HANDBOOK OF NOISE CONTROL

OTHER McGRAW-HILL HANDBOOKS OF INTEREST

AMERICAN INSTITUTE OF PYHSICS · American Institute of Physics Handbook
AMERICAN SOCIETY OF MECHANICAL ENGINEERS · ASME Handbooks:
  Engineering Tables   Metals Engineering—Processes
  Metals Engineering—Design   Metals Properties
AMERICAN SOCIETY OF TOOL AND MANUFACTURING ENGINEERS:
  Die Design Handbook   Handbook of Fixture Design
  Manufacturing Planning and   Tool Engineers Handbook
    Estimating Handbook
ARCHITECTURAL RECORD · Time-Saver Standards
BEEMAN · Industrial Power Systems Handbook
BRADY · Materials Handbook
BURINGTON · Handbook of Mathematical Tables and Formulas
BURINGTON AND MAY · Handbook of Probability and Statistics with Tables
CARRIER AIR CONDITIONING COMPANY · Handbook of Air Conditioning System
  Design
CARROLL · Industrial Instrument Servicing Handbook
CONDON AND ODISHAW · Handbook of Physics
CONSIDINE · Process Instruments and Controls Handbook
CONSIDINE AND ROSS · Handbook of Applied Instrumentation
CROCKER · Piping Handbook
DAVIS · Handbook of Applied Hydraulics
DUDLEY · Gear Handbook
EMERICK · Heating Handbook
FACTORY MUTUAL ENGINEERING DIVISION · Handbook of Industrial Loss
  Prevention
FLUGGE · Handbook of Engineering Mechanics
HARRIS · Handbook of Noise Control
HARRIS AND CREDE · Shock and Vibration Handbook
HEYEL · The Foreman's Handbook
HUSKEY AND KORN · Computer Handbook
JURAN · Quality Control Handbook
KALLEN · Handbook of Instrumentation and Controls
KING AND BRATER · Handbook of Hydraulics
KNOWLTON · Standard Handbook for Electrical Engineers
KOELLE · Handbook of Astronautical Engineering
KORN AND KORN · Mathematical Handbook for Scientists and Engineers
LASSER · Business Management Handbook
LAUGHNER AND HARGAN · Handbook of Fastening and Joining of Metal Parts
LEGRAND · The New American Machinists' Handbook
MACHOL · System Engineering Handbook
MAGILL, HOLDEN, AND ACKLEY · Air Pollution Handbook
MANAS · National Plumbing Code Handbook
MANTELL · Engineering Materials Handbook
MARKS AND BAUMEISTER · Mechanical Engineers' Handbook
MAYNARD · Industrial Engineering Handbook
MAYNARD · Top Management Handbook
MORROW · Maintenance Engineering Handbook
PERRY · Chemical Engineers' Handbook
PERRY · Engineering Manual
ROSSNAGEL · Handbook of Rigging
ROTHBART · Mechanical Design and Systems Handbook
SHAND · Glass Engineering Handbook
STANIAR · Plant Engineering Handbook
STREETER · Handbook of Fluid Dynamics
TOULOUKIAN · Retrieval Guide to Thermophysical Properties Research Literature

HANDBOOK

OF

NOISE CONTROL

Edited by

Cyril M. Harris, Ph.D.

Professor of Electrical Engineering and Architecture
Columbia University

McGRAW-HILL BOOK COMPANY
New York   San Francisco   Toronto   London   Sydney

Handbook of Noise Control

Library of Congress Catalog Card Number: 56-12268

10 11 12 – MAMM – 7 6

ISBN 07-026808-8

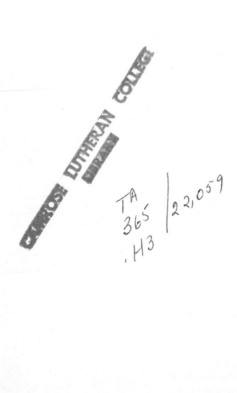

PREFACE

People do not like noise. By definition, it is *unwanted* sound. It may interfere with speech communication on jobs or in leisure activities; in certain respects it may affect behavior; it may produce a temporary hearing loss, and if the noise level is high enough, it may be responsible for permanent damage to hearing.

Noise control is therefore a matter of considerable social and economic importance. This has become increasingly true in recent years. In consequence it has brought together individuals of widely varying vocations who share a vital interest in the problem: acoustical engineers, physicists, electrical engineers, designers of military equipment, aeronautical engineers, mechanical engineers, ventilation engineers, builders, architects, city planners, public health officials, industrial hygienists, otologists, physiologists, psychologists, transportation authorities, industrial designers, business executives, lawyers, and compensation experts. This range of interests is reflected in the contributors who have cooperated in the writing of this handbook. They are divided equally among government, university, and industrial organizations.

Although there have been many scientific articles on various aspects of noise, and lengthy technical reports have been issued by government agencies and industrial organizations, this is the first book to be published in the United States on the general subject of noise control.

Over the years there has been an increasingly large quantity of material published on noise, some of which is more popularly than accurately written. A need has therefore developed for an authoritative work covering the entire field. Consideration was given to the division of the field into separate volumes, each with its own author. But since all areas of noise control are interrelated, such separate volumes cannot treat these interrelationships as effectively as can a single work; furthermore, useless duplication of material would result. A handbook type of presentation has permitted a highly unified treatment of the specialized areas—each one covered by an expert in his field.

The chapters in this handbook are included in the following general groupings: properties of sound, effects of noise on man, vibration control, instrumentation and noise measurement, techniques of noise control, noise control in buildings, sources of noise and examples of noise control,

v

noise control of machinery and electrical equipment, noise control in transportation, community noise, and the legal aspects of noise problems.

In the writing of this book many authorities have spent much time and effort preparing their respective chapters. Their labor, willing collaboration, diligence, and patience have been immense. Thanks are due also to their colleagues who read and commented on the chapters during their preparation.

Many of the authors are with the Department of Defense in either a civilian or military capacity. Some are with other departments of the government. The material which they present has been released for publication, but the opinions expressed are not official and therefore do not necessarily reflect views of the relevant agency.

The wealth of technical information contained in this volume has been gathered through diligent effort on the part of the contributors. In this regard, publications of the Acoustical Society of America have been particularly helpful. Much of the material is heretofore unpublished; we are greatly indebted to the many industrial organizations, government agencies, and engineering consultants who have been credited throughout the book. Special thanks are due to the Department of Defense, to the American Standards Association, to the Controller of Her Brittanic Majesty's Stationery Office, and to the Director of Building Research for permission to reproduce material in this handbook.

Cyril M. Harris

CONTENTS

HANDBOOK OF NOISE CONTROL

Chapter 1

INTRODUCTION AND TERMINOLOGY

Cyril M. Harris, Ph.D.

Columbia University

INTRODUCTION

What Noise Is. A sonorous melody pouring forth from a radio may be very pleasant to one family in a dwelling, but it is a nuisance to those neighbors who are trying to sleep; it is unwanted, it is noise. By definition, *noise is unwanted sound.*

Unfortunately, most of the machines that have been developed for industrial purposes, for high-speed transportation, or to make life more enjoyable, by furnishing additional comfort, reducing the drudgery of everyday living, and speeding up our daily routines to provide additional leisure hours, are accompanied by noise. Since noise affects man in a number of ways—his hearing, his ability to communicate, and his behavior—noise control, from both economic and medico-legal standpoints, has become tremendously important. In addition, noise control has become a matter of significance because it can make the world a pleasanter place in which to live. The chapters that follow will consider the various effects of noise on man, noise measurements, methods of noise control, practical applications of noise-control techniques, and the legal aspects of the noise problem.

How Noise Is Transmitted. Noise may reach a listener by any one of a number of paths. Suppose, for example, he hears a piano in the apartment overhead. Some of the sound may be transmitted to the listener along a direct air path out of the window of the apartment overhead, along an outside path, and through his window. Some of the sound radiated by the piano will strike the walls, forcing them into minute vibration; a fraction of this vibratory energy will travel through the building structure, forcing other wall surfaces elsewhere in the building to vibrate and to radiate sound. Alternatively, some of the vibratory energy may be communicated through the frame of the piano to the floor, entirely along a solid path, setting the floor into vibration and thereby radiating sound in the apartment below.

For convenience, in engineering problems, one may represent the transmission of sound from a source to a listener by the diagram shown in Fig. 1.1. Actually, the block labeled *source* may represent not one, but many sources of vibratory energy, e.g., it may include all the airplanes in the sky above a specified area. As indicated above, the *paths* may be numerous. Finally, the block labeled *receiver* may represent a single person, a group of people, an entire community, or a delicate piece of equipment whose operation is affected by noise.

Statistical Aspect of the Source, Path, and Receiver. In the field of noise control it is always important to bear in mind the statistical aspect of the elements of the block diagram of Fig. 1.1. First, the noise generators represented by the block labeled *source* may vary in number and their outputs may vary in time—as, for example, the case of vehicular traffic at an intersection.

The *path* by which noise reaches our ears from a source is also statistical in nature. For example, consider an airplane circling a listener on the ground. Because of inhomogeneities in the atmosphere, there will be a multitude of variations in the transmission path. These statistical variations in the propagation characteristics of the atmosphere may result in a wide fluctuation in sound level at the listener's ears. As another illustration, consider the noise level in an office which is separated from a noisy factory by a partition with a door in it. When the door is opened, the transmission path is altered. Thus, the noise level in the office varies statistically, depending among other factors on the frequency with which the door to the factory area is opened.

FIG. 1.1. Schematic diagram in which the heavy solid arrows represent the transmission of sound from a source to a listener. The block labeled *source* may represent more than one sound source; the *paths* may be numerous; and the *receiver* may represent a single person, a group of people, an entire community, or equipment whose operation is affected by noise. The broken arrows indicate interaction between the various elements of the block diagram.

The *receiver* in Fig. 1.1 has its statistical aspects as well. Suppose it represents a large group of people. The actual number in the group may vary from time to time, the threshold of each person in the group will be different, and each of these thresholds may vary with time.

Interaction between Source, Path, and Receiver. Although the source, path, and receiver are shown as separate elements in the block diagram of Fig. 1.1, there is considerable interaction among them—they are not independent elements.

The output of a sound *source* is not always a constant but may depend on both the path and the receiver. In a technical sense, we say that when the output of a noise source has been so influenced by its surroundings, the "radiation impedance" of the source has been altered by its environment. Another type of influence of the environment on the output of a source may take place when the source is a person speaking. If he talks to a nearby listener in a small room, his speech power may be relatively low, but in a large hall or at some distance out of doors, his power will automatically increase. In fact, the talker is influenced by the receiver as well as the path. If he knows the listener is hard of hearing, he will raise his voice. Another illustration of the influence of the path and receiver on the source is provided by the operator of a noisy machine who varies its operation according to the environmental conditions in which this source of disturbance is placed and the people he may annoy by its operation.

It is not always realized that the characteristics of the *path* may be influenced by both the source and receiver. For example, it is shown in Chap. 21 that the attenuation provided by mufflers and acoustic filters depends to a considerable extent on the characteristics of both the source and the receiver, i.e., the attenuation of the path is not a constant independent of the source and receiver.

Likewise, the reaction of the *receiver* depends upon the characteristics of the path and source. For example, a housewife may go about her chores unaffected by the sound from airplanes that pass overhead. She may be uninfluenced by the rattle of dishes in her cupboard if they are set into vibration by a noisy refrigerator. However, should the rattle of the dishes be caused by airplane noise, her reaction may be entirely different. Thus, it is apparent that there is considerable interaction among the source, path, and receiver, just as there may be among the many components of which the source, path, or receiver may be constituted.

WHAT NOISE CONTROL IS

Noise control is the technology of obtaining an acceptable noise environment, at a receiver, consistent with economic and operational considerations; the receiver may be a person, a group of people, an entire community, or a piece of equipment whose operation is affected by noise. When the word "acceptable" is employed, such questions as the following are raised: Acceptable under what conditions? Acceptable to whom? There is usually no unique answer to such questions for a given noise problem because of the complexity of the economic and operational considerations which are involved, and because all the elements may vary with time.

Noise control is not the same as noise reduction. In a specific problem, the amount of noise reduction required to achieve acceptable results sometimes may be obtained simply by applying all the various noise-reduction techniques listed in a following section. But this procedure may be unnecessarily costly and wasteful, and it may result in needless interference with normal operations. In contrast, from the standpoint of good noise-control technique, the same problem would be analyzed systematically to determine how acceptable conditions might be achieved in the most economical way. In unusual cases the solution to some noise control problems may even suggest a noise *increase*, rather than a noise reduction. Consider, for example, the waiting room in a physician's office that is separated from his consultation room by a partition which provides so little sound insulation that private conversations can be overheard in the waiting room. Acceptable conditions in the waiting room could be achieved by the construction of a partition providing greater air-borne sound insulation. A possible alternate solution is to *increase* the noise level in the waiting room by installing another noise source there (for example, a fan) so as to "mask" the conversation that would otherwise be overheard. While this latter solution has its disadvantages, it is much more economical—and therefore may be more desirable under some circumstances. It illustrates once again that "noise control" and "noise reduction" are not always synonymous.

ECONOMIC IMPORTANCE OF NOISE CONTROL

Because noise can affect man's ability to communicate with his neighbors by speech, because noise may affect his behavior, because noise may have some permanent damaging effect on his hearing, and because he simply may regard it as being annoying, noise is a problem of very great economic importance in modern society. For example, quantitative relationships can be obtained to show how one's ability to understand speech is reduced by the influence of noise (Chap. 9). Thus when the noise level in business or educational institutions is high enough to interfere with speech communication, economic losses are sustained. Compensation cases involving claims for many millions of dollars as a result of permanent hearing damage are now in the courts (Chap. 38). Another aspect of the economic importance of noise is shown by the effects of noise on property values. For example, the noise from the operation of an airfield or from a factory may influence the value of the land in the surrounding area (Chap. 37). For economic reasons, a considerable effort is being made by industry to develop products that are quiet,* and by the business world to achieve quiet conditions in their offices and factories. While it is not always possible to state explicit relationships between noise and its effects on man, or for the laboratory scientist—at this time—to demonstrate that some of these effects even exist, it is of utmost significance that business and industry are spending considerable amounts of money annually to achieve conditions of quiet. During the past 10 years in the United States, the total dollar sales of acoustical materials have increased from about 10 to 60 million dollars. It may be argued that this increase is the result of sales promotional effort; to some extent this is true, as it is with most products. On the other hand, such rapid growth can be fully accounted for only on the basis of the fact that people do not like noise. They are annoyed by it. They are distracted by it. Noise is a public nuisance. Many business firms find their customers object to noise. Furthermore, their employees prefer not to work in a noisy environment. People like quiet. They are willing to pay for it.

NOISE-CONTROL TECHNIQUES

Throughout this handbook, various methods for controlling noise are considered in detail. In general, these measures may be classified in three categories: (1) noise

---

* In some industries it is important that noises associated with their products have a certain quality. For example, automobile manufacturers consider it desirable that the noise produced by the slamming of an automobile door have a "big-car quality."

reduction at the *source*, (2) noise control of the *transmission* path, and (3) the use of noise protective measures at the *receiver*. Which method, or which combination of methods, is employed depends on the amount of noise reduction that is required and on economic and operational considerations. In solving a specific noise-control problem, the relative benefit to be gained from the application of each technique must be evaluated from the system point of view and compared with its respective cost.

In addition to the techniques described below, which have general application in the field of noise control, measures that may be employed in special problems are described in the specific chapters where they have application. For example, a method is described in Chap. 29 for controlling noise from transformer substations which is based on the principle of "noise cancellation." Here, the reduction in noise at the receiving position is achieved by generating a second sound source which is just "out of phase" with the original source of disturbance, so as to cancel it. Although this technique has limited application (primarily for steady, pure-tone sources, such as transformer noise), it has been used successfully over small areas.

Noise Control at the Source. Important methods of controlling noise at its source include (1) the reduction of the amplitude of the exciting forces, (2) the reduction of the response of various components of the system to these exciting forces (components that generate noise when excited or that transmit vibratory energy to surfaces that will radiate sound), and (3) changes in operating procedure. It may be impractical for the purchaser of equipment to employ any of the measures listed below which involve equipment modification. In this case, he may best reduce the noise at its source by the selection of the quietest source or the quietest components of which the source is comprised, consistent with other requirements.

Reduction of the Exciting Forces.

a. REDUCTION OF IMPACTS OR IMPULSIVE FORCES.

b. BALANCING OF MOVING MASSES. (See Chaps. 12 and 30 for a discussion of the balancing of shafts of rotating machinery.)

c. BALANCING OF MAGNETIC FORCES. (In electric motors and generators, both *b* and *c* must be considered. See Chap. 30.)

d. REDUCTION OF FRICTIONAL FORCES BY PROPER ALIGNMENT AND LUBRICATION. (See Chap. 23.)

e. THE USE OF DYNAMIC COMPENSATION. So-called "dynamic absorbers" provide a compensating force which is out of phase with the exciting force and hence reduce the total energy transmitted to the structure (Chap. 14).

f. VIBRATION ISOLATION. The vibration isolation of the components of a source, or of the entire source itself, can be effective in greatly reducing the exciting forces (see Chaps. 12 and 13).

Reduction of the Response of Noise-radiating Components in the System to the Exciting Forces. When components in a system are set into vibration, they will radiate sound. Application of the following techniques can reduce this noise at its source.

a. ALTERATION OF THE NATURAL FREQUENCY OF A RESONANT ELEMENT. A panel may be set into strong vibration when the frequency of the exciting force corresponds with, or is near, the natural frequency of the panel. Under these conditions, the vibration of the panel, and hence the noise which is produced by it, may be reduced by altering the natural frequency of the panel. For example, this may be done by increasing the mass of the panel (which will lower the natural frequency), by increasing its stiffness (which will raise the natural frequency), or by changing the dimensions of the panel.

b. INCREASING THE ENERGY DISSIPATION. Vibration-damping materials (Chap. 14) may be applied to the radiating surfaces. In this way, very substantial reductions in noise output may be obtained.

Changes in Operating Procedure. Changes in the usual procedure of operation may be effective as a noise-control technique. Thus some factories, adjacent to residential areas, suspend or reduce noise operations at night, when the normal activity in a community diminishes and the general background noise is decreased. Without this background noise to "mask" it, the factory noise becomes more noticeable. Because of this and because of possible interference with sleep, factories that would otherwise operate on a 24-hour-a-day basis curtail their operations at night.

Control of the Transmission Path. Another general technique of noise reduction is that of controlling the transmission path so as to reduce the energy that is communicated to the receiver. This may be done in a number of ways:

a. SITING. In the open air, maximum attenuation should be provided by increasing—in so far as possible—the distance between the source and the receiver. Since many noise sources do not radiate uniformly in all directions, by altering the relative orientation of the source and receiver a considerable reduction in noise level at the receiver may be possible. For example, the orientation of an airport runway may be an important consideration in reducing noise in an adjacent community. Where possible, a site should be chosen that will take advantage of the natural terrain to provide additional shielding of the receiver from the source.

b. BUILDING LAYOUT. The careful planning of the location of rooms within a building, with respect to the relative position of the noise sources and those areas where quiet conditions are desired, may result in a considerable economy by reducing the extent of the noise-control measures that would otherwise be required.

c. PATH DEFLECTION. Barriers in the open air can be effective when they are large in size compared with the wavelength of the noise to be deflected (Chap. 3). For example, deflecting surfaces which make an angle of 45° with respect to the horizontal have been used in the noise field of jet aircraft engines to reflect the high frequencies upward toward the sky. The use of barriers or partial partitions in rooms is discussed in Chap. 22.

d. ENCLOSURES. Considerable attenuation may be provided by the use of a properly designed enclosure around a noise source or around the receiver (Chap. 20).

e. ABSORPTION. One of the most effective means of attenuating sound in its transmission path is by means of absorption. For example, suppose a number of machines are in operation in a large office. Most of the noise from these sources that reaches workers on the opposite side of the room will have been reflected by the ceiling, walls, and floor. Therefore, the use of sound absorption in the form of acoustical materials on the ceiling, or carpet on the floor, will provide attenuation in the path between the source and receiver (Chap. 18). If noise is communicated by a ventilating duct, attenuation along this path may be employed in the form of a sound-absorptive lining (Chap. 27).

f. IMPEDANCE MISMATCH (acoustic filters, mufflers). The flow of acoustic energy along the path from source to receiver can be impeded by discontinuities which reflect the energy back toward the source (i.e., by an "impedance mismatch"). In dwellings, this may be provided by a break in the building construction (Chap. 19). Sound transmission in the open air can be similarly impeded. For example, the stack of an exhaust blower can be designed to provide the greatest reflection of acoustic fan-noise energy at its outlet, in order to minimize the radiation of blower noise from the stack. Acoustic filters and mufflers operate on this principle, although some mufflers may also include absorption in the transmission path (Chap. 21).

Protective Measures at the Receiver. The following noise-control techniques may be employed where the noise level at the receiver is considered to be excessive.*

Use of Personal Protective Equipment. Where noise levels in an environment are excessive, the use of earplugs, earmuffs, noise helmets, or small booths may reduce the levels to a point where the noise hazard will be reduced to a condition of acceptability (Chap. 8).

Education and Public Relations. In some cities where noise has been a serious problem, both industrial and government installations have improved their relations with the community by interesting it in their noise problem and by showing the com-

---

* One manufacturer found that for a particularly noisy operation in his factory, the combination of all the techniques described above, including that of personal protective measures, would not provide sufficient protection for his workmen at an economical price. The most practical solution was the use of a closed-circuit television system for monitoring the operation and the use of appropriate remote-controlled devices in the noisy areas. Such extreme measures are seldom necessary.

munity that constructive steps were being taken to minimize the disturbance. A dramatic example of this took place at an Air Force base in Wisconsin, where public discontent was turned to public pride as the result of the application of noise-control techniques, public education to the problem, and a good public-relations policy.

Exposure Control. Under some circumstances it is impracticable to reduce extremely intense noise levels in areas where people must work to levels which are considered acceptable for the usual working period. As indicated in Chap. 34, a noise level that is unacceptable for one period of time may be acceptable for a shorter period. Therefore one noise-control technique is the rotation of personnel so that work assignments in the intense noise area are for a limited period of time only.

HOW MUCH NOISE REDUCTION IS REQUIRED

The following steps are taken to determine the amount of noise reduction required in a specific problem:

1. *Determine the noise level in the environment where the receiver is located, under existing or expected conditions.* This may be done by measurements or from estimates based on available data.
2. *Determine what noise level is acceptable.* This information is provided by an appropriate criterion.
3. *Use the difference between 1 and 2 as the noise reduction that must be provided to obtain an acceptable environment.* This noise reduction is usually determined as a function of frequency.

Determination of Noise Level in the Receiver Environment. Noise measurements should furnish data that is statistically significant for the selection or evaluation of noise-control procedures. This requires the use of the appropriate equipment for the job, accurate calibration, the taking of data in the various frequency bands under properly controlled conditions, and the evaluation of other factors which influence the measurements—for example, the effects of the environment (Chaps. 16 and 17).

Under some circumstances it is impracticable or impossible to make noise measurements on various sources. In such cases one frequency can obtain a useful engineering estimate from information provided by existing data, which specifies the conditions of measurement. Many noise analyses are given throughout this handbook. By way of illustration in this chapter, data from one type of noise survey are shown in Appendix 1.1.

Noise Control Criteria. A *criterion* is defined as a standard of judging. Noise control criteria provide standards for judging the acceptability of noise levels under various conditions and for various purposes.

Criteria can be stated for man's tolerance to vibration, for risk of damage to hearing as a result of exposure to high-intensity noise, for reliable speech communication in the presence of noise, for acceptable noise levels in different types of buildings, for community reaction to noise, etc. Such criteria are statistical in nature. For example, a noise level that may constitute a damage risk to the hearing of one person may not have a significant effect on another. Furthermore, the reactions of people are not time-invariant. Thus how they react depends to a large extent on their previous history and how they intercommunicate. A community may react to airplane noise entirely differently after a series of airplane crashes than it did before.

To illustrate the statistical aspect of such criteria, consider a factory in which there is a continuous noise level of very high intensity, in an area where men spend eight hours a day. A damage-risk criterion could be established here which would indicate a "safe" upper limit for the noise spectrum. If the noise level does not exceed this limit, 99 per cent of the factory population would be protected against risk of damage to their hearing; but if, for example, this limit were raised by x db, then only 90 per cent would be protected. After the noise-control engineer has been provided with information which specifies the percentage of the group that is to be protected, the length of exposure time per man, and the amount of hearing loss that is considered significant, he may use such a criterion to determine the level to which the noise must be reduced. Thus the difference between this level and the existing level, obtained by appropriate measurements, indicates the noise reduction in decibels that must be provided. The desired results then may be obtained by application of noise-control techniques described in detail in the chapters which follow.

TERMINOLOGY

Throughout this handbook, definitions of terms used in noise-control work are given in various chapters. (In particular, see Chap. 2, *Physical Properties of Noise*, and Chap. 12, *Principles of Vibration Control*.) For convenience definitions of terms which are used frequently in the general field of noise control are assembled here. Many of these definitions are quotations, with permission, from *American Standard Terminology* (Z24.1-1951), American Standards Association.† These definitions have been denoted by an asterisk(*). Others have been modified from this standard or are proposed revisions. For terms which are not listed below, the reader is referred to the index.

Absorption Coefficient (Acoustical Absorptivity) (α). The sound-absorption coefficient of a surface which is exposed to a sound field is the ratio of the sound energy absorbed by the surface to the sound energy incident upon the surface. The absorption coefficient is a function of both angle of incidence and frequency. Tables of absorption coefficient which are given in the literature usually list the absorption coefficients at various frequencies, the values being those obtained by averaging over-all angles of incidence.

Acoustic, Acoustical. The qualifying adjectives acoustic and acoustical mean containing, producing, arising from, actuated by, related to, or associated with sound. *Acoustic* is used when the term being qualified designates something that has the properties, dimensions, or physical characteristics associated with sound waves; *acoustical* is used when the term being qualified does *not* designate explicitly something which has such properties, dimensions, or physical characteristics.

Acoustics. Acoustics is the science of sound, including (*a*) its production, transmission, and effects, or (*b*) the qualities that determine the value of a room or other enclosed space with respect to distinct hearing.

Acoustic Impedance. The acoustic impedance of a sound medium on a given surface lying in a wave front is the impedance obtained from the ratio of the sound pressure (force per unit area) on that surface by the flux (volume velocity, or linear velocity multiplied by the area) through the surface. When concentrated rather than distributed impedances are considered, the impedance of a portion of the medium is based on the pressure difference effective in driving that portion and the flux (volume velocity). The acoustic impedance may be expressed in terms of mechanical impedance divided by the square of the area of the surface considered. (Velocities in the direction along which the impedance is to be specified are considered positive.)

Acoustical Ohm.* An acoustic resistance, reactance, or impedance has a magnitude of 1 acoustical ohm when a sound pressure of 1 microbar produces a volume velocity of 1 cu cm per sec.

Acoustic Power. (See *Sound Power*.)

Acoustic Power Level. (See *Sound Power Level*.)

Acoustic Reactance. Acoustic reactance is the imaginary component of the acoustic impedance.

Acoustic Refraction. Acoustic refraction is the process by which the direction of sound propagation is changed because of spatial variation of the wave velocity in the medium.

Acoustic Resistance.* Acoustic resistance is the real component of the acoustic impedance.

Acoustic Scattering. Acoustic scattering is the irregular and diffuse reflection, refraction, or diffraction of a sound in many directions.

Ambient Noise. Ambient noise is the all-encompassing noise associated with a given environment, being usually a composite of sounds from many sources near and far.

Amplitude of a Periodic Quantity. The amplitude of a periodic quantity is the maximum value of the quantity.

Anechoic Room. (See *Free-field Room*.)

† Copies of this standard, as well as others in the field of acoustics, vibration, and mechanical shock, are available from the American Standards Association. Inc., New York 17, N.Y.

Angular Frequency (ω). The angular frequency of a periodic quantity is its frequency in radians per unit time, usually radians per second. It is thus the frequency multiplied by 2π.

Antinodes. An antinode is a point, line, or surface in a vibrating body or system at which the amplitude of motion, relative to that at a node, is a maximum.

Antiresonant Frequency.* An antiresonant frequency is a frequency at which antiresonance exists.

Articulation (Per Cent Articulation) and Intelligibility (Per Cent Intelligibility). Per cent articulation or per cent intelligibility of a communication system is the percentage of the speech units spoken by a talker or talkers that is understood correctly by a listener or listeners. The word "articulation" is customarily used when the contextual relations among the units of the special material are thought to play an unimportant role; the word "intelligibility" is customarily used when the context is thought to play an important role in determining the listener's perception. The kind of speech material used is identified by an appropriate adjective in phrases such as "syllable articulation," "individual sound articulation," "vowel (or consonant) articulation," "word articulation," "discrete word intelligibility," "discrete sentence intelligibility."

Articulation Score. (See *Discrimination for Speech.*)

Audio Frequency (Sonic Frequency). An audio frequency is any frequency corresponding to a normally audible sound wave, roughly from 15 to 20,000 cps.

Audiogram (Threshold Audiogram).* An audiogram is a graph showing hearing loss, per cent hearing loss, or per cent hearing as a function of frequency.

Audiometer.* An audiometer is an instrument for measuring hearing acuity. Measurements may be made with speech signals, usually recorded, or with tone signals.

Aural Critical Band. The aural critical band is that frequency band of sound, being a portion of a continuous-spectrum noise covering a wide band, that contains sound power equal to that of a simple (pure) tone centered in the critical band and just audible in the presence of the wide band noise. In order to be just audible in a wideband continuous noise, the level of a simple tone in decibels must exceed the spectrum level of the continuous noise (at the same frequency) by 10 times the logarithm to the base 10 of the ratio of the critical bandwidth to unit bandwidth.

Aural Harmonic.* An aural harmonic is a harmonic generated in the auditory mechanism.

Band Pressure Level.* The band pressure level of a sound for a specified frequency band is the effective sound pressure level for the sound energy contained within the band. The width of the band and the reference pressure must be specified. The width of the band may be indicated by the use of a qualifying adjective: e.g., octave-band (sound pressure) level, half-octave band level, third-octave band level, 50-cps band level. If the sound pressure level is caused by thermal noise, the standard deviation of the band pressure level will not exceed 1 db if the product of the bandwidth in cycles per second by the integration time in seconds exceeds 20.

Beats. Beats are periodic variations that result from the superposition of two simple harmonic motions of different frequencies f_1 and f_2. They involve the periodic increase and decrease of the amplitude at the beat frequency $(f_1 - f_2)$.

Characteristic Impedance. The characteristic impedance of a medium is the ratio of the effective sound pressure at a given point to the effective particle velocity at that point in a free plane progressive sound wave. The characteristic impedance is equal to the product of the density by the speed of sound in the medium, i.e., (ρc).

Characteristic Impedance of Air ($\rho_0 c$). (See *Characteristic Impedance.*) Values of the characteristic impedance of air for various temperatures and pressures are given in Fig. 2.8.

Circular Frequency. (See *Angular Frequency.*)

Compliance. Compliance is the reciprocal of stiffness.

Compressional Wave.* A compressional wave is a wave in an elastic medium which causes an element of the medium to change its volume without undergoing rotation.

Continuous Spectrum.* A continuous spectrum is the spectrum of a wave, the components of which are continuously distributed over a frequency region.

Coupled Modes. Coupled modes are modes of vibration which are not independent but which mutually influence one another because of energy transfer from one mode to the other.

Critical Band. (See *Aural Critical Band.*)

Critical Speed. Critical speed is the rotating speed of a system which corresponds to a resonant frequency of the system.

Cycle.* A cycle is the complete sequence of values of a periodic quantity which occur during a period.

Cycle per Second (cps). A unit of frequency. In many European countries the cycle per second is called the *Hertz*.

Cylindrical Wave.* A cylindrical wave is a wave in which the wavefronts are coaxial cylinders.

Damage-risk Criterion. A damage-risk criterion specifies the maximum sound pressure levels of a noise, as a function of frequency, to which people should be exposed if risk of hearing loss is to be avoided. This criterion includes a specification of the time of exposure, amount of hearing loss considered significant, and the percentage of the population to be protected.

Dead Room.* A dead room is a room which is characterized by an unusually large amount of sound absorption.

Decibel (db). The decibel is a unit of level which denotes the ratio between two quantities that are proportional to power; the number of decibels corresponding to the ratio of two amounts of power is 10 times the logarithm to the base 10 of this ratio. In many sound fields, the sound-pressure ratios are not proportional to the square root of the corresponding power ratios, so that strictly speaking the term *decibel* should not be used in such cases; however, it is common practice to extend the use of the unit to these cases (see, for example, *Sound Pressure Level*).

Degrees of Freedom. The number of degrees of freedom of a mechanical system is equal to the number of independent displacements which are possible. In general, it is equal to the minimum number of independent coordinates required to define completely the position of the system at any given instant.

Difference Limen (Differential Threshold) (Just Noticeable Difference).* A difference limen is the increment in a stimulus which is just noticed in a specified fraction of the trials. The relative difference limen is the ratio of the difference limen to the absolute magnitude of the stimulus to which it is related.

Diffracted Wave. A diffracted wave is one whose front has been changed in direction by an obstacle or other nonhomogeneity in a medium, otherwise than by reflection or refraction.

Diffraction.* Diffraction is that process which produces a diffracted wave.

Diffuse Sound Field (Random-incidence Sound Field). A diffuse sound field is a sound field such that the sound pressure level is everywhere the same, and all directions of energy flux are equally probable.

Discrimination for Speech (Articulation Score). The discrimination for speech, or articulation score, of an ear is the percentage of items in an appropriate form of test, usually monosyllabic words, that is correctly repeated, written down, or checked by the listener. This form of test is usually administered at an acoustic level well above the threshold for speech. The normal value of discrimination (or articulation score) for each test must be determined empirically.

Discrimination Loss. Discrimination loss is the difference between the normal discrimination score for the test and the score obtained for the ear under test.

Distortion.* Distortion is a change in wave form. Noise and certain desired changes in wave form, such as those resulting from modulation or detection, are not usually classed as distortion.

Doppler Effect.* The Doppler effect is the phenomenon evidenced by the change in the observed frequency of a wave in a transmission system caused by a time rate of change in the effective length of the path of travel between the source and the point of observation.

Doppler Shift.* The Doppler shift is the magnitude of the change in the observed frequency of a wave due to the Doppler effect.

Double Amplitude. (See *Peak-to-peak Amplitude*.)

Echo. An echo is a wave which has been reflected or otherwise returned with sufficient magnitude and delay to be perceived as a wave distinct from that directly transmitted.

Efficiency. The efficiency of a device with respect to a physical quantity which may be stored, transferred, or transformed by the device is the ratio of the useful output of the quantity to its total input.

Effective Sound Pressure (p) (Root-mean-square Sound Pressure). The effective sound pressure at a point is the root-mean-square value of the instantaneous sound pressures, over a time interval at the point under consideration. In the case of periodic sound pressure, the interval must be an integral number of periods or an interval long compared to a period. In the case of nonperiodic sound pressures, the interval should be long enough to make the value obtained essentially independent of small changes in the length of the interval. The term "effective sound pressure" is frequently shortened to "sound pressure."

Flutter Echo.* A flutter echo is a rapid succession of reflected pulses resulting from a single initial pulse.

Forced Oscillation (Forced Vibration). The oscillation of a system is forced if the response is imposed by the excitation. If the excitation is periodic, the oscillation is steady-state.

Free Field. A free sound field is a field in a homogeneous, isotropic medium free from boundaries. In practice it is a field in which the effects of the boundaries are negligible over the region of interest. The actual pressure impinging on an object (e.g., a microphone) placed in an otherwise free sound field will differ from the pressure which would exist at that point with the object removed, unless the acoustic impedance of the object matches the acoustic impedance of the medium.

Free-field Room (Anechoic Room). A free-field room is a room in which essentially free-field conditions exist.

Free Oscillation (Free Vibration). Free oscillation of a system is the oscillation of some physical quantity of the system when there are no externally applied driving forces. Such oscillation is maintained by the transfer of energy between elastic restoring forces and inertia forces. The oscillation may arise from initial displacements, velocities, or a force suddenly applied and withdrawn.

Free Progressive Wave (Free Wave).* A free progressive wave is a wave in a medium free from boundary effects. A free wave in a steady state can only be approximated in practice.

Frequency (f). The frequency of a function periodic in time is the reciprocal of the period. The unit is the cycle per unit time, e.g., cycles per second (cps) or kilocycles per second (kc or kcps).

Fundamental Mode of Vibration.* The fundamental mode of vibration of a system is the mode having the lowest frequency.

Fundamental Frequency. The fundamental frequency of a periodic quantity is equal to the reciprocal of the shortest period during which the quantity exactly reproduces itself.

g. The quantity g is the acceleration produced in a mass by the force of gravity; it is approximately equal to 32.2 ft per sec^2 = 386 in. per sec^2 = 981 cm per sec^2.

Harmonic.* A harmonic is a sinusoidal quantity having a frequency which is an integral multiple of the fundamental frequency of a periodic quantity to which it is related.

Hearing Loss. The hearing loss of an ear at a specified frequency is the amount, in decibels, by which the threshold of audibility for that ear exceeds the normal threshold.

Hearing Loss for Speech.* Hearing loss for speech is the difference in decibels between the speech levels at which the average normal ear and the defective ear, respectively, reach the same intelligibility, often arbitrarily set at 50 per cent.

Hertz (Hz). (See *Cycle per Second*.)

Impedance. An impedance is the complex ratio of a forcelike quantity (force, pressure, voltage) to a related velocitylike quantity (velocity, volume velocity, or current).

Infrasonic Frequency (Subsonic Frequency).* An infrasonic frequency is a frequency lying below the audio-frequency range.

Instantaneous Sound Pressure.* The instantaneous sound pressure at a point is the total instantaneous pressure at that point minus the static pressure at that point.

Intensity (I). The sound intensity measured in a specified direction at a point is the average rate at which sound energy is transmitted through a unit area perpendicular to the specified direction at the point considered. Only in plane or spherical free progressive sound waves is the intensity related to the average pressure p by the equation $I = p^2/\rho_0 c$, where $\rho_0 c$ represents the characteristic impedance of air.

Intensity Level (Sound-energy Flux-density Level) (L_I). The intensity level, in decibels, of a sound is 10 times the logarithm to the base 10 of the ratio of the intensity of this sound to the reference intensity. The reference intensity shall be stated explicitly; however, a commonly used reference is 10^{-16} watt per sq cm in a specified direction. In a plane progressive wave, there is a known relationship between sound-energy flux density and sound pressure, so that sound-energy flux-density level can be deduced from a measurement of sound pressure level. In general, however, there is no simple relationship between the two and a measurement of sound pressure level should not be reported as intensity level.

Jerk. Jerk is a vector which specifies the time rate of change of the acceleration of a particle; jerk is the third derivative of the displacement of the particle with respect to time.

Just Noticeable Difference. (See *Difference Limen*.)

Level. In communication and acoustics, the level of a quantity is the logarithm of the ratio of that quantity to a reference quantity of the same kind. The base of the logarithm, the reference quantity, and the *kind* of level must be specified.

Level above Threshold (Sensation Level) (L_S). The level above threshold of a sound is the pressure level of the sound in decibels above its threshold of audibility for the individual observer.

Line Spectrum.* A line spectrum is the spectrum of a wave, the components of which are confined to a number of discrete frequencies.

Live Room.* A live room is a room which is characterized by an unusually small amount of sound absorption.

Loudness (N). Loudness is the intensive attribute of an auditory sensation, in terms of which sounds may be ordered on a scale extending from soft to loud. Loudness depends primarily upon the sound pressure of the stimulus, but it also depends upon the frequency and wave form of the stimulus.

Loudness-level Contours. Loudness-level contours are curves which show the related values of sound pressure level and frequency required to produce a given loudness level for the typical listener.

Loudness Level (L_N). The loudness level, in phons, of a sound is numerically equal to the sound pressure level in decibels, relative to 0.0002 microbar, of a pure tone of frequency 1,000 cps, consisting of a plane progressive sound wave coming from directly in front of the observer, which is judged by normal observers to be equivalent in loudness.

Masking.* Masking is the amount by which the threshold of audibility of a sound is raised by the presence of another (masking) sound. The unit customarily used is the decibel.

Maximum Sound Pressure.* The maximum sound pressure for any given cycle of a periodic wave is the maximum absolute value of the instantaneous sound pressure occurring during that cycle. In the case of a sinusoidal sound wave this maximum sound pressure is also called the pressure amplitude.

Mean Free Path.* The mean free path for sound waves in an enclosure is the average distance sound travels between successive reflections in the enclosure.

Mechanical Impedance. Mechanical impedance is the impedance obtained from the ratio of force to either velocity or displacement during simple harmonic motion. The ratio of force to velocity is designated, *velocity impedance;* the ratio of force to displacement is designated *displacement impedance.*

Mel.* The mel is a unit of pitch. By definition, a simple tone of frequency 1,000 cps, 40 db above a listener's threshold, produces a pitch of 1,000 mels. The pitch of any sound that is judged by the listener to be n times that of a 1-mel tone is n mels.

Microbar, Dyne per Square Centimeter.* A microbar is a unit of pressure commonly used in acoustics. One microbar is equal to one dyne per sq cm.

Modal Number. In general, a vibratory system can be analyzed in terms of its normal modes. The modes may be arranged in a discrete sequence associated with a set of ordered integers which are called modal numbers.

Modal Shape. A modal shape is one of the characteristic shapes of a vibrating body or system. It corresponds to a normal mode of vibration.

Modulation.* Modulation is the process or the result of the process whereby some characteristic of one wave is varied in accordance with some characteristic of another wave.

Natural Frequency (f_n). Natural frequency is the frequency of free oscillation of a system. In a damped system, the natural frequency is a quasi-frequency in that the motion is not periodic but is generally taken as the frequency at which the velocity reverses sign. For a multi-degree-of-freedom system, the natural frequencies are the frequencies of vibration in normal modes.

Nodes. Nodes are the points, lines, or surfaces in a standing-wave system where some characteristic of the wave field has essentially zero amplitude.

Noise. Unwanted sound.

Noise Reduction Coefficient (NRC). The noise reduction coefficient of a material is the average, to the nearest multiple of 0.05, of the absorption coefficients at 250, 500, 1,000, and 2,000 cps.

Noise Level. The acoustical noise level is the sound level.

Normal Mode of Vibration. In an undamped multi-degree-of-freedom system undergoing free vibration, a normal mode of vibration is a pattern of motion assumed by the system in which the motion of every particle is simple harmonic with the same period and phase. Vibration in a normal mode thus occurs at a natural frequency of the system. In general, any composite motion of a system is analyzable into a summation of normal modes. (The terms *natural mode, characteristic mode,* and *eigen mode* are synonymous with normal mode.)

Normal Threshold of Audibility. The normal threshold of audibility at a given frequency is the modal value of the minimum sound pressure level, at the entrance to the external auditory canal, which at that frequency produces an auditory sensation in a large number of persons with normal ears and in the age group from 18 to 30 years, inclusive.

Octave Band Pressure Level.* The octave-band pressure level of a sound is the band pressure level for a frequency band corresponding to a specified octave. (The location of the octave-band pressure level on a frequency scale is usually specified as the geometric mean of the upper and lower frequencies of the octave.)

Oscillation.* Oscillation is the variation, usually with time, of the magnitude of a quantity with respect to a specified reference when the magnitude is alternately greater and smaller than the reference.

Overload Level. The overload level of a component or system is that level at which operation ceases to be satisfactory as a result of signal distortion, overheating, etc. In an acoustical system, sound pressure level is to be understood, unless otherwise specified.

Partial Nodes.* Partial nodes are the points, lines, or surfaces in a standing-wave system where some characteristic of the wave field has a minimum amplitude differing from zero.

Particle-velocity.* In a sound wave the particle-velocity is the velocity of a given infinitesimal part of the medium, with reference to the medium as a whole, due to the sound wave. The terms "instantaneous particle-velocity," "effective particle-velocity," "maximum particle-velocity," and "peak particle-velocity" have meanings which correspond with those of the related terms used for sound pressure.

Peak Level. The peak level is the maximum instantaneous level that occurs during a specified time interval. In acoustics, peak sound pressure level is to be understood, unless some other kind of level is specified.

Peak Sound Pressure.* The peak sound pressure for any specified time interval is the maximum absolute value of the instantaneous sound pressure in that interval. In the case of a periodic wave, if the time interval considered is a complete period, the peak sound pressure becomes identical with the maximum sound pressure.

Peak-to-peak Amplitude (Double Amplitude). The peak-to-peak amplitude of an oscillating quantity is the algebraic difference between the extremes of the quantity.

Per Cent Articulation. (See *Articulation*.)

Per Cent Hearing.* The per cent hearing at any given frequency is 100 minus the per cent hearing loss at that frequency.

Per Cent Hearing Loss (Per Cent Deafness).* The per cent hearing loss at a given frequency is 100 times the ratio of the hearing loss in decibels to the number of decibels between the normal threshold levels of audibility and feeling. (A weighted mean of the per cent hearing losses at specified frequencies is often used as a single measure of the loss of hearing.)

Per Cent Intelligibility. (See *Articulation*.)

Period.* The period of a periodic quantity is the smallest value of the increment of the independent variable for which the function repeats itself.

Periodic Quantity.* A periodic quantity is an oscillating quantity, the values of which recur for equal increments of the independent variable.

Phase of a Periodic Quantity.* The phase of a periodic quantity, for a particular value of the independent variable, is the fractional part of a period through which the independent variable has advanced, measured from an arbitrary origin. In the case of a simple sinusoidal quantity, the origin is usually taken as the last previous passage through zero from the negative to positive direction. The origin is generally so chosen that the fraction is less than unity.

Phon.* The phon is the unit of loudness level.

Pitch. Pitch is that attribute of auditory sensation in terms of which sounds may be ordered on a scale extending from low to high; it depends primarily on frequency of the sound stimulus, but also on the sound pressure and wave form of the stimulus.

Plane Wave.* A plane wave is a wave in which the wavefronts are everywhere parallel planes normal to the direction of propagation.

Power Level (L_w). Power level, in decibels, is 10 times the logarithm to the base 10 of the ratio of a given power to a reference power. The form of power (e.g., acoustic) and the reference power must be indicated. The reference power used throughout this handbook for sound-power level is the picowatt (i.e., 1 $\mu\mu$watt), and the symbol *dbp* is employed to indicate both the unit of power level (the decibel) and the reference power (the picowatt). In sound recording, a reference electric power often used is the milliwatt, and the symbol *dbm* is employed to indicate both the unit of power level (the decibel) and the reference power (the milliwatt).

Power (Level) Gain. Power-level gain in decibels is the excess of the output power level in decibels over the input power level in decibels. By reason of the properties of logarithms, it is also 10 times the common logarithm of the ratio of the output power to the input power. Ordinarily, the name of this quantity can be shortened without ambiguity to power gain in decibels.

Power Spectrum Level. The power spectrum level of a sound at a specified frequency is the power level for the acoustic power contained in a band 1 cps wide, centered at the specified frequency. In this handbook, it is expressed in decibels re 1 picowatt (1 $\mu\mu$watt), i.e., dbp.

Pressure Spectrum Level (L_{ps}). The pressure spectrum level of a sound at a specified frequency is the effective sound pressure level for the sound energy contained within a band 1 cps wide, centered at the specified frequency. Ordinarily this has significance only for sound having a continuous distribution of energy within the frequency range under consideration. The reference pressure used throughout this text is 0.0002 microbar.

Pure Tone. * A pure tone is a sound wave, the instantaneous sound pressure of which is a simple sinusoidal function of the time.

Random-incidence Sound Field. (See *Diffuse Sound Field.*)

Random Noise. Random noise is a fluctuating quantity (such as sound pressure) whose instantaneous amplitudes occur, as a function of time, according to a normal (Gaussian) distribution.

Rate of Decay. * The rate of decay is the time rate at which the sound pressure level (or velocity level) is decreasing at a given point and at a given time. The commonly used unit is the decibel per second.

Recognition Differential. The recognition differential for a specified aural detection system is that excess of the signal level over the noise level presented to the ear which results in a 50 per cent probability of detection of the signal. The bandwidth of the system, within which signal and noise are presented and measured, must be specified.

Relative Velocity. * The relative velocity of a point with respect to a reference frame is the time rate of change of a position vector of that point with respect to the reference frame.

Resonance. Resonance of a system under forced vibration exists when any small increase or decrease in the frequency of excitation causes a decrease in the response of the system.

Resonant Frequency (f_r). A resonant frequency is a frequency at which resonance exists.

Reverberation. Reverberation is the sound that persists at a given point after direct reception from the source has stopped.

Reverberation Chamber (Reverberation Room). A reverberation chamber is an enclosure in which all the surfaces have been made as sound-reflective as possible. Reverberation chambers are used for certain acoustical measurements.

Reverberation Time (t_{60}). The reverberation time for a given frequency is the time required for the average sound pressure level, originally in a steady state, to decrease 60 db after the source is stopped. Usually the pressure level for the upper part of this range is measured and the result extrapolated to cover 60 db.

Root-mean-square Sound Pressure. (See *Effective Sound Pressure.*)

Sabin (Square-foot Unit of Absorption). The sabin is a measure of the sound absorption of a surface; it is the equivalent of 1 sq ft of perfectly absorptive surface.

Sabine Absorption. The Sabine absorption in a room is the sound absorption (a) defined by the Sabine reverberation-time equation

$$t_{60} = 0.049 \frac{V}{a}$$

where t_{60} is the reverberation time in seconds, V is the volume of the room in cubic feet, and a is the total (Sabine) absorption in sabins (square-foot units). In metric units,

$$t_{60} = 0.161 \frac{V}{a}$$

where V is the volume of the enclosure in cubic meters and a is the total Sabine absorption in square meters.

Sabine Coefficient. The Sabine coefficient of a sound-absorptive surface is the ratio of the Sabine absorption, attributable to that surface, divided by its area.

Sensation Level. (See *Level above Threshold.*)

Signal. A signal is (1) a disturbance used to convey information; (2) the information to be conveyed over a communication system; (3) a signal wave.

Simple Harmonic Motion. A simple harmonic motion is one in which the relationship between time t and displacement x can be expressed in the form $x = A \sin(\omega t + \phi)$, where A is the amplitude, ω the angular frequency, and ϕ the phase angle.

Simple Sound Source. * A simple sound source is a source which radiates sound uniformly in all directions under free-field conditions.

Sone. * The sone is a unit of loudness. A simple tone of frequency 1,000 cps, 40 db above a listener's threshold, produces a loudness of 1 sone. The loudness of any sound that is judged by the listener to be n times that of the 1-sone tone is n sones. A millisone is equal to 0.001 sone.

Sound. (a) Sound is an alteration in pressure, stress, particle displacement, or shear, etc., in an elastic medium, or (b) sound is an auditory sensation evoked by the alterations described above. In case of possible confusion, the term "sound wave" or "elastic wave" may be used for concept (a) and the term "sound sensation" for concept (b). Not all sound waves evoke an auditory sensation. The medium in which the sound exists is often indicated by an appropriate adjective, e.g., air-borne, structure-borne.

Sound Absorption.* Sound absorption is the process by which sound energy is diminished in passing through a medium or in striking a surface.

Sound Absorption Coefficient. (See *Absorption Coefficient.*)

Sound Energy.* The sound energy of a given part of a medium is the total energy in this part of the medium minus the energy which would exist in the same part of the medium with no sound waves present.

Sound Energy Density.* The sound energy density at a point in a sound field is the sound energy contained in a given infinitesimal part of the medium divided by the volume of that part of the medium. The commonly used unit is the erg per cubic centimeter.

Sound Field.* A sound field is a region containing sound waves.

Sound Energy Flux.* The sound energy flux is the average rate of flow of sound energy for one period through any specified area. The commonly used unit is the erg per second.

Sound Intensity (Sound Energy Flux Density).* The sound intensity in a specified direction at a point is the average rate of sound energy transmitted in the specified direction through a unit area normal to this direction at the point considered.

Sound Level. Sound level, in decibels, is the *weighted* sound pressure level obtained by use of a sound-level meter whose weighting characteristics are specified in the latest revision of the American Standards Association standard on sound-level meters. The reference pressure is 0.0002 microbar, unless otherwise specified.

Sound-level Meter. A sound-level meter is a device which is used to measure sound pressure level or weighted sound pressure level, constructed in accordance with the standard specifications for sound-level meters set up by the American Standards Association. The sound-level meter consists of a microphone, an amplifier to raise the microphone output to useful levels, a calibrated attenuator to adjust the amplification to values appropriate to the sound levels being measured, and an instrument to indicate the measured sound level; optional weighting networks are included to adjust the over-all frequency characteristic of the response; provision is made for an output connection to additional measuring equipment.

Sound Power of a Source (W)**.** The sound power of a source is the total sound energy radiated by the source per unit of time.

Sound Power Level (L_w)**.** The sound power level of a sound source, in decibels, is 10 times the logarithm to the base 10 of the ratio of the sound power radiated by the source to a reference power. Throughout this handbook, the reference power is 1 picowatt (1 $\mu\mu$watt). To indicate the 1-picowatt-reference power, the letter p is affixed to the abbreviation for decibel, that is, dbp.

Sound Pressure Level (L_p)**.** The sound pressure level, in decibels, of a sound is 20 times the logarithm to the base 10 of the ratio of the pressure of this sound to the reference pressure. The reference pressure employed throughout this text is 0.0002 microbar. In many sound fields the sound-pressure ratios are not proportional to the square root of corresponding power ratios and hence cannot be expressed in decibels in the strict sense; however, it is common practice to extend the use of the decibel to these cases.

Sound Pressure Spectrum Level. (See *Pressure Spectrum Level.*)

Sound Reduction between Rooms. The sound reduction, in decibels, between two rooms is the amount by which the mean square sound pressure level in the source room exceeds the level in the receiving room. If a common partition separates two rooms, the first of which contains a sound source, the sound reduction between the two rooms is equal to the transmission loss of the partition *plus* a function of the total absorption in the second room and the area of the common partition.

Sound Reflection Coefficient (Acoustical Reflectivity). The sound reflection coefficient of a surface not a generator is the fraction of incident sound reflected by the surface. The angle of incidence, angle of reflection, and characteristic of sound observed must be specified, e.g., power or pressure amplitude at normal incidence.

Sound Transmission Coefficient. (See *Transmission Coefficient.*)

Specific Acoustic Impedance (Unit-area Acoustic Impedance).* The specific acoustic impedance at a point in the medium is the complex ratio of sound pressure to particle velocity.

Specific Acoustic Reactance.* Specific acoustic reactance is the imaginary component of the specific acoustic impedance.

Specific Acoustic Resistance.* Specific acoustic resistance is the real component of the specific acoustic impedance.

Spectrum. The spectrum of a function of time is a description of its resolution into components which are sinusoidal functions of time, each of different frequency and (usually) different amplitude and phase; spectrum is also used to signify a continuous range of components, usually wide in extent, within which waves have some specified common characteristic, e.g., audio-frequency spectrum.

Speed of Sound (*c*). The speed of sound in air is given by $(1.40P_s/\rho)^{\frac{1}{2}}$, where P_s is the atmospheric pressure and ρ is the density of air (see Chap. 2).

Spherical Wave.* A spherical wave is a wave in which the wavefronts are concentric spheres.

Standing Waves.* Standing waves are periodic waves having a fixed distribution in space which is the result of interference of progressive waves of the same frequency and kind. Such waves are characterized by the existence of nodes or partial nodes and antinodes that are fixed in space.

Stationary Waves.* Stationary waves are standing waves in which the energy flux is zero at all points.

Strength of a Sound Source (Strength of a Simple Source).* The strength of a sound source is the maximum instantaneous rate of volume displacement produced by the source when emitting a wave with sinusoidal time variation. The term is properly applicable only to sources of dimensions small with respect to wavelength.

Subharmonic.* A subharmonic is a sinusoidal quantity having a frequency which is an integral submultiple of the fundamental frequency of a periodic quantity to which it is related. For example, a wave, the frequency of which is half the fundamental frequency of another wave, is called the second subharmonic of that wave.

Threshold Audiogram. (See *Audiogram*.)

Threshold of Audibility (Threshold of Detectability).* The threshold of audibility for a specified signal is the minimum effective sound pressure of the signal that is capable of evoking an auditory sensation in a specified fraction of the trials. The characteristics of the signal, the manner in which it is presented to the listener, and the point at which the sound pressure is measured must be specified. The ambient noise reaching the ears is assumed to be negligible, unless otherwise stated.

Threshold of Feeling (or Discomfort, Tickle, or Pain).* The threshold of feeling (or discomfort, tickle, or pain) for a specified signal is the minimum effective sound pressure of that signal which, in a specified fraction of the trials, will stimulate the ear to a point at which there is the sensation of feeling (or discomfort, tickle, or pain).

Transmission Coefficient (Acoustical Transmittivity). The sound-transmission coefficient of a partition is the fraction of incident sound transmitted through the partition. The angle of incidence and the characteristic of sound observed must be specified, e.g., pressure amplitude at normal incidence.

Transmission Loss. Transmission loss is the reduction in the magnitude of some characteristic of a signal, between two stated points in a transmission system. The characteristic is often some kind of level, such as power level or voltage level; in acoustics, the characteristic that is commonly measured is sound pressure level. If the levels are expressed in decibels, then the transmission loss is likewise in decibels.

Transmission Loss of a Partition (*T.L.*). The sound transmission loss of a partition, in decibels, is -10 times the logarithm to the base 10 of the power transmittivity of the partition. It is equal to the number of decibels by which sound incident on a partition is reduced in transmission through it. It is thus a measure of the air-borne sound insulation of the partition. Unless otherwise specified, it is to be understood that the sound fields on both sides of the partition are diffuse.

Ultrasonic Frequency.* An ultrasonic frequency is a frequency lying above the audio-frequency range.

Velocity.* The velocity of a point is the time rate of change of a position vector of that point with respect to an inertial frame.

Velocity Level.* The velocity level, in decibels, of a sound is 20 times the logarithm to the base 10 of the ratio of the particle velocity of the sound to the reference particle velocity. The reference particle velocity shall be stated explicitly. In many sound fields the particle-velocity ratios are not proportional to the square root of corresponding power ratios and hence cannot be expressed in decibels in the strict sense; however, it is common practice to extend the use of the decibel to these cases.

Velocity of Sound. (See *Speed of Sound*.)

Voltage (Level) Gain. Voltage-level gain in decibels is the excess of the output voltage level in decibels over the input voltage level in decibels. By reason of the properties of logarithms, it is also 20 times the common logarithm of the ratio of the output voltage to the input voltage. Ordinarily the name of this quantity can be shortened without ambiguity to voltage gain in decibels.

Volume Unit (VU).*   The volume unit (VU) is a unit for expressing the magnitude of a complex electric wave, such as that corresponding to speech or music.   The volume in VU is equal to the number of decibels by which the wave differs from reference volume.

Volume Velocity.   Volume velocity is the rate of flow of the medium through a specified surface due to a sound wave.

Wave.   A wave is a disturbance which is propagated in a medium in such a manner that at any point in the medium the quantity serving as a measure of the disturbance is a function of the time, while at any instant the quantity serving as a measure of the disturbance at a point is a function of the position of the point.

Any physical quantity which has the same relationship to some independent variable (usually time) that a propagated disturbance has, at a particular instant, with respect to space, may be called a wave.

Wavefront.*   The wavefront of a progressive wave in space is a continuous surface which is a locus of points having the same phase at a given instant.

Wave Interference.*   Wave interference is the phenomenon which results when waves of the same or nearly the same frequency are superposed and is characterized by a spatial or temporal distribution of amplitude of some specified characteristic differing from that of the individual superposed waves.

Wavelength (λ).   The wavelength of a periodic wave in an isotropic medium is the perpendicular distance between two wavefronts in which the displacements have a difference in phase of one complete period.

White Noise.   White noise is noise of a statistically random nature having equal energy per unit frequency bandwidth over a specified total frequency band.

APPENDIX 1.1

The following graphs are illustrative of data of the type described under *How Much Noise Reduction Is Required*.   In this survey, measurements of noise sources were taken within 2 to 5 ft of a machine and in the vicinity of the machine operator.   There may be considerable variation in the output of such machines even though they are supposedly identical.   Measurements of noise levels in areas where men worked were taken at some distance from the chief noise sources; usually several could be heard.   In any specific cases, actual levels in such areas will depend not only on the number and types of machines, but also on the amount and location of sound-absorptive surfaces in the area.   [*Data after Karplus and Bonvallet, Am. Ind. Hyg. Assoc. Quart.,* **14:** 4 (*December,* 1953).]

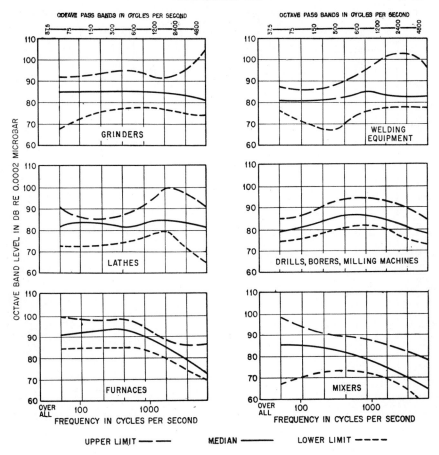

UPPER LIMIT — —   MEDIAN ———   LOWER LIMIT — — — —

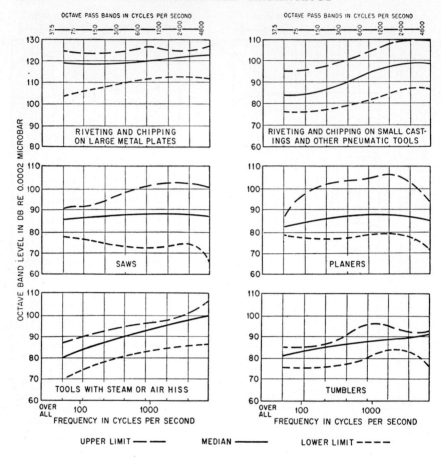

UPPER LIMIT —— ——   MEDIAN ————   LOWER LIMIT —— —— ——

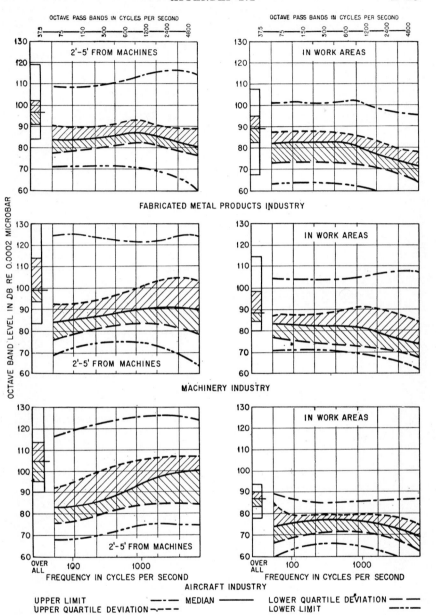

OCTAVE BAND LEVEL IN DB RE 0.0002 MICROBAR

FABRICATED METAL PRODUCTS INDUSTRY

MACHINERY INDUSTRY

AIRCRAFT INDUSTRY

UPPER LIMIT ———— MEDIAN ———— LOWER QUARTILE DEVIATION — —
UPPER QUARTILE DEVIATION —·—— LOWER LIMIT ———·———

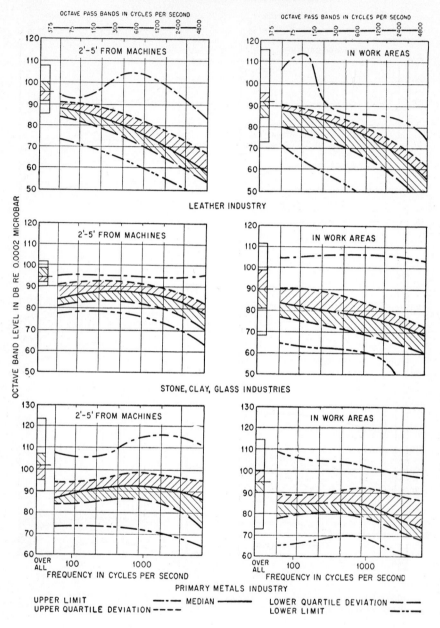

LEATHER INDUSTRY

STONE, CLAY, GLASS INDUSTRIES

PRIMARY METALS INDUSTRY

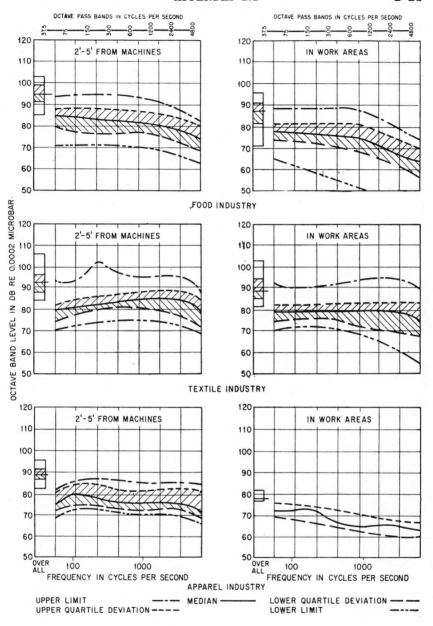

OCTAVE PASS BANDS IN CYCLES PER SECOND

2'-5' FROM MACHINES

IN WORK AREAS

FOOD INDUSTRY

OCTAVE BAND LEVEL IN DB RE 0.0002 MICROBAR.

2'-5' FROM MACHINES

IN WORK AREAS

TEXTILE INDUSTRY

2'-5' FROM MACHINES

IN WORK AREAS

FREQUENCY IN CYCLES PER SECOND

APPAREL INDUSTRY

| UPPER LIMIT | —·—·— | MEDIAN | ——— | LOWER QUARTILE DEVIATION | — — — |
| UPPER QUARTILE DEVIATION | — — — — | | | LOWER LIMIT | —··—··— |

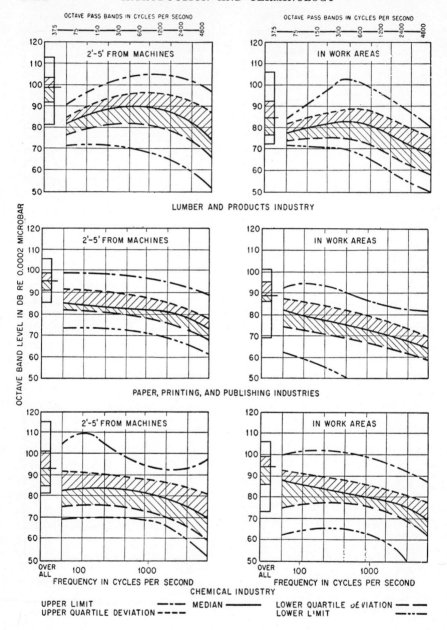

LUMBER AND PRODUCTS INDUSTRY

PAPER, PRINTING, AND PUBLISHING INDUSTRIES

CHEMICAL INDUSTRY

Chapter 2

PHYSICAL PROPERTIES OF NOISE
AND THEIR SPECIFICATION

Robert W. Young, Ph.D.

U.S. Navy Electronics Laboratory

INTRODUCTION

Sound. When an automobile horn is blown, a physical disturbance called *sound* is created in the air. Someone standing nearby may report that he has *heard* the sound of the horn. Thus *sound* is defined in two ways: as the physical disturbance—in this case in the air—and as the sensation in the ear of the listener. According to the first definition, sound exists even if there is no one present to perceive the physical disturbance. Moreover, the disturbance called sound can travel through any elastic medium, such as water or steel.

Noise. Usually the sound of a violin is referred to as music—something pleasing to the ear. If, however, the same physical disturbance exists when quiet is desired, the sound is called a noise. *Noise is defined as unwanted sound.*

Sounds called musical are usually rather regular disturbances of the air; irregular and erratic disturbances are usually unpleasant to hear and are termed noise. Thus noise, in a general sense, is any more or less random disturbance.

At any location there is always some noise. Usually the noise comes from many sources near and far; it may be reflected from walls, and parts of it probably come from all directions. This composite all-encompassing noise associated with a given environment is called *ambient noise.*

WAVE MOTION

Frequency. Most sounds in air are produced by the vibration of some solid material. For example, in the usual automobile horn there is a diaphragm driven rapidly back and forth. The air in contact with this diaphragm is likewise moved to and fro. The number of such motions per unit time is the same for both the diaphragm and the air; the "how often" is called the frequency.

Consider the sound of a small vacuum cleaner that is dominated by a strong whine. When suitable vibration-measuring equipment was attached to the nozzle of this vacuum cleaner, a magnified picture of its mechanical vibration was drawn like that in Fig. 2.1a. The location of the straight horizontal zero line represents the rest position of the nozzle, and the oscillating line represents the up-and-down displacement of the nozzle while the motor was running. The upward direction is marked positive in the figure, the downward negative. The sequence of up-down movements is repeated again and again; this is a *periodic motion.* Each unique sequence of motions is a *cycle.* The time required for the point on the nozzle to move through one cycle is the *period*, namely, $\frac{1}{220}$ sec. The *frequency* of the periodic motion is the number of cycles that occur per unit time. Usually the second is the unit of time, and the unit of frequency is thus the cycle per second (abbreviated cps).* Frequency f is the reciprocal of the period T:

$$f = \frac{1}{T} \tag{2.1}$$

In this example, therefore, $f = 220$ cps.

Sometimes the term angular frequency (or pulsatance) is used; this is (Greek omega) $\omega = 2\pi f$.

Displacement. The curve in Fig. 2.1a can be described by the sine function of trigonometry; it is therefore called a sine wave:

$$x = A \sin 2\pi f t \tag{2.2}$$

The distance x that the nozzle was moved from its position of rest, at a time t, is called the *displacement*. The maximum displacement is defined as the *displacement amplitude A*. The total extent of the motion is $2A$; this is the *double amplitude* or peak-to-peak amplitude. In the particular example of the vacuum-cleaner nozzle, the double amplitude was 0.002 in., in which case $A = 0.001$ in.

Velocity. Figure 2.1a represents the motion of only one point on the vacuum cleaner. At zero time this "particle" had its maximum upward speed; at the peak of the displacement its speed was zero. As it moved downward through its position of rest its velocity was a maximum, being negative (downward). These facts may be checked by comparing Figs. 2.1a and b. The *velocity u* of the *particle* shown in Fig. 2.1b is a cosine wave given by

$$u = (2\pi f A) \cos 2\pi f t \tag{2.3}$$

$$\text{or} \quad u = (2\pi f A) \sin \left[2\pi f \left(t + \frac{T}{4} \right) \right] \tag{2.4}$$

$$\text{or} \quad u = (2\pi f A) \sin \left(2\pi f t + \frac{\pi}{2} \right) \tag{2.4a}$$

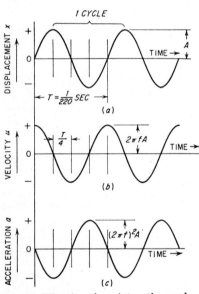

FIG. 2.1. Vibration of a point on the nozzle of a vacuum cleaner.

These descriptions are mathematically equivalent. The cosine wave has the same shape as the sine wave, but it is displaced in time by a quarter of a period. The particle velocity leads the displacement by a time $(T/4)$, and the two waves are said to differ in phase by $2\pi f(T/4) = 2\pi f(1/4f) = \pi/2$.

The maximum particle velocity is the *velocity amplitude*, $2\pi f A$. For the vacuum-cleaner nozzle, the velocity amplitude was $2\pi \times 220 \times 0.001 = 1.38$ in. per sec.

Acceleration. It is apparent from Fig. 2.1b that the velocity of the "particle" changes periodically in direction and magnitude. The time rate of change of velocity is *acceleration*:

$$a = -(2\pi f)^2 A \sin 2\pi f t \tag{2.5}$$

The *acceleration amplitude* is $(2\pi f)^2 A$; in the case of the vacuum cleaner the acceleration amplitude was 1,911 in. per sec per sec. In view of Eq. (2.2), the acceleration is also

$$a = -(2\pi f)^2 x = -\omega^2 x \tag{2.6}$$

* In many countries the unit of frequency is called the *Hertz*, abbreviated *Hz*.

Simple Harmonic Motion. A motion that can be described by a sine wave is called *simple harmonic motion.* Simple harmonic motion is characterized by the fact [see Eq. (2.6)] that the acceleration is at all times proportional to the displacement but oppositely directed.

Root-mean-square Amplitude. One way of describing the magnitude of a wave motion has already been illustrated, namely, its peak or maximum value called the amplitude. For some purposes, other ways of describing the magnitude of a wave are more convenient or significant. A very useful kind of mean value of a wave is its *root-mean-square* amplitude; that is, the square root of the mean squared displacements during one period. For a sine wave, such as the one in Fig. 2.2a that has an amplitude of 3 units, the rms amplitude is 2.12 units, or 0.707 times the maximum value. The rms value is also known as the *effective* value.

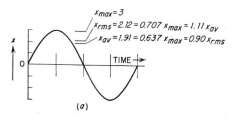

(a)

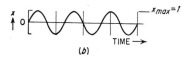

(b)

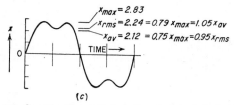

(c)

FIG. 2.2. Combination of 3 sin $2\pi ft$ and $+\sin 6\pi ft$; in phase.

Rectified Average. Sometimes the average value of a sound wave is wanted. More exactly, this is the mean value of a rectified wave; the average is taken over a period of motion without regard to whether the displacement is positive or negative. In the case of x, the sine wave in Fig. 2.2a, the rectified-average amplitude is 1.91 units, and $x_{av} = 0.637 x_{max}$.

In Phase. Figure 2.2b shows a sine wave having three times the frequency and one-third the amplitude of the wave pictured at Fig. 2.2a. Both waves cross their respective zero positions in the same direction at the same time; they are therefore said to be *in phase.*

Superposition. In many situations where the total motion is not large the result of superposing two simple oscillations is merely the sum of the two individual motions. This is the principle of *superposition.* If, in accordance with this principle, the sine waves of Fig. 2.2a and b are added together, the result is that shown at c. The maximum (peak), rms, and average values have again been computed; the results are shown in the figure. The ratios between these values are no longer the same as they were for the sine wave. Also (note carefully!) the maximum value of the combination is a little *less* than that of the single large wave alone.

Out of Phase. Figure 2.3 depicts a similar combination of sine waves, but here there is a phase difference of π or 180° between the two constituent waves. That is, at a starting time where both displacements are zero one motion is directed upward and the other is directed downward. For the individual sine waves the maximum, rms, and rectified-average values are the same as in Fig. 2.2. When the two waves are combined, however, the results as listed at Fig. 2.3c are different—except that the rms amplitude is still 2.24. One of the important characteristics of the rms value is that it remains the same regardless of the relative phases of the constituent waves of a complex motion.

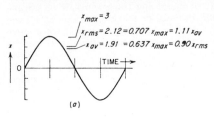

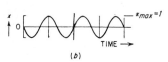

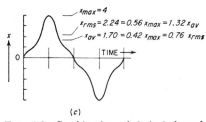

(a)

(b)

(c)

FIG. 2.3. Combination of $3 \sin 2\pi ft$ and $-\sin 6\pi ft$; out of phase.

Square Wave. A waveform often used for electrical tests is the periodic square wave pictured in Fig. 2.4a. For example, there is a constant positive value for half the period and then an equal negative value for the other half of the period. Under such circumstances the maximum, rms, and rectified-average values are all equal, in this example, to 3 units. The average value is, of course, zero.

A related waveform is the pulsed wave shown in Fig. 2.4b. The positive displacement is 3 units for 1 millisecond (abbreviated msec) and then for the remainder of the period (which is 4 msec) the displacement is zero. This sequence is repeated again and again. In this example, the rms displacement is only one-half the maximum value and the average is only one-fourth the maximum value.

Averaging Time. In all the above examples the mean values have been taken over a complete period. The results would be the same if they were taken over a very long time since the waves are repetitive. If, however, one averages over only a fraction of a period, the results will depend upon the averaging time. For example, suppose that

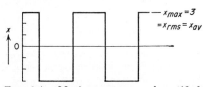

FIG. 2.4a. Maximum, rms, and rectified-average values of a square wave.

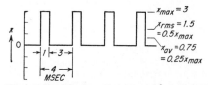

FIG. 2.4b. Maximum, rms, and average values of a particular pulsed wave.

the wave of Fig. 2.4b were averaged during 5 msec to include two successive displacements. The maximum value would still be $x_{max} = 3$, but $x_{rms} = 1.9 = 0.63x_{max}$ and $x_{av} = 1.20 = 0.40x_{max}$. The usual solution to such a predicament is to require that the averaging time be reasonably long in comparison with a period.

SOUND WAVES

Sound Pressure. The atmospheric pressure changes a little from day to day, and on high mountains it is less than at sea level. At any one location, however, it is relatively constant for at least a few seconds. In metric units, the typical atmospheric pressure is about a million dynes per square centimeter. A shorter name for this amount of pressure is the bar, so that *one dyne per square centimeter is a microbar.*

Suppose that sensitive equipment is arranged to measure the atmospheric pressure several hundred feet away from an automobile horn. While the horn is sounding, the atmospheric pressure fluctuates a small amount. The fluctuating part of the air pressure is called *sound pressure*. The sound pressure can be either positive or negative, depending upon whether the total pressure at any instant is in excess or below the average atmospheric pressure. At the distance of 400 ft from the horn the maximum excess pressure may be a millionth of the atmospheric pressure, in which event the sound-pressure amplitude is 1 dyne per sq cm, or 1 microbar.

Speed of Sound. The air-borne disturbance (the sound generated by the automobile horn) travels on and on through the atmosphere. It takes time for sound to pass through the air. The rate at which the disturbance travels through the medium is the *speed of sound* (or *velocity of sound*, if the direction is specified also). At a room temperature of 68°F (20°C) this speed is 1,127 ft per sec (344 m per sec). It is the wave motion—the sound—that travels at this speed. This must not be confused with the particle velocity, which is the rate at which a given particle of air moves to and fro when the sound wave passes. As indicated in Eq. (2.3), the particle velocity of a sine wave is proportional to the frequency, but the speed of sound through the air does not change with the frequency. The speed does, however, increase with the temperature, at the rate of 1.1 ft per sec per degree Fahrenheit (i.e., 60.7 cm per sec per degree centigrade).

Wavelength. The distance that a sound wave travels in one period is the *wavelength* of the sound. Since the speed of sound differs from one medium to another the wavelength changes proportionally. The Greek letter lambda (λ) is used to represent wavelength. Then if c is the speed of sound, T the period, and f the frequency,

$$\lambda = cT = \frac{c}{f} \tag{2.7}$$

The wavelength of the sound given off by the vacuum-cleaner nozzle in the previous example which vibrated at a frequency of 220 cps is thus $\lambda = 1,127/220 = 5.1$ ft, or 1.6 meter. Wavelengths in air for different frequencies can be read from Fig. 2.5.

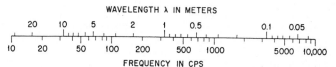

Fig. 2.5. Wavelength in air vs. frequency, under ordinary conditions.

Wavelength is an important acoustical parameter. For example, sound having a wavelength much larger than the size of an obstacle is little affected by the presence of the obstacle; it will bend around it. Figure 2.6 illustrates how a sound wave in passing through a picket fence is disturbed only a little by it, but the sound soon travels on the same as if the fence were not present at all. This bending of the sound around obstacles is *diffraction*.

If the wavelength of the sound is small in comparison with the size of the obstacle the sound will be reflected or scattered in many directions and the obstacle will cast a shadow. This is suggested by Fig. 2.7, where the dotted lines indicate sound reflected back from the wall. This picture is much simplified; actually some sound is diffracted into the "shadow" and there is significant reflection from the ground. As a consequence of diffraction, a wall is of little value as a shield against sound of low frequency (long wavelength), but it can be an effective barrier against high-frequency (short-wavelength) sound (see Chap. 3 for details).

Divergence. In open air where sound can spread spherically in all directions without encountering reflecting surfaces the sound pressure decreases as the distance from the source increases. Specifically, this is the case of *spherical divergence*, in which the sound pressure varies in inverse proportion to the distance. Thus

$$p = p_x \left(\frac{r_x}{r}\right) = (\text{const}) \frac{1}{r} \tag{2.8}$$

where p_x is the sound pressure at some particular distance r_x from the acoustic center of the source, and p and r are the sound pressure and distance, respectively, at the point of measurement. The relationship expressed by Eq. (2.8) is the *inverse-distance law* (frequently called the "inverse-square law"); it states that the product of the sound pressure by the distance is constant. Applied to the case of the automobile horn, for which the sound pressure was observed to be $p_x = 1$ microbar at a distance $r_x = 400$ ft, this equation tells us (if there are no reflections) that the sound pressure at a distance of 100 ft should be $p = 1 \times (400/100) = 4$ microbars.

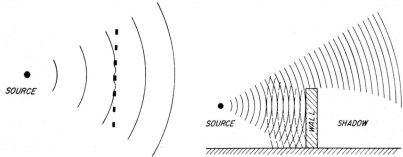

Fig. 2 6. Sound wave passing through a picket fence. This is a plan view; cross sections of the pickets are shown.

Fig. 2.7. Reflection of sound of short wavelength by a wall, and the resulting shadow.

Absorption of a fraction of the sound simply as a consequence of traveling through the air also causes a reduction in sound pressure that can be quite significant at great distances.

Acoustic Free Field. In a place where sound can travel freely without reflection the sound waves are called *free progressive waves* traveling in a *free field*. For certain tests free-field conditions are necessary and often outdoor measurements are impractical. For such tests, special rooms have been built in which the sound-absorptive construction of the walls, floor, and ceiling is such that practically no sound is reflected from them. These are called *free-field rooms* or *anechoic* (echo-free) *rooms*. Rooms in which much of the sound is absorbed upon reflection from the boundaries but in which a "free field" does not exist are sometimes referred to as *dead rooms* (or lagged rooms).

Reverberation. In an ordinary room a great deal of the sound is reflected from the walls. Thus, the sound at a given position in the room is made up of that which travels directly from the source plus sound that comes from other directions as a result of reflection. Under such circumstances the sound pressure does not decrease so rapidly as predicted by the inverse-distance relation* of Eq. (2.8). Nonuniformity of absorption and of shape of bounding surfaces tends to increase the scattering of sound within the room. When conditions are such that the sound waves are traveling equally in all directions and the sound pressure is everywhere the same within the room then the sound field is *perfectly diffuse*. As a consequence of reflections from the boundaries of a room the sound persists after the source has stopped; this persisting

* For a detailed discussion, see Chap. 18.

sound is called *reverberation*. The effect is most noticeable in a *reverberant room* where the walls do not absorb sound readily and the sound persists for a considerable time.

Intensity. Sound waves can be described by any of several characteristics, such as the displacement of particles of the medium, the particle velocity, or the sound pressure. The last named is the characteristic commonly measured because most microphones used in noise-measuring instruments respond to sound pressure. However, for some purposes one wants to know the energy or power associated with sound waves. Apparatus for direct measurement of sound power is not readily available, but this quantity can be calculated from sound-pressure measurements under certain conditions.

The passage of a sound wave is accompanied by a flow of sound energy. The power per unit area thus transmitted, in the direction of travel, is the *intensity*. This is given by

$$I = up \cos \phi \qquad (2.9)$$

where u is the rms particle velocity of the wave, p the rms sound pressure, and ϕ the difference in phase between the two. If the sound wave is traveling through a free field

$$u = \frac{p}{\rho c} \qquad (2.10)$$

where ρ is the density of the medium and c the speed of sound therein. In a free field, sound pressure and particle velocity are in phase, so that $\cos \phi = 1$, and the intensity in the direction of propagation is

$$I = \frac{p^2}{\rho c} \qquad (2.11)$$

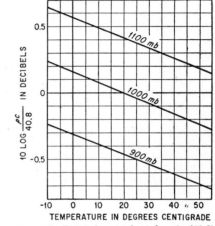

FIG. 2.8. Dependence of $10 \log (\rho c/40.8)$ on temperature for several barometric pressures.

Perpendicular to this direction the intensity is zero. In the technical sense, the word *intensity* is meaningful only if the direction is specified. Equations (2.10) and (2.11) apply only in free progressive plane or spherical waves.

The quantity ρc is called the *characteristic impedance* of the medium through which the sound travels. For air at a typical barometric pressure of 1,000 millibars (29.5 in. Hg) and a temperature of 20°C (68°F), $\rho c = 40.8$ cgs units. This value is used for illustrative calculation throughout this handbook. The characteristic impedance changes with temperature and barometric pressure (see Fig. 2.8).

Equation (2.11) is true for any consistent set of units. Suppose, however, that the intensity is wanted (expressed in microwatts per sq cm) for a free progressive wave in air, and that in a certain situation the sound pressure is 50 microbars (dynes per sq cm). Then

$$I = \frac{p^2}{10\rho c} = \frac{50^2}{10 \times 40.8} = 6.1 \ \mu\text{w per sq cm} \qquad (2.11a)$$

Sound Power. Consider an imaginary sphere of radius r surrounding a sound source, in a free field, that is emitting sound power W. The area of the sphere is $4\pi r^2$; so the average power unit per area (that is, the average intensity in the radial direction) is

$$I_{\text{av}} = \frac{W}{4\pi r^2}$$

The subscript "av" has been used on I_{av} to emphasize that this equation is true, on the average, over the sphere; it does not necessarily give I for any one direction. In view of Eq. (2.11) there is an average squared sound pressure p_{av}^2 that corresponds to I_{av}, so that

$$W = \frac{4\pi r^2 p_{av}^2}{\rho c} \tag{2.12}$$

If one wants sound power expressed in microwatts, distances in centimeters, and sound pressures in microbars (dynes per square centimeter),

$$W = \frac{4\pi r^2 p_{av}^2}{10\rho c} = 0.0309 r^2 p_{av}^2 \quad \mu\text{w} \tag{2.12a}$$

If the distance is in feet and the sound pressure in microbars,

$$W = 28.6 r^2 p_{av}^2 \quad \mu\text{w} \tag{2.12b}$$

For example, when a man shouts, on the average the sound pressure 1 ft in front of his lips is about 5 microbars. This means he is producing a sound power of

$$W = 28.6 \times 1^2 \times 5^2 = 701 \ \mu\text{w} = 0.0007 \text{ watt}$$

Remember that Eq. (2.12) is for sound escaping in all directions; if the sound is restricted to a hemisphere, for a given sound pressure the necessary sound power is only half as great.

The wide spread in sound power that may be encountered is illustrated in Table 2.1. Obviously these must be orders of magnitude only; e.g., there are noisy automobiles and quiet automobiles, yet there is only one entry in the table. Moreover, these are long-time average values. If a really quantitative statement of sound power were intended, more details of the method of averaging would be needed. For example, even in connected speech, the silent parts are estimated to occupy 35 per cent of the time; so *while sound is being produced* the power is accordingly greater than the value listed in Table 2.1. (The column headed *Power Level* is explained below.)

Table 2.1. Sound Powers Produced by a Few Sources

Source	Power	Power level, dbp
Jet airplane	10 kilowatts	160
Pneumatic chipping hammer	1 watt	120
Automobile at 45 mph	0.1 watt	110
Piano	20 milliwatts	103
Conversational speech, connected	20 microwatts	73
Small electric clock	0.02 microwatt	43
Soft whisper	0.001 microwatt	30

Directivity Factor. It is common for sound sources to radiate more sound in one direction than in others. The sound pressure in front of a speaker's mouth, for high-frequency sound, is likely to be ten times as great as that in the opposite direction. Low-frequency (long-wavelength) sound from the mouth is more uniformly radiated in all directions. In general, a sound source that is small in comparison with the wavelength of sound it produces tends to be an omnidirectional source; a sound source large in comparison with the wavelength of the sound produced is apt to be directional.

The directivity factor is a term often employed to describe how directional a source is. The *directivity factor Q* is defined as the ratio of the mean square sound pressure, at some fixed distance and specified direction, to the mean square sound pressure at the same distance but averaged over all directions from the source. The distance must be sufficiently great that the sound appears to come from a single point called the *acoustic center* of the source. Thus if p_d^2 is the squared sound pressure in the specified direction and p_{av}^2 is the squared pressure averaged over all directions, the directivity factor for the specified direction is

$$Q = \frac{p_d{}^2}{p_{av}{}^2} \tag{2.13}$$

When this equation is combined with Eq. (2.12) it follows that the sound pressure in the specified direction is related to the total power output of the source by

$$p_d = \left(\frac{\rho c Q W}{4\pi r^2}\right)^{\frac{1}{2}} \tag{2.14}$$

If one chooses to measure p_d in microbars, W in microwatts, and r in feet and to take $\rho c = 40.8$ cgs units, in a free field

$$p_d = \frac{0.186(QW)^{\frac{1}{2}}}{r} \tag{2.14a}$$

If r is in centimeters instead of feet, then Eq. (2.14a) becomes

$$p_d = \frac{5.69(QW)^{\frac{1}{2}}}{r} \tag{2.14b}$$

The *directivity factor* for a microphone that receives sound is defined in a similar fashion as for a sound source: it is the ratio of the square of the open-circuit voltage produced in response to sound waves coming from the specified direction to the mean square voltage for sound coming from all directions. Sometimes the directivity factor is stated without the direction's being specified; under such circumstances one can only assume that the direction is that of maximum response.

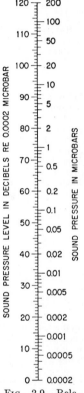

FIG. 2.9. Relation between sound pressure and sound pressure level.

LEVELS AND THE DECIBEL

Sound Pressure Level. The sound pressure near a powerful engine may well be greater than 200 microbars. This is a million times the sound pressure that is just audible to a very sensitive ear. To ease the handling of this wide range of sound pressure it has become customary to deal with *sound pressure level* instead of sound pressure. The logarithmic relation between the two is indicated in Fig. 2.9. Notice that instead of a million-to-one ratio of sound pressure one can deal with only 120 units of sound pressure *level*. A logarithmic scale is useful for other reasons also; for example, calculations concerning pressure which would require multiplication can instead be done by addition.

The usual unit of sound pressure level is the *decibel* (abbreviated db). It is of such nature that doubling any sound pressure corresponds to an increase of sound pressure level of 6 db. For example, in Fig. 2.9, note that the sound pressure level corresponding to a sound pressure of 1 microbar is 74 db; that corresponding to 2 microbars is 80 db. A change of sound pressure by a factor of 10 corresponds to a change in sound pressure level of 20 db.

The sound pressure level L_p in decibels, corresponding to a sound pressure p, is defined by

$$L_p = 10 \log \frac{p^2}{p_0{}^2} = 20 \log \frac{p}{p_0} \quad \text{db} \tag{2.15}$$

where p_0 is a *reference pressure*. Here as elsewhere in this handbook the common logarithm to the base 10 is to be understood unless there is a specific notation to the contrary. A useful table for calculating the number of decibels corresponding to a given pressure ratio is included as Appendix 2.1.

Reference Pressure. *The reference pressure commonly employed for noise measurement is* 0.0002 *microbar, i.e.,* 0.0002 *dyne per sq cm, and is the one used throughout* this handbook. Thus sound pressure level may be understood here to mean simply

$$L_p = 20 \log \frac{p}{0.0002} \qquad \text{db} \qquad (2.16)$$

The reference pressure of 0.0002 microbar is approximately the threshold of hearing at 1,000 cps. A reference pressure serves to fix a 0-db mark in a scale of sound pressure level: as in Fig. 2.9, the "zero level" *corresponds* to the reference quantity. The "re" in this figure means "with reference to."

Typical Sound Pressure Levels. Some idea of the sound pressure levels associated with common sound sources may be gained from Table 2.2. The sound-pressure levels given here are for a wide frequency band; the distribution of sound pressure level in narrower bands is illustrated in a later section, *Plotting Noise Measurements*. Notice that in many cases a distance is specified; if a source is localized a distance or position

Table 2.2. Wide-band Sound Pressure Levels for a Variety of Sounds

Sound Pressure Level L_p, db	Source
140	
130	Hydraulic press, distance 3 ft
120	Bass drum at 3 ft, peak
110	Automobile horn, distance 3 ft
100	DC-6 airliner, inside
90	Automatic lathe, distance 3 ft
80	Automobile at 40 mph, inside
70	Office with tabulating machines, ambient noise
60	Conversational speech, distance 3 ft
50	Residential kitchen, ambient noise

must be given to make the quoted sound pressure level meaningful. Only for ambient noise generated by a multiplicity of sources can the distance be omitted. Most of the levels in Table 2.2 are long-time averages. For the bass drum, however, the peak sound pressure level is given; obviously its long-time average would be much lower—particularly in quiet music!

Other Levels. Other kinds* of levels are also employed in acoustics. *Power level* in decibels corresponding to power W is

$$L_w = 10 \log \frac{W}{W_0} \qquad \text{db} \qquad (2.17)$$

---

* The general relationship for a *level*, in the specialized logarithmic sense of the word in acoustics, is

$$L = \log_r \frac{q}{q_0} \qquad (2.17a)$$

where q is the quantity whose level is being obtained, q_0 is the reference quantity of like kind, and r is the base of the logarithm. Thus, the level of a quantity is the logarithm of the ratio of that quantity to a reference quantity. The base of the logarithm and the reference quantity must be specified. Since there are many *kinds* of levels, the type of level involved must be specified, e.g., *voltage* level.

The decibel is a unit of level when $r = 10^{1/10}$ and the quantities q and q_0 are in some idealized situation proportional to power. That is, the decibel is used as a unit of level of quantities such as voltage squared and sound pressure squared. Strictly, the decibel is thus a unit of "pressure-squared" level, but the usual convention is to shorten this to pressure level. With a little juggling in accordance with the rules of logarithms it follows that

$$L = 10 \log_{10} \frac{q}{q_0} \qquad \text{db} \qquad (2.17b)$$

which is of the same form as Eqs. (2.17) and (2.18). Other units of level, which are seldom used, are the neper (for ratios of amplitudes) and the bel, for which $r = 2.718$ and 10, respectively. Thus 10 db = 1 bel = 1.15 nepers.

where W_0 is a reference power. A useful table for calculating the number of decibels corresponding to a given power ratio is included as Appendix 2.2. If W is expressed in watts, the standard reference $W_0 = 1$ micromicrowatt (1 picowatt) is used throughout this handbook. The letter p is generally appended to "db" to indicate that the reference power is 1 picowatt.* Table 2.1 gives the power level of a few typical noise sources.

The *voltage level* corresponding to voltage v is

$$L_v = 10 \log \frac{v^2}{v_0^2} = 20 \log \frac{v}{v_0} \quad \text{db} \tag{2.18}$$

Spectrum Level. Many complex sounds may reasonably be assumed to be made up of a large number of small noises distributed continuously in frequency. For noise of this kind it is sometimes convenient to employ the sound-pressure spectrum level L_{ps}. This is the sound pressure level for a band 1 cps wide; more descriptively, it is the "pressure-squared per cps" level. Usually it is necessary to measure in bands wider than 1 cps; what is measured directly is the sound pressure level within some passband between frequencies $(f_2 - f_1)$. The width of this passband depends upon characteristics of the measuring equipment; what is measured is the *band-pressure level*, L_{band}.

In general, the conversion from one band-pressure level to another band-pressure level is accomplished by subtracting from the first level ten times the logarithm of the ratio of the respective bandwidths. For example, suppose that a band level L_{200} has been measured with a passband $(f_2 - f_1) = 200$ cps and the question later arises what the band level L_{50} would have been had the measurements been made in a 50-cps band centered (geometrically) within the 200-cps band. The result is

$$L_{50} = L_{200} - 10 \log {}^{200}\!/_{50} = L_{200} - 6 \text{ db}$$

Similarly, the 1-cps band level (the *spectrum level L_{ps}*) can be computed from the band level L_{band}, which has been measured for the band $(f_2 - f_1)$, by

$$L_{ps} = L_{band} - 10 \log \frac{f_2 - f_1}{1} \quad \text{db} \tag{2.19}$$

Examples of the use of spectrum level are given later in this chapter in the section entitled *Plotting Spectrum Level*.

Directional Gain. When a source is directional, the amount by which the sound pressure level L_d in some specified direction exceeds the level L_{av} of the mean square sound pressure (at the same distance and averaged over all directions) is called the *directional gain* (or *directivity index*); that is,

$$G = L_d - L_{av} \quad \text{db} \tag{2.20}$$

Upon comparison with the definition of directivity factor Q employed in Eq. (2.13) and recalling the definition of sound pressure level, it will be seen that

$$G = 10 \log Q \quad \text{db} \tag{2.21}$$

Usually the direction employed for reference is the direction of maximum response, but this is not a necessary requirement. The directional gain can be either positive or negative, depending upon whether the reference direction specified is one of greater-than-average or less-than-average response.

The directional gain can be used to relate the sound-power level of a source to the sound pressure level at a given distance and direction. By combining Eqs. (2.14), (2.16), and (2.17), and recalling that $p_0 = 0.0002$ microbar and $W_0 = 1$ micromicrowatt, in a direction for which the gain is G,

$$L_p = L_w + G - 20 \log \frac{r}{r_0} + 10 \log \frac{\rho c}{40.8} + 29.1 \text{ db} \tag{2.22}$$

---

* A reference power of 10^{-13} watt has been employed in some previous publications. To convert a power level in db which has been referred to 10^{-13} watt to a power level which is referred to 10^{-12} watt, merely subtract 10 db from the power level re 10^{-13} watt.

where the distance r is in centimeters and $r_0 = 1$ cm. If, however, the distance is in feet the final term is -0.6 db instead of 29.1 and can often be disregarded. The variation of $10 \log \left(\dfrac{\rho c}{40.8} \right)$ with temperature and barometric pressure is given in Fig. 2.8.

If L_p is sound pressure level based on the mean square sound pressure averaged over all directions, then $G = 1$, and for $\rho c = 40.8$ cgs units and r in feet,

$$L_p = L_w - 20 \log r - 0.6 \text{ db} \tag{2.22a}$$

If r is in meters, then for the above conditions Eq. (2.22a) becomes

$$L_p = L_w - 20 \log r - 10.9 \text{ db} \tag{2.22b}$$

This equation holds for sound spreading out in a sphere. If the sound is restricted to a hemisphere, for a given sound power the sound pressure level is increased by 3 db.

Divergence. It was shown in Eq. (2.8) that, in a free field, sound diverges *spherically* and the sound pressure varies inversely as the distance. Let the sound pressure level at the particular distance r_x be

$$L_x = 20 \log \frac{p_x}{0.0002} \quad \text{db} \tag{2.23}$$

so that the sound pressure level at any distance r is

$$L_p = L_x - 20 \log \frac{r}{r_x} \quad \text{db} \tag{2.24}$$

This is the logarithmic form of the inverse-distance law. The equation says that if r is doubled (that is, if $r = 2r_x$) the sound pressure level drops 6 db; if the distance is halved the sound pressure level increases 6 db. This 6-db change for a doubling of distance is a convenient test for the existence of a free field.

If sound is constrained to travel as if from a line source (instead of a point source) the sound waves are cylindrical in shape instead of spherical, and the sound pressure varies inversely as the square root of distance. Correspondingly, the sound pressure level drops only 3 db for each doubling of the distance, when *cylindrical divergence* exists. For plane waves all parts of the wave travel in the same direction and the divergence is zero.

PLOTTING NOISE MEASUREMENTS

Bandwidth. Electrical filters used for analyzing noise reject signals of frequency below a lower "cutoff" frequency and above the upper "cutoff" frequency. Signals between these two frequencies are passed by the filter; so this intermediate region is called the passband. The difference between the cutoff frequencies is the *bandwidth*.

The following passbands often are included in filters intended for noise measurements: 75 to 150 cps, 150 to 300 cps, 300 to 600 cps, 600 to 1,200 cps, 1,200 to 2,400 cps, 2,400 to 4,800 cps. Note that in each case the ratio of the cutoff frequencies is 2:1. This frequency ratio defines the interval called the octave in music; so these passbands are called octave bands. The bandwidth increases in proportion to frequency. A noise-measuring device which incorporates such filters is called a *proportional bandwidth* or *constant-percentage bandwidth analyzer* (see Chap. 16).

Octave Band. Figure 2.10 is an example of one type of graph plotted from measurements of noise in successive octave bands. The particular band limits are shown at the top of the graph. The sound pressure level in any one octave band is the *octave-band sound pressure level* or, briefly, the *octave-band level*. Notice, for example, that the sound pressure level in the band 600 to 1,200 cps was found to be 64 db; this value is plotted on the vertical line at the center of the band, given by $\sqrt{600 \times 1{,}200} = 850$ cps. Such a plot of the different octave- (or other) band levels in relation to frequency is called a *spectrum*. The actual experimental data are represented by the plotted points. Connecting lines are useful, however, to help to estimate the octave-band levels at intermediate frequencies and to bring out the general shape of the spectrum.

Half-octave Band. Sometimes more detailed information about a noise spectrum is needed than can be obtained with octave bands. Half-octave bands may then be employed. The cutoff frequencies for half-octave bands commonly used are listed at the top of Fig. 2.11. The open circles in this figure show how the sound spectrum of Fig. 2.10 appears when measured in half-octave bands.*

Third-octave Bands. When still more detailed information is required, third-octave† bands can be used. The previously plotted noise spectrum is shown for one-third octave bands in Fig. 2.12. These bands are usually identified by their rounded center frequencies, which are shown near the bottom of the figure: 100, 125, 160, 250 cps, etc. In addition to affording a little better resolution than is possible with wider bands, it is an advantage with third-octave bands that the center frequencies are multiples by 10 of the basic 10 numbers, no matter how far the range is extended. Sometimes it is convenient to number each band; such numbers are shown at the top of Fig. 2.12. These band numbers are simply 10 times the logarithm of the center frequency of the band; e.g., the band centered at 1,000 cps is No. 30.

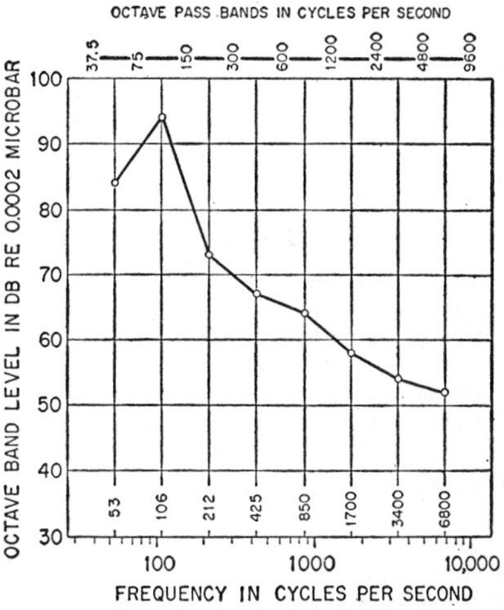

Continuous Distribution. Many noises are such that the sound is distributed essentially continuously in frequency (meaning that all frequencies are present) within a given passband; if the width of the passband is reduced, the measured sound pressure level is decreased. That is, a narrow band does not permit so much noise to pass as does a wideband. Notice, for example, that the half-octave band level read at 1,000 cps in Fig. 2.11 is 59 db whereas the octave-band level read at this same frequency in Fig. 2.10 is 62 db. Since many noise analyses are given in terms of octave bands, sometimes it is con-

FIG. 2.10. Example of a plot of noise measurements by octave bands. The sound source was a blower driven by a motor having a pronounced hum. These data are averages of measurements made in a reverberant room at distances of 10 to 30 ft from the motor.

venient to compute (for reasonably continuous spectra) the corresponding octave-band levels by adding 3 db to the observed half-octave band levels. Similarly, octave-band levels can be computed by adding 5 db to third-octave band levels.

Interpretation. Consider the observed sound pressure level near 120 cps in Figs. 2.10 to 2.12. The level at this frequency is the same, namely, 94 db, irrespective of the width of the passband. This happens when the predominant sound within the band is a tone of a single frequency. Such tones can often be identified by listening, or from information such as known multiples of the power-line frequency. A vertical bar has been drawn at 120 cps in Figs. 2.11 and 2.12 to indicate that this peak is thought to be due to a simple tone—not to continuously distributed noise. The

---

* Another comparison of measurements made in octave, half-octave, and third-octave bands is given in Chap. 17.

† These bands are usually described as being one-third octave wide. It is evident that for 10 successive bands to be exactly contiguous their width would have to be represented by the frequency ratio $10^{1/10} = 1.2589$. For practical purposes this ratio is indistinguishable from the ratio corresponding to a true one-third octave division; namely $2^{1/3} = 1.2599$. Moreover, the spacing of the bands (aside from rounding) is based exactly on $10^{1/10}$: every 10 bands the frequency is increased by a factor of 10.

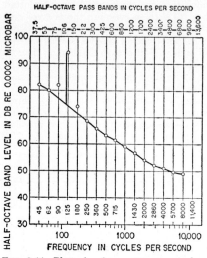

FIG. 2.11. Plot of noise measurements by half-octave bands. The sound source was the same motor blower as in Fig. 2.10.

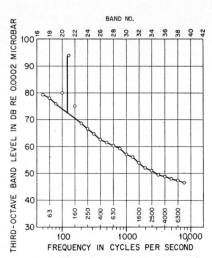

FIG. 2.12. Plot of noise measurements by third-octave bands. The source was the same motor blower as for Fig. 2.10.

vertical bar represents an *interpretation* in contrast to the open circles, which represent the actual measurements. It will be noticed in Fig. 2.11 at 90 and 180 cps, and in Fig. 2.12 at 100 and 160 cps, that the curves have been drawn *below* the observed points. This is also by way of interpretation. A practical filter does not reject completely signals outside the nominal passband, and the examples of Figs. 2.11 and 2.12 illustrate how the strong signal at 120 cps may affect the readings in the adjacent band. See Chap. 16 for a further discussion of filter characteristics.

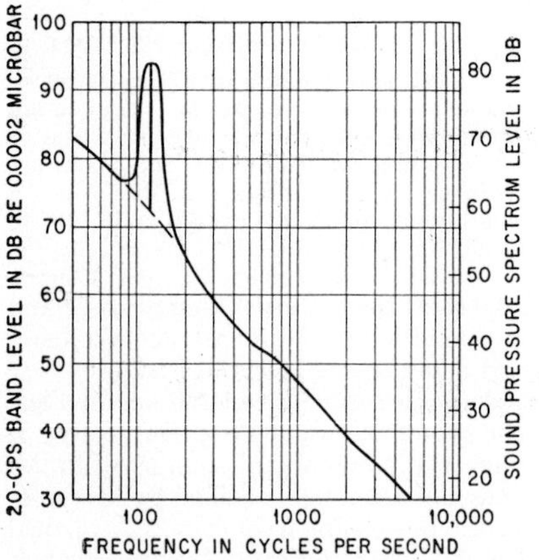

Constant-width Band. Another kind of sound analyzer in common use for noise analysis is one in which the bandwidth is fixed and usually not very wide—perhaps on the order of 20 cps. The frequency location of such a constant-width band can be shifted over the frequency range of interest (for example) by rotation of a dial. This kind is called a constant (or fixed) bandwidth analyzer.

If the sound pressure level measured with a constant-width band is constant over a wide frequency range, the spectrum is described as "flat" and the noise is called *white noise*. Otherwise expressed, in a white noise the mean sound pressure squared is uniform and continuous with frequency. A white noise may also be a *random noise* in which the instantaneous amplitudes of the components of the noise

FIG. 2.13. Example of plot of noise measurements by 20-cps band. The noise is the same as in Fig. 2.10. The solid bar at 120 cps and the adjacent dashed lines have been added as interpretation.

are distributed in time in accordance with the normal (Gaussian) distribution. Random noise, however, does not necessarily have a flat spectrum.

Figure 2.13 shows how the blower-motor noise plotted in Fig. 2.10 appears when measured with an analyzer having a 20-cps passband. Notice the marked difference

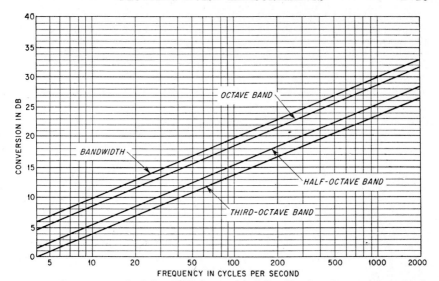

FIG. 2.14. Conversion in decibels, to be subtracted from band level to obtain spectrum level. Use the upper curve when the actual width of the passband is given. Read from the appropriate one of the lower three curves when the center frequency of a band is given. The conversion is appropriate only for distributed noise.

in the shape of these two curves. The right-hand scale of sound-pressure spectrum level is discussed below.

Spectrum Slope. The approximate shape of a spectrum, or part of the spectrum, often is described by its slope. However, care is necessary in the use of such a description. For example, in Fig. 2.10 in the region from 200 to 4,000 cps the downward slope is a little over 4 db per octave, but in Fig. 2.13 over the same interval, the downward slope is about 7 db per octave. This 3 db per octave difference in slope always appears when measurements made with a band of constant width are compared with those made with proportional bands, because the latter being progressively wider accept more and more distributed noise as the frequency increases.

Plotting Spectrum Level. One way to compare data obtained with analyzers of different bandwidths is to reduce all observations to what would have been obtained with a common bandwidth of 1 cps. This may be accomplished by the use of sound pressure spectrum level. As indicated in Eq. (2.19), the spectrum level of a noise can be calculated from measurements in wider bands by subtracting a conversion from the observed band level. The conversion is ten times the logarithm of the number of cps in the band. It can be obtained graphically by two different methods from Fig. 2.14.

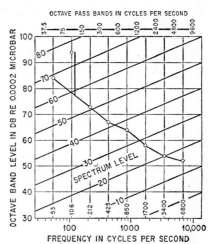

FIG. 2.15. Example of plot of noise spectrum by octave bands, with added spectrum-level grid. The data are the same as in Fig. 2.10.

The first method depends upon knowledge of the actual width of a passband in cps. Suppose, for example, that the conversion is required for a passband of 20 cps. From the top curve labeled *bandwidth* in Fig. 2.14, the conversion for a width of 20 cps is seen to be 13 db. This conversion can be applied to the 20-cps band levels plotted in Fig. 2.13. For example, at 1,000 cps the observed band level is 47 db; so the calculated spectrum level at 1,000 cps is 47 − 13 = 34 db. This and other values of spectrum level can be read directly from the scale added on the right side of Fig. 2.13.

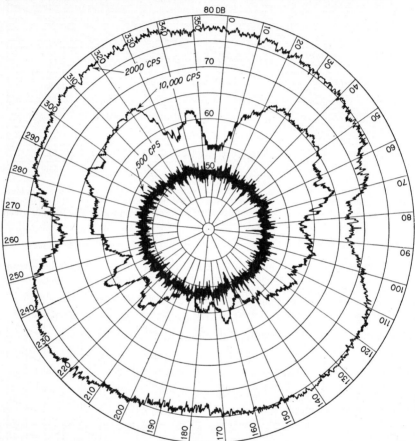

Fig. 2.16. Directional response patterns of sound radiated from a high-speed electric hand grinder running under no load at 22,000 rpm. The sound pressure level was measured in third-octave bands centered at the frequencies indicated. The microphone was rotated about the grinder at a distance of 30 in., in a plane containing the axis of the grinder; the grinder chuck was at 0°. (*Courtesy of General Engineering Laboratory, General Electric Company.*)

The second method of finding the conversion depends upon the use of a proportional band, such as an octave, and the center frequency of the band. Suppose the problem is to compute the spectrum level at 1,000 cps, having been given the half-octave band level of just over 59 db, as read from Fig. 2.11. From Fig. 2.14 the conversion for a half-octave band at 1,000 cps is 25.4 db; so the computed spectrum level at this frequency is about 59 − 25 = 34 db—the same result obtained above for the 20-cps band.

Oblique Grid. The conversion from band level to spectrum level can be accomplished automatically by the use of a graph containing the additional oblique grid shown in Fig. 2.15, where the original data from Fig. 2.10 have been replotted. For example, note that the octave band level at 3,400 cps can be read from the regular scale to be 54 db, and, in relation to the sloping grid, the spectrum level is 20 db at this frequency.

A particular convenience of the added grid is that the spectrum level can be read directly when desired, yet the band-level scale is still available for reading the sound pressure level of the simple tone after it has been identified.

It is evident that subtracting a conversion leads merely to the average spectrum level over the measurement band. Nothing is learned thereby about the distribution of sound within the passband.

Directional Patterns. The way sound is radiated differently in different directions is often described by the use of a polar plot such as that shown in Fig. 2.16. The source of sound was a high-speed electric hand grinder running with no load at 2,200 rpm. The measuring microphone was 30 in. away and it was rotated about the grinder in a plane containing the axis of the grinder. The figure shows the graph automatically traced out by the measuring equipment; the wiggly lines give some indication of the variability of the sound pressure level. The measurement bands were one-third octave wide centered at 500, 2,000, and 10,000 cps, respectively.

Notice that at 500 cps the sound pressure level (if the rapid fluctuations are smoothed out) varied only between 49 and 52 db. At 2,000 cps the maximum sound pressure level was 78 db and the minimum 67 db. At 10,000 cps there was a minimum sound pressure level in the direction of the chuck (0°) and there were broad maxima near 30° and 320°.

The equipment also measured the mean square sound pressure level in all directions, at a distance of 30 in. These sound pressure levels in the third-octave bands centered at 500, 2,000, and 10,000 cps were 51, 75, and 61 db, respectively. These values are seen to be plausible from Fig. 2.16, particularly if it is recalled that the directional pattern is not necessarily the same in all planes through the axis of the grinder.

In view of Eq. (2.22a) and the distance of $2\frac{1}{2}$ ft, it follows that the sound-power levels (re 1 micromicrowatt) produced by the grinder were 59.5, 83.5, and 69.5 db, respectively, in the third-octave bands at 500, 2,000, and 10,000 cps. The corresponding sound powers are 0.9, 224, and 9 μw.

The directional gain can be determined readily from the information available. In the 320° direction, for example, the observed sound pressure levels were 51, 78, and 66 db, respectively, at 500, 2,000, and 10,000 cps. The directional gains, for this direction, are accordingly 0, 3, and 5 db. The value $G = 0$ db means that at 500 cps the sound pressure level in the 320° direction is the same as the mean square sound pressure level for all directions. At 2,000 cps, however, there is a gain of 3 db over the mean and at 10,000 cps there is a gain of 5 db.

The directional gain is associated with a specific direction. For example, *at* 0° the observed sound pressure levels read from Fig. 2.16 are 49.5, 77, and 54.5 db at 500, 2,000, and 10,000 cps, respectively. Accordingly, *for this direction,* $G = -1.5$, 2.0, and -6.5 db. When these values are substituted in Eq. (2.22), the results for the power levels are the same as before—as they should be.

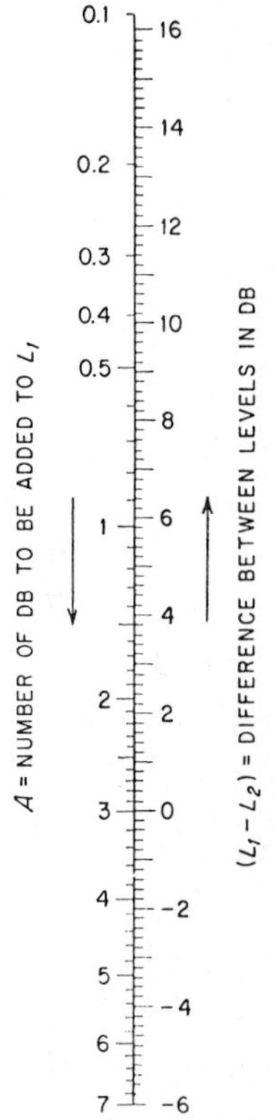

Fig. 2.17. Chart used in combining sound pressure levels. Left scale shows the number of decibels A to be added to sound pressure level L_1 to obtain the level resulting from the combination of L_1 and L_2.

COMPUTATIONS WITH THE DECIBEL

Combining Sound Levels. Figure 2.17 may be used to compute the sound pressure level that will exist if two or more sounds, measured separately, are combined. The desired result is *not* obtained by simply adding the individual sound pressure levels together.

For example, suppose that two ventilating fans each produce a sound pressure level of 80 db at a given location when run separately. The difference between these two levels is 0 db. According to Fig. 2.17, 3 db should be added to the "individual" level to obtain the "combination" level. Thus, when the two fans are run at the same time the total sound pressure level is 83 db.

As a second example, suppose the noise level of one fan alone is $L_1 = 80$ db, and that of the second fan alone is $L_2 = 76$ db. Since $L_1 - L_2 = 4$ db, from Fig. 2.17 it follows that 1.5 db should be added to L_1 to obtain the level of the combination: $80 + 1.5 = 81.5$ db.

If one of two levels being combined is much lower than the other, the combination level will not be much greater than the higher level. In any case a level which results from two noise sources is never more than 3 db above the higher of the two individual levels.

Wideband Level from Octave-band Measurements. Occasionally a "wideband" level is wanted after measurements have been made in narrower bands. Suppose that, in connection with a problem involving the interference of noise with speech, the sound pressure level in the band 300 to 4,800 cps is wanted for the noise whose spectrum is plotted in Fig. 2.10. The band levels read from the figure for the successive octave bands within the limits 300 to 4,800 cps are:

Center frequency, cps.	425	850	1,700	3,400
Octave-band level, db.	67	64	58	54

Since the bands are contiguous, the wideband level desired is simply the "combination" level of the several octave-band levels. The octave-band levels may be combined in any order. (However, it is advisable to start with the highest levels because one can then judge easily the importance of continuing the addition of the lower levels.) The first two levels to be combined are 67 and 64 db; the difference is 3, and 1.8 db should be added to the first to obtain the combination level. This combination level is in turn to be combined with 58 db, and so on. For extended calculation the following form is convenient:

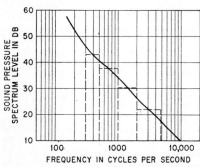

FIG. 2.18. Noise spectrum of motor and blower given in sound-pressure spectrum level from Fig. 2.13. The spectrum blocks used for wideband calculation are shown by dashed lines.

L_1, db	L_2, db	$(L_1 - L_2)$, db	A, db
67	64	3.0	1.8
1.8			
68.8	58	10.8	0.3
0.3			
69.1	54	15.1	0.1
0.1			
69.2			

The new combination level each time is called L_1, and the difference $(L_1 - L_2)$; A is obtained from Fig. 2.17. It is evident that when $(L_1 - L_2)$ is as great as 15 db the calculation can be stopped, unless there remain a large number of small levels which combined would be comparable with the combination level thus far calculated. Thus the sound pressure level for the band 300 to 4,800 cps is found to be 69.2 db.

Wideband Level from Spectrum Level. The problem of finding the sound pressure level for the band 300 to 4,800 cps can be solved by a similar computation if the data available are expressed as spectrum levels. Consider, for example, the noise spectrum shown in Fig. 2.18, which has been transcribed from Fig. 2.13. The spectrum has been arbitrarily approximated by a number of contiguous rectangular blocks whose tops are at the spectrum level of the actual noise at the center of the block (on this logarithmic frequency scale). This is equivalent to using the spectrum level at the geometric center frequency of the band; this is accomplished graphically without actual calculation of the frequency. The spectrum level L_{ps} corresponding to each block has been entered in the following table:

Band limits, cps	C, db	L_{ps}, db	L_b, db	L_{comb}, db
300–500	23.0	43.0	66.0	66.0
500–1,000	27.0	37.8	64.8	2.5
1,000–2,000	30.0	30.1	60.1	68.5
				0.5
2,000–4,800	34.5	22.0	56.5	69.0
				0.2
300–4,800				69.2

The first step is to convert the spectrum levels to band levels L_b. This is done by adding the conversion C read from Fig. 2.14; for example, the bandwidth of the band extending from 300 to 500 cps is 200 cps, for which $C = 23$ db. The band level for this band is thus $23.0 + 43.0 = 66.0$ db. This band level is combined with the next band level of 64.8 db, and that combination is combined with 60.1 db. The computation can be done compactly as indicated at the right, since part of the task can be done mentally. That is, the difference $L_1 - L_2 = 66.0 - 64.8 = 1.2$ db and from Fig. 2.17 can be read the quantity $A = 2.5$ to be added to $L_1 = 66.0$ db. The final result is the sound pressure level 69.2 db for the band 300 to 4,800 cps. Had the spectrum been more irregular, it is evident that narrower blocks would have been needed to approximate the spectrum.

Background Noise. Any noise may be considered a "signal" when it is a noise to be measured; at least momentarily it is a "wanted" sound. If the noise to be measured is the ambient noise there is always other noise within the measuring equipment that sets the lower limit to the measurement of the "signal." The total of all noise that interferes with the measurement of the desired signal is called *background noise;* this is made up of the ambient noise plus any other interference present. For example, this other interference may arise within the electrical measuring equipment. The magnitude of this background noise should always be determined to ensure that the signal can be measured.

A straightforward test is to note the reading in each measurement band when the signal is off. For reliable measurements, the background noise level should be at least 10 db below the signal level. The amount by which the signal level exceeds the background noise level is commonly referred to as the "*signal-to-noise ratio* in db"; a more descriptive name is the "signal-over-noise level."

Sometimes it is necessary to measure the noise from a machine that is not in a quiet location. The measuring microphone thus picks up *both* the machine sound of interest (the signal) and the general background noise. That is, one actually measures the signal-plus-noise level. Usually the signal can be turned off and the background noise alone can be measured. If the background noise level is less than the noise level of the machine to be measured, correction for the presence of extraneous noise may be feasible. The procedure is explained in Chap. 17.

Appendix 2.1

The following tables give the number of decibels corresponding to a given pressure ratio. These values are computed from Eq. (2.15). For example, if the sound-pressure ratio is 2.55, the corresponding number of decibels is 8.13. For large ratios, the answer can be obtained in two steps. For example, suppose the sound-pressure ratio is 146. Then $146 = 20 \times 7.3$; the corresponding number of decibels is $26.02 + 17.27 = 43.29$.

Pressure ratio	.00	.01	.02	.03	.04	.05	.06	.07	.08	.09
1.0	.00	.09	.17	.26	.34	.42	.51	.59	.67	.75
1.1	.83	.91	.98	1.06	1.14	1.21	1.29	1.36	1.44	1.51
1.2	1.58	1.66	1.73	1.80	1.87	1.94	2.01	2.08	2.14	2.21
1.3	2.28	2.35	2.41	2.48	2.54	2.61	2.67	2.73	2.80	2.86
1.4	2.92	2.98	3.05	3.11	3.17	3.23	3.29	3.35	3.41	3.46
1.5	3.52	3.58	3.64	3.69	3.75	3.81	3.86	3.92	3.97	4.03
1.6	4.08	4.14	4.19	4.24	4.30	4.35	4.40	4.45	4.51	4.56
1.7	4.61	4.66	4.71	4.76	4.81	4.86	4.91	4.96	5.01	5.06
1.8	5.11	5.15	5.20	5.25	5.30	5.34	5.39	5.44	5.48	5.53
1.9	5.58	5.62	5.67	5.71	5.76	5.80	5.85	5.89	5.93	5.98
2.0	6.02	6.06	6.11	6.15	6.19	6.24	6.28	6.32	6.36	6.40
2.1	6.44	6.49	6.53	6.57	6.61	6.65	6.69	6.73	6.77	6.81
2.2	6.85	6.89	6.93	6.97	7.01	7.04	7.08	7.12	7.16	7.20
2.3	7.24	7.27	7.31	7.35	7.38	7.42	7.46	7.50	7.53	7.57
2.4	7.60	7.64	7.68	7.71	7.75	7.78	7.82	7.85	7.89	7.92
2.5	7.96	7.99	8.03	8.06	8.10	8.13	8.17	8.20	8.23	8.27
2.6	8.30	8.33	8.37	8.40	8.43	8.47	8.50	8.53	8.56	8.60
2.7	8.63	8.66	8.69	8.72	8.76	8.79	8.82	8.85	8.88	8.91
2.8	8.94	8.97	9.01	9.04	9.07	9.10	9.13	9.16	9.19	9.22
2.9	9.25	9.28	9.31	9.34	9.37	9.40	9.43	9.46	9.48	9.51
3.0	9.54	9.57	9.60	9.63	9.66	9.69	9.71	9.74	9.77	9.80
3.1	9.83	9.86	9.88	9.91	9.94	9.97	9.99	10.02	10.05	10.08
3.2	10.10	10.13	10.16	10.18	10.21	10.24	10.26	10.29	10.32	10.34
3.3	10.37	10.40	10.42	10.45	10.48	10.50	10.53	10.55	10.58	10.60
3.4	10.63	10.66	10.68	10.71	10.73	10.76	10.78	10.81	10.83	10.86
3.5	10.88	10.91	10.93	10.96	10.98	11.01	11.03	11.05	11.08	11.10
3.6	11.13	11.15	11.17	11.20	11.22	11.25	11.27	11.29	11.32	11.34
3.7	11.36	11.39	11.41	11.43	11.46	11.48	11.50	11.53	11.55	11.57
3.8	11.60	11.62	11.64	11.66	11.69	11.71	11.73	11.75	11.78	11.80
3.9	11.82	11.84	11.87	11.89	11.91	11.93	11.95	11.98	12.00	12.02
4.0	12.04	12.06	12.09	12.11	12.13	12.15	12.17	12.19	12.21	12.23
4.1	12.26	12.28	12.30	12.32	12.34	12.36	12.38	12.40	12.42	12.44
4.2	12.47	12.49	12.51	12.53	12.55	12.57	12.59	12.61	12.63	12.65
4.3	12.67	12.69	12.71	12.73	12.75	12.77	12.79	12.81	12.83	12.85
4.4	12.87	12.89	12.91	12.93	12.95	12.97	12.99	13.01	13.03	13.05
4.5	13.06	13.08	13.10	13.12	13.14	13.16	13.18	13.20	13.22	13.24
4.6	13.26	13.27	13.29	13.31	13.33	13.35	13.37	13.39	13.41	13.42
4.7	13.44	13.46	13.48	13.50	13.52	13.53	13.55	13.57	13.59	13.61
4.8	13.63	13.64	13.66	13.68	13.70	13.72	13.73	13.75	13.77	13.79
4.9	13.80	13.82	13.84	13.86	13.88	13.89	13.91	13.93	13.95	13.96
5.0	13.98	14.00	14.01	14.03	14.05	14.07	14.08	14.10	14.12	14.13
5.1	14.15	14.17	14.19	14.20	14.22	14.24	14.25	14.27	14.29	14.30
5.2	14.32	14.34	14.35	14.37	14.39	14.40	14.42	14.44	14.45	14.47
5.3	14.49	14.50	14.52	14.54	14.55	14.57	14.58	14.60	14.62	14.63
5.4	14.65	14.66	14.68	14.70	14.71	14.73	14.74	14.76	14.78	14.79
5.5	14.81	14.82	14.84	14.86	14.87	14.89	14.90	14.92	14.93	14.95
5.6	14.96	14.98	15.00	15.01	15.03	15.04	15.06	15.07	15.09	15.10
5.7	15.12	15.13	15.15	15.16	15.18	15.19	15.21	15.22	15.24	15.25
5.8	15.27	15.28	15.30	15.31	15.33	15.34	15.36	15.37	15.39	15.40
5.9	15.42	15.43	15.45	15.46	15.48	15.49	15.51	15.52	15.53	15.55

Appendix 2.1 (*Continued*)

Pressure ratio	.00	.01	.02	.03	.04	.05	.06	.07	.08	.09
6.0	15.56	15.58	15.59	15.61	15.62	15.64	15.65	15.66	15.68	15.69
6.1	15.71	15.72	15.74	15.75	15.76	15.78	15.79	15.81	15.82	15.83
6.2	15.85	15.86	15.88	15.89	15.90	15.92	15.93	15.95	15.96	15.97
6.3	15.99	16.00	16.01	16.03	16.04	16.06	16.07	16.08	16.10	16.11
6.4	16.12	16.14	16.15	16.16	16.18	16.19	16.21	16.22	16.23	16.25
6.5	16.26	16.27	16.29	16.30	16.31	16.33	16.34	16.35	16.37	16.38
6.6	16.39	16.40	16.42	16.43	16.44	16.46	16.47	16.48	16.50	16.51
6.7	16.52	16.53	16.55	16.56	16.57	16.59	16.60	16.61	16.63	16.64
6.8	16.65	16.66	16.68	16.69	16.70	16.71	16.73	16.74	16.75	16.76
6.9	16.78	16.79	16.80	16.82	16.83	16.84	16.85	16.87	16.88	16.89
7.0	16.90	16.91	16.93	16.94	16.95	16.96	16.98	16.99	17.00	17.01
7.1	17.03	17.04	17.05	17.06	17.07	17.09	17.10	17.11	17.12	17.14
7.2	17.15	17.16	17.17	17.18	17.20	17.21	17.22	17.23	17.24	17.26
7.3	17.27	17.28	17.29	17.30	17.31	17.33	17.34	17.35	17.36	17.37
7.4	17.39	17.40	17.41	17.42	17.43	17.44	17.46	17.47	17.48	17.49
7.5	17.50	17.51	17.52	17.54	17.55	17.56	17.57	17.58	17.59	17.61
7.6	17.62	17.63	17.64	17.65	17.66	17.67	17.69	17.70	17.71	17.72
7.7	17.73	17.74	17.75	17.76	17.78	17.79	17.80	17.81	17.82	17.83
7.8	17.84	17.85	17.86	17.88	17.89	17.90	17.91	17.92	17.93	17.94
7.9	17.95	17.96	17.98	17.99	18.00	18.01	18.02	18.03	18.04	18.05
8.0	18.06	18.07	18.08	18.09	18.11	18.12	18.13	18.14	18.15	18.16
8.1	18.17	18.18	18.19	18.20	18.21	18.22	18.23	18.24	18.26	18.27
8.2	18.28	18.29	18.30	18.31	18.32	18.33	18.34	18.35	18.36	18.37
8.3	18.38	18.39	18.40	18.41	18.42	18.43	18.44	18.46	18.47	18.48
8.4	18.49	18.50	18.51	18.52	18.53	18.54	18.55	18.56	18.57	18.58
8.5	18.59	18.60	18.61	18.62	18.63	18.64	18.65	18.66	18.67	18.68
8.6	18.69	18.70	18.71	18.72	18.73	18.74	18.75	18.76	18.77	18.78
8.7	18.79	18.80	18.81	18.82	18.83	18.84	18.85	18.86	18.87	18.88
8.8	18.89	18.90	18.91	18.92	18.93	18.94	18.95	18.96	18.97	18.98
8.9	18.99	19.00	19.01	19.02	19.03	19.04	19.05	19.06	19.07	19.08
9.0	19.09	19.09	19.10	19.11	19.12	19.13	19.14	19.15	19.16	19.17
9.1	19.18	19.19	19.20	19.21	19.22	19.23	19.24	19.25	19.26	19.27
9.2	19.28	19.29	19.30	19.30	19.31	19.32	19.33	19.34	19.35	19.36
9.3	19.37	19.38	19.39	19.40	19.41	19.42	19.43	19.44	19.44	19.45
9.4	19.46	19.47	19.48	19.49	19.50	19.51	19.52	19.53	19.54	19.55
9.5	19.55	19.56	19.57	19.58	19.59	19.60	19.61	19.62	19.63	19.64
9.6	19.65	19.65	19.66	19.67	19.68	19.69	19.70	19.71	19.72	19.73
9.7	19.74	19.74	19.75	19.76	19.77	19.78	19.79	19.80	19.81	19.82
9.8	19.83	19.83	19.84	19.85	19.86	19.87	19.88	19.89	19.90	19.90
9.9	19.91	19.92	19.93	19.94	19.95	19.96	19.97	19.97	19.98	19.99

Pressure ratio	0	1	2	3	4	5	6	7	8	9
10	20.00	20.83	21.58	22.28	22.92	23.52	24.08	24.61	25.11	25.58
20	26.02	26.44	26.85	27.24	27.60	27.96	28.30	28.63	28.94	29.25
30	29.54	29.83	30.10	30.37	30.63	30.88	31.13	31.36	31.60	31.82
40	32.04	32.26	32.47	32.67	32.87	33.06	33.26	33.44	33.63	33.80
50	33.98	34.15	34.32	34.49	34.65	34.81	34.96	35.12	35.27	35.42
60	35.56	35.71	35.85	35.99	36.12	36.26	36.39	36.52	36.65	36.78
70	36.90	37.03	37.15	37.27	37.39	37.50	37.62	37.73	37.84	37.95
80	38.06	38.17	38.28	38.38	38.49	38.59	38.69	38.79	38.89	38.99
90	39.09	39.18	39.28	39.37	39.46	39.55	39.65	39.74	39.83	39.91
100	40.00									

Appendix 2.2

The following table gives the number of decibels corresponding to a given power ratio. These values are computed from Eq. (2.17). If the power ratio is greater than unity, the higher power exceeds the lower one in level by the number of decibels given below; if the power ratio is less than unity, the higher power is *less* than the lower one in level by the number of decibels given below. As an example, suppose that two power levels differ by 4 db; the table shows the ratio of the two powers to be 2.51. If, however, the difference in power level is −4 db, the second power is greater than the first, and the ratio is 0.398.

Power ratio	− db + ← →	Power ratio	Power ratio	− db + ← →	Power ratio	Power ratio	− db + ← →	Power ratio
1.000	0	1.00	0.355	4.5	2.82	0.126	9.0	7.94
0.977	0.1	1.02	0.347	4.6	2.88	0.123	9.1	8.13
0.955	0.2	1.05	0.339	4.7	2.95	0.120	9.2	8.32
0.933	0.3	1.07	0.331	4.8	3.02	0.118	9.3	8.51
0.912	0.4	1.10	0.324	4.9	3.09	0.115	9.4	8.71
0.891	0.5	1.12	0.316	5.0	3.16	0.112	9.5	8.91
0.871	0.6	1.15	0.309	5.1	3.24	0.110	9.6	9.12
0.851	0.7	1.18	0.302	5.2	3.31	0.107	9.7	9.33
0.832	0.8	1.20	0.295	5.3	3.39	0.105	9.8	9.55
0.813	0.9	1.23	0.288	5.4	3.47	0.102	9.9	9.77
0.794	1.0	1.26	0.282	5.5	3.55	0.1000	10.0	10.0
0.776	1.1	1.29	0.275	5.6	3.63	0.0977	10.1	10.2
0.759	1.2	1.32	0.269	5.7	3.72	0.0955	10.2	10.5
0.741	1.3	1.35	0.263	5.8	3.80	0.0933	10.3	10.7
0.724	1.4	1.38	0.257	5.9	3.89	0.0912	10.4	11.0
0.708	1.5	1.41	0.251	6.0	3.98	0.0891	10.5	11.2
0.692	1.6	1.45	0.246	6.1	4.07	0.0871	10.6	11.5
0.676	1.7	1.48	0.240	6.2	4.17	0.0851	10.7	11.8
0.661	1.8	1.51	0.234	6.3	4.27	0.0832	10.8	12.0
0.646	1.9	1.55	0.229	6.4	4.37	0.0813	10.9	12.3
0.631	2.0	1.59	0.224	6.5	4.47	0.0794	11.0	12.6
0.617	2.1	1.62	0.219	6.6	4.57	0.0776	11.1	12.9
0.603	2.2	1.66	0.214	6.7	4.68	0.0759	11.2	13.2
0.589	2.3	1.70	0.209	6.8	4.79	0.0741	11.3	13.5
0.575	2.4	1.74	0.204	6.9	4.90	0.0724	11.4	13.8
0.562	2.5	1.78	0.200	7.0	5.01	0.0708	11.5	14.1
0.550	2.6	1.82	0.195	7.1	5.13	0.0692	11.6	14.5
0.537	2.7	1.86	0.191	7.2	5.25	0.0676	11.7	14.8
0.525	2.8	1.91	0.186	7.3	5.37	0.0661	11.8	15.1
0.513	2.9	1.95	0.182	7.4	5.50	0.0646	11.9	15.5
0.501	3.0	2.00	0.178	7.5	5.62	0.0631	12.0	15.9
0.490	3.1	2.04	0.174	7.6	5.75	0.0617	12.1	16.2
0.479	3.2	2.09	0.170	7.7	5.89	0.0603	12.2	16.6
0.468	3.3	2.14	0.166	7.8	6.03	0.0589	12.3	17.0
0.457	3.4	2.19	0.162	7.9	6.17	0.0575	12.4	17.4
0.447	3.5	2.24	0.159	8.0	6.31	0.0562	12.5	17.8
0.437	3.6	2.29	0.155	8.1	6.46	0.0550	12.6	18.2
0.427	3.7	2.34	0.151	8.2	6.61	0.0537	12.7	18.6
0.417	3.8	2.40	0.148	8.3	6.76	0.0523	12.8	19.1
0.407	3.9	2.46	0.145	8.4	6.92	0.0513	12.9	19.5
0.398	4.0	2.51	0.141	8.5	7.08	0.0501	13.0	20.0
0.389	4.1	2.57	0.138	8.6	7.24	0.0490	13.1	20.4
0.380	4.2	2.63	0.135	8.7	7.41	0.0479	13.2	20.9
0.372	4.3	2.69	0.132	8.8	7.59	0.0468	13.3	21.4
0.363	4.4	2.75	0.129	8.9	7.76	0.0457	13.4	21.9

Appendix 2.2 (*Continued*)

Power ratio	− db + ← →	Power ratio	Power ratio	− db + ← →	Power ratio	Power ratio	− db + ← →	Power ratio
0.0447	13.5	22.4	0.0251	16.0	39.8	0.0141	18.5	70.8
0.0437	13.6	22.9	0.0246	16.1	40.7	0.0138	18.6	72.4
0.0427	13.7	23.4	0.0240	16.2	41.7	0.0135	18.7	74.1
0.0417	13.8	24.0	0.0234	16.3	42.7	0.0132	18.8	75.9
0.0407	13.9	24.6	0.0229	16.4	43.7	0.0129	18.9	77.6
0.0398	14.0	25.1	0.0224	16.5	44.7	0.0126	19.0	79.4
0.0389	14.1	25.7	0.0219	16.6	45.7	0.0123	19.1	81.3
0.0380	14.2	26.3	0.0214	16.7	46.8	0.0120	19.2	83.2
0.0372	14.3	26.9	0.0209	16.8	47.9	0.0118	19.3	85.1
0.0363	14.4	27.5	0.0204	16.9	49.0	0.0115	19.4	87.1
0.0355	14.5	28.2	0.0200	17.0	50.1	0.0112	19.5	89.1
0.0347	14.6	28.8	0.0195	17.1	51.3	0.0110	19.6	91.2
0.0339	14.7	29.5	0.0191	17.2	52.5	0.0107	19.7	93.3
0.0331	14.8	30.2	0.0186	17.3	53.7	0.0105	19.8	95.5
0.0324	14.9	30.9	0.0182	17.4	55.0	0.0102	19.9	97.7
						0.0100	20.0	100.0
0.0316	15.0	31.6	0.0178	17.5	56.2	10^{-1}	10	10
0.0309	15.1	32.4	0.0174	17.6	57.5	10^{-2}	20	10^2
0.0302	15.2	33.1	0.0170	17.7	58.9	10^{-3}	30	10^3
0.0295	15.3	33.9	0.0166	17.8	60.3	10^{-4}	40	10^4
0.0288	15.4	34.7	0.0162	17.9	61.7	10^{-5}	50	10^5
0.0282	15.5	35.5	0.0159	18.0	63.1	10^{-6}	60	10^6
0.0275	15.6	36.3	0.0155	18.1	64.6	10^{-7}	70	10^7
0.0269	15.7	37.2	0.0151	18.2	66.1	10^{-8}	80	10^8
0.0263	15.8	38.0	0.0148	18.3	67.6	10^{-9}	90	10^9
0.0257	15.9	38.9	0.0145	18.4	69.2	10^{-10}	100	10^{10}

Chapter 3

PROPAGATION OF SOUND IN THE OPEN AIR

ISADORE RUDNICK, PH.D.

University of California at Los Angeles

INTRODUCTION

The effects of propagation of sound in the open air to be considered in this chapter depend very much on the nature and distribution of the sound sources and upon the ever changing characteristics of the atmosphere. Because of the fact that the atmosphere is neither homogeneous nor quiescent, the propagation of sound in this medium presents a complicated statistical problem. Since much of the basic micrometeorological data upon which such calculations might be based are not available, reliable engineering solutions to many of the practical problems encountered in noise control in the open air are not yet available. Therefore much of the material presented in this chapter is of a theoretical nature—in contrast to the engineering approach stressed in the chapters which follow.

In the analysis given below, unless otherwise stated a point source of sound is assumed. When more than one such source is present their combined effect depends on whether they are (1) independent sound sources, e.g., airplanes on an airfield, a crowd of people, etc., or (2) sound sources in a fixed phase relationship, e.g., a number of loudspeakers in a public-address system. In the former case one calculates the sound level at a distant point by determining the sound level at that point for each of the sound sources and then adding the sound powers. Calculations for the latter case are generally more difficult, and one is not always able to carry them out. Suffice it to say that it is necessary to find the sound pressure amplitude at the observation point for each sound source, and to add them with due regard to phase.

Consider now a point source of sound. What is the sound level at a distant point? The following factors are important in determining this:

1. Divergence decrease, due to spreading out of the sound energy.
2. Attenuation of sound in the air.
3. Effect of fog.
4. Reflection by and diffraction around solid obstacles such as fences.
5. Refraction, and shadow formation by wind and temperature gradients.
6. Scattering of sound by small-scale temperature and wind variations.
7. Reflection and absorption at the ground.

Each of these is treated separately in this chapter. Under certain conditions the cumulative effect is the sum of the separate effects, but this is not generally the case. Some circumstances in which one effect can interfere with and modify another effect are discussed.

DIVERGENCE DECREASE DUE TO SPREADING OF SOUND WAVES

Ordinarily, the decrease in sound pressure level as one moves away from a source is affected most by the divergence of the sound waves which are radiated by the source.

The sound pressure amplitude from a point source varies inversely as the distance from the source.   An equivalent statement is: There is a drop in sound pressure level of 6 db with each doubling of distance away from such a source.

At distances large compared with the size of a nondirectional sound source the source can be treated as a point source, even though it is relatively large.   The location of the equivalent point source is then somewhere near the center of the sound emitter.   For example, at large distances, a noisy shop building with sound being emitted equally through all walls can be considered as a point source located at the center of the building.

Two procedures for obtaining the sound pressure level L_p in decibels at a distance r from such a point source can be used, depending on the data available.

1. From Eq. (2.24) if the sound pressure level L_x in decibels at a distance r_x is known, then L_p at distance r is

$$L_p = L_x - 20 \log_{10} \frac{r}{r_x} \qquad \text{db} \qquad (3.1)$$

2. Equations (2.22a) and (2.22b) give the sound pressure level at any distance from a nondirectional source in a free field in terms of the sound power level of the source L_w (re 1 micromicrowatt).   If the source is on the ground, similar expressions may be obtained by the addition of 3 db to account for ground reflection.*   Thus if r is expressed in feet,

$$L_p = L_w - 20 \log r + 2.4 \qquad \text{db} \qquad (3.2)$$

If r is expressed in meters,

$$L_p = L_w - 20 \log r - 7.9 \qquad \text{db} \qquad (3.2a)$$

A sound source may not radiate equally in all directions.   An example of this is the noise from an airplane.   In such a case Eq. (3.2) does not apply but Eq. (3.1) may be used provided (1) r and r_x are both sufficiently far away from the source so that the directional pattern of the sound does not change with distance (for some jet airplanes this minimum distance may be taken to be 200 ft) and (2) r and r_x are measured in the same direction with respect to the sound source.

ATTENUATION OF SOUND IN AIR

The attenuation constant, which may be expressed in decibels per 100 ft or in decibels per meter, is made up of two parts.   One part, which is unimportant except for very high frequencies, is due to the combined action of the viscosity, heat conductivity of the air, and a relaxation behavior of the rotational energy states of the molecules of the air.   This attenuation constant α_1 can be considered to be independent of the humidity of the air.   The second part is due to a relaxation behavior of the vibrational

---

* Equation (3.2) is derived on the assumption that the sound is radiated into a solid angle of 2π, as if, for example, the source is on a perfectly reflective surface.   "Suppose that a point source is placed infinitesimally close to a reflective wall of infinite extent and that the volume-velocity of the source is maintained constant.   Under these conditions the radiation resistance of the source and its image will be doubled, so that the power output of each will be twice as great as that of the source when it is in a free field.   However, twice as much power is required to maintain the constant volume-velocity.   Hence, at any point on the source side of the reflecting plane, the intensity will be increased by a factor of 4 and the pressure will be increased by a factor of 2.   As the source recedes from the wall the radiation resistance varies as $1 + [(\sin x)/x]$ times its value in a free field.   Here, x is 4π times the distance from the wall divided by the wavelength.   At large distances from the reflector, $(\sin x)/x$ approaches zero so that the radiation resistance of the source is the same as it would be in a free field.   Thus the effect of the wall is merely to double the intensity."[20]

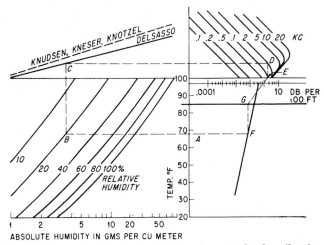

FIG. 3.1. Nomogram for obtaining the attenuation due to molecular vibration relaxation absorption coefficient α_2. Illustrated is an example in which the temperature is 68°F, the relative humidity is 20 per cent, and the frequency is 2,000 cps. The attenuation is then 0.9 db per 100 ft. The curve marked Kneser, Knudsen, and Knotzel is based on separate measurements by the latter two[2,3] and is recommended by Kneser. The curve marked Delsasso is based on recent measurements[5] which are close to those of Knudsen and Obert.[4] It is difficult to choose between these data, but the use of Delsasso's results is recommended.

states of the oxygen molecules in the air. This behavior is strongly dependent on the presence of water molecules. Consequently this second attenuation coefficient α_2 depends on humidity. The total attenuation coefficient α is given by

$$\alpha = \alpha_1 + \alpha_2 = 4.34 \times 10^{-9}f^2 + \alpha_2 \quad (3.3)$$

where α_1 and α_2 are in decibels per 100 ft, and f is frequency in cycles per second.

Figure 3.1 is a nomogram which gives the value of α_2. For example, suppose α_2 is desired at a frequency of 2,000 cps for air at a temperature of 68°F and a relative humidity of 20 per cent. (1) Enter the vertical temperature scale at A. (2) Draw a horizontal line to the 20 per cent humidity curve and find the point B. (3) Draw a vertical line to the curve indicated and find point C. (4) Draw the horizontal line from C to the 2,000-cps curve and find D. (5) Draw the vertical line from D to E. Going back to A the horizontal line AF is drawn; then the vertical line FG. (6) Join F and G and read 0.9 db per 100 ft for α_2. At this same frequency α_1 is 1.74×10^{-4} db per 100 ft.

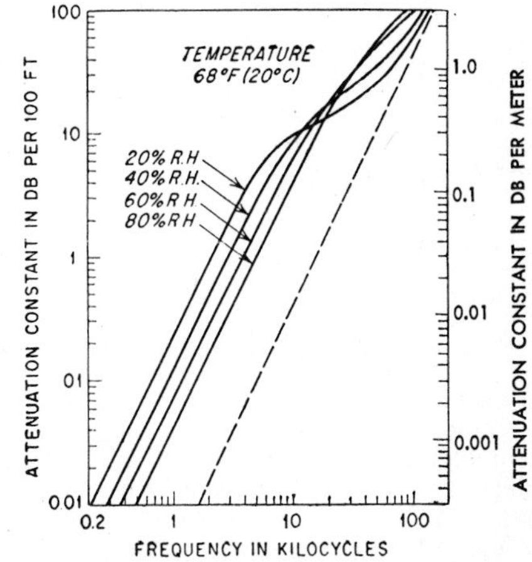

In Eq. (3.3) the pressure is assumed to be the normal pressure at sea level. Corrections for 5 or 10 per cent deviations from this can usually be neglected. How-

FIG. 3.2. The attenuation coefficient in decibels per meter for air at a temperature of 68°F and relative humidities of 20, 40, 60, and 80 per cent. The solid curves give the total attenuation coefficient α; the dotted curve gives the contribution to this total of α_1.

ever, if the pressure is quite different from normal sea-level pressure, the attenuation is changed significantly and the calculations are then made as follows: Let x be the ambient pressure in units of normal sea-level atmospheres. Then α_1 is $4.34 \times 10^{-9} f^2/x$. To determine α_2 the nomogram in Fig. 3.1 is used, determining the attenuation for a frequency f/x. The true attenuation is this value multiplied by x. As an example, determine α at a frequency of 1,000 cps at a point where the pressure is one-half normal sea-level pressure; i.e., $x = \frac{1}{2}$. The temperature is 68°F and the relative humidity is 20 per cent. Then $\alpha_1 = 4.34 \times 10^{-9} \times (1,000)^2 \times 2 = 8.7 \times 10^{-3}$ db per 100 ft. The frequency value in using the nomogram is 2,000 cps and as before an attenuation of 0.9 db per 100 ft is found. The true value of α_2 is then $0.9 \times \frac{1}{2} = 0.45$ db per 100 ft.

The solid curves of Fig. 3.2 are plots of α at 68°F for various humidities. The dotted line is the asymptote to which all the curves tend; it is α_1.

EFFECT OF FOG

At a distant point from a source it is not unusual for the sound pressure level to be higher during foggy weather than in clear weather. The attenuation in fog can be considered to be practically negligible. The lessening of attenuation during foggy weather can generally be ascribed to the absence of wind and to the homogeneity of the temperature so that sound shadows (to be discussed later) are not present.

REDUCTION OF NOISE BY WALLS OR FENCES

Walls or fences usually are not efficient noise barriers, but there are situations when this may be the only possible method of noise control. If the sound reduction required is not too great the erection of such barriers may be useful. Figure 3.3 shows the reduction which may be obtained. The barrier height and angle θ are illustrated in

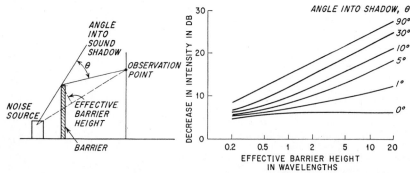

FIG. 3.3. Shielding provided by barriers. (*A. J. King, after Ref. 17.*)

the sketch and the decrease in level at the observation point is seen to be a function of these two quantities. Note that the higher the fence the greater the decrease in sound level. Note also that, when the fence is higher than the source and observation point, θ is maximized and the greatest benefits are obtained if the fence is closer to either the source or receiver rather than midway between them. The results shown in Fig. 3.3 must be regarded as approximate since no account is taken of reflection at the ground.

SOUND REDUCTION BY BUSHES AND TREES

For bushes and trees to be effective in containing noise in an open work area or reducing noise in residential areas, the density of growth must be very high and the depth of treatment great. If trees are used the leaf level should extend almost to ground level. Systematic studies of the attenuation provided by bushes and trees have not been made. However, measured transmission losses through various types of jungle (see Fig. 3.4) are useful as a guide. These data indicate that bushes and trees provide only slight attenuation. Therefore, as a practical matter, the use of plants as a sound barrier can be justified only when the effects desired are marginal, or when other avenues of approach are either unprofitable or exhausted.

REFRACTION OF SOUND RAYS BY TEMPERATURE AND WIND GRADIENTS

The velocity of sound in air is determined by (1) the wind velocity and (2) the temperature. The velocity of sound also depends on the humidity but the effect of this can be neglected. The dependence of sound velocity c on temperature is given by

$$c = c_0 \sqrt{\frac{T}{T_0}} \qquad (3.4)$$

where T is the absolute temperature in degrees Kelvin or in degrees Rankin,* and c_0 is the sound velocity at the absolute temperature T_0. The resultant velocity is then the vector sum of the wind velocity and c, the latter vector being taken normal to the wavefront.

Sound waves propagated through an atmosphere in which the wind velocity and temperature are functions of space (when they are also rapidly varying functions of time they will lead to fluctuations in sound energy with which we are not concerned at the moment) will suffer refraction and possibly reflection.

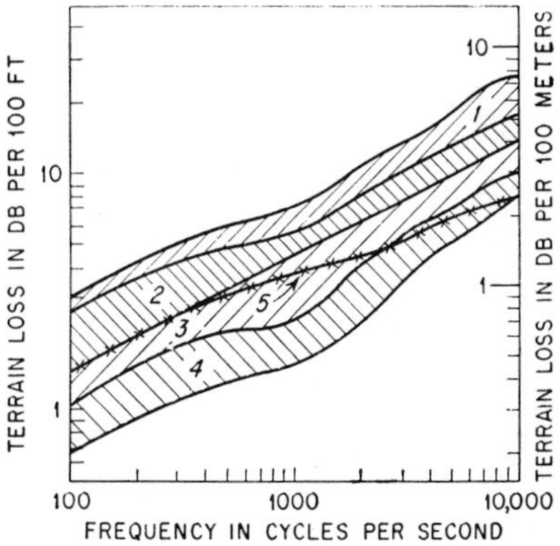

FIG. 3.4. A chart based on measurements in tropical jungles. Zone 1, very leafy; one sees a distance of approximately 20 ft, penetration by cutting. Zone 2, very leafy; one sees a distance of approximately 50 ft, penetrated with difficulty but without cutting. Zone 3, leafy; one sees a distance of approximately 100 ft, free walking if care is taken. Zone 4, leafy; one sees a distance of approximately 200 ft; penetration is rather easy. Zone 5, very leafy undergrowth, large bracketed trunks; one sees a distance of approximately 300 ft; penetration is easy. (*After Eyring.*[6])

Before discussing these effects, consider the type of temperature and wind structure that may be encountered in the atmosphere.†

Temperature Structure of the Atmosphere. An "ideal" atmosphere at complete rest would tend to approach a uniform temperature by virtue of the conduction of heat from regions of higher to regions of lower temperature. The pressure and density would decrease exponentially with height but the temperature would be constant. However, the actual atmosphere is in a continual state of motion and agitation; heat is transferred from lower to higher altitudes by the circulation of air currents. Some idea of how the temperature varies with height can be obtained by assuming that the air masses move adiabatically from a lower altitude to a higher altitude, and again to a new altitude without any loss of heat by conduction. The pressure at any given height is determined by the weight of the atmosphere above this point; the pressure and temperature are related by the adiabatic law for perfect gases (the assumption of a perfect gas is justified for the accuracy of results required here). In such an atmosphere the temperature varies with height according to the law

$$\frac{dT}{dh} = -\frac{g}{R}\frac{\gamma - 1}{\gamma} = -\Gamma \qquad (3.5)$$

where g = gravitational acceleration
     R = gas constant per gram
     γ = ratio of specific heats
     h = height above ground

* $T_{\text{Rankin}} = T_{\text{Fahrenheit}} + 459°$.
† For further details see Ref. **7.**

Inserting appropriate values for g, γ, and R one finds approximately $\Gamma = 0.3°C$ per 100 ft. Γ is known as the adiabatic lapse rate.

The *actual* temperature structure of the atmosphere deviates markedly from that of Eq. (3.5). There appears to be a very rough approximation to the adiabatic lapse rate below about 45,000 ft, excluding the layer of air near the earth's surface. It is a matter of common experience that in the lowest layer the temperatures encountered cover a wide range and are subject to cyclic variations. The temperature gradient as a function of height is of principal interest. The gradient very near the ground is generally much greater than Γ. Figure 3.5 shows the mean gradient (expressed in units of

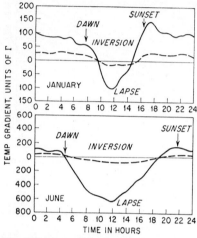

FIG. 3.5. Mean diurnal variation of temperature differences between heights of 1 in. and 1 ft (full line) and 1 ft and 4 ft (dotted line) over short grass in (*a*) winter and (*b*) summer in southern England. The differences are in multiples of the adiabatic lapse rate—approximately 0.3°C per 100 ft. (*After Best.*[18])

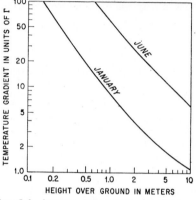

FIG. 3.6. Average temperature gradients at noon as a function of height above ground. (*After Best.*[18])

$\Gamma = 0.3°C$ per 100 ft) averaged over two low-height regions in southern England in a winter month and a summer month. Figure 3.6 shows how the temperature gradient varies with height above ground, given again in terms of units of Γ. Note that the gradient varies markedly with time of day. From slightly after sunrise to just before

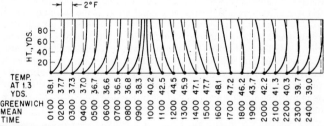

FIG. 3.7. Profiles of temperature taken in southern England in the spring. (*After Johnson and Heywood.*[19])

sunset the gradient is negative, whereas nighttime hours are characterized by an inversion. Figure 3.7 shows some measured temperature profiles over a 24-hr period taken between 1.1 and 85 yd in southern England, in the spring. The negative gradient during the day and the positive gradient (inversion) at night can be understood from the following considerations. Dry air is relatively transparent to most of the electromagnetic radiation energy from the sun. During the day this energy striking the earth's ground surface heats it. The temperature reached by the surface depends on its nature. For example,[8] it was found that on the hottest days the maximum surface temperature of a tar-macadam layer was 60°C (140°F); of a sand layer 55°C (130°F); of a grass-covered surface 44°C (111°F). The air in contact with the surface heats up and, being hotter than the air a little distance above the surface, rises. The heat which is absorbed by contact with the earth's surface then is transported to higher altitudes by convection. For this reason a negative temperature gradient may exist during the daytime hours which may be very large near the surface. In contrast, shortly before sundown the earth's surface will cool (by radiation and conduction); it will cool the air in contact with it, and a positive temperature gradient near the earth will result. At higher heights the gradient will remain negative so that an inversion layer is generated. The top level of this inversion layer rises during the night as more and more of the lower-level air is cooled. The air below this level is characterized by comparative stability since the density decreases with increasing height.

From the above discussion it is clear that, during overcast conditions, the gradient will be small at all hours.

Wind Structure of the Atmosphere. The important region for most sound-propagation problems related to noise control is below heights of 3,000 ft. Here the wind structure is much affected by local conditions and time of day. In inland areas the wind at the lowest heights reaches a maximum in the daytime and a minimum at night. At intermediate heights, the variation may be 180° out of phase, the maxima occurring at night and minima in the daytime. The height at which this reversal occurs may be 120 ft for moderate winds, being lower than this for light, and higher than this for strong winds. In coastal areas the land and sea breezes tend to override the above-mentioned diurnal changes.

The wind profile depends on the roughness of the ground and the temperature profile. There are theoretical reasons for assuming the following wind structure:

$$\bar{u} = 5.8u_f \log_{10} \frac{h + z_0}{z_0} \tag{3.6}$$

where h is the height above ground, $\bar{u}$ is the average wind velocity, z_0 is a *roughness length* determined by the nature of the ground's surface; and u_f is the *friction velocity*, which is determined by the surface. Table 3.1 lists some representative values of z_0 and u_f.[8]

Observations of the wind profile indicate that Eq. (3.6) holds quite well under conditions when the temperature lapse rate is adiabatic. During temperature inversions the wind speed increases more rapidly with height and during periods of great temperature-lapse rate the wind-speed profile is more gradual.

Refraction of Sound Rays in the Atmosphere. Now consider the problem as to how temperature and wind structures affect sound propagation. Suppose a point source in a quiescent atmosphere in which there is a temperature inversion (Fig. 3.8). Since

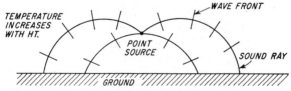

FIG. 3.8. Rays and wavefronts for an atmosphere with temperature inversion.

the velocity is higher where the temperature is higher Eq. (3.4) shows that the top of the wavefronts will travel faster than the bottom of the wavefronts and each wavefront as it travels will bend toward the ground. Moreover, this behavior is symmetrical with respect to a vertical axis through the sound source. On the other hand, during a temperature-lapse condition the rays rise and there is a limiting ray which just grazes the ground at a distance x from the source and which defines a shadow region as illustrated in Fig. 3.9—there is no corresponding shadow region for temperature-inversion conditions.

The same reasoning may be applied to an atmosphere as regards wind structure, as shown in Fig. 3.10. With a typical wind profile there will be a shadow region upwind and no shadow region downwind. This accounts for the oft-observed difficulty in hearing upwind from a source. It is important to emphasize that this is because the wind velocity normally *increases* with height.

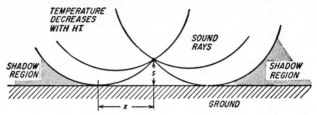

FIG. 3.9. Sound rays for an atmosphere with temperature lapse showing formation of shadow region.

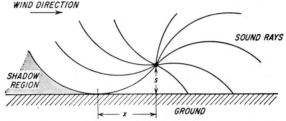

FIG. 3.10. Sound rays for an atmosphere with wind gradient, showing shadow formation upwind.

An important difference between the effects of temperature and wind is that while reciprocity holds so far as the former is concerned it does not hold so far as the latter is concerned. That is, a source and receiver at the ground may be interchanged and there will be no difference at the receiver when we have only a temperature gradient. But in the presence of a wind gradient the sound level at the receiver is much greater when it is in a downwind position than after the interchange of position.

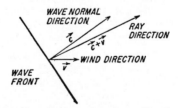

FIG. 3.11. Construction of ray direction.

Sound-ray Equations. Suppose (1) the temperature and wind velocity are functions only of height, and (2) there is no vertical component of the wind velocity. This assumes a stratified medium which is consistent with the previous discussion. Let the z coordinate direction be taken vertically. If u and v are, respectively, the x and y components of wind velocity, then $u = u(z)$, $v = v(z)$. Since the temperature is a function of height, the velocity of sound is too, i.e., $c = c(z)$. Consider a wavefront whose normal N has the direction cosines l, m, n (Fig. 3.11).

The energy flow corresponding to an infinitesimal section of the wavefront will be in a direction which is the vector sum of c (taken in the direction $\overrightarrow{N}$) and the wind velocity. The path traced out by such a section is the ray path. It is the path of energy flux and in general its direction is *different* from the direction of the wave normal (they coincide only in the absence of wind). The parametric equations for the ray are

$$\frac{dx}{dt} = u + cl$$

$$\frac{dy}{dt} = v + cm \qquad (3.7)$$

$$\frac{dz}{dt} = cn$$

u, v, and c are presumed to be known functions of z; if l, m, and n were similarly known functions of the space coordinates it would be possible to solve Eq. (3.7) for the ray paths.

The way in which l, m, and n vary is obtained by considering the refraction problem. It can be shown that for a given ray

$$u + \frac{c}{l} = \text{const} = u_0 + \frac{c_0}{l_0} = u_p + c_p \qquad (3.8)$$

This equation is just Snell's law of refraction for moving media. The meaning of this equation is that $(u + c/l)$ has the same value at each point for a given ray. The subscript zero is used to denote the values of u, c, and l at the source; the subscript p is used to denote their values at the peak of a ray (where $l_p = 1$).

Calculation of Ray Paths in Absence of Wind. Equations (3.7) and (3.8) are sufficient to determine ray paths. As an example of their use, consider the case in which there is no wind ($u = v = 0$). Assume the ray is in the xz plane. Equation (3.7) becomes

$$\frac{dx}{dt} = c \cos \theta$$

$$\frac{dy}{dt} = 0$$

$$\frac{dz}{dt} = c \sin \theta$$

Equation (3.8) becomes

$$\frac{c}{\cos \theta} = K$$

where θ = the angle the ray makes with the horizontal. Introducing the differential length $ds = (dx^2 + dz^2)^{1/2}$ we find that

$$\frac{dc}{dz} + K \frac{d\theta}{ds} = 0$$

and we see that, if dc/dz is a constant (c is a linear function of height), then $d\theta/ds$ is a constant and the ray is the arc of a circle of radius

$$r = \frac{ds}{d\theta} = -\frac{K}{k} = \frac{c_0}{k \cos \theta_0}$$

where

$$c = c_0 + kz \qquad (3.9)$$

This result is reasonable, as indicated by the following discussion. Suppose a section of the initial wavefront is drawn and extended down to the extrapolated level at which the velocity would be zero; suppose it is now rotated about this point. Then all points of the line so drawn will move with a velocity which is proportional to the distance above this plane. But this is just the condition required by $c = c_0 + kz$. Thus the rays will be circles whose centers lie on the plane at which the velocity would be 0, i.e.,

$$z = \frac{-c_0}{k}$$

(see Fig. 3.12). To find the peak height of travel h as a function of range requires but a simple geometrical construction. For values of $h \ll 2c_0/k$

$$h = \frac{R^2 k}{8 c_0} \qquad (3.10)$$

when the source and receiver are on the ground and R is the distance between them.

If the temperature gradient is linear

$$T = T_0 + b_1 z$$

It is very often a sufficient approximation when one has a linear temperature gradient to use Eq. (3.9) with

$$k = \frac{b_1}{2} \frac{C_0}{T_0}$$

Discussion of Effect of Wind Gradient. As a further example of the use of the sound ray Eqs. (3.7) and (3.8) consider the effect of a wind gradient. The cross-wind component has no effect on the wave normal. It serves only to carry the waves parallel to themselves. The resultant effect is generally much less important than that due to the wind component in the direction of propagation. Conse-

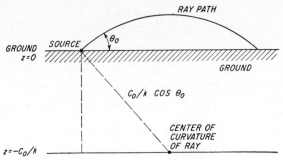

Fig. 3.12. Construction of ray paths when a linear sound-velocity gradient exists. $z = -c_0/k$ is the level at which extrapolation yields zero sound velocity.

quently only the latter component is discussed here. Let x be the direction of propagation. From Eq. (3.7)

$$\frac{dz}{ds} = \frac{c \sin \theta}{\sqrt{u^2 + 2uc \cos \theta + c^2}}$$

where θ is the angle the wave normal makes with the horizontal. From Eq. (3.8)

$$r = \frac{ds}{d\theta} = \frac{c \sin \theta}{\cos \theta[(du/ds) \cos \theta + (dc/ds)]}$$

whence

$$r = \frac{\sqrt{u^2 + 2uc \cos \theta + c^2}}{\cos \theta[(du/dz) \cos \theta + (dc/dz)]}$$

Now if $u \ll c$ and $\theta \ll \pi/2$, then

$$r = \frac{u_0 + c_0/\cos \theta_0}{(du/dz) \cos \theta + (dc/dz)} \tag{3.10a}$$

For $\theta = 0°$ (and very small θ) a wind gradient has the same effect as a sound-velocity gradient. Thus for propagation downwind, a wind gradient of 0.57 ft per sec per 100 ft will balance the effect of an adiabatic lapse rate of 0.3 per 100 ft for all rays close to the horizontal. In the upwind direction, their effects add.

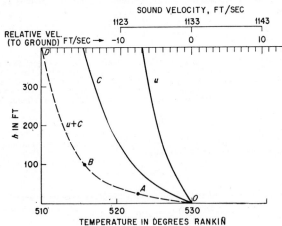

Fig. 3.13. Illustration of method of graphically plotting sound rays. See text for discussion.

Simplified Method of Plotting Sound Rays. Utilizing the fact that a linear "resultant" sound-velocity $(u + c)$ gradient causes a circular ray, the center of curvature lying at the height at which the extrapolated sound velocity is zero, the following simple graphical method for plotting sound rays has been developed.

A set of coordinate axes giving the sound velocity c (the upper horizontal axis in Fig. 3.13) as a function of the height (vertical axis) is set up. An auxiliary horizontal coordinate system is plotted with aid of Eq. (3.4), giving the temperature corresponding to the sound-velocity coordinates. This is shown as the lower horizontal coordinate axis. The temperature as a function of height is plotted as shown by curve c. The sound velocity relative to that at the ground is listed as a horizontal coordinate (upper axis). The wind-velocity component in the source-receiver direction is next plotted using the "velocity relative to that at the ground" coordinates and is shown as curve u. A wind blowing from the source to receiver is counted positive. The example shown is one in which the component in the source-receiver direction is toward the source, the magnitude increasing until it is 6.8 mph at a height of 400 ft. The algebraic sum of a and c is obtained and is shown as the dotted curve $(u + c)$.

The $(u + c)$ curve is now approximated by a series of straight lines. In Fig. 3.13 the straight lines chosen are those determined by OA, AB, BD. The height at which the lines would give zero "resultant" sound velocity is determined. For line OA this is $1,130 \times 25/6.6 = +4,300$ ft. For line AB it is $1,120 \times 7\frac{5}{8} = +10,500$ ft. For line BD it is $1,115 \times 300/6.8 = +49,500$ ft.

Referring now to Fig. 3.14, a very large plot is made of the horizontal and vertical space coordinates. The levels corresponding to points A, B, and D are indicated by the dotted lines as shown. The heights of 4,300, 10,500, and 49,500 ft are indicated by the full lines. The position of the source is located on these coordinates. In the example chosen it is at 75 ft. A beam compass is placed with its pivot point of (1) on the 10,500 level and the curve ab is drawn. At b the ray enters the region below A and accordingly the pivot point of the compass is moved to point (2) on the 4,300-ft level, being careful to keep the direction of the beam of the compass unchanged. At c the ray rises above the A level and the pivot point is moved to point (3) as indicated. At d the ray rises above the B level, the pivot point is shifted to the 49,500-ft level as shown, and the ray is continued.

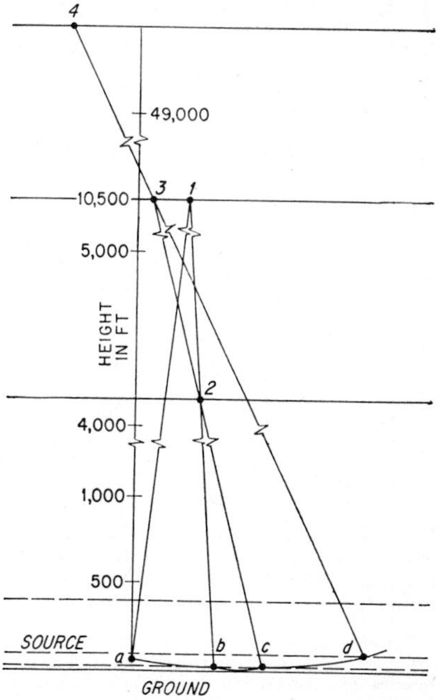

Shadow Ranges. The distance to the edge of the shadow regions x may be calculated as a function of the source height h_s, in the following way: Whether a shadow region exists at the position of an observer depends on his height. If the observer's height is equal to that of the source, the observer will be in the shadow region for all distances greater than $2x$.

FIG. 3.14. Illustration of method of graphically plotting sound rays. See text for discussion.

In general, the shadow region may be calculated in the following way:

Assuming (1) that the sound-velocity gradient and wind gradients are constant and (2) shallow-angle ray propagation, the rays are circles and the results of Eq. (3.10) apply so that

$$x^2 = 2h_s r = \frac{2h_s(u_0 + c_0/\cos \theta_0)}{(du/dz) \cos \theta + (dc/dz)} \tag{3.11}$$

The value of x has been calculated for a source 10 ft above the ground in the presence of a wind of 7 mph, assuming a velocity gradient appropriate to thin grass 20 in. high (see Table 3.1). The temperature gradients used were those which exist at a height of 5 ft; they are given in Fig. 3.5. Figure 3.15 shows polar plots giving the shadow boundary for the above conditions at noon and midnight in the summer and winter. (The wind structure is assumed the same for all cases.)

Table 3.1. Representative Value of z_0 and u_f for Natural Terrain Surfaces

Type of surface	z_0, ft	u_f, ft/sec
Very smooth (mud flats, ice)	3.3×10^{-5}	0.53
Lawn, grass up to 4 in. high	3.3×10^{-3}	0.87
Thin grass up to 4 in. high	2.3×10^{-2}	1.2
Thick grass up to 4 in. high	7.7×10^{-2}	1.5
Thin grass up to 20 in. high	0.17	1.8
Thick grass up to 20 in. high	0.3	2.1

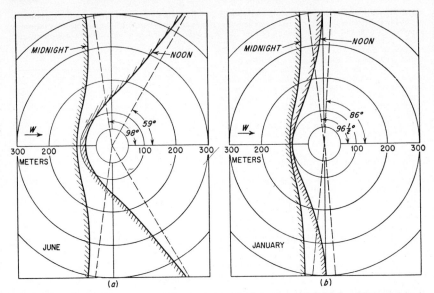

FIG. 3.15. (a) Example of shadow formation around a source 10 ft high. The receiver is also located 10 ft above ground. The average wind velocity measured 10 ft above ground is 7 mph. (b) Example of nighttime shadow formation with the same source and receiver geometry as in (a). (*After Ingard.*[9])

Variation of Sound Pressure within the Shadow. Using the optical analogy one may say that the "shadow" edge is not sharp and the shadow itself is not black but things get grayer and grayer as one recedes into the shadow zone. The shadow edge is sharper and the shadow blacker the higher the frequency.

Three factors affect the way in which the sound pressure decreases in the shadow zone:

1. Temperature inhomogeneities and turbulence in the air.
2. The magnitude of the temperature and wind gradient.
3. The acoustic nature of the ground.

Little is known in a quantitative way of the effect of temperature inhomogeneities and turbulence in the shadow region. However, measurements show that the rate of decrease of sound pressure in the shadow zone is limited by the energy scattered into shadow from inhomogeneities outside this zone.[10]

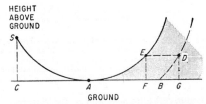

FIG. 3.16. Path of energy flow to point D in shadow is by way of $SABD$.

The second and third factors listed above are best treated together. The problem of propagation in a medium has been analyzed considering a constant-temperature-lapse rate over a plane boundary which was characterized by a constant normal acoustic impedance ratio $Z/\rho_0 c_0 = (\theta + i\varphi)$. It was found that the way in which energy travels from the source S to the observing point D in the shadow is over the path $SABD$ (Fig. 3.16) where BD is parallel to the limiting ray AE. In this shadow region the sound pressure drops as the result of the acoustic field behaving as a damped cylindrical wave. Thus the sound pressure at point D (see Fig. 3.16) is

$$p = p_E \left(\frac{CF}{CG}\right)^{\frac{1}{2}} e^{-k(AB)} \tag{3.12}$$

where CF, CG, and AB are the distances indicated. E is at the same height as D and p_E is the sound pressure at E; k is the attenuation constant given by

$$k = 1.01 \left(\frac{\omega}{c_0} \frac{1}{h_0^2}\right)^{1/3} - \frac{\theta}{2h_0} \tag{3.13}$$

where h_0 = height at which the absolute temperature = 0
c_0 = sound velocity at ground
$\omega = 2\pi f$

This is an approximation which holds for $|Z/\rho_0 c_0|^2 \ll \omega h_0/c_0$. At 100 cps and ordinary lapse rates this means the approximation is good for $|Z/\rho_0 c| \ll 50$.

For high-impedance boundaries

$$k = 0.44 \left(\frac{\omega}{c_0 h_0^2}\right)^{1/3} + 0.98 \left(\frac{\omega}{c_0 h_0^2}\right)^{1/3} \left|\frac{\rho_0 c_0}{Z}\right| \cos\left(\frac{\pi}{3} + \psi\right) \tag{3.14}$$

where $\tan \psi = \phi/\theta$. This result holds for $|Z/\rho_0 c_0|^2 \gg \omega h_0/c_0$.

Note that the attenuation coefficient for a pressure-release surface given by Eq. (3.13) is 2.3 times greater than that for a rigid surface given by Eq. (3.14).

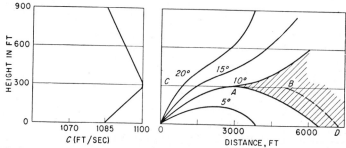

FIG. 3.17. Ray formation for an inversion at ground and lapse rate at higher altitudes.

As numerical examples of the use of these results, the following values are cited. For a temperature gradient of 0.27°F per ft, in addition to the attenuation resulting from the cylindrical divergence, there will be an attenuation rate of 78 db per 100 ft for ground with impedance $Z = \rho_0 c$, 58 db per 100 ft for ground with impedance $Z = 10\rho_0 c$, and 35 db per 100 ft for ground with infinite impedance, when the frequency is 500 cps.

Anomalous Effects Produced by Temperature Gradients. *An Inversion Near the Ground and Temperature Lapse at Higher Heights.* Consider an atmosphere with the temperature structure indicated in Fig. 3.17 and no wind. The ray paths for sound radiated from a 500-cps source will then be as

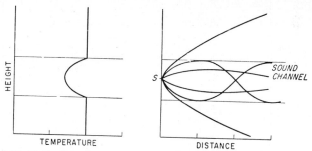

FIG. 3.18. Illustration of a temperature structure leading to a sound channel.

shown at the right. Using Eq. (3.8) with $c_p = 1,100$ ft per sec, $c_0 = 1,085$ ft per sec, and $u_p = u_0 = 0$, we find the limiting ray occurs at an angle given by

$$\cos \theta_{\lim} = \frac{1,085}{1,100}$$

so that $\theta_{\lim} = 10°$. The range to the shadow will be given by Eq. (3.10) where $h = 300$ ft.

$$k = \frac{1,100 - 1,085}{300} = 0.05$$

and $c_0 = 1,085$, whence $R = 7,200$ ft.

In the shadow the intensity should drop off as a damped cylindrical wave, with the damping coefficient being given by Eq. (3.13) with $\theta = 1$, and h_0 being equal to 11,000 ft.

The above description is accurate provided the ground is a good absorber so that (for example) the 5° ray is not reflected.

Sound Channels. In Fig. 3.17 if the ground is a very good reflector the layer below 300 ft acts as a sound channel, all rays with angles less than 10° being "trapped" in this region.

It is possible, although there have been no important instances reported in the literature, that such a sound channel can occur at an elevated layer. The temperature structure shown in Fig. 3.18 would lead to such a channel. Slightly inclined sound rays from a source placed in such a low-temperature layer would be trapped. If there are variations in temperature in the xy plane it would be possible for sound emanating from a source outside the layer to be similarly trapped.

SOUND PROPAGATION NEAR THE GROUND IN A HOMOGENEOUS UNIFORM ATMOSPHERE

Equations (3.12) to (3.14) are appropriate for a sound source and receiver near the ground in a quiescent atmosphere which has a temperature-lapse rate. Here an atmosphere that is uniform ($h_0 = \infty$) is considered. Moreover the ground is assumed to have a constant characteristic impedance—this replaces the assumption of an earth boundary with constant normal surface impedance.

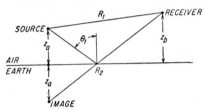

FIG. 3.19. Image of point source.

As a general rule, sand and soil are porous, having a noninfinite flow resistivity. Thus the characteristic impedance of the ground will be quite different from the product of its mean density and compressional wave velocity ρc and may, under many circumstances, be within an order of magnitude of the characteristic impedance for air. Consequently, air-borne sound waves impinging on such a porous earth surface will be only partially reflected. An appreciable portion of this energy will be propagated through the pores of the ground, and attenuated. Unfortunately there is a paucity of published values of the characteristic impedance and propagation constants for various types of earth, although some data are available for frequencies above 10,000 cps.

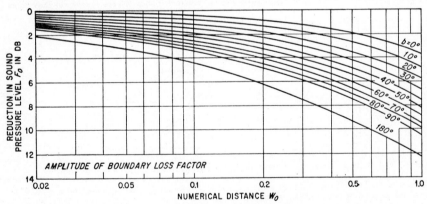

FIG. 3.20a. Graph of F_0 in terms of the numerical distance w_0 and b (see text).

The attenuation which results from propagation over the ground can be determined from the following analysis. Consider a point source of sound somewhere near an earth boundary. If the terrain is infinite in acoustic impedance, a condition approximated by concrete or asphalt surfaces, the sound field due to a point source can be obtained by adding the fields due to the original source and its geometrical image, as illustrated in Fig. 3.19. (However, if the acoustic impedance of the ground is noninfinite, the concept of a geometrical image is no longer valid.) The acoustic pressure under these conditions is given by[13]

$$p = \frac{e^{ik_1R_1}}{R_1} + \frac{e^{ik_1R_2}}{R_2}[(1 - R_p)F + R_p \tag{3.15}$$

where

$$R_p = \frac{Z_2 \cos \theta_1 - \rho c \cos \theta_2}{Z_2 \cos \theta_1 + \rho c \cos \theta_2} \tag{3.16}$$

$$F = 1 + i2w^{1/2}e^{-w} \int_{-iw^{1/2}}^{\infty} e^{-u^2}\, du \tag{3.17}*$$

$$w = w_0 e^{ib} = i\, \frac{2k_1R_2}{(1 - R_p)^2}\, \frac{(\rho c)^2}{Z_2^2}\, \frac{\cos^2 \theta_2}{\sin^2 \theta_1} \tag{3.18}$$

$\cos^2 \theta_2 = 1 - k_1^2/k_2^2 \sin^2 \theta_1$
k_1 = propagation constant of air
k_2 = propagation constant of ground
ρc = characteristic acoustic impedance of air
Z_2 = characteristic acoustic impedance of the ground

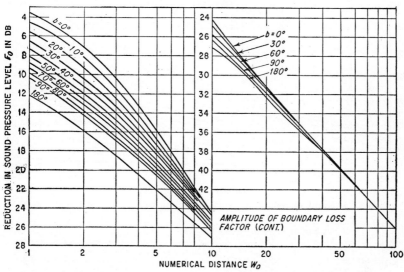

Fig. 3.20b. Graph of F_0 in terms of the numerical distance w_0 and b (see text).

* The function F may be expanded as follows: For small values of w, a convenient expansion of the error integral leads to

$$F = 1 + i(\pi w)^{1/2}e^{-w} \left(w - \frac{w^2}{3 \cdot 1!} + \frac{w^3}{5 \cdot 2!} - \frac{w^4}{7 \cdot 3!} + \cdots \right)$$

For large values of w the semiconvergent series below is convenient:

$$F = -\left[\frac{1}{2w} + \frac{1 \cdot 3}{(2w)^2} + \frac{1 \cdot 3 \cdot 5}{(2w)^3} + \cdots \right]$$

It is seen that, as w approaches 0, F approaches 1; as w approaches infinity, F approaches 0. Furthermore, w is porportional to k_1R_2 so it is evident that, for values of either r_0, or $z_a + z_b$, very large compared with a wavelength in air, F will approach 0. (Since w is a function of the impedance and the propagation of the ground, the values of either r_0, or $z_a + z_b$, which are necessary before F is inappreciable, will vary with the nature of the ground.) As F approaches 0, the amplitude p approaches the following value:

$$p = \frac{e^{ik_1R_1}}{R_1} + R_p\, \frac{e^{ik_1R_2}}{R_2}$$

Thus at great distances or great heights the solution approaches that of a plane incident wave whose direction of propagation is that corresponding to the ray.

The solution is a function of the sum of the heights of the receiver and source. Thus if all other variables are held constant, the last term of Eq. (3.16) will remain constant when z_a and z_b are varied provided their sum is constant.

Source and Receiver on the Ground. Of particular interest are the results obtained when the source and receiver are both at the surface of the ground. In this case $\theta_1 = 90°$, $R_1 = R_2$, and grazing incidence is always obtained. Then $R_p = -1$, and Eq. (3.15) becomes

$$p = 2F \frac{e^{ik_1R_1}}{R_1}$$

It is seen that there will be a decrease of sound pressure with distance which is caused by two factors (1) spherical divergence—the $1/R_1$ factor; (2) the variation of F with distance.

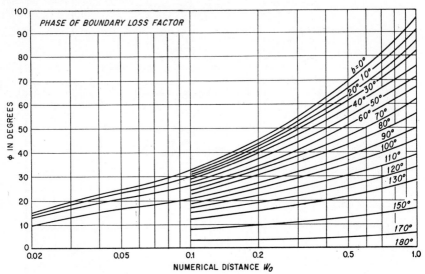

Fig. 3.20c. Graph of ϕ in terms of the numerical distance w_0 and b (see text).

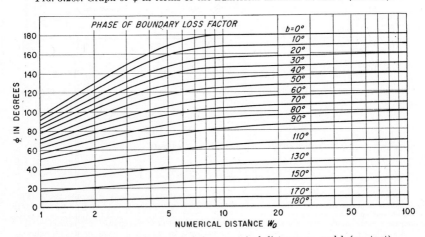

Fig. 3.20d. Graph of ϕ in terms of the numerical distance w_0 and b (see text).

In order to see the significance of the decrease in sound pressure with distance due to the function F, consider the case where $k_2 \ll k_1$ and k_2 is real, which is usual when the surface of the ground is nonporous. Then, if the receiver is only a small height above the ground, the reflection coefficient R_p will equal 1. At these small heights w is very large and F is very small; so $p = 2e^{ik_1R_1}/R_1$. Consequently, the added decrease in pressure because the ground is not a perfect reflector is given by the function F, and F may be called the "boundary loss factor."

An important feature of the solution is that, in the limit of very large separation, and when the heights of the source and receiving point are such that the sound is at grazing incidence with the ground, the amplitude, as above, varies as $1/R^2$.

Values of F are conveniently given in terms of w_0 and b [see Eq. (3.18)]. Writing $F = F_0 e^{i\varphi}$ the values of F_0 and φ are given in terms of w_0 and b in Figs. 3.20a, b, c, and d.

Example. Using the above solution, determine the distance at which there will be a 6-db drop in sound pressure level as a result of ground absorption for the case where both source and receiver are at ground level. Let us assume the frequency is 200 cps, the characteristic acoustic impedance of the ground is $3\rho c(1 + i)$, and the value of $k_2 = k_1 \cdot 3(1 + i)$. (Note: Having assumed a solution of the form $e^{i(k_1 x - \omega t)}$, a positive imaginary part means a negative reactance.) Then

$$w = 0.028 k_1 R e^{i0.055}$$

From Fig. 3.20b, $b = 0.055$ radians $= 3.2°$, $F_0 = 6$ db when $w_0 = 15.5$. Therefore $k_1 R = 550$ or $R/\lambda = 88$. Assuming the wavelength is 5.5 ft, we obtain $R = 485$ ft.

Laboratory measurements, made as a function of distance and height above a mineral-wool surface boundary, show the results to be in good agreement with theory.[14]

Case in Which the Boundary Has Constant Normal Specific Acoustic Impedance. If the boundary has a constant normal specific acoustic impedance the mathematics is more tractable. Solutions appropriate to this case have been obtained.[15,16]

When the velocity of sound in the earth is very low, its normal acoustic impedance is very nearly independent of angle of incidence. As a practical matter, very often any departures from constancy of normal impedance introduce changes which are unimportant.

REFERENCES

1. Kneser, H. O.: *Akust. Z.*, **5**: 256 (1940).
2. Knudsen, V. O.: *J. Acoust. Soc. Amer.*, **5**: 112 (1933).
3. Knotzel, H.: *Akust. Z.*, **5**: 245 (1940).
4. Knudsen, V. O., and L. Obert: *J. Acoust. Soc. Amer.*, **7**: 249 (1936).
5. Delsasso, L. P.: Summary Report of Research under Contract W-28-099-ac-228, USAF, University of California, Los Angeles, 1953.
6. Eyring, C. F.: *J. Acoust. Soc. Amer.*, **18**: 257 (1946).
7. Sutton, O. G.: "Micrometeorology," McGraw-Hill Book Company, Inc., New York, 1953.
8. Johnson, N. K., and L. Davies: *Quart. J. Roy. Meteorol. Soc.*, **53**: 45 (1927).
9. Ingard, K. U.: *Proc. Fourth National Noise Abatement Symposium*, **4**: 1953.
10. Ingard, K. U., A. F. Kuckes, and I. Dyer: *J. Acoust. Soc. Amer.*, **26**: 135A (1954).
11. Pridmore-Brown, D. C., and K. U. Ingard: *J. Acoust. Soc. Amer.*, **27**: 36 (1955).
12. Nyborg, W. S., I. Rudnick, and H. K. Schilling: *J. Acoust. Soc. Amer.*, **22**: 422 (1950).
13. Rudnick, I.: *J. Acoust. Soc. Amer.*, **19**: 348 (1947).
14. Lawhead, R. B., and I. Rudnick: *J. Acoust. Soc. Amer.*, **23**: 541 (1951).
15. Ingard, K. U.: *J. Acoust. Soc. Amer.*, **23**: 329 (1951).
16. Lawhead, R. B., and I. Rudnick: *J. Acoust. Soc. Amer.*, **23**: 546 (1951).
17. Redfearn, S. W.: *Phil. Mag.* (ser. 7), **30**: 223 (1940).
18. Best, A. C.: *Geophys. Mem.*, **65**: 40 (1935).
19. Johnson, N. K., and G. S. P. Heywood: *Geophys. Mem.*, **77**
20. Knudsen, V. O., and C. M. Harris: "Acoustical Designing in Architecture," p. 58, footnote, John Wiley and Sons, Inc., New York, 1950.

Chapter 4

THE HEARING MECHANISM

Hallowell Davis, M.D.

Central Institute for the Deaf

INTRODUCTION

For a better understanding of many problems in noise control, some knowledge of the mechanism of hearing is helpful. The ear is a biological detector of sound, a physical mechanism that can be injured by too intense a sound. Chapter 7 is devoted to the effects of noise on hearing, Chap. 8 to the protection of the hearing mechanism against injury, and Chap. 38 to the legal aspects of the disabilities that result from such injury when it does occur. In this connection we must know not only the anatomy and something of the normal functions of the ear, but also the disabilities of hearing that may arise from other causes such as infection or old age. These points are reviewed in the present chapter. Also the description of the mechanism of the detection of sound enables us to understand better the problems of audiometry in industry (Chap. 6) and the basic problems of the loudness of noise (Chap. 5).

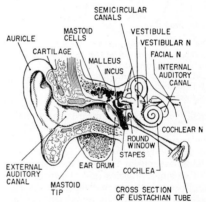

Fig. 4.1. In this semidiagrammatic drawing of the ear, the inner ear is shown with the temporal bone cut away to reveal the semicircular canals, the vestibule, and the cochlea. The cochlea has been turned slightly from its normal orientation to show its coils more clearly. The opening for nerves through the bone to the brain cavity of the skull is quite diagrammatic. The Eustachian tube actually runs forward as well as downward and inward. The muscles of the middle ear are omitted. (*Davis.*[5])

ANATOMY OF THE HEARING MECHANISM[2,5,6,10,13]

External and Middle Ear. Figure 4.1 shows a semidiagrammatic section through the *external ear* and the *middle ear* with their approximate relationship to the *cochlea*, which is the auditory portion of the inner ear. The *inner ear* also contains sense organs for acceleration and orientation to gravity, located in the *semicircular canals* and the *vestibule*. The external ear includes the *auricle* and also the *external auditory canal*.

The external auditory canal has a cross section of about 30 to 50 sq mm, a length of about 27 mm, and a volume of about 1 cu cm. The cross section varies in shape from individual to individual, from circular to a long oval.   The ranges of size and of shape render very difficult the design of any universal model of earplug.

The external canal serves to carry the sound from the auricle to the eardrum, to protect the eardrum from mechanical injury by foreign bodies and from drying.   The canal is lined with skin, which is increasingly sensitive as we go inward, particularly in the deeper portion where it lies directly on bone.   Wax, secreted by the skin, serves as protection.   The flexibility and the sensitivity of the skin are both important limiting factors in the performance and for the wearability of earplugs.

The *tympanic membrane*, which is popularly called the *eardrum*, closes off the external canal diagonally.   It is round in outline and about 7 mm in diameter.   It is an inwardly directed cone with an included angle of about 135° having an area between 50 to 90 sq mm.   The material, connective tissue, and the shape of the membrane combine to make the cone rather stiff.   At least at frequencies below 2,400 cps, the cone and the little bone, the malleus, that is attached to it move as a whole as a rigid body.   The conical shape does not extend quite to the edges of the membrane.   The edges are thus fairly flexible and permit the unified movement of the large central portion.   At higher frequencies the membrane vibrates in segments.

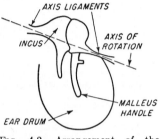

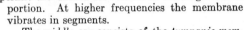

The *middle ear* consists of the *tympanic membrane*, the air-filled cavity of the middle ear beyond the membrane, and two openings into the inner ear, the *oval window* and the *round window*. The latter, about 2 sq mm in area, is closed by a flat elastic membrane.   The oval window is closed by a thin plate of bone, the footplate of the *stapes* (stirrup), supported by a flexible ring-shaped ligament.   The area of the footplate is about 3.2 sq mm.   The stapes is the smallest of a chain of three little bones (the *ossicles*) that are contained in the middle ear, the other two being the *incus* (anvil) and *malleus* (hammer) which connect the stapes to the tympanic membrane.   The "handle" of the malleus is firmly attached to the cone-shaped tympanic membrane from the tip of the cone diag-

Fɪɢ.   4.2.   Arrangement   of   the ossicles, showing how the mass is distributed around the axis of rotation.   The maximum displacement of the drum membrane occurs at its lower edge.   (*Bárány.*[15])

onally backward and upward nearly to its edge.   The head of the malleus and the body of the incus are interlocked and firmly held together by ligaments so that, except at the very highest sound pressures, they move as a single unit.   They are suspended by ligaments so that their freest movement is rotation around an axis that passes almost tangential to the upper posterior edge of the tympanic membrane (Fig. 4.2).

Two small muscles (not shown in the figures), the *tensor tympani*, attached to the long process of the malleus, and the *stapedius*, attached to the neck of the stapes, restrain somewhat the movements of the ossicles.   The movement of the footplate of the stapes in the oval window is like a bell-crank lever around an axis that passes tangential to the posterior edge of the footplate.   Here the suspensory ligament is narrower while at the mobile anterior end it is wider and more elastic.   At very high sound pressures the stapes may move in another mode of vibration, rocking (or "rolling") around the long axis of its footplate.   This pattern of movement gives relatively much less pistonlike displacement of the footplate.

Inner Ear.   The inner ear is a series of channels and chambers that are so complicated in shape that they are known as the *labyrinth*.   The labyrinth is not accessible to easy view, as Fig. 4.1 might suggest, but is actually buried in the substance of the temporal bone in the base of the skull.   The bony canals of the labyrinth are filled with a clear watery fluid known as *perilymph* and in it a corresponding series of delicate membranous tubes and sacs that contain a rather similar clear fluid known as *endolymph*.   The membranous tubes and sacs also contain the sensory cells of the inner ear and their specialized supporting structures.

We are here concerned only with the organ of hearing: i.e., the *cochlea* and the central portion of the *vestibule* to which the cochlea connects and into which the oval window opens.

The *cochlea* is coiled like a snail in a flat spiral of 2½ turns. The canal within it is about 35 mm long and ends blindly at the apex. The canal is partly divided into an upper (*vestibular*) and a lower (*tympanic*) gallery (scala) by a spiral shelf of bone that protrudes outward from the inner wall of the passage like a shelf along the inner wall of a circular staircase. The division between the two galleries is completed by a fibrous flexible membrane, the *basilar membrane*, that stretches across from the lower edge of the bony shelf to the spiral ligament that attaches it to the outer wall (see Fig. 4.3). The basilar membrane and the shelf both terminate a millimeter or two short of the end of the galleries so that the two galleries join at the apex of the cochlea. The opening that joins them is called the *helicotrema;* its size is between 0.25 and 0.40 sq mm. The basilar membrane is about 32 mm long and it tapers in width from about 0.5 near the apex to about 0.05 mm at the base of the cochlea near the open window.

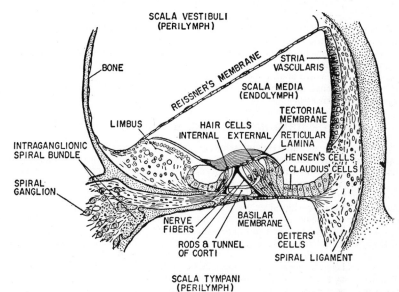

FIG. 4.3. Cross section of the cochlear partition showing the sensory structures. This drawing is based on a section about midway between the round window and the apex in the guinea pig. The human ear is very similar. Certain details, notably the width of the basilar membrane, vary systematically with position up and down the spiral of the cochlea. (*Davis.*[16])

On the vestibular surface of the basilar membrane lies the membranous tube that contains the sensory cells, their supporting structures, and the endolymph. The space within this tube is the *scala media*. The sensory cells and their supporting structures are known as the *organ of Corti*. The round window opens into the tympanic gallery near the base of the cochlea not far from the oval window but is separated from it by the "*cochlear partition*," which includes the basilar membrane, the sensory structures attached to it, and also the thin partition, known as *Reissner's membrane*, which separates the *scala vestibuli* from the endolymphatic space within the scala media.

The sensory cells, known as *hair cells* because of the tufts of tiny hairlike structures that extend from their upper ends, are embedded in the organ of Corti that lies on the upper surface of the basilar membrane (Fig. 4.3). Just above the organ of Corti and attached to it by fibrous networks along its edges lies another structure, the *tectorial membrane*. The tectorial membrane is also attached by one edge to a firm supporting structure, the *limbus*. The outer ends of the hairs of the hair cells are embedded in the tectorial membrane and bend when any shearing motion takes place between it and the organ of Corti. The upper surface of the organ of Corti, facing the tectorial membrane, is a rather stiff plate (the "reticular lamina" in Fig. 4.3). The upper ends of the hair cells form part of this plate. The lower ends of the hair cells are held in specialized supporting structures, and the endings of the *auditory nerve fibers* spread over the lower ends of the hair cells.

The hair cells are arranged systematically in several rows lengthwise of the organ of Corti. One row lies just inward of the rods of Corti (see Fig. 4.3) toward the limbus. These are known as the *internal hair cells*. The others, the *external hair cells*, are arranged in three parallel rows on the opposite side of the rods of Corti. Each external hair cell is about 8 microns in diameter; the internal hair cells are slightly larger. There are about 3,500 internal and about 20,000 external hair cells in each ear.

The sense of hearing is served by the *cochlear portion of the auditory nerve*. The cell bodies of its nerve fibers lie close to the organ of Corti but within the bony structure of the central core of the cochlea. They extend along the length of the cochlea to form the so-called *spiral ganglion*, which contains about 27,000 nerve cells.

The relation between nerve cells and hair cells is not simple. Some nerve fibers make connections with one or two hair cells each. This seems to be the dominant arrangement for the internal hair cells. For the external hair cells, however, most nerve fibers make connections with quite a number of hair cells along the way. Furthermore, each hair cell usually receives connections from several nerve fibers. The functional significance of this complicated multiple distribution of the nerve fibers is not known, although a complicated netlike distribution of nerve fibers is found in some other sense organs also.

HOW THE HEARING MECHANISM FUNCTIONS[2,3,4,6,7,8,9,11,12,13]

The ear is one of the external sense organs. It is specialized to receive and to respond to a particular form of energy, air-borne acoustic vibratory energy, over a frequency range of about nine octaves and a dynamic range of more than 120 db. Its output is nerve impulses in the auditory nerve. These impulses convey auditory information to the brain. We are not here concerned with the way the information is encoded in the nerve impulses, or with how acoustic energy stimulates these nerve impulses, or with the way in which the inner ear performs a partial acoustic analysis of sounds with respect to their sound pressure, their frequency, and their time of arrival. All these are problems of the physiology of hearing. For purposes of noise control it is enough to know that the outer ear conducts acoustic energy to the middle ear and that the middle ear serves as an impedance-matching device to deliver the energy efficiently to the inner ear. Furthermore, we should know that the inner ear may be harmed by certain diseases and also by excessive noise.

At the other end of the system, we know too little about the relations of nerve impulses to thought or action to make neuroanatomy and neurophysiology of any practical importance for noise control. It is not difficult, however, to measure the over-all sensitivity and powers of discrimination of the human auditory mechanism, as we do by "tests of hearing" in the popular sense. This is the province of psycho-acoustics, and more specifically of audiometry. These aspects of hearing, including the problem of loudness, will be covered in later chapters.

External Ear.[2] The acoustic effect of the auricle is almost negligible, largely because the side of the head forms an even larger acoustic baffle nearby in almost the same plane.

In a free field the external canal is an acoustic resonator having a natural frequency of about 3,000 cps. It has very little effect below 1,000 cps, but at 3,000 cps the sound pressure level just in front of the eardrum is 10 to 12 db higher, on the average, than that measured just at the entrance to the canal. The difference in sound pressure level falls again at higher frequencies to about 3 db at 7,000 cps. The resonance of the external canal is one of the factors that determines human auditory sensitivity.

Middle Ear.[2,13] When the ear is excited by a sharp click, the handle of the malleus oscillates at about 1,300 to 1,500 cps. Some distortion of quick transient sounds is therefore unavoidable. The oscillations are heavily damped but the damping is not quite critical. At higher frequencies other minor resonances may appear.

At low frequencies the ear is sensitive mainly to changes in pressure rather than to the particle-velocity of the vibrating air and the eardrum behaves like an elastic membrane whose displacements are proportional to the applied sound pressure.   The air entrapped in the middle ear acts as a cushion and is partly responsible for the simple acoustic behavior of the eardrum.   Near its natural frequencies, however, the ear does not act in a manner strictly analogous to a pressure microphone.

The force which results from the sound waves acting on the drum membrane is transmitted to the fluid that fills the inner ear through a system of two levers in tandem.   The first is the drum-malleus-incus combination that rotates as a unit around the axis of the suspensory ligaments of the malleus and incus (Fig. 4.2).   The second is the stapes, rocking on its "heel."

The *force* exerted by the stapes on the fluid is about the same as the force exerted on the movable drum membrane by the sound wave in the air.   The area of the footplate of the stapes is, however, much smaller than that of the rigid moving section of the drum.   The *pressure* delivered by the stapes is therefore considerably greater than the pressure of the air-borne sound wave, perhaps an increase as much as 22 : 1.

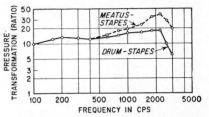

In more technical language, the middle ear partially matches the impedance of the external air to that of the fluids of the inner ear.   The matching of impedances results in more efficient transfer of energy from air to inner ear with less loss by reflection of sound back from the eardrum. There is some disagreement as to the "normal" percentage of energy transmitted at different frequencies.   It seems to be rather low, perhaps 10 per cent or less, at 300 cps and to rise to a maximum of nearly 100 per cent at about 1,500 cps, which is the usual natural frequency of the

Fig. 4.4. Pressure transformation in the external and middle ear. The pressure at the stapes is increased over the pressure at the outer end of the auditory canal (meatus) and at the drum by the ratios shown.   The increase in pressure at the drum over the pressure at the outer end of the canal is due to the resonance of the canal. (*Békésy.*[17])

eardrum as a whole.   At higher frequencies the efficiency of transfer falls off somewhat (Fig. 4.4).

Minor resonances of various parts of the system and more complicated patterns of vibration of the drum membrane show their effects at higher frequencies.   These variations have not yet been fully evaluated, but many individual audiograms (i.e., threshold curves) deviate rather consistently from the smooth average curve.   The deviations are probably best explained in terms of minor anatomical differences.   They are small, however, compared with the deviations due to abnormalities of the inner ear. Also, as the mass and the stiffness of various parts of the transmission system are modified by disease, notably by chronic otitis media or by otosclerosis, the efficiency of transfer of acoustic energy may be further and greatly reduced at all frequencies.

Bone Conduction.[2] Conduction of acoustic energy to the inner ear by any path other than through the air of the external canal, the drum membrane, and the ossicles, is called *bone conduction*.   An example is hearing a tuning fork whose stem is pressed against the forehead.   One's own voice is an important source of bone-conducted sound.

Although only a very small fraction of air-borne acoustic energy is converted to solid-borne vibration in the head, if air-borne sound is sufficiently intense this vibration may be detected by bone conduction.

Bone-conducted vibrations do not stimulate the auditory nerve directly but, in one way or another, they set up exactly the same patterns of vibration of the cochlear partition as does air-conducted sound.

A major problem related to bone conduction is the identification and evaluation of the several different paths that may be followed, often simultaneously, by the acoustic energy.   This becomes important in studying the effectiveness of earplugs, earmuffs, and helmets as protection against intense noise, and also in diagnosing the nature of a hearing loss.

One mechanism of bone conduction is the vibration of the head as a whole. This is the chief mode at frequencies below 200 cps. If it were not for the shape and manner of suspension of the ossicles, energy would be transferred very effectively to the ossicles by this to-and-fro movement because of their inertia.

At the frequency of 800 cps the front and back of the head move in opposite directions with a nodal line of compression between. At higher frequencies still more complicated modes of vibration of the skull appear.

Whatever the frequency, the skull must be considered as a whole. It is not surprising that in bone conduction the energy reaches the right ear at very nearly the same intensity as the left ear, regardless of whether the energy is applied over-all (as in a sound field), to the forehead, to the right mastoid, or to the left mastoid.

Tissue Conduction. An important effect that should probably be called "tissue conduction" is the transfer of acoustic energy by an earplug moving as a whole like a piston. The elasticity of the skin of the external ear canal makes such transmission not only possible but inevitable. Perhaps, also, the auricle may transmit some acoustic energy past a plug along the cartilaginous wall of the ear canal rather than by true bone conduction that involves the skull as a whole.

Protective Actions.[2,6,9,13] The middle ear seems to protect the delicate sensory structures of the inner ear from possible injurious effects of very intense sounds. The extent of this protection is not very clear, however.

Mode of Vibration. One mechanism of protection is the change in the mode of vibration of the stapes. This action has been demonstrated clearly for very low frequencies, i.e., about 10 cps. The sound pressure level at which protection occurs is revealed by a decrease in the loudness of the tone and the beginning of a pricking sensation in the middle ear. The amplitude of displacement at which the change in the pattern of vibration occurs is considerable. It is uncertain whether at higher frequencies the change occurs at sound pressure levels below those which cause acute pain in the ear.

The Intra-aural Reflex. The muscles of the middle ear are generally believed to afford some protection by contracting reflexly in response to loud sounds, very much as the eyelids close reflexly when a bright light is flashed in the eye. Such contraction of the stapedius, rocking the footplate of the stapes outward, can be observed in patients who have large holes in their eardrums. The tensor tympani tends to pull the long process of the malleus inward and thus oppose the action of the stapedius. No movement of the entire drum membrane can be seen, however. The net result seems to be merely a stiffening of the ossicular chain. The natural frequency of the middle ear is presumably altered somewhat, and changes in transmission are of the order of 5 or 10 db. In any case, the reaction time is at least 10 msec, so that even this small amount of protection is not effective against steep acoustic wavefronts from impacts or explosions.

Nonlinear Distortion. Some protection to the inner ear may also be afforded by the nonlinear response of the middle ear to intense sounds. For small amplitudes the displacement of the stapes seems to be proportional to the pressure applied to the eardrum, but, as in all mechanical systems, as the pressure is increased the amplitude of displacement finally ceases to be proportional to it. The system is then said to be "overloaded." The inner ear is protected to the extent that extreme displacements of the stapes are thus reduced. A larger proportion of the energy is dissipated within the middle ear or reflected back from the drum.

The situation is complicated, however. Some of the energy in an overloaded transmission system is transformed to higher frequencies that are multiples of the original frequency, resulting in so-called "harmonic distortion." Also, if more than one frequency is present, new frequencies of vibration will be produced that correspond to the sum and to the difference between these frequencies and/or their harmonics. The production of higher harmonics and of sum and difference tones in the ear has been amply demonstrated. The element in the system which is responsible for this nonlinear distortion and the consequent aural harmonics is a matter of considerable debate. Apparently the drum membrane is not responsible unless it is displaced by a relatively large static pressure. Some nonlinear behavior results from the action of the footplate of the stapes.

Another source of nonlinearity is within the inner ear. The sensory structures themselves may be "overloaded" and thus subjected to possibly dangerous mechanical stresses. There is good evidence that some processes in the inner ear are in fact nonlinear, even at rather moderate sound pressure levels, but until more is known about the exact site and nature of the nonlinear process the appearance of nonlinearity cannot be accepted automatically as a danger signal. A system that is "overloaded" in the sense of becoming nonlinear in its response is not necessarily in danger of breaking.

Further evidence for nonlinearity in the middle ear is the appearance of "subharmonics," which are submultiples of the exciting frequency. Such subharmonics can be produced in mechanical systems that have more than one degree of freedom, particularly when they are excited at frequencies above the natural frequency of one of their modes of vibration. The ear is such a system; and such subharmonics radiated back from the middle ear have been demonstrated at sound levels near or above the threshold for discomfort or tactile sensations in the ear. They clearly are generated in the middle ear.

The nonlinearity of the ear and the production in it of harmonics, subharmonics, and sum and difference tones are mentioned here not only because of their protective action but also to illustrate the complexity of the acoustic behavior of the ear at high sound pressure levels. All these effects can be demonstrated at sound levels such as may be encountered in some industrial or military situations and some of them at levels well below those which cause pain or even discomfort. They suggest that mechanical limits of some sort are being reached, but their significance as possible warning signals or an indication of protective actions has not yet been adequately assessed. But in any case, we must also reckon with the distortion as causing deterioration of acoustic signals such as speech that are received at high sound pressure levels.

AUDITORY SENSITIVITY

The Auditory Area. The least sound pressure needed to make a tone audible, i.e., the *"threshold" pressure*, depends on the frequency of the tone. To a lesser extent, it also depends on whether the sound pressure is measured at the entrance to the auditory canal (minimum audible pressure) or in a free field (minimum audible field), whether the tone is steady or interrupted, whether other tones or noise are sounding, the direction of the source (in a free field), and so on. Practice in listening may improve performance by several decibels, and even under similar conditions normal ears differ considerably in sensitivity.

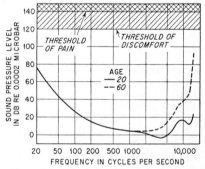

Fig. 4.5. The "auditory area." The lowest curve shows the threshold of hearing for binaural listening in a free field. (*After Robinson and Dadson.*[14]) The threshold of discomfort is frequently considered to be 120 db, and the threshold of pain 140 db.

It is possible to define an auditory stimulus in several ways: for example, in terms of: (1) the sound pressure as measured at the eardrum by a probe-tube microphone, (2) the sound pressure at the entrance to the auditory canal, or (3) the pressure measured in an acoustic free field at the position that is later to be occupied by the center of the listener's head. The position usually chosen for the specification of the free-field threshold contour is at the entrance to the auditory canal, not at the tympanic membrane. The free-field measurement with no listener present is the one employed almost exclusively in other problems relevant to noise control. The threshold of hearing for two-ear (binaural) listening in a free field for normal young adults, under good conditions, is quite close to the standard reference level of 0 db (0.0002 microbar) between about 800 and about 5,000 cps (see Fig. 4.5). Above 5,000 cps the threshold curve rises steeply to cross the threshold of pain at about 20,000 cps.

The upper intensity limit of "the auditory area" is sometimes taken as the threshold of discomfort, which is a sound pressure level of about 120 db independent of frequency.

More often the threshold of pain, at 140 db, is considered the boundary, but, as far as we know, sounds above 140 db continue to sound louder with increasing sound pressure until the loudness is reduced by "auditory fatigue" or by acoustic injury.

The pain, and also tactile sensations of pricking or tickle, come from the middle ear. The "discomfort" experienced at 120 db seems to be an auditory sensation.

The lower frequency limit of hearing is vague because hearing merges into sensations of vibration. For practical purposes it lies somewhere between 20 and 50 cps.

The dynamic range of hearing extends from a sound pressure level of about 0 db (0.0002 microbar) to 140 db, or 2,000 microbar. The amplitude of vibration of the drum membrane at 2,000 cps increases from an unbelievably small 10^{-9} cm (one-tenth the diameter of a hydrogen atom) to $\frac{1}{10}$ mm at 140 db.

The ability of the ear to discriminate small differences of pressure, frequency, and time lie in the domain of psychophysics. The central nervous system elaborates in complicated fashion the information provided by the ears. Statements as to just noticeable differences in frequency or in sound pressure must, in order to be meaningful, be accompanied by detailed specifications as to the conditions and methods of measurement.

Auditory Fatigue. The sensitivity of the ear is not constant. Both the threshold for a tone and its loudness may vary considerably as the result of previous exposure to sounds of the same or of different frequencies. The short-term changes produced by sounds below 90 or 100 db are essentially an adjustment of some physical or chemical balance in the sense organ, rather than fatigue in the sense of exhaustion. They are analogous to the processes of dark adaptation or light adaptation in the eye.

Louder sounds produce longer-lasting changes in threshold that increase with continuing exposure. Complete recovery takes place after these *temporary threshold shifts* but it may require hours or even days (see Chap. 7). Temporary shifts of 20 to 30 db are the rule in young ears in many noisy industrial situations. This condition may properly be called "auditory fatigue," although it is difficult to draw the line between physiological fatigue and pathological injury followed by repair. Individual ears vary greatly in their susceptibility to temporary threshold shift. It is not known whether the same ears that show large temporary threshold shifts are also the ones that are most susceptible to cumulative permanent hearing loss of the industrial or presbycusis type.

Auditory Localization. An important auditory ability is the localization of the source of a sound. The important clues are differences in sound pressure and in the time of arrival of corresponding sound waves at the two ears. It is primarily a binaural sense, although a person with only one good ear can localize sound to some extent if allowed to move his head about. Rudiments of the sense of echo location, which is highly developed in bats, appear in humans in the feeling of space given by reverberation of sound and by our ability to sense, by echoes of sounds that we ourselves produce, the presence of a nearby reflecting surface even when we are not conscious of just how we do so.

HEARING IMPAIRMENTS[5]

External Ear. *Foreign Bodies and "Otitis Externa."* Accident and disease may affect the external and the middle ear. One affliction of the external ear is the presence of foreign material, including insects and water. Water remaining in the external ear not only interferes with the conduction of sound but also softens and weakens the skin that lines the canal and makes easy the entry of infections. Such infections, although they may develop slowly and never form an acute inflammation or abscess, may be very stubborn and irritating. This is particularly true of the fungus and low-grade bacterial infections that are so prevalent in hot moist tropical climates. In such parts of the world the cleanliness and integrity of the external canal must be guarded most carefully, and in the presence of infection of any sort the use of insert-type earplugs for protection against noise may bring even worse attendant discomfort and dangers.

Impacted Wax. Nature's defense against insects and water is the wax, or "cerumen," that is formed by skin glands in the ear canal. But sometimes wax is formed in excessive amounts and forms a hard mass that may stick to or press against the drum membrane or may completely plug the canal. Unskilled efforts to remove wax by means of matchstick, hairpins, cotton, etc., are likely only to force it more deeply into the canal and favor *impaction*, as formation of a plug is called.

The transmission loss produced by a plug of wax may be as much as or more than is given by the very best artificial earplugs. It may reduce the sensitivity of that ear to the level of the bone-conducted sound picked up by the skull.

Middle Ear: Conductive Hearing Loss. *The Drum Membrane.* Acoustic transmission across the middle ear may be reduced in many ways. The drum may be torn and perhaps malleus and incus lost also, from either mechanical injury, destruction by disease, or deliberate removal by a surgeon in order to check the further progress of infection. The amount of the hearing loss depends, first, on the reduction or loss of the pressure transformation that is normally performed by the drum and ossicles, and, second, on the presence of some mechanical barrier to the transmission of sound pressure to the oval and round windows. Such a barrier might be fluid or pus in the middle ear or it might be the scars of "adhesions" produced by an old chronic infection, or perhaps a protective skin graft deliberately placed by an otologic surgeon.

The hearing loss produced by a small slit or hole in an eardrum may be negligible, not more than 5 db. A larger hole may cause a loss of 20 db or even more.

The loss after a "radical mastoid operation" may be as little as 25 db or as much as 45 db in a normal ear. In a pathologic ear the operation often improves the hearing, but there is always a residual hearing loss of about 25 db because of the lack of a normal ossicular chain. The final hearing depends on the amount of scar tissue about the only ossicle left in a radical operation, namely, the stapes. All these conductive hearing losses affect all frequencies but are usually more severe at some frequencies than at others.

Simple static pressure on the drum membrane, either from excess air trapped in the middle ear or more often a deficiency of air due to increase of barometric pressure outside without the normal equalization through the Eustachian tube, will reduce transmission. The difference in static pressure puts the drum membrane and the ligaments of the ossicular chain on the stretch and thereby restricts the amplitude of movement. The stiffness of the transmission system is increased and its response may become nonlinear.

Otitis Media. Fluid or pus in the middle ear causes great reductions in acoustic transmission. The loss may be even greater if bands of scarlike fibrous tissue called "adhesions" are also formed. Fluid, pus, and adhesions are caused by infection of the middle ear, or *otitis media*. The infection may be acute or chronic, single or recurrent. The usual original source of the infections is the nose or throat in the form of a head cold or a sore throat. The Eustachian tube and the middle ear are in direct communication with the pharynx and are actually outpocketings of the respiratory tract; so that the close relation of otitis media to the common cold is not surprising.

Otosclerosis. Another cause of conductive deafness is otosclerosis. This condition particularly afflicts adolescents and young adults. A strong hereditary factor is shown by its tendency to run in families and to appear in white persons but not in Negroes. In otosclerosis an abnormal bonelike tissue invades the bony capsule of the inner ear. If the growth occurs at the edge of the oval window or in the stapes it is likely to join the footplate to the bone of the skull with a bony ridge. The condition has been described as "a sort of arthritis of the ossicular chain." It is not painful and causes no symptoms except a progressive loss of hearing and, sometimes, head noises. Furthermore, loss of hearing occurs only when and to the extent that the stapes becomes mechanically fixed in the oval window. The resulting hearing loss may be as much as 60 db, the greatest encountered in any form of conductive hearing loss. More or less "nerve deafness" or "cochlear deafness" may also be present in otosclerotic ears and cause a still greater total loss of hearing.

The common feature of all types of conductive deafness is that they affect the transmission of acoustic energy. The interference with hearing can be understood in anatomical and physical terms. The sense organ itself remains intact and still responds when adequate acoustic energy is delivered to it. This can usually be accomplished by bone conduction. The conductive physical character of a hearing loss is revealed by a loss of sensitivity for air-borne sound while sensitivity remains practically normal for bone-conducted sound.

Barotrauma. The possibility of injury to the drum membrane from differences in static pressure (*barotrauma*) between the outer atmosphere and the air within the middle ear is greatly reduced by the action of the *Eustachian tube* that connects the middle ear with the pharynx above the soft palate. The inner end of this tube is usually closed, but it normally opens from time to time when we swallow or yawn and allows replenishment of the gas absorbed from the middle ear by the blood stream. It also allows equalization of differences that may occur suddenly from changes of altitude, as in an airplane or an elevator. If the tube does not open and equalize the static pressure, the drum membrane and the suspensory system of the ossicles are put under strain. This reduces their acoustic transmission and it also causes discomfort or even acute pain. The common cold causes swelling of the lining of the Eustachian tube and hinders its opening.

Inner Ear. *Nerve Deafness and Cochlear Deafness.* In addition to *conductive loss*, hearing loss may be due to injury to the sense organ or to the auditory nerve. Both types have been called *nerve deafness* or sometimes *perceptive deafness.* Unlike conductive hearing loss, nerve loss shows reduced sensitivity for bone conduction as well as for air conduction.

Disease of the cochlea can often be distinguished from injury to the auditory nerve, and the term "cochlear deafness" is coming into increasing use. The condition known as "Ménière's syndrome" is an important class of cochlear deafness. It seems to be an irritative process that usually affects the semicircular canals and other parts of the labyrinth as well as the cochlea and is characterized by acute attacks of dizziness and vertigo, by tinnitus, by hearing loss, and also by inability to make out words even when the sounds can be heard. The attacks are generally attributed to changes in the blood supply to the ear.

A very common but quite different cochlear defect is the degeneration of some of the hair cells and particularly the external hair cells near the basal end of the cochlea. Sometimes all the hair cells beyond a rather sharp transition zone may degenerate and frequently the nerve fibers also. This condition gives the clinical picture of "abrupt high-tone hearing loss." The audiogram is normal up to a certain frequency and then falls off very sharply. In other cases the fall of sensitivity as a function of frequency is not so abrupt. Here the transition from normal to degenerated hair cells is presumably less abrupt. The hearing loss is not very different from that in a "nerve deafness" caused by the pressure of a tumor on the auditory nerve.

Tinnitus and Diplacusis. *Tinnitus,* or "ringing in the ears," seems to be a symptom of any sort of irritation of the sense organ. A little such "head noise" is so common as to be normal. Tinnitus may be greatly increased by the mechanical insult of exposure to very loud sound. The basis for it is presumably the spontaneous discharge of irritated hair cells or nerve fibers, like the itching or smarting of irritated skin.

Diplacusis means that both ears do not hear the same pitch for a given sound. It may be a simple mistuning. Small differences in the pitch heard for a given frequency are quite normal. They are averaged in the brain and pass unnoticed. Another variety of diplacusis is an abnormality in the "quality" of a tone, which sounds harsh, buzzing, or multiple instead of smooth, single, and musical. Such distortion is another common accompaniment of local irritation, fatigue, or mild injury to the organ of Corti. It may be induced by exposure to a single-frequency tone at high sound pressure.

Central Deafness. Disorders of hearing that arise in the brain are of a complex nature. They may be of importance in connection with problems of compensation and rehabilitation. Certain brain injuries disrupt to various degrees the normal function of the recognition of sounds and interpretation of their meaning. Auditory sensitivity may be normal but the words fail to have meaning. The term *sensory aphasia* refers to this condition.

Sometimes a person becomes partially or totally deaf for strictly psychological reasons. Such *psychogenic deafness* has an unconscious emotional basis and is well recognized by psychiatrists. The lack of response to sound is perfectly real and is not to be confused with malingering. Such psychogenic deafness may combine with a peripheral, physically determined hearing loss and greatly increase the patient's disability.

Presbycusis.[1] *Presbycusis* is the loss of sensitivity for tones of high frequency that is to be expected as part of the average aging process. (These data are given in Figs. 7.1 and 7.2.) The upper limit of hearing on the frequency scale usually begins to fall off in early adult life. Very characteristic also is a so-called "4,000-cps dip" in the audiogram. The "4,000-cps dip" may or may not be due to past exposure to some very intense noise. Such dips are commoner and tend to be deeper and wider in men than in women, and to increase with age. The average expected hearing loss at sixty years of age is 32 db for men and 17 db for women. These are average expectations and there are many and wide individual deviations. The basis of the hearing loss is a degeneration, for no presently assignable cause other than age, of some of the hair cells toward the basal end of the cochlea.

Industrial Hearing Loss and Acoustic Trauma.[1] *Industrial hearing loss* has long been recognized under the names "boilermakers' deafness" and "weavers' deafness." Repeated exposure to very intense noise, all day and every day for months and years, causes a gradual cumulative loss of hearing. The loss is typically a high-tone loss. It usually begins at 4,000 cps. Sometimes the high-frequency cutoff is quite abrupt on the audiogram, but more often it is gradual. The loss is apparently due to degeneration of external hair cells, and, like presbycusis, it is not conductive but is a "nerve" or "cochlear" hearing loss. No present test of hearing can reliably distinguish presbycusis from industrial hearing loss. It is believed that the two effects are additive, as though the exposure to noise merely accelerated the natural progress of presbycusis, and there is no clear evidence that a preexisting hearing loss from presbycusis or from previous noise exposure either sensitizes or immunizes the ear with respect to possible further injury by noise. Of course, to the extent that a conductive impairment, as in otosclerosis or otitis media, reduces the intensity of the noise that reaches the cochlea it acts like a protective device and reduces the probability of industrial hearing loss. There are large individual differences in the amount of permanent hearing loss from a given exposure. The relations of hearing loss to noise exposure involve frequency, sound level, temporal distribution, schedule of exposure and recovery, overall duration, etc., and are too complex for brief summary (see Chap. 7).

"*Acoustic trauma*" is a term sometimes applied to cumulative permanent hearing loss from repeated exposures to noise, i.e., "industrial hearing loss." It would reduce confusion and misunderstanding, however, if this term were reserved for the effects of explosions, blast, blows on the head, or even a single brief exposure to a very intense noise. In animal ears such injury to the organ of Corti is well known. The end result is a degeneration of the sensory cells or even the whole organ, but with a tendency to spare both the extreme basal and the extreme apical ends. The hearing loss may be very severe shortly after the injury but it tends to recover considerably before stabilizing. The eardrum and ossicles as well as the organ of Corti may be injured by blast.

Acute acoustic trauma has been studied experimentally quite extensively in animals, but chronic cumulative hearing loss has not. The latter condition is well known, but not yet adequately studied, in man. Acoustic trauma in man is also known, but for obvious reasons it has not been well studied experimentally.

REFERENCES

1. American Standards Association: The Relations of Hearing Loss to Noise Exposure; A Report by Exploratory Subcommittee Z24-X-2 of the American Standards Association, American Standards Association, New York, 1954.
2. Békésy, G. v., and W. A. Rosenblith: chap. 27 in "Handbook of Experimental Psychology" (S. S. Stevens, ed.), John Wiley & Sons, Inc., New York, 1951.
3. Békésy, G. v.: *J. Acoust. Soc. Amer.*, **25**: 770 (1953).
4. Békésy, G. v.: *Ann. Otol. Rhinol. & Laryngol.*, **63**: 448 (1954).

5. Davis, H. (ed.): "Hearing and Deafness: A Guide for Laymen," Rinehart & Company, Inc., New York, 1947.
6. Davis, H.: chap. 28 in "Handbook of Experimental Psychology" (S. S. Stevens, ed.), John Wiley & Sons, Inc., New York, 1951.
7. Davis, H.: The Biophysics and Physiology of the Inner Ear, *Physiol. Revs.* (in press).
8. Licklider, J. C. R.: *Experientia*, **7:** 128 (1951).
9. Stevens, S. S., and H. Davis: "Hearing: Its Psychology and Physiology," John Wiley & Sons, Inc., New York, 1938.
10. Stuhlman, O.: "An Introduction to Biophysics," chap. 7, John Wiley & Sons, Inc., New York, 1943.
11. Tasaki, I., H. Davis, and J. P. Legouix: *J. Acoust. Soc. Amer.*, **24:** 502 (1952).
12. Wever, E. G.: "Theory of Hearing," John Wiley & Sons, Inc., New York, 1949.
13. Wever, E. G., and M. Lawrence: "Physiological Acoustics," Princeton University Press, Princeton, N.J., 1954.
14. Robinson, D. W., and R. S. Dadson: *Brit. J. Appl. Phys.*, **7:** 166 (1956).
15. Bárány, E.: *Acta Oto-Laryngol.*, suppl. 26, 1 (1938).
16. Davis, H., and associates: *J. Acoust. Soc. Amer.*, **25:** 1180 (1953).
17. Békésy, G. v.: *Akust. Z.*, **6:** 1 (1941).

Chapter 5

THE LOUDNESS OF SOUNDS

W. A. Munson
Bell Telephone Laboratories

INTRODUCTION

Loudness. When a person moves from a quiet to a noisy environment, he is usually acutely aware of the loudness of the noise. He may find the noise too loud to converse easily, or so loud that it is distracting, or too loud to sleep, etc. In this chapter methods of measuring the loudness of a noise are described, and it is shown that loudness can be computed from measurements of the sound-pressure spectrum of a sound.

It should be kept in mind, however, that equally loud sounds are not always equivalent in other respects. For instance, two noises that are equal in loudness may differ in the degree to which they interfere with or mask speech. A high-pitched noise with most of its energy beyond the range of speech sounds could be quite loud without detracting much from ease of conversation, while other noises, no louder, would make it difficult to carry on a conversation without shouting. So the extent to which a noise masks or interferes with hearing another sound is quite different from loudness. The same remarks apply to the annoyance of a noise, since equal loudness does not necessarily mean equality of annoyance. It is important in noise-control work to consider other factors besides loudness, and the reader will find appropriate discussions of the annoying effect of noise and the masking of speech by noise in other chapters of this book.

The term "loudness" pertains only to the magnitude of the auditory sensation a person experiences and should not be confused with other distinguishing characteristics of a sound. For instance, a noise may be high- or low-pitched, penetrating or dull, disturbing or soothing, but all can be assigned a loudness value. Loudness cannot be measured directly with an ordinary sound-level meter unless the characteristics of the ear are built into the device. This is difficult to accomplish because of the complexity of the ear, so that sound-level meters are simply designed to measure sound pressure level, but they may partially simulate the ear by use of frequency-weighting networks.

If one wishes to know how loud a noise is, several different procedures are available: (1) A simple but very approximate method is to obtain weighted sound-level meter measurements of the noise and to convert these measurements to loudness values, but this is frequently not adequate. (2) Another possibility is the "sound jury" method, which is based upon comparison, by a group of people, of the noise with a standard reference sound. (3) A third method depends upon an analysis of sound pressure in filter bands and computation of loudness from the measurements. Each method has its advantages and shortcomings with which one must be familiar before the right choice can be made.

The fundamental measurement on which all loudness determinations are based is a loudness-judgment test by a group of observers. This is often called a "sound jury" test, and much time and thought have been spent on methods of increasing the precision of this type of measurement. As one might expect, the precision of loudness judgments can be improved if observers are permitted to compare the unknown loudness with the reference sound.

Phon Scale. Acousticians have chosen a 1,000-cps tone for the standard reference, and the results of loudness-judgment tests are usually given by stating the sound pressure level of a 1,000-cps tone that has been found to be equal in loudness to the unknown. For example, if the observers find, on the average, that a 1,000-cps reference tone having a pressure level of 60 db appears to be equally as loud as a noise, the noise is then said to have a loudness level of 60 *phons*. As in other sound pressure measurements, the reference pressure for the phon is 0.0002 microbar. The term *"phon" is the name for the unit of loudness level* and whenever used implies that a sound jury measurement is involved either directly, or indirectly as in the case of computations intended to predict the results that a sound jury would obtain if a test were made.

Loudness Contours. Using the technique of comparison with a reference tone, the loudness levels of single-frequency tones covering the full range of frequencies the ear can hear have been measured. The results are shown in Fig. 5.1. These curves, called *equal-loudness contours*, show the free-field sound pressure levels of tones that are equally loud. For example, the sound pressure levels of all tones having a loudness level of 20 phons lie on the curve marked 20. The lowest curve shows the sound pressure levels of all tones at the threshold of hearing for the average young adult with good hearing. Loudness contours exhibit two very noticeable characteristics. The first is that above 1,000 cps the curves change rapidly with frequency to form complex shapes. This is believed to be due to the distortion of the sound field about the head of the listener. If the sound originates from a diffuse source these irregularities would probably be changed.

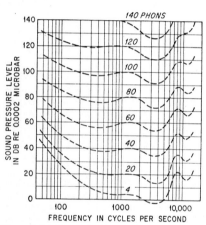

FIG. 5.1. Equal-loudness-level contours. (*Robinson and Dadson.*[16])

The second interesting characteristic is the tendency for the curves to bunch together at low frequencies, but not at frequencies above 500 cps. This indicates that low-frequency tones increase in loudness more rapidly than high frequencies when the level is raised. The explanation for this requires an understanding of the hearing mechanism and the relationship between the loudness sensation experienced by a listener and the pattern of stimulation of the auditory nerves in the ear.

Loudness contours have also been constructed from the results of sound jury measurements of the loudness level of bands of thermal noise. The frequency bands used were 250 mels wide (see section on *Mel Scale*) and the resulting contours were similar to, but not the same as, the pure-tone curves.

Sone Loudness Scale. An important distinction is made in acoustics between the two terms "loudness" and "loudness level." The unit of loudness level is the "phon," which has already been defined. The unit of loudness is the *sone;* for every phon value there is a corresponding sone value given by Fig. 5.2. This transfer function is called the "sone loudness scale," and it has an important role in the computation of loudness from sound-pressure measurements. Within certain limits, it may be defined by the equation[12,13]

$$\log_{10} N = 0.03L_N - 1.2 \tag{5.1}$$

where N = loudness, sones
L_N = loudness level, phons

By definition, a loudness of 1 sone has been arbitrarily selected to correspond to a loudness level of 40 phons. The data of Fig. 5.2 are presented in tabular form in Appendix 5.1.

The use of the sone scale can be explained by first considering the loudness of a very simple sound having two components which are widely separated in frequency, such as 300 and 2,000 cps. Let us suppose that each component alone is equal in loudness to a 1,000-cps tone having a sound pressure level of 70 db. Each component would then have a loudness level of 70 phons or, referring to Fig. 5.2, a loudness of 8 sones. Now if the 300- and 2,000-cps components are sounded together, it has been found that a sound jury would *not* judge the loudness level of the combination to be

$$(70 + 70) = 140 \text{ phons}$$

but instead the verdict would be close to 80 phons. Examination of Fig. 5.2 will show that 8 + 8, or 16 sones, corresponds to a loudness level close to 80 phons, so it is seen that *well-separated components of a sound are additive on the sone scale, but not on the phon scale.*

Another use of the sone scale is the qualitative description of noise-reduction magnitudes. If a noise has been reduced from 8 to 2.6 sones, it is correct to say that the loudness is about one-third of its former value. This is usually more meaningful to most people than to say that the noise has been reduced from 70 to 54 phons, the phon values equivalent to 8 and 2.6 sones, respectively. The sone scale is also used to estimate loudness reduction in communication problems involving one- and two-ear listening conditions. The sone value of a sound is halved when only one ear is used, and hence the additional loudness level required to bring the sound back to a loudness equal to two-ear listening can be found from Fig. 5.2. There has been considerable speculation and experimentation by psychologists to determine whether the sone scale is a valid scale of loudness magnitudes, but its usefulness as a transformation in computing loudness levels is seldom denied.

LOUDNESS EVALUATION

Several different methods are available for evaluating the loudness of a noise. Each has its advantages and disadvantages and no one method is completely satisfactory for all applications. The procedures described here should be considered an introduction to a subject that should be followed closely in current literature for recent developments. These procedures provide methods of loudness evaluation that have been found useful in noise-reduction engineering.

Sound-level Meter Measurements. The subject of sound-level meters is fully treated in Chaps. 16 and 17. With these instruments measurements can be made rapidly with a minimum of effort and for many applications they are to be preferred over other more complicated methods. A sound-level meter usually consists of a mi-

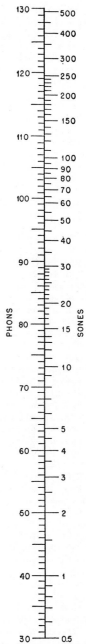

FIG. 5.2. Nomogram giving the relationship between loudness in sones and loudness level in phons, as computed from Eq. (5.1).

crophone, amplifier, frequency-weighting networks, calibrated attenuator, and indicating device such as a meter or a recorder (see Chap. 16). This equipment is designed to measure some aspect of the sound pressure, and to be successful as a method of evaluating loudness, there must be some assurance of close correlation between sound pressure and loudness. For many specific types of noises this correlation can be checked by sound jury tests, and in these cases the sound-level meter measurement may be quite satisfactory.

The point to notice is that the correlation must be established for a given type of sound-level meter used on a given type of noise before the results can be used with confidence. After this has been done, the sound-level meter is usually the method of choice because of its simplicity—provided the problem does not require an analysis of the noise to determine details of the loudness spectrum.

Sound Jury Measurements. All the basic loudness data are derived from sound jury tests in which a group of people listen first to one sound, then to another, and try to decide which is louder. Or they may try to adjust the loudness of one until the two sounds are equally loud. There are many different forms of the test, but no method has been found which is as accurate as could be desired. People seem to differ greatly in their judgments of the loudness of sounds, particularly when the sounds are unlike in quality.

In order to determine just how precise a loudness-judgment test is, as many as 100 different observers have been used on a single jury. The variance undoubtedly depends somewhat upon the similarity of the sound under test to the standard reference tone, but in general most noises bear little resemblance to a 1,000-cps tone. It can be expected that for many sounds the probable error of a single observer's test will be of the order of ± 6 phons. The error cannot be reduced much by taking large numbers of observations with the same observer, although some improvement is possible if the tests are days or weeks apart. For a jury of 10 people, the probable error of the average result will still be about ± 2 phons and much of the fundamental work on loudness is of this order of precision.

In order to obtain a variance as low as this, numerous precautions should be taken to obtain judgments that are independent. Some observers are easily influenced by a knowledge of the results of previous tests or the judgments of other observers. It is important to alternate the order in which an observer listens to the unknown sound and the reference tone, and to control the duration of the listening period. Tests should be short so observers will not be fatigued, and since work of this kind can become very monotonous, some form of motivation is desirable.

Computed Loudness. Loudness measurements with a sound jury have been made on many different types of noise and the results were found to be related to the sound-pressure spectrum. On the basis of this information, several methods have been devised for computing the loudness of a sound when the pressure spectrum is known. For a given noise spectrum, there will be differences in the value of loudness computed by the various methods employed. However, if the spectrum is reduced in level because of the application of noise-reduction techniques, the per cent loudness reduction calculated by the various methods will be in much closer agreement than their absolute magnitudes. The choice of the method used to compute loudness depends to a large extent on the form of the original data, and therefore on the equipment available to the engineer; the choice will also depend on the spectrum and the required accuracy.

Noise-control engineers usually prefer to compute the loudness of a noise from measurements of the sound pressure employing bandpass filters rather than use the long and tedious sound jury method, because in addition to the saving in time, the computation shows which part of the sound spectrum contributes most heavily to the loudness. Having this information, the steps taken to control the noise can be directed toward reduction of the noise components which will be most effective in diminishing the loudness.

Because of the lack of precision in the fundamental data on loudness it is unreasonable to expect extreme accuracy when using a computational method for obtaining the loudness level of a noise, and for many applications a short computation based **upon** engineering approximations is adequate.

LOUDNESS-COMPUTATION PROCEDURES

The loudness-computation procedures described here are:

1. The Equivalent Tone method.[2,3,4]
2. The Corrected Equivalent Tone method.[19]
3. The Equivalent Noise method.[18]

The first step in any loudness-computing method is to obtain a reliable sound analysis using appropriate bandpass filters to measure the sound pressure level, over the entire range of audible frequencies, of the noise whose loudness is to be evaluated. The techniques and equipment for making these measurements are described in Chaps. 16 and 17. In most such engineering evaluations, octave-band analyses have been used. Frequently, greater detail in analysis may be desirable in computing the loudness of the noise. In this

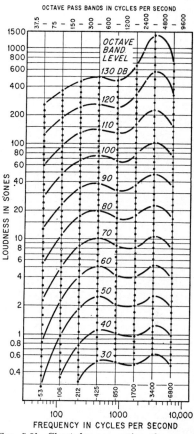

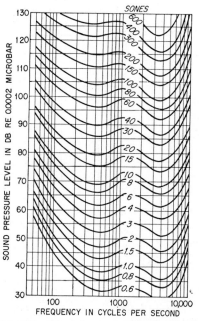

FIG. 5.3a. Chart for converting the sound pressure level of a pure tone in decibels to its corresponding loudness value in sones.

FIG. 5.3b. Chart for converting the sound pressure level of an octave band of noise to the equivalent loudness of that band in sones.

case a half-octave or third-octave analysis may be made. The loudness-computation procedures described here may be used with data obtained from octave, half-octave, or third-octave analyses, by the methods outlined below.

Equivalent Tone Method. The loudness of a noise can be computed from its octave-band analysis in the following way: First, tabulate the octave-band sound pressure levels. Next, consider that the noise in each band may be replaced by an "equivalent" pure tone having a frequency corresponding to the center of the band, and which produces the same octave-band sound pressure level. From the appropriate chart of Fig. 5.3 determine the loudness of each of these pure tones. Finally, to obtain the total loudness of the noise, add the loudness of each of these equivalent tones—this sum represents the total loudness.*

For example, consider the noise whose octave-band spectrum is given as (a) in Fig. 5.4. The octave-band levels for this spectrum are tabulated in Table 5.1. The corresponding loudness values for each band are obtained conveniently from Fig. 5.3b. Note that the sound pressure level in the first octave (37.5 to 75 cps) of the noise is

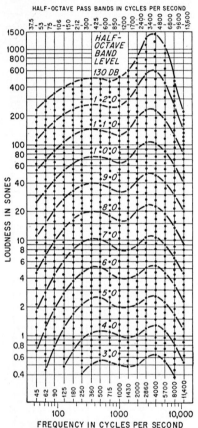

FIG. 5.3c. Chart for converting the sound pressure level of a half-octave band of noise to the equivalent loudness of that band in sones.

96 db. Referring to Fig. 5.3b it is seen that the corresponding loudness value is 21 sones. In the second band (75 to 150 cps) the sound pressure level is 87 db and the corresponding loudness is 18 sones. These, and the corresponding values for the remaining bands, are tabulated in Table 5.1. The total loudness of the noise is found by summing the corresponding values for each of the eight octave bands; in this example the sum is 86 sones.

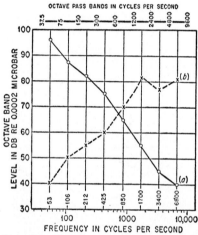

FIG. 5.4. Noise spectra whose loudness values are calculated by different methods, in Tables 5.1 and 5.4. The octave-band analyses shown are: (a) a spectrum having its energy predominantly in the low-frequency range; and (b) a spectrum having its energy predominantly in the high-frequency range.

The simplicity of the octave-band Equivalent Tone method has resulted in its widespread use. However, it has certain limitations, as noted below. The term "Equivalent Tone" method is used because of the assumption that the sound pressure level in an octave band produces the same loudness as a single tone having a frequency equal to the mid-band frequency and having the same sound pressure level. Comparison of Fig. 5.3a with the equal loudness-level contours of Fig. 5.1 will show that the chart for converting octave-band sound pressure levels to loudness values is truly a plot of loudness contours for tones. The only changes made are the smoothing of the high-

* The procedure for computing loudness from a sound pressure level analysis in octave bands also can be made rapidly if Fig. 5.3a is drawn in the form of a transparency that can be placed over the plot of octave-band measurements such as those of Fig. 5.4.

frequency portions of the curves in Fig. 5.3a so they are applicable to persons having an average age of thirty to forty years, listening under conditions where diffraction effects of the head are diminished, e.g., listening in a room where the sound field is somewhat diffuse.

Limitations of the Octave-band Equivalent Tone Method. The octave-band Equivalent Tone method is subject to errors on certain types of noise which, for some applications, are too large to be neglected. If the noise has a component in the first octave band, its loudness can vary as much as 100 per cent if the frequency of this component changes from one side of the band to the other, as can be seen from Fig. 5.3a; although the computing procedure would show no change in loudness for this frequency shift. The only way to avoid this type of error is to measure with half-octave or narrower filters to determine the frequency of the component more accurately.

Table 5.1. Octave-band Loudness Computation by Corrected Equivalent Tone Method for a Spectrum Having Its Energy Predominantly in the Low-frequency Range. See Curve (a) in Fig. 5.4

Group No.	Frequency band, cps	Octave-band level, db	Uncorrected loudness, sones	Loudness, factor	Correction factor	Corrected loudness, sones
1	37.5–75	96	21	1	1	21
	75–150	87	18	0		0
	150–300	82	20	0		0
2	300–600	75	14	1	0	0
	600–1,200	65	7	0		0
3	1,200–2,400	55	3	1	1	3
4	2,400–4,800	45	2	1.5	1	3
5	4,800–9,600	40	1	1.5	1	1.5
Total loudness, sones			86			**28.5**

Another source of error becomes important when the first two or three octaves contribute heavily to the loudness and the remaining octaves are relatively unimportant. Under these conditions the total loudness will be overestimated. On the other hand, the total loudness will be underestimated if the last three octaves contribute heavily to the loudness of a noise and other octaves are of lesser importance. Any attempts to correct these errors on a theoretical basis usually complicate and lengthen the method more than is justified for most applications. A correction, which is usually adequate and can be very quickly applied, is given below.

Corrected Equivalent Tone Method (Octave Bands). The accuracy of the Equivalent Tone method of loudness computation, described above, can be improved greatly by the correction procedure which is given by the following steps (for half-octave and third-octave band computations, see the next section):

1. Measure and tabulate the octave-band levels of the noise whose loudness is to be computed.
2. Determine the value of the "uncorrected" loudness contribution in sones that corresponds to each octave band. This may be done by finding the loudness of a pure tone whose frequency is at the center of the band and whose level is equal to the octave-band level; the values may be obtained conveniently by the use of Fig. 5.3b.
3. Now separate the octave bands into five groups, as indicated in Table 5.1.

4. Assign a *loudness factor* to each uncorrected value of loudness obtained in step 2. (This factor accounts for differences in mel-band width of the various octave bands.) The loudness factors for the bands in Group 1 are either 0 or 1—the factor 1 being assigned to the octave having the greatest loudness value, and the factor 0 to the other two octaves. The loudness factors for the bands in Group 2 are either 0 or 1—the factor 1 being assigned to the octave having the greater loudness value, and the factor 0 being assigned to the smaller. The loudness factors for Groups 3, 4, and 5 (1,200 to 2,400, 2,400 to 4,800, and 4,800 to 9,600 cps, respectively) are 1, 1.5, and 1.5, respectively (for example, see Table 5.1).

5. Now assign a *correction factor* of 0 or 1 to each octave band. (This factor accounts for the masking effect of one band on another which reduces the over-all loudness value. This reduction in the calculated value may result from the assignment of a correction factor of 0, as indicated below.) Inspect all bands having a loudness factor of 1 or 1.5 and assign to the loudest band a correction factor of 1. If two or more have the same maximum value, select the one having the lower frequency and assign a correction factor of 1 to it. If the uncorrected loudness of this band is 8 *sones or more, but less than* 35 *sones*, assign a correction factor of 0 to the next higher group of frequencies. If the loudness is 35 *sones or more*, assign a correction factor of 0 to the next two higher groups of frequencies. Inspect the remaining bands having loudness factors of 1 and repeat the above process until all groups have been assigned correction factors of unity or 0. In cases where a subsequent step would change a correction factor previously assigned, the initial value should be retained.

6. The total loudness of the noise is now obtained by summing the corrected loudness contributions; these corrected loudness contributions are simply the uncorrected values of each band, multiplied by their respective loudness and correction factors.

An example of this loudness-computation method is given in Table 5.1 for a noise spectrum which is shown as (*a*) in Fig. 5.4. Here the energy is predominantly in the low-frequency region. The corrected total loudness in this example is 28.5 sones. A similar computation of the loudness of the noise whose spectrum is shown as (*b*) in Fig. 5.4 yields a value of 58 sones.

Corrected Equivalent Tone Method (Half-octave Bands). The computation of loudness of a noise based on measurements of half-octave band levels is similar to the loudness-computation method given in the preceding section, but the grouping of the components is different:

1. Measure and tabulate the half-octave band levels of the noise whose loudness is to be computed.

2. Determine the value of the "uncorrected" loudness contribution in sones that corresponds to each half-octave band. This may be done by finding the loudness of a pure tone whose frequency is at the center of the band and whose level is equal to the half-octave band level; the values may be obtained conveniently by the use of Fig. 5.3c.

3. Now separate the half-octave bands into eight groups, as indicated in Table 5.2.

4. Assign a *loudness factor* to each uncorrected value of loudness obtained in step 2. (This factor accounts for differences in mel-band width of the various half-octave bands.) The loudness factors for the bands in Group 1 are either 0 or 1—the factor 1 being assigned to the half octave having the greatest loudness value, and the factor 0 to the other three half octaves. In a similar manner, assign loudness factors to the half-octave bands in Groups 2 and 3—a factor of 1 for the loudest band and 0 for the others. The loudness factors for the remaining groups are all unity (for example, see Table 5.2).

5. Now assign a *correction factor* of 0 or 1 to each half-octave band. (This factor accounts for the masking effect of one band on another which reduces the over-all loudness value. This reduction in the calculated value may result from the assignment of a correction factor of 0, as indicated below.) Inspect all bands having a loudness factor of 1 and assign to the loudest band a correction factor

of 1. If two or more have the same maximum value, select the one having the lower frequency and assign a correction factor of 1 to it. If the uncorrected loudness of this band is 8 sones or more, but less than 35 sones, assign a correction factor of 0 to the next higher group of frequencies. If the loudness is 35 sones or more, assign a correction factor of 0 to the next two higher groups of frequencies. Inspect the remaining bands having loudness factors of 1 and repeat the above process until all groups have been assigned correction factors of unity or 0. In cases where a subsequent step would change a correction factor previously assigned, the initial value should be retained.

6. The total loudness of the noise is now obtained by summing the corrected loudness contributions; these corrected loudness contributions are simply the uncorrected values of each band, multiplied by their respective loudness and correction factors.

Table 5.2. Half-octave Band Loudness Computation by Corrected Equivalent Tone Method for a Spectrum Having Its Energy Predominantly in the Low-frequency Range. See Fig. 5.5a

Group No.	Frequency band, cps	Half-octave band level, db	Uncorrected loudness, sones	Loudness factor	Correction factor	Corrected loudness, sones
1	37.5–53	96	18	1	1	18
	53–75	91	15	0		0
	75–106	86	15	0		0
	106–150	83	16	0		0
	150–212	80	16	0		0
	212–300	77	15	0		0
2	300–425	74	13	1	0	0
	425–600	70	10	0		0
	600–850	64	7	0		0
	850–1,200	59	4	0		0
3	1,200–1,700	54	3	1	1	3
	1,700–2,400	50	2	0		0
4	2,400–3,400	44	2	1	1	2
5	3,400–4,800	41	2	1	1	2
6	4,800–6,800	38	1	1	1	1
7	6,800–9,600	36	1	1	1	1
8	9,600–13,600	34	0	1	1	0
Total loudness, sones						**27**

An example of this method of loudness computation is shown in Table 5.2 for a noise whose spectrum is given as (a) in Fig. 5.5. Here the total loudness is 27 sones, which is approximately the same loudness as that obtained in Table 5.1 where the same noise was measured by filters having a bandwidth of one octave.

Corrected Equivalent Tone Method (Third-octave Bands). The computation of loudness of a noise based on measurements of third-octave band levels is similar to the loudness-computation method given in the preceding section, but the grouping is different:

1. Measure and tabulate the third-octave band levels of the noise whose loudness is to be computed.
2. Determine the value of the "uncorrected" loudness contribution in sones that corresponds to each third-octave band. This may be done by finding the loudness of a pure tone whose frequency is at the center of the band and whose level is equal to the third-octave band level; the values may be obtained conveniently by the use of Fig. 5.3a.
3. Now separate the third-octave bands into eight groups, as indicated in Table 5.3.
4. Assign a *loudness factor* to each uncorrected value of loudness obtained in step 2. (This factor accounts for differences in mel-band width of the various third-octave bands.) The loudness factors for the bands in group 1 are either 0 or 1—the factor 1 being assigned to the third octave having the greatest loudness value, and the factor 0 to the other seven third octaves. In a similar manner assign loudness factors to the third-octave bands in the remaining groups—a factor of 1 for the loudest band and 0 for the others (for example, see Table 5.3).

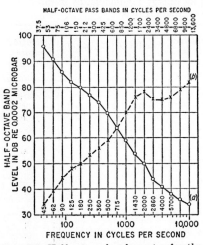

Fig. 5.5. Half-octave band spectra for the noise sources whose octave-band spectra are given in Fig. 5.4.

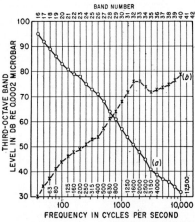

Fig. 5.6. Third-octave band spectra for the noise sources whose octave-band spectra are given in Fig. 5.3.

5. Now assign a *correction factor* of 0 or 1 to each third-octave band. (This factor accounts for the masking effect of one band on another which reduces the over-all loudness value. This reduction in the calculated value may result from the assignment of a correction factor of 0, as indicated below.) Inspect all bands having a loudness factor of 1 and assign to the loudest band a correction factor of 1. If two or more have the same maximum value, select the one having the lower frequency and assign a correction factor of 1 to it. If the uncorrected loudness of this band is 8 sones or more, but less than 35 sones, assign a correction factor of 0 to the next higher group of frequencies. If the loudness is 35 sones or more, assign a correction factor of 0 to the next two higher groups of frequencies. Inspect the remaining bands having loudness factors of 1 and repeat the above process until all groups have been assigned correction factors of unity or 0. In cases where a subsequent step would change a correction factor previously assigned, the initial value should be retained.
6. The total loudness of the noise is now obtained by summing the corrected loudness contributions; these corrected loudness contributions are simply the uncorrected values of each band, multiplied by their respective loudness and correction factors.

An example of this method of loudness computation employing third-octave band analysis data is given in Table 5.3.   This computation is for the noise spectrum shown as (a) in Fig. 5.6.   Note that this spectrum is for the same noise whose octave and half-octave band spectrum is shown as (a) in Figs. 5.4 and 5.5.   There is good agreement in the loudness values obtained in Tables 5.1, 5.2, and 5.3.

Table 5.3. Third-octave Band Loudness Computation by Corrected Equivalent Tone Method for a Spectrum Having Its Energy Predominantly in the Low-frequency Range.   See Fig. 5.6a

Group No.	Mid-band frequency, cps	Third-octave band level, db	Uncorrected loudness, sones	Loudness factor	Correction factor	Corrected loudness, sones
1	40	95	13	0	1	0
	50	92	14	1		14
	63	89	14	0		0
	80	86	14	0		0
	100	83	14	0		0
	125	81	14	0		0
	160	79	14	0		0
	200	78	14	0		0
2	250	75	13	1	0	0
	315	73	12	0		0
	400	71	11	0		0
	500	68	9	0		0
3	630	64	7	1	1	7
	800	61	5	0		0
	1,000	57	3	0		0
4	1,250	54	3	1	1	3
	1,600	51	2	0		0
5	2,000	48	2	1	1	2
	2,500	45	2	0		0
6	3,150	41	1	1	1	1
	4,000	39	1	0		0
7	5,000	37	1	1	1	1
	6,300	36	1	0		0
8	8,000	34	0	1	0	0
	10,000	32	0	0		0
Total loudness, sones						**28**

Equivalent Noise Method.   Another method of computing loudness is based upon measurements of the loudness of bands of noise.[18]   The results of such measurements are plotted in Figs. 5.7 to 5.9, which show the loudness as a function of the sound pressure level of octave, half-octave, and third-octave bands, respectively.   The computational procedure is applicable to spectra that are reasonably continuous in frequency, and not interrupted in time.

This computing procedure is essentially the same for the evaluation of the loudness of data in the form of octave, half-octave, or third-octave analyses.   These steps are taken:

1. Tabulate the sound pressure levels in the various bands.
2. Find the loudness corresponding to each band, from Fig. 5.7 or 5.8 or 5.9, depending on whether the tabulated data are for octave, half-octave, or third-octave bands.
3. The loudness of the band having the greatest number of sones is left unchanged in value (i.e., it is multiplied by a correction factor of 1.0). The loudness values of the remaining bands are multiplied by a correction factor of 0.3, or 0.2, or 0.15, respectively, depending on whether the tabulated data are for octave, half-octave, or third-octave bands.
4. The total loudness of the noise is the sum of the loudness values of the various bands multiplied by their respective correction factors.

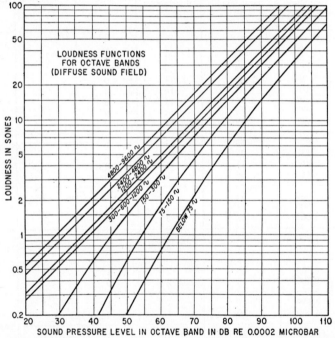

FIG. 5.7a. Chart for use in computing loudness by the Equivalent Noise method. This chart shows the loudness in each octave band as a function of the sound pressure level in the band. These data are presented in the form of a nomogram in Fig. 5.7b. (*Stevens.*[18])

An example of the application of the Equivalent Noise method is given in Table 5.4 for the noise spectrum shown as curve (a) of Fig. 5.4. This noise has its energy predominantly in the low-frequency range. Here the total loudness is computed to be 44 sones. If similar calculations are carried out for the loudness of the noise whose spectrum is given as curve (b) in Fig. 5.4, a total loudness of 55 sones is obtained.

For convenience, the steps to be taken in loudness computation by the Equivalent Noise method are outlined below separately for computations based upon octave, half-octave, and third-octave band analyses:

Octave-band Computations:

1. Tabulate the sound pressure levels for each of the eight octave bands.
2. From Fig. 5.7b, determine the loudness value for each octave band and enter these values in the table.
3. Inspect the loudness values obtained in (2), and determine which band is the

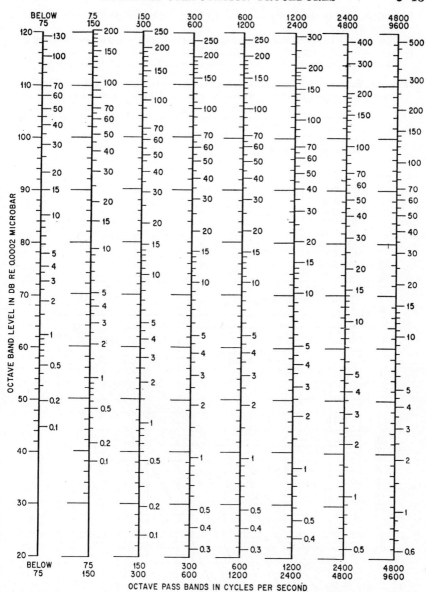

FIG. 5.7b. Nomograms for computing loudness by the Equivalent Noise method. From each nomogram determine the loudness in each octave band. Next multiply all values but the loudest by a correction factor of 0.30; the correction factor for the loudness value of the loudest band is 1.0. The total loudness is then computed by summing the loudness values for the various bands multiplied by their respective correction factors. (S. S. Stevens.[18])

loudest. Leave this loudness value unchanged (i.e., multiply it by a correction factor of 1).

4. Multiply the loudness values of all the other bands by a correction factor of 0.3.
5. Now obtain the sum of the loudness values of the various bands multiplied by their respective correction factors—this represents the total loudness of the noise.

Table 5.4. Example of a Loudness Computation by the Equivalent Noise Method. These Calculations Are Carried Out for a Noise Whose Spectrum Is Shown as Curve (a) in Fig. 5.4

Frequency band, cps	Octave band level, db	Uncorrected loudness, sones	Correction factor	Corrected loudness, sones
37.5–75	96	25	1.0	25
75–150	87	18	0.3	5
150–300	82	18	0.3	5
300–600	75	12	0.3	4
600–1200	65	6	0.3	2
1200–2400	55	4	0.3	1
2400–4800	45	3	0.3	1
4800–9600	40	2	0.3	1
Total loudness, sones				**44**

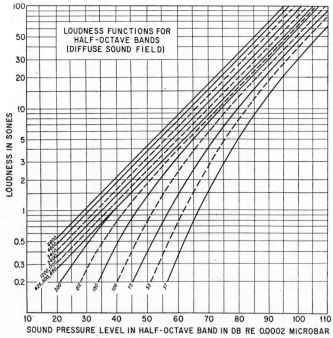

FIG. 5.8. Chart for use in computing loudness by the Equivalent Noise method when the noise analysis is given in terms of the sound pressure levels in half-octave bands. The loudness of these bands is given as a function of the half-octave band levels. (See text: S. S. Stevens.[18])

Half-octave Band Computations:

1. Tabulate the sound pressure levels for each of the 16 half-octave bands.
2. From Fig. 5.8, determine the loudness value for each half-octave band and enter these values in the table.
3. Inspect the loudness values obtained in (2), and determine which band is the loudest. Leave this loudness value unchanged (i.e., multiply it by a correction factor of 1).
4. Multiply the loudness values of all other bands by a correction factor of 0.2.
5. Now obtain the sum of the loudness values of the various bands multiplied by their respective correction factors—this represents the total loudness of the noise.

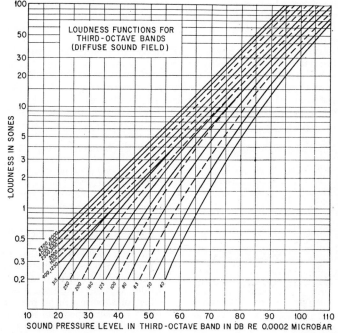

FIG. 5.9. Chart for use in computing loudness by the Equivalent Noise method when the noise analysis is given in terms of the sound pressure levels in third-octave bands. The loudness of these bands is given as a function of the third-octave band levels. (See text; S. S. Stevens.[18])

Third-octave Band Computations:

1. Tabulate the sound pressure levels for each of the 20 third-octave bands.
2. From Fig. 5.9, determine the loudness value for each third-octave band and enter these values in the table.
3. Inspect the loudness values obtained in (2), and determine which band is loudest. Leave this loudness value unchanged (i.e., multiply it by a correction factor of 1).
4. Multiply the loudness values of all other bands by a correction factor of 0.15.
5. Now obtain the sum of the loudness values of the various bands multiplied by their respective correction factors—this represents the total loudness of the noise.

SHORT-DURATION SOUNDS

Some sounds, such as hammer blows, footsteps, and noise from machines such as punch presses, are of such short duration that ordinary sound-analysis methods are not suitable for obtaining a frequency spectrum. Neither can the conventional methods of computing loudness be used.   A discussion of the measurement of short sounds is given in Chap. 16.

Sound-meter measurements of impact sounds serve a very useful purpose, although the absolute values may not agree closely with sound jury measurements.   When the time constant of the device is of the order of 50 to 100 msec, the meter readings can be used as an estimate of loudness before and after noise-reduction treatment if measurements are made on the same type of sounds.   For sounds that appear to be of quite different character to the ear, the use of a sound-level meter for loudness evaluation should be regarded with suspicion until verified by sound jury measurements.

Sound Jury Measurements of Short Sounds.   When a person compares a long sample of a steady sound to the loudness of a short sample of the same sound, the latter will appear to be reduced in loudness if the duration is less than 0.2 sec.   Maximum loudness occurs when the sample is about 0.5 sec, but there is very little change between 0.2 and 0.5 sec.   The loudness of samples longer than 1.0 sec decreases slowly as the ear fatigues.

Sound jury measurements of steady sounds are frequently made with 1-sec exposures to the reference and the unknown sound.   Comparison of impact sounds with a 1-sec reference is difficult because of the large difference in durations.   Since the loudness of the reference is not changed much by reducing the length to 0.2 sec, the shorter value is preferred.   The complexity of sound jury tests on short noises has spurred the search for alternative methods of evaluating the loudness of this type of sound.   One method under investigation is based upon the use of a distributed energy noise to mask the impact sound.[20]   A calibrated source of noise is introduced into the sound field at a level just high enough so that the impact sound cannot be heard.   The level of the masking noise is then considered a measure of the unknown sound.

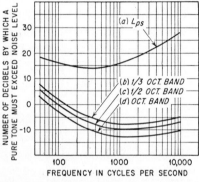

Fig. 5.10. Graph showing the number of decibels which a pure tone must be raised above the level of noise for the tone to be just audible in the presence of the noise. The upper curve shows the amount which the tone must exceed the sound-pressure spectrum level before it becomes audible. Curves are also given showing the amount by which the tone must exceed various band levels to be just audible.   (See text.)

MASKING EFFECT OF NOISE

When a noise is so loud that it prevents a person from hearing another sound, the sound is said to be *masked* by the noise. Under certain conditions the masking effect of a noise can be predicted if its sound pressure spectrum level is known.

Masking of Tones by Noise.   A low-frequency pure tone must be at least 14 to 18 db higher than the sound pressure spectrum level of a noise before it can be heard above the noise.   At high frequencies the difference is even greater, as can be seen from Fig. 5.10.   Curve *a* shows the amount by which the tone must exceed the sound pressure spectrum level before it becomes audible.   Curves *b*, *c*, and *d* show the amount by which the tone must exceed the band levels for octave, half-octave, and third-octave bands of noise, respectively, in order to be just audible.   At very high and very low levels, the difference is greater than those shown, but for most applications the values given are sufficiently accurate.

As an example of the use of the masking curve, consider a 200-cps pure tone that is masked by a noise.   If the noise has a sound pressure spectrum level of 70 db at 200 cps, then the tone must have a sound pressure level of $70 + 14 = 84$ db before it becomes audible above the noise.   Figure 5.3*a* shows that a 200-cps tone at a sound pressure level of 84 db would normally have a loudness of about 24 sones, but in this case it is barely audible because it is masked by noise.

However, raising the level of the tone only 15 db from 84 to 99 produces a large change in loudness. At 99 db, the loudness is 60 sones without masking and $60 - 24 = 36$ sones with masking. This rapid growth of loudness is typical of masked sounds; hence the observation that masking an unwanted sound is not effective unless it is nearly complete. Thus, as occurs in certain types of noise-reduction problems, where a pure tone must be masked by a noise, to be effective it is necessary that the noise be sufficiently high in level to mask the tone completely—partial masking of the tone usually will not provide significant reduction in the loudness of the tone.

Masking of Noise by Noise. A noise with a distracting characteristic such as the clatter of dishes or the screech of brakes can be masked by more acceptable sounds such as the smooth noise of a fan. When there are no prominent single-frequency tones present, satisfactory masking is usually achieved when the sound-pressure spectrum level of the unwanted noise does not exceed the spectrum level of the masking sound.

LOUDNESS PATTERNS

When a sound impinges upon the ear, the vibrations of the eardrum are conducted to the inner part of the ear where the nerves leading to the brain are spread out along a flexible partition called the basilar membrane (see Chap. 4). The vibrations stimulate these nerve endings and initiate large numbers of short-duration pulses of electrochemical energy which travel up the nerve tracts to the central nervous system. The nerve endings in the ear extend along the length of the basilar membrane, and the characteristics of this structure are such that high frequencies produce nerve pulses at the end close to the entrance of the inner ear and low frequencies do the same at the far end.

A very low level pure tone stimulates nerve endings in a localized area, but as the level of the tone is increased, the area spreads so that additional nerves are involved and also the pulsing rate increases on the nerve fibers initially stimulated. There is considerable evidence that the spreading effect is greater for low frequencies than for high, and this is believed to be a predominant factor in the rapid increase in loudness of low frequencies with level.

Since the pulses that go to the brain when a sound is heard do not originate in a single nerve but come from a large number of nerve endings that are distributed in space along the basilar membrane, it seems reasonable to assume that the loudness perceived is an integrated function of all the pulses.

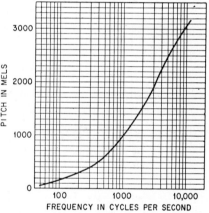

Fig. 5.11. Relation between the pitch in mels and frequency in cps. (*After Ref. 6.*)

While no conclusive proof has been found, it is significant that all successful loudness-computing methods have been based upon an integration procedure. This hypothesis can be expressed analytically by the equation

$$N = \int \frac{dN}{dn}\, dn \tag{5.2}$$

where N is the loudness of a sound, dN/dn is the loudness contribution from a small element of the frequency range, and dn is the bandwidth of the frequency element on a scale proportional to the number of nerve endings included.

The Mel Scale. *Pitch* may be defined as that aspect of auditory sensation in terms of which sounds may be ordered in a scale running from "low" to "high." Although it is chiefly a function of the frequency of the sound it is also dependent on the sound pressure level and composition of the sound. The scale which is employed in ordering

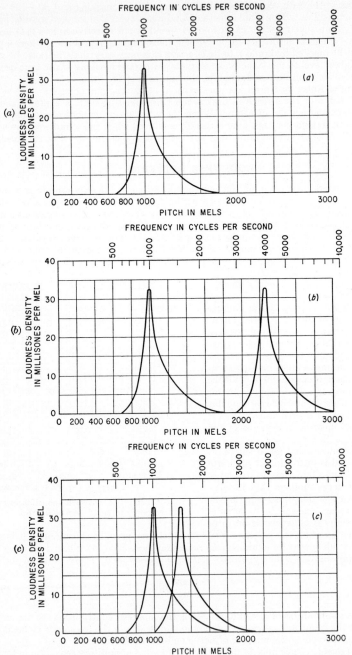

FIG. 5.12. (a) Loudness pattern for a 1,000-cps tone at a loudness level of 70 phons. (b) Loudness pattern for a 1,000-cps tone and a 4,000-cps tone, both having a loudness level of 70 phons. (c) Loudness level for a 1,000-cps tone and a 1,500-cps tone, both having a loudness level of 70 phons (see text).

sounds in terms of pitch is the "mel scale." It is related to frequency by the curve shown in Fig. 5.11. The unit of pitch is called the *mel* and this subjective scale has the property of direct proportionality to the magnitude of the sensation of pitch. A 2,000-mel tone will appear to be double the pitch of a 1,000-mel tone.

Apparently, the pitch in mels is roughly proportional to the number of nerve fibers terminating on the basilar membrane up to the point of maximum stimulation by the tone, counting from the apex end of the cochlea. Therefore, pitch may be expressed in terms of n in Eq. (5.2).

Loudness Patterns. As indicated in Eq. (5.2), dN/dn is the loudness contribution from a small element of frequency range. Therefore, a plot of dN/dn as a function of frequency is called a *loudness pattern;* since frequency and pitch are related by the plot shown in Fig. 5.11, a loudness pattern may also be shown as the graphical relationship between the loudness density dN/dn and the pitch n. An example of such a relationship is shown in Fig. 5.12a, which gives the loudness pattern for a 1,000-cps tone having a loudness level of 70 phons. Since N represents the total loudness it may be obtained by integrating the area under this curve.

Figure 5.12b shows the loudness patterns for two pure tones, one at 1,000 cps having a loudness level of 70 phons, and the other at 4,000 cps having a loudness level of 70 phons. The total loudness if they were sounded simultaneously is given by Eq. (5.2); the total loudness is simply the sum of the areas under the two curves. Figure 5.12c shows the loudness patterns when the 4,000-cps tone in this example is lowered in frequency to 1,500 cps. Here the loudness patterns from the two tones overlap. The sum of the areas under each separate curve is therefore somewhat greater than the area under the loudness pattern that would exist if the tones were sounded simultaneously. For this reason any loudness-computation technique essentially based upon an integration procedure must employ a correction factor to avoid summing the same area twice. Since the "Equivalent Tone method" of loudness computation, described earlier, is—in effect—such an integration procedure, a correction factor is required if greatest computational accuracy is to be obtained.

REFERENCES

1. Fletcher, H., and W. A. Munson: *J. Acoust. Soc. Amer.*, **5**: 82 (1933).
2. King, A. J.: *Engineering*, **146**: 199 (1938).
3. Beranek, L. L., J. L. Marshall, A. L. Cudworth, and A. P. G. Peterson: *J. Acoust. Soc. Amer.*, **23**: 261 (1951).
4. Mintz, F., and F. G. Tyzzer: *J. Acoust. Soc. Amer.*, **24**: 80 (1952).
5. Fletcher, H., and W. A. Munson: *J. Acoust. Soc. Amer.*, **9**: 1 (1937).
6. Stevens, S. S., and J. Volkmann: *Am. J. Psychol.*, **53**: 329 (1940).
7. Munson, W. A., and M. B. Gardner: *J. Acoust. Soc. Amer.*, **22**: 177 (1950).
8. Churcher, B. G., and A. J. King: *J. Inst. Elec. Engrs. (London)*, **81**: 57 (1937).
9. Garner, W. R.: *J. Acoust. Soc. Amer.*, **26**: 73 (1954).
10. King, A. J., R. W. Guelke, C. R. Maguire, and R. A. Scott: *J. Inst. Elec. Engrs. (London)*, **88**: 3 (1941).
11. Pollack, I. J.: *J. Acoust. Soc. Amer.*, **23**: 654 (1951).
12. Robinson, D. W.: *Acustica*, **3**: 344 (1953).
13. Geiger, P. H., and F. A. Firestone: *J. Acoust. Soc. Amer.*, **5**: 25 (1933).
14. Ham, L. B., and J. S. Parkinson: *J. Acoust. Soc. Amer.*, **3**: 511 (1932).
15. Davis, A. H.: *J. Inst. Elec. Engrs. (London)*, **83**: 249 (1938).
16. Robinson, D. W., and R. S. Dadson: *Brit. J. Appl. Phys.*, **7**: 166 (1956).
17. Quietzsch, G.: *Akust. Beih.*, **1**: 49 (1955).
18. Stevens, S. S., *J. Acoust. Soc. Amer.*, **28**: 807 (1956).
19. Munson, W. A. (unpublished).
20. Hardy, H. C., F. G. Tyzzer, and H. H. Hall: *J. Acoust. Soc. Amer.*, **27**: 1003 (1955).

Appendix 5.1. Table Relating Loudness Level in Phons and Loudness in Sones Based on Eq. (5.1)*

Loudness level	0	0.1	0.2	0.3	0.4	0.5	0.6	0.7	0.8	0.9
0	0.062	0.063	0.063	0.064	0.064	0.065	0.065	0.066	0.066	0.067
1	0.067	0.067	0.068	0.068	0.069	0.069	0.070	0.070	0.071	0.071
2	0.072	0.072	0.073	0.073	0.074	0.074	0.075	0.075	0.076	0.076
3	0.077	0.077	0.078	0.079	0.079	0.080	0.080	0.081	0.081	0.082
4	0.082	0.083	0.084	0.084	0.085	0.085	0.086	0.087	0.087	0.088
5	0.088	0.089	0.090	0.090	0.091	0.092	0.092	0.093	0.093	0.094
6	0.095	0.095	0.096	0.097	0.097	0.098	0.099	0.099	0.100	0.101
7	0.102	0.102	0.103	0.104	0.104	0.105	0.106	0.107	0.107	0.108
8	0.109	0.110	0.110	0.111	0.112	0.113	0.113	0.114	0.115	0.116
9	0.117	0.117	0.118	0.119	0.120	0.121	0.122	0.122	0.123	0.124
10	0.125	0.126	0.127	0.128	0.129	0.129	0.130	0.131	0.132	0.133
11	0.134	0.135	0.136	0.137	0.138	0.139	0.140	0.141	0.142	0.143
12	0.144	0.145	0.146	0.147	0.148	0.149	0.150	0.151	0.152	0.153
13	0.154	0.155	0.156	0.157	0.158	0.159	0.160	0.162	0.163	0.164
14	0.165	0.166	0.167	0.168	0.170	0.171	0.172	0.173	0.174	0.176
15	0.177	0.178	0.179	0.180	0.182	0.183	0.184	0.186	0.187	0.188
16	0.189	0.191	0.192	0.193	0.195	0.196	0.198	0.199	0.200	0.202
17	0.203	0.204	0.206	0.207	0.209	0.210	0.212	0.213	0.215	0.216
18	0.218	0.219	0.221	0.222	0.224	0.225	0.227	0.228	0.230	0.232
19	0.233	0.235	0.237	0.238	0.240	0.241	0.243	0.245	0.247	0.248
20	0.250	0.251	0.253	0.255	0.257	0.259	0.261	0.262	0.264	0.266
21	0.268	0.270	0.272	0.274	0.275	0.277	0.279	0.281	0.283	0.285
22	0.287	0.289	0.291	0.293	0.295	0.297	0.299	0.301	0.304	0.306
23	0.308	0.310	0.312	0.314	0.316	0.319	0.321	0.323	0.325	0.328
24	0.330	0.332	0.334	0.337	0.339	0.342	0.344	0.346	0.349	0.351
25	0.354	0.356	0.358	0.361	0.363	0.366	0.369	0.371	0.374	0.376
26	0.379	0.382	0.384	0.387	0.390	0.392	0.395	0.398	0.401	0.403
27	0.406	0.409	0.412	0.415	0.418	0.420	0.423	0.426	0.429	0.432
28	0.435	0.438	0.441	0.444	0.448	0.451	0.454	0.457	0.460	0.463
29	0.467	0.470	0.473	0.476	0.480	0.483	0.486	0.490	0.493	0.497
30	0.500	0.503	0.507	0.511	0.514	0.518	0.521	0.525	0.529	0.532
31	0.536	0.540	0.543	0.547	0.551	0.555	0.559	0.563	0.566	0.570
32	0.574	0.578	0.582	0.586	0.590	0.595	0.599	0.603	0.607	0.611
33	0.616	0.620	0.624	0.629	0.633	0.637	0.642	0.646	0.651	0.655
34	0.660	0.664	0.669	0.674	0.678	0.683	0.688	0.693	0.697	0.702
35	0.707	0.712	0.717	0.722	0.727	0.732	0.737	0.742	0.747	0.753
36	0.758	0.763	0.768	0.774	0.779	0.785	0.790	0.796	0.801	0.807
37	0.812	0.818	0.824	0.829	0.835	0.841	0.847	0.853	0.859	0.865
38	0.871	0.877	0.883	0.889	0.895	0.901	0.908	0.914	0.920	0.927
39	0.933	0.940	0.946	0.953	0.959	0.966	0.973	0.979	0.986	0.993
40	1.00	1.01	1.01	1.02	1.03	1.04	1.04	1.05	1.06	1.06
41	1.07	1.08	1.09	1.09	1.10	1.11	1.12	1.13	1.13	1.14
42	1.15	1.16	1.16	1.17	1.18	1.19	1.20	1.21	1.21	1.22
43	1.23	1.24	1.25	1.26	1.27	1.27	1.28	1.29	1.30	1.31
44	1.32	1.33	1.34	1.35	1.36	1.37	1.38	1.39	1.39	1.40

* Compiled by S. S. Stevens, Ref. 18.

Appendix 5.1. Table Relating Loudness Level in Phons and Loudness in Sones Based on Eq. (5.1) (*Continued*)

Loud-ness level	0	0.1	0.2	0.3	0.4	0.5	0.6	0.7	0.8	0.9
45	1.41	1.42	1.43	1.44	1.45	1.46	1.47	1.48	1.49	1.51
46	1.52	1.53	1.54	1.55	1.56	1.57	1.58	1.59	1.60	1.61
47	1.62	1.64	1.65	1.66	1.67	1.68	1.69	1.71	1.72	1.73
48	1.74	1.75	1.77	1.78	1.79	1.80	1.82	1.83	1.84	1.85
49	1.87	1.88	1.89	1.91	1.92	1.93	1.95	1.96	1.97	1.99
50	2.00	2.01	2.03	2.04	2.06	2.07	2.08	2.10	2.11	2.13
51	2.14	2.16	2.17	2.19	2.20	2.22	2.23	2.25	2.27	2.28
52	2.30	2.31	2.33	2.35	2.36	2.38	2.39	2.41	2.43	2.45
53	2.46	2.48	2.50	2.51	2.53	2.55	2.57	2.58	2.60	2.62
54	2.64	2.66	2.68	2.69	2.71	2.73	2.75	2.77	2.79	2.81
55	2.83	2.85	2.87	2.89	2.91	2.93	2.95	2.97	2.99	3.01
56	3.03	3.05	3.07	3.10	3.12	3.14	3.16	3.18	3.10	3.23
57	3.25	3.27	3.29	3.32	3.34	3.36	3.39	3.41	3.43	3.46
58	3.48	3.51	3.53	3.56	3.58	3.60	3.63	3.66	3.68	3.71
59	3.73	3.76	3.78	3.81	3.84	3.86	3.89	3.92	3.94	3.97
60	4.00	4.03	4.06	4.08	4.11	4.14	4.17	4.20	4.23	4.26
61	4.29	4.32	4.35	4.38	4.41	4.44	4.47	4.50	4.53	4.56
62	4.59	4.63	4.66	4.69	4.72	4.76	4.79	4.82	4.86	4.89
63	4.92	4.96	4.99	5.03	5.06	5.10	5.13	5.17	5.21	5.24
64	5.28	5.31	5.35	5.39	5.43	5.46	5.50	5.54	5.58	5.62
65	5.66	5.70	5.73	5.78	5.82	5.86	5.90	5.94	5.98	6.02
66	6.06	6.11	6.15	6.19	6.23	6.28	6.32	6.36	6.41	6.45
67	6.50	6.54	6.59	6.63	6.68	6.73	6.77	6.82	6.87	6.92
68	6.96	7.01	7.06	7.11	7.16	7.21	7.26	7.31	7.36	7.41
69	7.46	7.52	7.57	7.62	7.67	7.73	7.78	7.84	7.89	7.94
70	8.00	8.06	8.11	8.17	8.22	8.28	8.34	8.40	8.46	8.51
71	8.57	8.63	8.69	8.75	8.82	8.88	8.94	9.00	9.06	9.13
72	9.19	9.25	9.32	9.38	9.45	9.51	9.58	9.65	9.71	9.78
73	9.85	9.92	9.98	10.1	10.1	10.2	10.3	10.3	10.4	10.5
74	10.6	10.6	10.7	10.8	10.9	10.9	11.0	11.1	11.2	11.2
75	11.3	11.4	11.5	11.6	11.6	11.7	11.8	11.9	12.0	12.0
76	12.1	12.2	12.3	12.4	12.5	12.6	12.6	12.7	12.8	12.9
77	13.0	13.1	13.2	13.3	13.4	13.5	13.5	13.6	13.7	13.8
78	13.9	14.0	14.1	14.2	14.3	14.4	14.5	14.6	14.7	14.8
79	14.9	15.0	15.1	15.2	15.3	15.5	15.6	15.7	15.8	15.9
80	16.0	16.1	16.2	16.3	16.4	16.6	16.7	16.8	16.9	17.0
81	17.1	17.3	17.4	17.5	17.6	17.8	17.9	18.0	18.1	18.3
82	18.4	18.5	18.6	18.8	18.9	19.0	19.2	19.3	19.4	19.6
83	19.7	19.8	20.0	20.1	20.3	20.4	20.5	20.7	20.8	21.0
84	21.1	21.3	21.4	21.6	21.7	21.9	22.0	22.2	22.3	22.5
85	22.6	22.8	22.9	23.1	23.3	23.4	23.6	23.8	23.9	24.1
86	24.3	24.4	24.6	24.8	24.9	25.1	25.3	25.5	25.6	25.8
87	26.0	26.2	26.4	26.5	26.7	26.9	27.1	27.3	27.5	27.7
88	27.9	28.1	28.2	28.4	28.6	28.8	29.0	29.2	29.4	29.7
89	29.9	30.1	30.3	30.5	30.7	30.9	31.1	31.3	31.6	31.8
90	32.0	32.2	32.4	32.7	32.9	33.1	33.4	33.6	33.8	34.1
91	34.3	34.5	34.8	35.0	35.3	35.5	35.8	36.0	36.3	36.5
92	36.8	37.0	37.3	37.5	37.8	38.1	38.3	38.6	38.9	39.1
93	39.4	39.7	39.9	40.2	40.5	40.8	41.1	41.4	41.6	41.9
94	42.2	42.5	42.8	43.1	43.4	43.7	44.0	44.3	44.6	44.9

Appendix 5.1. Table Relating Loudness Level in Phons and Loudness in Sones Based on Eq. (5.1) (*Continued*)

Loud-ness level	0	0.1	0.2	0.3	0.4	0.5	0.6	0.7	0.8	0.9
95	45.3	45.6	45.9	46.2	46.5	46.9	47.2	47.5	47.8	48.2
96	48.5	48.8	49.2	49.5	49.9	50.2	50.6	50.9	51.3	51.6
97	52.0	52.3	52.7	53.1	53.4	53.8	54.2	54.6	54.9	55.3
98	55.7	56.1	56.5	56.9	57.3	57.7	58.1	58.5	58.9	59.3
99	59.7	60.1	60.5	61.0	61.4	61.8	62.2	62.7	63.1	63.6
100	64.0	64.4	64.9	65.3	65.8	66.3	66.7	67.2	67.6	68.1
101	68.6	69.1	69.6	70.0	70.5	71.0	71.5	72.0	72.5	73.0
102	73.5	74.0	74.5	75.1	75.6	76.1	76.6	77.2	77.7	78.2
103	78.8	79.3	79.9	80.4	81.0	81.6	82.1	82.7	83.3	83.9
104	84.4	85.0	85.6	86.2	86.8	87.4	88.0	88.6	89.3	89.9
105	90.5	91.1	91.8	92.4	93.1	93.7	94.4	95.0	95.7	96.3
106	97.0	97.7	98.4	99.0	99.7	100	101	102	103	103
107	104	105	105	106	107	108	108	109	110	111
108	111	112	113	114	115	115	116	117	118	119
109	119	120	121	122	123	124	124	125	126	127
110	128	129	130	131	132	133	133	134	135	136
111	137	138	139	140	141	142	143	144	145	146
112	147	148	149	150	151	152	153	154	155	156
113	158	159	160	161	162	163	164	165	167	168
114	169	170	171	172	174	175	176	177	179	180
115	181	182	184	185	186	187	188	190	191	193
116	194	195	197	198	199	201	202	204	205	206
117	208	209	211	212	214	215	217	218	220	221
118	223	224	226	228	229	231	232	234	236	237
119	239	241	242	244	246	247	249	251	252	254
120	256	258	260	261	263	265	267	269	271	272
121	274	276	278	280	282	284	286	288	290	292
122	294	296	298	300	302	304	307	309	311	313
123	315	317	319	322	324	326	329	331	333	335
124	338	340	343	345	347	350	352	355	357	360
125	362	365	367	370	372	375	377	380	383	385
126	388	391	393	396	399	402	405	407	410	413
127	416	419	422	425	428	431	434	437	440	443
128	446	449	452	455	458	461	465	468	471	474
129	478	481	484	488	491	495	498	501	505	508
130	512	516	519	523	526	530	534	537	541	545
131	549	553	556	560	564	568	572	576	580	584
132	588	592	596	600	605	609	613	617	622	626
133	630	635	639	644	648	653	657	662	666	671
134	676	680	685	690	695	699	704	709	714	719
135	724	729	734	739	744	750	755	760	765	771
136	776	781	787	792	798	803	809	815	820	826
137	832	838	843	849	855	861	867	873	879	885
138	891	898	904	910	917	923	929	936	942	949
139	955	962	969	976	982	989	996			

Chapter 6

AUDIOMETRIC TESTING IN INDUSTRY

Aram Glorig, M.D.

American Academy of Ophthalmology and Otolaryngology
Subcommittee on Noise in Industry

J. Donald Harris, Ph.D.

U.S. Naval Medical Research Laboratory
New London, Connecticut

AUDIOMETRY IN GENERAL

One of the primary characteristics of the ear is its ability to detect weak sounds. Testing to determine the weakest sound to which a person responds is known as *threshold audiometry*.   Many types of sound stimuli and many different "responses" have been used for audiometry, but practically all audiometry of significance for industry depends upon sinusoidal waves (often called "pure tones") for stimuli, and a response on the part of the subject such as pushing a button or lifting a finger.

Industry has a proper concern with (1) whether a person's hearing is, and remains, adequate to sustain his work, and (2) whether industrial noise will cause deterioration of hearing enough to affect the person's life in general.   An industrial hearing conservation program should therefore be designed with both considerations in mind, to maintain work efficiency and to protect the worker.

There is no question whatever that some industrial noises are producing irreversible hearing losses; this is in part due to particular susceptibility to damage in some individuals, and in part to the general level of industrial noise.   More and more industrial plants are finding that, unless the hearing of personnel is examined before employment, or before reassignment to potentially noisier work spaces, management is liable without recourse for demonstrated hearing loss—even though in some cases that loss may have existed undetected by management prior to employment or reassignment. Therefore, a proper audiometric program may provide adequate protection for both employers and employees in cases of industrial hearing loss.

This chapter outlines some audiometric tests suitable for use in industry and considers how it may be decided which test or tests should be selected for any particular situation, how the equipment may be kept in calibration, how the tests should be administered, and how the results may be interpreted.

PURE-TONE AUDIOMETRY

The use of pure tones in hearing tests, today easily accomplished with the development of vacuum tubes, was introduced many decades ago with sets of tuning forks often running from 64 through 8,000 cps, with the continuously variable Galton whistle, and with a variety of Helmholtz resonators and acoumeters. Today, the sensitivity of the ear for tones of various frequencies is given in terms of the sound pressure level needed to evoke 50 per cent correct response at each frequency.

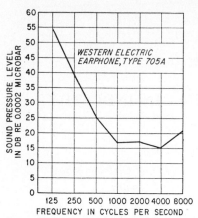

The base line from which hearing loss is calculated is called the *normal threshold of hearing*. If, in order to produce a sensation of hearing at a certain frequency, an individual ear needs 10 db more sound pressure level than the normal threshold of hearing, the ear is said to have a 10-db hearing loss at that frequency. The normal threshold of hearing, which has been standardized in the United States, is shown in Fig. 6.1. It is based upon earphone listening tests of a cross section of the population and is not the same as the "minimum-audible-field" curve given in Fig. 4.5, which represents the average threshold of hearing for a group of young adults facing a pure-tone source of sound in a free field.

FIG. 6.1. Normal threshold of hearing, based on earphone listening tests on a cross section of the population. (*After Ref. 1; see Appendix 6.2.*)

The relationship between hearing loss and the ability to understand speech[2] varies from person to person so that no such relationship is exact. However, one classification is given in Table 6.1.[3]

In representing a particular ear's hearing loss, a convenient system is the graphed audiogram. Printed forms have been prepared which have a horizontal line for

Table 6.1. Scale of Degrees of Hearing Loss*,†

Class	Name	Loss for speech, db‡	Remarks
A	Normal...............	Not more than 15 in worse ear	Both ears within normal limits. No difficulty with faint speech
B	Near normal...........	More than 15 but not more than 30 in *either* ear	Has difficulty only with faint speech
C	Mild impairment........	More than 30 but not more than 45 in *better* ear	Has difficulty with normal speech but not with loud speech
D	Serious impairment......	More than 45 but not more than 60 in *better* ear	Has difficulty even with loud speech
E	Severe impairment......	More than 60 but not more than 90 in *better* ear	Can hear only amplified speech
F	Profound impairment...	More than 90 in *better* ear	Cannot understand even amplified speech
G	Total loss of hearing in *both* ears		Cannot hear any sound

* Prepared by the Committee on Hearing of the National Research Council. From Ref. 3.

† This scale refers solely to hearing and does not take into consideration a man's competence with hearing aids, lip reading (speech reading), etc.

‡ The classes are defined by "decibels loss of hearing for speech." Until suitable technical facilities for direct measurement by speech audiometry are available, the loss of hearing for speech shall be calculated from pure-tone air-conduction measurements by averaging the hearing losses at 500, 1,000, and 2,000 cps, or at 512, 1,024, and 2,048 cps if the available audiometers are so calibrated. A person should be classified one class lower than indicated by the average value if, with an average loss of 10 db or more, his hearing loss for any one of the three frequencies is greater by 25 db (or more) than the least of his three losses.

"audiometer 0-db hearing loss" extending from low frequencies on the left to high frequencies on the right; space is provided below this line for parallel lines representing hearing loss in 10-db steps. Figure 6.2 illustrates one form in common use. By way of illustration, a normal audiogram has been plotted on this chart. A common convention is that frequency shall be plotted logarithmically and that the distance vertically between 10-db steps shall be the same as the distance horizontally between half octaves. On this set of coordinates the ear's audiogram is drawn as a series of straight lines connecting the plotted hearing losses at all frequencies.

The pure-tone audiometer is an instrument designed to make these measurements of hearing loss conveniently. It is basically a "pure-tone" generator, and attenuator (electrical resistance) calibrated in decibels, and an earphone for producing the acoustic stimulus. At any frequency provided by the instrument a pure tone can be presented

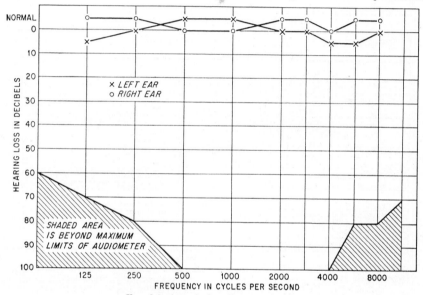

Fig. 6.2. A typical audiogram chart.

to a subject at some easily heard loudness, and gradually reduced until the 50 per cent threshold is reached.

The National Bureau of Standards has developed an "artificial ear" coupler (Type 9A) for calibrating audiometer earphones. It connects the audiometer earphone with a condenser microphone.[1] The cylindrical cavity between the two units has a volume of about 5.7 cu cm. The microphone indicates the sound pressure generated in the coupler volume by the earphone when known voltages are applied to the earphone. One can then relate this to the sound pressure levels in the coupler corresponding to the normal threshold ("zero hearing loss").

Simple Air-conduction Audiometry. The diagnosis or even the rough classification of a hearing disorder is a special medical problem, involving not only a patient's ear but his whole person and personality, and must be recognized as such. Many other tests are employed in complete audiometric examination besides the audiogram obtained with an earphone, described above. Nevertheless air-conduction audiometry alone (named from the fact that the air-borne route to the eardrum is largely utilized) can serve to identify in a short time, and with considerable accuracy, those ears which are normal in hearing and those ears which are not. If an ear can hear weak sounds well, then not much can be amiss. Air-conduction audiometry is the best single predictor of what the ear can or cannot hear, and is in consequence the backbone of any hearing testing program.

High noise levels may cause irreparable damage to hearing (see Chap. 7). To detect early losses in hearing due to noise, the aid of accurate air-conduction audiometry is invaluable. It is advisable to make *preemployment* air-conduction audiograms so that they may serve to evaluate any changes in hearing which may develop later. This initial audiogram is known as a preplacement audiogram since it is taken after the man is employed but before he is actually at work in the industrial plant. (For a preemployment test, screening tests are available and are described later.) It is important that the *preplacement* audiogram be taken in a standard manner and with equipment adjusted to the normal threshold standard, and capable of maintaining stable long-term performance. If not, data cannot accurately be compared as a succession of follow-up audiograms are collected, or compared with audiograms from other sources.

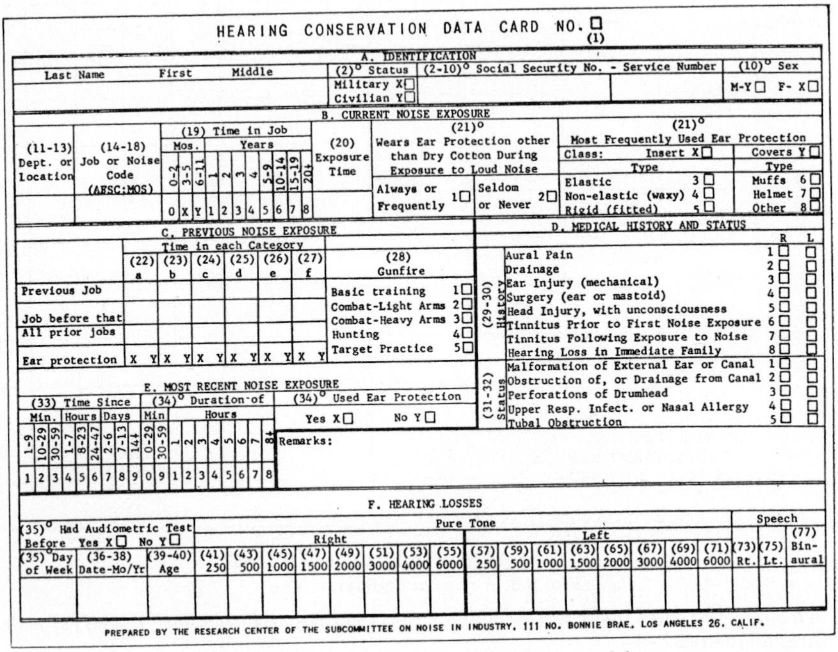
HEARING CONSERVATION DATA CARD NO. ☐ (1)

A. IDENTIFICATION
Last Name | First | Middle | (2)° Status: Military X☐ Civilian Y☐ | (2-10)° Social Security No. - Service Number | (10)° Sex: M-Y☐ F- X☐

B. CURRENT NOISE EXPOSURE
(11-13) Dept. or Location | (14-18) Job or Noise Code (AFSC:MOS) | (19) Time in Job: Mos. 0-2, 3-5, 6-11; Years 1, 2, 3, 4, 5-9, 10-14, 15-19, 20+ (0 X Y 1 2 3 4 5 6 7 8) | (20) Exposure Time | (21)° Wears Ear Protection other than Dry Cotton During Exposure to Loud Noise: Always or Frequently 1☐; Seldom or Never 2☐ | (21)° Most Frequently Used Ear Protection: Class: Insert X☐ — Type: Elastic 3☐, Non-elastic (waxy) 4☐, Rigid (fitted) 5☐; Covers Y☐ — Type: Muffs 6☐, Helmet 7☐, Other 8☐

C. PREVIOUS NOISE EXPOSURE
Time in each Category: (22) a, (23) b, (24) c, (25) d, (26) e, (27) f
Previous Job / Job before that / All prior jobs / Ear protection X Y X Y X Y X Y X Y X Y
(28) Gunfire: Basic training 1☐; Combat-Light Arms 2☐; Combat-Heavy Arms 3☐; Hunting 4☐; Target Practice 5☐

D. MEDICAL HISTORY AND STATUS (R L)
(29-30) History: Aural Pain 1; Drainage 2; Ear Injury (mechanical) 3; Surgery (ear or mastoid) 4; Head Injury, with unconsciousness 5; Tinnitus Prior to First Noise Exposure 6; Tinnitus Following Exposure to Noise 7; Hearing Loss in Immediate Family 8
(31-32) Status: Malformation of External Ear or Canal 1; Obstruction of, or Drainage from Canal 2; Perforations of Drumhead 3; Upper Resp. Infect. or Nasal Allergy 4; Tubal Obstruction 5

E. MOST RECENT NOISE EXPOSURE
(33) Time Since: Min. 1-9, 10-29, 30-59; Hours 1-7, 8-23; Days 24-47, 2-6, 7-13, 14+ (1 2 3 4 5 6 7 8 9) | (34)° Duration of: Min 0-29, 30-59; Hours 1, 2, 3, 4, 5, 6, 7, 8+ (0 9 1 2 3 4 5 6 7 8) | (34)° Used Ear Protection: Yes X☐ No Y☐
Remarks:

F. HEARING LOSSES
(35)° Had Audiometric Test Before Yes X☐ No Y☐
(35) Day of Week | (36-38) Date-Mo/Yr | (39-40) Age | Pure Tone — Right: (41) 250, (43) 500, (45) 1000, (47) 1500, (49) 2000, (51) 3000, (53) 4000, (55) 6000; Left: (57) 250, (59) 500, (61) 1000, (63) 1500, (65) 2000, (67) 3000, (69) 4000, (71) 6000 | Speech: (73) Rt., (75) Lt., (77) Bin-aural

PREPARED BY THE RESEARCH CENTER OF THE SUBCOMMITTEE ON NOISE IN INDUSTRY, 111 NO. BONNIE BRAE, LOS ANGELES 26, CALIF.

FIG. 6.3. A typical audiometric follow-up record form.

Together with a preplacement audiogram there should be collected information on the employee's medical history pertaining to hearing, the noises to which he has previously been exposed, the previous use of ear-protective devices, and a number of similar items. A sample audiometric follow-up form is shown in Fig. 6.3. Where thousands of audiograms must be analyzed in an industrial plant it is often convenient to punch the coded audiogram and other information on I.B.M. cards. A suggested list of desirable information and a coding system to be used with an I.B.M. card are given in Appendix 6.1. Such charts are particularly useful in industrial audiometry where the results of thousands of charts must be tabulated.

Where the industrial physician or the safety engineer has information that noise levels in a work space are reaching limits possibly injurious to hearing, the preplacement audiogram should be followed up within 1 month and again 5 months later by other audiograms taken under closely similar conditions. Follow-up audiograms are especially useful if taken during the temporary-employment period. If a transfer is in order, it may then be possible to transfer the man to another job within the plant without seniority difficulties.

Occasionally an ear may exhibit a hearing loss, usually in the higher frequencies, after 1 or 6 months' exposure to intense noise. If a hearing loss has not developed after 6 months, it should be sufficient to check hearing only once a year thereafter.

Equipment. Minimum specifications for pure-tone audiometers for general diagnostic purposes, set up by the American Standards Association,[1] are given in Appendix 6.2. Instruments meeting the specification are all adjusted to a uniform normal threshold standard. Essential components of such an audiometer include an electronic sine-wave oscillator, an attenuator calibrated in 5-db steps, a tone interrupter, and an earphone in a cushion and headband.

The oscillator must produce a "pure" tone at least at the octave intervals in the range from 125 through 8,000 cps. Some audiometers employ a continuously variable frequency dial very useful for diagnosis; some use fixed-frequency steps and usually incorporate intermediate points above 1,000 cps. The oscillator output is adjusted at the factory so that, at any frequency, when the attenuator dial reads "0 db" the acoustic output of the earphone corresponds to the ASA specifications for the normal threshold audibility.

The attenuator is constructed so that, as its dial changes from "0-db loss" to, say, "10-db loss," the voltage delivered to the earphone increases by 10 db. The voltage range should extend 10 db below "0-db loss" and to 75 to 95 db above, depending upon frequency.

The tone interrupter must allow the operator of the audiometer to initiate or terminate the tone at will, without audible click.

The last major component is the earphone. It is important to realize that each audiometer is usually matched at the factory to a particular earphone, or perhaps a pair of earphones. A note should be attached to all audiometers stating the serial number of the earphone or earphones supplied as original equipment. If a different earphone is used, the acoustic output may no longer meet the specifications. The earphone is the most easily damaged part of the audiometer and must not be dropped or otherwise mistreated. It comes encased in a special cushion which encloses a certain volume of air between it and the eardrum. The acoustic loading provided by this volume enters into the original calibration; the cushion must not be changed for one of a different type without specific information on the effect produced. Different cushions on the same earphone may change the acoustic output by as much as 6 to 8 db or more.

Usually a headband is provided with spring enough to hold two earphones firmly on the head. The older system of having the subject hold the earphone to his ear has been found to allow the transmission of muscular tremor to the ear, partially masking the lower frequencies, and leaving the ear not under test exposed to distracting sounds. One of the two earphones may be a dummy, the headband being switched to test the other ear.

Calibration. By calibrating an audiometer one refers to the adjustments, if any, necessary to ensure that the frequency and hearing loss dials meet the ASA specifications (see Appendix 6.2). The frequencies produced must be within ±5 per cent of the indicated dial frequency. The "0" hearing-loss dial setting must produce an acoustic output in the Type 9A coupler within ±4 db of the sound pressure level in the specifications. Furthermore, at each frequency, the difference in decibels between any two hearing-loss dial settings must agree with the difference in acoustic output within ±1.5 db.

The complete audiometer is factory calibrated and meets fairly rigid standards of precision. However, it is not unusual that after a time, or with mistreatment, the acoustic output at the "0-db" hearing-loss dial setting will change at one or more frequencies. To correct for this possibility (and to correct possible frequency drift, noisy attenuators, worn earphone cords, etc.) audiometers should be returned to the factory for overhaul and recalibration approximately once per year.

In the interim, however, it is possible to check, roughly, the calibration of the audiometer's acoustic output without the expense involved in assembling an "artificial ear" coupler (Type 9A) and associated equipment which is available in audiometer factories and in many larger laboratories.

Two factors must be checked, the voltage to the earphone, and the acoustical efficiency of the earphone. It is easy to measure the voltage at some level, say 60 db, above 0-db hearing loss. A record is made of this voltage at each audiometric frequency when the audiometer is known to be in calibration. An occasional check assures that the system is correct up to the point of the earphone. The efficiency of the earphone can be checked subjectively or objectively. Artificial ears are now available consisting of a seat for an earphone, a small air cavity, and a microphone leading to a voltmeter.* Such equipment may be used for checking changes in the acoustic output level of the audiometer.

Normal-hearing ears can be used as a means of determining changes in the acoustic output of an audiometer. When the instrument is known to be correct, several audiograms are taken under conditions where the noise level is low. Every few weeks, or oftener if a change is suspected, another set of audiograms is taken as before.

The dates of factory calibration, of the collection locally of objective data, and/or subjective data, should be carefully preserved. In many cases such information is valuable as court evidence.

Test Environment. A common factor contributing to inaccuracy in audiometry is the apparent reduction in sensitivity as a result of masking which occurs when the test is done in a noisy room. The quietest location possible should be selected, and a check should be made to determine if it is acceptable. If, during any normal working day, the audiogram for a normal-hearing ear does not shift from that taken during the quiet of the night, it is clear that the audiometric work space is sufficiently quiet. If a sound-level meter with an octave-band analyzer is available, data may be obtained from which it is possible to determine the threshold shift, caused by noise in the testing room, by the use of Fig. 6.4. These figures contain corrections for the fact that the earphone cushions now supplied with most audiometers will

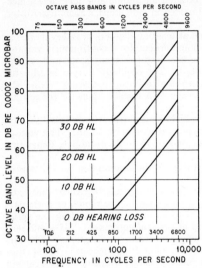

FIG. 6.4. Minimum acceptable octave-band noise levels for audiometric rooms. The curves show the sound pressure levels in octave bands that will just mask the audiometer test tones at a certain setting of the hearing-loss dial. A listener with normal hearing can just hear the test tones when the audiometer dial is at zero hearing loss if the room noise does not exceed the levels of the "0-db hearing loss" contour. Screening tests at 10, 20, or 30 db can be conducted in rooms if the noise levels do not exceed the correspondingly labeled contours. (*After Webster and Cox, revised from Refs. 4 and 5.*)

cut out a certain amount of ambient noise.

Such levels will allow one to perform most diagnostic tests. There are, however, numerous individuals who are 10 db or more better than audiometric zero; to test these at their threshold it would be necessary that the levels listed above be reduced by 10 to 15 db.

Many industrial plants have a room available somewhere in their administrative or medical departments which can be modified for this purpose. Perhaps the application of acoustical material is all that is required. A good solution is to find the quietest space available and to build a soundproof booth according to the principles of Chaps. 19 and 20. If such an installation is found not to be satisfactory, then either the location must be changed or an acoustical engineer must be consulted regarding a specially constructed sound-treated room-within-a-room.

* Manufacturers include Ballantine Laboratories, Boonton, N.J.; Brush Electronics Co., 3405 Perkins Ave., Cleveland 14, Ohio; and Allison Laboratories, Puente, Calif.

For industrial audiometry the booth need accommodate only the subject. Communication is easy with simple visual signals through a small window. Occasionally a claustrophobe will object to a very small room, but the number of these is very small. In a survey of 3,600 individuals tested in booths about 3 by 4 ft inside, no one objected to the small size, and no difficulty was encountered because the operator was outside the booth.

Test Procedure.[6–9] *Instructions to Subject.* The subject is seated so that he cannot see the operator's manipulation of the dials, which should be operated in such a way that the subject receives no aural cues. It is desirable that his back be toward the operator. Tell him he will hear soft and loud sounds, and both high and low tones, and that first one ear will be tested and then the other. One test procedure is as follows: Instruct the subject to raise his finger each time he hears a sound in the earphone, and to keep his finger up as long as he hears the sound, no matter how faint it may be. Tell him to lower his finger only when he no longer hears the sound. Now place the earphones over his ears, making sure each earphone is centered over the canal, and that the cushions fit snugly. At this point close the booth door and present one or two tones of different frequencies and at a few easily heard sound levels until you are sure the subject understands what is expected of him.

Testing for Thresholds. Starting with 1,000 cps, obtain threshold for the better ear by starting with a level well above threshold (40 db is a good level for an ear presumed to be not much different, if any, from normal). Reduce subsequent levels in 10-db steps, with one or two interruptions at each level, until the subject fails to respond. At that point go back to the last clearly heard level, and decrease in 5-db steps, giving at least four interruptions at each level; continue in this fashion until the subject fails to respond. Then the levels should be raised in 5-db steps until correct responses are again obtained. Then reduce the levels again until it is clear just what that least intense level is which yields 50 per cent response or better. That dial setting is entered on the audiogram card as threshold. (Although psychophysical thresholds are generally based on a 50 per cent response, the relatively coarse steps of the audiometer make it impossible to insist on a 50 per cent response criterion for threshold in all cases. It is necessary to accept anything between 50 to 100 per cent response as "threshold.")

Then proceed to 2,000, 3,000, 4,000, and 6,000 cps in that order. Next retest at 1,000 cps to check for learning, and proceed to 500 cps (and also to 250 cps if called for by legal requirements). The same procedure is used on the opposite ear.

Caution: When using the often-interrupted signal, do not set up a rhythm. Many subjects will respond to such a rhythm in anticipation of the next move. If a frequency is encountered where the threshold is uncertain, return to it again just before completing the test. Remember that in many instances this is the first time the subject will have undergone a hearing test; make instructions very explicit and repeat as often as desired. Finally, remember that listening for a faint tone is tiring—do not prolong the test unnecessarily. If responses become inconsistent beyond reasonable expectation, it is sometimes better to terminate the test and repeat it later on.

Recording Data. The maintenance of easily accessible and readable records is extremely important. Where it is anticipated that only a few audiograms will be collected, the small chart forms distributed by audiometer manufacturers are convenient. Where it is anticipated that many audiograms may be collected on the same ear, it is time-consuming and inexact to pass the eye from one card to another. Here, the chart of Fig. 6.3 is convenient. One glance at a single sheet of paper will encompass the status of an ear over a period of months or years. A more comprehensive discussion of this subject is given in Appendix 6.1.

Technician Training. An audiologist in a diagnostic hearing center should have received months of instruction and supervised practice. But the typical industrial audiometric program is not, and should not attempt to be, a diagnostic hearing center. The training which a reasonably intelligent and, especially, a well-motivated audiometrist must have to serve well in the industrial audiometer booth can be minimized. With proper instruction, good audiometrists for this purpose can be trained in 6 to 8 hr. The instruction should include about 2 hr of lecture on the anatomy and physiology of the ear, the fundamentals of psychoacoustics, the audiometer, and the importance of the hearing-conservation program and of their key place in it. The remaining 4 to 6 hr should be spent in actual collection of air-conduction audiograms, without and with masking, but with no other complications, under the close personal supervision of skilled audiologists.

With such a program, scores of individuals have been trained with test-retest accuracy within about ±5 db on sample audiograms. Well-motivated individuals with a minimum of training will supply better audiometry than poorly motivated though well-trained audiologists.

Variations of Air-conduction Audiometry. *Group Testing.* A saving in time is available in a system which couples a group of matched earphones to a single audiometer and elicits paper-and-pencil response from a group of subjects. At a certain frequency and sound pressure level (selected just as in individual audiometry), the subjects receive 1, 2, or 3 short spurts of tone and are asked to write down or cross out the number they heard. Then the sound pressure level is reduced and another group of spurts presented. This system is only a very slight extension of the stimulus-response setup in individual audiometry.

A system of group audiometry for a complete seven-frequency audiogram takes 15 to 20 min for the maximum recommended number of subjects, 25. It has been

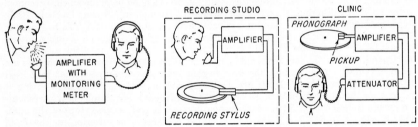

Fig. 6.5. Schematic diagram of equipment for speech audiometry. The input may be direct, may be fed from either a microphone or the pickup of a phonograph, and the output may be fed to either an earphone or a loudspeaker. (*Hirsh.*[8])

shown that with only reasonable care the difference between test and retest is almost indistinguishable from the difference between this test and good individual audiometry on the same subjects.

Sample answer blanks and other material on this test have been summarized in Ref. 10, together with notes on how the equipment may be assembled.

Sweep-frequency Screening. It may not be desired to obtain a complete audiogram for each ear, but only to be sure that all ears meet certain minimum requirements. By a screening technique, ears which do not meet minimum requirements may be identified within 1½ to 2 min testing time.

Minimum specifications for screening audiometers have been published.[11] A precise sampling of threshold acuity at each frequency is not provided by a screen, but much valuable information is provided very quickly, and sweep-frequency screening audiometry can have a definite role in industrial applications. If an ear can hear 500, 1,000, and 2,000 cps at 20 db on the audiometer dial, it will have little or no trouble with conversational speech. Accordingly a screen at this level makes an appropriate preemployment test for ability to handle the demands of ordinary conversation. Such a test may be used to survey the personnel of an entire industrial plant rapidly to screen out those with hearing loss, for purposes of further study and placement.

With sweep-frequency screening, variations using group testing are available which reduce the testing time per man to a negligible amount.[12]

Speech Audiometry. Speech which originates from either a microphone or a phonograph output, amplified and led to an earphone, may be used as the stimulus for a so-called "speech audiometer." The American Standards Association has promulgated minimum acceptable characteristics for such systems[13] (see Fig. 6.5). When a

.microphone is used, the speaker watches a volume-indicating meter while he talks, in an effort to maintain constant intensity. This is referred to as "monitored live-voice" audiometry. When a phonograph is used the system is referred to as "recorded-voice" audiometry.

In many industrial situations the recorded voice cannot be used, especially with subjects having difficulties with the English language or even with the regional dialects of most standardized recorded tests, or with children, or with those of slower personality complexes unable to follow the speed of testing. The acuity of an ear for speech sounds should not be incorrectly assessed because of such irrelevancies. These reasons are among those which account for the use of pure-tone audiometry in industry as of today in preference to speech audiometry.

Diagnostic Audiometry. Air-conduction audiometry is useful for determining what stimuli the ear can or cannot hear, and thus is of great practical value to industry and to the individual whose hearing is under consideration; but through pure-tone audiometry has other, largely medical, values. Using certain special tests now available with commercial equipment, much better approach can be made to diagnosis, and therefore to treatment.

The otologist now finds it possible to determine whether certain therapy is really aiding the patient significantly. If not, he can try other approaches. Thus audiometry can be helpful in treatment. The air-conduction audiogram alone has great clinical significance. A number of disorders have quite characteristic audiogram shapes.

Another diagnostic method is known as bone-conduction audiometry (see Chap. 4). It is possible to generate sine waves in a bone-conduction vibrator and create the sensation of a pure tone when the vibrator is applied with some pressure to the mastoid bone. The route or routes of the vibrational waves through the head between the point of application of the rod, and the cochlea, involve circuitous pathways. Part of the energy of sound transmitted by bone conduction bypasses the middle-ear route and creates wave motion within the fluids of the cochlea itself. This path, directly through the skull, provides a method of threshold evaluation which has a major diagnostic value: in case the eardrum or ossicles are even seriously defective, it may still be fairly well ascertained whether the cochlea and auditory nervous system are capable of normal functioning. If the bone-conduction data are normal, but the air-conduction data are not, it can be said with confidence that the locus of the disorder lies peripheral to the cochlea. If *both* are defective, and similar in configuration, it is considered to indicate a cochlear or nerve disorder.

Other techniques and tests with diagnostic audiometers are available. In some patients, for example, one ear may be normal or nearly so, the other ear seriously deaf. It is necessary to mask out the normal ear in order to assess the defect in the other ear.

Most diagnostic audiometers today have provisions for two separate electronic channels from the oscillator circuit and two earphones, so that the patient can match the loudness of a tone in one ear with the loudness of the same tone (independently controlled in sound pressure) in the other ear. An abnormally rapid growth of loudness in an ear, as sound pressure increases, is known as *recruitment,* and its presence is of considerable importance in diagnosis.

There are ways of utilizing the bone-conduction vibrator attachment to the audiometer in such a way as to derive the same clinical information as some otologists obtain from tuning-fork examinations. Such signs as referred localization of sound, air-conduction vs. bone-conduction thresholds for the same bone-conduction vibrator amplitude, tests for malingering, stapes fixation, distortion, tinnitus, etc., may all be performed with the diagnostic audiometer in competent hands.

The use of these techniques is not required in the usual industrial program. The place in industry of diagnostic audiometry is with those relatively few individuals for whom it must be decided whether some industrial condition, usually noise, has caused the defect shown up by air-conduction audiometry, or whether some condition connected in no way with the work environment lies at the bottom of the disorder. Industry should have the services of a competent otologist at its disposal for these decisions. He should be able to perform, or have an experienced audiological assistant

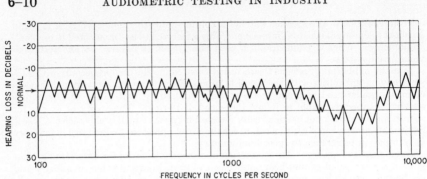

FIG. 6.6. Audiogram obtained with a Model E524 Békésy-type audiometer showing a 15-db loss at 4,000 cps.   (*Courtesy of Grason-Stadler Co.*)

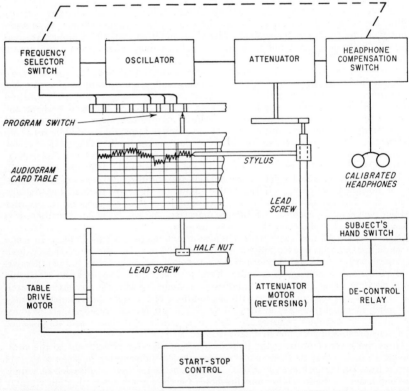

FIG. 6.7. Block diagram of Model ARJ-3 Automatic Audiometer.   When the start control is pushed, the table drive motor starts and the decontrol relay permits the subject's hand switch to operate the attenuator motor.   As the attenuator motor turns, this changes the signal strength to the earphones as well as operates the recording stylus via the lead screw. The moving table operates the program switch, which in turn controls the homing selector switch.   The selector switch changes frequency, selects the earphone, and introduces the proper compensation in the earphone circuit.   When the stop control is activated, the table drive motor stops, and the decontrol relay takes control away from the hand switch and causes the attenuator motor to reduce the earphone signal to zero.   (*McMurray and Rudmose.*[15])

(trained far beyond the usual industrial audiometrist) perform, and he should interpret the tests mentioned here for bone-conduction as well as air-conduction audiometry with masking, and tests for malingering, recruitment, speech reception, and referred localization of sound, all with equipment and procedures which meet American Standards Association minimum specifications. In many cases, even with such complete diagnostic audiometry, it is impossible to assess with high confidence the relative contribution of the work environment to a particular hearing loss. In many cases the diagnosis will depend not upon any one test, but upon the otologist's judgment when such tests are considered together with such data as subject's age, the progressive nature of the defect, its configuration with respect to the spectrum of the industrial noise involved, and perhaps other factors.

Automatic Audiometry. The various audiometric methods described above depend on the manual operation of an audiometer by a technician. One of the principal sources of error in the threshold determination results from the influence of poorly motivated or poorly trained technicians. Much variability in the measured threshold values is due to this factor alone. The use of audiometers described in this section avoids this difficulty by presenting the entire test to the subject automatically. The technician merely instructs the subject, and he starts and stops the equipment. The initial cost of automatic audiometers is higher than for manual instruments, but this may be compensated for because of lower personnel costs since automatic audiometers

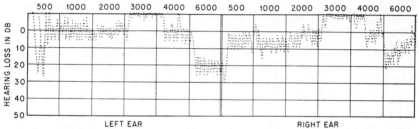

FIG. 6.8. Audiogram obtained with a Model ARJ-3 Automatic Audiometer. (*Courtesy of Rudmose Associates.*)

do not require highly trained operators. It has been found that, in general, subjects have no more difficulty in responding to automatic audiometers than to those which are manually operated. Furthermore, on the basis of considerable research and individual studies, measurements made with automatic audiometers have proved as reliable as those made with manually operated instruments.

The first widely used automatic audiometer was of the "Békésy" type,[14] which, in principle, operates as follows: An oscillator whose frequency is continuously variable starts at the lowest frequency to be tested and slowly sweeps over the entire frequency range, reaching the highest frequency at the end of the test. The attenuator, which adjusts the level of the tone presented to the subject, is automatically controlled by a hand switch so that the level decreases when the hand-switch button is depressed, and the level increases when the button is released. Thus the level of the tone is adjusted by the subject to values which vary about his threshold, thereby determining the threshold and providing some estimate of the variability of his absolute threshold. The horizontal position of a marking stylus on an audiogram chart is synchronized with the oscillator frequency, and the vertical position is controlled by the hand switch which the subject holds. Thus an audiogram such as that shown in Fig. 6.6 can be obtained.

Another type of automatic audiometer, shown schematically in Fig. 6.7, has been developed which is similar in operation to the Békésy type except that here the threshold (air conduction) is tested at specific frequencies: 500, 1,000, 2,000, 4,000, and 6,000 cps.[15] The subject operates an attenuator which is synchronized with the writing stylus and the oscillator so as to record the threshold values on an audiogram card which moves from right to left, providing an audiogram such as that shown in Fig. 6.8. A complete test can be performed in 6 to 7 min. The operator need only instruct the subject and start the card carrier. Experience has shown that two or three of these instruments can be operated simultaneously by one attendant because of the automatic operation.

An automatic audiometer makes it possible to test from 1 to 50 subjects simultaneously for mass screening tests.[16] This instrument presents a specified number of pulses at each of five frequencies at a fixed sound pressure level, variable between 0 and 50 db. The instrument is energized by pressing a hand-switch button and the test proceeds to completion automatically. Each subject records his answers on a prepared form. The attendant seats the subjects, instructs them, and initiates the test by pressing the starting button. The test is completed in about 2 min.

RATING SCALES

While the evaluation of air-conduction audiograms in clinical terms is a problem for the medical profession, interpretive classifying schemes can be presented for use by industry in making up a job-classification system for employees with a hearing loss. Such rating methods are important from the standpoint of determining the percentage compensable hearing loss. At the present time there is no uniform procedure in the United States for evaluating this loss, although many systems for evaluating hearing loss have been proposed.[17-20] See Chap. 7 for a discussion of *speech average loss*.

Wisconsin. For a discussion of compensable hearing loss in the state of Wisconsin see the following chapter.

A.M.A. Computational Method. The American Medical Association has proposed a tentative method for converting pure-tone audiometric data into a single score for percentage hearing loss.[21] The audiometric losses at the frequencies 500, 1,000, 2,000, and 4,000 cps are multiplied by 0.15, 0.30, 0.40, and 0.15, respectively. The total is considered to be the "weighted db loss for speech." The total is then converted to a percentage loss by means of a sigmoid conversion graph which takes into account the fact that a 10-db loss near normal or near total loss is of less significance than a 10-db loss from, say, 30 to 40 db. A table is provided in Ref. 21 to simplify these calculations. The reference further indicates that percentage *binaural* hearing loss can be computed by adding the loss for the worse ear together with 7 times the loss for the better ear, and dividing by 8.

For example, consider an audiogram in which the hearing in the right ear is 5, 5, 10, 20, and 50 db at the frequencies 250, 500, 1,000, 2,000, and 4,000 cps, respectively; the losses in the left ear at these frequencies are 20, 25, 25, 65, and 80 db, respectively. From the table in Ref. 21 the loss in the right ear, according to the A.M.A. system, is 11 per cent, while in the left ear it is 50 per cent. The combined loss for both ears would be computed to be $[11 + (7 \times 50)]/8 = 45$ per cent.

New York State. State laws have not generally followed the A.M.A. system. In New York State the monaural hearing loss is computed as the average of the losses at 250, 500, 1,000, 2,000, and 4,000 cps, multiplied by 0.8. Thus in the above example for the left ear the loss would be computed as $9\frac{0}{5} \times 0.8 = 14.4$ per cent; the left ear would have a loss computed to be $21\frac{5}{5} \times 0.8 = 34.4$ per cent.

REFERENCES

1. Anon.: Standard Z24.5-1951, American Standards Association, New York, 1951.
2. Steinberg, J. C., and M. B. Gardner: *J. Acoust. Soc. Amer.*, **11**: 270 (1940).
3. Corliss, E. L. R.: *Natl. Bur. Standards* (*U.S.*) *Circ.* 534, Mar. 2, 1953.
4. Webster, J. C.: *J. Acoust. Soc. Amer.*, **26**: 782 (1954).
5. Cox, J. R., Jr.: *Noise Control*, **1**: 25 (1955).
6. Fowler, E. P.: Tests for Hearing, chap. 11 in "Medicine of the Ear," 2d ed. (E. P. Fowler, Jr., ed.), Thomas Nelson & Sons, New York, 1947.
7. Bunch, C. C.: "Clinical Audiometry," The C. V. Mosby Company, St. Louis, 1943.
8. Hirsh, I. J.: "The Measurement of Hearing," McGraw-Hill Book Company, Inc., New York, 1952.

9. Watson, L. A., and T. Tolan: "Hearing Tests and Hearing Instruments," The Williams & Wilkins Company, Baltimore, 1949.
10. Harris, J. D.: *J. Acoust. Soc. Amer.*, **17**: 73 (1945). This work began on the basis of W. A. Munson, Trial Tests of Pulsing Tone Audiometer, unpublished research memorandum, Case 20871-2, Bell Telephone Laboratories, 1937.
11. Anon.: Standard Z24.12-1951, American Standards Association, New York, 1951.
12. Glorig, A., and R. R. Wilke: *J. Acoust. Soc. Amer.*, **24**: 450 (1952).
13. Anon.: Standard Z24.13-1953, American Standards Association, New York, 1953.
14. v. Békésy, G.: *Acta Oto-Laryngol.*, **35**: 411 (1947).
15. McMurray, R. F., and W. Rudmose: *Noise Control*, **2**: 33 (January, 1956).
16. Glorig, A.: *Proc. Intern. Course in Paedo-audiology*, Groningen University, Netherlands, 1953.
17. Fletcher, H.: *J. Acoust. Soc. Amer.*, **22**: 1 (1950).
18. Fowler, E. P.: *J. Acoust. Soc. Amer.*, **13**: 373 (1942).
19. Fletcher, H.: "Speech and Hearing in Communication," D. Van Nostrand Company, Inc., Princeton, N.J., 1953.
20. Davis, H.: *Laryngoscope*, **58**: 761 (1948).
21. Carter, H. A.: *J. Am. Med. Assoc.*, **133**: 396 (1947).

Appendix 6.1.　Hearing Conservation Data Card and I.B.M. Code*

INSTRUCTIONS FOR FILLING OUT THE HEARING CONSERVATION DATA CARD

The hearing conservation data card is broken down into six major categories:

A. Identification of individual.
B. Current noise exposure.
C. Previous noise exposure.
D. Medical history and status.
E. Most recent noise exposure.
F. Hearing losses.

ADDITIONAL DATA. Such additional data as are desired to meet local needs and objectives may be recorded on supplementary sheets attached to the present data card. The present form represents the minimum data that are required for a proposed nationwide research study. The recommended codes and conventions must be followed to make the data most useful for such study and easy to copy or microfilm efficiently and without confusion. Uniformity in the form and coding of data for statistical study is very important.

CARD NUMBER. On the first card that is used for each individual, place the number 1 in the square at the top of the card (the numbers in the parentheses are for the use of the key-punch operator). As additional cards are used for the same person, enter the number of the card in the square at the top of each new card. For example, if it is the person's second audiogram, which is placed on a second card, enter the number 2 in this square.

A. *IDENTIFICATION*

Name. Record the subject's name, last name first.

Military Status. Check the appropriate box to indicate whether the subject is a military or civilian employee.

Social Security Number—Service Number. Record the subject's social security number or his service number, or both, in the proper space. If the subject is a military employee, make certain that the service number is recorded, and if he is a civilian employee, make certain that the social security number is recorded.

Sex. Indicate the person's sex by checking the appropriate square.

B. *CURRENT NOISE EXPOSURE*

Department or Location. Record the department number or the coded location or area where the subject generally works. For example, department 103 or area 5 or section 3 in hangar 6, etc.

Job or Noise Code. Record the utilization AFSC, MOS, or job or noise-exposure code (to be developed), which best describes the subject's work. Where possible, the job code

* The material contained in this appendix has been prepared by the Research Center of the Subcommittee on Noise in Industry, A.A.O.O., Aram Glorig, Director; it was revised in consultation with the Armed Forces, N.R.C. Committee on Hearing and Bio-acoustics.

should include information about the noise and the subject's exposure to it. An example of such a code is presented in a following section of this appendix.

Time in Job. Determine the length of time, in years, or months if less than 1 year, that the subject has been working in the coded job environment. Circle the number in the square that is directly below the column heading containing this length of time. For example, if the subject has been working in the coded job environment for 7 years, circle the number 5.

Exposure Time. Record the number of hours that the employee is subjected to his major noise exposure on a "typical" day. If less than 1 hr, record the number of minutes. If the exposure time cannot be determined, because of a complicated or irregular noise exposure, place an X in this square.

Wears Ear Protection Other than Dry Cotton during Exposure to Loud Noise. Ask the subject if he wears ear protection other than dry cotton on the job. If he answers "yes," determine how frequently he wears ear protection when exposed to loud noise (90 db or greater), and check the appropriate square. If he answers "no," check "never."

Most Frequently Used Ear Protection. If the subject indicates that he wears ear protection other than dry cotton, determine the *class* of ear protection he most frequently uses, insert or covers, and check the proper square. Also determine the *type* of ear protector within this class that he most frequently uses, and check the appropriate square.

C. *PREVIOUS NOISE EXPOSURE.*

Time in Each Category. A tentative code containing six categories for recording previous exposure to noise is presented in the following section. These categories are based upon the over-all noise level of various job operations, broken down into 10-db steps. Category a represents those jobs having an over-all noise level of 80 to 90 db, while category f represents jobs having an over-all noise level of 130 db or more. Record the number of years, or months if less than 1 year, that the employee has worked in each of these categories on his previous job, on the job before that, and on all prior jobs.

Ear Protection. Determine how frequently the subject used ear protection other than dry cotton on all previous jobs within each category. If on all previous jobs within a given category the subject "seldom" or "never" wore ear protection, leave blank the space for ear protection in that column. If he indicates that he "always" or "frequently" wore ear protection, encircle the letter under the appropriate column according to the code used in column 21 for the class of ear protection most frequently used. For example, if the subject worked for a total of 3 years in category e, and he frequently wore insert plugs when exposed to noise in that category, encircle the letter x in that column.

Gunfire. If the subject has had military basic training in which he was exposed to gunfire, check box 1. If he has had combat and used guns of 50 caliber or less, check "light arms," and if he used guns of greater than 50 caliber, check "heavy arms." If the subject has gone hunting ten or more times during his life (excluding air rifles), check "hunting," and if he has engaged in target practice ten or more times (excluding basic training), check "target practice."

D. *MEDICAL HISTORY AND STATUS*

History. Check the proper boxes to indicate the presence of the corresponding data for each ear.

Check "Ear Injury (Mechanical)" if the subject has received any ear injury caused by a blow by a foreign object.

Check the first square behind "Hearing Loss in Immediate Family" if a blood relative (grandparent, parent, brother, sister, son, or daughter) had a hearing loss which started before the age of forty. If more than one blood relative had such a hearing loss, check both the squares behind this category.

Check "Tubal Obstruction" if the drumhead is not seen to move, or pressure there is not felt by the subject, on performing the Valsalva maneuver.

E. *MOST RECENT NOISE EXPOSURE*

Time Since. Determine the length of time which has elapsed since the end of the subject's last exposure to noise. Circle the number in the square that is directly below the column heading containing this length of time. For example, if it has been 45 min, circle the number 3.

Duration of. Determine the number of minutes' or hours' duration of the most recent noise exposure. Circle the number in the square that is directly below the column heading containing this length of time.

Used Ear Protector. Check the proper box to indicate whether ear protection was worn during the most recent noise exposure.

F. HEARING LOSSES

Had Audiometric Test Before. If it is the very first audiometric test the person has ever had, check "no." If he has had a previous pure-tone audiogram, given by any agency, check "yes."

Day of Week. Record the day of the week, i.e., Monday, Tuesday, etc., on which the test is given.

Date. Record in numbers the month and the last two digits of the year that the test is given. For example, if the test is given in June, 1956, record 6/56.

Age. Record the age of the subject as the number of years at his last birthday.

Pure Tone. Record the hearing loss in decibels in the appropriate space for each frequency. The recommended frequencies are 500, 1,000, 2,000, 3,000, 4,000, and 6,000 cps. In addition, 250 and 1,500 cps are optional.

Speech Reception. The determination of speech-reception thresholds by means of recorded spondee word lists is optional.

It is recommended that the hearing conservation data card be filed with the subject's medical records after the data have been transferred to an I.B.M. card.

TENTATIVE CODE FOR OVER-ALL NOISE LEVELS AT MACHINES*

a (80–89 db)

Lathe, automatic
Liming machine
Welder, arc

b (90–99 db)

Boring machine
Drill, pneumatic
Drill, radial, vertical, etc.
Grinders, castings, pipe, metal parts, etc.
Jointer, wood
Lathe, engine
Lathe, turret, other than ram type
Leveler, steel plates
Mill, bloomer, strip steel
Mill, strip steel
Milling machine
Polisher, metal tubes
Ram, pneumatic, sand molds
Rivet bucking, fuselage
Router, aluminum stock
Sand muller
Sander, wood
Scarfing, acetylene welding equipment
Screw machine, automatic
Shaper, small steel parts
Shear, steel plate
Welder, butt, electric
Welder, gas, on steel
Welding machine, tube

c (100–109 db)

Conveyor, strip steel
Forging manipulator
Furnaces, oil, gas, electric
Grinder, pedestal, on small tools
Hammer, forging
Hammer, pneumatic, peening
Hammering machine, rotary, on steel tubes
Hoop machine, steel wire
Jolt squeeze machine, sand molding
Lathe, automatic, wood

Lathe, turret, ram type
Mill, roughing, steel plates
Planer, wood
Pointing machine, steel parts
Press, pneumatic
Press, punch, automatic
Push-up machine, sand molding
Rivet bucking, wings
Riveting gun, pneumatic, wing assembly
Riveting hammer, fuselage assembly
Sand slinger
Saw, circular, cutting metal
Saw, cutoff, circular, wood
Saw, friction, steel
Shakeout, castings
Shot blast, small castings
Surfacer, wood
Tumbler, small castings
Vibrator, pneumatic, sand molds
Wrench, pneumatic

d (110–119 db)

Air hoist, pneumatic
Chipper, pneumatic, castings
Core blower, sand cores
Corrugating machine, sheet steel
Cutting machine, hardened tools
Decoiler, steel coils
Hammer, bumping, on thin metal
Hammer, drop, automatic
Internal-combustion-engine test
Nail machine
Riveting jig, wing assembly
Sandblast machine, on hand tools

e (120–129 db)

Chipper, pneumatic, tank
Engine airplane, propeller
Riveting gun, pneumatic, subassembly

f (130 db or over)

Engine, jet
Riveting hammer, pneumatic, on steel tank

* Adapted from H. B. Karplus and G. L. Bonvallet, *Am. Ind. Hyg. Assoc. Quart.*, **14**: 4 (December, 1953). See Appendix 1.1.

TENTATIVE CODE FOR OVER-ALL NOISE LEVELS IN AREAS*

a (80–89 db)

Furnace, annealing
Grinding
Machine shop, lathes, presses, etc.
Machining, aluminum
Milling machines
Sand molding
Spraying, varnish, etc.
Veneer department
Welding arc
Wood finishing, sanding, plaining, jointing, etc.

b (90–99 db)

Castings, cleaning
Core room
Fabrication, steel, handling, cutting
Foundry operations, sand slinging, etc.
Furniture making, planers, jointers, saws, etc.
Hammer, drop forge
Mill, bloomer, roughing, strip, etc.
Mill shop, wood

Power plant, alternators, etc.
Ramming, pneumatic
Riveting, routers, aircraft
Sawing, logs, etc.
Screw machine, automatic
Shot blast room
Steel pouring
Wire drawing

c (100–109 db)

Chipping, castings, etc.
Conveyor
Furnace, electric
Hammer, drop, automatic
Molding, push-up machines, etc.
Punch press, automatic
Riveting, pneumatic, large steel plate tanks
Tumblers

d (110–119 db)

Shakeouts
Chipping, pneumatic, cleaning steel tank welds

* Adapted from H. B. Karplus and G. L. Bonvallet, *Am. Ind. Hyg. Assoc. Quart.*, **14**: 4 (December, 1953). See Appendix 1.1.

TENTATIVE JOB CODE*

Boring machine operator...........	01-b
Chipper operator pneumatic on castings...........................	02-d
Chipper operator pneumatic, on tanks...........................	02-e
Core blower......................	03-d
Drill operator....................	04-b
Grinder operator on castings, pipe, metal parts, etc...............	05-b
Grinder operator, pedestal, on small tools.........................	05-c
Hammer operator, bumping........	06-d
Hammer operator, drop...........	07-d
Hammer operator, forging.........	07-c
Hammer operator, pneumatic, peening...........................	08-c
Hammering machine operator, rotary, on steel tubes..................	09-c
Lathe operator, automatic.........	10-a
Lathe operator, engine, turret, other than ram type.................	10-b
Liming machine operator..........	11-a
Milling machine operator..........	12-b
Punch press operator..............	13-c
Riveter, pneumatic, wing, fuselage assembly......................	14-c
Riveter, pneumatic, subassembly....	14-e
Riveter, pneumatic, on steel tanks..	14-f
Rivet bucker, fuselage.............	15-b
Rivet bucker, wings...............	15-c
Router operator, aluminum stock...	16-b
Saw operator, metal...............	17-c
Shaper operator, small steel parts...	18-b
Shakeout operator, castings........	19-c
Tumbler operator, small castings....	20-c
Welder, arc......................	21-a
Welder, gas......................	21-b
Engine, airplane, propeller.........	22-e
Engine, jet......................	22-f

* The two digits are used to separate jobs having the same over-all noise level, and the letters correspond to the categories representing the over-all noise level of each job. This value can best be obtained by sound-level measurements, but where this is not possible, a close approximation can be obtained from the classifications given in the previous sections.

INSTRUCTIONS FOR PUNCHING THE HEARING CONSERVATION DATA CARD

I. GENERAL INSTRUCTIONS

Punch the information on the hearing conservation data card into the columns on the I.B.M. card indicated in the parentheses above each item of information. For example, punch the hearing conservation data card number into column (1) on the I.B.M. card.

A small letter "o" behind a parenthesis indicates that an over-punch is to be placed in that column. When one of these columns is encountered, hold the I.B.M. card in that column, by depressing the extended space key, until both sets of information have been punched into the card. For example, hold the I.B.M. card in column (2)° until both military or civilian status *and* the first digit of the social security or service number have been punched.

Within each column, punch the number or letter* that is either checked, encircled, or written in for that item of information. For example, in column (10)° punch the last digit of the social security or service number which is written in, and the letter in front of the square that is checked under "sex."

Where there is no information for a particular item, punch a zero into the column containing that information.

II. SPECIFIC INSTRUCTIONS

CARD NUMBER

(1) Punch the number written in the square at the top of the card. For numbers 10 through 19, punch the unit digit *and* an X punch: for numbers 20 through 29, punch the unit digit *and* a Y punch; and for numbers 30 through 39, punch the unit digit *and* an X and Y punch.

A. IDENTIFICATION

Name. The name is not punched into the I.B.M. card.

(2)° *Status.* Holding the card in column 2, over-punch the appropriate letter.

(2–10)° *Social Security Number—Service Number.* If, under status, "military" is checked, punch the service number in columns 2 through 10. If "civilian" is checked, punch the social security number into these columns. If the number punched into these columns contains less than nine digits, fill in the remaining columns with zeros through column 10, holding the card in this position.

(10)° *Sex.* Over-punch the appropriate letter.

B. CURRENT NOISE EXPOSURE

(11–13) *Department or Location.* Punch the numbers that are written in the square.

(14–18) *Job or Noise Code.* Punch the numbers that are written in the square. If there are less than five digits in this square, fill in the remaining columns with zeros through column (18).

(19) *Time in Job.* Punch the number that is encircled.

(20) *Exposure Time.* If less than 1 hr, punch a zero. If 1 hr or more, punch the number of hours written in the square, unless this number is larger than eight. If the number is eight or larger punch an 8. If there is an X in this square, punch an X over-punch.

(21)° *Ear Protection.* Holding the card in column (21), punch the number checked under "Wears Ear Protection Other Than Dry Cotton During Exposure to Loud Noise," the letter over-punch for the class, and the number for the type checked under "Most Frequently Used Ear Protection."

C. PREVIOUS NOISE EXPOSURE

(22–27)° *Time in Each Category.* Add up the time in each category, and punch the appropriate columns according to the code used in (19) *Time in Job*, except that, if the total time in a particular category is less than 1 year, punch a zero. Use the over-punch to punch in the letters encircled for ear protection under the appropriate columns. Punch zeros in each of the blank columns.

(28) *Gunfire.* Punch the number, or numbers, checked.

D. MEDICAL HISTORY AND STATUS

(29–30) *History.* Punch the numbers checked for the right ear in column (29), and the numbers checked for the left ear in column (30).

(31–32) *Status.* Punch the numbers checked for the right ear in column (31), and the numbers checked for the left ear in column (32).

E. MOST RECENT NOISE EXPOSURE

(33) *Time Since.* Punch the number that is encircled.

(34)° *Duration of, and Used Ear Protector.* Holding the card in column (34) with the extended space key, punch the number that is encircled, and the letter that is checked.

F. HEARING LOSSES

(35)° *Had Audiometric Test Before*, and *Day of Week.* Holding the card in column (35), punch the letter that is checked, and the number corresponding to the day of the week that

---

* The X punch is sometimes referred to as an 11 punch, and the Y punch is sometimes referred to as a 12 or R punch.

I.B.M. CODE FOR HEARING CONSERVATION DATA CARD

Data	Column No.	Code
CARD NUMBER	(1)	Direct transposition of unit digit, using an X punch to indicate 10–19, a Y punch to indicate 20–29, and an X and Y punch to indicate 30–39
A. *IDENTIFICATION*		
Status	(2)°	Military —X
		Civilian —Y
Social security number or service number	(2)–(10)°	Direct transposition
Sex	(10)°	Male —Y
		Female —X
B. *CURRENT NOISE EXPOSURE*		
Department or location	(11)–(13)	Direct transposition of supplementary code
Job or noise code	(14)–(18)	Direct transposition of supplementary code
Time in job	(19)	0–2 months—0
		3–5 months—X
		6–11 months—Y
		1 year —1
		2 years —2
		3 years —3
		4 years —4
		5–9 years —5
		10–14 years —6
		15–19 years —7
		20⁺ years —8
Exposure time	(20)	0–59 min —0
		1 hr —1
		2 hr —2
		3 hr —3
		4 hr —4
		5 hr —5
		6 hr —6
		7 hr —7
		8 hr —8
		Indeterminate—X
Ear protection, frequency	(21)°	Always or frequently—1
		Seldom or never —2
Ear protection used		
Class	(21)°	Insert —X
		Covers —Y
Type	(21)°	Elastic —3
		Nonelastic —4
		Fitted —5
		Muffs —6
		Helmet —7
		Other —8
C. *PREVIOUS NOISE EXPOSURE*		
Category a	(22)°	0–11 months—0
b	(23)°	1 year —1
c	(24)°	2 years —2
d	(25)°	3 years —3
e	(26)°	4 years —4
f	(27)°	5–9 years —5
		10–14 years —6
		15–19 years —7
		20⁺ years —8

I.B.M. CODE FOR HEARING CONSERVATION DATA CARD (*Continued*)

Data	Column No.	Code
Ear protection	(22)°–(27)°	Insert —X Covers —Y
Gunfire	(28)	Basic training —1 Combat—light arms —2 Combat—heavy arms —3 Hunting —4 Target practice —5
D. *MEDICAL HISTORY AND STATUS*		
History—Right ear	(29)	Aural pain —1 Drainage —2 Ear injury (mechanical) —3 Surgery (ear or mastoid) —4
Left ear	(30)	Head injury, with unconsciousness —5 Tinnitus prior to first exposure —6 Tinnitus following exposure —7 Hearing loss in immediate family —8
Status—Right ear	(31)	Malformation of external ear or canal —1 Obstruction of, or drainage from canal —2 Perforation of drumhead —3
Left ear		Upper respiratory infection or nasal allergy —4 Tubal obstruction —5
E. *MOST RECENT NOISE EXPOSURE*		
Time since exposure	(33)	1–9 min —1 10–29 min —2 30–59 min —3 1–7 hr —4 8–23 hr —5 24–47 hr —6 2–6 days —7 7–13 days —8 14^+ days —9
Duration of exposure	(34)°	0–29 min —0 30–59 min —9 1 hr —1 2 hr —2 3 hr —3 4 hr —4 5 hr —5 6 hr —6 7 hr —7 8^+ hr —8
Used ear protection	(34)°	Yes —X No —Y
F. *HEARING LOSSES*		
Had audiometric test before	(35)°	Yes —X No —Y
Day of week	(35)°	Monday —1 Tuesday —2 Wednesday—3 Thursday —4

I.B.M. CODE FOR HEARING CONSERVATION DATA CARD (*Continued*)

Data	Column No.	Code
		Friday —5
		Saturday —6
		Sunday —7
Date—Month	(36)	January —1
		February —2
		March —3
		April —4
		May —5
		June —6
		July —7
		August —8
		September —9
		October —0
		November —X
		December —Y
Year	(37)–(38)	Direct transposition
Age	(39)–(40)	Direct transposition
Audiometric data—pure tone	(41)–(42)	Direct transposition where possible
250* cps	(41)–(42)	
500	(43)–(44)	
1,000	(45)–(46)	Minus value X punch over unit digit
Right ear 1,500*	(47)–(48)	
2,000	(49)–(50)	100—rounded down to 99
3,000	(51)–(52)	
4,000	(53)–(54)	No response—0Y
6,000	(55)–(56)	
Audiometric data—pure tone		
Left ear 250* cps	(57)–(58)	
500	(59)–(60)	
1,000	(61)–(62)	Direct transposition where possible
1,500*	(63)–(64)	
2,000	(65)–(66)	Minus values X punch over unit digit
3,000	(67)–(68)	
4,000	(69)–(70)	100—rounded down to 99
6,000	(71)–(72)	No response—0Y
Audiometric data—speech reception*		
Right ear	(73)–(74)	
Left ear	(75)–(76)	Same as for pure tone
Binaural	(77)–(78)	
PROJECT NUMBER	(79)–(80)	Assigned

* Optional.

is written in the square. Use the following code to designate the day of the week: Monday, 1; Tuesday, 2; Wednesday, 3; Thursday, 4; Friday, 5; Saturday, 6; and Sunday, 7.

(36–38) *Date.* Punch the numbers written in the square.

(39–40) *Age.* Punch the numbers written in the square.

(41–72) *Pure-tone Thresholds.* Punch the numbers written in the squares into the appropriate columns on the I.B.M. card. Two columns are used for each frequency, but only the first of the two columns is indicated in the parentheses. Use an X punch over the unit digit to indicate a minus threshold, and round 100 down to 99 so that it will fit into the two columns. If a frequency is left blank, *skip over the columns that contain that frequency.* If a frequency is marked "NR" punch a 0Y in the columns for that frequency.

(73–78) *Speech-reception Thresholds.* Punch the same as pure-tone thresholds.

(79–80) Punch the project number that has been assigned to you.

After punching the I.B.M. cards, return the hearing conservation data cards to the medical department.

Appendix 6.2. American Standard Specification for Audiometers for General Diagnostic Purposes[1]

1. Scope and Purpose

1.1. The audiometer covered by this specification is a device designed for general diagnostic use and to determine the hearing acuity of individuals. The audiometer described is an electroacoustic generator with associated air- and bone-conduction receivers, and provides pure tones of selected frequencies and intensities which cover the major portion of the auditory range. A device for interrupting the tone is provided. The results of measurements with this audiometer determine an individual's auditory threshold as a function of frequency.

1.2. This specification has been prepared with the objective that the measurements obtained with any audiometer shall truly represent a comparison of an individual's auditory threshold with the normal threshold.

2. Definitions

2.1. Normal Threshold of Audibility. The normal threshold of audibility for air conduction at a given frequency is the modal value of the minimum sound pressures, at the entrance to the ear canal, which produce a pitch sensation in a large number of normal ears of individuals between eighteen and thirty years of age. The threshold values accepted for the purposes of this specification shall be those determined by the National Health Survey of 1935–1936.

2.2. Hearing Loss. The hearing loss of an ear corresponds to the ratio of the threshold of audibility for that ear to the normal threshold of audibility and is expressed in decibels.

3. Requirements

3.1. General. Audiometers shall be designed to furnish readings which give an individual's hearing threshold in terms of hearing loss in decibels relative to a reference normal threshold. Provision shall be made for both air- and bone-conduction measurements. The frequencies of the pure tones generated shall be indicated in cycles per second, and the hearing loss shall be indicated in decibels. The only audible sound should be that which is radiated by the air- and bone-conduction receivers; the chassis and audiometer cabinet shall be so constructed that no audible sound is radiated from them. All audiometers shall be designed to operate on one or more of the following electric power supplies: 117 volts, 60 cps, a-c; 117 volts, d-c; batteries, or such supply as regional requirements demand. They shall have a nameplate giving the manufacturer's name, the serial number, and, if power-line operated, the voltage (or voltages), and frequency (or frequencies) of the power supply, and the power consumed by the audiometer.

3.2. Power Supply. Tests for compliance with the requirements of Section 3.3 shall be made at line voltages of 110 and 125 volts, for audiometers designed for nominal 117-volt operation, or at the extremes of the usable range of battery voltages recommended by the manufacturer. For audiometers designed for other line voltages, tests shall be made at the extremes of a proportionate range of voltages. Tests for compliance with the requirements of Sections 3.4, 3.5, 3.6, 3.7, and 3.8 shall be made at a line voltage of 117 volts, or at the voltage indicated on the nameplate of the audiometer, or at the battery voltages recommended as operating voltages by the manufacturer. When a range of voltage is indicated on the nameplate, tests shall be made at the mean voltage.

3.3. Frequencies. Audiometers shall produce sounds of at least the following definitely identified frequencies: 125, 250, 500, 1,000, 2,000, and 4,000 cps for both air- and bone-conduction measurements, and also 8,000 cps for air-conduction measurements. Each frequency generated by the audiometer shall have a value within ±5 per cent of the corresponding frequency reading.

3.4. Hearing-loss Intervals and Hearing-loss Range for Air-conduction Measurement. Hearing-loss dial range shall extend from −10 db (below threshold) by intervals of 5 db or less to at least the values given in Table 1.

Each measured difference (interval) between successive hearing-loss readings shall not differ from the nominal interval in decibels by more than 0.3 of the interval at each of the above indicated frequencies. That is, if the nominal interval is 5 db, the measured interval shall be not less than 3.5 db or more than 6.5 db.

The intervals shall be determined by measurement of the electrical input to the earphone, with the earphone coupled to the coupler shown in Fig. 1.

3.5. Sound-pressure Output of the Air-conduction Earphones.   Measurements of sound-pressure output of air-conduction earphones shall be made with a coupler having the acoustical characteristics of the coupler shown in Fig. 1.   The sound pressure produced by the earphones at each hearing-loss reading shall not differ from the indicated value, as

TABLE 1

Frequency Reading, cps	Hearing-loss Readings, db above Threshold
125	65
250	80
500	85
1,000	95
2,000	95
4,000	90
8,000	75

referred to normal threshold, by more than 4 db at the indicated frequencies of 125, 250, 500, 1,000, 2,000, and by not more than 5 db at frequencies of 4,000 and 8,000 cps.   The sound pressures corresponding to normal threshold have been determined for several types of earphones by the National Bureau of Standards, and are based on the threshold determinations made by the U.S. Public Health Service.   The threshold determinations are published in the Preliminary Reports of the National Health Survey Hearing Study Series, Bulletin 5, page 10, 1935–1936.

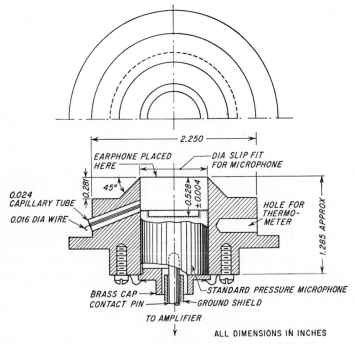

FIG. 1. Coupler for use with air-conduction earphones.

3.5.1. *Line Voltage Variation.*   The acoustic output level at the 60-db setting shall not depart by more than ±1 db from its value at the line voltage of 117 volts when the line voltage is varied from 105 to 125 volts.   In audiometers designed for power sources of other voltages, the output level shall not depart by more than ±1 db from its value at normal line voltage when the voltage is varied over an equivalent proportion above and below the normal voltage.

3.5.2. *Loudness Balance.* The sound pressures in this coupler which correspond to normal threshold for any particular type or configuration of earphone are determined by loudness balancing against a laboratory standard earphone.* The loudness balance test should be performed by a jury of not less than six persons with normal hearing.

The threshold pressures† of this earphone are as shown in Table 2.

TABLE 2. Threshold Pressures of Laboratory Standard Earphone*

Frequency, cps	Pressure, db above 1 dyne per sq cm
125	−19.5
250	−34.4
500	−49.2
1,000	−57.3
2,000	−57.0
4,000	−58.9
8,000	−53.1

* These pressures apply only to the Western Electric type 705-A earphone.

3.5.3. *Measurement of Sound-pressure Output.* The sound-pressure output of the audiometer shall be measured directly at hearing-loss settings of 60 db. The sound-pressure output may be obtained at all other hearing-loss dial settings by combination of the pressures measured at 60 db with the results of the hearing-loss interval measurements made under Section 3.4. It may be measured acoustically at practical levels, if equipment is available and shall be measured electrically at all other levels.

3.6. Harmonics in the Output of Air-conduction Earphones. The sound pressure of the fundamental signal shall be at least 25 db above the sound pressure of any harmonic. The harmonic shall be measured at the frequencies and hearing-loss readings shown in Table 1, even though some audiometers may be designed with higher maximum intensities. The measurements shall be made with the coupler shown in Fig. 1. The distortion requirements shall apply at all levels up to the values shown in Table 1, but will normally be measured at the values shown in Table 1.

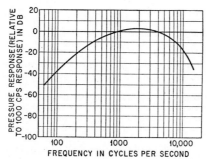

Fig. 2. Pressure response-frequency characteristic of equipment for measurement of noise in air-conduction earphone.

3.7. Noise in Air-conduction Earphones. The rms weighted sound pressure produced by the earphone in the coupler shown in Fig. 1, due to all frequencies except the signal frequency and its harmonics, shall be either less than 1×10^{-3} dynes per sq cm, or at least 60 db below the sound pressure due to the signal frequency and its harmonics at all specifically designated frequencies and hearing-loss dial settings.

3.7.1. *Measurement of Weighted Sound Pressure.* The measurement of weighted sound pressure shall be made with an equipment having the pressure response-frequency characteristics shown in Fig. 2. The weighted sound pressure due to any frequency distribution of sound energy shall be the sound pressure due to a 1,000-cps sound which gives the same reading on the equipment.

3.7.2. *Tests for Compliance with Noise Requirements.* Tests for compliance with the requirements of this section shall be made with a power supply voltage TIF (telephone

* The Western Electric 705-A earphone has been found suitable as a laboratory standard earphone.
† These threshold pressures have been determined by loudness balancing with the earphones used in the National Health Survey Hearing Study.

influence factor) of not less than 80 or more than 120, if d-c power is specified.   If a-c power is specified, the voltage TIF shall be not less than 15 or more than 25.   The frequency weighting characteristics* for TIF measurements are as shown in Fig. 3.

All tests for compliance with the noise requirements of this section should be made with the oscillator inoperative but with the remainder of the audiometer circuit in normal operating condition.

3.8. Bone-conduction Receivers.   Bone-conduction receivers shall not radiate sound to such an extent that the sound reaching the tympanum through the auditory meatus might influence the validity of the bone-conduction measurement.   As judged by an observer with normal hearing, the sound received at the ear via air radiation from the bone conductor shall have a sensation level at least 5 db below the level which the receiver generates by bone conduction when in contact with the head.   This measurement is made as follows:

(*a*) The bone-conduction threshold is determined in the usual manner.

(*b*) Then, with the receiver in approximately the same position as in the threshold measurements, the driver element or contact area is covered with the soft flesh at the end

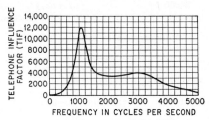

Fig. 3. Frequency weighting network for TIF measurements.

of the operator's finger to create a closure comparable to that created when the receiver is on the mastoid.   Care should be taken that no direct contact is made between the finger and the skull.

(*c*) The threshold at which any auditory sensation is perceived should then be noted and should be at least 5 db above the direct bone-conduction threshold.

(*d*) A jury of at least six persons with normal hearing should perform this test and the mean of the results should be taken.

Determination of the air radiation from bone-conduction receivers is not required at frequencies above 2,000 cps.

3.9. Shock Hazard.   Audiometers shall be free from electric-shock hazard.   A shock hazard shall be considered to exist at an exposed live part if the open-circuit potential is more than 25 volts and the current with a 1,500-ohm load is more than 5 ma.

3.10. Audiogram Blanks.   The results of hearing-loss measurements made with an audiometer shall be plotted on cross-section paper.   The abscissas shall be frequency in cycles per second on a logarithmic scale and the ordinates shall be hearing loss in decibels on a linear scale.   One octave on the frequency scale shall be the same distance as 20 db on the hearing-loss scale.

3.11. Tone Interrupter.   The tone interrupter shall be so designed and constructed that during operation no transients or extraneous frequencies are audible to the normal ear.   It is recommended that after operation of the switch the time required for the test tone to rise to a value which is within ± 1 db of the required sound pressure shall be not less than 0.1 sec and not more than 0.5 sec.

* A complete description of the manner in which telephone influence factor measurements are made is contained in a paper by J. M. Barstow, P. W. Blye, and H. E. Kent, *Trans. Am. Inst. Elec. Engrs.*, **54**: 1307 (1935).

Chapter 7

HEARING LOSS RESULTING FROM NOISE EXPOSURE

WAYNE RUDMOSE, PH.D.

Southern Methodist University and Rudmose Associates, Inc.

INTRODUCTION

The measurement of the effects of noise upon hearing has a long history. As early as 1880 reference[1] was made to some of the effects of railroad noise upon hearing. Others[2,3,4] dealt with the problem of occupational deafness among boilermakers as early as 1890. In fact, at least a hundred authors have written one or more papers on the general subject of the effects of noise upon hearing. A "Bibliography on Hearing"[5] contains all such references up through 1952.

In spite of the efforts of so many people, no one had an opportunity to survey any large quantity of data which contained sufficient information relevant to the problem to establish relationships between hearing loss and noise exposure until the formation of the American Standards Association Committee Z24-X-2 in 1952. As a result of the cooperation of industry with this committee, data were made available for analysis, and the committee's findings are contained in the publication "The Relations of Hearing Loss to Noise Exposure."[6] Much of the information in that report is contained in this chapter; however, new interpretations are presented in a form which may be more useful to industry.

Many of our states operate under laws which deal with occupational deafness only as a traumatic injury (see Chap. 38). In some of these states the concept of traumatic injury, normally associated with a sudden accident resulting in partial or total loss of hearing, has been broadened to cover cases where it is felt hearing losses accrue in a matter of a few days because of an exposure to some unusual noise. This chapter does not consider traumatic injury, but loss of hearing due to extended noise exposure. As will be seen later, there appear to be no sharp breaks in the functional relationships between hearing loss and noise exposure, at least for the noises being produced by industry today. Hence there is no simple exposure level beyond which hearing loss suddenly changes from insignificant to important. Such a situation automatically cloaks the problem in a degree of uncertainty.

Nevertheless industry must have as many positive answers as possible. However, any such answers may lead to misunderstanding since statements can be withdrawn from context and used incorrectly if modifying sentences are not always placed in juxtaposition to offset such practices. Especially since the matter of occupational deafness is closely allied with legal proceedings, a great deal of verbal qualification is associated with writings on this subject. Here, to avoid such wordage, the following statement is made. The data presented are in general tentative, and in many cases represent extrapolations and interpretations that cannot, as yet, be fully justified.

The statistical approach has been used, and in such cases the information serves to guide industry in matters dealing with groups of employees. Certain results are given in terms of average values, 20 percentiles, etc. Such results cannot apply to an individual; this fact must always be kept in mind.

In matters of industrial hygiene there is always the question, "What is a safe level?" So it is with the problem of occupational deafness in relation to noise exposure. Various criteria or suggestions for criteria relating hearing loss to noise exposure have been published.[7-10] At the time the ASA Committee Z24-X-2 started its work, all published criteria were thoroughly investigated at the time as the first step in the committee's activities. The results of this investigation led to the conclusion that all the criteria at that time were essentially "best guesses" of qualified individuals. But "guesses" leave much to be desired.[11] Unfortunately the matter of criteria still remains unsettled, but with the recent recommendations of a medical advisory committee,[12] the first step has been taken which now permits a rather realistic approach to the problem if the noise exposure is limited to the one area in which the greatest amount of information is available.

For a fuller understanding of the contents of this chapter, some knowledge is helpful of the physical characteristics of sound, the procedures for determining the threshold of hearing, and the methods for measuring noise. Such matters are discussed in Chaps. 2, 6, and 17, respectively. In general, industrial noise is measured in terms of the sound pressure levels existing within certain frequency limits. Where sound pressure levels in octave bands are plotted, the resulting chart is called an "octave spectrum." An employee's hearing is measured over a range of frequencies by determining the weakest sound pressure level of a pure tone that he can hear at each frequency selected for test. The data from such measurements, when properly plotted, constitute an "audiogram." Finally, the third item associated with this problem is the length of time the employee remains in the noise, called *exposure*.

The following comments concerning the general nature of the relation of hearing loss to noise exposure relate to average data obtained from measuring the hearing of a group of people—they do not, in general, apply to any specific individual. Hearing losses tend to increase the longer the exposure. If the group is removed from the noise, the hearing losses tend to become less. However, if exposures are repeated over and over the hearing losses become permanent, and removal from the noise will not completely restore hearing to its value prior to any noise exposure.

Hearing losses due to noise exposure tend to reach a maximum, for frequencies in the 3,000 to 6,000 cps range, for any given exposure. Hearing losses are usually less for test frequencies both above and below the above range. For this reason, if the mean audiogram of a group shows a maximum hearing loss at 4,000 cps, one can generally conclude that this hearing loss is a result of noise exposure.

One of the first facts to be learned is that hearing loss, measured as a function of frequency, is *not* the image of the noise spectrum. Furthermore, high-frequency noise does not produce hearing losses at low frequencies. Within general limits, industrial noise as it exists today produces essentially the same type of hearing loss, regardless of the character of the noise. Different classes of noise merely alter the severity of the hearing loss, not the general nature of the loss. For this reason a noise that sounds "loud" or "interferes with speech" may not be producing much permanent hearing loss in spite of the natural reaction of the employees to feel that this is a noise to be avoided. On the other hand, a less loud or obnoxious noise may actually be causing more damage to hearing. In a sense, one "cannot trust uneducated ears" to assess the potentialities of a noise to produce permanent loss of hearing.

Occupational deafness concerns itself with the ability of employees to understand speech—not, for example, with the ability of employees to appreciate high-fidelity music. The nature of speech is such that it is only the values of hearing loss in the frequency range 500 to 2,000 cps that are important. Hearing losses below and above this limited range do not appreciably affect one's ability to understand speech. Actually hearing losses below 500 cps are usually less or at most equal to the hearing loss at 500 cps. But hearing losses above 2,000 cps may be much greater than the loss at 2,000 cps. This fact, coupled with the fact that high-frequency noise does not produce low-frequency hearing loss, forces one to the conclusion that, as far as speech perception is concerned, it is the level of the noise *below* 1,000 cps that is important. Noise *above* 1,000 cps has little or no effect upon deafness as it relates to speech perception.

Another salient feature is that there are tremendous variations among the hearing losses measured on individuals who have equal exposures to a given noise. Some may sustain no hearing losses, while others may sustain severe hearing losses. This variation in susceptibility makes it most difficult to assess the severity of a noise exposure. There are, as yet, no acceptable tests to determine susceptibility other than the practice of repeat audiometry. By repeating the measurement of hearing tests at reasonable intervals of a year or less, the highly susceptible employee can be detected by noting the change in hearing loss measured at frequencies above 2,000 cps, where changes occur at the greatest rate with increased exposure.

DEFINITIONS

Noise has been defined in Chap. 1 as any unwanted sound. Other definitions which are pertinent to this chapter are:

Steady noise is characterized by sound pressure levels, as measured in octave bands, that do not fluctuate rapidly with time. Fluctuations occurring at the rate of a few decibels per second satisfy this requirement. Rotating and reciprocating machinery usually produces steady noises.

Impulse noise is characterized by sound pressure levels, as measured in octave bands, that fluctuate at a moderate rate, say, greater than a few decibels per second. Steady hammering, riveting, etc., typify such noise sources.

Impact noise is characterized by sound pressure levels, as measured in octave bands, that fluctuate at an extremely fast rate with time. Drop forges, occasional hammering, etc., are examples of devices producing this type of noise.

An *octave spectrum* of a noise is the tabulation of sound-pressure levels as measured in contiguous frequency bands, each an octave in frequency width. Present practice in many industrial noise problems is to measure the noise below about 10,000 cps and cover this range in seven or eight octave bands.

Pure-tone threshold is the minimal sound pressure level of a pure tone that can be heard when no masking noise is present. A masking noise is any noise that interferes with the measurement of a threshold.

Hearing losses are those irreversible threshold shifts which constitute a permanent departure from a specified base line. Usually the base line is the "normal" threshold but occasionally it is a "biological" base line.

Normal threshold is defined here as the average threshold of a group of individuals eighteen to thirty years old who have no otological malfunction and have never been exposed to undue noise. For a more complete discussion of this concept, see Chap. 6.

Biological Base Line. Some of the hearing-loss data of industry used in the Z24-X-2 report were taken under conditions where there was no opportunity to check the calibration of the instrument used. Because of this unavoidable situation, a biological base line was used to correct the calibration. Rather than use the absolute value of the audiometric data, a control group was established by selecting all persons below the age of thirty years who had not been exposed to excessive noises during their regular work, and who had been tested with the equipment in question. The average audiogram of this control group becomes the biological base line, or "normal hearing," for persons tested with this equipment. There are many advantages[13] to using a control group and thus establishing a biological base line.

Temporary threshold shift is any threshold shift that is not permanent with time. It is generally true that any individual exposed to moderate or intense noise will experience a temporary loss of hearing at some frequencies. When the person remains away from the noise, the shift in threshold diminishes and, in general, becomes zero. The matter of how much of an individual's hearing loss is temporary and how long it will take for the temporary loss to diminish to zero are questions that cannot be answered at present.

Exposure refers to the length of time employees are subjected to a noise.

Continuous exposure, usually expressed in years, denotes the time spent by the employees in the noise in the course of a regular work schedule. This takes into account the fact that the employee is normally in the noise 8 hr out of 24; that during this 8-hr period there are "coffee breaks," lunch periods, etc.; and that during a year's exposure there are vacations, sick leaves, etc.

Intermittent exposure refers to exposures that cannot be classed as continuous. For example, an airline pilot flies for several hours one day and possibly does not fly at all the next day. Obviously there are many cases of exposure where the degree of intermittency is difficult to assess. The correlation of data taken under such conditions with data taken for continuous exposure or under different degrees of intermittent exposure must be carried out with considerable judgment.

Sorting octave is an arbitrary name given to a particular octave band. In analyzing the Z24-X-2 data it was shown that the hearing loss at a given frequency produced by exposure to a noise correlates better with the sound pressure level in a particular octave than it correlates with the sound pressure level in any of the other octave bands. This special octave is called the sorting octave.

Trend curves is an arbitrary name given to a set of contours which are useful in estimating the amount of hearing loss to be expected from a noise exposure. Until such relations have been adequately established by experimental facts, the word "trend" appears to serve the useful purpose of indicating the tentative nature of the relationships.

Speech average loss (hearing loss for speech) is the value of the arithmetic average of the hearing losses measured at 500, 1,000, and 2,000 cps. The individual hearing losses, as well as the "speech average losses," are expressed in decibels.

Speech hearing loss is the difference in decibels between the speech levels at which the average normal ear and the defective ear, respectively, reach the same intelligibility.

PRESBYCUSIS

Presbycusis is the normal loss of hearing with increasing age. As individuals become older, they sustain hearing losses at the higher frequencies even though they have not been exposed to noise. The average hearing losses attributable to presbycusis increase with increasing frequency; however there is no "notch" like that frequently observed in the average hearing losses resulting from noise exposure. Many people spend most of their working lives in noisy places and while still working reach an age at which some loss of hearing is to be expected as the normal result of the process of aging. It would certainly be illogical to attribute to the noise that part of a hearing loss which might, according to expectations, have occurred in any case. The contribution of presbycusis to the hearing loss of groups must be removed in order to obtain consistent relationships between hearing loss and noise exposure.

Presbycusis curves for men and women are shown in Figs. 7.1 and 7.2. In the correction for presbycusis, the effects of age are separated from the effects of noise by the simple process of subtraction. This method involves an assumption that should be recognized explicitly, namely, that hearing losses which result from noise exposure and presbycusis are additive and there is no interaction between them. To a first approximation this assumption seems valid as presbycusis loss and the irreversible hearing loss induced by noise are both of the same type, called "nerve deafness" or "perceptive" deafness. The pathologist cannot distinguish between them under the microscope; both involve the permanent loss of some sensory cells and their nerve fibers.

There is no reason to suppose that presbycusis protects the ear from further injury by noise, as otosclerosis is believed to do. On the other hand, there is no indication that presbycusis makes the ear more sensitive to injury.

Since the relationships between hearing loss and noise exposure are statistical in nature, and since the presbycusis data are likewise statistical, it appears best to apply the presbycusis correction as a statistical correction. Thus, in determining the hearing loss of a group of men having an average exposure time and an average age, the presbycusis correction is determined for the average age and then subtracted from the average gross hearing loss. This difference represents the average hearing loss attributed to the noise.

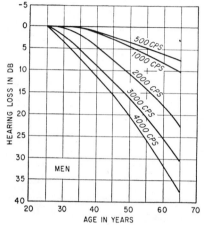

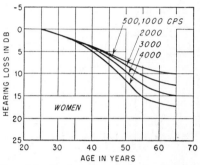

FIG. 7.1. Presbycusis curves for men: average hearing loss to be expected with age. These curves were plotted from data obtained in large population studies.[14,15,20] In these studies, the reference line (zero hearing loss) was the average hearing loss of the group between eighteen and thirty years of age. (*After ASA Z24-X-2 Report.*[6])

FIG. 7.2. Presbycusis curves for women: average hearing loss to be expected with age. These curves are similar to those of Fig. 7.1, except that there were no data on women in one[20] survey, and these curves are based on the other two[14,15] surveys. (*After ASA Z24-X-2 Report.*[6])

CONTINUOUS EXPOSURE TO STEADY NOISE

Our knowledge is the greatest for the case of continuous exposure to steady noises. The relationships between hearing loss and continuous exposure to steady industrial noises are shown in Figs. 7.3, 7.4, and 7.5. These curves, which are referred to as "trend curves," represent the condensation of a large amount of data, which places a number of limitations upon their use—limitations that must be understood clearly by the user.

Figure 7.3a shows the average hearing loss in decibels at 1,000 cps for a group of employees who were exposed continuously to steady noise for the exposure time shown. One of the limitations referred to above is that these curves apply only to steady noises which have an octave spectrum analysis which falls within the shaded area shown in Fig. 7.3b. The technique for analyzing a noise by the use of octave-band filters is described in Chap. 17. The problem of identifying which of the various octave levels should be used has been simplified by the introduction of the "sorting octave." The sound pressure levels in the sorting octave have been shown to represent the best single number which correlates hearing loss with noise exposure. The meaning of the sorting octave is illustrated by the following example.

Example. As an example of the use of Figs. 7.3, 7.4, and 7.5, assume that a group of employees work for 20 years in a given industrial noise. The mean age of these employees at the end of 20 years' exposure will be taken arbitrarily as fifty years. Assume that the octave analysis of the noise shows that the sound pressure level in the 300- to 600-cps band (the sorting octave for this chart) is 95 db.

1. To determine the loss at 1,000 cps, enter Fig. 7.3 on the abscissa corresponding to 20 years' exposure; follow this vertical exposure line until it intersects the contour labeled

95 db, the sound pressure level in the sorting octave, i.e., the sorting-octave band level. The hearing loss corresponding to this intersection is about 12 db. This represents the average loss of this group which is due to exposure to the noise. To determine the total average hearing loss of the group, the presbycusis correction must be added. From Fig. 7.1, the average hearing loss at 1,000 cps for a mean age of fifty years is approximately 5 db. Thus our hypothetical group of men employees would be expected to have an average total hearing loss of (12 + 5) = 17 db at 1,000 cps.

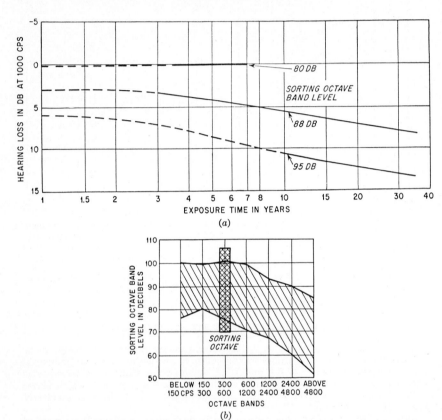

Fig. 7.3. Estimated average trend curves for net hearing loss at 1,000 cps after continuous exposure to steady noise; corrected for presbycusis; not corrected for temporary threshold shift. The broken-line portions are extrapolations. Note that the scale of exposure time starts at 1 year and is logarithmic. The shaded area of Fig. 7.3b represents the limits of the spectra on which these trend curves are based. The crosshatched area identifies the sorting octave. (After ASA Z24-X-2 Report.[6])

2. From Fig. 7.4, at 2,000 cps the average hearing loss is about 18 db. The presbycusis correction for 2,000 cps and fifty years age is about 11 db. Adding these two figures gives a mean total hearing loss at 2,000 cps of about 29 db.

3. Following a similar procedure the hearing loss at 4,000 cps can be determined by using Fig. 7.5. Note that in this case the sorting octave is different, i.e., it is the sound pressure level in the 1,200- to 2,400-cps band. Assume that the level in this band is 85 db. For 20 years' exposure the average hearing loss is about 26 db. The presbycusis correction is 20 db, making a total average hearing loss at 4,000 cps of 46 db. Thus the above hypothetical group would have average hearing losses of 17, 29, and 46 db at 1,000, 2,000, and 4,000 cps, respectively.

Similar calculations can be made to correspond to any other industrial situation that satisfies the limitations imposed by the trend curves. For the present, the complete octave analysis of steady noises should be taken to assure the user of the trend curves that the noise is within the limits given in the *b* parts of Figs. 7.3 to 7.5. Once that is determined, then it is only the sound pressure levels in the 300- to 600-cps and 1,200- to 2,400-cps bands that are used in estimating the average hearing losses to be expected.

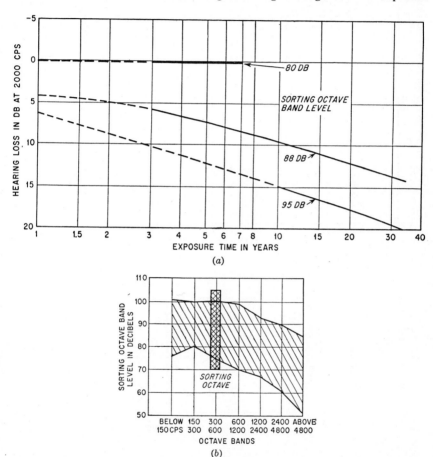

(a)

(b)

Fig. 7.4. Estimated average trend curves for net hearing loss at 2,000 cps after continuous exposure to steady noise; corrected for presbycusis; not corrected for temporary threshold shift. The broken-line portions are extrapolations. Note that the scale of exposure time starts at 1 year and is logarithmic. The shaded area of Fig. 7.4b represents the limits of the spectra on which these trend curves are based. The crosshatched area identifies the sorting octave. (*After ASA Z24-X-2 Report.*[6])

A second limitation upon the use of the trend curves is that extrapolations should not be made to levels which exceed, by more than 5 db, those given on charts. There is no a priori reason to believe that the shapes of the trend curves remain constant as the sound pressure level in the sorting octave increases.

A third limitation is that the exposure to the noise must satisfy the definition of continuous exposure. Intermittency of exposure cannot be interpreted, as yet, as an equivalent amount of continuous exposure.

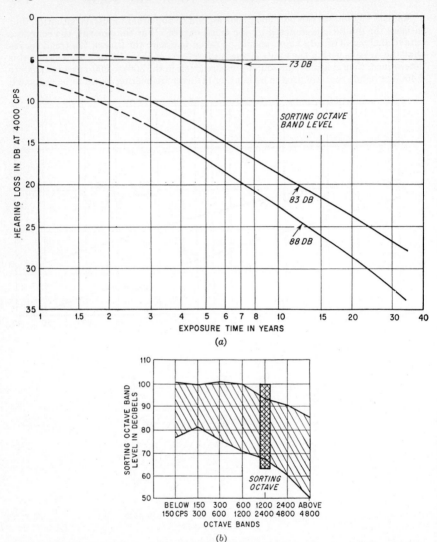

FIG. 7.5. Estimated average trend curves for net hearing loss at 4,000 cps after continuous exposure to steady noise; corrected for presbycusis; not corrected for temporary threshold shift. The broken-line portions are extrapolations. Note that the scale of exposure time starts at 1 year and is logarithmic. The shaded area of Fig. 7.5b represents the limits of the spectra on which these trend curves are based. The crosshatched area identifies the sorting octave. (*After ASA Z24-X-2 Report.*[6])

A fourth limitation is that the trend curves can be used to estimate only the average hearing loss of a group of persons exposed to noise. Individual variations in susceptibility to noise exposure are so great as to overlap considerably the curves shown for other octave levels. The fact that two trend curves are separated by only, say, 7 db does not mean that the total distribution of hearing losses for a group of employees is limited to 7 db. This point will be discussed in detail later.

A fifth limitation is that the hearing losses shown on the trend curves are a composite of temporary and permanent hearing loss. Just how much of the hearing loss is temporary has not been established; however, later data will permit the assignment of reasonable estimates to the amount of temporary hearing loss present in the total loss.

It should be noted that trend curves for estimating hearing loss at 500 cps have not been given since some of the data from which the trend curves were originally developed were ambiguous due to the presence of masking noise in the test room. Thus the omission of 500-cps trend curves is due to lack of data and not due to the feeling that such curves are unimportant.

Statistical Distribution of Hearing Losses. Since the trend curves yield average hearing losses, the usefulness of such data is limited. Experience has shown that some individuals who are exposed to noise develop compensable hearing losses under conditions where the average employee, exposed to the same noise for the same length of time, has no compensable hearing loss. To determine the seriousness of a noise exposure, relationships are required, therefore, relating the distribution of hearing losses in some manner with the average hearing loss. With such relationships the hearing losses to be equaled or exceeded by, say, 20 per cent of the employees can be estimated.

Industrial data are not yet available to permit the establishment of such relationships for persons exposed to noise. However, there are available data obtained at various world and state fairs which can be used. A distribution function obtained from such data should not be applied to cases involving noise exposure without the realization that faulty answers may result. Nonetheless such distribution functions can be extremely useful. There is ample evidence to indicate that the distribution data for noise-exposed individuals have at least an equal and possibly greater "spread" for hearing losses greater than the average hearing loss than do the distribution data for non-noise-exposed individuals. Such knowledge permits proper guidance in extrapolating data obtained by using distribution data based on non-noise-exposed persons.

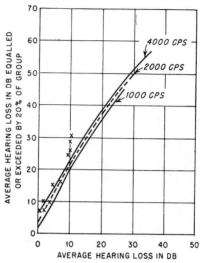

FIG. 7.6. The relationships between average hearing loss of a group and the average hearing loss equaled or exceeded by 20 per cent of the group. The smooth curves are based on Fair data and the crosses represent data from groups exposed to steady noises. The frequencies associated with the curves are the frequencies at which the averages are computed. The chart should be restricted to cases of continuous exposure to steady noise with levels less than 100 db in the 300- to 600-cps octave. The average values of hearing loss must include the effects of presbycusis. (*From Ref. 21.*)

Data obtained at the 1940 World's Fair,[14] the 1950 San Diego County Fair,[15] and the 1954 Wisconsin State Fair[16] have been used to obtain the information plotted in Fig. 7.6. The smooth curves are based on a composite of the "Fair" data. These functions show that, for hearing losses measured within the frequency range 1,000 to 4,000 cps, the 20 percentile is roughly twice the average hearing loss as long as the average loss is less than about 20 db. Also the spread of hearing losses above the mean value of the hearing loss increases with frequency within the above range; however, the difference in spread is not striking.

The crosses shown in Fig. 7.6 are data obtained from isolated cases of noise-exposed individuals. Caution should be exercised in drawing any quantitative conclusion about the differences in distribution spreads of hearing losses for noise- and non-noise-exposed groups. At least, however, there is the inference that the spread based on noise-exposed groups is equal to or greater than the distribution spread based on the non-noise-exposed population.

Using Fig. 7.6, the hypothetical example of the last section takes on more meaning. The average hearing losses for this fifty-year-old group were 17, 29, and 46 db at 1,000, 2,000, and 4,000 cps, respectively. It is now seen that 20 per cent of this group would be expected to have hearing losses equal to or exceeding 31, 49, and 68* db at 1,000, 2,000, and 4,000 cps, respectively.

Pure-tone Hearing Loss Related to Speech Loss. The hearing losses of our hypothetical group are expressed in terms of the decibel shift in threshold from the "normal" threshold. Until one has considerable experience, these decibel numbers carry little connotation in terms of the ability of an individual with this hearing loss to understand speech. Just how much of a handicap is a hearing loss of 31, 49, and 68 db at 1,000, 2,000, and 4,000 cps?

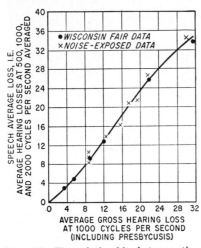

FIG. 7.7. The relationship between the average value of the mean hearing losses measured at 500, 1,000, and 2,000 cps and the average gross hearing loss at 1,000 cps. Use of the curve is restricted to cases of continuous exposures to steady noises with sound pressure levels less than 100 db in the 300- to 600-cps octave. (*From Ref. 21.*)

Quite naturally the answer to such a question was originally couched in the "percentage loss of hearing" concept. Experience has shown that there is as yet no unique relationship between hearing losses measured using pure tones and the "percentage loss of hearing." In 1946 it was shown for a large number of clinical observations that the very simple arithmetic mean (in decibels) of the hearing losses at 500, 1,000, and 2,000 cps correlates best with the hearing loss for speech.[17] A little later (1950) the suggestion was made that the average value of the two smallest values of hearing loss measured at 500, 1,000, and 2,000 cps is a more satisfactory value to correlate pure-tone audiometry with hearing loss for speech.[18] An attempt has been made to introduce the concept of the social-adequacy index for hearing;[19] however, at present the trend is toward the use of the simple average value of the hearing losses measured at 500, 1,000, and 2,000 cps, here called "speech average loss" as the number to correlate with hearing loss for speech. The use of the term "percentage loss of hearing" should be avoided, irrespective of the method of calculation.

Since the trend curves have not been developed for 500-cps hearing loss, it has been necessary to obtain a relationship between the hearing loss at 1,000 cps and the speech average loss. Figure 7.7 is based upon the Wisconsin Fair data[16] and the Z24-X-2 data.[6] For this reason, the use of this chart must be restricted to cases of continuous exposures to steady noises, and the sound pressure levels of the noise in the 300- to 600-cps octave must be less than 100 db. The crosses in Fig. 7.7 are isolated cases taken from noise-exposed groups. The solid curve is based upon data from non-noise-exposed groups and, because of the large sample size, should have a high validity. (There is evidence, however, to indicate that the extreme upper part of the curve may be in doubt.) The fact that the crosses fall within a reasonable range of the smooth curve indicates that, for noise exposures as limited by the data, the nonnoise data and the noise data are in agreement. Continuing with our hypothetical example, 20 per cent of the employees have a 1,000-cps hearing loss equal to or greater than 31 db.

* Extrapolated. This value appears conservative, since obviously the ordinate values of the functions in Fig. 7.6 must reach 90 db (considered total deafness) before the abscissa values reach 90 db.

Figure 7.7 permits the determination of the "speech average loss," which is equaled or exceeded by 20 per cent of the group. This "speech average loss" is 34½ db; hence 20 per cent of the group will possess a speech average loss of 34½ db or more.

Determination of Percentage Compensable Hearing Loss. The final step in the evaluation of the severity of the noise exposure experienced by the hypothetical group is the determination of the possible cost of compensation resulting from the exposure. Naturally this step differs from state to state as compensation laws are regulated by the individual states (see Chap. 38).

The state of Wisconsin appointed a Medical Advisory Committee which made recommendations[12] that can be used to calculate the percentage compensable hearing loss if the "speech average loss" is known. Figure 7.8 is a plot of the tables recommended by the Committee. Basically the Committee recognizes the fact that there

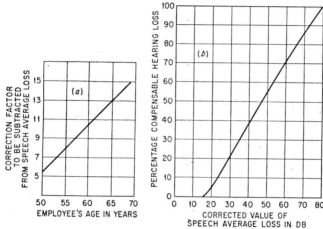

Fig. 7.8. The Advisory Medical Committee to the State of Wisconsin relates the percentage of compensable hearing loss to the speech average loss. This relationship is shown in (b). Before the speech average loss can be used in chart (b), it must be corrected for the effects of temporary threshold shift and presbycusis. These correction factors are shown in (a). The correction factor is taken as 5 db for all ages below fifty years. The correction factor is to be subtracted from the "speech average loss" to obtain the corrected value of speech average loss. (From Ref. 21.)

are effects of temporary threshold shift and presbycusis to be considered. Figure 7.8a shows the correction factor to be applied to the "speech average loss." Figure 7.8b shows the percentage compensable hearing loss as a function of the corrected "speech average loss."

Returning to the hypothetical example, we see that the average hearing loss at 1,000 cps of the group was 17 db. Using Fig. 7.7, the "speech average loss" is seen to be 19 db. Applying the Wisconsin correction factor (5 db for 50 years), the corrected "speech average loss" is 19 − 5½ = 11½ db. According to the committee, an individual does not receive compensation until the corrected "speech average loss" exceeds 16 db. Therefore, the average employee in the hypothetical group does not sustain sufficient hearing loss in 20 years of exposure to warrant any compensation.

Consider, however, 20 per cent of the group. The corrected "speech average loss" which is equaled or exceeded by 20 per cent of the group is 34½ − 5½ = 29 db. According to Fig. 7.8b, 20 per cent of the group will have 20 per cent or greater compensable hearing loss.* If this loss had occurred in only one ear, then the compensation would be 20 per cent of his weekly rate for a period of 32 weeks. If this loss has occurred in both ears, then the compensation would be 20 per cent or more of his

---

* It is entirely fortuitous that 20 per cent of the group should sustain 20 per cent or more compensable hearing loss.

weekly rate for a period of 60 weeks.   The maximal amount of compensation cannot exceed $3,500.

Thus for the hypothetical group, the knowledge of (1) the average age of the group, (2) the length of exposure, and (3) the octave spectrum of the noise is all that was required to arrive at a figure of compensable hearing loss.   The procedure has been outlined step by step.   However, Fig. 7.9 eliminates the need for carrying out the steps just mentioned.   The four charts in Fig. 7.9 are for employee's ages of thirty-five, forty-five, fifty-five, and sixty-five years at the time their percentage compensable hearing loss is determined.   The abscissa is the sound pressure level of the steady noise in the 300- to 600-cps octave band; the contour lines are years of continuous

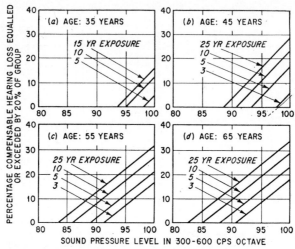

Fig. 7.9. Charts showing the percentage of compensable hearing loss (as recommended by the Advisory Medical Committee for the State of Wisconsin) to be equaled or exceeded by 20 per cent of the group as a function of noise exposure.   Each chart is for a different age at the time of compensation.   Charts are restricted to cases of continuous exposure to steady noises with sound pressure levels less than 100 db in the 300- to 600-cps octave.

exposure; and finally the ordinate is the percentage of compensable hearing loss sustained or exceeded by 20 per cent of the group.   All these charts are based upon the recommendations of the Wisconsin Medical Committee.

*Damage-risk Criteria.** As far as the Medical Advisory Committee for the state of Wisconsin is concerned, Fig. 7.9 can be used to establish reasonable criteria.   Recall that Fig. 7.9 is based in part upon Fig. 7.6.   In discussing Fig. 7.6 it was pointed out that the relations for noise-exposed groups might well lie above the curves obtained from non-noise-exposed groups.   If this were so, then for an average hearing loss of 17 db at 1,000 cps, 20 per cent of the group would be expected to have a hearing loss in excess of approximately 38 db.†   This value, converted to "speech average loss" by Fig. 7.7 and corrected by Fig. 7.8a, would yield a corrected "speech average loss" of about 33 db.   According to Fig. 7.8b, this would correspond to 25 per cent compensable hearing loss.   This loss corresponds more closely to what would be estimated using Fig. 7.9d.   It is therefore recommended that Fig. 7.9d be used for employees over forty-five years of age and Fig. 7.9b be used for employees less than thirty-five years of age.

Thus if one uses Fig. 7.9d, it is seen that, if 80 per cent of the employees over forty-five years of age are to sustain no compensable hearing loss, the sound pressure levels

* Also see the discussion on *Damage Risk Criteria* in Chap. 34.

† It is interesting to note that, if Fig. 7.6 is modified in this manner, Fig. 7.9b, c, and d coalesce and become a single chart given by Fig. 7.9d.

in the 300- to 600-cps octave should be within the range 83 to 90 db, depending on the exposure time. Stated in another manner, a sound pressure level in the 300- to 600-cps octave of 95 db would imply that 20 per cent of the employees would sustain 12½ per cent or more compensable hearing loss in 5 years of continuous exposure to the steady noise. If the employees were less than thirty-five years old after 5 years of employment, then 20 per cent of this young group would have sustained only 5 per cent or more compensable hearing loss in the 5 years of exposure to sound pressure levels of 95 db in the 300- to 600-cps octave.

It is hoped that Fig. 7.9 will form the foundation for industry to set its own criteria for noise exposure. It is obvious that no single number can be chosen as an undeniable criterion. Whether the matter is one of fully protecting 80 or 90 per cent of the

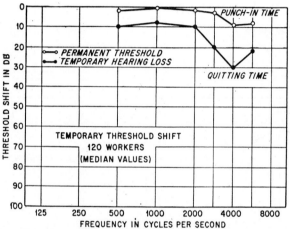

Fig. 7.10. The median temporary threshold shift found in 120 employees exposed for one day to a noise whose spectrum is relatively "flat" and whose over-all sound pressure level is 105 db. The top curve represents the median permanent threshold of the group. The bottom curve represents the median shifted threshold. The tests were made just prior to the noise exposure and immediately after leaving the noise exposure. (*A. Glorig et al.*)

workers or just 50 per cent is a policy decision industry must make. Certainly it seems reasonable that industry will try to protect as high a percentage of its employees as possible.

Temporary Threshold Shift. The significance of Figs. 7.3 to 7.5 is limited by the fact that these curves are not corrected for temporary threshold shift since sufficient correction data are not available. This temporary shift is illustrated by Fig. 7.10. Recently, the results of some work[20] published by the Subcommittee on Noise in Industry indicate the following general findings concerning temporary threshold shifts.

1. Exposure to steady-state noise with octave-band sound pressure levels of 85 to 95 db for a full workday produces an average temporary threshold shift of about 10 db for frequencies above 1,000 cps.
2. Exposure to intermittent and/or nonsteady noise with octave-band sound pressure levels of 80 to 120 db for a full workday produces an average temporary threshold shift of about 5 db for frequencies above 1,000 cps.
3. The extent of the temporary threshold shift in the individual is influenced by the amount of hearing loss he already has (resting threshold). Normal thresholds may be shifted as much as 35 db at frequencies above 1,000 cps. Impaired thresholds (45 db or more) may be shifted 5 db or less.
4. In steady-state exposures, it appears that the larger proportion of the temporary threshold shift has already occurred by midday.

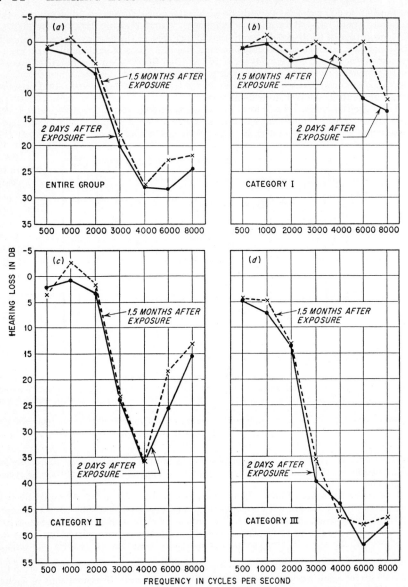

FIG. 7.11. Recovery at seven frequencies as a function of the interval of time between the cessation of exposure and the measurement of hearing loss. The median age of the 36 persons was thirty-one years, and they had, on the average, been exposed to the noise for more than 10 years. The group was divided into three subgroups called Categories I, II, and III, on the basis of amount of total hearing loss. There were 13 persons in Category I, 12 in Category II, and 10 in Category III. One person had hearing losses too large to be classified in Category III. (*After ASA Z24-X-2 Report.*[6])

Since temporary threshold shifts occur as indicated above, there arises the question of how much time should elapse between cessation of exposure to noise and the audiometric test. Most indications seem to point to the fact that, for a large majority of industrial noise exposure, a time lapse of 15 to 20 min is sufficient to minimize the effects of short-term recovery. Certainly, where possible, audiometric testing should be done in the early part of the working shift.

In measuring "long-time" recovery, a waiting time following exposure of the order of 48 hr is usually adequate from an industrial point of view. Normally industry is not required to measure "long-time" recovery, as this need arises only when an

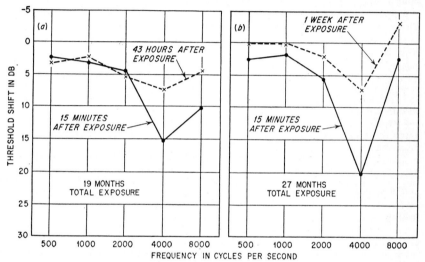

Fig. 7-12. Threshold shifts at five frequencies as a function of the interval of time elapsed between the cessation of exposure and the measurement of hearing loss. Threshold shifts were measured in terms of a control group. The noise to which the people were exposed had sound pressure levels between 90 and 95 db in all octaves below 4,800 cps. Twenty men and women were exposed to the noise for 19 months, 16 of them for 27 months. The mean age of the group was twenty-eight years. For more complete information, see Ref. 13. (*After ASA Z24-X-2 Report.*[6])

employee shows an unusual change in his hearing as judged by repeat audiograms. Such an employee then becomes a special case for study by the medical department. The 48-hr figure is based in part upon the data presented in Figs. 7.11 and 7.12. These data show the amount of recovery measured in two different situations. Figure 7.11 shows the hearing of 36 people 1½ months after cessation of exposure to a noise whose octave-band spectrum is almost uniform. The sound pressure levels in the 300- to 600-cps band and the 1,200- to 2,400-cps band were 93 and 91 db, respectively. Figure 7.11a represents the entire group; b, c, and d represent a division of the group into three categories on the basis of the amount of initial hearing loss. Category I has the smallest initial hearing loss, Category III the largest. The median age is thirty-one years for the entire group, and twenty-seven, thirty-three, and thirty-six years for Categories I, II, and III, respectively. The average exposure of the group was more than 10 years.

On each part of the figure the solid line is the mean audiogram taken 48 hr after the last previous exposure to the noise; the broken line 1½ months after exposure. During this 1½-month period, repairs were made in the part of the plant where the group usually worked, and the group was exposed to noise whose sound pressure levels were about 20 db lower in each octave band. The sound pressure levels of this noise ranged from 70 to 75 db in the octaves between 75 and 4,800 cps.

Figure 7.11b, c, and d shows that greater recovery takes place when the initial hearing loss is small, especially when the people are young.   Category I, which had the smallest initial hearing loss, was also the youngest group.   The pattern of recovery of Category I is not unlike that of Fig. 7.12, and this similarity lends additional support to the conclusion that, as irreversible hearing losses become greater, the amount of reduction in temporary threshold shifts seems to become smaller.

Figure 7.12 presents mean threshold shifts measured at different intervals of time after exposure.   The spectrum of the exposure noise shows sound pressure levels between 90 and 95 db for octaves below 4,800 cps.   The levels in the low and high sorting octaves were 93 and 95 db, respectively.

Figure 7.12a shows the mean audiogram of the group after 19 months of exposure. The audiograms were taken during the working day, about 15 min following the cessation of exposure to noise.   The broken line shows the audiogram of the same group 43 hr later.

Figure 7.12b shows a similar pair of audiograms for the same group exposed to the same noise after the total exposure had been 27 months; the interval between cessation of exposure and test was 1 week.   These young adults (mean age twenty-eight years) with rather small permanent hearing losses showed considerable recovery, especially at the higher frequencies, after a week of rest from the noise.

In both studies (Figs. 7.11 and 7.12) the greatest reduction in threshold shift occurred at 4,000 cps and above.   Below 4,000 cps the average reduction was never more than 5 db.

The Effect of Extreme Low-frequency Noise.   Occasionally there arises a noise situation where the sound pressure levels below 150 cps are greater than 100 db, yet the sound pressure level in the 300- to 600-cps band (the low sorting octave) may be about 80 db or lower.   The only data available covering such an environment are not extensive; however, they do indicate that, for continuous exposures up to 13 years, little permanent loss in hearing has been sustained.   This indicates that the trend curves still appear valid even though the low-frequency sound pressure levels may be above 100 db.   However, if the sound pressure levels below 150 cps reach 110 db or more, caution must be exerted in evaluating the effects of this noise exposure upon hearing.

INTERMITTENT EXPOSURE TO STEADY NOISE

No general relations such as given earlier exist for cases where exposure ceases to be continuous and the noises cease to be steady.   At present only a few isolated cases are available for study and these data are totally inadequate for use in advancing any hypothesis.   These cases are presented here since they may prove beneficial in cases where industrial situations are somewhat similar to the examples shown.   They may also serve as a point from which "educated guesses" may find their foundation.

A study of airline pilots illustrates the effect of intermittent exposure to steady noise. The average hearing losses (corrected for presbycusis) of 446 pilots are plotted in Fig. 7.13 as a function of exposure measured in thousands of air hours.

Figure 7.13a shows mean net hearing losses as a function of exposure time for 2,000, 3,000, and 4,000 cps.   The pilots show closer similarity between the losses at 3,000 and 4,000 cps than between those at 2,000 and 3,000 cps, but the accuracy of these data is questionable.*   It is possible that these pilots had sustained some permanent hearing loss from prior exposure to noise.

Figure 7.13b shows net hearing loss as a function of exposure time for the tenth percentile of the group: only 10 per cent of the pilots had hearing losses equal to or greater than these.   The contrast between this 10 per cent curve and the mean values is clear. Differences of this order of magnitude are not inconsistent with the amount of spread shown in Fig. 7.6.

---

* The relatively large losses at these two frequencies for exposure times shorter than 1,000 hr suggest the possibility that the calibration of the audiometer was in error by about 5 db at 3,000 cps and possibly even at 4,000 cps.   The audiometric tests were made a number of years ago, however, and the calibrations cannot be rechecked.

An average spectrum measured in the pilot's compartment of the airplane that most of the airlines were using at the time the audiograms were taken, a Douglas DC-3, is shown in Fig. 7.13c. This spectrum does not represent the only noise to which the pilots had been exposed. All of them trained on other airplanes, and some probably

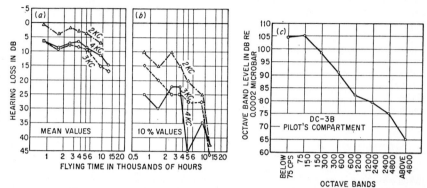

Fig. 7-13. Net hearing loss (corrected for presbycusis) of 446 airline pilots as a function of thousands of hours of flying time. Audiometric data were obtained several hours after exposure to the noise. (a) Mean net hearing loss. (b) Net hearing loss at the tenth percentile; only 10 per cent of the pilots had a larger hearing loss than these 10 per cent values. (c) Average noise spectrum measured in the pilot's compartment of a DC-3B airplane. This spectrum is typical of the ambient noise to which the pilots were exposed for most of the exposure time. (*After ASA Z24-X-2 Report.*[6])

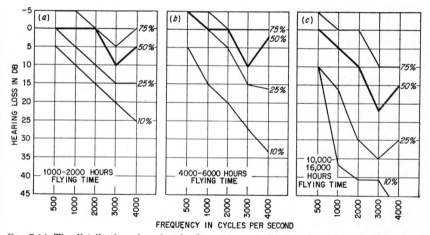

Fig. 7.14. The distribution of net hearing losses (corrected for presbycusis) of airline pilots, as a function of five test frequencies, for different ranges of flying time. The audiograms were taken several hours after exposure to the noise. (*After ASA Z24-X-2 Report.*[6])

had been exposed to noises of quite different character. In addition, they were all exposed to higher noise levels during take-off and to sounds from their communication equipment. The sound pressure levels of these noises are difficult to determine, but these exposures should not be neglected. When these uncertainties are added to the fact that their exposure was intermittent and not on a fixed schedule, it becomes clear that the exposure of the pilots cannot be specified accurately.

Figure 7.14 shows the spread of the audiometric data when the pilots are divided into three groups on the basis of length of exposure. As length of exposure increases, the hearing-loss curves diverge, and this divergence points up individual differences in susceptibility.

A second study of intermittent exposure concerns 132 men who made the final ground check of jet engines before the airplanes left the factory. The airplanes were all in the open and no acoustic protection was provided at the source of the noise. Protection was provided for the ears, however, and all persons near the run-ups were required to wear earplugs. In this plant audiograms had been taken bimonthly for almost 4 years. Workers were transferred if they showed sizable threshold shifts. The number so shifted was less than 1 per cent of the workers so employed, and very few showed any threshold shift whatever.

From these two studies of intermittent exposure to noise one may conclude that intermittency tends to reduce somewhat the hearing losses that occur compared with those which would occur if the exposure were continuous, although there are not enough data to indicate quantitative relationships.

NONSTEADY NOISES

A wide variety of industrial-noise situations encompasses those cases described as intermittent exposure to nonsteady noises. For purpose of analysis, nonsteady noises differ from steady noise chiefly in the practical difficulties encountered in attempts to measure them. The standard sound-level meter has no provision for recording the quick variations in sound pressure associated with nonsteady noise (see Chaps. 16 and 17). In particular, the quick sharp peaks are missed. A high-speed level recorder or an assembly that includes an oscilloscope could overcome these difficulties. But even if an accurate analysis were made of the shape of the spectrum at a given instant, there would still remain the problem of recording the rapid changes of the spectrum from one instant to another. Since the necessary measurements have not yet been standardized, the operation that causes the noise is specified, and no attempt is made to correlate particular aspects of these noises with the hearing losses that result from exposure to them.

Intermittent Exposure: Riveting Noise. Audiometric data have been obtained on a group of people employed in the wing-assembly section of an aircraft factory where the riveting was intermittent, as far as any individual was concerned. The noise level at an employee's ear would rise and fall as a function of the riveting processes. At a riveter's ear the sound pressure levels in octave bands ranged from 91 to 97 db above 150 cps when the person actually was riveting. At a bucker's ear, under conditions of rivet bucking, they ranged from 96 to 107 db in this same frequency range. If riveting was not taking place in the immediate vicinity of a person, the background levels varied from about 82 to 95 db over the frequency range above 150 cps. The background noise was not sufficient in the 300- to 600-cps band (88 db) to produce a significant threshold shift over the exposure time interval from 1 to 6 years. But, in the 1,200- to 2,400-cps band where the sound pressure level was 95 db for the background noise, a significant threshold shift should have been observed just due to the background noise. No significant threshold shift was observed at this frequency, however, because a program of conservation of hearing was in effect, and earplugs were issued to the people in this part of the plant. It appears as if the use of plugs were protecting the ears against hearing loss at 4,000 cps by virtue of reducing the noise above 1,200 cps. Fortunately the background levels in the 300- to 600-cps band were not too high. Apparently the combination of nonsteady noise and this intermittency of exposure combines with the use of earplugs to protect the individual.

Use of Earplugs. If a company is using earplugs or is preparing to initiate a program involving their use, it is worthwhile obtaining audiograms on employees before and after insertion of the plugs. Such measurements give an indication of the effectiveness of the plug. Frequent rechecks of their hearing have in some cases tended to encourage the use of plugs by the employees.

The use of earplugs represents one method of protecting the worker. However, plugs must be well designed and properly fitted to ensure reduction in noise in the 300- to 600-cps band. These levels seem to correlate better with hearing losses at

1,000 and 2,000 cps; hence, to protect the ear from losses at 1,000 and 2,000 cps means that the sound pressure levels in the 300- to 600-cps band, and in neighboring bands, must be reduced. A plug which, to the individual, appears to reduce the loudness and "annoying" effect of the noise, may not be protecting the ear satisfactorily. Thus a plug that reduces the sound pressure levels above 1,000 cps may appear to be serving its purpose but affords only a slight amount of protection against hearing losses below 2,000 cps. Only periodic audiometric measurements or some other procedure which

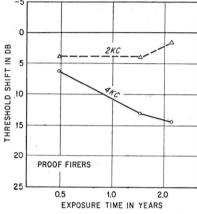

FIG. 7.15. Threshold shifts at three frequencies after exposure to gun noise. Audiometric data were taken approximately 20 min after exposure to the noise. (*After ASA Z24-X-2 Report.*[6])

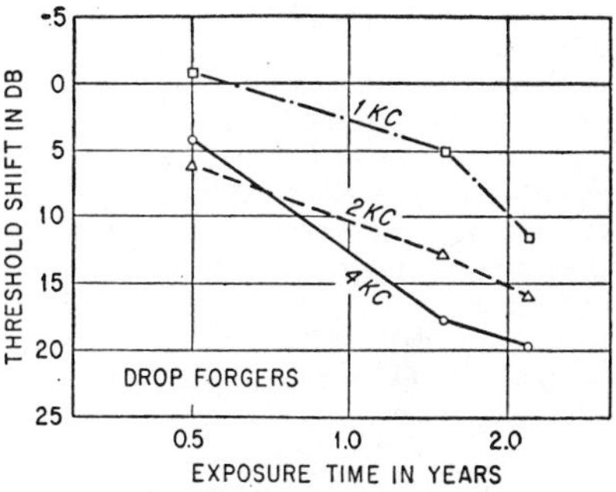

FIG. 7.16. Threshold shifts at three frequencies after exposure to drop-forge noise. Audiometric data were taken approximately 20 min after exposure to the noise. (*After ASA Z24-X-2 Report.*[6])

yields data pertaining to the attenuation afforded by the plug when inserted in a particular person's ear will provide data to assay the effectiveness of that plug in protecting that particular employee from hearing losses. See Chap. 8 for further information on earplugs.

Impulsive Noise: Proof Firing. In the proof-firing room of a gun factory, gun barrels are checked by firing a single supercharged shell through the barrel. The noise thus produced is a nonsteady noise of the kind that is called "impulsive." The proof firers work in a fairly large "live" room, reverberation within which keeps the sound pressure levels from decaying rapidly.

An analysis of the audiometric data taken on these workers is presented in Fig. 7.15. Threshold shifts at 2,000 and 4,000 cps are plotted as a function of exposure time (note the expanded scale of exposure time). There is a measurable threshold shift at 4,000 cps, but at 2,000 cps the data are indecisive.

Impact Noise: Drop Forge. Large drop forges produce peak sound pressures that are above 130 db sound pressure level. The spectrum* of the noise changes so rapidly after the instant of the impact that the spectrum at three different instants of time would have to be presented to give a fair description of the event. A detailed study must be made before it is possible to determine the physical properties of this noise that correlate with hearing loss.

Threshold shifts measured on 35 drop-forge operators are plotted in Fig. 7.16 as a function of exposure time. The threshold shifts appear to increase markedly with exposure time, and, in a period as short as 2 years, sizable shifts have taken place at all three test frequencies.

It should be specifically noted that Figs. 7.15 and 7.16 have "threshold shifts" as their ordinates. Threshold shifts can be obtained only if a program of repeat audiometry is in effect, since the term is defined as the difference between two audiograms.

*See Chap. 17.

If audiograms are taken once a year, then threshold shifts calculated with these audiograms represent the change in threshold occurring within the interval of 1 year. A threshold shift gives no indication as to the absolute value of the hearing loss. If the time interval is no greater than a year, presbycusis effects are normally not considered for frequencies below 2,000 cps.

In working with threshold shifts, the accuracy of audiometric data assumes significance. Present audiometers are normally calibrated in 5-db steps, and operator techniques may easily account for a one-step difference in evaluating thresholds. Thus a difference of as much as 10 db may exist between repeat audiograms that could be due to operational techniques. Unless noise exposures are severe, the expected threshold shifts may well be masked by measurement difficulties. Threshold-shift data primarily are useful where large time intervals exist between initial and final tests, or where exposure is severe, as in the drop-forge case, and threshold shifts are large.

Relation of Threshold Shifts to Initial Audiograms. The question continually arises as to the advisability of assigning a person to a noisy operation if he already has a certain amount of hearing loss. Some people believe that a hearing loss indicates susceptibility to noise exposure, and hence the employee with a hearing loss will lose hearing at a rate greater than the normal rate while others believe that an initial hearing loss may represent the loss of the "tender nerves" in the ear, leaving only the "tough nerves." Data from the Z24-X-2 report[6] indicate that threshold shifts are essentially independent of the absolute value of the initial audiogram, at least for cases of exposure to impulsive and impact noises.

PRESENT STATE OF KNOWLEDGE

The present state of knowledge regarding the relationships of hearing loss to noise exposure leaves much to be desired. There are a great many questions that cannot be answered. On the other hand, there are certain things that can be said with some degree of certainty, and these are the statements summarized here.

In general, the average audiogram resulting from noise exposure shows the least permanent loss of hearing for frequencies below 1,000 cps. Hearing losses increase for frequencies above 1,000 cps until they reach a maximum at approximately 4,000 cps. In many instances the average hearing loss at 6,000 or 8,000 cps is less than it is for 4,000 cps.

The audiogram of noise-exposed employees is not the image of the octave analysis of the noise to which they have been exposed. It is the energy of the noise lying below 1,000 cps which is primarily responsible for producing loss of hearing as judged by speech loss. In fact, it is the sound pressure level in the 300- to 600-cps octave band which seems most useful in evaluating the effect of steady noises upon loss of hearing.

The arithmetic average of the pure-tone hearing losses measured at 500, 1,000, and 2,000 cps, called the "speech average loss," is also approximately the speech reception loss. For this reason it is recommended that the speech average loss be used as the single number representing the severity of the hearing loss. The pure-tone audiogram can be used to estimate the speech reception loss for employees. The use of the term "percentage hearing loss" should be avoided.

If 80 per cent of all employees who are continuously exposed to steady noise are to receive no compensable hearing loss, the sound pressure level in the 300- to 600-cps octave band should be less than 90 db and the exposure time should be less than 3 years. These figures are based upon the Wisconsin Medical Advisory Committee's recommendations. If the noise remains steady, the percentage compensable hearing loss increases logarithmically with exposure time.

Temporary threshold shifts are greatest for normal hearing and may approach 15 db for exposures to noises with octave levels of the order of 100 db. If appreciable hearing loss exists (a "speech average loss" of the order of 20 db or more), temporary threshold shifts are generally on the order of less than 5 db for frequencies below 2,000 cps if the r,oise has octave sound pressure levels less than 100 db. Most of the temporary threshold shift occurs in the first 4 hr of the day's exposure.

Employees vary greatly in their susceptibility to noise exposure. For cases of continuous exposure to steady noises (octave levels less than 100 db), 20 per cent of the employees have hearing losses in excess of two times the average hearing loss of the group. The average employee sustains his hearing loss at a gradual rate with respect to time. Little is known about how rapidly hearing loss increases in the more susceptible employees as a function of time.

Since speech reception loss is the principal guide in evaluating the seriousness of a hearing loss; and since the energy of the noise below 1,000 cps appears to be primarily responsible for producing hearing loss which affects the speech reception loss, the practice of correlating the ability to carry on speech in the noise with the potentiality of the noise to produce speech hearing loss is not necessarily valid. The energy of the noise which masks speech is higher in frequency than the energy of the noise which produces hearing loss for speech.

At present there is no conclusive evidence that temporary threshold shift and permanent hearing loss are related in a one-to-one fashion.

The only accepted way to determine the susceptibility of an employee to noise exposure is to determine the "short-time" threshold shifts by means of repeat audiometry.

For most of the exposures encountered in industry, the average permanent threshold shift of a group of employees due to noise exposure is independent of the average audiogram of the group at the beginning of the exposure. Hence a group of employees with preplacement audiograms showing hearing losses outside the range of normalcy will sustain the same increase in hearing loss (on the average) as will employees with normal preplacement audiograms. The total loss of hearing after years of exposure, however, will be greater for the group who started with some initial hearing loss.

Even though hearing losses for frequencies above 2,000 cps do not affect speech reception, these hearing losses should be measured. Threshold shifts due to noise exposure are generally greater for frequencies above 2,000 cps than are threshold shifts for frequencies below 2,000 cps. Hence repeating audiograms at 4,000 cps is most useful in detecting susceptibility.

All the statements regarding hearing losses and threshold shifts should be considered as applying to both ears. The "Fair" data and the Z24-X-2 data show that the average hearing losses for the right ears of a group are essentially the same as those for the left ears. The Wisconsin Fair[16] data indicate statistically significant differences between the right and left ear; however, these differences are less than about 4 db.

REFERENCES

1. Moos, S.: *Arch. Otolaryngol.*, **9**: 319 (1880).
2. Holt, E. E.: *Trans. Am. Otol. Soc.*, **3**: 34 (1882).
3. Barr, T.: *Proc. Phil. Soc., Glasgow*, **17**: 223 (1886).
4. Habermann, J.: *Arch. Ohrenhlk.*, **30**: 1 (1890).
5. Stevens, S. S., J. C. G. Loring, and D. Cohen: "Bibliography on Hearing," Harvard University Press, Cambridge, Mass., 1953.
6. American Standards Association: "The Relations of Hearing Loss to Noise Exposure," American Standards Association, New York.
7. Rosenblith, W. A.: *J. Acoust. Soc. Amer.*, **13**: 220 (1942).
8. Beranek, L. L.: "Acoustics," p. 416, McGraw-Hill Book Company, Inc., New York, 1954.
9. Kryter, K.D.: *Arch. Ind. Hyg. and Occupational Med.*, **5**: 117 (1952).
10. Hardy, H. C.: *J. Acoust. Soc. Amer.*, **24**: 756 (1952).
11. Sterner, J. H.: *Sch. Publ. Hlth. Inst. Industr. Hlth.*, University of Michigan, Ann Arbor, 1952.
12. Fox, M. S.: *Noise Control*, **1**: 74 (January, 1955).
13. Cox, J. R., R. H. Mansur, and C. R. Williams: *Arch. Ind. Hyg. and Occupational Med.*, **8**: 36 (1953).
14. Steinberg, J. C., H. C. Montgomery, and M. B. Gardner: *J. Acoust. Soc. Amer.*, **12**: 291 (1940).

15. Webster, J. C., H. W. Himes, and M. Lichtenstein: *J. Acoust. Soc. Amer.*, **22**: 473 (1950).
16. Informal communication from A. Glorig.
17. Carhart, R.: *J. Speech Disorders*, **11**: 97 (1946).
18. Fletcher, H.: *J. Acoust. Soc. Amer.*, **22**: 1 (1950).
19. Davis, H.: *Laryngoscope*, **58**: 761 (1948).
20. Quarterly Report No. 6, Subcommittee on Noise in Industry of the Committee on Conservation of Hearing of the American Academy of Ophthalmology and Otolaryngology, Apr. 1 to June 30, 1955, p. 8.
21. Rudmose, W., and A. Glorig: These data are being prepared for publication.
22. Bunch, C. C.: *Arch. Otolaryngol.*, **9**: 625 (1929).

Chapter 8

EAR PROTECTORS

J. Zwislocki, D. Tech. Sci.

Psycho-acoustic Laboratory.   Harvard University

INTRODUCTION

The Need for Ear Protection.   In many industrial and military situations, it is not practical or economical to reduce the noise to levels that present neither hazards to hearing nor annoyance.   In all such situations personal ear protectors are of great value and should be recommended.   They are capable of reducing the noise level at the ear by 10 to 45 db, and occasionally to 50 db, depending on their make and the sound frequency.   A personal ear protector or a combination of personal ear protectors often permits the reduction of noise at the ear, if not to a pleasant level, at least to a harmless one.

Ear protectors can also improve speech communication.   The widespread belief that ear protectors impair hearing acuity holds true only in a quiet environment where ear protectors are not usually necessary.   At noise levels justifying their use, they not only do not impair hearing acuity but may even improve it.   A possible exception is an intermittent noise with periods of silence between the bursts of noise.

Kinds of Ear Protectors.   Ear protectors can be divided into four categories according to their position relative to the ear: earplugs, semi-inserts, earmuffs, and helmets.

Earplugs are inserted into the ear canal and usually remain there without any additional means of support.   *Semi-inserts* close the entrance to the ear canal without being inserted into it and are supported by a headband.   They have not been used generally as ear protectors, but rather as part of an earphone system.   Usually they carry a small receiver of the hearing-aid type at the outer end.   Nevertheless they can provide high sound attenuation.   *Earmuffs* cover the entire outer ear in much the same way as an earphone mounted in an earphone socket (cushion).   They may be held in place by a headband or a helmet, or they may be a part of some other head covering.   *Helmets* cover most of the head surface.   They are not commonly used for ear protection alone; usually they combine this function with protection of the head against cold or injury.   They may act also as a support for earphones or earmuffs.

Figure 8.1 shows examples of the four basic kinds of ear protectors.   Each has advantages and disadvantages compared with the others.

Earplugs, when correctly inserted, provide high sound attenuation, are unobtrusive, and do not interfere with head covers, masks, goggles, or other devices worn on the head.   Because they are small, they can be carried in a pocket.   Earplugs are the least expensive ear protectors.   On the debit side, they are often uncomfortable and may cause pain in the auditory canal, or even, in the extreme case, inflammation, especially in a tropical climate.   The variability in shape and size of ear canals makes a good fit difficult and usually necessitates several sizes.   This in turn complicates the production and distribution of earplugs and introduces the possibility of incorrect selection. As a consequence, the performance of earplugs is likely to be highly variable.[5,23,34]

Semi-inserts have some of the advantages of earmuffs and earplugs and some of their disadvantages. One size can provide high sound attenuation and a satisfactory fit for almost any person. Comfort is not a critical problem. The semi-insert is smaller than the earmuff and interferes less with other devices worn on the head. However, like the earmuff, it requires a means of support, and for this reason it is more cumbersome than an earplug.[22]

Earmuffs need be made in only one size, and their shape is less critical than that of an earplug. Almost anyone can be fitted satisfactorily with little difficulty. For this reason the variability of performance is smaller and the problem of comfort less critical.[5,34] Earmuffs have several disadvantages, however. Their average sound attenuation for frequencies under 1,000 cps is usually lower than that of earplugs.[5,8,9,27,28,40,43] Together with their means of support, they are rather large and cumbersome and conflict with almost everything else worn on the head. Their price is high compared with earplugs.

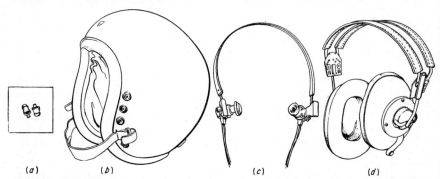

Fig. 8.1. The four kinds of ear protectors: *a*, earplugs; *b*, helmet; *c*, semi-insert; *d*, earmuffs.

Helmets are the largest and usually the most expensive of all ear protectors. They have to be made in several sizes. At present their acoustic action does not seem to improve significantly the effectiveness of earmuffs. For these reasons, the use of helmets for the purpose of ear protection alone does not seem justified. However, a helmet can be very practical as an ear protector when it performs some other function at the same time, as is mentioned above. The acoustic importance of the helmet may increase when sound attenuation at the ear reaches such a high level that transmission through the skull becomes a controlling factor. In this situation a helmet covering the greater part of the head can introduce additional transmission loss.[8,9]

Basic Requirements for Ear Protectors. Every ear protector, irrespective of type, must comply with the requirements of (1) sound attenuation, (2) comfort, and (3) absence of adverse effect on the skin. In addition there are three other requirements whose importance depends on the conditions of use: (4) conservation of speech intelligibility, (5) ease of handling, and (6) durability.

1. The first requirement, sound attenuation, is obvious. It determines the amount of protection of the ear. The degree of sound attenuation necessary depends on the sound pressure, the kind of noise, and the duration of exposure. The exact nature of these interrelations is still obscure, but it can be stated quite generally that the amount of sound attenuation provided by an ear protector should be sufficient to keep the noise level below the safety limit whenever such limit has been established (see Chap. 7). The ear protector will not always be capable of attaining this limit. Even the best ear protectors do not attenuate more than 25 to 35 db on the average, while an attenuation of 40 to 50 db may be advisable under some circumstances.

2. Although comfort may appear to be a secondary requirement at first glance, it must be realized that an uncomfortable ear protector becomes intolerable after prolonged wear and has to be removed. Consequently, it becomes useless even if it provides a high initial sound attenuation. The annoyance produced by noise of very high sound pressure to some extent masks the discomfort caused by ear protectors. Consequently the requirement of comfort is most acute in a noise of moderate sound pressure, where ear protectors are used for psychological rather than for physiological reasons, for example, to eliminate the distraction caused by irregular noise, or to facilitate sleep.

3. A third factor, which in itself justifies discarding otherwise satisfactory ear protectors, is a toxic effect on the skin. An ear protector may lead to inflammations that cannot be controlled except by discontinuing its use. Fortunately nontoxicity is the easiest requirement to fulfill.[23,32]

4. Whenever the noise level is low enough to permit speech communication, the acoustic performance of the ear protector should be such as to assure the highest possible speech intelligibility. In a continuous noise, speech is most intelligible when the ear protector has a flat frequency characteristic.[13,17,23] But for intermittent noises special devices have been developed.[5,18,37,38]

5. Ear protectors are effective only when used correctly. This is more easily achieved when their application is simple. If they are difficult to handle, the probability of incorrect use increases, and with it the variability of their performance.

6. The durability of an ear protector is an economic factor and becomes important when large quantities are purchased. In general, more durable devices are more economical in the long run. This is especially true of the more expensive ear protectors, such as earmuffs and helmets.

SOUND ATTENUATION AT THE EAR

Factors Determining Sound Attenuation. Ear protectors are older than the present century. But only since World War II have they been investigated systematically in the laboratory. This has resulted in a better understanding of the way they work, how best to use them, and what can be expected of them, and has speeded up their improvement.

The factors determining the sound attenuation provided by ear protectors are now fairly well known.

The ear protector introduces an insertion loss between the sound source and the eardrum of the listener. This is accomplished first by a change in the sound field and, second, by transmission loss between the outer and inner surfaces of the ear protector. The first factor is usually considered negligible, although for large units, such as helmets, this may not be quite obvious. The second factor, the transmission loss, can be defined here as the ratio of the sound pressure at the inner surface of the ear protector to the sound pressure at its outer surface p_i/p_o.

Even with the best ear protector, external sound cannot be excluded completely from the ear. Acoustic vibrations are transmitted not only through the ear canal but also through the skull (bone conduction). If an ideal helmet were used, acoustic vibrations would be transmitted through the rest of the body (Fig. 8.2). These secondary pathways are very ineffective, however, and the exclusion of sound transmission through the ear canal should afford sufficient protection in most situations.[1,2,4,8,9,40]

Sound transmission to the "protected" ear can be illustrated by an electrical network analogous to the mechanical system.[8,9,36,37,40] One such circuit is shown in Fig. 8.2b. The electrical analogy does not, of course, represent the acoustic situation exactly, and its validity is limited to frequencies that are not too high, but it helps to make clear what is happening.

Any ear protector, irrespective of its type, can transmit sound in three ways: (1) through air leaks, (2) by propagation through its material, and (3) through the vibration of the whole device as a rigid body. This last pathway depends critically on the mechanical properties of the layer of flesh that separates the ear protector from the bony structure of the head. These properties, together with sound conduction through the body and the skull, control the sound attenuation at the ear.[8,9,40]

It can be seen from Fig. 8.2 that sound attenuation depends not only on the impedance of the ear protector, but also on the impedance behind it.[8,9,36,37,40,43]

Earplug System.[8,9,44] Figure 8.3a shows schematically an earplug secured in the auditory canal. The attenuation it provides can be deduced from the analogous

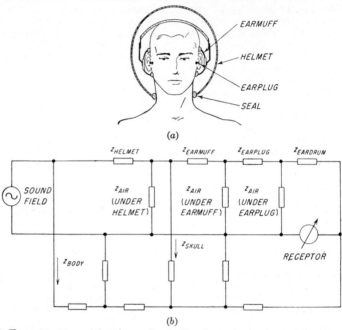

(a)

(b)

FIG. 8.2. Ear protectors on the human head: (a) schematic representation; (b) analogous electrical network, showing sound transmission to the ear through the three ear protectors, the skull, and the body. Z = impedance.

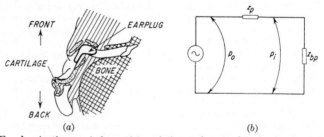

(a)   (b)

FIG. 8.3. Earplug in the ear (schematic) and the analogous electric circuit of the system

circuit of Fig. 8.3b and is given by the equation

$$\frac{p_i}{p_o} = \frac{Z_{bp}}{Z_p + Z_{bp}} \tag{8.1}$$

The impedance behind the earplug Z_{bp} is produced by the compliance of the air cushion between the earplug and the eardrum, in parallel with the impedance of the eardrum coupled to the mechanisms of the middle and inner ear (Fig. 8.4). The impedance presented by the eardrum can be approximated for frequencies below

2,000 cps by a damped resonator with a natural frequency of approximately 1,300 cps. The air volume between the earplug and the eardrum amounts to about 0.5 cu cm with a cross-sectional area of 0.5 sq cm.

The impedance of the earplug itself can be represented by three branches[8,9,44] (Fig. 8.4) symbolizing (1) air leakage between the earplug and the wall of the ear canal (m_l, R_l), (2) sound transmission through deformation of the earplug $(Z_{material})$, and (3) vibration of the earplug as a rigid body caused by the flexibility of the skin lining the auditory canal (m_p, C_s, R_s). Of these three pathways of sound transmission, air leaks and deformation can be effectively eliminated.

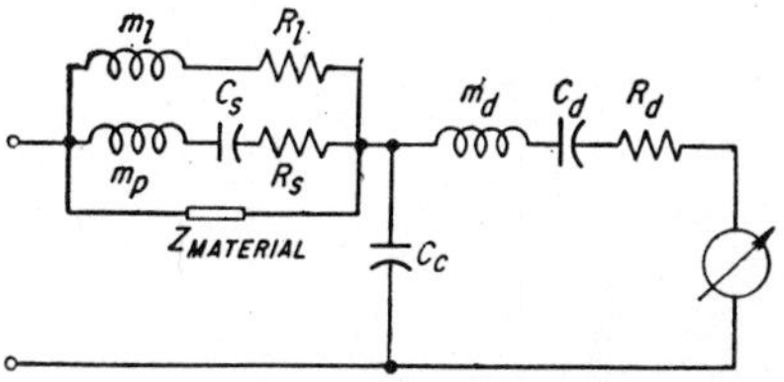

Air leakage decreases the attenuation at the ear for low frequencies and, if large enough, can nullify it almost completely.[9,23,37] Figure 8.5 shows the effect of an experimental air leak produced with a cylindrical tube 0.15 cm in diameter and 1 cm long.[37] For comparison, a curve calculated for a leak 0.05 cm in diameter and 2 cm long is also included.[9]

When an earplug consists of a hollow body made of a soft resilient material, sound transmission through the material may be considerable. Figure 8.6 demonstrates the improvement in sound attenuation produced by filling such a plug with compact cotton wool.[42]

In contrast to the two other channels of sound transmission, the vibration of the

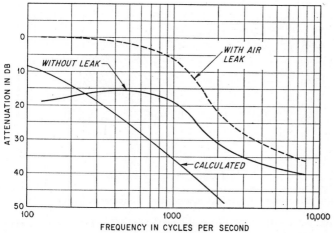

FIG. 8.4. Analogous electrical network of the earplug in the ear (detailed). m_l and R_l = mass and resistance of an acoustic leak, respectively; m_p = mass of the earplug; C_s and R_s = compliance and resistance of the skin lining the auditory meatus; $Z_{material}$ = impedance for sound transmission through deformations of the earplug; C_c = compliance of air volume enclosed between earplug and eardrum; m_d, C_d, R_d = impedance components of the eardrum.

earplug as a rigid body cannot be eliminated, because the flexibility of the skin lining is an anatomical constant. The impedance of the best earplug one can make is shown, therefore, by the middle branch of the circuit in Fig. 8.4 (m_p, C_s, R_s). Numerical

FIG. 8.5. Effect of an air leak on attenuation provided by earplugs. The broken line shows the attenuation obtained experimentally with a cylindrical leak 1 mm in diameter and 2 cm long.[37] The continuous line was calculated for a leak 0.05 cm in diameter and 2 cm long.[8,9]

values established for one earplug, the V-51R (unfortunately on only one subject)[9] give: mass of the earplug $m_p = 0.5$ g, skin compliance $C_s = 2.06 \times 10^{-7}$ cm per dyne, skin resistance $R_s = 4.4 \times 10^3$ dyne sec per cm.

With the help of the values for the impedance behind the earplug and for the impedance of an earplug moving as a rigid body, the sound attenuation at the ear can be calculated.[8,9,44]   The result is shown by the solid curve in Fig. 8.7.[44]   The shaded area indicates the attenuation limit set by bone conduction; the broken lines indicate the attenuation actually obtained by some of the most effective earplugs[23,30,32] under laboratory conditions.   This attenuation can be improved somewhat by increasing the inertia of the earplug.   Experience shows, however, that this is impractical because

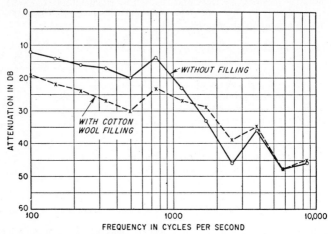

FIG. 8.6. Improvement in sound attenuation produced by filling a hollow earplug of soft elastic material with compact cotton wool.[42]

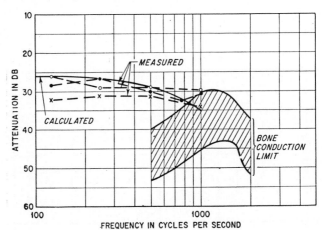

FIG. 8.7. Calculated maximum attenuation curve for earplugs[44] and the highest attenuation measured for three different earplugs (averages of a number of listeners).[23,32,42]

making the mass a little larger does not help much,[8,9,42] and too large a mass decreases comfort.

Acoustically, *semi-inserts* behave much like earplugs, and the electrical and mathematical models of the earplug system are applicable to them.   Only the numerical values must be changed.   Unfortunately, pertinent data are lacking.

Earmuff System.[8,9,43]   A pair of earmuffs in its position of use is shown schematically in Fig. 8.8 together with the electrical network analogous to the mechanical system of one earmuff.   The attenuation at the ear is described by an equation similar to the one that applies to the earplug. It gives the ratio of sound pressures at the inner and outer sides of the earmuff

$$\frac{p_i}{p_o} = \frac{S_o}{S_i} \frac{Z_{bm}}{Z_m + Z_{bm}}$$

(8.2)

where S_o is the "outer effective area" approximately equal to the portion of the head surface delimited by the outer rim of the sealing cushion; S_i is the "inner effective area" delimited on the head by the inner rim of the sealing cushion; Z_m is the impedance of the earmuff; and Z_{bm} is the impedance behind the earmuff. The equation shows that, in order to have a high sound attenuation (small p_i/p_o), S_o/S_i and Z_m must be as large as possible and Z_{bm} as small as possible.

A small S_o/S_i means a narrow sealing cushion. Too narrow a cushion is uncomfortable, however, and increases the probability of an air leak. The average value for S_o/S_i seems to lie around 2.

The components of Z_m are shown in Fig. 8.8. The branch m_l, R_l represents an air leak; $Z_{material}$ symbolizes the impedance presented to acoustic waves penetrating

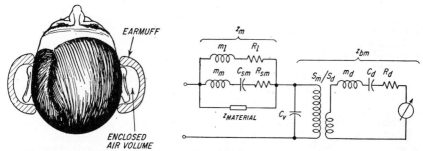

FIG. 8.8. Schematic representation of the earmuffs on the head and the analogous electrical network of the earmuff system. Z_m = impedance of the earmuff; Z_{bm} = impedance behind the earmuff; m_l, R_l = mass and resistance of an air leak; m_m = mass of earmuff; C_{sm}, R_{sm} = impedance components of the flesh and the sealing cushion; $Z_{material}$ = impedance for sound transmission through deformations of the earmuff; C_v = compliance of air volume enclosed under earmuff; s_m/s_d = ratio of the area delimited on the head by the sealing cushion and the cross-sectional area of the auditory meatus; m_d, C_d, R_d = impedance components at the eardrum.

through the earmuff by way of its deformation, and m_m, C_{sm}, R_{sm} the impedance due to the vibration of the earmuff as a rigid piston.

Leakage between the sealing cushion and the skin must be avoided because, as with the earplug, it decreases sound attenuation at low frequencies. When a substantial attenuation is required above 100 cps, an eventual air leak should not exceed 0.03 cm in diameter for an air volume enclosed under the earmuff of 5 cu cm, and should stay below 0.25 cm when the volume amounts to 300 cu cm. These values are given on the assumption of an air passage 0.5 cm long.[40,43]

Sound transmission by way of deformation of the earmuff, i.e., through the material of the earmuff, is more difficult to control than sound transmission through the material of an earplug. The difficulties stem from the earmuff's much larger surface. Theoretically, this transmission channel could be eliminated by making the earmuff of a rigid material. The whole earmuff cannot be made rigid, however, because it must adapt to the contours of the head surface around the ear. At the least, the part of the earmuff designed to provide a tight seal around the ear must be highly compliant. Sound transmission through this compliant layer can be decreased by using a material with high internal viscosity.[40] If the viscosity is not sufficiently high, the attenuation is decreased for all frequencies except for a frequency range in which an antiresonance occurs. Interaction between the compliance of the soft part and the inertia of the rigid part of the earmuff causes this antiresonance. These considerations apply to

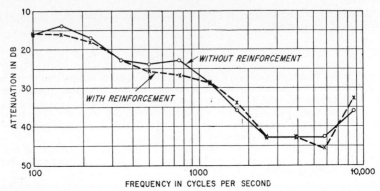

FIG. 8.9. Improvement in sound attenuation of an earphone socket as a result of metal reinforcement of its shell.[41]

earphone sockets as well as earmuffs.[40,43] Figure 8.9 shows the effect of reinforcing a bulky but flexible earphone socket with a metal plate.[40]

Sound transmission due to vibration of the earmuff as a rigid piston cannot be decreased below a limit set by the flexibility of the flesh lining of the skull and the maximum mass of earmuff that is compatible with comfort. Under the most favorable circumstances, sound attenuation provided by devices such as earmuffs or earphone sockets is determined by the middle branch of the circuit in Fig. 8.8. When the mechanical impedance of the cushion is high, the influence of its compliance is negligible; therefore C_{sm} represents the compliance of the flesh lining alone. High impedance can be achieved by filling a hollow cushion that has soft elastic walls with a highly viscous material (putty or wax) that is malleable at body temperature[41,43] (Fig. 8.10). Such a cushion has a high impedance through its resistive component and at the same time adapts easily to the contours of the side of the head. Experiments reveal that the mechanical compliance of the flesh lining presented to the earmuff is of the order of 3×10^{-9} cm per dyne.[43] This value seems to agree with direct impedance measurements on the head.[2,7]

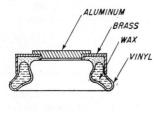

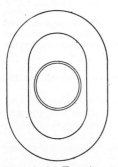

FIG. 8.10. Experimental earmuff HZM-9-A which consists of a rigid earphone socket with a soft hollow cushion filled with wax (CZM-7). The earphone has been replaced by an aluminum plug.[43]

When the sealing cushion is soft and has a low internal viscosity (for instance, sponge rubber), its compliance adds to the compliance of the flesh lining,[40] and the resulting compliance can be half or even a smaller fraction of C_{sm}. The compliance of the flesh lining controls the attenuation at low frequencies, and the mass of the earmuff is the determining factor above the resonance frequency which usually lies around 200 cps. For comfort, however, the weight of an earmuff must be limited to approximately 200 grams.[40]

The last factor to be discussed in connection with the sound attenuation provided by earmuffs is the impedance behind the earmuff (Z_{bm} in Fig. 8.8).[40,43] As Eq. (8.2) shows, sound attenuation is inversely proportional to Z_{bm} when the impedance of the earmuff itself is sufficiently large.

The impedance behind the earmuff consists mainly in the air volume enclosed behind the earmuff. This volume is usually large enough to make negligible the effect on the

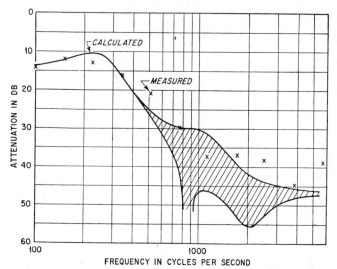

FREQUENCY IN CYCLES PER SECOND

FIG. 8.11. Sound attenuation provided by earmuff of Fig. 8.10. The shaded area corresponds to indeterminate attenuation because of unknown phase relation between sound transmitted through the earmuff and sound transmitted through the skull.[43]

middle ear (eardrum). The mechanical impedance of an air-filled enclosure is inversely proportional to the volume of the enclosure and directly proportional to the square of the cross-sectional area of the opening leading to it. In simple earmuffs this "effective area" is determined by S_i. Consequently, in order to obtain high sound attenuation at the ear (small Z_{bm}), the earmuff should enclose a large air volume but should have a small S_i. This leads to a deep earmuff. The area S_i is limited by the dimensions of the pinna.

In earmuffs available commercially, the enclosed air volume varies between 25 and 300 cu cm and the inside effective area S_i between 25 and 40 sq cm. Thus mechanical compliance of the air volume lies within the limits 1×10^{-8} and 3×10^{-7} cm per dyne.

Commercial earphone sockets enclose an air volume of 5 to 25 cu cm and have an S_i of 15 to 40 sq cm. The mechanical compliance of the air they enclose varies between 1×10^{-8} and 1.5×10^{-8} cm per dyne.

Figure 8.10 shows a small experimental earmuff consisting of a brass shell and a hollow sealing cushion with elastic walls, filled with wax malleable at body temperature.[43] The hard shell together with the high internal viscosity of the sealing cushion ensures that the earmuff vibrates as a rigid piston and that the factors determining its impedance are reduced to the compliance and resistance of the skin and to the mass of the earmuff. The enclosed air volume amounts to about 24 cu cm and $S_i = 24$ sq cm.

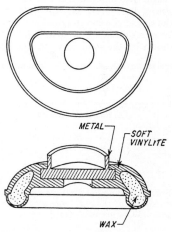

FIG. 8.12. Experimental earmuff consisting of a Grason-Stadler earphone socket (CZW-6), with the earphone replaced by a brass plug of equal weight.

The mass is 150 grams. The curve and the shaded area of Fig. 8.11 give attenuation values calculated on the basis of Eq. (8.2), and the crosses the values measured. The agreement is good below 1,000 cps, where the assumption of long waves compared with the linear dimensions of the ear-

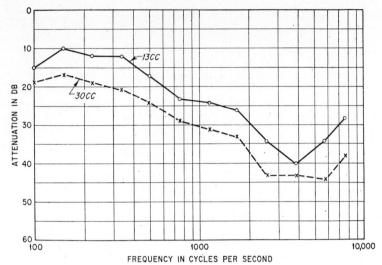

FIG. 8.13. Attenuation provided by the earmuff of Fig. 8.12 with two different volumes of air enclosed.

muffs holds true. The shaded area represents the uncertainty due to the unknown phase relation between the sound transmitted through the earmuff and the sound transmitted by bone conduction.[43]

The sound attenuation provided by an earphone socket depends on the impedance of the earphone mounted in it. Figure 8.12 shows a small circumaural socket consisting of soft resilient vinylite surrounding a core of viscous material. In the figure, the socket contains a metal plug instead of earphones. In this condition the enclosed air space amounts to about 14 cu cm, and the socket provides the sound attenuation shown by the solid curve in Fig. 8.13. Replacing the metal plug by a PDR-10 earphone of the same weight increases the sound attenuation by about 7 db (broken line). The addition of the PDR-10 earphone seems to have approximately the same effect as an addition of 15 cu cm of air volume. Static measurements confirm that behind its diaphragm the PDR-10 earphone contains a cavity of this order of magnitude.

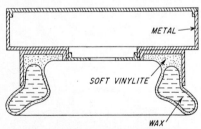

FIG. 8.14. Experimental earmuff HZM-9-B consisting of the earphone socket CZW-7 and a 50 cu cm resonator.[43]

Earmuffs tend to attenuate high-frequency sound more than low frequencies. This effect can be diminished by adding one or more Helmholtz resonators.[43] One assembly shown in Fig. 8.14 (HZM-9-B) consists of the HZM-9-A earmuff and a resonator with 50 cu cm of air volume and an opening 1 cm in diameter. The solid line of Fig. 8.15 gives the sound attenuation obtained with this device. The addition of a second resonator, in series with the first but tuned to a lower frequency, changed the attenuation characteristic to that shown by the broken curve. Finally, the dotted line reproduces the attenuation curve obtained with the earphone socket of Fig. 8.14, with the earphone replaced by an insert containing four resonators in series. The total air volume enclosed by this device amounts to 109 cu cm. It follows from Fig. 8.15 that resonators can affect substantially the attenuation provided by earmuffs and make possible a better adaptation of the attenuation characteristic to the conditions of use.

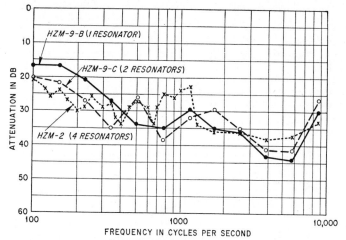

FIG. 8.15. Attenuation curves of three earmuffs equipped with different numbers of resonators connected in series.[43]

Earplug-Earmuff Combination. Sometimes, in order to obtain maximum sound attenuation in extremely strong noise, earmuffs are worn in addition to earplugs. The acoustical action of such a system follows from the analogous electric circuit of Fig. 8.16. The attenuation provided by the earmuff is given by the following equation:

$$A_m = \frac{Z_v(Z_p + Z_{bp})}{Z_m(Z_p + Z_{bp} + Z_v) + Z_v(Z_p + Z_{bp})} \tag{8.3}$$

which simplifies to

$$A_m = \frac{Z_v}{Z_m + Z_v} \tag{8.4}$$

because $Z_p \gg Z_{bp} \gg Z_v$. Thus the sound attenuation provided by the earmuff is practically independent of the earplug. The attenuation provided by the earplug follows from

$$A_p = \frac{Z_{bp}}{Z_p + Z_{bp}} \tag{8.5}$$

and is independent of the earmuff. Therefore, the total attenuation A should amount to

$$A = A_m \times A_p \tag{8.6}$$

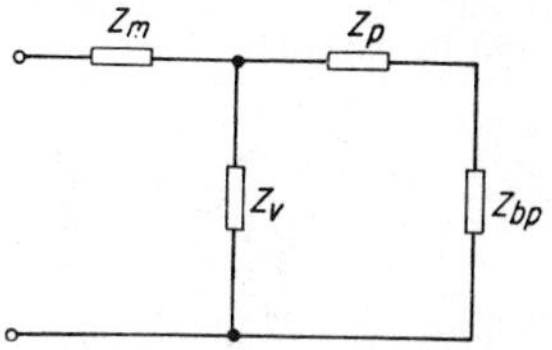

FIG. 8.16. Electrical analogous network of earplug and earmuff combination. Z_m = impedance of earmuff; Z_v = impedance of air volume enclosed under the earmuff; Z_p = impedance of earplug; Z_{bp} = impedance behind the earplug.

If A_m and A_p are expressed in decibels, denoted by A_m' and A_p' respectively, then the total attenuation of the combination, expressed in decibels, A' is given by an equivalent expression

$$A' = A_m' + A_p' \tag{8.7}$$

If an earmuff attenuates 20 db and an earplug 25 db, the total attenuation might be expected to be 45 db. Experiments show, however, that simple addition does not occur and that the total is appreciably less. Figure 8.17 shows this discrepancy.[8,9] At the present time no explanation is generally accepted. At least three possibilities must be taken into consideration: (1) sound may reach the ear through the mouth and the Eustachian tube (sound attenuation of earplugs of high quality seems to decrease somewhat when the mouth is open); (2) the level of sound transmission through the skull may be reached; and (3) the vibration of the earmuff may be transmitted to the earplug through the flesh lining and the cartilaginous structures of the outer ear.

Bone Conduction.[1,2,4] Because there have been some differences in interpretation of the term "bone conduction," it is defined, for the purposes of this chapter, as an acoustical transmission channel to the inner ear that involves vibration of the bony structures other than the ossicles of the middle ear. There seem to be three channels of bone conduction: (1) the elastic deformation of the skull leading to deformations of the middle and inner ear; (2) the vibration of the skull as a rigid body, producing

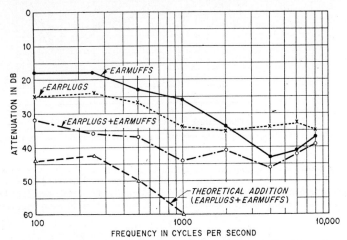

Fig. 8.17. Measured attenuation curves of: (1) earplugs; (2) earmuffs; (3) earplugs and earmuffs together; (4) theoretical addition of attenuations in decibels provided by earplugs and by earmuffs.[8,9]

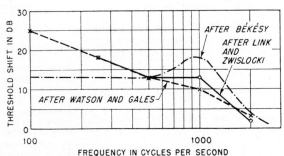

Fig. 8.18. Improvement of bone conduction caused by the closure of the auditory meatus by an earplug.[4,14,31]

inertia displacements in the middle and inner ear; and (3) the relative movement between the skull and the lower jaw.[1,2,4] This movement causes vibration of the cartilage of the auditory canal, and in this way air-borne sound is produced which reaches the inner ear through the eardrum. This transmission channel is often called the "osseotympanic" pathway. This becomes important when the ear is closed by an earplug or earmuff and sound generated by the deformation of the ear canal cannot radiate into the surrounding air. Thus closure of the external ear increases bone conduction. The effect of earplugs on bone conduction is shown in Fig. 8.18.[2,14,31] It is similar for small earmuffs and earphone sets, but it decreases as the enclosed volume increases.

The ratio between bone conduction and air transmission of sound into the ear can be regarded as the upper limit of sound insulation at the ear that is provided by earplugs and earmuffs. It is usually defined as the ratio of the relative thresholds of hearing in an acoustic free field. Unfortunately, this ratio has not yet been measured with sufficient precision; only crude estimates are available which have been deduced from indirect measurements. Figure 8.19 shows the uncertainty that exists. The figure presents two different ratios of bone to air transmission as a function of frequency, each determined by the same author but by two different methods.[4] The dots in Fig. 8.19 indicate the highest attenuation values that were obtained at the ear in tests made in the acoustic free field.[44] Resonators with semi-inserts were used in

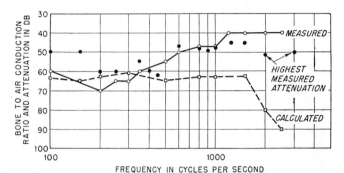

FIG. 8.19. Bone to air conduction ratio obtained for open ears by two different procedures.[4] The dots represent highest attenuation values obtained at the ear when resonators were used.

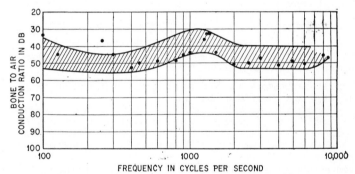

FIG. 8.20. Bone to air conduction ratio when the ears are closed by earplugs. The width of the band indicates the scatter of data. The dots represent the highest attenuation values obtained with an earplug-earmuff combination.

these tests. They gave maximum attenuation at their natural frequency. Except for the frequency range below 200 cps these attenuation maxima agree approximately with the measured bone conduction.

When the ears are closed with earplugs or are covered with earmuffs that have no resonators or other sound-absorbing devices, the bone conduction to air transmission ratio is shifted in accordance with the curves of Fig. 8.18. In this situation the limit of sound attenuation set by bone conduction can be expected to lie in the band shown in Fig. 8.20, which has been determined from the data of reference.[2,4,9,14,31,40] The dots of Fig. 8.20 are actual maximum attenuation values obtained with the earplug-earmuff combination under optimal laboratory conditions.[9,40,44]

Expected Limits of Sound Attenuation at the Ear. The ratio between bone conduction and air transmission of sound into the ear constitutes the absolute limit of acoustic insulation at the ear for earplugs and earmuffs. By excluding the direct transmission from the surrounding air to the skull, an ideal helmet could improve the sound attenuation by 5 to 10 db. The only channel left then is sound conduction through the body.[8,9] As Fig. 8.19 indicates, it is possible to reach the absolute limit of bone conduction, i.e., with the ears free, by using ear protectors containing sound-absorptive devices. Such ear protectors are still in the experimental stage, however. For the present, a more realistic attenuation limit is shown by the shaded band of Fig. 8.20. Experience shows that even this limit is extremely difficult to attain, especially at frequencies below 700 cps. Here the impedance of the flesh lining of the auditory canal or around the ear and the mass of the ear protector determine the highest sound attenuation that can be obtained with earplugs or earmuffs without imperiling comfort. Figure 8.21 shows the practical attenuation limits predicted for earplugs, earphone sets, and earmuffs without resonators.[8,9,40,43,44] Above 500 to 800 cps these limits merge with the bone-conduction limit of Fig. 8.20.

Sound Attenuation vs. Speech Communication. The problem of speech communication in noise is treated extensively in Chap. 9; certain aspects of this problem are closely connected with ear protectors.

Three different situations can be distinguished: a signal can be transmitted (1) through an earphone with the sound-attenuating device outside the path of the signal;

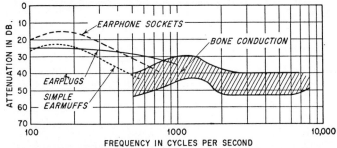

Fig. 8.21. Upper limit of sound attenuation at the ear provided by earplugs, earphone sockets, and earmuffs without resonators.[40,43,44]

(2) through an earphone when at least part of the ear protector is in the path of the signal; or (3) through the surrounding air.

The first situation occurs when an earphone mounted in a tightly sealing socket acts as an ear protector. Under such circumstances speech intelligibility is best when the noise attenuation is the highest possible, because the signal-to-noise ratio improves proportionally with the attenuation. A sound-excluding helmet would constitute added protection.

The second situation occurs when an earplug is added. The earplug decreases the sound pressure level of both the noise and the signal about equally. When attenuation of the signal can be compensated by increasing the signal level in the receiver the signal-to-noise ratio improves, and with it the speech intelligibility.[24] When the maximum output of the receiver has been reached, however, further improvement of the signal-to-noise ratio becomes impossible. Articulation scores show that even then speech intelligibility improves as long as the speech level does not fall below about 75 db. In practice such a reduction of the speech level is unlikely, since a signal level can be as high as 110 db and earplugs do not attenuate more than 30 to 35 db. Consequently, wearing earplugs under earphones is always beneficial in a continuous loud noise.[13]

When the signal is transmitted through the surrounding air, both signal and noise are always affected by the ear protector. The signal-to-noise ratio cannot be improved substantially. It follows from experiments that the attenuation of both speech and noise does not affect communication adversely so long as the speech remains above about 75 db at the ear. At noise levels above 85 db, the speech may be more intelligible.[13]

The conditions are somewhat different in intermittent noise when the intervals between the bursts of noise are long enough to permit substantial recovery of hearing.[16] Especially when the bursts are short, speech intelligibility may be far better than when the noise is continuous, and ear protectors may decrease the intelligibility by impairing the hearing during the quiet periods. In order to overcome this difficulty, ear protectors have been devised with selective sound attenuation. Some have been designed to act as valves and cut down excessive amplitudes of sound pressure without affecting the speech waves, although their effectiveness has not been proved.[5,18] Others act as acoustic resonators or low-pass filters, which attenuate the most harmful and annoying frequencies above 1,000 cps but let the lower frequencies through.[15,20,37,39] It has been shown that such devices permit better speech intelligibility in quiet than do ear protectors that attenuate all speech frequencies by approximately equal amounts. Some of these selective earplugs have been found to provide adequate protection in most situations involving noise.[38] They are particularly effective against gun blast.[20]

COMFORT AND OTHER REQUIREMENTS

Pressure. Pressure exercised by an ear protector on the skin is the most direct cause of discomfort. If the pressure is strong and continues for a relatively long period of time, the pain may become intolerable. Two factors are involved, the total force with which the ear protector is pressed against the skin, and the distribution of the pressure.

The total force exercised by an earplug results from the ratio between its cross-sectional dimensions and the corresponding dimensions of the ear canal. A small earplug is more comfortable than a large one. The pressure exercised by earmuffs and semi-inserts varies proportionally with the force applied by their supporting means. A helmet creates a more complicated situation and the total force depends partly on size, partly on weight.

When the total force is distributed over a large area, the resulting pressure is smaller than when it is concentrated on a few spots. For this reason an earplug shaped to fit the contours of the auditory canal and made of a soft material that permits individual adaptation is much more comfortable than a poorly shaped or hard one. The same is true for the sealing cushion of an earmuff or a semi-insert. In order to ensure a large area of contact with the skin, earmuffs and semi-inserts should not only be of a size and shape compatible with the anatomy, but they should also be made of a soft material.

When the area of contact between the ear protector and the skin is large, the total force acting on the flesh lining must be limited to a value that permits proper circulation of the blood.

A certain amount of pressure on the skin is necessary to hold the ear protector in place and to provide sound attenuation. As the pressure diminishes, the impedance of the skin decreases and the vibration of the ear protector as a rigid body increases. With too little pressure air leaks may be created.

It is difficult to specify the maximum pressure acceptable for earplugs. Experience shows that, on the average, three to five sizes are sufficient to fit most ears. The largest size that can be tolerated affords the maximum sound attenuation. Earmuffs should be applied against the sides of the head with a force varying between 500 and 1,000 grams.[23] Pressure on the very sensitive pinna should be avoided as far as possible. Pressure limits have not yet been specified for semi-inserts but pressure just sufficient to hold the semi-insert in place seems to provide adequate sound attenuation.

Weight. The weight of an ear protector affects comfort directly because the force of gravity presses the device against the skin, and indirectly because the force required to hold the device in place increases as the weight increases. The following weights are suggested: an earplug should weigh on the order of 1 to 5 grams, an earmuff or an earphone mounted in a socket below 200 grams, and a semi-insert assembly around 15 grams. Too little weight is not good since sound attenuation becomes lower as the weight decreases.

Temperature. Ambient temperature can affect both the acoustic performance and the comfort of an ear protector. Some materials, such as waxes, become very soft at high temperatures, and air leaks and increased sound conduction through the material may result. In other devices, a moderate softening of the material at body temperature may improve the tightness of seal and comfort.

Temperature may raise more serious problems with large ear protectors, such as earmuffs and helmets, than with small ones. By providing heat insulation they tend to raise the temperature of the head. In a cold climate this may be welcome but in a hot climate it may be very annoying. In addition to the discomfort caused by heat, evaporation of perspiration is almost impossible and excessive condensation takes place. Muffs made in part of absorbent materials improve this situation. They have other disadvantages, however. They cannot be washed, and if they are not changed frequently they may become unhygienic. Consequently earmuffs should cover the smallest possible area of the head surface; the area of contact with the skin of helmets should also be kept to a minimum; and if possible, ventilation should be provided.

Time Factor. The longer discomfort exists, the more annoying it becomes. For a short period of time even hard poorly shaped earplugs can be tolerated. On the other hand, ear protectors that seem quite comfortable during the first minute may become intolerable after $\frac{1}{2}$ hr or so. Several kinds of earplugs can be worn during short periods of exposure to intense noise, but very few are sufficiently comfortable to wear for an 8-hr period, or during a whole day or night. In addition to the direct discomfort caused by pressure, long wear accentuates the adverse effects of temperature and toxicity.

Toxicity. Some materials affect the skin chemically and cause inflammation. As a matter of fact, any material can probably cause skin irritation under some circumstances. Toxic effects cannot be eliminated completely, because some are the result of an allergy. Materials are available, however, that cause allergy only in exceptional cases and are otherwise practically free from toxic effect on the skin, even over long periods of use. Polymerized chloroprenes (neoprene) and polyvinyl chloride copolymers (vinylite) are generally nontoxic when compounded with nontoxic plasticizers.[23,32] Since the testing of new materials takes a great deal of time, it seems advisable, for the present, to use these and other materials known from experience to be chemically neutral to the skin.

Washability. If an ear protector is designed for repeated use it should be washable. It should be resistent not only to water and soap but also to some antiseptic, such as alcohol. Smooth surfaces of impermeable material lend themselves better to cleaning than do absorbent materials such as chamois or porous materials such as sponge rubber.

The requirement of washability should not be applied indiscriminately, however. Some earplugs are intended to be thrown away after one use and do not require washing. For some purposes disposable earplugs are more readily accepted than the "permanent" washable ones. Earmuffs are too expensive to be used only once, but they can be isolated from the skin by a disposable tissue or other inexpensive material.

Durability. Durability, like washability, is not a general requirement. It is superfluous for very inexpensive earplugs designed to be used only once. "Permanent" devices, however, which may be less costly in the long run, should last as long as possible. Consequently they should be reasonably rugged and made of a material resistant to aging. Many factors can speed up the aging process, but the most important seem to be ear wax, perspiration, humidity, light, oxygen, and eventually some active chemicals contained in the air. Materials of the neoprene or vinylite type, when compounded with appropriate ingredients, are resistant to most of these influences and may last for two or more years without objectionable changes. Most of the soft resilient materials, however, show a tendency either to contract and harden with time or to expand and become soft.[32]

Ease of Handling. Ease of handling is often slighted; yet it contributes a lot to the performance of an ear protector. A complicated device or one that has to be applied with precision may give excellent results in the laboratory and fail in the field because of incorrect use. The way in which an ear protector is to be applied should be as obvious as is practicable; its performance should not depend heavily on precise placement. Three properties facilitate easy placement: mechanical simplicity, symmetry, and adaptability.

Mechanical simplicity presents no great difficulty, since most earplugs have no movable parts, and the supporting systems of earmuffs are so simple that instructions are not necessary for their use. Although asymmetrical ear protectors are usually better adapted to the anatomy, symmetrical ear protectors are more likely to be applied correctly. However, symmetrical devices usually perform efficiently in only one position, and the unit designed for the right ear should be distinguishable from the one designed for the left ear, the front from the back, the top from the bottom. Usually a compromise is reached and the residual adaptation to the head or ears is left to the compliance of the material. The most widely accepted solution for resilient earplugs is symmetry about the horizontal plane, so that the right and left units are identical. The wearer must pay attention to placing the device correctly in the ear, and the existing asymmetry should be made obvious in order to decrease the likelihood of mistakes. Earmuffs have different degrees of symmetry. Nevertheless, except for those mounted in a helmet, earmuffs and earphone sockets should be symmetrical in at least one plane, i.e., the top the same as the bottom, the right unit no different from the left.

With malleable ear protectors asymmetry presents no problems. Malleable earplugs are either spheres or cylinders, and they adapt completely to the contours of the ear canal. In addition, a malleable or at least a highly compliant material makes the device less sensitive to exact placement, and the stability of performance increases.

EVALUATION OF EAR PROTECTORS

The evaluation of ear protectors is important to those who design them, buy them, use them, as well as to those who are concerned with damage to hearing. Unfortunately, the standards for testing ear protectors have not yet been worked out fully and no standards or criteria exist for their acceptability. It is not possible, therefore, to present either a generally accepted method for testing them, or minimum requirements. We must limit ourselves to suggestions consistent with the experience of laboratory and field experiments. In conformity with basic requirements outlined above, these tests concern primarily sound attenuation, comfort, and toxicity. They comprise laboratory tests, usually preliminary in character, and field tests.

Attenuation Tests.* Of the various tests on ear protectors, those of sound attenuation at the ear are the most widely known. These tests are still not entirely satisfactory, because they cannot be reproduced from one laboratory to another with sufficient agreement. Most present-day tests use human subjects and psychophysical methods, but efforts continue to replace the "subjective" methods by "objective" physical tests [5,26,29] These efforts have failed to a large degree for obvious reasons. The sound attenuation provided by an ear protector is usually dependent at least in part on the anatomical and mechanical properties of the head and especially of the ear. The most important of them are the impedance of the middle ear, the mechanical impedance of the flesh lining of the ear canal, the flexibility of the cartilages of the outer ear, the shape of the ear canal, the mechanical properties of the flesh lining of the skull (especially around the pinna), the mechanical properties of the pinna, and finally all the factors determining bone conduction. It is doubtful whether all these parameters can be duplicated in a physical instrument with materials that will keep their mechanical properties over long periods of time.

Purely physical methods can be used to test the mechanical properties of the ear protector itself. Devices like those used for the evaluation of earphones would be adequate. In such a test ear protectors should provide higher sound attenuation than at the real ear. When this is not so, it is probable that sound transmission through the deformation of the ear protector lowers the attenuation.

Another objective attenuation test is to place the ear protector on a human subject and measure the sound pressure at the entrance to the ear canal, usually with a probe-

* Acceptance of a standard by the American Standards Association pending.

tube microphone. The attenuation value is given by a comparison with the sound pressure measured with the same microphone in the same position when no ear protector is present.[5,29,36]

These tests must be performed without distortion of the proper functioning of the ear protector. The probe tube should be flexible. It should be introduced through the body of the ear protector so that the seal on the surface of the skin remains unchanged. The impedance of the microphone terminated by the probe tube must be high, in order not to affect appreciably the impedance of the cavity behind the ear protector. This method is appropriate for large devices such as earmuffs and helmets. Even then, however, its advantages are uncertain.

The variability of "subjective," i.e., psychophysical, tests probably comes largely from difference in the fitting of ear protectors rather than from inaccuracy of the threshold or loudness determinations, and the problem of fitting is the same in the probe-tube method. Consequently, tests with a probe tube cannot be expected to give much more accurate results or reduce the number of subjects necessary to achieve a statistically significant result. Nevertheless it may be less time-consuming.

Psychophysical measurement of sound attenuation provided by ear protectors is undoubtedly the most widely used.[5,23,33,34,41,43] Sound attenuation is defined as the hearing loss introduced by the device under test. For this purpose the threshold of audibility is measured once with and once without the ear protector in place. The difference in decibels is taken as the measure of sound attenuation. Sometimes loudness matching replaces the threshold determination, but this is a more complicated procedure.[23,34]

The order in which the thresholds are determined may affect the attenuation values obtained. For this reason the test should be balanced; i.e., if one listener is tested first without ear protection and then with ear protection, the next one should be tested first with ear protection, then without it, and so forth. In the next session, the subjects who started without ear protection in the first session are tested first with ear protection. In the third session the order is reversed again.[41,43]

Both pure tones and bands of noise serve as stimuli. Most experimenters prefer pure tones, because they require simpler equipment and the relation between the attenuation and the frequency is well determined. Measurements with bands of noise give not the average attenuation of the band, but the minimum attenuation encountered at one particular frequency, which remains unknown. In order to obtain precise attenuation characteristics, as many frequencies as possible should be tested—at the least the following: 125, 250, 500, 1,000, 2,000, 3,000, 4,000, 6,000, and 8,000 cps. Most commercial audiometers produce these frequencies. The tests should be performed with a loudspeaker, not with earphones, because earphones depart too much from the conditions in which ear protectors are normally used. In most tests the listener sits facing a loudspeaker at 1 to 2 m distance in a room with highly sound-absorptive walls, preferably a free-field room (anechoic chamber). The sound field thus produced is well determined. In some tests the subject listens with one ear, in others with both ears. Theoretically, monaural listening is more nearly correct, but it is difficult to exclude satisfactorily the ear not under test. Binaural listening gives the attenuation values produced at the ear at which the attenuation is least. And comparisons of monaural and binaural tests confirm that the average attenuation obtained binaurally can be expected to lie below the average attenuation obtained monaurally.[5]

Any psychophysical method can be used for the determination of the threshold of hearing, so long as the same method is applied to the threshold measurements both with and without the ear protector. The method should not require complicated maneuvers on the part of the listener. Audible background noise must be excluded from the test room and the listener should sit as quietly as possible. Since noise affects thresholds taken without ear protectors more than those with ear protectors, the attenuation measured is lowered. For this reason, both the examiner and any noisy equipment should be outside the test room. Usually, the listener's head is fixed by a support.

Correct placement of the ear protector plays a critical role in the sound attenuation, particularly with earplugs. Even with the best earplug, air leaks may result if the wrong size is used or the device is positioned inaccurately. The instructions for use of the device may be of more importance than the quality of the device itself. In laboratory experiments it may even be necessary for the examiner to insert the ear-plugs into the listener's ears the first time. For tests, however, the listener should perform this operation himself. Otherwise the test conditions depart too far from the field conditions. It is a good idea to position the ear protectors while listening to a moderately loud noise. Since movements of the lower jaw or the entire head may displace the ear protector and decrease sound attenuation, such movements should be included in the tests.

These tests should be performed on at least 10 listeners with normal hearing and evaluated statistically. Because of variability of fit it seems advisable to repeat the measurement at least three times on each subject. The values measured may increase somewhat with the experience of the subject.

Tests of Comfort and Toxicity. Although comfort probably can be evaluated quantitatively, no such tests have been devised as yet. For instance, it is possible to measure the time during which the subject is able to keep the ear protector on the head. A really comfortable device should be wearable for a whole day. Usually, however, a simple qualitative inquiry decides whether the ear protector is comfortable.

The same is true of toxicity. The only reliable test seems to consist in having a group of people wear the ear protector, or at least a piece of the material it is made of, in close contact with the skin for several days.[32] If no skin irritation occurs in the great majority of subjects (90 to 95 per cent) the device may be considered satisfactorily nontoxic.

Criteria of Acceptability. The criteria of acceptability of ear protectors are even less well specified than the methods of testing. With respect to sound attenuation this results from insufficient information on the harmful effects of noise. The limits between harmless and dangerous noise intensities seem to be vague and probably depend on the kind of noise, the duration of exposure, periods of rest, and the individual listener (see Chap. 7). The minimum noise attenuation required depends, therefore, on the conditions of use. Consequently, a standard of acceptability is not a simple matter. Wide use of ear protectors in the field may result in a self-regulatory mechanism that will eliminate the inferior devices. Nevertheless, it can be stated quite generally that the amount of sound attenuation provided by an ear protector should be sufficient to keep the noise level below a safety limit whenever such a limit is known. This must apply to all frequency bands.

Experience shows that uncomfortable ear protectors are rejected immediately and that skin irritations caused by toxic material soon become evident. Because these effects manifest themselves promptly, the chance that a large population might be harmed seems remote. Thus protection of hearing presents the only serious problem. Acoustic trauma develops slowly and may not be noticed for a long period of time (see Chaps. 4 and 7). Careful audiometric tests are of great help here (see Chap. 6). If tests are performed on a number of young people with reasonably normal hearing, working in the same noise conditions, they can reveal promptly any hearing loss caused by the noise, and at the same time the effectiveness of ear protectors. These tests require several days, usually starting after the week-end's rest. Two audiograms are taken each day, one before the noise begins and one immediately after it stops.[38,39] The difference between the two thresholds gives the temporary hearing loss. Ear protectors may be considered effective if they eliminate this shift of the auditory threshold almost completely (within 5 to 10 db). If there is no appreciable temporary hearing loss, it seems reasonable to expect that no permanent loss will occur. Obviously, these tests must be performed in a quiet room; otherwise small hearing losses cannot be detected.

COMMERCIAL EAR PROTECTORS

The variety of ear protectors and the slow improvement in them indicate that, even though ear protectors give the impression of being very simple devices, individual ear protection presents complex and difficult problems. Only a few typical ear protectors which are widely used are presented here, together with some recent developments. The availability of data about them has played a role in their inclusion, and mention here does not mean that they are necessarily the best. The attenuation curves given here do not represent any average data taken by a standardized procedure because no such data exist. These curves were obtained by individual investigators by different methods. For this reason, results obtained in different laboratories, and even in the same laboratory by different investigators, are not directly comparable with each other. Sometimes the agreement is good; occasionally the differences are pronounced. All the attenuation data reproduced here have one thing in common: they were obtained as average hearing loss produced at the threshold of audibility by the ear protector in an acoustic free field on a number of listeners with normal hearing.

Earplugs. One of the oldest and simplest ways of protecting the ear against intense noise is to press dry cotton wool into the ear canal. The earplug formed in this way is very comfortable but provides little sound attenuation (Fig. 8.22).[23] Substantial improvement can be achieved by soaking the cotton wool in oil or wax. There are prefabricated earplugs consisting of cotton or foam rubber impregnated with wax.

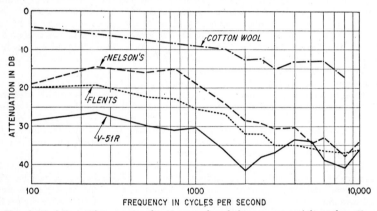

Fig. 8.22. Attenuation curves of cotton wool and three commercial earplugs.[23]

Usually they come in a cylindrical shape and can be kneaded into shape with the fingers. Their main advantages are their comfort and the low cost per piece. They cannot be washed, however, and for this reason they should be used only once, for their sticky surface tends to accumulate dirt. Their resilience is low and not always sufficient to provide a tight seal. As an example, the attenuation characteristic of one such earplug, Flents Anti-Noise Ear Stopples, is given in Fig. 8.22.

Figure 8.22 also shows the attenuation characteristics of two earplugs of the "permanent" type. One is Nelson's Ear Stopper. It consists of a hard spherical globule of colorless plastic terminated in a T-shaped handle that facilitates insertion and removal. It is manufactured in three sizes. This kind of earplug is considered the least comfortable and attenuates the low sound frequencies less than the cotton-wax earplugs. Its advantages are low cost, washability, and durability.

The other permanent earplug is the V-51R Ear Warden (pictured in Fig. 8.23).[23] It consists of a capsule of soft neoprene or vinylite with a bell-shaped cup at its tip which improves the seal and the retention in the ear. The capsule has a shape roughly adapted to the contours of the average ear canal. A flange at the outer end prevents too deep insertion. Three sizes are available. The V-51R Ear Warden provides high sound attenuation at all frequencies and is reasonably comfortable. It is washable and can last for years.

Another example of a soft elastic earplug is the Selectone[39] (Fig. 8.24), which differs from the V-51R Ear Warden mainly in the lack of a sealing cap and a cover closing the capsule at its outer end. The cover creates an insulated volume of air inside the earplug. The properties of the Selectone are similar to those of the V-51R Ear Warden except for one additional feature. One model of this earplug (Selectone K) contains two tiny holes, one connecting the inner cavity with the outside air, the other with the air volume enclosed in the ear canal. The system acts as a two-section low-pass filter, giving a high attenuation at the higher frequencies, which are considered the

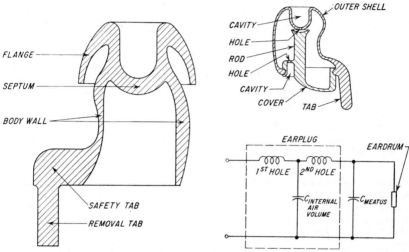

FIG. 8.23. The V-51R Ear Warden.[23]

FIG. 8.24. Selectone ear protector Type K (A. Lindinger) acting as a two-section low-pass filter, and its analogous electrical network.[39]

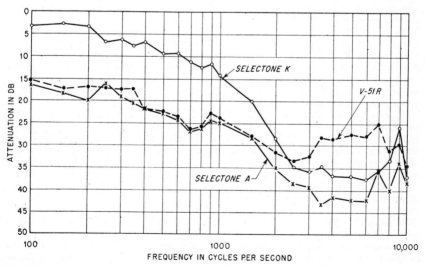

FIG. 8.25. Attenuation curves of Selectone A, Selectone K (low-pass filter), and V-51R Ear Warden determined under the same conditions.[39]

most harmful, and almost no attenuation at the lower frequencies. An analogous electric circuit is also shown in Fig. 8.24. Selectone's low-pass filter characteristic is intended to provide better speech intelligibility in intermittent and interrupted noise than do earplugs that attenuate all frequencies evenly. The attenuation characteristics of the two Selectone models are shown in Fig. 8.25, together with an attenuation curve obtained for V-51R under the same experimental conditions.

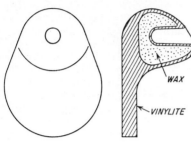

Fig. 8.26. Semiplastic earplug HZP-3 (Maico Co.).[42]

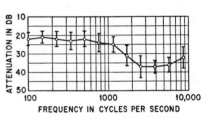

Fig. 8.27. Attenuation curve of the HZP-3 earplug. Vertical lines indicate the standard deviation (10 listeners).[42]

The earplug shown in Fig. 8.26 resulted from an effort to combine the good qualities of the malleable earplugs with those of the elastic ones and is called a semiplastic earplug.[42] It consists of a malleable core surrounded by thin and very soft elastic walls. A reentrant portion of the wall increases the shape and volume adaptability. The basic shape conforms to the contours of the average ear canal. Laboratory experiments indicate that it is more comfortable than other permanent elastic earplugs and provides equal sound attenuation. The attenuation characteristic of the semiplastic earplug, determined under conditions similar to those of Fig. 8.25, is given in Fig. 8.27. One size fits the majority of ears. In contrast to the malleable wax plugs, it can be washed.

Earphone Sockets. From the great number and variety of earphone sockets we choose two classic models (Figs. 8.28 and 8.29) and one that represents a recent development (Fig. 8.12).

Earphone socket MX-41/AR is a small "supra-aural" socket consisting of a shell of solid neoprene and a soft layer of spongelike material providing a tight seal against the pinna (Fig. 8.28). Together with an ANB-H-1 earphone mounted in an HB-7 headband it gives the attenuation shown by the solid line in Fig. 8.30. The chief advantage of the MX-41/AR socket is the small volume it encloses (6 cu cm), which ensures good signal transmission from the earphone. It has the disadvantage of exercising pressure on the sensitive pinna.

"Circumaural" sockets, of which the NAF-48490-1 is a typical example (Fig. 8.29), are usually more comfortable.[22] The NAF-48490-1 socket consists of a large shell of solid neoprene which holds the earphone in its center and of a chamois ring filled with kapok at the periphery. The soft ring, called a "doughnut," ensures the seal around the ear and keeps the shell of the socket at a sufficient distance from the head to avoid uncomfortable pressure on the pinna. One of the advantages of the chamois cushion is the absorption of perspiration. On the other hand, it is not washable. Another disadvantage is the large volume enclosed between the earphone and the ear which decreases the efficiency of the earphone. The attenuation provided by the NAF-48490-1 socket with the ANB-H-1A earphone and CQT-49510 headband is shown in Fig. 8.30 (broken line).

The semiplastic earphone socket of Fig. 8.12 is also of the circumaural type.[41] In contrast to the NAF-48490-1, it consists of one hollow piece of soft vinylite containing a core of highly viscous malleable material. This design ensures high adaptability to the contours of the head portion surrounding the ear and provides a tight seal without

FIG. 8.28. U.S. Air Force MX-41/AR earphone socket with ANB-H-1 earphone and HB-7 headband.[22]

uncomfortably high pressure. Some people find it too small. The whole surface of the socket is smooth and easy to wash. In order to decrease the volume that couples the earphone to the ear to about 13 cu cm, the socket had to be made asymmetrical and, although the right and left units are identical, the front differs from the back. The sound attenuation is provided mainly by the viscosity of the core material and not by stiffness as in other sockets (dash-dot line of Fig. 8.30).

Earmuffs. Any earphone socket in combination with a dummy earphone can be used as an earmuff. There are, however, several earmuffs designed exclusively for ear protection. Usually they provide higher sound attenuation than do earphone sockets. A few examples follow.

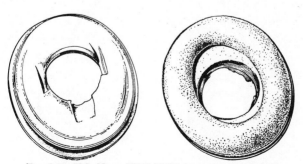

FIG. 8.29. U.S. Navy NAF-48490-1 earphone socket.[22]

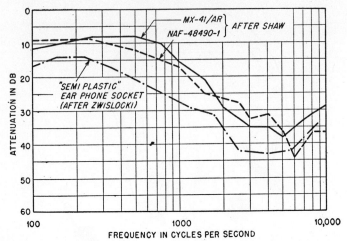

F‍IG. 8.30. Sound attenuation provided by the earphone sockets shown in Figs. 8.12, 8.28, and 8.29.[22,41]

The Kindel ear protector shown in Fig. 8.31 is a small light earmuff consisting of a double-walled metal shell and a very soft flexible sealing cushion. It appears to be comfortable and has a simple headband that makes it less cumbersome than other earmuffs. Unfortunately, it does not attenuate sound frequencies below 1,000 cps by any substantial amount, and even above this frequency sound attenuation does not reach the level attained by other models (Fig. 8.34).

The Noisefoe, shown in Fig. 8.32, provides better sound attenuation (Fig. 8.34). It consists of a plastic shell lined on the inner side with foam rubber which also ensures the seal against the head. Provision is made to secure the muff on the head with a standard headband used for earphones. The Noisefoe is also available mounted in a specially designed cap. It is then called "Earsaver." Despite these practical provisions the Noisefoe (Earsaver) is a rather bulky object. Because of the large surface of contact between the foam rubber and the skin it tends to overheat the skin.

The Straightaway Sound Protector (Fig. 8.33) is the largest and most cumbersome of the earmuffs, but it provides by far the most sound attenuation (Fig. 8.34). It consists of a hard plastic shell sealed to the head by a soft cushion of foam plastic.

F‍IG. 8.31. Kindel ear protector.

FIG. 8.32. Noisefoe (Mine Safety Appliance Co.).

FIG. 8.33. Straightaway Sound Protector (David Clark Co.).

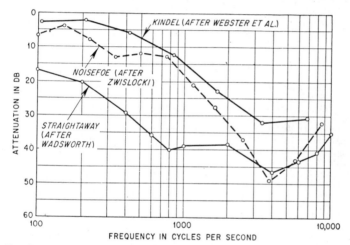

FIG. 8.34. Attenuation curves of earmuffs shown in Figs. 8.31 to 8.33.[33,43]

It encloses an air volume of about 300 cu cm,* filled in part by an absorbent foam plastic.

Semi-inserts.[22] Semi-inserts have been used mainly in connection with earphones. Because they can offer high sound attenuation and could easily be used as ear protectors, the attenuation characteristic of one of them (Harvard Design C-6, see Fig. 8.1) is shown in Fig. 8.35. The C-6 is a flexible and reasonably soft semi-insert, made of neoprene that is shaped to fit the entrance to the auditory canal. It is mounted, together with hearing-aid earphones, on a specially designed headband. In order to add stability and comfort to the system the headband does not press directly on the

* Wadsworth, personal communication.

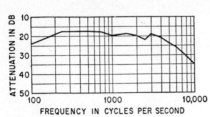

FIG. 8.35. Attenuation curve of semi-inserts C-6 (Fig. 8.1).[22]

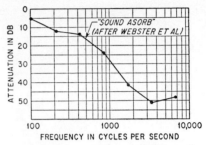

FIG. 8.36. Attenuation curve of the Sound Asorb helmet shown in Fig. 8.1 (Bill Jack Scientific Instruments Co.).[33]

inserts, but on a secondary spring. The headband itself rests on the temporal bone. The system is adequate, although substantial improvements appear possible.

Helmets. Most helmets do not contribute to sound attenuation but serve only as supporting means for earphones or earmuffs. There are helmets, however, which can be considered as ear protectors in themselves. The Sound Asorb helmet, shown in Fig. 8.1, is an example. It consists of a Fiberglas shell lined on the inside with sound-absorbing materials and cloth. Foam-rubber cushions provide a seal around the ears. The helmet can be used with or without earphones. It is, of course, a large and heavy object and it does not attenuate sound better than earmuffs (Fig. 8.36). It should not be used, therefore, when only ear protection is required. Since it provides protection against crash and wind blast it is useful in situations where combined protection is needed.

REFERENCES

1. Bárány, E. A.: *Acta Oto-Laryngol.*, suppl. 26, 1938.
2. Békésy, G. v.: *Akust. Z.*, **4**: 113 (1939).
3. Békésy, G. v.: *Acta Oto-Laryngol.*, **35**: 411 (1947).
4. Békésy, G. v.: *J. Acoust. Soc. Amer.*, **20**: 743 (1948).
5. Dickson, E. D. D., et al.: Acoustics Laboratory, Department of Otorhinolaryngology, Central Medical Establishment, Royal Air Force, FPRC Report 884, 1954.
6. Egan, J. P., et al.: OSRD Report 1491, U.S. Department of Commerce, Washington, D.C., 1943, PB 22545.
7. Franke, E. K.: *J. Acoust. Soc. Amer.*, **24**: 410 (1952).
8. Gierke, H. E. v.: *Am. Ind. Hyg. Assoc. Quart.*, **15**: 1 (1954).
9. Gierke, H. E. v., and D. R. Warren: Benox Report, ONR Project NR144-079, University of Chicago, 1953, p. 47.
10. Griffin, D. R., et al.: OSRD Report 826, U.S. Department of Commerce, Washington, D.C., 1942, PB 22844.
11. Kietz, H., and H. Z. Zangemeister: *Z. Laryngol. Rhinol. Otol.*, **31**: 3 (1952).
12. Knudsen, V. O.: *J. Acoust. Soc. Amer.*, **11**: 29 (1939).
13. Kryter, K. D., et al.: OSRD Report 3541, U.S. Department of Commerce, Washington, D.C., 1944, PB 22912.
14. Link, R., and J. Zwislocki: *Arch. Ohren-, Nasen-, u. Kehlkopfheilk. ver. Z. Hals-, Nasen-, u. Ohrenheilk.*, **160**: 347 (1951).
15. Lüscher, E., and J. Zwislocki: *Industrielle Organisation*, 1948.
16. Miller, G. A., and J. C. R. Licklider: *J. Acoust. Soc. Amer.*, **22**: 167 (1950).
17. Miller, G. A., F. M. Wiener, and S. S. Stevens: Summary Technical Report NDRC Division 17, vol. 3, Washington, D.C., 1946.
18. Neely, K. K.: Defence Research Medical Laboratory, Canada, Report 100-1, 1952.
19. Neff, W. D.: Benox Report, ONR Project NR144-079, University of Chicago, 1953, p. 37.
20. Rüedi, L., and W. Furrer: *Practica oto-rhino-laryng.*, **6**: 255 (1944); **8**: 177 (1946).
21. Shaw, W. A., et al.: Report IC-116, Harvard University, Psycho-Acoustic Laboratory, 1945.

22 Shaw, W. A., et al.: OSRD Report 6113, U.S. Department of Commerce, Washington, D.C., 1945, PB 22851.

23. Shaw, W. A., et al.: OSRD Report 5122, U.S. Department of Commerce, Washington, D.C., 1945, PB 22849.

24. Snow, W. B., and W. D. Neff: U.S. Department of Commerce, Washington, D.C., 1943, PB 50822, pp. 28ff.

25. Stevens, S. S.: IC-15 in OSRD Report 1572, U.S. Department of Commerce, Washington, D.C., 1943, PB 22550.

26. Tolhurst, G. C., and S. N. Morrill: U.S. Naval School of Aviation Medicine, Pensacola, Fla., Joint Report NM 001 064.01 Report No. 16.

27. Tolhurst, G. C.: U.S. Naval School of Aviation Medicine, Pensacola, Fla., Special Report 55-2, 1955.

28. Tolhurst, G. C.: U.S. Naval School of Aviation Medicine, Pensacola, Fla., Special Report 55-6, 1955.

29. Veneklasen, P. S., et al.: Report from Harvard University Electro-Acoustic Laboratory, published by Psycho-Acoustic Laboratory in PNR-6, 1946, section J.

30. Watson, N. A.: OSRD 536, U.S. Department of Commerce, Washington, D.C., 1942.

31. Watson, N. A., and R. S. Gales: *J. Acoust. Soc. Amer.*, **14**: 209 (1943).

32. Watson, N. A., and V. O. Knudsen: *J. Acoust. Soc. Amer.*, **15**: 153 (1944).

33. Webster, J. C., et al.: U.S. Navy Electronics Laboratory, San Diego, Calif. *Tech. Mem.* TM-77, January, 1955.

34. Webster, J. C.: *Noise Control*, **1**: 34 (September, 1955).

35. Wheeler, D. E.: p. 93 in "Noise," University of Michigan Press, Ann Arbor, Mich., 1952.

36. Wilkie, D. R.: *J. Acoust. Soc. Amer.*, **24**: 191 (1952).

37. Zwislocki, J.: *J. Acoust. Soc. Amer.*, **23**: 36 (1951).

38. Zwislocki, J.: *Industrielle Organisation*, 1951.

39. Zwislocki, J.: *J. Acoust. Soc. Amer.*, **24**: 762 (1952).

40. Zwislocki, J.: *J. Acoust. Soc. Amer.*, **27**: 146 (1955).

41. Zwislocki, J.: *J. Acoust. Soc. Amer.*, **27**: 155 (1955).

42. Zwislocki, J.: *J. Acoust. Soc. Amer.*, **27**: 460 (1955).

43. Zwislocki, J.: *J. Acoust. Soc. Amer.*, **27**: 1154 (1955).

44. Zwislocki, J.: unpublished data.

Chapter 9

EFFECTS OF NOISE ON SPEECH

Mones E. Hawley

Radio Corporation of America

Karl D. Kryter, Ph.D.

Operational Applications Laboratory
Air Force Cambridge Research Center

INTRODUCTION

This chapter is concerned with the effects of noise on speech as a means of communication. Certainly one of the most serious consequences of noise is that it prevents us from understanding what other people are saying whether they are talking to us directly or talking over a telephone or public-address system. The understanding of spoken *words* is defined here as *intelligibility*. Identification of the speaker or his emotions from the sound of his voice is not included in the term.

Intelligibility is a psychological factor and psychological techniques are required to measure it; but a speech-communication system consists of equipment on which many physical measurements can be made. Much work has been done by scientists and engineers on the relations between these psychological and physical measurements, but many problems remain unsolved. However, it is possible for the engineer to solve most speech-communication problems by means of a series of approximations and estimates which are given in this chapter. Provision must be made for minor modifications in the communication system to correct for inaccuracies in these approximations.

In this chapter there is, first, a description of the statistical properties of speech which are pertinent to intelligibility and methods of measuring speech intelligibility. Next, the effectiveness of noise in masking speech is discussed, and it is shown that speech intelligibility can be predicted from physical measurements of the noise and on the equipment. Some equipment especially useful where intelligibility is a problem will then be described. Finally some examples of speech-communication systems used in various noisy conditions are presented.

THE STATISTICS OF SPEECH

When a person speaks he generates continuously changing complex sound pressure waves. Speech sounds vary widely in both spectrum and over-all level as a function of the time. Furthermore, the frequency of occurrence of speech sounds in connected discourse differs greatly. One can analyze speech microscopically, looking at the characteristics of each speech sound; but for the purposes of this handbook, it is the macroscopic viewpoint that is of interest, i.e., the long-term averages of data for a large number of people. On the average, a talker speaking in a raised voice produces a sound-pressure spectrum which approximates that shown in Fig. 9.1. This is a smoothed average curve taken from a large number of determinations on male subjects.[1-5] There may be considerable deviations from this spectrum owing to changes in talking level or individual differences, and there would be a different curve for female voices. This sound-pressure spectrum is here used as being representative of average speech.

The average over-all level of speech is not so easily determined. What is a "normal" speaking level under one set of conditions is abnormally low or high for another set of conditions. The differences in individuals are great, and reverberation time, noise level, and many other factors influence this normal level. However, over-all sound pressure levels, as measured on a sound-level meter at a distance of 1 m from the talker, are usually between 65

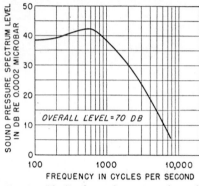

FIG. 9.1. Idealized speech spectrum for male voices at 1 meter from the talker's lips. (*From Ref. 2.*)

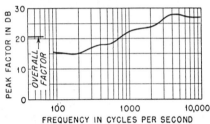

FIG. 9.2. Difference in decibels between peak pressures of speech measured in short (⅛-sec) intervals and the rms pressure averaged over a long (75-sec) interval. (*From Ref. 2.*)

and 75 db for most talkers under most conditions when instructed to speak in a "normal" tone of voice.[2,4,5,6] It is assumed here that the average over-all level, with the talker in the quiet, is 66 db at a distance of 1 meter.

A very important characteristic of speech is that it has an irregular waveform with a high peak factor. That is to say, the peak instantaneous sound pressures are high compared with the long-term rms sound pressure. Figure 9.2 shows the magnitude of this peak factor as a function of frequency. The variations in this peak factor with differences in talking level have not been determined, but it is believed that the values shown are reasonable for a wide range of conversational speech levels.

It is the high peak factor and the transient nature of speech which make it difficult to measure speech levels, although a number of means are available: (1) the volume indicator, frequently called a VU meter because its reading is in "volume units" (VU); (2) the sound-level meter; (3) the cathode-ray oscilloscope; and (4) the integrator, integrating either sound pressure or sound pressure squared. Each of these devices has its advantages and disadvantages. All will give different values for the same speech sample.

The VU meter is an instrument, primarily used for radio-broadcast work, having characteristics which are very carefully defined in a standard.[7] The device is widely used for monitoring broadcast and recording material, and experienced audio engineers usually agree on the interpretation of the meter fluctuations. In some cases the VU meter gives misleading indications because it is affected by the talker's speaking rate and by his individual peak factor; in addition, peak clipping or other peak-factor distortion also may give misleading indications.

The sound-level meter is not especially designed for speech measurements, but it can be used for this purpose. The transient response of the meter, on either the slow or fast scales, differs from that of the VU meter.[8]   An oscilloscope is very useful for monitoring speech because clipping of the peaks or distortion of the waveform caused by overloading is quite obvious.   The oscilloscope is also a very valuable tool for speech measurements because the peak readings can be observed directly, and the long-term rms sound pressure of speech can be calculated.

The use of an integrator with a linear or a square-law detector is a more sophisticated means of determining speech level.[2-5]   However, such equipment is too complicated for the requirements of most design engineers.

INTELLIGIBILITY TESTS

A procedure known as speech-intelligibility testing is usually employed to determine how well speech can be understood over a given speech-communication system.   No measuring instrument other than people can be used to measure the intelligibility of a system, but a great deal can be done to standardize the method of measurement so that results taken in one set of circumstances may be compared with those obtained in another.   In order to facilitate the comparison of such measurement between laboratories, it is useful to have a standardized test.   The American Standards Association has issued a standard for intelligibility tests which contains details of a method, including test procedure, material, selection of subjects and their training, talker and listener levels and their measurement, the experimental design, the use of recordings, the reporting of results, and lists of words normally used in these tests.[9]   Both "articulation" tests and "intelligibility" tests have been used for measuring the performance of communication systems.   It is generally accepted practice to refer to a test as an articulation test when the reception of individual speech sounds, regardless of context or meaning, is the measure of performance, and to refer to a test as an intelligibility test when the reception of a word, phrase, or sentence is the measure of performance.   As the result of redundancy within and among speech sounds and in meaningful phrases and sentences, intelligibility tests are usually considerably easier and give higher scores on a given communication system than articulation tests.   A number of monosyllabic words divided into lists that are phonetically balanced to represent everyday speech have been designated by the American Standards Association for normal intelligibility-testing purposes.

A speech-intelligibility test is made in the following way: A carefully controlled experiment is set up in which trained talkers read specially selected lists of words to trained listeners who write down the words they hear.   The ambient noise level and spectrum at the talkers and listeners are representative of the conditions under which the communication system will be used.   The performance of a given system is reported as the percentage of words correctly received.   This score is called the word-intelligibility score.   The intelligibility of different possible systems is compared by comparing the word scores, usually using a few hundred words for each system.   Notice that no absolute measurements are made; only comparisons are meaningful because so much depends on the ability and training of the crew.   It is possible, however, to make measurements at different laboratories and to maintain the same rank order among systems.   The results of intelligibility tests are usually evaluated by statistical analysis to determine whether the observed differences between the systems, between the talkers, and between the various repetitions of the tests are statistically significant.

One of the first things the speech-communications systems designer must do is decide upon the intelligibility which is required under his conditions of operation. Word scores higher than 90 per cent are seldom essential.   Usually scores of 70 per cent are quite acceptable, and in many cases word scores as low as 50 per cent are adequate.   Proper names are quite difficult to understand over speech-communication systems and present severe problems if noise levels are high.   It is estimated that a paging system should have a word-articulation score of 85 per cent or better for the listeners regularly to identify the correct name out of a large number of possibilities.[10]

These scores are for isolated words. Of course, for connected discourse the resulting scores would be very much higher. The relationship between scores for words and sentences is shown as a function of signal-to-noise ratio in Fig. 9.3. High intelligibility is usually expensive, and the designer frequently must make several designs before he arrives at a satisfactory compromise between intelligibility and equipment cost and complexity.

One of the ways to reduce the required word-intelligibility score is through the use of standardized phraseology and voice procedures, preferably by limiting the vocabulary to a relatively small number of polysyllabic words. It is found that within broad limits the greater the reduction in the size of the vocabulary used the greater is the increase in speech intelligibility under a given signal-to-noise ratio.[11,12] The use of standardized voice procedures is particularly important when power, weight, size, or cost limitations placed upon the equipment prevent optimum engineering of a given communication system.[13-18] This principle is applied to radio-telephone communications for air-traffic control where a limited number of standardized phrases and words are used according to specific regulations. Standardized voice procedures also have real value when noise levels are such that the speech signal cannot be made greater in intensity than the noise without running the risk of damaging the ear. In situations where a low signal-to-noise ratio cannot be avoided, the use of standardized phrases or words can mean the difference between obtaining satisfactory or unsatisfactory speech intelligibility. In addition, the use of standardized phraseologies provides a margin of safety for emergency conditions that place unusual stress upon a communication system, for example, sudden increases in noise level or the use of inept talkers.

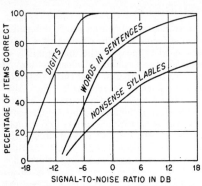

FIG. 9.3. Showing the relationship between intelligibility scores and signal-to-noise ratio. The same communication equipment and test crew were used for all three functions. (*From Ref. 11.*)

However, first consideration must be given to overdesigning to whatever extent is practical in order to achieve a communication system that will provide adequate intelligibility in all emergencies without the need of standardized phraseologies and voice procedures. There are dangers in relying on the possible use of small standardized vocabularies; one is that, under conditions of emergency, the standardized procedures may be forgotten or the standardized vocabulary may prove too small to cope with the situation. Another problem confronting military personnel is that, particularly in wartime, it is frequently impossible to devote sufficient time to the training of the people who are to use the communication system. Thus they may not be familiar with the standardized phraseology and may be forced to use normal but longer, less accurate phrases or sentences in their communications. The decision rests with the user of a communication system as to what use, if any, will be made of standardized phraseologies and voice procedures.

Training of the users in proper use of the equipment is a most valuable assist to the communication-systems designer. There is a great difference in the fundamental intelligibility of talkers.[19-26] The ability of listeners to understand speech also varies, but both talkers and listeners can be improved greatly by training. If possible, only a limited number of talkers should use a communication system, particularly a paging or public-address system. It has been shown that both talkers and listeners improve consistently when they use a communication system for a long period of time, but the talkers and listeners who were best initially usually remain best. It is worthwhile to spend some time on the selection of paging-system operators and other announcers.

THE INFLUENCE OF NOISE ON SPEECH PERCEPTION

Three kinds of noise need to be distinguished in so far as influence on speech is concerned: (1) continuous wide-range random noise such as that produced by most machinery or by escaping air; (2) continuous, discrete spectrum noise, for example, noise produced by transformers; and (3) intermittent noise such as that caused by impact machinery or by guns. The effects of continuous noise on speech intelligibility have been studied far more thoroughly than the effects of impulsive noise.[27-35] Continuous noise masks certain information bearing elements of speech quite continuously, and for the most part the impulsive noise masks speech only temporarily, although in between impulses the listener's hearing threshold remains raised so that he does not hear so well as he normally would. For example, a repetition of a spoken message will not improve intelligibility greatly in the presence of continuous noise; but if the noise is impulsive, repetition may very well spell the difference between complete and very limited intelligibility. A further difference between continuous and impulsive noise will be pointed out later when the effect of peak clipping is discussed.

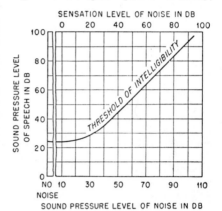

FIG. 9.4. The shift in threshold of intelligibility for sentences in connected discourse as a function of the level of wide-spectrum noise. The threshold of intelligibility is defined, in this case, as the speech level at which the listener obtains the meaning of nearly every sentence. (*From Ref. 35.*)

The results of masking of speech by continuous wideband noise are illustrated in Fig. 9.4. The ordinate of this graph gives the amount by which the sound-pressure level of speech must be increased in the presence of noise in order for the speech to have the same intelligibility as the no-noise condition. It will be noticed that, as the noise level approaches 20 db, the threshold of intelligibility of speech rises only slightly. For more than 40 db of noise, the change in the threshold of intelligibility of the speech is directly proportional to the change in the level of the masking noise.

The effect of noise on speech greatly depends on the spectrum of the noise. If the noise, which is transmitted by a speech-communication system, is concentrated in one band of frequencies, a great deal of intelligibility may still be obtained, particularly if this band is suppressed by the system. If the noise occurs in the middle of the speech band, filtering is not worth the trouble and better results can be obtained by merely increasing the speech-signal level at the listener.

THE PREDICTION OF WORD INTELLIGIBILITY

The physical characteristics of a speech-communication system are more easily measured than the psychological ones, such as the rating of speech intelligibility. Therefore, it is highly desirable to find the relationship between the physical and psychological measures applicable to the system. Such a function is shown in Fig. 9.5 in which word and sentence intelligibility scores are plotted against articulation index. The *articulation index* is a measure of the system's potential intelligibility and is derived from the physical measurements on the system. The exact relationship between word scores and articulation index will change for different crews and for different kinds of test conditions. However, the curve shown in Fig. 9.5 is representative of that obtained by several different laboratories with several different crews and under a reasonably wide range of conditions.[36-38] This curve is applicable to most speech-communication system problems that are likely to be encountered by the reader. It should be emphasized, however, that all the determinations which lead to this transfer function were made with thoroughly trained crews, a situation which may not always exist.

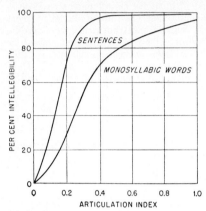

FIG. 9.5. The intelligibility of sentences and words as a function of articulation index.

Two factors are used to compute articulation index: signal-to-noise ratio and bandwidth. Experiments have shown that only the frequencies lying between about 200 and 6,100 cps contribute to speech intelligibility.[30] It has also been possible to determine the frequency bands which seem to contribute equally to intelligibility if the signal-to-noise ratios in the bands are equal. The abscissa of Fig. 9.6 shows the 200- to 6,100-cps region broken into 20 such bands. Earlier it was shown (Fig. 9.4) that the masking of speech (at least at the threshold of intelligibility) by noise is a linear factor. Experiments have demonstrated that a 30-db change in signal-to-noise ratio will span the entire range of word intelligibility scores from 0 to almost 100 per cent.[30]

For the purposes of articulation-index computation, one assumes that equal increments (in decibels) of the signal-to-noise ratio contribute equal increments of articulation index in each band and that the bands are linearly additive. Thus each of

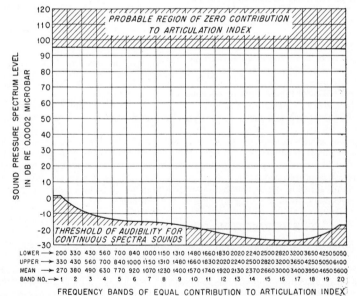

FIG. 9.6. Chart showing auditory area available for speech communications. The frequency scale is divided into 20 bands of equal importance to the calculation of the articulation index. (*From Ref. 36.*)

20 bands can contribute a maximum of 0.05 to the articulation index and each decibel of the signal-to-noise ratio in the band will contribute $\frac{1}{30}$ of this.[36] With these assumptions, one can use a work sheet such as that shown in Fig. 9.6. If the measure of speech sound pressure level and of the noise are chosen such that they are equal

when word intelligibility score is 0 and are 30 db apart when word intelligibility score is 100 per cent, the two sound-pressure spectrum levels can be plotted against the "equal-articulation-index contribution bands" and the signal-to-noise ratio in each band can be computed directly. This choice is based on experiments in which it was found that a speech signal having a long-term rms sound pressure level 12 db below the rms sound pressure level of the noise will be barely detectable. Thus the minimum contribution to articulation index is made at a signal-to-noise ratio of -12 db and a practical maximum is at a signal-to-noise ratio of $+18$ db. The reason negative signal-to-noise ratios give some speech intelligibility is due to the dynamic nature of the speech signal, as shown in Fig. 9.2. It is convenient when using the work sheet in Fig. 9.6 to plot the long-term rms speech spectrum plus 12 db. It is common practice to call this level "speech peaks." When this is done, signal-to-noise ratios ranging from 0 to 30 db can be used directly in computing the articulation index.

The method of obtaining the proper speech spectrum depends on how the speech level is measured. If a sound-level meter is used, employing the flat weighting network, an over-all speech level of 3 db lower than the meter reading should be used. For a standard VU meter, the true long-term speech level will be about 4 db lower than the VU meter readings. The speech spectrum shown in Fig. 9.1 can be moved up or down to give the proper over-all level. However, if an oscilloscope is used to determine the speech sound pressure level, the following procedure should be followed:

1. Determine on the oscilloscope the highest speech peaks that occur during a reasonably long (30 sec or more) sample of speech.
2. Apply to the oscilloscope a 1,000-cps sinusoidal signal such that the peaks are as high as the speech peaks.
3. Determine the rms voltage of this sinusoidal signal.
4. Subtract 17 db from this voltage; this is the proper over-all rms voltage of speech.
5. Using the microphone-sensitivity calibration, determine the sound pressure level required to produce this input voltage at the oscilloscope.
6. Use the sound pressure level thus obtained as the over-all spectrum level, and plot the speech spectrum on the work sheet as before, adding 12 db to allow for the peak pressure of speech which contributes to intelligibility.

Note that there is an upper and a lower limit to the useful sound-pressure spectrum levels. The lower limit is the threshold of audibility for continuous spectrum sounds, and the upper limit is uniformly 95 db for the peaks of speech (rms +12 db). This upper limit is an estimate of the level at which some kind of overloading seems to occur at the ear and further increases in sound pressure do not increase intelligibility.

It should be noted that only the first 30 db of the signal-to-noise ratio in any band contributes to intelligibility, and negative signal-to-noise ratios do not decrease it, but it is obvious that a given articulation index may be obtained by any one of a large number of combinations of signal-to-noise ratios and bandwidth. But there are limitations. Abrupt changes in the frequency spectrum of the signal or of the noise may cause inaccuracies in the prediction method. For reasonably smooth values, however, the method works fairly well, but particular caution is indicated in its use in noise whose spectral components fall predominantly in either the lower or upper end of the audible range of frequencies.

It is important to remember that the speech signal which is used in articulation-index computations is the signal after it has gone through the entire communication system, that is, from the talker through his microphone, the amplifier, a loudspeaker or headset, and finally to the listener. Similarly the noise is the composite total of noise reaching the listener's ears: noise picked up by the talker's microphone, noise in the transmission channel, and noise from the listener's environment. It is important to study how these various components affect the signal and noise spectra and to select components which give the highest intelligibility.

Figure 9.7 gives a self-explanatory schematic demonstration of steps to be taken in the application of the 20-band method for calculating the intelligibility score to be expected of a given communication system used in noise. An example is worked out at the end of the chapter.

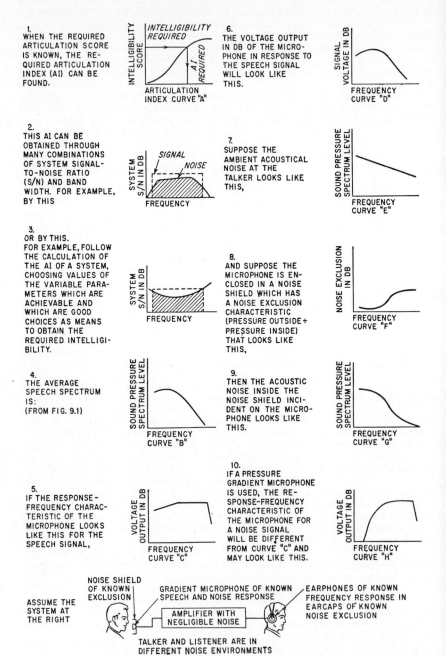

1.
WHEN THE REQUIRED ARTICULATION SCORE IS KNOWN, THE REQUIRED ARTICULATION INDEX (AI) CAN BE FOUND.

ARTICULATION INDEX CURVE "A"

6.
THE VOLTAGE OUTPUT IN DB OF THE MICROPHONE IN RESPONSE TO THE SPEECH SIGNAL WILL LOOK LIKE THIS.

FREQUENCY CURVE "D"

2.
THIS AI CAN BE OBTAINED THROUGH MANY COMBINATIONS OF SYSTEM SIGNAL-TO-NOISE RATIO (S/N) AND BAND WIDTH. FOR EXAMPLE, BY THIS

FREQUENCY

7.
SUPPOSE THE AMBIENT ACOUSTICAL NOISE AT THE TALKER LOOKS LIKE THIS,

FREQUENCY CURVE "E"

3.
OR BY THIS.
FOR EXAMPLE, FOLLOW THE CALCULATION OF THE AI OF A SYSTEM, CHOOSING VALUES OF THE VARIABLE PARAMETERS WHICH ARE ACHIEVABLE AND WHICH ARE GOOD CHOICES AS MEANS TO OBTAIN THE REQUIRED INTELLIGIBILITY.

FREQUENCY

8.
AND SUPPOSE THE MICROPHONE IS ENCLOSED IN A NOISE SHIELD WHICH HAS A NOISE EXCLUSION CHARACTERISTIC (PRESSURE OUTSIDE + PRESSURE INSIDE) THAT LOOKS LIKE THIS,

FREQUENCY CURVE "F"

4.
THE AVERAGE SPEECH SPECTRUM IS:
(FROM FIG. 9.1)

FREQUENCY CURVE "B"

9.
THEN THE ACOUSTIC NOISE INSIDE THE NOISE SHIELD INCIDENT ON THE MICROPHONE LOOKS LIKE THIS.

FREQUENCY CURVE "G"

5.
IF THE RESPONSE-FREQUENCY CHARACTERISTIC OF THE MICROPHONE LOOKS LIKE THIS FOR THE SPEECH SIGNAL,

FREQUENCY CURVE "C"

10.
IF A PRESSURE GRADIENT MICROPHONE IS USED, THE RESPONSE-FREQUENCY CHARACTERISTIC OF THE MICROPHONE FOR A NOISE SIGNAL WILL BE DIFFERENT FROM CURVE "C" AND MAY LOOK LIKE THIS.

FREQUENCY CURVE "H"

ASSUME THE SYSTEM AT THE RIGHT

NOISE SHIELD OF KNOWN EXCLUSION

GRADIENT MICROPHONE OF KNOWN SPEECH AND NOISE RESPONSE

AMPLIFIER WITH NEGLIGIBLE NOISE

EARPHONES OF KNOWN FREQUENCY RESPONSE IN EARCAPS OF KNOWN NOISE EXCLUSION

TALKER AND LISTENER ARE IN DIFFERENT NOISE ENVIRONMENTS

Fig. 9.7. A schematic presentation of the prediction of the intelligibility

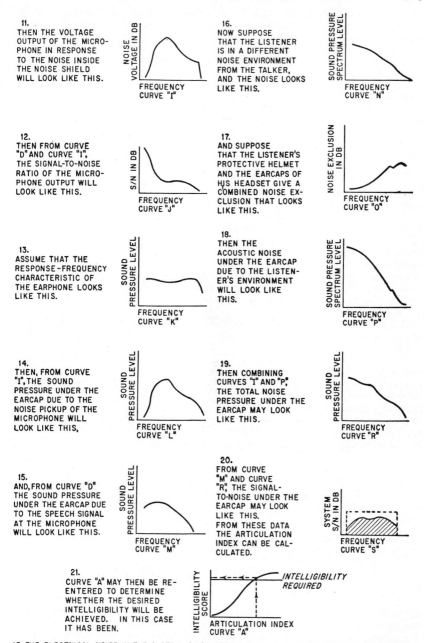

11. THEN THE VOLTAGE OUTPUT OF THE MICRO-PHONE IN RESPONSE TO THE NOISE INSIDE THE NOISE SHIELD WILL LOOK LIKE THIS.

NOISE VOLTAGE IN DB / FREQUENCY
CURVE "I"

16. NOW SUPPOSE THAT THE LISTENER IS IN A DIFFERENT NOISE ENVIRONMENT FROM THE TALKER, AND THE NOISE LOOKS LIKE THIS.

SOUND PRESSURE SPECTRUM LEVEL / FREQUENCY
CURVE "N"

12. THEN FROM CURVE "D" AND CURVE "I", THE SIGNAL-TO-NOISE RATIO OF THE MICRO-PHONE OUTPUT WILL LOOK LIKE THIS.

S/N IN DB / FREQUENCY
CURVE "J"

17. AND SUPPOSE THAT THE LISTENER'S PROTECTIVE HELMET AND THE EARCAPS OF HIS HEADSET GIVE A COMBINED NOISE EX-CLUSION THAT LOOKS LIKE THIS.

NOISE EXCLUSION IN DB / FREQUENCY
CURVE "O"

13. ASSUME THAT THE RESPONSE-FREQUENCY CHARACTERISTIC OF THE EARPHONE LOOKS LIKE THIS.

SOUND PRESSURE LEVEL / FREQUENCY
CURVE "K"

18. THEN THE ACOUSTIC NOISE UNDER THE EARCAP DUE TO THE LISTEN-ER'S ENVIRONMENT WILL LOOK LIKE THIS.

SOUND PRESSURE SPECTRUM LEVEL / FREQUENCY
CURVE "P"

14. THEN, FROM CURVE "I", THE SOUND PRESSURE UNDER THE EARCAP DUE TO THE NOISE PICKUP OF THE MICROPHONE WILL LOOK LIKE THIS,

SOUND PRESSURE LEVEL / FREQUENCY
CURVE "L"

19. THEN COMBINING CURVES "I" AND "P", THE TOTAL NOISE PRESSURE UNDER THE EARCAP MAY LOOK LIKE THIS.

SOUND PRESSURE LEVEL / FREQUENCY
CURVE "R"

15. AND, FROM CURVE "D" THE SOUND PRESSURE UNDER THE EARCAP DUE TO THE SPEECH SIGNAL AT THE MICROPHONE WILL LOOK LIKE THIS.

SOUND PRESSURE LEVEL / FREQUENCY
CURVE "M"

20. FROM CURVE "M" AND CURVE "R", THE SIGNAL-TO-NOISE UNDER THE EARCAP MAY LOOK LIKE THIS. FROM THESE DATA THE ARTICULATION INDEX CAN BE CAL-CULATED.

SYSTEM S/N IN DB / FREQUENCY
CURVE "S"

21. CURVE "A" MAY THEN BE RE-ENTERED TO DETERMINE WHETHER THE DESIRED INTELLIGIBILITY WILL BE ACHIEVED. IN THIS CASE IT HAS BEEN.

INTELLIGIBILITY SCORE / ARTICULATION INDEX
CURVE "A"

INTELLIGIBILITY REQUIRED

IF THE ELECTRICAL NOISE IN THE SYSTEM IS LOW COMPARED WITH THE ACOUSTIC NOISE PICKED UP BY THE MICROPHONE (CURVE "D"), CURVES "D", "I", AND "J" WILL REPRESENT THE VALUES OF SIGNAL, NOISE AND S/N, RESPECTIVELY OF THE EARPHONE INPUT.

of a speech-communication system for use in noisy environments.

Speech Interference Level. It is noted in the procedures just described that the audible sound spectrum is divided into 20 bands that are not harmonically related. Inasmuch as most laboratories are not equipped with passband filters that will permit quick analyses of the speech and noise into the 20 bands required, the 20-band method of calculating speech intelligibility is not practical for many engineering applications. It is possible, of course, to approximate these levels by converting measures made in octave, half-octave, or third-octave band steps into appropriate values for the 20 bands.

For reasons of simplicity, a method has been proposed for estimating maximum tolerable noise levels for satisfactory speech intelligibility in which acoustical measures of the noise are made by means of octave-band filters and a sound-level meter. In this procedure the arithmetic average of the decibel level over-all of the noise in each of the octave bands 600 to 1,200 cps, 1,200 to 2,400 cps, and 2,400 to 4,800 cps is found. It has been determined that, when the arithmetic average of the octave-band levels of wideband noise in decibels is 12 db below the over-all rms level of undistorted speech at the listener's ear, in general, nearly 100 per cent of sentences will be heard correctly. This level of noise (12 db below the average over-all level of undistorted speech) is called the *speech interference level* (SIL) for reliable speech communications and is equivalent to an articulation index computed according to the 20-band method of 0.4. In effect the SIL tells us how intense the speech signal at the listener's ear must be for a given noise condition in order to be heard reliably. In order to prevent discomfort and possible damage to the ear, the average over-all rms level of the speech signal should not be permitted to exceed about 110 db at the listener's ear even though, by such limitation, a satisfactory speech interference level is not attained. The peaks of speech in terms of level per cycle will be about 95 db when the over-all rms level is 110 db. As mentioned previously, speech above that level at the listener's ear will not contribute to intelligibility.

The problem of speech communication in an engine room can serve as an example of how to use the speech interference level concept. The noise levels are shown in Table 9.1.

The speech interference level is so high in the engine room that with open-ear listening to a loudspeaker or person-to-person speech we could not expect reliable communications. A speech level that exceeded this SIL by 12 db, our criterion for reliable communications, would be of such great intensity that it would hurt the listener's ears and be relatively unintelligible. However, through the use of earplugs, or proper earphone cushions, sufficient noise can be excluded from the listeners' ears so that a satisfactory speech interference level is realizable. This is shown as the second column of Table 9.1, which gives the estimated sound pressure level, by octave,

Table 9.1

Octave band, cps	Sound pressure level L_p, db	L_p estimated under ear-plugs or earphones, db
600–1,200	107	88
1,200–2,400	99	74
2,400–4,800	96	71
	SIL = 101	SIL = 78

at the listener's ear as the result of noise exclusion. The gain of the system presenting the speech signal can be adjusted to provide an over-all rms speech level of 90 db at the listener's ear. This level would not be excessively loud and would exceed the speech interference level by 12 db, meeting our criterion for reliable speech communications.

The communication engineer will note that, in computing speech interference levels by the octave-band method, it is assumed the response-frequency characteristics of all components of a speech communication system are uniform or substantially so.

When frequency discrimination is appreciable, the speech interference level method should not be used.   Also, this method may not be applicable if the noise is predominantly in the frequency region below 600 or above 4,800 cps.   Although it has obvious advantages over the 20-band method of predicting speech intelligibility in terms of simplicity, the speech interference level method should be used only as a rough yardstick by the engineer in those situations where it is applicable.   For more detailed and useful information concerning the expected performance of a communication system, the 20-band method is recommended.

Person-to-person Speech.   It is necessary on occasion to evaluate the interference effects of noise in office, factory, and military work spaces where a public-address system or interphone is not desired or felt necessary.   The speech interference level can be used to provide a quick and, under some conditions of noise, accurate estimation of the probable intelligibility of speech communications carried out on a direct person-to-person basis.

In order to use the speech interference level method for this situation, the following steps are required:

1. Obtain the arithmetic average of the decibel levels of noise in the octave bands 600 to 1,200 cps and 1,200 to 2,400 cps and 2,400 to 4,800 cps.   This is the speech interference level.
2. Consult Table 9.2 to determine maximum distances between talker and listener and voice level required to permit reliable speech communications for a given speech interference level.

If the speech interference level exceeds the values in Table 9.2, difficulties and misunderstandings in speech communications may be expected.

Table 9.2. Speech Interference Levels (in Db re 0.0002 Microbar) Which Barely Permit Reliable Conversation at the Distances and Voice Levels Indicated

Distance, ft, between source and listener	Normal voice level, db	Raised voice level, db
0.5	71	77
1	65	71
2	59	65
3	55	61
4	53	59
5	51	57
6	49	55
12	43	49

It has been suggested in the past that higher speech interference levels are tolerable if the talkers increase their vocal effort to that of a shout, which will provide a speech level that is 12 db greater than that obtained with the "raised" voice level utilized in the computations of speech interference levels in the second column of Table 9.2. However, recent research data indicate that we cannot rely on the intelligibility of very loud or shouted speech.[40]   Not only is there some question as to whether the talker will be able to maintain the vocal effort required for shouting but the intelligibility of the speech deteriorates at these high levels even though a relatively high signal-to-noise ratio is maintained.

An additional variable that must be given some consideration in evaluating the effects of noise on person-to-person speech is that of lip reading.   The speech interference levels presented in Table 9.2 assume that the listener obtained no appreciable cues regarding the speech signal as the result of observing the facial, lip, and mouth movements of the talker.   This is true at the rather high signal-to-noise ratios required for speech interference level but recent tests show that in intense noise and at low signal-to-noise ratios even unpracticed observers are able to improve their intelligibility test scores by as much as 30 percentage points by watching the talker's face.

In summary, in intense noise we do not gain in communication effectiveness what we might expect by increasing voice level to a raised or shouting level, but this factor is to some significant degree compensated for in person-to-person speech by "lip reading." It is important to bear these factors in mind when attempting to predict what the intelligibility of person-to-person speech communication will be in a given noise environment.

Criterion of Acceptable Performance. Before turning to a discussion of the components of a speech-communication system, a final word regarding criterion of performance of a speech-communication system in noise is in order. It has become generally accepted practice that a system which will score 70 per cent correct or better with a trained crew of talkers and listeners on the American Standards Association word test is acceptable for military, industrial, office, and general operations; this level of system performance would be predicted by an articulation index of 0.4 and by speech interference levels calculated on the basis of acoustical measurements of the noise and speech signal at the ear of the listener.

The intelligibility of sentences and standardized phrases and messages used in normal day-to-day operations will be at or near 100 per cent over a system meeting this criterion. Systems or person-to-person speech communications that fall below this level of performance require improvement if possible. This improvement, of course, is obtainable by better equipment design or usage and control or reduction of interfering noise.

THE COMPONENTS OF A SPEECH-COMMUNICATION SYSTEM

The Talker and His Environment. The first element in the speech-communication system is the talker and his environment. As noted above, the speech spectrum which was shown in Fig. 9.1 may change with differences in talking level.[6] There are many reasons why this level changes. Among these are (1) normal differences among individuals;[2,3,4,5] (2) noise at the talker's environment, which will cause him to talk louder; (3) fatigue, which will lower his talking level; (4) speaking into an enclosure such as a gas mask, respirator, diving helmet, or oxygen mask, which in general will make it harder for him to talk;[41,42] (5) talking at high altitude in the case of airplanes, where the rarefication of the gas in the talker's vocal tract causes his talking level to drop because of the bad impedance match obtaining with the vocal folds;[43,46] and (6) the ability of the talker to hear himself, for when such a so-called side-tone signal is loud, his talking level will drop.[47] Not all these factors can be measured with any great exactness, but the speech-communication systems designer should try to take as many into account as he possibly can and should, whenever possible, set up experiments which simulate the condition of talking so that he may observe variations in the talker's speech spectrum. The noise in the talker's environment will, of course, determine the signal-to-noise ratio at the microphone; consequently the sound-pressure spectrum of this noise must be measured if articulation-index calculations are to be performed. Another important factor in the talker's environment is the reverberation. If the reverberation time is long, it may affect the talker's manner of speaking and will certainly reduce the word-articulation score by masking the speech signal with echoes of previous speech sounds. Some indicative and qualitative results have been published, but, unfortunately, no reliable quantitative information regarding this effect is available.[48-53]

Microphones (Also See Chap. 16). The next element in the system is the microphone. In so far as intelligibility is concerned it makes very little difference whether a carbon, dynamic, crystal, or condenser microphone is used provided they have the same response-frequency and distortion characteristics. It is important that the output-input characteristic be linear enough and that the response-frequency characteristics be wide enough and smooth enough to make the articulation-index computation reasonably accurate. Normally it is desirable to have the bandwidth as wide as possible in order to get uniform response between 200 and 6,100 cps. A pressure microphone which is reasonably linear is quite satisfactory for most applications, but it is desirable to avoid nonlinearities such as sometimes occur in the case of carbon microphones where there is packing of the carbon granules.   When noise at the talker is a serious problem (100 db is a rough estimate of the level at which real difficulty will be encountered), a pressure-gradient, or noise-canceling, microphone should be

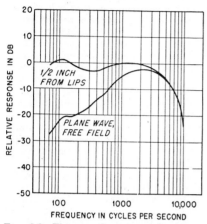

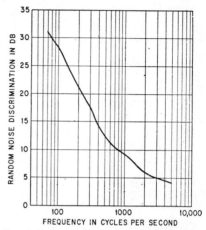

FIG. 9.8. The on-axis response-frequency characteristics of a commercial pressure-gradient microphone, RCA type. (*Courtesy of Radio Corporation of America.*)

FIG. 9.9. The random-noise discrimination of the microphone referred to in Fig. 9.8.

used.   This is a microphone which discriminates against noise or sound coming from a distance source with respect to sound coming from a close source.[58]   The response-frequency characteristics for a commercially available microphone of this kind for both a close source and a distant source are shown in Fig. 9.8.   It should be noted that the difference between these two curves, which is called the axial noise discrimination of the microphone, is greatest at low frequencies and is smallest at high frequencies.

A pressure-gradient microphone is a dipole device, and its directional characteristics look like a pair of tangent spheres.   The ratio of response along the axis to the integral of the response to random angles of incidence is $3:1$.[54]   Thus, if one speaks along the axis of the microphone, a directional-efficiency term amounting to as much as 5 db may be added uniformly over the whole frequency range.   The random noise discrimination, which is the sum of the directional efficiency and the axial noise discrimination, is shown in Fig. 9.9 for this same microphone.

A noise shield for the microphone is another device which can improve the signal-to-noise ratio where noise at the talker is a serious problem (roughly 100 db or more).   Such a shield, one that is

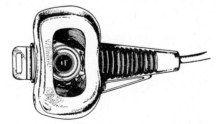

FIG. 9.10. A noise shield, type MX-1334/U, installed on a military pressure-gradient microphone, type M-34/AIC. (*Courtesy of Radio Corporation of America.*)

used with a military pressure-gradient microphone, is shown mounted on the microphone in Fig. 9.10.   The noise exclusion of this shield is shown in Fig. 9.11.   Experiments have shown that the addition of a noise shield of this size or larger does not interfere with the noise-canceling properties of these microphones; so the combination of low-frequency noise discrimination of the microphone and high-frequency noise exclusion of the noise shield produces a very good improvement in the signal-to-noise ratio throughout the frequency range.[59]

Most microphones do not have noise shields, but moderately good ones are not particularly difficult to construct from felt, rubber, or similar materials. Care must be taken to select a size large enough to prevent the introduction of standing-wave patterns and resonances that will change the response-frequency characteristics of the microphone. If the shield is too large, however, it will prove to be unwieldy. Provision must be made for exhalation without pressure build-up in the shield when talking at a high level. Experience has shown that a hole about 0.1 sq in. in area will provide a satisfactory vent; it should be located as far from the microphone as possible.[60] Some good noise shields have been developed for use on dictating equipment in courtrooms to prevent the dictator's voice from interfering with the proceedings. They also can be used to provide acoustic insulation to prevent noise in a room from interfering with speech which is spoken into a microphone.

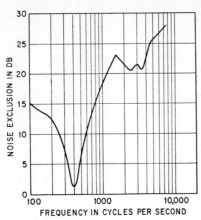

Fig. 9.11. The noise exclusion of the noise shield shown in Fig. 9.10.

Amplifiers. There are two modifications of conventional audio amplifiers which are used to improve intelligibility of speech-communication systems. The first of these is the incorporation of an *automatic volume control (AVC)* in the amplifier to compensate for differences in talking level which are caused by the factors noted previously. The function of AVC is to keep the output of the amplifier nearly constant

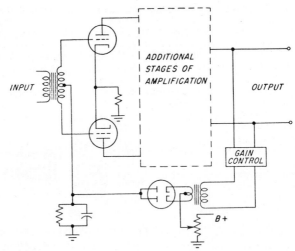

Fig. 9.12. Simplified automatic volume control or compressor circuit. (*From Ref. 63.*)

regardless of variations in the input. Quite normally an AVC system will compress variations of 30 to 40 db at the input into variations of approximately 5 db at the output. The two most frequently used methods of obtaining AVC action are (1) to employ a nonlinear circuit element with a relatively long time constant and the desired output-input characteristics in the amplifier, and (2) to use a portion of the amplifier output, rectified and applied as a bias to the first amplifier stage (sometimes to other stages too), to regulate the output by controlling the gain.   A typical AVC circuit of the latter kind is shown in Fig. 9.12.

In all cases several characteristics are important.   The first is the attack and release times.   The attack time is the time it takes the amplifier to stabilize its gain after an input signal is applied.   Similarly, the release time is the time it takes the gain of the amplifier to return to normal after the signal is removed.   If the attack time is too long, parts of words will come through at uncomfortably high levels; on the other hand, circuit complexity and transient problems limit the designer in his desire to make the time short.   It is also possible to have an initial reduction in gain which is applied as soon as the press-to-talk switch is depressed.[59]   This will prevent the noise which is present before the talker begins to speak from being transmitted by the amplifier at

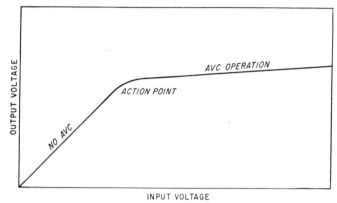

FIG. 9.13. Output-input characteristic of an automatic volume control circuit.

full gain.   When the talker speaks, his voice signal will take control of the AVC. Under some circumstances the gain of the amplifier may be dictated and controlled by the noise level at the listening location.   For example, in a restaurant at rush hour, the gain is increased because the noise level is high, while in the quieter periods the gain is reduced and the relative signal-to-noise ratio will remain nearly the same. The release time of the AVC circuit should be short enough to prevent the transmitted noise level from rising between words and phrases, and to compensate for changing input levels.   Here the communication-system designer must determine what causes the changing inputs and design his AVC characteristic accordingly.   If, for example, the input changes are caused by the talker's turning his head in the course of his normal duties, then the release time should be short.   But if the variations in input are caused by different talkers or by fatigue or different conditions of use of the talker's microphone, then the release time should be considerably longer.   Experiments performed on a number of systems indicate that intelligibility is not affected markedly by a wide variation in the attack and release time in AVC.[59]   Attack times of the order of $\frac{1}{10}$ sec are easily obtained and are usually quite satisfactory.   Release times as long as 10 sec and in some cases 30 sec are desirable.   The point at which AVC action begins in an amplifier is often called the action point (see Fig. 9.13).   For a limited-gain amplifier the higher the action point, the higher maximum output and the smaller the range of input for which AVC action is obtained.   The lower the action point, the greater the AVC range but the lower the maximum output.   This is a compromise which the communication-system designer will also have to work out. Finally, there is the operating characteristic slope shown in Fig. 9.13.   The wider the range of inputs over which AVC is to act, the more difficult it is to keep the AVC characteristic slope small.   However, for speech communication a moderate slope is usually quite acceptable.

Another special modification of conventional audio amplifiers which is used to improve the intelligibility for operation under noisy conditions is *peak clipping*.[38,59,65-76] As illustrated in Fig. 9.14, the peaks of the input voltage wave are clipped; then the signal may be reamplified so that the clipped peaks are equal to the level of the peaks before clipping. The result of this is that the long-term average signal level is increased without increasing the peak power-handling capacity of the amplifier.

Clipping and reamplification improve intelligibility when one of three conditions exists: (1) The electrical signal coming to the listener's loudspeaker or headset has a very good signal-to-noise ratio and the ambient noise at the listening location is so

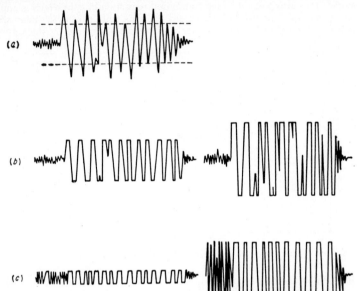

FIG. 9.14. A representation of the waveform of the word "Joe" when undistorted (a) after 6-db peak clipping, and (b) after 20-db peak clipping; (c) at the right, the waves of (b) and (c) are shown reamplified until their peak-to-peak amplitudes equal the peak-to-peak amplitude of (a). (*From Ref. 73.*)

high that the listener needs peak levels of unclipped speech which are above the threshold of discomfort in order for him to get maximum intelligibility. In this case peak clipping makes it possible for one to raise the average signal level to a satisfactory value without having the peaks exceed the threshold of discomfort of the listener. (2) The signal entering the clipper has a high signal-to-noise ratio; the power-handling capacity of the link between the clipper and the listener's headset or loudspeaker is limited. The benefits are particularly great if the speech signal is weak because of limited power or if the listener is in intense noise. This is the situation one normally encounters in the case of a person in a noisy room or vehicle listening over a communication system to a talker who is speaking from a quiet location. (3) The noise in the system preceding the clipper is impulsive with a high-peak factor. In this case clipping can be used to clip the noise far more than the speech.

On the other hand, peak clipping and reamplification impair intelligibility when the signal-to-noise ratio before the clipper is low because of low-frequency noise and the noise newly introduced into the system after the clipper is also low. In this case the noise in the channel before the clipper is intermodulated with the speech signal and the result is a definite loss in speech intelligibility.

If the existing situations do not meet any of these conditions, one cannot be sure whether peak clipping will improve speech intelligibility. Preliminary measurements have indicated that under most conditions peak clipping which does not exceed 12 db will not be detrimental to speech intelligibility. Peak clipping greater than 12 db will not impair and will frequently improve intelligibility unless the signal-to-noise ratio entering the clipper is quite low, but will make the speech sound

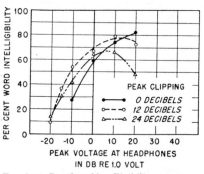

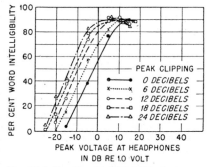

Fig. 9.15. Results of intelligibility tests conducted with the talkers in the quiet and the listeners in ambient airplane noise. (*From Ref. 70.*)

Fig. 9.16. Results of intelligibility tests conducted with the speakers and listeners in the presence of simulated airplane noise. The over-all effect of noise picked up at the microphone can be observed by comparing these results with those in Fig. 9.15. It is seen that, when the microphone picks up noise, 24 db of clipping is not so beneficial as 12 db of clipping. A dynamic microphone (non-noise-canceling) was used. (*From Ref. 70.*)

somewhat harsh and unnatural. Intelligibility test results for different degrees of peak clipping are shown in Figs. 9.15 and 9.16.

Two common methods of peak clipping are used. In one, peak clipping is obtained by merely overdriving the amplifier. That is, the operating point of the output tube is placed halfway between (1) the grid cutoff point due to grid current on the positive swings of the control grid, and (2) the cutoff point due to the grid's going negative with respect to cathode on negative swings. The operating range is then chosen so that these cutoffs come at the proper clipping levels. The operating range and the operating point are controlled by selection of the proper plate load and cathode-bias resistors. Some-times a resistor placed in series with the

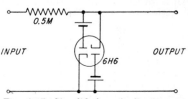

Fig. 9.17. Simplified peak-clipping circuit.

control grid of the output tube helps sharpen the corners of the clipped waveform on positive swings of the grid. The other method of clipping is to use a pair of diodes "back to back" as shown in Fig. 9.17 to limit the signal passing through the amplifier by providing a shunting path when signal levels exceed the biasing voltage on the batteries.

Both AVC and peak clipping require gain that is not used to give higher listening levels. In the case of peak clipping the gain is used to obtain a level to clip. In the case of AVC it is used to obtain the control signal. Because normally the gain of the amplifier is limited by considerations such as feedback, number of tubes, power drain, and cost, the relative improvement in intelligibility which is obtained in the two methods when the same amount of gain is available presents a difficult choice. In some cases the choice is clear. In many, only experimentation will determine which procedure gives the higher intelligibility.

If AVC and peak clipping are both used in a system, it is a problem to determine the best relative location of the two in the system. Some of the following considerations should be kept in mind by the experimenter and designer:

1. There is little reason to have AVC follow peak clipping unless the only action of the clipper is to eliminate peaks of impulsive noise.
2. AVC ahead of the clipper will reduce the amount of gain required in the clipper portion but will not reduce the over-all gain.
3. If radio links are present, AVC in the audio amplifier may eliminate the need for it in radio transmitters or receivers.
4. If loudspeakers are used, AVC may make it easier to prevent acoustic feedback.
5. If several speech signals are mixed at a listening station, AVC on each input will reduce cross talk and maintain the outputs nearly uniform; AVC in the station amplifier must occur before mixing to accomplish the same results.
6. Peak clipping of mixed signals will introduce intermodulation distortion.
7. Peak clipping should not be applied to a system having poor signal-to-noise ratio.
8. If side tone (a system permitting the talker to hear himself by feeding back to his ear some of the microphone signals) is taken out of the amplifier after AVC action, the talker has little idea how his voice output changes.
9. However, it is less important for the talker to hear his voice level change than for him to hear his signal-to-noise level change; AVC does not alter the signal-to-noise ratio.
10. Electronic-circuit considerations make it difficult to apply AVC action after the signal has been amplified to a level suitable for side tone.

Although under some conditions intelligibility can be improved by tilting the response-frequency characteristic positively (rising response with increase in frequency) before any peak clipping is introduced, the systems designer is discouraged from using this technique unless he performs experiments showing its value under his conditions. This warning is given for two reasons: first, the amount of tilting which will give best results seems to depend on the signal-to-noise ratio of the input to the tilting network, and, second, the emphasis of the high-frequency portion of the speech spectrum usually will be disliked by the listeners. In fact, the users usually prefer response-frequency characteristic of a speech system having its high-frequency components deemphasized; if adequate intelligibility can be obtained with a gradual rolling off of the frequencies above 3,000 cps, this response characteristic may be used.

Loudspeakers. Most listening over speech-communications systems is done through loudspeakers. These loudspeakers fall into two general types: the first is the horn loudspeaker which provides high efficiency and the second is the direct radiator loudspeaker which usually has better response at low frequencies than a horn loudspeaker unless the latter is very large.

In order to choose the proper loudspeaker, the system designer must first determine the required sound pressure level and spectrum at the listener's ears. This is done by measuring or estimating the noise level and spectrum and using the articulation-index computations to determine the signal-to-noise ratio as a function of frequency. Then the designer must examine the response-frequency characteristics, the sensitivities, the power-handling capacities, and the directional characteristics of the loudspeakers available to him, to determine which one will best serve the purpose when installed at the planned locations. The electrical power required for the loudspeaker to produce the desired sound pressure must be within the manufacturer's rated limits or the loudspeaker will be damaged. The output requirements for the amplifiers are usually determined by this process of starting with the sound pressure required and working backward through the system.

Acoustic feedback is a very important consideration in the installation of loudspeakers. If a microphone connected to the input of the speech-communication system is near the loudspeaker, it is likely that the system will oscillate at the frequency at which the system gain is highest. This oscillation, sometimes called "squeal," is caused by the microphone's picking up sound energy from the loudspeaker directly or after reflections in the room and feeding this energy into the amplifier and loudspeaker, from which it comes out at higher level than before.   This process is repeated, building up each time, until the overload limit of some component of the system is reached.   The feedback level is then stabilized.

The obvious cure is to reduce the gain of the amplifier, but this gain reduction may reduce the intelligibility to an unacceptable value.   In such cases, other methods are necessary.

A system with a uniform response-frequency characteristic will be less likely to feed back than one with peaks in the characteristic.   Sometimes the peaks can be eliminated by the proper choice of components; sometimes electrical compensation is required.   In large reverberant chambers acoustic feedback can be eliminated by using a velocity or unidirectional microphone.   Sometimes it is necessary to build a high-pass filter to reduce the system gain at low frequencies (below 100 or 200 cps) where reverberation is most troublesome.   In severe cases a shield for the microphone or a booth for the talker may be required.   Another possible solution, applicable particularly outdoors or in rooms with low reverberation, is to place the microphone at a point where the directional characteristics of the loudspeaker give a low sound level.   In systems utilizing multiple microphones and loudspeakers, it may be possible to connect relays in the system so that, when a microphone press-to-talk switch is actuated, the loudspeakers in the immediate vicinity are cut off.

Acoustic feedback is usually eliminated by trial and error.   When testing for feedback, the engineer should talk into the system, simulating conditions of actual use. Frequently a system that is normally well-behaved will feed back when a loud noise or speech signal is introduced.   If a close-talking microphone is used, the experimenter must be careful to hold his mouth as close (or closer) to the microphone as the talkers will in normal use because these microphones are susceptible to feedback at the resonant frequencies of the mouth cavity.   If the engineer utters loud sustained vowel sounds with his lips close to the microphone, he should be able to discover any feedback difficulties.

Headsets.   If a very high noise level prevails in the vicinity of the listener, the highest intelligibility probably will be obtained if he wears a headset.   There are two reasons: the first is that high signal levels can be obtained with relatively low power because the earphone is closely coupled to the ear, and the second is that the earcap in which the earphone is mounted will attenuate the ambient noise somewhat and thus give a higher signal-to-noise ratio for the same sound pressure due to the electrical signal.   The problem of signal-to-noise ratio at the listener's ear when he is wearing a headset is a fairly complicated one.   First, it must be remembered that the electrical input to the earphone consists of the combination of speech signal and the noise which has been introduced previous to the headset.   This electrical signal is then transformed into acoustic sound pressure which is mixed with the sound pressure due to the listener's environmental noise.   Thus, the signal-to-noise ratio at his ear is a combination of the speech signal introduced originally and the noises introduced all along the line.   If, as is frequently the case, both the talker and the listener are in very loud noise, and the noise introduced between the microphone and the earphone is negligible compared with the other noise in the system, we may designate these two noises as N_T and N_L.   The signal-to-noise ratio at the listener's end will be the signal divided by N_T plus N_L.   If a first-order pressure-gradient microphone without a noise shield is used then the N_T will be small at low frequency and large at high frequency. If the conventional earcap is used by the listener, N_L will be small at high frequency and large at low frequency.   The sum of the noises will thus be reasonably large throughout the whole frequency band and the signal-to-noise ratio will be poor throughout.   A noise shield used at the microphone end will give a good signal-to-noise ratio coming out of the microphone at high frequency and thus preserve the good signal-to-noise ratio which can be obtained at the headset for the listener's noise.   Similarly, if a device can be used which will give high signal-to-noise ratios at the listener's end, reducing the N_L term greatly, the good signal-to-noise ratio provided by the noise-discrimination properties at the microphone will be preserved and the over-all signal-to-noise ratio will be good throughout the frequency spectrum.   Unfortunately, the noise exclusion of earcaps on headsets is quite poor at low frequency.   A normal earcap will provide only about 5 db of noise insulation at frequencies below approximately 800 cps.   The noise exclusion then rises sharply until it has reached 20 db or more at about 1,500 to 2,000 cps.   It is usually then reasonably uniform from there on out. Noise-exclusion curves for a number of earcaps are given in Chap. 8.

The earcap is also important because it determines the size of the cavity through which the earphone is coupled to the ear.   If this cavity is small, high sound pressures can be obtained with small amounts of power at the earphone.   If the cavity is large, it requires large amounts of power to produce the same sound pressure at the ear. There is a disadvantage in the use of small cavities formed by the earcap, however. This disadvantage is that, in order to obtain small cavities, it is necessary for the earcap to rest against the pinna or external fleshy part of the ear.   If the headset must

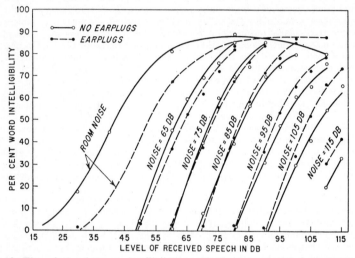

Fig. 9.18. The relation between intelligibility and speech level with noise level as the parameter.   In loud noise Ear Wardens improve intelligibility.   (*From Ref. 93.*)

be worn for any lengthy period of time, it will be uncomfortable.   If a doughnut sort of cushion is used to surround the pinna completely, a large cavity will be formed. In order to get equally high sound pressures, a larger amount of power must be obtained from the amplifier and the power-handling capacity of the earphone must be greater, usually resulting in a larger, heavier earphone which is more uncomfortable to wear. It is possible, of course, to get the same signal-to-noise ratio at the listener by means of greater acoustic installation of the earcap instead of increasing the power-handling capacity of the earphone.   To do this, however, requires that the earcap must be larger and heavier and, once again, the headset becomes uncomfortable to wear. Insert earphones which partially or entirely enter the ear canal may solve most of these problems, but they introduce new problems, as discussed in Chap. 8.

Earplugs.   If the noise is sufficiently intense, the listener's ears may need protection. Ordinary ear sockets will do some good, of course, but their low-frequency insulation is poor.   Earplugs that are inserted in the ear canal provide considerably greater attenuation (see Chap. 8).   Figure 9.18 shows the results of some experiments performed during World War II.   Note that in the low noise levels word-intelligibility scores without earplugs are approximately the same as or slightly higher than with them, but at higher noise levels the scores are higher with earplugs than without.   The apparent reason is that the listener does not perceive words so well at high levels as he does at more moderate levels (when the signal-to-noise ratio is the same) because of "overloading" and distortion in the auditory system at high levels.   The earplugs reduce the over-all levels of both the speech and noise to more moderate levels without affecting the signal-to-noise ratio. Whenever the effective masking level of the noise is less than 75 db, the use of earplugs will reduce intelligibility at low signal-to-noise ratios. In somewhat greater, but moderate noise levels, speech intelligibility will not be appreciably altered by the wearing of earplugs; and at high noise levels, as previously mentioned, intelligibility will be improved through the use of earplugs.

EXAMPLE OF OVER-ALL SYSTEM DESIGN

As an example of the above-described methods, the following communication problem and its solution are described. A factory has a diesel power plant containing an engine room and a control room. In the latter a large number of pumps are used to supply the factory with pneumatic and hydraulic power. Communication from the engine room to the rest of the factory is necessary only occasionally, but

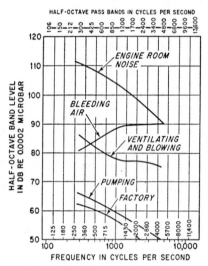

Fig. 9.19. Half-octave band noise analysis for various noise conditions.

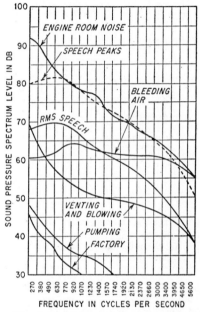

Fig. 9.20. Noise and speech spectra for various conditions. The spectra are shown as sound-pressure spectrum levels vs. frequency.

communication from the control room to the factory is required almost constantly. Two-way communication between the control room and the engine room is also required. Because the power-plant engineers must move about freely, they do not wear headsets, but in the engine room they wear earplugs for protection.

For the most part, only a limited number of standardized messages will be exchanged between the engine and control rooms and repetitions are possible. Therefore, 70 per cent word intelligibility is considered adequate for this noncritical situation; from Fig. 9.5 the corresponding articulation index is 0.4.

A half-octave band analysis of the noise levels in the engine room, the control room, and the rest of the factory is shown in Fig. 9.19 for the different conditions of use. The variation of the noise in the control room complicates the problem. First consider the signal-to-noise ratios at a microphone in each condition. In Fig. 9.20 the noise levels of Fig. 9.19 have been plotted in terms of pressure-spectrum levels on an articulation-index computation sheet. The speech spectrum of Fig. 9.1 has also been plotted here, but with 28.4 db added uniformly—28.4 db to convert from 1 in to 1.5 in. an average talking distance for a pressure microphone. Also shown is the speech-peak curve, 12 db higher. It should be noted, however, that, if this speech-peak curve lies uniformly 12 db above the noise curve, the articulation index of the system may be as high as 0.4 ($12\frac{2}{30}$ = 0.4). An equivalent statement is that, if at the microphone the entire noise spectrum lies at or below the long-term rms speech spectrum, the system intelligibility is potentially adequate. However, noise at this level will be quite audible and may be objectionable to the listeners.

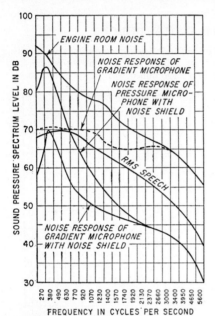

FIG. 9.21. The engine-room noise spectrum and the noise output of (a) a pressure-gradient microphone with a uniform close-source response characteristic, (b) the same microphone used with a noise shield, and (c) a pressure microphone with a uniform response characteristic and used with the same noise shield. The speech output of all three is the same.

Look first at the problem of talking from the control room to the engine room. The three rather different noise spectra in the control room are (1) bleeding air to test the lines, (2) various venting and blowing operations during pneumatic build-up and relief, and (3) normal pumping operation. These represent maximum octave-band measurements during each operation. Bleeding air is of such short duration (3 to 5 sec) that communication is not essential; therefore, it is not necessary to design for this condition. A comparison of the "bleeding air" and "rms speech" curves in Fig. 9.20 shows that the signal-to-noise ratio is too low to permit the over-all system articulation index to reach 0.4. In the case of the venting and blowing and the normal pumping operations, the rms speech spectrum lies well above the noise throughout nearly all the intelligibility spectrum; so an ordinary pressure microphone will provide a speech signal that is adequate.

The same is true of the factory noise, but in the case of the engine room the noise levels are so high that practically no intelligible speech will be transmitted over an unshielded pressure microphone. Therefore, consider using a pressure-gradient microphone having a uniform response characteristic and the random-noise discrimination shown in Fig. 9.9. A noise shield might be used with it. In Fig. 9.21 the noise-exclusion characteristic shown in Fig. 9.11 has been added to the noise-discrimination curve to give an over-all curve of signal-to-noise improvement.

Note that the microphone noise discrimination by itself is certainly insufficient to provide adequate intelligibility, but that, if a noise shield is used on a pressure microphone, the signal-to-noise ratio is improved sufficiently above 700 cps to compensate for the poor signal-to-noise ratio below that frequency. Adequate intelligibility seems assured with this shield, but the low-frequency noise coming over the system is sure to prove highly objectionable, especially when heard in the relative quiet of the factory. If an electrical high-pass filter is introduced to eliminate both speech signal and noise at low frequencies, the voice quality will be so adversely affected that users are sure to complain. Therefore, it seems advisable to use both a gradient microphone and a noise shield which together will give the signal-to-noise ratio also shown in Fig. 9.21.

Having thus chosen microphone equipment which will give sufficiently good signal-to-noise ratio under all the conditions, let us turn to the listening problem. All listening is to be done over loudspeakers. The noise level in the engine room is so high

(124 db over-all) that everyone wears earplugs having sound-attenuation characteristics similar to those given in Chap. 8. Both the loudspeaker signal and the noise will be reduced by this amount so the signal-to-noise ratio at the listener will not be affected, but it will be possible for the loudspeaker usefully to generate peak sound pressures above 120 db without the listeners' finding them particularly uncomfortable. Figure 9.22 shows the response-frequency characteristics and sensitivities of two loudspeakers potentially suitable for the engine and control room, respectively. It is assumed that only the more sensitive (curve B) will be adequate for reproducing the speech in the engine room.

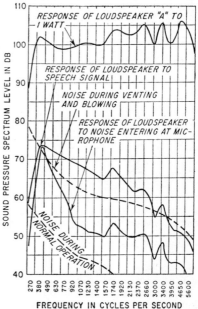

In calculating the acoustic-output spectrum of the loudspeaker, it is estimated that, for compartments of the size found in this factory, a distance of 6 ft represents approximately the distance at which uniform level (due to reinforcement by reflection from the compartment walls) is reached. Therefore, general coverage

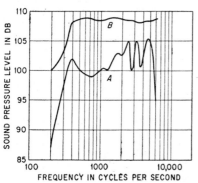

FIG. 9.22. Free-field response-frequency characteristics of two loudspeakers for the control room and the engine room measured at 6 ft with 1-watt sine wave applied to the loudspeakers.

FIG. 9.23. The control-room noise spectra and the spectra at 6 ft due to speech and noise at the microphone as reproduced by loudspeaker A of Fig. 9.22.

is estimated on the basis of the calculated output level of 6 ft, starting with the on-axis response to the loudspeaker measured in a dead room.

Consider first the control room. Figure 9.23 shows the noise spectra for venting and blowing and by normal operation. It also shows response curve A from Fig. 9.22 plotted at the proper level for 1-watt pure tone and the response of the loudspeaker to the rms speech spectrum at a level which appears satisfactory for intelligibility. The curve for noise picked up by a gradient microphone with a noise shield and reproduced by the loudspeaker is also shown. This noise and the ambient noise add to give the total noise over which speech must be understood. In the case of normal operation, the microphone noise is clearly limiting, but during the venting and blowing operation, both noise sources must be considered at low frequencies. The articulation index is 0.46.

Note that the power-handling capacity of the required amplifier may be easily calculated, for at 400 cps the rms speech curve lies 28 db below the 1-watt pure-tone response curve. Thus, if an audio amplifier having a uniform response-frequency characteristic is used, the long-term rms power delivered over all frequencies would be just 1 watt. (From Fig. 9.1 the over-all long-term rms speech level is 28 db above the spectrum level at 400 cps.) Instantaneous speech peaks occur as much as 20 db above the long-term rms. To accommodate them would require an amplifier capable of delivering 100 watts. Common practice is to allow a 10- to 12-db peak factor; thus, an amplifier capable of delivering 20 watts with perhaps 5 per cent harmonic distortion should be very suitable.

In the engine room the loudspeaker problem is a very severe one. In Fig. 9.24 the engine-room noise spectra is shown again. The response curve B from Fig. 9.22 is plotted at the proper level for 1-watt pure tone. The response of the loudspeaker to an rms speech spectrum at a level suitable for adequate intelligibility is shown, together with the loudspeaker response to the noise picked up at the pressure microphone in the control room during venting and blowing operations. If the sum of the noise entering the system at the microphone and the engine-room noise is used, the speech spectrum shown will give an articulation index of 0.41.

The calculation of the power required from the amplifier is done in the same manner as for the control room. The long-term rms speech level lies 28 db above the spectrum level at 400 cps. (Note that this will be 127 db sound pressure level, acceptable only because earplugs are worn.) From Fig. 9.24 the spectrum level required from the amplifier at 400 cps is 0.2 watt. The long-term rms speech level must be 63 watts. A 20-db instantaneous peak factor would raise the power-handling capacity to 6,300 watts. Therefore, 8 db of peak clipping will be introduced so that the maximum instantaneous peak power will be 1,000 watts. Thus an amplifier capable of delivering 1,000 watts would be required for the 12 peak factor commonly allowed for and used in the articulation-index computation. Enough loudspeakers must be used to give a total peak power-handling capacity of 1,000 watts.

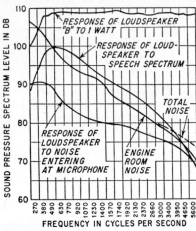

Fig. 9.24. The engine-room noise spectra and the spectra at 6 ft due to speech and noise at the microphone as reproduced by loudspeaker B of Fig. 9.22.

In a similar manner, the reader may determine the loudspeaker level and amplifier requirements for listeners in the factory.

REFERENCES

1. Sacia, C. F., and C. J. Beck: *Bell System Tech. J.*, **5**: 393 (1926).
2. Dunn, H. K., and S. D. White: *J. Acoust. Soc. Amer.*, **11**: 278 (1940).
3. Stevens, S. S., J. P. Egan, and G. A. Miller: *J. Acoust. Soc. Amer.*, **19**: 771 (1946).
4. Rudmose, H. W., et al.: *J. Acoust. Soc. Amer.*, **20**: 503 (1948).
5. Benson, R. W., and I. J. Hirsh: *J. Acoust. Soc. Amer.*, **25**: 499 (1953).
6. Licklider, J. C. R., M. E. Hawley, and R. A. Walkling: (Abstract), *J. Acoust. Soc. Amer.*, **27**: 207 (1955).
7. IRE Standards on American Recommended Practice for Volume Measurements of Electrical Speech and Program Waves, 1953, *Proc. IRE*, **42**: 815 (1954).
8. American Standard 224.3-1944, American Standards Association, New York.
9. American Standard Z24.23-1955 (Pending), American Standards Association, New York.
10. Hawley, M. E.: Unpublished data.
11. Miller, G. A., G. A. Heise, and W. Lichten: *J. Exptl. Psychol.*, **41**: 329 (1951).
12. Hirsh, I. J., E. G. Reynolds, and M. Joseph: *J. Acoust. Soc. Amer.*, **26**: 530 (1954).
13. Abrams, M. H., and J. E. Karlin: OSRD 1919, Harvard University Psycho-acoustic Laboratory, 1943, PB 22906.
14. Abrams, M. H., and J. E. Karlin: NDRC Research on Sound Control, IC 32, Harvard University Psycho-acoustic Laboratory, 1943, PB 77772.

15. Abrams, M. H., et al.: OSRD 4023, September, 1944, PB 19805.
16. Moser, H. M.: *Speech Monogr.*, **13**: 47 (1946).
17. Abrams, M. H., et al.: Harvard University Psycho-acoustic Laboratory, PB 15215.
18. Frick, F. C., and W. H. Sumby: *J. Acoust. Soc. Amer.*, **24**: 595 (1952).
19. Curtis, J. F.: OSRD 3862, 4261, 1944, PB 12171, 12176.
20. Egan, J. P.: Harvard University Psycho-acoustic Laboratory, OSRD 3802, November, 1944, PB 22848.
21. Snidecor, J. C., et al.: OSRD 3176, January, 1944 (ATI-14587).
22. Whan, F. L.: *Quart. J. Speech*, **30**: 261 (1944).
23. Black, J. W.: *Speech Monogr.*, **13**: 64 (1946).
24. Black, J. W., and H. M. Mason: *J. Acoust. Soc. Amer.*, **18**: 441 (1956).
25. Shoup, F. C.: *Speech Monogr.*, **13**: 59 (1946).
26. Kelly, J. C., and M. D. Steer: (Abstract) *Quart. J. Speech*, **38**: 167 (1952).
27. Fletcher, H.: "Speech and Hearing," D. Van Nostrand Company, Inc., Princeton, N.J. (2d ed., 1953).
28. Miller, G. A.: *Psychol. Bull.*, **41**: 105 (1944).
29. Egan, J. P., and F. M. Wiener: *J. Acoust. Soc. Amer.*, **18**: 435 (1946).
30. French, N. R., and J. C. Steinberg: *J. Acoust. Soc. Amer.*, **19**: 90 (1947).
31. Radley, W. G.: *J. Inst. Elec. Engrs. (London)*, **95**: 201 (May, 1948).
32. Fletcher, H., and R. H. Galt: *J. Acoust. Soc. Amer.*, **22**: 89 (1950).
33. Hawkins, J. E., Jr., and S. S. Stevens: *J. Acoust. Soc. Amer.*, **22**: 6 (1950).
34. Miller, G. A.: "Language and Communication," McGraw-Hill Book Company, Inc., New York, 1951.
35. Licklider, J. C. R., and G. A. Miller: p. 1040 in "Handbook of Experimental Psychology" (S. S. Stevens, ed.), John Wiley & Sons, Inc., New York, 1951.
36. Beranek, L. L.: *Proc. IRE*, **35**: 880 (1947).
37. Pollack, I.: *J. Acoust. Soc. Amer.*, **20**: 259 (1948).
38. Martin, D. W.: *J. Acoust. Soc. Amer.*, **22**: 614 (1950).
39. Kryter, K. D.: Unpublished data.
40. Pickett, J. M.: (Abstract), *J. Acoust. Soc. Amer.*, **27**: 1000 (1955).
41. Egan, J. P., et al.: OSRD 1816, 1943, PB 19773.
42. Morrow, C. T.: *J. Acoust. Soc. Amer.*, **19**: 645 (1947).
43. Kryter, K. D., J. C. R. Licklider, and E. B. Newman: *Am. Psychol.*, **1**: 281 (1946).
44. Weichbrod, J.: *J. Acoust. Soc. Amer.*, **18**: 161 (1946).
45. Clark, K. C., et al.: *J. Acoust. Soc. Amer.*, **20**: 776 (1948).
46. Kryter, K. D.: *J. Appl. Psychol.*, **32**: 503 (1948).
47. Black, J. W.: *J. Speech Disord.*, **16**: 56 (March, 1951).
48. Knudsen, V. O., and C. M. Harris: "Acoustical Designing in Architecture," Chap. 9, John Wiley & Sons, Inc., New York, 1950.
49. Vermeulen, R.: *Philips Tech. Rev.*, **3**: 139 (1938).
50. Shultz, C.: A Graphical Analysis of the Influence of Reverberation upon Articulation, M. S. thesis in electrical engineering, MIT, January, 1948.
51. Haas, H.: *Acustica*, **1**: 49 (1951).
52. Lee, B. S.: *J. Acoust. Soc. Amer.*, **22**: 824 (1950).
53. Muncey, R. W., A. F. B. Nickson, and P. Dubout: *Acustica*, **3**: 168 (1953).
54. Olson, H. F.: "Elements of Acoustical Engineering," 2d ed., D. Van Nostrand Company, Inc., Princeton, N.J., 1947.
55. Beranek, L. L.: "Acoustic Measurements," John Wiley & Sons, Inc., New York, 1949.
56. Richardson, E. G.: "Technical Aspects of Sound," vol. I, Elsevier Publishing Company, Amsterdam, 1953.
57. Beranek, L. L.: "Acoustics," McGraw-Hill Book Company, Inc., New York, 1954.
58. Hawley, M. E., and A. H. Kettler: *J. Acoust. Soc. Amer.*, **22**: 365 (1950).
59. Radio Corporation of America: Unpublished data.
60. Hawley, M. E., and W. F. Meeker: Unpublished data.
61. Reich, H. J.: "Theory and Applications of Electron Tubes," 2d ed., McGraw-Hill Book Company, Inc., New York, 1944.
62. Terman, F. E.: "Radio Engineers' Handbook," McGraw-Hill Book Company, Inc., 1943.
63. Frayne, J. G., and H. Wolfe: "Elements of Sound Recording," John Wiley & Sons, Inc., New York, 1949.
64. Langford-Smith, F.: "Radiotron Designer's Handbook," 4th ed., Radio Corporation of America, Harrison, N.J., 1952.
65. Licklider, J. C. R., M. I. Stein, and S. S. Stevens: Harvard University Psycho-acoustic Laboratory, September, 1944 (ATI-14701).
66. Kryter, K. D., et al.: Harvard University, October, 1944 (ATI-14597).

67. Kryter, K. D., et al.: Harvard University Psycho-Acoustic Laboratory, March, 1945 (ATI-64131).
68. Gross, N. B., and J. C. R. Licklider: Harvard University Psycho-Acoustic Laboratory, PNR 11, 1946.
69. Licklider, J. C. R.: *J. Acoust. Soc. Amer.*, **18**: 429 (1946).
70. Kryter, K. D., J. C. R. Licklider, and S. S. Stevens: *J. Acoust. Soc. Amer.*, **19**: 125 (1947).
71. Dean, M. H.: *Tele-Tech.*, May, 1947.
72. Licklider, J. C. R., and I. Pollack: *J. Acoust. Soc. Amer.*, **20**: 42 (1948).
73. Licklider, J. C. R., D. Bindra, and I. Pollack: *Am. J. Psychol.*, **61**: 1 (1948).
74. Licklider, J. C. R.: *J. Acoust. Soc. Amer.*, **22**: 820 (1950).
75. Pollack, I.: *J. Acoust. Soc. Amer.*, **24**: 538 (1952).
76. Saxe, R. K., and R. E. Lacy: (Abstract), *Proc. IRE*, **42**: 613 (March, 1954).
77. McLachlan, N. W.: "Loudspeakers," Oxford University Press, New York, 1934.
78. Morse, P. M.: "Vibration and Sound," 2d ed., McGraw-Hill Book Company, Inc., New York, 1948.
79. Kinsler, L. E., and A. R. Frey: "Fundamentals of Acoustics," John Wiley & Sons, Inc., New York, 1950.
80. Hunt, F. V.: "Electroacoustics," Harvard University Press, Cambridge, Mass., 1954.
81. Hopkins, H. F., and N. R. Stryker: *Proc. IRE*, **36**: 315 (March, 1948).
82. Salmon, V.: *Audio Engng.*, **35**: 13; **42** (August, 1951).
83. Hardy, H. C., H. H. Hall, and L. G. Ramer: *Proc. Natl. Electronics Conf.*, **8**: 99 (1952).
84. Brittain, F. H.: *J. Brit. Inst. Radio Engrs.*, **13**: 105 (February, 1953).
85. Olson, H. F.: *Trans. IRE*, P.G.A., AU-1, 7 (1953).
86. Veneklasen, P. S.: *Trans. IRE*, P.G.A., AU-1, 5 (1953).
87. Wente, E. C., and A. L. Thuras: *J. Acoust. Soc. Amer.*, **3**: 44 (1931).
88. Olson, H. F., and F. Massa: *J. Acoust. Soc. Amer.*, **6**: 250 (1935).
89. Egan, J. P., et al.: OSRD 901, October, 1942 (ATI-14635).
90. Egan, J. P., et al.: Harvard University Psycho-Acoustic Laboratory, OSRD 1491, NDRC 17-3-23, June, 1943, PB 22545.
91. Martin, D. W., and L. J. Anderson: *J. Acoust. Soc. Amer.*, **19**: 63 (1947).
92. Mott, E. E., and R. C. Miner: *Bell System Tech. J.*, January, 1951.
93. Kryter, K. D.: *J. Acoust. Soc. Amer.*, **18**: 413 (1946).

Chapter 10

EFFECTS OF NOISE ON BEHAVIOR

Donald E. Broadbent

Applied Psychology Research Unit
Cambridge, England

Behavior in response to noise can normally be measured in three ways. (1) A man may be asked to report on his own feeling or sensations. In the case of noise, this usually means enquiring about the *annoyance* which the noise is causing the man. (2) *Physiological* measurements may be applied, such as metabolism, rate of breathing, tension in the muscles, and similar indicators of the man's bodily state. (3) The man may be required to perform some task, and his *efficiency* on that task measured. This last type of measurement is from several points of view the most satisfactory. It is directly related to questions of practical importance, such as industrial efficiency, whereas the other two kinds of measurement have only an indirect relation. Furthermore, this type of measurement is usually more suited to statistical methods and gives results which are from this point of view of greater scientific value than the opinions expressed by the man concerned. It is also common to find that the three types of measure do not agree in estimating the importance of some environmental conditions. A man may say that he is unaffected by his long working hours and yet show in the time he takes to perform certain operations that his efficiency has declined. Conversely, he may express violent dislike for a task and yet be able to perform it perfectly satisfactorily. Similarly, he may show unaffected efficiency when physiological changes are certainly taking place in his body, or altered efficiency with no detectable physiological change. In such cases of disagreement, the hardheaded industrialist or soldier will usually prefer the measure of proficiency. Yet this is perhaps a short-sighted view. Complaints of annoyance by noise may well correlate with other forms of verbal behavior, such as legal action, which will have a cash value. Any physiological effect may similarly be a herald of high sickness absence or other unpleasant consequences in the future, even though it is not related to present efficiency. Although the greater proportion of this chapter will be devoted to questions of efficiency, therefore, we shall also consider the other two types of measure.

ANNOYANCE

Is a Nuisance Harmful? There is a widespread agreement that some noises are annoying to almost all people, and probably any particular noise is annoying to some person. This causes much confusion, since many who find noise annoying will argue that it is also a menace to health or efficiency. Others, knowing that efficiency on the tasks in which they are interested is unimpaired, may feel that annoyance is unimportant and may be led to argue against any effect of noise on behavior at all. But there is in nature no necessary connection between the pleasantness of some stimulus and its effects.   Medicine is often evil-tasting, and some pastimes have ill effects on health.   Yet this does not make the pleasant or unpleasant quality of stimuli an airy and unreal matter to be ignored.   Suppose we consider the behavior of animals, since they are not influenced by social custom and can be brought up experimentally to avoid differences in experience between different animals.   Yet if we present to a rat some saccharine every time it performs a particular response, that response will become more probable.   But saccharine is not, as far as we know, biologically useful to the rat.   An opposite result follows from administering electric shock even though the shock is too weak to cause physiological damage.   In a similar, although much more complex, fashion, a human being may dress in clothes of particular color or avoid food of a certain taste.   Sounds do not differ from other kinds of stimuli in being attractive or repellent; and people will take action to produce sounds they like and to avoid or to reduce sounds which they do not like.   There are a fair number of sounds which fall in the latter category for the majority of people, and woe betide the manufacturer who introduces such a sound into a neighborhood.   Other sounds may differ more widely from person to person in their annoyance value.

The widespread dislike of certain sounds needs no more explanation than the taste of the rat (and of many humans) for saccharine.   It is a theoretical problem of some interest, but to the practical man it may simply be taken as a fact of life, like the wetness of water or the need to pay income tax.   Individual differences in the type of sound which will annoy a person, however, may deserve more attention, since they can produce much unnecessary conflict.   A person who is undisturbed may well feel that the annoyance expressed by another is artificial and unnecessary, particularly when the sound concerned is of low intensity.   But it must be realized that an individual may truly be annoyed by a stimulus which is neutral to other people.   Let us consider again our animal results, since animals can hardly be suspected of avoiding a stimulus merely because they have some grudge against the experimenter.   To a normal rat, it may be a matter of indifference whether the walls of his box are striped or plain.   Yet if he has been given a shock in a striped room he will make strenuous efforts to avoid or get out of any other striped room.   Conversely, an animal which is used to hearing a click when its food is delivered will continue to respond without food provided that it is given clicks as a reward.   In everyday terms, a sensation may acquire associations beyond its natural meaning.   One and the same piece of music may be highly pleasant to one person because it is associated with pleasant memories, and violently unpleasant to another person to whom it recalls failure and unhappiness.   The importance of such associations may perhaps be revealed in a recent public-opinion poll survey on annoyance by aircraft noise.[1]   Eighty per cent of those who complained of aircraft noise reported some fear in connection with aircraft, either fear of machines crashing on the house or else unwillingness to fly themselves.   It seems unlikely that such a high percentage would be obtained from an unselected group of people.   Such emotional associations undoubtedly play a part in producing complaints about particular noises.

In all this, noises are no different from other sensory stimuli.   There can be unpleasant sights as well as unpleasant sounds; most people are offended by an untidy house or factory in full view of their own windows.   But for purely physical reasons noise arouses more complaints, because it is more likely to spread from the person who produces it to some other person who is not concerned with it.   Mr. Brown need not concern himself with Mr. Jones's taste in pin-ups, since he cannot see into Mr. Jones's room.   Even if he enters he can keep his gaze demurely on his feet.   But Mr. Brown may try his neighbor's patience considerably by playing Mozart too loudly on his phonograph.   This point, and indeed all the present discussion, may seem to some so obvious as not to be worth saying.   But it is clear from the literature that noise is often regarded as quite peculiar in its effects.   Examples which have become classic are claims that noise is responsible for an increase in mental disorders or for the decline in the birth rate: papers making such claims, and others of minor importance, are cited in excellent bibliographies[2,3] and because they are excessively numerous are not included in the references to this chapter.   There is no evidence to support such claims and it is likely that the large proportion of complaints from annoyance by noise as compared with complaints against other stimuli is due simply to the physical peculiarities of sound. Glaring lights or bad smells can be equally annoying if they manage to reach our senses. We must therefore guard against two errors. First, the annoyance produced by some sounds does not mean that they are bad for health, any more than an unsightly billboard is bad for health. Second, because annoyance is unrelated to health, it does not follow that it can be ignored. One would not deliberately spoil the beauty of a landscape. As far as possible most societies try to reduce annoyance for all their members, though difficulties arise when the pleasure of one section conflicts with that of another. The solution of such difficulties lies rather in the province of the political theorist than of the scientist; but in western societies there may often be penalties attached to a production of too much annoyance for too many fellow citizens.

A final point emerges from this analysis of annoyance. It should often be possible to reduce annoyance, either by training or by compensating advantages. Repeated experience of a noise without the unpleasant associations which have made it annoying should cause the sound to become emotionally neutral under suitable conditions, and as we shall see, it is indeed true that annoyance and other effects of noise decline when the noise is familiar. Even where this is not possible, it is of the nature of pleasant and unpleasant stimuli that they can be weighed up one against the other. Thus annoyance due to the presence of a factory may be balanced by the prosperity which that factory brings to the neighborhood; or annoyance due to aircraft noise be balanced by the assurance of protection against air attack. These considerations are valid up to a point but must not be overworked. Once an emotional reaction is established, it may well be self-sustaining and will not die away with exposure to the situation. Equally there is ample evidence that too violent a conflict of motives has unfortunate psychological effects.

The Most Annoying Noises. There are three sources from which we may obtain information concerning the annoyance produced by a noise. The simplest method is simply to observe cases in which legal action or considerable agitation has resulted from a noise. This method is of course somewhat uncontrolled, but it has the advantage of a very high validity when one is considering practical problems of noise reduction. That is, no question arises about the readiness of people, who say they are annoyed, to take legal action. A more controlled technique is to conduct a public-opinion poll in localities of particular interest. Here there is a slight doubt whether a person who complains to a pollster does in fact really feel deeply on the subject and is likely to take other steps. But there is no doubt that the sounds about which the questions are asked are realistic ones. That is, they are the sounds normally heard in everyday life and do not differ from the normal environment in familiarity, intensity, or any other aspect. The third method is to take subjects into a laboratory, to present sounds to them, and to ask them to rate the sounds in order of annoyance or to adjust one sound until it is equally annoying compared with another. This method is of course the most controlled, but it may suffer from a lack of realism. Fortunately, there is a good deal of agreement between the various methods, at least in some characteristics of the sounds likely to be annoying.

Loudness. The louder the sound the more likely it is to produce annoyance. This is a common finding in the laboratory experiments, and it appears to be confirmed by public-opinion polls. For example, in Table 10.1 the incidence of complaints by residents about aircraft noise is tabulated against the intensity of the noise to which that area is subjected. The aircraft-noise level was actually not continuous but is taken as the level which was exceeded at the peak on 25 per cent of the occasions on which aircraft were overhead. Obviously complaints become more frequent as the intensity increases. Another example may be taken from an inquiry which was concerned with residential noise.[4] If dwellers in houses were compared with dwellers in apartments, the latter were more likely to be troubled by noise arising from the activities of their neighbors. This is not merely because the sounds made by neighbors are inaudible from one house to another, because a distinction was made in the results between people who noticed their neighbors' noise and people who were troubled by it. The proportion of those who notice who are troubled is higher in the

Table 10.1. Annoyance to Residents from Aircraft*

Aircraft sampled noise level, db	Degree of annoyance, %		
	No	Moderate	Great
50–60	63	31	6
61–66	42	40	18
67–72	33	36	31
73–78	15	37	48
79	12	26	62

* From H. Davis et al., Ref. 1.

apartments, and this is presumably due to the higher intensity to which they are exposed.

This general relation between intensity and annoyance indicates that noise abatement is likely to be an effective means of combating annoyance, despite the emotional factors which are involved in it. At the same time, our previous discussion will make it clear that no critical level is to be expected below which nobody will find a sound annoying. The proportion of people who complain will vary also with the situation in which the complaints are recorded. In residential areas, as Table 10.1 shows, a noise level of 60 db may produce a sizable number of complaints. In industrial situations, the level is likely to be higher. Some studies suggest that an appreciable amount of annoyance may begin when the level rises above 90 db.[5,6] This level may quite well be related to the fact that speech will begin to become difficult to understand at normal intensities in a noise of this level. One of the areas in which further research is needed is the extent of annoyance produced by noise in situations with varying amounts of speech in progress. A level of 90 db would presumably be more annoying in an office than in a foundry. It is also likely that individuals who are particularly liable to be annoyed by noise will avoid work in which levels of 80 or 90 db are present, and thus the level of complaint may be kept lower in any particular factory than it would be in an unselected sample of persons.

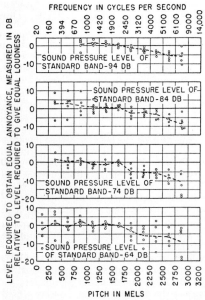

FIG. 10.1. The sound pressure level of noise which sounds equally annoying at various frequencies. Note that in general a high-pitched noise is more annoying than a low-pitched noise of the same sound level. (*Kryter.*[2])

It may also be noted that the relation with loudness which has been mentioned applies chiefly to meaningless noises. There are some reports that a meaningful sound such as speech may become more annoying when it is sufficiently faint to be about the threshold of intelligibility.[7] This is presumably the inverse of the effect, noted earlier, of a noise becoming annoying when it interferes with speech. Faint speech is particularly annoying because the listener is unable to make out what is being said. The annoyance is thus of a rather different kind from that produced by primarily unpleasant sounds.

Pitch. Many studies agree that a high-pitched noise is more annoying than an equally loud low-pitched noise. By high-pitched we mean, in this connection, from about 1,500 cps upward. The effect has been found both for pure tones and for bands of noise. It should be noted, however, that the difference between different pitches may decline after prolonged exposure to the noise. There are also considerable differences between different people, as indeed there are in comparing the loudness of sounds of different pitch. Nonetheless, it appears a fair practical guide to action that reduction of high-frequency components pays larger dividends than reduction of low-frequency components in a noise.[8,9,10] (See Fig. 10.1.)

It has also been reported that exceptionally low pitch in a sound, in the region of 100 cps, makes it more annoying than a noise more toward the middle of the audible spectrum. That is, both extremes of the spectrum were found more annoying than the middle.[10] There is also a view, derived from case studies of noises which have produced complaints, that a noise containing substantial pure-tone elements is more annoying than one whose energy is more evenly distributed.[11] These points are not so heavily supported as the greater annoyance arising from high frequencies but suggest that there may be more in the effect of different pitches than has so far been established.

The discussion so far applies to steady noises. The question of varying or warbling pitch belongs with the general question of varying or intermittent sounds and will be considered later. We may note, however, that in one study a pattern of tones was presented, and the changes in annoyance resulting from various types of pattern determined. Once again when the average frequency of the tones was high the pattern was more annoying; but in addition it was observed that a very wide range of frequencies was also particularly annoying. The listeners reported that their perception of the pattern alternated between listening to the pattern as a whole and hearing a high-pitched pattern against a low-pitched background or a low-pitched pattern against a high-pitched background. In some way this rather ambiguous sound was more annoying. This finding also suggests that more research on more complex aspects of pitch would be fruitful.[12]

Intermittent and Irregular Noise. The third feature of noises which is very commonly found to be related to their annoyance is the degree of variability in the noise itself. A sound which is modulated in intensity or frequency is found to be much more annoying. There is also some evidence that people do not become accustomed to such noises so quickly as they do to steady ones.[7,13] The opinion has been expressed, though very cautiously, that changes in intensity are of greater importance from this point of view than changes in frequency.[12]

There are perhaps two factors in this effect, although both operate in the same direction. On the one hand, there is the greater annoyance produced by exposing an individual to a noise only at fairly long intervals. An example is the case of aircraft noise in residential areas, since aircraft pass over only periodically. This occasional exposure is more annoying to some people than a continuous exposure to noise of the same level. There is some evidence that complaints of aircraft noise are less frequent in neighborhoods which have a high permanent noise level.[11] The form of annoyance produced by a sound which is continually present but changing in its various characteristics is logically distinct and may be due to different causes. A complex pulsating sound which is continuously present cannot be said to allow the listener opportunity to become used to quiet and so be unduly offended by the noise. Nevertheless, such pulsating sounds are sometimes reported as more annoying than less complex sounds.[12] Pure sine waves are not so annoying as more abrupt waveforms. (This may appear to conflict with the point made earlier, that a noise with energy concentrated in one part of the spectrum was more annoying than a wider-band noise. The contradiction may perhaps be explained by the fact that the earlier statement was derived from case histories. Real-life noises, even if the energy is relatively concentrated at particular frequencies, are probably not sine waves. A good guess might be that the most annoying waveform is a strongly periodic but nonsinusoidal one, such as that of an automobile horn or a human scream. Such a sound would have a more uneven spectrum than a white noise but a less even one than a sine wave.)

Rhythm is another feature of noises which is related to variability. In the experiments on patterns of sound, which we have already mentioned, it was found that the pattern became more annoying if the length of some steps in the sequence of sound was greater than that of others.[12] That is, a rhythmic noise was more annoying than an evenly repeating one. Worse still, however, was the introduction of random changes in the time taken by each step in the pattern of sounds. A slight effect of rhythmic sounds has been shown on tasks requiring a different rhythm.[7] But the effect is very slight and will of course depend upon the nature of the task which is being performed. The same experiments on patterns of sound[12] showed that up to a point the annoyance was increased by introducing silent intervals between parts of the pattern. This raises the interesting possibility that quieting one part of a process might make the remaining, and now intermittent, noise more annoying.

It is worth noting that the three features which make sounds particularly annoying are all features which, in ordinary language, make sounds likely to secure attention. That is, if a man is observed in a situation in which he must distribute responses between several sources of stimulation, he is more likely to respond to intense stimuli, to stimuli which have not recently been presented, and to high-pitched sounds. The annoyance seems to follow this attention-getting quality of the sound; although of course the causal relation may be in the opposite direction.

Localization. When we leave the three dimensions of pitch, loudness, and intermittency, we find ourselves on much less certain ground. The relation to annoyance of the features of sounds which we are now going to consider is less established than those which have gone before. But there are suggestions in the literature which may at least serve as guides for further investigation. Localization, for example, is a topic which figures in some complaints. Certain points about it are more or less obvious. A sound which repeatedly changes its localization may fairly be assumed to be more annoying than one which remains stationary, by analogy with the effects of changes in other dimensions. In addition, uncertain localization may provoke in human beings feelings of curiosity and even of insecurity which may interfere with other occupations and prove annoying. A sound whose source is not confidently known may be a nagging intellectual problem. In the same way, a motorist may be very concerned about a sudden metallic screaming noise until he identifies it as a passing aircraft. Definite localization allows a noise to be identified in this way more rapidly and so may reduce its annoyance. The same effect may of course be produced by verbal explanation, and it may often be more practical to explain the source of a new noise to those likely to hear it rather than attempt to modify the noise to make it more easily localized.

But there is more to the effects of localization than this. Several studies have shown that speech can be most easily understood in noise when the localization of the speech and noise sources is different.[14,15] If the noise is not definitely localized, it will be more difficult to adjust one's position relative to the person with whom one is holding a conversation, so as to secure maximum intelligibility. In places where speech is used, therefore, an indefinitely localized noise is likely to be particularly annoying. No studies of the effect of noise on efficiency in dealing with other than auditory signals appear to have varied localization in any systematic way. But the experiments showing the larger effects seem to have used indefinitely localized noises, and it may be that the distracting effect of a noise even on visual signals is less easily overcome by familiarity when the noise is not tied down to one special direction. The reasons already given, however, are sufficient to explain complaints about indefinitely localized noises.

Perhaps the only way in which localization can usually be modified is by reducing reflection from walls in workplaces and other situations where delayed echoes are to be expected. Up to a certain value of the time delay between the arrival of a sound and its echo, localization will be unaffected by the presence of echoes. With such short intervals, the echo is fused with the original sound and increases its apparent loudness, but the apparent localization is that of the first sound to reach the ears.[16] The presence of sound-absorptive material on the walls which produce echoes will therefore in small rooms affect annoyance primarily by reducing the sound pressure level. But in very large spaces the time interval between the arrival of the original sound and of its echo will become too great for fusion of the two to occur in subjective experience. Localization will then become indeterminate and annoyance therefore may be increased. The length of the time interval, between the original sound and its echo, necessary for the two to be heard separately varies according to the type of sound, being apparently as low as 5 for sharp clicks but as high as 40 in more complex sounds such as speech.

Avoidable or Unnecessary Sounds. The annoyance produced by a sound can be balanced by compensating advantages. Conversely, it seems that a sound which has no good reason for its existence is liable to produce severe complaints. Illustrations may be found again in a survey of British homes.[4] Of those who notice the sound of delivery trucks in their homes, only 10 per cent are troubled by the noise. But of those who hear noises made by neighbors' pets, nearly 40 per cent are troubled. Another example appears in Table 10.2. The proportion of those who are troubled by the banging of doors is higher than that of those who are troubled by water-closet noises, if each is considered in relation to the percentage who notice the noise. Admittedly, in both examples there is a possible alternative explanation that the noise producing more complaints is intrinsically more annoying. The sharp onset of a door

Table 10.2. Annoyance to Residents from Domestic Noise*

	Notice		Are troubled		Sleep is disturbed	
	Own dwelling, %	Neighbor's, %	Own dwelling, %	Neighbor's, %	Own dwelling, %	Neighbor's, %
Doors banging.............	39	41	13	15	8	11
Water closet..............	44	27	9	6	6	5
Baby crying..............	15	12	3	3	3	3
Children playing in other rooms..................	25	27	5	7	2	4
Radio in other rooms.......	52	58	5	10	4	6
Piano or other musical instrument in other rooms..	10	14	1	3	...	1
Conversation in other rooms	29	31	3	7	2	4
People moving in other rooms	48	48	5	8	4	6
All persons..............	82	83	25	30	18	24

* From D. Chapman, Ref. 4.

slam, in particular, seems likely to be more startling than the slower rise of a water-closet noise. However, the person complaining is less likely to be easily satisfied in the former case than in the latter.

Inappropriateness to One's Own Activity. Table 10.2 shows another interesting point, that on the whole there is a slight tendency to object to one's neighbor's noise more than one's own. The difference is slight, but when one remembers the probable difference in level in the opposite direction it is important. From the analysis of annoyance which we made earlier, it is not surprising that this difference exists. In most adults there are relatively permanent preferences which are peculiar to the individual, so that one man's noise is another man's music. In addition, to any individual a sound which would be quite welcome at one time may well be very unwelcome at another. The most serious extreme of these changes in preference within an individual is reached by the need for times of sleep or rest. That a need for sleep exists is not seriously questioned by anybody, although little is known about it scientifically. It is equally agreed that a sufficiently intense stimulus of any kind will awake a sleeper; the intensity of stimulus required is in fact sometimes used as a measure of the depth of sleep. Noises likely to interrupt sleep will therefore give rise to more annoyance than those which occur at times when most people are not sleeping.

It is often observed in real life that people become accustomed to sleeping in noise levels which to the uninitiated are too high, so that the city dweller may actually have difficulty in sleeping in the country. Little scientific information is available on the extent to which this adaptation takes place. Further knowledge about sleep itself is required before one can do more than recommend that unavoidable noises should be made as far as possible in the daytime. Besides disturbance of sleep, other examples of inappropriate noises causing annoyance may be provided by sounds which, while innocent in themselves, disturb the reverent atmosphere of a church service; or by a funeral march emerging from a radio at a party. General rules can hardly be formulated on this subject.

Individual Differences in Annoyance. To some extent the fact that a noise may annoy one person and leave another indifferent is doubtless to be explained by differences in past experience or by mere idiosyncrasy. Certainly individuals dislike one particular noise out of all proportion to its physical qualities. There is considerable evidence, however, that some individuals are inclined to complain of many noises, and indeed of many other stimuli. In one study it was found that over 80 per cent of those greatly annoyed by aircraft noise were preoccupied with other physical problems of their communities, including other noises, litter, and similar topics.[1] This is of some importance, because a questionnaire in which the subject is presented with a list of possible annoying situations and asked to indicate how many of them do in fact annoy him has been found useful in psychiatric screening. A large number of annoyances are related to difficulties in personal adjustment.[17] Complaints about noise are no exception to this rule. In one study four groups of workers totaling over two hundred were interviewed by a psychiatrist and the number of nervous symptoms present in each individual noted.[18] When the same individuals were asked if they were unaffected by noise, if they slightly disliked it, or if they were seriously annoyed by it, there was a significant relationship with the number of symptoms present. Another investigation, which was concerned with the problem of diagnosing neurotics, presented several questionnaires of different types to two equally large groups of subjects.[19] One group was composed of those who had found it necessary to consult a psychiatrist and the other of persons who had not and might therefore be fairly described as in some sense normal. Four of the questionnaires were concerned with annoyances, and all of them showed more annoyances among the neurotic group. The questionnaire concerned particularly with noise annoyances showed the largest correlation and was indeed one of the best questionnaires at differentiating the two groups. There is in fact good evidence for the opinion sometimes met in the field that complaints about noise come disproportionately from neurotic people. This fact, however, is so clearly liable to misinterpretation that two cautions should be added. On the one hand, there is no evidence that neurotics are more commonly met with among persons who have been exposed to noise. That is, there is no ground for supposing that noise produces neurosis. On the other hand, an individual who expresses dislike of a noise to which his fellows are indifferent is not therefore neurotic. Even if he were so, one is not justified in ignoring the likes and dislikes of another person simply because he helps psychiatrists to earn a living.

The question of individual differences in efficiency in noise may be connected with that of differences in annoyance; it will be dealt with later.

Conclusions on Annoyance. In brief, annoyance is something distinct from harm to health or efficiency. It must not therefore be ignored. Physical characteristics of sounds, such as intensity, high frequency, and modulation, tend to increase annoyance on the average. But there will be large differences between various cases, and each will need consideration on its merits.

PHYSIOLOGICAL MEASURES

Measures of Startle or Emotional Response. A sudden unexpected sound such as a pistol shot produces a widespread change in bodily activity.[20,21,22] There is a rise in blood pressure, a rise in pressure inside the head, and an increase in sweating. The heart rate increases, there are changes in breathing, and there may be sharp contraction of the muscles over the whole body.   These changes are often regarded as an emergency reaction of the body, increasing the effectiveness of any violent muscular exertion which may be required.   Under primitive conditions an unexpected stimulus might be likely to call for such exertion.   Such a simple statement does not do justice to the full complexity of these bodily changes, but it serves to make them intelligible.   Their importance is twofold; first, such a widespread response may be expected to interfere with other activities at the time when the sound occurs.   Second, too frequent an occurrence of such changes might well be harmful to health.   For example, one of the features of such emotional patterns is that digestion ceases.   It has in fact been shown that a short exposure to noise produces a decrease in the contractions which convey food through the body, and in the flow of saliva and gastric juices.[23]   However desirable in emergencies, this kind of change is obviously not wanted for long periods.   But fortunately all experiments in which repeated measures were taken indicate that the effect of the noise wears off rapidly when it is presented again and again.   One very thorough test found that exposure for 20 hr to jet-engine noise was sufficient to remove any effect on pulse rate, respiration rate, blood pressure, metabolism, acuity of vision, heartbeat, and a number of more technical tests.[24]

Recent studies of bodily responses to stress are revealing measures which may be more sensitive.   One of the glands involved in the pattern of response to emergency situations is the adrenal cortex, and the level of its activity may be determined by counting the number of cells of a certain type in the blood.   By this measure it has been shown that animals continue to show bodily changes when exposed to noise, even after quite repeated exposure.[25]   A brief report indicates that this is also true of aircraft assembly workers even when accustomed to noise.[26]   At the same time, in mice there did not appear to be any permanent change in the adrenals or any other organs, as there would be in stresses likely to cause ill health.[25]   The amount of change in the blood count was less than that produced by picking the animals up and handling them, or by allowing several animals to meet each other and fight.   Although further research will no doubt lead us to a valuable understanding of the body's response to intense stimulation, at present the evidence is that no undue and unhealthy response appears in prolonged noise.

Measures of Effort.   If one measures the activity of the muscles, usually by picking up electrical potentials from the skin above them, or if one measures the energy expended by the man, by observing how much oxygen he consumes, one may hope to detect the effort which his task is costing him.   It has often been suggested that, when efficiency is not impaired by noise, a compensating effort is being made.   But although a number of short experiments do show increased energy expenditure (metabolism) when working in noise, experiments which are continued for some time have always so far shown a reduction in metabolism to the normal level.[24,27]   It is arguable that energy expenditure by the whole body is not a very sensitive index of effort, since one part of the body may increase its activity while another part is decreasing.   There is some evidence for this from the electrical activity of the muscles.   In general, muscle potentials increase when first working in noise but afterward decline.   It has been reported that the decline in muscles which are not being used for the task is greater than that in muscles which are directly being employed for the work.[28]   As indicated below, the question whether the tension finally returns to normal, even in muscles required by the task, is obscured by individual differences between people.   The size of the rise in tension when the noise is heard varies with the intensity of the noise, and also with the meaningfulness of the sound.[29]   That is, if a man is told to react by pressing a key when he hears a sound, the muscle tension in his arm increases more when the noise occurs than if he is told to ignore the sound.   The effect of intensity is greater when a reaction is to be made to the noise.

A fair conclusion seems to be that in early stages of work in noise increased effort is required to maintain performance but that on the average such effort is not present when the noise has become familiar.   It may still possibly be present in some individuals.   One study, using more subjects than are usually employed in physiological researches, showed a relation between muscle-tension changes and efficiency of work in glare and noise.[30]   Persons who maintained their level of work in the distracting conditions showed a larger increase in muscle potentials than those whose performance was less efficient. When differences in effort were minimized, by making the rate of work depend on the apparatus rather than on the choice of the worker, there was some evidence for a more universal increase in tension. This finding is relevant to data on individual difference in efficiency of work.

Exceptional Physiological Effects. Certain other effects of noise do not fit into the categories given above but may nonetheless be termed physiological. First, there are effects of extremely high intensity noises. At sound levels of 140 db or more, there may be a number of unpleasant bodily sensations, such as feelings of vibration in the head, movement of the air in the nose, and loss of equilibrium.[31,32] These effects border upon those of vibration, since the disturbances of equilibrium, for example, are probably due to vibration of the labyrinthine sense organs which control posture. Similarly the vibration of the eyeballs by these very high intensities may cause disturbances of vision. These effects may well disturb efficiency temporarily, but the levels required to produce them are naturally somewhat uncommon; and if the ears are unprotected in such intensities the noise will be painful. At these very high intensities there may be some heating of the skin. Animals with hair on their skins, such as rats or guinea pigs, may suffer from burns because of the energy absorbed.[33,34] A hairless skin, however, seems to lessen this effect considerably. In any case, it is highly undesirable for human beings to be exposed to such conditions because of the effects on hearing and on efficiency.

Possible Permanent Effects on Efficiency from Exposure to Very High Intensities. Although there are many complaints of permanent effects, sometimes under the heading of "supersonic sickness," there is no very convincing evidence of such effects. Persons reporting disability following exposure to such intense noises are usually found to be suffering from some other complaint, and particularly neurotic ones (see the section on *Individual Differences in Annoyance* above). Although it is difficult to prove a negative, the weight of informed opinion is that there are no permanent effects. One study investigated the performance of men who had been working on aircraft engines on certain tests previously found to distinguish people with injured brains from normal persons.[35] The aircraft workers did worse on these tests. But, as the author points out, these men had been subject to emotional stress in their work as well as to noise, since they were anxious about the possible dangers of the task. Any permanent effect on them might be due to this other stress and not to the noise. There is also the danger in such an investigation that people who are by nature somewhat unusual will thrust themselves forward for testing. Another similar tentative investigation was carried out on animals and showed that rats after exposure to a loud noise were less well able to learn a new maze, although they retained performance on one which they had learned before receiving the noise.[36] Here again it is possible that the animals had transferred the avoidance reaction which they normally have to an unpleasant stimulus to the whole experimental situation, just as the animals mentioned in the first section on annoyance were trained to escape from a room with striped walls. Such a general distaste for the experiment is not uncommon in animal work which involves unpleasant stimuli. Further work should undoubtedly be conducted on the general lines of these investigations, but it may be doubted whether positive results will emerge.

Sensory Interaction. It has been found that under some conditions a very faint light may be more easily visible if it is accompanied by sound, while under other conditions the effect may be reversed. The practical importance of these effects is rather slight, though they are of theoretical interest.[37,38]

EFFICIENCY

Methods of Measuring Efficiency Effects. A great deal of research effort appears to have been wasted in the past through failure to recognize the precautions essential to measurement of human performance. A number, possibly the majority, of studies of effects of noise are scientifically unacceptable. There are two main avenues of investigation, industrial studies on the one hand and laboratory research on the other.

Some of the weaknesses in procedure apply to both these avenues; others apply only to industrial investigation, although industrial studies are an essential complement to laboratory ones if we are to ensure that differences found in the laboratory are really important in practice.

The major weakness of industrial studies is lack of control of other conditions besides the noise which is being investigated. Changes in the auditory environment of a worker are commonly linked with a move to a new building, a change in the work which is being done; change in the temperature, lighting, and other conditions of work; or similar alterations in the circumstances of the job. Any change in performance may be due to these other changes and not to reduction in noise. This criticism disposes of almost all industrial investigations which have been reported. In addition there are two other dangers to which industrial researches are particularly prone. One of them is the contaminating effect of annoyance. In an earlier section it was indicated that a sound might be annoying without necessarily affecting efficiency. But if some feature of the conditions of work is annoying, the worker may stay home unduly long when he is ill, spend longer in the rest room, and similarly reduce his output. In more subtle form this difficulty may appear as that of suggestion. The very fact that an investigator is spending time on noise may cause the workers to believe that they should work better in quiet. This will then have an effect on efficiency, although the effect is not really due to the noise. A second weakness of industrial experiments is that any change in conditions of work may produce a temporary improvement in efficiency. This is particularly true of changes which imply that the management is considering the well-being of the workers. The attitude of the man toward his work becomes more favorable, just as it does if unpleasant conditions are removed; but this does not mean that the noise is truly affecting his efficiency. To put the distinction in monetary terms, it may be very expensive to reduce noise in a workplace, compared with the cost of painting the walls and installing a new canteen. If the effect of reducing the noise is merely to improve the workers' attitude, the latter techniques may be preferable. The final point may be made concerning industrial researches that they have usually measured output, with some attention to absenteeism. Mistakes and accidents are very rarely recorded in investigations of noise, although they have proved good indexes of other environmental conditions; in the section on practical conclusions from the known data, it will be argued that they should be especially useful in studying noise.

Studies in the laboratory, as well as industrial studies, are open to certain other possible weaknesses of technique. First, there is considerable chance fluctuation in the performance of any one person, and there is also considerable variation between different individuals. To establish an effect of noise it is necessary, therefore, to report sufficient data for an estimate of this chance variation to be formed, and for the effect which is being claimed to be compared with the chance variation. If a coin is tossed once and comes down heads, we cannot therefore conclude that the coin is biased. Second, performance may vary from one time to another because of other outside causes, in addition to the chance fluctuation. For example, a man may work better because he has become practiced. On the other hand, he may work worse because he has become fatigued. The best way of overcoming this difficulty is to employ two groups of people as subjects for the experiments. One may either give one group noisy conditions throughout and the other group quiet conditions throughout; or else one may start one group under quiet conditions and then change to noisy conditions, while reversing the order of presentation in the second group. A third technique which is rather less satisfactory is to keep one group of subjects but to change them from quiet to noise and then back to quiet again, or vice versa. The weakness of this technique is that a man's performance may first rise and then fall when conditions are kept uniform throughout; we usually say that he has improved with practice and then become fatigued. An industrial experiment, in particular, is likely to have some outside circumstances which may change during the course of an experiment in such a way as to produce first a rise and then a fall in performance. For example, if a group was to work in noise for a year, then in quiet for a year, and then in noise again, it would be quite possible for a change in the general economic situation to produce an atmosphere of prosperity during the second year which was lacking before and after, and which might well be reflected in greater production. Naturally if one changes from quiet to noise and back again repeatedly, the risk of some outside factor of this sort becomes less. If a group works in noise and quiet on alternate days for a year, it would be very bad luck indeed if the economic situation had been particularly bad on alternate days throughout that time. Most of the better investigations of noise effects have therefore used a method of this type, in which noise and quiet are alternated repeatedly. The two-group technique, however desirable, is often impracticable, because it requires the observation of large numbers of people. This is because the difference between different people causes the chance factor in the experiment to be high, and many results must therefore be obtained to ensure a positive conclusion. Even so, there is the danger in the single-group technique that, when two or more conditions of work are rapidly alternated, performance will not adjust itself to each of them in turn but will rather take up an average level.

The last possible snag is that the condition under which a person first meets a task may influence his performance on that task on subsequent occasions even though the conditions are altered. Thus in another field it has been shown that the crew on an aircraft who are given a test after returning from a flight do badly both on that occasion and also later after rest, while those who are first tested after rest do well both on that occasion and also after flying.[39] Similar effects have been noticed in some noise experiments. But these difficulties should be detectable by careful consideration of the results, and with modern methods of statistical analysis confident conclusions may be drawn.

The control of noise has been exercised in different ways in different experiments. In the industrial case, the use of sound-absorptive material or of earplugs has been employed. Both these alternatives have their disadvantages, as they introduce extra changes in the situation. A suggestion has recently been made that an industrial experiment utilizing two kinds of earplug of different efficiency would be valuable.[11] In laboratory experiments, the quiet condition has normally been the usual circumstances of the laboratory, and the noise has been artificially produced. In the early experiments naturally arising noises such as machinery or recordings of traffic or office noise were used. More recently, laboratory experimenters have tended to use electronically generated noise and to specify it physically with an exactness denied to the earlier workers. Studies giving some indication of the spectrum of the noise, however, as well as the level, are still in the minority, and as yet there is no study of the effect of noise on efficiency which has reported the autocorrelation function or some similar index of the periodicity of the waveform. As is now known, a sound which recurs periodically at some frequency may be heard as having a pitch of that frequency even though the energy in its spectrum is not particularly high at that point. This point is, however, probably an unnecessary refinement; but the different sound levels and spectra employed by different workers may well influence their conflicting results. An additional control which has some merit is the use in recent experiments of an artificially generated steady level of noise at a low intensity as the quiet control. This prevents small incidental sounds from entering the laboratory and disturbing performance.

The tasks used in laboratory studies may be divided into tests of particular functions, such as dark vision or hand-steadiness tests, and tests of complex performances such as decoding, using simulated aircraft controls, or mental arithmetic. It will be found in the appropriate sections that tests of particular functions did not appear to show any effects, while the more complex tasks are divided, some showing effects and some remaining as efficient in noise as in quiet.

Results from Industrial Studies. So far as noise itself is concerned, there appears to be only a single study which cannot be immediately rejected for failures of technique of the type discussed in the previous section. This study is of the efficiency of weavers in Britain.[6,40] In this case ample data are available, including records from some subjects individually week by week for 6 months. There were three experiments, in all of which the noise was that naturally produced by the looms which had a sound level of 96 db. Comparatively quiet conditions were produced by earplugs which attenuated the noise by 10 to 15 db.   In one experiment 10 weavers were used who wore earplugs on alternate weeks for 6 months.   In each of the other experiments two groups were used, one wearing earplugs while the other did not.   One of these experiments lasted for 6 months and the other for a year.   All three experiments showed a gain in efficiency for the earplugs.   The gain was not very sizable when considered in relation to the amount produced, being only 1 per cent.   But in weaving production depends to a great extent upon the loom, and the change in the efficiency of the workers themselves was about 12 per cent.

It is difficult after this interval to assess the value of the latter two experiments. The degree of equality between the two groups was not demonstrated before the earplugs were issued to one of them, in either case.   The research belongs to the days when statistical methods of assessing significance were only beginning to be employed, and they were not in this case.   Individual data are not available for the workers in the latter two experiments.   In the first experiment, however, the data are given for each individual and it appears that every one of the 10 workers did better when wearing earplugs.   This is undoubtedly statistically significant and in view of the similarity of the results from the three experiments weakens statistical criticism of the second and third.   Perhaps more serious is the possibility that the groups wearing earplugs felt additional motivation from being used as subjects for an experiment, and so worked harder.   In the third experiment performance of the two groups was less widely different at the end of the year than it was at the beginning; and this might be due to the wearing off of such an increase in motivation. The authors make the point that the two groups separated and came together cyclically throughout the year and that the resemblance between the two levels of output at the end of the year is merely one of these cycles.   There is some indication that the two groups were about to diverge again.   The records are reproduced as Fig. 10.2.   The first group again has the advantage where this criticism is concerned, since any general increase

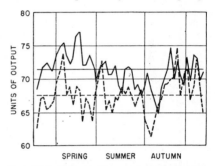

Fɪɢ. 10.2. Output of two groups of weavers, both exposed to noise but one group, indicated by the solid line, wearing earplugs. (*Weston and Adams,*[40] *by permission of the Controller, Her Majesty's Stationery Office.*)

in motivation should have affected performance of the group throughout, and not merely on the weeks when they were wearing earplugs.   A suggestion effect from current opinion that noise impaired work is not excluded in this group, nor of course in the other two experiments.   It should be noted that the opinions of the individual workers on the benefit derived from earplugs are also recorded and that some of them were markedly unfavorable.   This agrees with the experience of most people who have tried to make workers defend their ears.   Even the unfavorable workers showed an improvement in their performance when wearing earplugs, although there was a statistically insignificant difference between the favorable and unfavorable subgroups. Finally, although the first experiment thus seems to be less open to objection than the other two, the authors of the research were more doubtful of it.   This was because of chance differences in temperature and humidity between the weeks on which earplugs were worn and the weeks when the full noise was experienced; in other experiments temperature and humidity have been shown to affect performance.   The data on temperature and humidity from the first experiment are given in the report and do not seem in this case to show any connection with efficiency.   It may be that the authors were overcautious in suspecting their results.

The agreement between the three weaving experiments described above is impressive, and there is some answer to each of the possible criticisms that can be leveled against them.   But the evidence cannot be said to be overwhelming.   The most serious objection is probably the danger of suggestion or other influences upon the workers' attitude. It seems impossible to rule this out in industrial experiments except by the suggestion of using inefficient earplugs for one group. Perhaps it should be added that these criticisms of effects shown in industry do not necessarily mean that the results are false; they merely mean that the effect of noise is not proved to be true. In the light of the discussion under *An Interpretation of the Nature of Behavior in Noise* it is reasonable that weaving should show effects. Other industrial processes might not show corresponding effects.

Music in Industry. Although not noise by some definitions, music in factories has been the subject of several investigations. Its importance here is that the introduction of music during work is frequently supposed to improve production, rather than impair it. Although levels of intensity are not usually given, it seems likely that such music will reach levels comparable with those of the noises used in some experiments aimed at showing deleterious effects from sound stimulation. The popular opinion that music has a contrary effect thus serves to remind us that we cannot consider effects of noise purely from a physical standpoint. There is little doubt that the presence of music is regarded by the workers as a pleasant feature of the job and that it improves their attitude toward the task and the management. In some studies it has also been shown that production improves when music is present. As usual, there

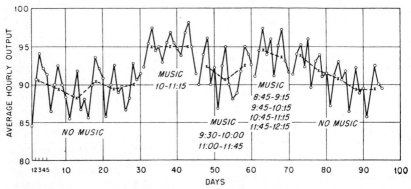

Fig. 10.3. Output in a light manual task under various conditions of noise presentation. (*Wyatt and Langdon,*[41] *by permission of the Controller, Her Majesty's Stationery Office.*)

is some doubt as to whether this production improvement is due to the attitude change or to a direct effect of the stimulus provided by the music. The effect on output from one of the earlier experiments is shown in Fig. 10.3. The task concerned in this case was the rolling of paper novelties by hand.[41] Three points are worth noting concerning the results; (1) There seems to be a difference between the different times of introduction of the music. (2) There appears to be a flywheel effect, such that production takes a little time to settle down to a new level. (3) This effect is merely an average one, an aspect not noted in the figure; some individuals do not benefit from the music. Other studies have also shown improvements in average output, with the same qualifications that individuals may not be affected and that particular schedules of music with particular types of work may fail to show any effect.[42,43,44] One sizable study on a skilled task which had remained stable for some time, so that work habits were fairly fixed, did not show any improvement in average output despite an improvement in the workers' attitude as measured by questionnaires.[45] This study in fact compared music and quiet conditions on randomly varied days within each of five experimental weeks. This may mean that the workers did not adjust their production to the changed conditions, as they did in the study in Fig. 10.3. On the other hand, production in the weeks before the start of the experiment was no lower than in the experiment itself; so it may be that the other differences between the two tasks were the significant ones. However, there do not appear to be any reports of music causing a deterioration in production, although it may possibly have some slight effect on accidents. Sound as such is clearly not necessarily a cause of low industrial efficiency. In comparing effects of music with effects of noise, the fact that industrial noise levels may rise considerably above those due to music must be remembered; and it is also of interest that music is probably best used for short periods and not continuously throughout the day. The conception that a change in the background stimulation present during a task may improve performance is one which is common to a number of studies of prolonged work. It is noted in the previous section that the effect is sufficiently marked to be a normal hazard in assessing effects of changes in conditions on industrial performance. The use of music appears to be a method of deliberately producing changes in the surroundings. As will be seen in the following section, meaningless noises sometimes produce a corresponding improvement in performance. Music has the advantage that attitudes favorable to the work and to the management are induced, as well as a change in the surroundings which opposes monotony. Both factors therefore operate in the same direction and may produce enhanced performance on suitable tasks.

The Effects of Unfamiliar Noises. It is widely agreed that a novel or unusual noise will produce some decline in the efficiency of work when it is first heard. This effect is considered separately from that of prolonged noise since the latter is more confused and controversial.

In a typical experiment, each subject was presented with a series of letters among which digits were interspersed.[46] The task was to add up the series of digits. When a series of such sums had been done, the noise was turned on and continued while another series of sums was done. It was then turned off again and a final series of measurements taken. The noise was provided by an automobile horn mounted 2 ft from the subject. The effect was that the first few sums after the onset of noise were slowed down but that the time per sum then returned to normal. A very important point is that a similar slowing down occurred when the noise was stopped. Once again, performance rapidly returned to normal; but the interest of the finding is that it suggests that the effect of the noise was primarily that of a change in the conditions of work, rather than any effect peculiar to intense sounds. Similar results have also been found using an even more complex task, in which the subject was required to observe a letter through a slot, to encode it into another letter using a code supplied, to take this second letter and encode it into a digit using one of three codes varying according to the color of the original presentation, and finally to press an appropriate key.[47] In this case an assortment of bells, buzzers, and other noise makers was used to provide the noise. Individual differences were evident in the results, but on the

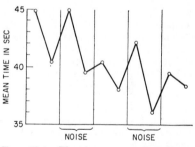

FIG. 10.4. The temporary disturbance caused by turning a noise on and off. (*Plotted from the data of Morgan.*[47])

whole findings appear to be similar to those already given. An initial slowing down was later replaced by unaltered performance, and indeed by improved performance in a majority of the subjects. There were signs of another deterioration when the noise was stopped. Typical results are shown in Fig. 10.4.

Logically, there are two possible aspects of unfamiliarity. There is the unfamiliarity of a noise which has never been heard before, and there is the unfamiliarity of a task which has not been practiced to any great extent. Both are usually regarded as important by investigators in this field, but experiments of the type mentioned earlier probably detect chiefly the effects of familiarity and unfamiliarity of the noise. Performance on the task itself seems to have reached a plateau or constant level of efficiency before the noise is introduced. There remains the possibility that the effect of a given unfamiliar noise may be greater on an unpracticed task than on a practiced one. Oddly enough, no one appears to have done controlled experiments in which noises are repeatedly presented before the task is introduced, or in which the task is given varying degrees of practice before the noise is introduced. However, it seems fair to accept the evidence already given as showing that increasing familiarity with a noise will reduce its effect on a task for a constant level of practice. Perhaps the best evidence that a practiced task is less affected than an unpracticed one comes from an experiment using a fairly complex manual skill in which pegs had to be removed from a moving trolley which approached and receded from the worker at a speed dictated by a machine.[7] Some effect was shown on this task from clicking sounds delivered to the subjects through headphones in a rhythm different from that of the machine, although as usual the effect began to die away with continued exposure. When the same subjects were given a different kind of noise, no effect appeared on the task. Unfortunately, no other subjects were tested using this task and the second kind of noise, to show that this noise would have affected the task had it been less well practiced; the point was probably one of minor interest to the particular investigators, as their experimental design was well controlled in most respects.

Other experiments in the same series illustrated both the nature of the effects which may be obtained temporarily when noise is presented, and also the kind of changes which subjects say are taking place in their performance and which cause the noise to reduce its effect. In one experiment two groups of subjects were faced with the task of constructing an unfamiliar apparatus out of a number of pieces. One group received a noise during this task, and more rapid solutions of the problem were obtained in the quiet group. Only three of the noise subjects solved the problem in less than a quarter of an hour, while eight of the quiet subjects succeeded in a similar time, both groups containing 24 subjects. Applying modern statistics* to the results given in this report, the present writer has confirmed the investigators' tentative conclusion that the results are not due to chance. In another experiment the subjects were asked to solve, not one unfamiliar problem, but a succession of problems of similar type. The problems were to construct certain prescribed digit combinations on an apparatus in which digits could be moved into a register by pressing levers. Only a limited number of moves were allowed. Alternate problems were done in noise and in quiet. This task was at first impaired by noise, but the impairment disappeared until, on the fifth day of work, after the performance of fifty or more problems, the subjects were able to perform as well in noise as in quiet. Similarly, when the subjects were given groups of letters and told to form as many words as possible from these letters, they were at first impaired by noise but later recovered. In both these experiments the subjects reported that as time went on they discovered rules and mechanical techniques of solving the problems, and once this had been done the noise ceased to have any effect. For example, in the word-construction test a useful technique was to take one letter, to take each of the available vowels after this first letter, then to take each next consonant, and so on. This routine performance required little thinking and was undisturbed by noise. A typical comment, from a subject used in the manual-skill experiment, was that once the task was practiced he listened to the noise, but this did not affect the part of his mind which was occupied with doing a task. Noise levels were not stated in these reports[7] but were given elsewhere as being up to 90 db.[48]

Although the evidence for effects of practice on the task itself in reducing interference with the task by noise is not completely satisfactory, the opinion of most of the investigators seems to support it. There is also some evidence from experiments in which one task has to be combined with another task, after varying degrees of practice on the first task. A more practiced task does interfere less with the second occupation, although there is some limit to the extent to which this effect of learning can be used to combine different tasks. If a type of work involves reacting to a succession of different stimuli, and the order of the stimuli is random, there may be little benefit from previous practice in combining this task with another. Yet when the order of stimuli is predictable, practice at the task will mean that another task can be done at the same time more efficiently.[49] Practice at one task will also reduce interference with another at times between the occurrence of critical stimuli from the first task.[50]

* The technique used was a correlational one, rather than the more usual "chi-square method."

In the language of communication theory, interference between two tasks occurs only when a man is required to take in information from both tasks simultaneously. If one task presents a repeating series of stimuli, the information contained in this sequence is low after practice and there is then little interference with another task. In more everyday language, with an unfamiliar task one notices many features of the work which are not essential to its performance, and one cannot at the same time attend to some other work. In a practiced task, one attends only to what is crucial, and if the task is a repetitive one some other work may be done simultaneously. If it is unpredictable, it will be more difficult to combine with other occupations. Most actual tasks will lie between the two extremes, having crucial instants at which information is delivered to the man, and other times at which no such information is arriving. After practice one is aware of this and can alternate attention, dealing with a second task during the intervals in the first. If we take the further step of supposing that there is a tendency for attention to be directed to any change in the surroundings, such as the onset of a noise, it is not surprising that effects on performance due to this mechanism should be less on a practiced task. In other words, the initial response to any situation is diffuse and widespread. This applies whether the situation is a task presented by an experimenter or an interfering noise. It is pointed out in an earlier section that widespread muscle potentials may be detected early in performance but become more concentrated in particular parts of the body at later stages. When both task and irrelevant noise are producing widespread response, there is more likelihood of interference between responses due to the two stimuli. When response to the task has been concentrated in one part of the body and response to a noise has either disappeared or also been concentrated in a different part of the body there will be no interference between the two stimuli. But the worst effects of noise will be produced by a strange and unfamiliar sound on a strange and unfamiliar task, and the least effect of noise will be produced by a familiar sound upon a practiced task. Intermediate cases will be provided by familiar sounds and strange tasks, and by strange sounds with familiar tasks. But if this description is adopted, it is essential to remember that the word "response" may mean simply some event within the nervous system, not detectable outside. As long as this precaution is observed, it makes little difference whether one speaks of automatizing a task until it requires a low level of awareness, or of reducing the amount of information required to pass through the perceptual mechanism for successful performance, or of eliminating unnecessary responses which interfere and are interfered with when response to a noise is also present.

Although these different ways of describing the process of adapting to a novel noise are probably equivalent, they are not the only possible way in which this process can be regarded. A number of the earlier workers thought rather of a level of efficiency which was lowered by noise and raised again by compensating effort, the effort arriving somewhat late so that an initial drop in measured performance was redeemed only after the noise had been applied for a short time. The reason for viewing the situation in this way was the detectable change in various physiological measures which were referred to in an earlier section. That is, there might be rises in metabolism, in the pressure exerted on reaction keys, and so on. These additional processes seem to die out as the task goes on in noise. Although some reality corresponding to extra effort is undoubtedly present in some cases, it does not seem to be a sufficient explanation for the disappearance of the effect of noise after it has been present for a little while. Nor, if noise automatically lowers the level of efficiency and requires an effort to raise that level once more to the original, is it clear why the sudden cessation of a noise should be disturbing. One would rather expect a sudden spurt in performance followed by a decline to the normal level as effort was reduced. It seems easier to abandon the idea that noise automatically lowers the level of performance and to concentrate rather on the importance of changes in sensory stimulation. The importance of this change in viewpoint is that it means that work in a familiar noise, if efficiency is maintained, is not therefore requiring undue effort from the worker. The effect of an unfamiliar environment seems genuinely to die away, and not to require continued compensation by the worker.

Certain omissions in the literature have already been noticed. Perhaps even more surprising is the lack of any evidence on the kinds of noise which produce this effect most clearly. Since the reality of an initial disturbance in efficiency, lasting perhaps a few seconds with simple tasks and a few minutes with more complex ones, is accepted by most authorities, one might expect that some research would have been done with modern methods to compare the results of, say, bursts of noise, impact sounds, or pure tones. Such work would naturally require many experimental subjects since it would be necessary to use people with the same level of practice on the task, and without experience of the particular sound applied. Yet it should be a topic for research well within the resources of modern investigators. All that can be said is that most researches on the subject seem to have adopted noises which might be described as annoying, in view of what is said in the section on that subject. Thus automobile horns, bells, buzzers, and similar pulsating sounds figure prominently, while meaningful sounds of fairly low intensity are also particularly likely to cause the effect. Perhaps one reason for this neglect of the subject is that this effect of noise on efficiency is probably of little practical importance. Most industrial and military situations involve tasks which are to some extent practiced and noises which are to a large extent familiar. That an experimental subject faced with a completely new task may show a few seconds' delay when a striking and unusual noise begins is of little bearing for such practical situations; and recent research interests have been much more concerned with effects lasting at least over a matter of minutes. The transient effect of noise may conceivably be important to anybody concerned with the working conditions of men solving extremely new and unfamiliar problems, if the noises to which they are likely to be exposed are also very changeable and unfamiliar. Even then, the effect seems on the existing evidence to be only a question of a few seconds' delay in solution rather than a failure to reach solution; and in such work a delay of seconds is not usually thought important. Furthermore, small numbers of individuals are usually involved in any particular situation of this type, and the individuals may happen to be resistant to noise effects. Another possible field in which the effect may be noticed is in domestic life, since recreations frequently involve new and varying situations. The noises met under such circumstances will also be variable and may consist of a neighbor's radio on one occasion, the sound of a noisy vehicle a little later, an aircraft soon afterward, and so on. The interference produced on recreational activities may be detectable, and so indirectly contribute to annoyance and complaints. But these situations are somewhat special ones, and their practical importance is very doubtful. If the effects of noises on efficiency consist only of the brief distracting effect at their onset, there is little excuse for large-scale reduction of noise in the hopes of improving efficiency.

Sensory and Motor Functions Known to Be Unaffected by Noise. Once the initial effect of the beginning of a noise has worn off, a number of processes are definitely known to show no effect. These processes are specific sensory and motor ones, the position being more complicated in tasks which involve sensorimotor coordination, prolonged performance, and similar complexities of the type which one would normally describe as making the work more mental. It will simplify matters if we consider these complex tasks separately in the next section; the fact that more specific processes are generally agreed to be unaffected is important, and we shall now consider the particular functions which have been examined.

One of the first functions which should be mentioned is reaction time. If a subject is told to press a key as fast as possible when he sees a visual signal and is given a warning signal clearly and unmistakably a second or two before the main signal, the time he takes to react to the main signal is unaffected by the fact that he has been exposed to noise for some time. This fact was one of the earlier ones to be discovered, as reaction time was one of the first measures to be developed by psychologists; although an interesting measure in other ways, however, it rarely shows any effect of bad working conditions and noise is no exception in this respect. The early investigators showed the usual effect from the onset of an unfamiliar sound and also noted individual differences such that some people might go on being disturbed by a sound longer than others. Some persons indeed seem to have their performance improved by the noise. On the average, with a noise which has been present for some time a group of people will give the same reaction time as they would in quiet conditions which had been maintained for some time.[13] More recent studies have confirmed the finding using more modern techniques. Thus in an investigation in which simulated aircraft noise having a level of 115 db was compared with a 90-db level, no difference was found in choice reaction.[51] (A *choice reaction* is one in which several different signals are possible, in this case four, and several response keys are provided, so that the response is determined by the particular signal.) Similarly, with a simple reaction time using one possible signal and one key, a group of five subjects showed if anything a slight improvement in reaction time when working close to a jet engine in a noise level of about 130 db, while wearing ear defenders.[52]

Another function tested in a noise field of 115 db as opposed to 90 db was the ability to judge distances. The subjects were asked to adjust the distance of a movable wire to match that of a comparison wire and their accuracy was as great in the louder noise as in the quieter one. Two other visual functions which were compared in the noise fields of 115 and 90 db were dark vision and reversible perspective. In dark-vision tests the subject adapts his eyes to the dark for 20 min and then observes a test visual field in which a light is presented whenever he presses a key. The intensity of the light presented by the key is increased by the experimenter until the subject can see the light. The intensity at which this occurs gives a measure of the sensitivity of the eye to very faint illumination. This sensitivity was found to be lower in noise, but by such a very small amount that it did not reach the usual level of significance. Further investigation showed a similar insignificant difference. Although it may be that dark vision is slightly affected by noise, therefore, it does not seem to be badly impaired, and the results may be due to some cause which is not understood. For example, the threshold also changes from beginning to end of a week, for no apparent reason.

In reversible-perspective tests the subject looks at a figure which is ambiguous. A perspective drawing of a cube, for example, may be seen in one of two different orientations. If one watches the figure continuously for some time it will change spontaneously from one to the other of these orientations. The rate of change has sometimes been suggested as a measure of "fatigue" but was found to be so variable in this experiment that any effect of noise could not be detected. Another similar research which belongs with those just considered is a study of the threshold for visual contrast.[53] In this type of test the subject watches an illuminated field and has to detect an extra bright spot which appears within this field. The technique adopted by this study was for the experimenter to present the test light, at various possible illuminations, and for the subject to report its presence by pulling a trigger. The minimum brightness contrast between the light and its surroundings necessary for the subject to see the light was not affected by recorded tank noise having a noise level of 90 db as opposed to 45 db.

Motor Functions. Tests of body sway have been compared in noise fields of 115 and 90 db.[51] This type of measure is obtained by asking the subject to stand upright with some suitable recording gear attached to him and measuring the total amount by which he sways backward and forward or from side to side during a period of 30 sec. As far as the research was pressed, no effect of noise on this function could be found. Another measure of rather similar type was the steadiness of hand of the subjects. In this case each man was asked to hold a small stylus in a hole without making contact with the sides of the hole. There was no greater tendency to touch the side of the hole in the higher level of noise. If anything, the effect was in the opposite direction, which might perhaps mean that the subjects were being insulated from minor disturbing noises by the intense continuous one. However, the effect was not statistically significant. Motor functions connected with the eyes were also tested, notably the speed with which the eyes could be moved through a particular angle and the speed with which focus could be changed from near to a distant object or vice versa. The former seemed to show a definite effect on some subjects, but there were individual differences, and the effect was slight and was not pursued. The latter research ran into considerable difficulties because of spurious changes causing an apparent reduction in the speed of changing focus (accommodation) in noise. Relays used for the apparatus were found to give clues to the subject in the lower noise level and had to be moved to a different room. Although this reduced the apparent effect of noise it did not abolish it, but on one subject there still appeared to be an effect when he was wearing earplugs. The apparent effect might therefore be due to vibration of the eyes or of some part of the equipment resulting from the noise field. The effect of very high intensities on vision has been noted in the section on physiological measures. Although some of these functions might therefore conceivably show an effect of noise if research were pushed further, it is very unlikely that the effect is large enough to be of practical importance.

Another test of the motor type which was used to compare these same two levels of noise may be included here, although some would argue that it was a more complex type of task rather than a purely motor one. This is a test of the ability to follow a small target disk on a rotating phonograph turntable. The subject is provided with a stylus which he has to keep on the disk for as high a proportion of the time as he can. This is a task which has been used a great deal in studies of skilled performance; the reason for including it in the section on motor tasks is that the motion of the target is completely predictable. To a practiced subject, such as these were, any difficulty in the task is caused by failures to maintain a completely repetitive series of motions with his hand. Any such deviation will of course be reported by the sense organs and require corrective movement from the muscles, but this is equally true of hand steadiness or body sway. Some psychologists would argue that tests of this type should be distinguished from tasks in which information is transmitted through the man by presenting a series of different signals, to each of which there is a different possible response. While such tasks are being performed, there is no doubt feedback information being passed from the senses on the extent to which motor response is in agreement with the intentions of the human operator, but in addition there is information on the particular signals which are present because of the task and not because of the operator's action. Such tasks therefore appear to make a greater demand upon the human link in the system. In any event, the ability to perform the pursuit rotor test, as it is called, was as well maintained in the higher level of noise as in the lower level. A last example of a motor test may be taken once again from research using jet-aircraft noise with earplugs.[52] In this case, two hand dynamometers were employed, the subject being asked to squeeze with both hands as hard as he could. Four subjects showed little change in the jet noise, although if anything their performance improved on the right hand and deteriorated on the left.

It can be seen from the tests described above that the sense organs and muscles of a human being are not completely disorganized by the presence of an intense sound field. Any effects which have been found are extremely tentative and may well be due to some unsuspected feature of the experimental conditions. Any decline in the efficiency of more complicated tasks in noise is not due to failure of the simpler links in the nervous system. To recapitulate, most of the tests of sensory function indicated above presented a stimulus at a time when it was clearly expected by the subject or was even under his own control. There were normally intervals between each of the presentations of the stimulus, so that the task was not really continuous. Under such circumstances there is no doubt that the senses may be used as efficiently in noise as in quiet. Equally, tasks in which the movements required are simply repetitive, and no information is transmitted through the man, need show no decrement. A large variety of the tasks performed in noisy places are of this type: thus a man may have to enter a noisy engine shop to take down the readings of gauges or to tighten certain nuts. There is no reason to suppose that his efficiency will be lower in the noise.

Complex Tasks and Familiar Noises. The question to be considered in the present section is the most controversial in the general topic of efficiency in noise. If we take complex tasks rather than simple tests of sensory or motor function, practice them to a level at least sufficient to allow reasonably stable performance, and expose the worker to a sound which remains present for some time, shall we get any decline in efficiency? A number of studies have failed to show any effect under such circumstances. Yet they are clearly the conditions of greatest economic importance, as compared with the agreed effect of onset of the noise and lack of effect on simple sensory functions. There is as yet no widespread agreement about the reasons for the positive claims of some researches to show effects of noise, and the failure of others. A possible interpretation of the data does exist but cannot be said to be universally agreed. In consequence the method of presentation which we shall adopt is to outline as far as possible the known results in the present section and to give in the next section an interpretation of these results. This will mean that to some extent the present section will be a catalogue of data but will avoid the danger of too highly selective a presentation of the results in terms of a doubtful theory. Those who prefer to assimilate data to the framework of a general theory may consult the next section before examining the present one.

Intellectual Tasks. Classification of the results is not easy. In general, researchers have tended to use the same conditions for their "noise" and "quiet" and to vary their tasks. It will be easier to avoid repetition, therefore, if researches are considered in a more or less historical order rather than attempting to classify tasks on which effects have or have not been found. Where convenient, however, results on similar types of tasks will be put side by side. The earlier researchers, for instance, tended to use rather intellectual types of work, in which a succession of problems was to be solved, time taken or errors forming the score used. Two such tasks are described in an earlier section, since they showed effects of the onset of the noise.[46,47] These were a task of adding digits which had to be found among letters, and a task of carrying out two encoding operations on a presented letter. Neither of these studies showed any impairment by noise at the end of the work period, the initial effect having worn off. Another research used arithmetical problems, with records of actual street and office noise as the noise condition rather than the automobile horn of the first experiment and the bells and buzzers of the second. The records of office and street noise were played at sound levels which now seem rather low, the peaks being only 65 db for office noise and 75 db for street noise. Once again no detrimental effect was apparent when the sound and the task had become familiar.[27] It should be noted that these experiments, although repeated on successive days in some cases, involved work periods of the order of only 10 min. Another rather similar research employed a mechanical noise machine and music as the noisy conditions, with cancellation, addition, and transcription tests as the tasks. Once again there was little evidence of any decrement after the noise had become familiar.[54] To deviate slightly from a strict chronological order, two recent studies using modern techniques confirm the general trend of these earlier researches. In one case subjects were asked to carry out three clerical tests: one was of addition, each problem requiring the addition of nine five-place numbers.[55] The second test was of vocabulary, and required the subject to choose from four words a synonym for the given word. The third test was of number comparison, in which pairs of five-place numbers were given and the subject was required to detect any pairs which were dissimilar. Each test consisted, of course, of a number of problems of similar type, and equivalent sets of problems were prepared for use under the different noise conditions. The sound source used was recorded office-machine noise and was presented at the four 10-db steps from sound levels of 65 to 95 db, inclusive, the remaining two conditions employed being no noise and variation in the sound level of machine noise from 65 to 95 db randomly through the test period. The addition test took 5 min, the vocabulary test 1½ min, and the number-comparison test 3 min. In no case was there any significant difference between the various noise levels in the percentage of error on these tests. Speed and accuracy were not reported separately, probably because they showed nothing of particular interest. The longest test, the addition test, did show a steady trend as the noise intensity was increased. The percentage of correct responses declined with each increase in noise level, the drop becoming greater at the higher levels. But, like other results, this was not significant.

In the other recent research, intermittent bursts of noise from a noise generator were presented at sound levels of 100 db during the performance of a clerical test and a formboard test.[56] The bursts of sound varied from 10 to 50 sec in length and were present during half the time that testing was in progress. The clerical test consists of two subtests, each lasting 7 min, one being of the number-comparison type mentioned in the last research and the other being of a similar type but using pairs of names rather than pairs of numbers. The formboard test lasts 14 min and requires the subject to identify the result of assembling a given group of isolated plane figures. Two groups of subjects were employed; so that the same problems were given both in noise and in quiet. In all three tests more items were attempted in noise but less were correct. However, the statistical significance of the results is dubious, since of the 12 differences tested only 2 were significant. One of these was the percentage of correct responses in name checking, which were of course less frequent in noise, while the other comparison was the number of items attempted on the formboard. The latter score was higher in noise. There is always some doubt concerning the validity of statistical tests on one or two results chosen from a large number of possibilities. The criticism put forward is, in effect, that if we deal ourselves enough hands, sooner or later we shall get a winning one. Yet the significances in this case are fairly high and the results may well be correct; but, as the author says, they are unimportant from a practical point of view.

These studies, and certain others using similar types of problems,[57,58,59] suggest that paper and pencil work of this sort will not be likely to show effects of noise. If anything, there seems to be a tendency for faster work on the average. There may also be an unimportant increase in errors; both these findings are very slight but appear repeatedly in a number of experiments and may therefore be accepted as possible effects of noise. Similar findings also appear in certain studies using longer work periods and tasks which are somewhat less of the problem-by-problem type. For example, two groups of students were asked to read a chapter from a textbook, while one of the groups was exposed to recorded music.[60] This group read slightly more in $\frac{1}{2}$ hr than the quiet control group though not significantly so: they did, however, do significantly worse on a test of comprehension. In another research, six subjects performed a number of different tasks under a number of different temperature and noise conditions.[61] The tasks included number-comparison tests of the type mentioned several times already, mental multiplication of three-place by two-place numbers, the finding of particular locations in a grid of rows and columns, visual threading of mazes, the tracing of a circular pattern by two controls as in a lathe, and coding using a typewriter which presented the next item to be encoded as soon as one item had been handled. The noise was that of an electric fan and was administered at sound levels of 70, 80, and 90 db. The work period was of 4 hr, though the same task was not continually performed throughout this period. Yet the tasks were at least $\frac{1}{2}$ hr in length each and were therefore somewhat nearer to many practical situations than the short tests cited so far. Once again there was certainly no decline in the speed of work in the higher noise levels: on the multiplication and number-checking tasks the speed was significantly greater at a noise level of 90 db than at 70 db. An increase in errors also appears in the mental-multiplication and lathe tasks, being significant in both cases. On the other hand, the locations task showed significantly fewer errors at the highest noise level. It is difficult to decide why one such task should differ from the others, although it might possibly be argued that the locations task comes nearest to the simple sensory-function type of experiment, in which the subject knows exactly when he must look for the particular signal which he is required to distinguish.

Sensorimotor Tasks. The lathe task, described above, is a sensorimotor task, rather than an intellectual one. There are some early studies on such tasks, including typing and the striking of small target holes in a moving belt with a stylus, but they are open to objections on the ground of poor experimental technique. Detailed criticism may be found in the review of the literature already cited as including extra papers of insufficient importance to be examined here.[2] Among more recent studies, there is an experiment on the accuracy of tracking and of stereoscopic range finding with a gun-control system. In this case the work period was extremely long, by the standard of previous researches, being 4 hr on a single task. Extremely intense noises, having sound levels up to 120 or 130 db, were inserted for periods of 2 min in some cases and 3 min in others. No consistent deterioration in performance was found in any of the conditions of insertion of the noises. When they were introduced in the middle and end of the prolonged task, there was in fact an improvement.[62] This improvement may be compared with the improvement produced by short periods of music in factories during the working day. It seems to have come as a stimulus in the popular sense, relieving monotony and so keeping performance up to a high level.

Other sensorimotor tasks were studied in a research which compared aircraft noise having a sound level of 115 db with that of 90 db.[51] Besides the tests of visual and motor function which were mentioned above, tasks of translating written material into code and sorting 12 cards into 12 compartments were employed. Neither showed any difference between the two noise levels. Another task giving negative results was that of compensatory tracking using aircraft controls. (Compensatory tracking is the task of keeping an indicator, in this case the spot of a cathode-ray oscillograph and also a galvanometer needle, at a particular mark while outside disturbances attempt to remove it.) A rather similar task from the same research was to use aircraft controls to move a spot of light along a predetermined track. In this case the rate of work was set by the operator himself, and so the time taken to complete a given sequence of operations could be taken as a score, as well as the number of failures in keeping the light on the path. This test did appear to show a difference between the two noise levels, both in speed and in errors. Throughout this experiment the five subjects worked 7-hr days, the noise level being constant throughout each day. They did not, however, work at any one task for a long period. Each task was kept down to 15 min to keep motivation constant. Each subject spent one 15-min session on each of five tasks, then took a short rest and performed all five tasks again. Five such periods occupied the whole day. The sequence of high- and low-noise days was counterbalanced, 16 days in all being used. The subjects were all practiced on the tasks before the main experiment.

The discrepancy between the two tasks involving coordinated use of airplane controls was responsible for the rather skeptical phrasing used above to introduce the effect found on one task. A possible explanation is that this effect was spurious. A test of the speed of accommodation of the eyes was found to show a change with increasing noise level, which was afterward proved to be partly due to clues given to the subject by relays in the apparatus.[51] There were also relays in the apparatus connected to the aircraft-control task. Possibly, therefore, a similar explanation could be advanced, although no similar experiment demonstrating the effect of the relays seems to have been done. In view of the markedly negative results of most other tests used in this research, this explanation (that the results are spurious due to auditory clues) has usually been accepted. There is a slight difficulty, however, that the difference both in time per trial and in errors is much greater for the last period of the day than for the first. Indeed for the first period the quiet days show more errors than the noise ones, although the curves cross soon afterward. It may be conceivable that very faint audible clues from the apparatus should become helpful only after a relearning period each day, but such an interpretation seems somewhat forced. Another explanation which has been put forward is that the task showing an effect on noise was an unpaced one, in which the subjects worked at the limit of their ability in quiet, and so were impaired in noise. The other task required response only when demanded by the machine and it was recognized as being an easier task. Whatever the explanation, this result is clearly in an ambiguous position; in any case, the changes in speed and accuracy are only 5 per cent, and therefore probably of little practical importance.

A similarly ambiguous result has been obtained on a coordination test in which the hand is removed from a button (thus starting a clock), a pencil is removed from one hole and inserted in another, and the button is then pressed again to stop the clock. On two groups of subjects this task showed a retardation of a little over 5 per cent in jet-engine noise as compared with quiet conditions.[52] Unfortunately, while in the first group of three subjects all subjects showed the effect, in the second group of five subjects, two did not show it. The second group were tested under slightly different conditions and had received some jet noise because of accidental circumstances shortly before the instructions and first quiet control period. This result is not there fore statistically valid and is merely suggestive. In any event, as the subjects were not used to jet noise this may belong with the startle response discussed in an earlier section. Most authorities would agree that an unfamiliar noise would impair a delicate task, but this does not mean that a familiar noise would do likewise.

Visual Watchkeeping and Continuous Work. More positive conclusions appear in the next research to be considered, which compared the effects of two noises having sound levels of 70 and 100 db.[63] Three tasks were used, of types found to be particularly sensitive to the effect of other kinds of stress. Two of the tasks required the subject to watch a visual display, of steam gauges in the one case and of indicator lamps in the other, watching for rare signals upon which some action must be taken. The task in each case lasted 1½ hr, and only 15 signals were delivered during this time. The steam-pressure gauges were considerably harder to read, and a group of 10 subjects showed on the average better performance on quiet days than on noise days. The proportion of signals detected in less than 10 sec dropped by more than 30 per cent in the higher level of noise. On the easier task, however, a separate group of 20 subjects did not show any effect of noise. There were individual differences apparent in this group. There were also significant changes in the pattern of performance in noise, the center of the display showing a deterioration which was not shared by the ends of the row of lights; and there was a significant tendency for missed signals to be grouped together rather than appear at random throughout the work period. Detailed analysis of the trends in performance with time also showed that in noise performance began worse than in quiet, then became slightly better, and then deteriorated. The initial stages of this progress are similar to those frequently shown in other experiments described in the last section. But the later deterioration is less common, and suggested to the author that some subjects were making an effort in noise which they could not keep up. The relative decline from the first noise day to the second was statistically significant, although the difference between the second noise day and the second quiet day was not significant. The third task used in this research was a serial reaction task, in which the subject was faced with five lights and five contacts.[64] When a particular light was on, a particular contact was to be touched; as soon as a response was made another light lit up, and this continued without interruption. A work period of ½ hr was employed on this task, and scores of output of correct responses, number of incorrect responses, and number of short intervals of 1½ sec (in some experiments 2 sec), during which no response whatever was made, were recorded. It has long been known that in tasks of this sort the average rate of producing correct responses does not decline with prolonged performance until very long work periods have been undergone. But at a much earlier stage, after only 10 to 20 min work, the flow of responses begins to show momentary interruptions. In unpracticed subjects these may take the form of "blocks," that is, intervals without response;[65] in more practiced subjects they will rather become errors. (An error is of course not a badly coordinated response, but a response which is incorrectly chosen. That is, one of the contacts is struck, but not the contact corresponding to the signal light.) As the noise experiments involved practiced subjects errors were more important than blocks. A noise having a sound level of 100 db produced considerably more errors than the quieter condition. The blocks were increased but not significantly so, and the output of correct responses was decreased but very slightly and not significantly; individual variability was much more marked in the latter score than in the others, some subjects getting faster in noise and some slower. The size of the effect on accuracy was substantial, being of the order of 50 per cent. The result has been obtained in three experiments on separate groups of subjects; so that it seems reasonably well established. The first group of 18 subjects provided a simple comparison between the two conditions; the second group of 14 subjects were informed in advance, with carefully prepared faked graphs, that noise was expected to improve their performance, and the third group of 40 subjects were divided into subgroups and used to compare the effects of different kinds of noise. A result from this latter group will be mentioned again at the end of the section; in this case the worst noise was able to produce 100 per cent more errors than the best noise. To put these rather dramatic-sounding figures in perspective, it should be realized that the subjects were, under the worst conditions, producing about 2,000 correct responses for every 50 errors. As in the task of watching indicator lamps, it was found that the advantage of quiet conditions increased as the length of the work period increased. The first 5 min of the task would have shown an advantage for noise.

This research obviously gives more positive effects of noise than have been reported in the other experiments. Before considering the reasons for this, we should perhaps note some other experiments from different sources which confirm the general findings. First, it was mentioned in the last section that a research on the visual-contrast threshold had shown that as small a difference in brightness could be seen in a sound level of 90 db as in 45 db. The investigators had noted not only the level of brightness of a light which was detected but also the reaction time between the appearance of each light and the subject's response to it. In noise this time was consistently longer, except for the faintest stimulus. The change in reaction time is highly significant. The method of presenting the task in this case was somewhat different from many tests of sensory function. The subject was asked to observe the field of view through a telescope, for $12\frac{1}{2}$ min at a time. The appearance of each test stimulus was signaled by a light to his left eye shortly before the exposure of the stimulus. This light is specified as small and red, and may have been somewhat inconspicuous. Any delay in observing it would naturally be reflected in a long reaction time to the main stimulus. After each work period of $12\frac{1}{2}$ min, a break of $2\frac{1}{2}$ min was taken, and then another period was begun until a total time of 2 hr had been spent in the situation. This is a somewhat prolonged test involving the detection of signals at less definite times than in such a test as the dark-vision one, described in the last section, in which the subject presented the stimulus himself. It bears a close relation to the tasks of watching gauges and lights, and the similarity of the findings adds confidence to an acceptance of both sets of results. The only possible point of difference is over the effect of time in the noise. The authors of the contrast-threshold research rightly say that they have no evidence of an increase in the effect of noise with time; although, as is seen in Fig. 10.5, the difference in reaction times was larger at the end of the work period, the effect was not statistically significant and might have been due to chance. But since this research was done, another computational technique has become available;* the data from the contrast-threshold experiment have been recomputed by the present writer and give a highly significant relation with time in the noise. The agreement with the gauge- and light-watching experiment thus remains good.

One last piece of evidence supporting the conclusion that continuous searching for visual stimuli may produce slow reactions in noise comes from an early visual test. This was a test requiring the subject to detect particular patterns amongst a medley of confusing lines, and required close attention. A series of patterns was presented and the time taken to work through the test was used as the score. A statistically significant deterioration was found when this test was given in noisy surroundings as compared with quiet ones.[68] The noise was in this case that naturally arising in a generator room at a factory, as compared with normal quiet conditions. The test itself was done within a booth in controlled illumination so that other conditions beside the noise should have been reasonably constant. Putting these three researches together, it seems that a task involving continuous visual search, as opposed to detection of signals at an occasional known time with rest intervals in between, may show slow performance. The magnitude of the effect should not be overrated; in the last research cited the increase in time to do a test lasting nearly 1 min was only 3 sec.

---

* The analysis of variance, as used in the original research, treats time as a nominal rather than an ordinal scale.[66] The test used for recomputation[67] takes advantage of the gradual increase in the effect with successive intervals of time, as additional evidence against the null hypothesis. Because this test does not consider some of the possible alternatives to the null hypothesis, the validity of using it is similar to that of one-tail as opposed to two-tail tests. That is, it should only be employed when there are reasons for thinking that progressive increase or decrease in an effect are the major alternatives to the null hypothesis. In the present case the other researches provide these reasons.

In the research on contrast threshold, the increase in reaction time was only a small fraction of a second; and in the watching of indicator lamps and dials, although there was a large change in the proportion of signals seen within 10 sec, a less severe time criterion would have shown a smaller difference.   The effect is likely to be of practical importance only in cases where extreme speed is necessary, as, for example, in the detection of signals which indicate serious and dangerous faults developing in a machine, or in the inspection of items passing on a conveyor belt which will not be present for unlimited time.

Another research study is similar in the task used to the five-choice serial reaction task which was mentioned earlier.   That task did not allow any intervals for rest. Furthermore it showed that when the worker set his own rate of work the rate became more variable toward the end of a session, especially in noise.   This means that the effect would be more serious on a task in which the worker could not set his own rate of work but had to keep to that of a machine.   Any signal for response arriving at an instant of lowered efficiency would not be dealt with, and at instants of high efficiency the worker could not increase the speed of work to compensate.   This more damaging effect on a paced task, as opposed to an unpaced task, was shown for the effect of

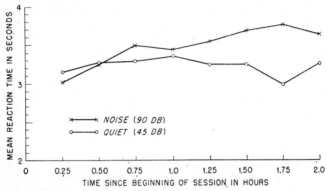

FIG. 10.5. Reaction time to an occasional faint visual signal in two levels of noise.   (*Plotted from the data of Broussard et al.*[53])

prolonged work, though not for the effect of noise.   The task to be described next resembled the five-choice task in requiring continuous activity but differed in other respects, including the fact that it was paced by a machine.   The subject was faced with three lights, each of which was flashing at a particular rhythm.   The rates of flash were different and formed a complex pattern such that the order of illumination of the lights did not repeat for a very long time.   The slowest light came on 9 times in 2 min while the fastest one came on 10 times in 1 min.   There was a key beneath each light, and the subject was required to press the key beneath a light when that light had flashed a prescribed number of times.   The number itself was varied from 4 to 10 but was constant for one testing session.   The worker thus had to keep count of three separate series of events at the same time, with no intervals in which he could be sure that nothing would happen.   On the average some light or other would come on every 3 sec but the unpredictable nature of the pattern would make it difficult to rely on any time in which nothing would happen.   This task was continued for 2 hr, two groups being tested, one of which was exposed for 1 hr of their session to a noise having a sound level of 110 db while the other group received relative quiet. The number of mistakes increased as time went on, was greater in the noise group, and became greater in the noise group relative to the quiet group as the period of exposure to the noise went on.   These results are clearly similar to those for errors on the unpaced five-choice reaction task.[69]   A number of real-life situations somewhat different from those usually studied in the laboratory are clearly parallel to this most ingenious task of counting lights.   In many cases a number of different activities must be kept going by alternating between them, without losing the thread of any of them. A simple example is that of cooking in which different items with different cooking times may all be in progress simultaneously. The type of immediate memory involved in such a task may require different functions from the more simply perceptual ones involved in the other tasks mentioned in this section. It was noted that the light flashing at the slowest rate, and the longest number of flashes required before a key pressing, seemed more sensitive than the modifications of the task which needed only a shorter span of memory; and this indicated the possible importance of memory functions. The distinction between perception and immediate memory, however, is difficult to make in many practical situations, although its reality or otherwise may be of great theoretical importance. This result, together with those from the serias reaction task, suggest that mistakes may rise rapidly in frequency in a prolonged talk of a type which does not allow any relaxation of attention.

To summarize, no clear and obvious distinction appears between tasks which show effects of noise and those which do not. Short paper and pencil tests appear to be quite insensitive to noise, and so are short tests of sensorimotor performance. When the average rate of work over a fair period is taken, there is no consistant decline in performance and there may be an improvement in some special cases. Mistakes are more likely to show effects but will be serious only in tasks in which effects of prolonged work are also serious; these appear on the whole to be tasks requiring completely

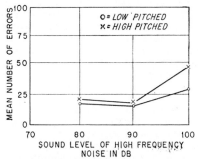

FIG. 10.6. Some evidence on the errors produced in one particular task by various levels of high- and low-pitched noise. (*Broadbent, unpublished data.*)

continuous alertness with no remission even for a matter of seconds. Speed of responding to an occasional visual signal, on the other hand, may be slowed down; provided that the measurement is made under prolonged conditions with, once again, little opportunity for free intervals without any danger of a signal. Prolonged performance as such or prolonged exposure to noise as such did not necessarily involve reductions in efficiency. Further clarification of the difference between tasks which show effects of noise and those which do not is undertaken in the next section.

The kinds of noise showing the most serious effects are not easy to specify since so many investigations have failed to find any effect at all. Some unpublished results are shown in Fig. 10.6, the score used being errors on the five-choice serial reaction task. Machinery noise having a fairly flat octave-band spectrum from 50 to 5,000 cps, with no marked periodic character, was recorded on magnetic tape. This recording was then used as a source of two types of noise by filtering above and below 2,000 cps. The errors in the high-pitched and low-pitched noises were compared at three sound levels. The effect of noise on errors appears above 90 db and seems to be more serious for the high-pitched noise. The difference between the effects of the high- and low-pitched noise at lower sound levels is not significant.

The remainder of the literature reveals no statistically satisfactory experiment showing effects of noise at sound levels lower than 90 db, although some have shown effects at this level. This does not necessarily prove that lower levels will not impair efficiency, but there is no positive evidence that they should do so. One of the experiments, unsatisfactory from a modern point of view, employed subjects for prolonged periods at a dotting task in which they were required to insert a stylus in holes appearing in a moving paper belt.[70] This is a task which the most recent results do suggest would show effects of noise, as was claimed, and the early study also found that high-pitched pure tones produced more errors than those lower in frequency. This statistically unsatisfactory confirmation of the more damaging effects of high frequencies is all that can be found in the literature. The same study found that a buzz from an audiometer was more effective than any pure tone except the highest frequencies. But the sounds appear to have been compared at equal sensation levels, that is, at equal numbers of decibels above threshold. This may mean that the broader band noise sounded louder than the pure tones to which it was compared. The more recent experiment used equal loudness levels. A rough rule is that the reduction of high frequencies is more important than that of low frequencies; if possible, over-all noise levels should be brought below 90 db.

An Interpretation of the Nature of Behavior in Noise. The various results given in the previous section are interpreted here to present an over-all picture of human performance in noise. The easiest way to introduce this view of human skill is to consider the familiar phenomenon of blinking. A blink lasts a definite time, and while the rate of blinking may go up and down within wide limits the time for which the eyes are closed for each blink is less variable. During the period for which the eyes are closed there is of course no visual information entering the nervous system; yet performance is only slightly affected, if at all, by this periodic interruption of the intake of information. Reasons for this lack of effect are easily found. If a novel object is presented, blinking may be temporarily suspended while the object is examined. The longer the visual task is continued, the more likely blinks are to appear, but for a short time at the beginning of the task they may be withheld. When a sequence of events has occurred repeatedly, on the other hand, there are two other mechanisms which allow blinking to take place without impairing efficiency. On the one hand, when it is known that incoming information will not be present for a certain specified time, a number of blinks may occur and thus reduce the necessity for blinking at a later time when a crucial signal is expected. On the other hand, if the sequence of events is completely predictable so that all its members after the first are known when the first occurs, then no information is provided by these later events and they need not be observed to be dealt with adequately.

Some concrete examples may make these mechanisms more understandable. A driver in heavy traffic where he is expecting to receive critical signals shows a low blink rate; the same driver in the open country when he knows it is safe to close his eyes occasionally shows a higher blink rate.[71] Experimentally, if a man is asked to follow a track appearing from behind a slit, and the track is sometimes straight for a definite period and then oscillates for a period, the blink rate is high before and after the oscillating portion of the track but not during it.[71,72] This shift in the distribution of blinks may allow efficient performance even though the number of blinks over a long period of time remains over the average the same. These examples illustrate the way in which the extent to which time of arrival of information is predictable will influence the occurrence of blinking.

A familiar and domestic example of the second behavioral mechanism which allows us to avoid ill effects from blinking is the ability to follow a familiar route in the dark. In a strange house one needs a light to go upstairs, while in one's own it may not be worth a few extra steps to reach the switch. Performance is determined by stored information, and visual stimuli are unnecessary. Experimentally, one may ask a man to follow an oscillating track with a pointer, and one finds that when he is unpracticed he shows errors either when he blinks naturally or when his vision of the task is interrupted by a shutter.[72] With a simple track, such as a sine wave, a practiced subject ceases to show such sizable errors from blinking or from mechanical interruption of his view. A complex and unpredictable track, of course, still defeats him on such occasions. So long in fact as the world continues to do what it has done in the past, his performance will show no sign of the effect of blinks; it is only when some unpredictable event occurs that we shall see that he is in error. If he is performing some practiced task, he will probably do something completely incorrect at such a time, and if the task is less familiar he will do nothing at all.   A motorist on a quiet road would perform quite incorrectly if the gentle curve he saw a moment ago were to straighten itself out during one of his frequent blinks.

The foregoing remarks apply only to blinking, but they have been shown to be true for that case, and they illustrate psychological mechanisms which are important for performance in noise.   It is likely that a man working in noise suffers from brief interruptions in the intake of information from a task he is supposed to be carrying out. These interruptions take place internally (Fig. 10.7) and not externally as blinks do. They can be withheld for a brief period so as to allow performance of a novel task, and their distribution in time will vary in such a way as to produce as little disturbance of the work as possible.   They will become serious in their effects on efficiency only in tasks in which no momentary relaxation is possible, in particular, in watch-keeping tasks in which stimuli are delivered at unpredictable times and in continuous tasks in which successive stimuli follow each other too closely to allow such an interruption in the intake of information.   For many purposes blinking provides a useful

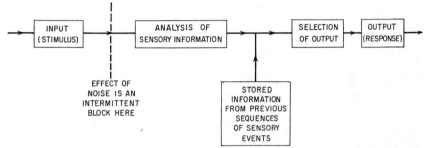

FIG. 10.7. A hypothetical information-flow diagram for the human nervous system, illus-trating the interpretation of noise effects given in the text.

analogy to illustrate the type of effect which is meant, but there are certain differences between the "internal blinks" and the external blinks, especially in the time scale of the effect.*   Thus a man working in noise will as time goes on show intermittent failures in his performance but in between these failures his work will not necessarily be less efficient.   As a background of continually changing stimulation seems to increase the efficiency of behavior,[74,75,76] the onset of noise and its cessation may produce work which is actually faster than that under normal conditions, during the intervals of time separating internal blinks.   It will be remembered that, in the section on industrial experiments, it was noted that short periods of music during the working day improved the rate of work.   Similarly, a number of laboratory experiments on noise suggest that performance may become faster in noise.   But this effect is independent of the increase in "internal blinks," so that work may become faster and less accurate or possibly more varied in speed in noise, or alternatively it may show an increase in errors without any increase in speed.   Finally, the evidence is not quite conclusive as to the nature of the "internal blink"; it might be due to a complete,

* An "internal blink" is suspected to last as long as 1 sec, but performance on one task may be maintained for several minutes before "internal blinking" commences.   There is also the point that the cutting off of incoming information does not seem to be absolute, as it is with overt blinking.   A stimulus which is easy to discriminate from its background may succeed in entering the nervous system even when one might expect intermittent failures of efficiency to be present.   This is shown by the task of watching indicator lamps, described in the last section, and has been shown in a number of different situations for the effects of prolonged performance.   A dim brief blip on a radar screen will, after prolonged watch, escape detection; but a bright clear blip may be detected as well at the end of a prolonged session as at the beginning.[73]   This affords no particular theoretical difficulty to a view which regards the efficiency of the perceptual system as being lowered intermittently, but it means that the simple analogy with blinking must be used with some caution.

though temporary, block in the analysis of all sensory information, or it might be due to analysis of information from some sense not used in the task. In ordinary terms, a mental blank or a shift of attention are the alternatives. There are reasons for believing the latter.* That is, the limited capacity of the human perceptual system makes it necessary for some incoming sensory information to be filtered out before reaching the main analyzing centers of the brain. Normally, irrelevant features of the surroundings are ignored and task stimuli control response. But after prolonged work in noise, the auditory stimulation may interfere with the task stimulation and so produce the effect we have called an "internal blink."

Individual Differences and the Effects of Attitudes on Efficiency. There are few data upon the types of individual most subject to effects from noise. A separate section on the topic is justifiable mostly on the grounds of recognizing the importance of individual differences, and of making suggestions to guide future research and practical action. It is a frequent feature of noise experiments that individual differences are noted, and this in itself is worth emphasizing to the practical man. There should be nothing surprising in finding that one person has a markedly lowered efficiency in a noisy place of work, while another does not.

The first and most obvious explanation of individual differences is that they are due to differences of attitude. A person who believes that noise will reduce his efficiency

* The evidence for an "attention-shifting" theory may be summarized as follows: First, it is by no means clear why an intense sound should produce complete blocks in activity. On the other hand, it is easy to see that an intense stimulus will offer severe competition in a contest to gain control of a limited-capacity perceptual mechanism. That is, the loud noise interferes more because attention wanders to the noise away from the task. Second, a high-pitched noise seems to be more effective than a low-pitched one, as noted in the last section. The attention-getting qualities of a high-pitched sound are commonly emphasized in literature based on everyday experience, and the greater probability of a rapid response to such a stimulus has been shown in unpublished experiments. There seems no reason why a stimulus which produces greater efficiency when it is a task stimulus should produce less efficiency when it is present during performance of a visual task, unless there is some competition between different stimuli for response.

Third, when prolonged watch keeping is performed on a visual display containing more than one source of information, the most efficiently observed part of the display does not remain the same as the watch is continued. There is a shift from one source of information to another.[77] Fourth, there is the question of the time taken to shift response from one sensory channel to another. Experiments in which one channel of information has been led to one ear and a different channel to the other ear of the same subject have shown that it is impossible to respond alternately to the signals reaching the two ears when those signals are separated by very short times. In ordinary language, one cannot shift attention instantaneously from one ear to the other. The minimum time necessary to listen to a spoken digit on one ear, to shift to the other ear and listen to a digit there, and to shift back in time for a second digit on the first ear, is $1\frac{1}{2}$ to 2 sec.[78] It varies from person to person, and these figures are for British sailors. In the five-choice serial reaction task, the momentary failures of performance which appear after prolonged work are also of $1\frac{1}{2}$ to 2 sec. This similarity fits very well with the interpretation that the worker is momentarily shifting attention from his task to his surroundings and then returning to the task. In more exact terms, an interruption in the intake of information from one ear to allow intake of information from the other ear requires about the same time as the interruption in reception of visual information appearing in the visual task. It is therefore consistent with the view that the interruption of visual performance is to allow reception of information from some other sensory channel. These arguments do not make a completely convincing case for the "attention wandering," or "shift in source of information," hypothesis. But they do seem to give it a reasonable probability. It may be noted, also, that there is some slight physiological evidence for its likelihood. In a recent investigation, electrodes were inserted into the cochlear nucleus of a cat. This nerve center lies between the ear itself and the higher centers of the brain, and shows electrical activity when a click is presented to the ear of the animal. But when a mouse was shown to the animal the cochlear nucleus showed no electrical activity following a click.[79] That is, there seemed to be an interruption in the intake of auditory information, while visual information of high priority is being handled. Apart from this isolated observation, there is little direct physiological evidence for a filtering of information as it enters the nervous system, but the evidence from psychological experiments seems reasonably strong.

is half defeated already.   If this were so, one might attack individual differences in
susceptibility by propaganda designed to show that noise does not impair efficiency.
Two researches have shown effects from such propaganda.   In one case music was
used as the auditory stimulus,[80] and in the other speech having a sound level of
70 db.[81]   Different groups of subjects were employed, some subjects being told that
noise would improve their performance, some that it would produce poorer performance, and some that an initial improvement would be followed by deterioration.
The results from each group differed, in a direction agreeing with the preliminary
briefing.   Obviously, therefore, poorer performance in noise can be the result of a
belief that noise impairs efficiency.   This may cause some misgiving about the positive
effects of noise cited earlier but it should be noted that these experiments on attitudes
used very faint noises compared with those giving effects of efficiency.   Furthermore,
in at least one of the positive cases a control experiment on effects of suggestion was
performed; it showed that the result could not be eliminated by suggestion and was
therefore unlikely to have been caused by it.   The rather limited effects on efficiency
considered earlier may therefore still be accepted; but we must also be aware of the
possibility that a spurious effect of noise may be caused at lower intensities by a hostile
attitude toward it on the part of the subject.   A factory manager who ridicules the
idea of effects of noise on efficiency is probably adopting a sound strategy, in so far
as he will minimize any suggestion effect on his workers.   At the same time, if this
attitude is carried so far as to ignore the deafening effects of noise and the possible
minor effects on efficiency, it may rebound since workers becoming aware of these
effects will shift their attitude to the opposite extreme.

It is not altogether satisfactory, however, to ascribe all individual differences to
differences in attitude.   One reason for this is that there is not a perfect correlation
between number of complaints and size of effect on efficiency.   In the industrial
study on weavers described earlier, it was found that the workers most hostile to
earplugs showed the least benefit from them, but the difference was so slight as to be
statistically insignificant.   Some individuals were hostile to earplugs and yet benefited
from them more than others who were keen on them.   A similar lack of correspondence between complaints and efficiency is found in other researches.   Nor is there any
evidence showing that neurotics show a greater effect on efficiency from noise, although
as mentioned previously they are more likely to express verbal annoyance at it.

The positive evidence about the personality or other features of people showing
large effects of noise is extremely scanty.   One study showed that the persons giving
the largest effect of noise were those who showed the largest improvement on the
second run of their performance in quiet as compared with their first run.[63]   This
rather curious relationship is more intelligible when it is realized that the latter score
is effectively a measure of liability to fatigue.   A person who shows a large decline in
performance when working over a long period but recovers rapidly with rest will score
highly on this measure.   This had previously been demonstrated in the task of
watching steam-pressure gauges.[77]   The result thus suggests that the persons who
show the greatest deterioration with prolonged work also show the greatest deterioration in noise.   In view of the fact that many studies claiming positive effects of
noise show that the difference between noise and quiet increases as the work period
increases, this individual difference is not surprising.   More interesting is the question
whether individual differences in susceptibility to noise or prolonged work can be
detected by some independent measure, applied possibly as a selection procedure.
Although in this same study an independent measure was found to correlate reasonably well, it was not of a type suited for selection testing.   It was of the type known
as a level-of-aspiration test, in which the subject is repeatedly asked to perform a task,
told of his previous performance, and asked to estimate his performance on the next
trial.   The difference between his known past score and his guessed subsequent score
is the measure of interest, but however suitable for research purposes it is clearly not
a test which would be very resistant to the more or less conscious faking employed
by applicants for work.   It is more useful to consider the other characteristics with
which such tests are known to correlate.   This particular level-of-aspiration test was
shown to correlate with educational attainment, although not with test intelligence.[82]

Thus, of two people who are equally intelligent the one who is least distractible will do better in academic work. This again is not surprising, and it is likely that many employers already regard educational attainment as some sort of index of conscientiousness. In the present state of the evidence, the most important point about individual differences is that experiments on effects of noise should be carried out on subjects from a population similar to that to which it is desired to apply the findings.

Practical Conclusions about Noise Reduction and Behavior. When one is considering whether to reduce a particular noise or not, in view of the probable expense of the operation, it may be valuable to bear in mind the various aspects of behavior in noise. Of the three possible measures of behavior, namely, verbal complaint, physiological damage, and effects on efficiency, the physiological effects can be neglected except at very high intensities. There is little evidence of any such effect at low intensities with a noise that continues for some time. Annoyance is a different matter; it is distinct from effects on efficiency and may be marked even with sounds that have no other effect on behavior at all. On the whole, noise reduction does reduce annoyance, even though annoyance may be produced by very faint sounds. If one is reducing noise on these grounds, to prevent complaints, high-pitched and intermittent or modulated sounds appear to be the ones worthy of the prime consideration. A good deal of variation in annoyance will occur, however, from one particular case to another. Questions of the history both of the noise and of the persons complaining will produce such variation, and it is to a large extent unpredictable by scientific methods.

The beginning of a noise will produce a startle effect that may interfere with performance on some task, and there may therefore be grounds in some cases for insulating workers from possible sources of variable noise such as roadways. The effect seems to be more marked on more complex and novel tasks, rather than practiced repetitive ones, so that the practical importance of such an effect on efficiency is slight. Once the noise has become familiar most sensory and motor functions will be unimpaired. There is some evidence, however, of an effect which has been described under *An Interpretation of the Nature of Behavior in Noise*. This effect will produce intermittent failures of efficiency interspersed by normal or even faster than normal performance. Because of this, output of work which is carried on at the worker's own speed will probably be unaffected. Mistakes may be increased, because the essence of the effect is that the worker does not notice unexpected features of the surroundings. Accidents also may show an effect of noise for this reason; they have not been investigated as a function of noise, although they are known to be highly sensitive indexes of effects of other stresses such as heat. Output may be affected if the work is paced by a machine, at a speed below the fastest which the human operator can handle. In such a case the intermittent failures of the human operator will cause failure to react, but it will not be possible to make this up by faster response between these intermittent failures. There may thus be a decline in output on paced tasks. The task would need to be one in which each element of the work is present only for a matter of a second or two, and thus this effect is not of general importance. Such conditions may be approximated in a high-speed inspection process, at the end of an assembly line, or similar operations. A good general conclusion, however, is that output will not be affected, but mistakes and accidents may be.

It is interesting to note that reported gains in industry from noise reduction have, in fact, been reported on tasks consistent with the view we have just put forward. The best research on the subject, as reported in the section on *Results from Industrial Studies*, was on weavers. The work of a weaver is of course largely a matter of watching machinery in order to take action if human intervention is needed. It is therefore precisely the sort of work which might be expected to show some effect of noise. Typing also might show an increase in errors in highly noisy conditions. Other industrial processes might not have reported such effects.

It is difficult to say very much about the types of noise producing the greatest effects on efficiency; but there is some evidence that high-pitched noises are once more those producing the worse effects. No effect on efficiency has yet been found with noise levels below 90 db, although unfortunately annoyance may still arise from such noises, and undoubtedly they will cause some harassing of speech communication. In general, effects on health or efficiency from noise seem to be somewhat slighter than is often thought. It must be borne in mind that unpleasantness is a quality of the environment distinct from effects on health or ability to work. Much of our civilization rests on the assumption that it is worth doing more to the environment than merely securing survival. Reduction of annoyance, or the pursuit of happiness, is not necessarily an ignoble end.

REFERENCES

1. Davis, H., et al.: C.H.A.B.A. Report No. 4, St. Louis, 1954.
2. Kryter, K. D.: *J. Speech Disorders Monog. Suppl.* 1, 1950.
3. Loring, J. C. G.: *J. Speech Disorders Monog. Suppl.* 3, 1953.
4. Chapman, D.: British National Building Studies, No. 2, H.M. Stationery Office, London, 1948.
5. Stevens, S. S., et al.: Part II, OSRD Report 274, Psychological Laboratory, Harvard University, Dec. 1, 1941.
6. Weston, H. C., and S. Adams: Part II, Report 65, Industrial Health Research Board, H.M. Stationery Office, London, 1932.
7. Pollock, K. G., and F. C. Bartlett: Part I of Report 65, Industrial Health Research Board, H.M. Stationery Office, London, 1932.
8. Laird, D. A., and K. Coye: *J. Acoust. Soc. Amer.*, **1**: 158 (1929).
9. Reese, T. W., and K. D. Kryter: Psycho-acoustic Laboratory, Harvard University, Mar. 17, 1944, PB 27306.
10. Pollack, I.: *Am. J. Psychol.*, **62**: 285 (1949).
11. Rosenblith, W. A., et al.: vol. II, U.S.A.F., WADC Tech. Report 52-204, 1953.
12. Miller, G. A.: *Psychol. Bull.*, **44**: 105 (1947).
13. Cassel, E. E., and K. M. Dallenbach: *Am. J. Psychol.*, **29**: 129 (1918).
14. Hirsh, I. J.: *J. Acoust. Soc. Amer.*, **22**: 196 (1950).
15. Broadbent, D. E.: *J. Acoust. Soc. Amer.*, **28**: 533 (1956).
16. Wallach, H., E. B. Newman, and M. R. Rosenzweig: *Am. J. Psychol.*, **62**: 315 (1949).
17. Eysenck, H. J.: "The Scientific Study of Personality," Routledge and Paul, London, 1952.
18. Culpin, M., and M. Smith: Report 61, Industrial Health Research Board, H.M. Stationery Office, London, 1930.
19. Bennett, E.: *Brit. J. Med. Psychol.*, **20**: 271 (1945).
20. Landis, C., and W. A. Hunt: "The Startle Pattern," Farrar and Rinehart, New York, 1939.
21. Kennedy, F.: *N.Y. State J. Med.*, **36**: 1927 (1936).
22. Davis, R. C.: *J. Exptl. Psychol.*, **15**: 108 (1932).
23. Smith, E. L., and D. A. Laird: *J. Acoust. Soc. Amer.*, **2**: 94 (1930).
24. Finkle, A. L., and J. R. Poppen: *J. Appl. Physiol.*, **1**: 183 (1948).
25. Anthony, A., and A. Ackerman: *J. Acoust. Soc. Amer.*, **27**: 1144 (1955).
26. Hale, H. B.: *Amer. J. Physiol.*, **171**: 732 (1952).
27. Harmon, F. L.: *Arch. Psychol.*, No. 147, 1933.
28. Freeman, G. L.: *Am. J. Psychol.*, **52**: 354 (1939).
29. Davis, R. C.: *J. Exptl. Psychol.*, **38**: 744 (1948).
30. Ryan, T. A., C. L. Cottrell, and M. E. Bitterman: *Am. J. Psychol.*, **63**: 317 (1950).
31. Parrack, H. O., et al.: Physiological Effects of Intense Sound, Engineering Division, Air Materiel Command, May 24, 1948.
32. Dickson, E. D. D., and D. L. Chadwick: *J. Laryngol. Otol.*, **65**: 154 (1951).
33. Allen, C. H., H. Frings, and I. Rudnick: *J. Acoust. Soc. Amer.*, **20**: 62 (1948).
34. von Gierke, H. E.: *J. Acoust. Soc. Amer.*, **21**: 55 (1949).
35. Halstead, W. C.: in The Benox Report, Chicago University, Dec. 1, 1953.
36. Gilbert, P. F., and G. C. V. Gawain: *U.S.A.F. Tech. Rept.* 6030, September, 1950.
37. Ryan, T. A.: *Psychol. Bull.*, **37**: 659 (1940).
38. Gregg, L. W., and W. J. Brogden: *J. Exptl. Psychol.*, **43**: 179 (1952).
39. Welford, A. T., R. A. Brown, and J. E. Gabb: *Brit. J. Psychol.*, **40**: 195 (1950).
40. Weston, H. C., and S. Adams: Report 70, Industrial Health Research Board, H.M. Stationery Office, London, 1935.
41. Wyatt, S., and J. N. Langdon: Report 77, Industrial Health Research Board, H.M. Stationery Office, London, 1937.
42. Humes, J. F.: *J. Appl. Psychol.*, **25**: 573 (1941).
43. Kerr, W. A.: *Appl. Psychol. Monog.*, No. 5, 1945.
44. Smith, H. C.: *Appl. Psychol. Monog.*, No. 14, 1947.

45. McGehee, W., and J. E. Gardner: *Pers. Psychol.*, **2** (4) (1949).
46. Ford, A.: *Amer. J. Psychol.*, **41**: 1 (1929).
47. Morgan, J. J. B.: *Arch. Psychol.*, No. 35, 1916.
48. Bartlett, F. C.: "The Problem of Noise," Cambridge University Press, Cambridge, 1934.
49. Bahrick, H. P., M. Noble, and P. M. Fitts: *J. Exptl. Psychol.*, **48**: 298 (1954).
50. Broadbent, D. E.: *Brit. J. Psychol.*, **47**: 51 (1956).
51. Stevens, S. S., et al.: Part I. OSRD Report 274, Harvard University, Dec. 1, 1941.
52. Miles, W. R.: in The Benox Report, Chicago University, Dec. 1, 1953.
53. Broussard, I. G., et al.: A.M.R.L. Report 101, Fort Knox, Nov. 6, 1952.
54. Obata, J., et al.: *J. Acoust. Soc. Amer.*, **5**: 255 (1934).
55. Hanley, T. D., and R. J. Williamson: U.S.N. Special Devices Center Tech. Report 104-2-2 1, Dec. 15, 1950.
56. Smith, K. R.: *Science*, **114**: 132 (1951).
57. Vernon, H. M., and C. G. Warner: *Personnel J.*, **11**: 141 (1932).
58. Tinker, M. A.: *Am. J. Psychol.*, **36**: 467 (1925).
59. Hovey, H. B.: *Amer. J. Psychol.*, **40**: 585 (1928).
60. Fendrick, P.: *J. Educ. Research*, **3**: 264 (1937).
61. Viteles, M. S., and K. R. Smith: *Trans. Am. Soc. Heating Ventilating Engrs.*, **52** (1291): 167 (1946).
62. Tufts College: NDRC Report to the Services, No. 37, Nov. 27, 1942.
63. Broadbent, D. E.: *Quart. J. Exptl. Psychol.*, **6**: 1 (1954).
64. Broadbent, D. E.: *Brit. J. Psychol.*, **44**: 295 (1953).
65. Bills, A. G.: *Am. J. Psychol.*, **43**: 230 (1931).
66. Stevens, S. S.: in "Handbook of Experimental Psychology," John Wiley & Sons, Inc., New York, 1951.
67. Jonckheere, A. R.: *Biometrika.*, **41**: 133 (1955).
68. Luckiesh, M.: *Elec. World*, **98**: 472 (1931).
69. Jerison, H. J.: *Am. Psychologist*, **9**: 399 (1954).
70. Laird, D. A.: *J. Appl. Psychol.*, **17**: 320 (1933).
71. Drew, G. C.: *Quart. J. Exptl. Psychol.*, **3**: 73 (1950).
72. Poulton, E. C., and R. L. Gregory: *Quart. J. Exptl. Psychol.*, **4**: 57 (1952).
73. Mackworth, N. H.: M.R.C. Spec. Rept. Ser. No. 268, H.M. Stationery Office, London, 1950.
74. Bexton, W. H., W. Heron, and T. H. Scott: *Can. J. Psychol.*, **8**: 70 (1954).
75. Kleitman, N.: "Sleep and Wakefulness," University of Chicago, Chicago, 1939.
76. Eccles, J. C., and A. K. McIntyre: *J. Physiol.*, **121**: 492 (1953).
77. Broadbent, D. E.: Applied Psychology Unit, Report 130, Cambridge, England, 1950.
78. Broadbent, D. E.: *J. Exptl. Psychol.*, **47**: 191 (1954).
79. Hernandez-Peon, R., H. Scherrer, and M. Jouvet: *Science*, **123**: 331 (1956).
80. Baker, K. H.: *J. Gen. Psychol.*, **16**: 471 (1937).
81. Mech, E. V.: *J. Psychol.*, **35**: 283 (1953).
82. Broadbent, D. E.: Applied Psychology Unit, Report 160, Cambridge, England, 1951.

Chapter 11

EFFECTS OF VIBRATION ON MAN

DAVID E. GOLDMAN, PH.D.

Naval Medical Research Institute

INTRODUCTION

This chapter is a survey of the present state of knowledge of the human body as a dynamic mechanical system and of the effects of vibration on man and his various parts, except for the very low frequencies concerned with motion sickness and for the auditory system which is discussed in earlier chapters. In recent years the need for such knowledge has become serious. The speed with which man has projected himself into the machine age has brought him closer than ever before to almost daily increasing concentrations of great mechanical power. So far, little widespread damage to man has resulted from vibratory energy, but injurious effects were first produced many years ago from the handling of vibrating tools and more recently from intense noise and from powerful vehicles and machinery. Further effects can be anticipated because of rapid advances in the development of higher-powered mechanical equipment.

Vibration may have a waveform which is simple or complex harmonic motion or it may be random "mechanical noise." What is now known of the effects of vibration on man deals primarily with the effects of simple wave shapes. The range of vibration frequencies of immediate interest begins at about 3 cps and may go as high as several million cycles per second. Below 3 cps, the human body responds to an alternating driving force as a unit and there is no internal relative motion. At very high frequencies, the absorption of vibration becomes very large and energy penetrates the body only a few millimeters at the most, at least with any reasonable amplitude. Frequencies below 3 cps are of considerable interest in connection with motion sickness but this problem is not considered here. The body may be exposed to vibration through contact with vibrating solids or by intercepting sound waves in air or water. The exposure may be incidental to certain procedures as in industrial, military, or other activity or may be deliberate as in the use of vibration in diagnosis and therapy or for experimental purposes.

The human body is the result of a long evolutionary process during which adaptation to many possible situations has been thoroughly accomplished. The body, among many other things, is a mechanical system of great complexity. It is neither homogeneous nor isotropic; its linear passive range is very small. Furthermore it is a system with built-in maintenance and repair facilities. Individual samples are by no means identical. Finally, one may not take the system apart for study or damage it in any way. Vibration measurements on the body thus present many special problems, some of which are discussed below.

Much of the information in this chapter is relatively new and much has still to be learned; so that the size of the different sections is based more on availability of material than on relative importance. It is impossible within a limited space to discuss in detail the many complex problems of reliability and interpretation of experimental data. The material will therefore be presented with little comment but it should be clearly understood that the situation is thereby being oversimplified and that the developments anticipated in the future may require important changes in viewpoint.

INSTRUMENTATION AND MEASUREMENT

It is a basic principle of experimental science that a system studied must be observed in such a way as to interfere as little as possible with the system's behavior. This principle in many cases is as simple in its application as in its formulation. However, the application of the principle to biological systems is often a matter of considerable difficulty. Measurements on excised tissues and organs are limited by the size, shape, instability, and environmental sensitivity of the material. This is even more the case with living systems. Anesthetized animals can be used for certain purposes but many of their mechanical and acoustical properties are quite different from those of human beings. The latter require nondestructive testing methods which are severely limited by the inaccessibility of the internal organs.

Whenever possible, and this is unfortunately not often, noncontact methods of measurement, such as optical, acoustical, and X-ray, made with devices away from the body, are to be preferred.

Such vibration measurements as cannot be made by external observations require the use of vibration pickups which are small and light enough so as not to introduce a significant mechanical load. This often means a weight limitation on the measuring equipment of a few grams. The mounting process must be noninjurious, and when subjective observations are being made, the procedure must be such as to produce a minimum of discomfort for the subject.

Of the vibration-measuring devices available, variable-reluctance pickups are frequently satisfactory for this purpose. They can be made with a weight of as little as 3 grams, a maximum dimension of $\frac{1}{2}$ in., low electrical impedance, and considerable sensitivity in the range from zero to a few hundred cycles per second. Crystal and capacitative pickups also lend themselves to size and weight requirements; they have a relatively high electrical impedance but are useful over a wide frequency range. Magnetic pickups are often less satisfactory because of the mass of the required magnetic material. For further details, see Chap. 15. Because of the lack of rigidity of the human body as a supporting structure, measurements of acceleration are usually preferable to those of velocity or displacement.

Conventional physiological measurements such as blood pressure, respiration rate or depth, electrocardiographic, metabolic, which may be entirely satisfactory in a fixed subject, become difficult when both the subject and instrument are exposed to vibration or intense sound. For example, mechanical vibration of electrodes placed on the skin can introduce potentials large enough to mask completely the phenomena to be studied.

Another situation arises when the observations to be made are subjective—that is, when made by the subject himself. The human mind far exceeds the body—itself complex—in complexity and lability. Hence extreme care is needed, when recording these responses, to avoid biasing the subject either through the characteristics of his physical environment or by the inadvertent suggestion of an attitude or point of view. The maintaining of a neutral situation with uniform motivation is one of the most important considerations in such psychological experimentation.

Application of vibratory forces to living subjects for experimental purposes requires great care to ensure that the exposure is as intended and does not include some other stimulus which may affect responses. Equipment for such purposes must usually be specially prepared and may be quite elaborate. For example, exposure to mechanical vibration should not be accompanied by intense noise when the object of the study is response to vibration alone.

Still another problem, in some ways closely related to those already mentioned, is the control of, and compensation for, the nonuniformity of the living systems studied.

People vary in size, shape, and in responsiveness. The use of adequate statistical experimental design is essential and almost always requires the carrying out of a large number of observations with carefully arranged controls.

EFFECTS OF VIBRATION ON MAN

Physical Effects. The physical effects of vibration on man are principally mechanical and secondarily thermal. Chemical effects occur only under very special conditions.

The mechanical effect of vibration on the body is to produce motion and relative displacement. The motion is very unevenly distributed and is affected by mode of excitation, frequency characteristics, and the spreading or concentration of vibratory energy. In extreme cases damage may occur. Large organs pull on supporting ligaments, and crushing injury to soft tissues is possible. A few examples are known or suspected. Riders of vehicles such as tanks, PT boats, or tractors occasionally complain of low back pain, traces of blood in the urine, and discomfort in the abdominal region. It is known that sacroiliac strain is not uncommon among truck drivers, but many of the complaints have not yet been separated from the domain of anecdote. The hand injuries to be discussed later are cumulative effects of the repeated blows or vibrations produced by hand-held vibrating or rotating tools. Lung hemorrhage can be produced in animals by very high-intensity low-frequency vibration (5 to 15 g at 5 to 20 cps) apparently because of the blows given by the vibrating heart to the lungs against the chest wall and vertebrae. These blows may injure the heart fatally. Mechanical injury to the auditory system is also well known.

At ultrasonic frequencies, mechanical injury to cells and tissues can be produced by the vibratory motion, by heating, or by cavitation which is readily produced in liquid media though probably rarely in tissues. Low-frequency air-borne ultrasound has been used to produce mechanical and thermal damage to insects at 19,000 cps and about 160 to 165 db. Mechanical injury to certain cells has been observed in liquids at frequencies near 1,000 cps, and at several hundred thousand cycles per second.[1,2]

Thermal effects are a direct consequence of losses by absorption of vibrational energy. None has been observed at low frequencies but many at ultrasonic frequencies where animals may be heated to a point beyond their capacity to dissipate the heat, with consequent thermal death. However, the levels required to produce such effects are well above those produced by present-day sources outside the laboratory. Since absorption in air increases with the square of the frequency, it now seems quite unlikely that air-borne ultrasound will become a hazard.

Biological Effects. Biological responses to vibration represent essentially a failure of the body to remain a passive system. The human body responds to stimuli presented to its receptor organs. There are nerve endings, sense receptors, more or less specialized and all providing information to one level or another of the nervous system which in turn controls the responses of the body and its parts. Accordingly, it is worthwhile to describe briefly the receptor system of the body as it relates to vibratory forces.

Perception of Vibration. Mechanical stimulation is detected by the auditory and vestibular systems, by numerous mechanical receptors embedded in the skin, and by a number of internally located proprioceptors. The vestibular organs—the semicircular canals and otoliths—respond to accelerations of the head and to changes in its position in the gravitational field. Their response times seem to be rather long and they are chiefly of importance at very low frequencies. It is through the vestibular system that the reactions of motion sickness seem to be mediated, although the higher nervous centers seem to play a leading role. However, at very high vibratory intensities, vestibular responses do occur at higher frequencies. Sound levels above 105 db produce small reflex head motions related to the time and space characteristics of the sound.[3] At sound levels above 140 db, it has been reported that there is a feeling of compulsion for orienting the body with respect to a sound source. With one ear exposed to an intense noise source there is a sensation of being pushed away from the exposed side. A displacement of the visual field toward the exposed side may occur. If the head is moved there is a feeling of exaggeration of the movement.   At levels above 155 db some of these sensations are present even though the subject wears ear protectors.   These effects seem to be most prominent near the middle of the audible frequency range, i.e., near 1,000 cps, but are less noticeable at low and high frequencies.[4]

Tactile receptors are of several kinds and are concerned with touch and pressure as well as vibration.   While it is not entirely clear just which receptors mediate which

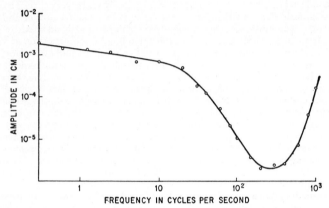

FIG. 11.1. Threshold of perception of tangential vibration applied to fingertip.   (*After von Békésy.*[5])

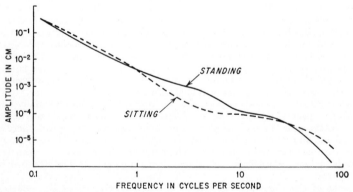

FIG. 11.2. Threshold of perception of standing or sitting man for vertical vibration.   (*After von Békésy.*[21])

type of stimulus, measurements have been made of vibration thresholds under a few conditions.   It is fairly well established that distortion of the skin is the controlling factor for vibration and for cutaneous pain.[5,6]   Figure 11.1 shows the frequency dependence of the threshold of the skin of the ball of the finger, one of the most sensitive areas of the body, to tangential vibration.   Figure 11.2 shows the sensation threshold for a man standing or sitting on a vertically vibrating platform, and Fig. 11.3 shows similar data for horizontal vibration.   These results were obtained under controlled laboratory conditions.   Additional, less accurate material is summarized in Fig. 11.4.

Adaptation plays an important role in long-duration exposures to vibration.   This term refers to the ability of the sense organs to adjust to long stimulation essentially by reducing their sensitivity—either in the nerve endings themselves, along the nervous transmission pathways, or in the higher centers of the central nervous system.

Proprioceptors, whose primary function is to provide the body with information as to its own motion, can also be stimulated by mechanical forces of external origin.   The

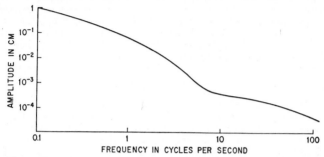

FIG. 11.3. Threshold of perception of standing and sitting man for horizontal vibration. (*After von Békésy.*[21])

stretch receptors of striped muscle, which respond to changes in muscle-fiber length, show evidence of responding to vibration by affecting the reflex response to a sudden pull on the muscle as, for example, in the knee jerk.[7]   Extreme stimulation may produce pain.

Physiological Responses to Vibration. The distinction between physiological and psychological responses is vague but convenient.   A physiological response is one which, while it may operate through the sensory system of the body, does not particularly involve the higher levels of the central nervous system as is the case in a psychological response.   One simple type of physiological response is the reflex—in which stimulation of some sensory system produces a nearly automatic reaction through some closely tied-in effector mechanism, such as a muscular or secretory one. One example is the contraction of the tensor tympani muscle of the ear in a protective response to intense sound.   Another is the head movements and compensating postural reactions from vestibular stimulation mentioned in the previous section.   Avoidance reflexes due to the pain produced by heat or overdistortion are also common. Still another specific response to vibration is inhibition of the knee jerk.[7]   Ordinarily, if a muscle is passively stretched, certain receptors in the muscle are stimulated and the nerve impulses so generated act on the motor nerves to the same muscle to produce a contraction.   This reflex is important for

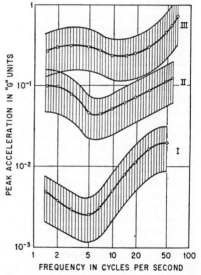

FIG. 11.4. Average peak acceleration at various frequencies at which subjects perceive vibration (I), find it unpleasant (II), or refuse to tolerate it further (III). The shaded areas are about one standard deviation on either side of the mean. Data averaged from seven sources. (*From Ref. 10.*)

the maintenance of posture.   However, when the system is subjected to intense mechanical vibration, there is produced a mechanical stimulation which may interfere with the reflex and inhibit it.

In addition to these more or less localized responses, there are those in which several of the control and adaptive systems of the body are involved. Severe shaking is a form of passive exercise and may bring with it changes in blood pressure, blood supply, respiration, and metabolism. With the vibration intensities ordinarily encountered in practice, these effects are weak and transient and possibly related to the more subjective reactions of discomfort.[7] Another aspect of these systemic responses involves the endocrine glands, one of whose functions seems to be an adaptation of the body to various applied stresses. Marked changes occur in the oestrous cycle, growth, and longevity of rats exposed for days or weeks to vibration of 2 to 4 cm amplitude at 2.3 cps.[8] A rapid fall occurs in the ascorbic acid (vitamin C) content of the rat adrenal gland after a relatively few minutes' exposure to low-frequency vibration, and this fall becomes greater as the vibratory acceleration increases.[9] Such findings are probably applicable to humans but no direct evidence of this exists as yet.

The occurrence of discomfort, even nausea and vertigo, in intense sound fields above about 145 db is a physiological response in so far as it is mediated through the sense organs and autonomic nervous system. However, like motion sickness, it seems to involve interaction with the higher levels of the central nervous system. Many subjective factors may play a part in these reactions which so far are hardly known beyond the level of casual observation and anecdote.

Psychological (Subjective) Responses. Vibration can affect people's attitudes, feelings, and work performance. They may like it, dislike it, or not care. The effects may be more or less direct responses to vibration or may involve emotional experiences and associations. Subjective responses are obviously of great practical importance but are the most difficult to record or interpret with any degree of certainty. The perception of vibration, while subjective, is at least capable of being studied accurately provided that proper precautions are taken. Discomfort or tolerance levels are, however, exceedingly difficult to deal with.

A comparison of discomfort and tolerance data from several sources, obtained for different purposes by observers with different backgrounds, nevertheless shows a rather surprising agreement to within a factor of about 3 (Fig. 11.4).[10] The data are only for 5- to 20-min exposures, and both vertical and horizontal vibration material had to be combined in order to get enough material for comparison. The personal experience of the author as well as several others working with mechanical vibration leads, however, to the belief that for exposures of a few minutes one can withstand without severe discomfort vibratory accelerations up to 1 g, at least up to 20 cps, and probably more at higher frequencies where the transmission through the body is less and the amplitudes are small enough to be taken up readily on the heel pads or other soft tissues. There is little information concerning very long exposures to vibration. Aircraft pilots and truck drivers find it very fatiguing, but no adequate studies have been carried out in this connection. Fatigue is a phenomenon difficult to define and harder to measure.

The effect of vibration on task performance is not understood either. Obviously mechanical interference with visual acuity and the performance of delicate muscular movement may occur at quite small amplitudes. A disturbance in visual acuity which has a maximum in the 40- to 80-cps range has been attributed to some sort of eyeball resonance, but difficulties do arise at lower frequencies when the amplitudes are large enough.[7] At present task-performance problems have to be studied individually with little chance of using the result of one study for application to another situation.

Pathological Responses to Vibration (Injuries). Outright injury from vibration fortunately is not common. The greatest current problems are those of hearing loss from high-level noise and hand injury from the continued use of vibrating hand tools. There is an extensive clinical literature on the characteristics of hand-tool injuries, which are variously known as "white fingers," "dead hand," "pneumatic-hammer disease," and "Raynaud's phenomenon."[11] These conditions are characterized by pain, numbness, and cyanosis of fingers exposed to cold. Sometimes there is evidence of minor bone or joint damage; sometimes there is stiffness and swelling of the fingers. The exact combination of symptoms varies with the amplitude and frequency of the vibration and with the manner of use of the tool. The vibration spectra show many high-amplitude harmonics up to several thousand cycles per second.   Many of these tools may, in fact, produce repeated sharp blows rather than smooth vibration. Pneumatic hammers or drills and hand-held drilling, grinding, and polishing tools are all possible sources of difficulty.   Light high-speed tools seem less apt to cause damage than slow heavy devices.   An attempt to produce controlled experimental lesions has been made.   Groups of rats were exposed for 10 to 12 hr per day, up to 1,000 hr, to vibrations of 8- to 9-g units at 60 and 120 cps.[12]   Changes in blood-vessel responses to cold were obtained and chronic changes were observed in the appearance of the paw capillaries, which became engorged and tortuous.   These results are an important step in the understanding of the injury processes.

INDUSTRIAL-HYGIENE AND PUBLIC-HEALTH ASPECTS OF VIBRATION

Since mechanical vibration of all kinds is so much a part of modern life, it is important to understand its effects and means of control.   Control is expensive—so is absence of control.   How much, then, should be tolerated?   The answer to this depends on a balancing of costs—in well-being, time, money, efficiency.   No simple answer is appropriate to all situations.   One cannot even say "let's have as little vibration as we can afford."   The establishment of clear-cut criteria or tolerance levels is at present a goal rather than an immediate possibility.

From the point of view of general public health one wants no injuries, no annoyance, no complaint.   Unfortunately, these matters are neither uniform nor readily controllable.   No one wants to be deprived of sleep because of excessive noise or shaking of his house but one man's soporific may give another man insomnia.   One man keeps his troubles to himself; another complains loudly.   Against this background, the word "tolerance" means whatever is acceptable to a given social group.

In industry the picture is different.   Exposure time is limited by working hours. Discomfort is less important since the prevailing attitude is that one is paid for it. The problem of injury or extreme discomfort remains, however, and to the extent permitted by custom and by workman's compensation costs, there is a strong temptation to think only in terms of direct monetary efficiency of output.   The word "tolerance" thus refers to the capacity of labor and management to put up with exposures to vibration.

For the armed forces, the problem is still different.   In peacetime, the attitude tends to approach that of industry.   In wartime, however, the factor of military effectiveness outweighs all else.   Injury to personnel is not desirable under any conditions, but battle is a matter of life and death and steps can be taken to reduce exposures to such mechanical hazards as these only to the extent that they improve, or at least do not decrease, fighting efficiency.   Another factor which enters is that, in a war, cost is a small matter indeed, although much military development takes place during peacetime.   Further, fighting usually constitutes so great a stress that it may be well worthwhile to avoid any other nontrivial stresses if at all possible.

The above refers to accidental undesired exposure to vibration.   However, vibration may also be desirable and useful.   The medical profession uses massage in physical therapy, and vibration is a convenient means of producing it.   Ultrasound has been very popular in Europe as a change from diathermy partly because of the ease with which it can be concentrated spatially and partly because of the claims for its mechanical effects.   The latter claims have not so far been substantiated; but as is so often the case, long series of trials and controlled experiments are required for final evaluation of any such procedure.

The great differences between these viewpoints and the unavoidable overlapping of their areas of influence serve only to complicate matters.   They should, however, emphasize the need for more knowledge of the production, effects, and control of vibration and for the continued education of all parties concerned who may be in a position to do something about it.

Methods of reduction of exposure to vibration are many.   There is reduction at the source or by the erection of barriers or isolating mountings.   There is the placing of protection on the man himself.   There is the reduction of exposure time either by reducing working shifts or by job rotation.   Finally, there is the acceptance by man of the exposure.

Since exposure occurs in mines, factories, small shops, during travel, and even at home, techniques for the control of vibration must be suited to the occasion, the pocket-book, and the subject's reactions—the latter sometimes crystallized into law.

Criteria.   The practical application of facts concerning noxious stimuli requires the establishment of criteria, safe limits, tolerance levels, or whatever one chooses to call them.   It is to be hoped that the preceding discussion has made it clear that there is still a lot to be learned before we can justify numerical criteria for exposure of man to mechanical vibration.   Part of the trouble arises out of the fact that it is often very difficult to avoid vibration.   This leads those who produce offending machinery to demand that those who complain justify their complaints.   Obviously, the more diffi-cult it is to control vibration and the more in time, money, and performance there is at stake, the harder it is to set acceptable limits.

In order to avoid complete frustration, however, one is forced to set down some tentative values and then hope that future work will either justify them or provide a reason for modification.   For the present the only possibility seems to the author to be the use of something like Fig. 11.4 or an equivalent.[13]   This requires a clear under-standing of the limitations.   The material refers to subjective effects produced pri-marily on adult males, standing or sitting on a vertically or horizontally vibrating platform or seat.   The exposure times are of the order of $\frac{1}{4}$ hr.   One can expect that subjects will "tolerate" more vibration for shorter times and less for longer times of exposure; no clear-cut definition of tolerance is available.   There is no specification of subject motivation or of the type or complexity of tasks which he may be called on to perform while exposed to vibration.   The data apply to simple waveforms at single frequencies in a limited range.

THE MECHANICAL CHARACTERISTICS OF THE BODY

Anatomical Structure.   The human body is required to perform a multitude of com-plex interrelated functions; so it is not surprising that it is also a mechanically intricate structure.   It has hard and soft solid components with reservoirs of liquid and gas. Structurally, it consists of a hard bony skeleton whose pieces are laced together and whose movement is controlled by muscle groups.   Soft visceral organs are supported inside.

An outline of the skeleton is shown in Fig. 11.5.   The slightly bowed vertebral column forms the central structural element.   It consists of a number of individual bony vertebrae having roughly cylindrical load-bearing elements separated by fibro-cartilaginous pads.   The skull rests on top of this column, and near the lower end several vertebrae fuse together to form the sacrum, which fits tightly into the pelvic bones to form the pelvic girdle.   At the bottom of each side of this girdle is an approxi-mately hemispherical hollow into which the head of the femur is fitted.   Below the femur are the tibia and fibula, which in turn rest on the ankle and foot bone complex.

The intervertebral joints are separated by fibrocartilaginous pads, the intervertebral disks.   The hip, knee, and ankle joints have cartilaginous layers on their articular surfaces.   The foot has a tough connective tissue pad at the bottom and a bony com-plex which acts to distribute applied loads.   In the sitting position the buttocks pro-vide a thick pad for insulation.   All these joints are held together primarily by liga-ments which are tough and flexible but relatively inextensible.   These ligaments form a more or less crisscross lacing which permits movement without stretching the liga-ments appreciably.   The sacroiliac joint is held together tightly and almost immov-ably.   The rib cage and shoulder girdles are supported in a relatively loose fashion, depending to a considerable extent on muscles as well as ligaments for their support.

In the ideal standing position, a plumb line through the center of gravity passes through the lower lumbar and upper sacral vertebrae, slightly behind the hip-joint sockets, a bit in front of the knee joints and of the ankle joints.   Upward, the line passes in front of the thoracic curve of the vertebrae and finally through the support at the base of the skull.   Vertical thrusts may be taken up by compression of the pads

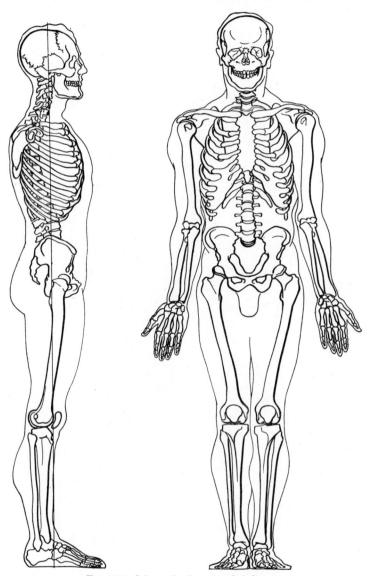

FIG. 11.5. Schematic diagram of skeleton.

of the joints, cartilage being relatively soft. At the pelvis there is often a slight forward-turning moment, especially in older adults. The action of the thrust on the vertebral column may be as much a bending or straightening as a compression of the intervertebral pads. Since the body has lateral symmetry, no sideways forces or turning moments are found if the body posture remains symmetrical. However, since this is often not the case, asymmetrical forces are frequently of importance as a consequence of vertical thrusts or tensions. Minor abnormalities in posture or structure thus may introduce problems in relation to exposure to vibration.

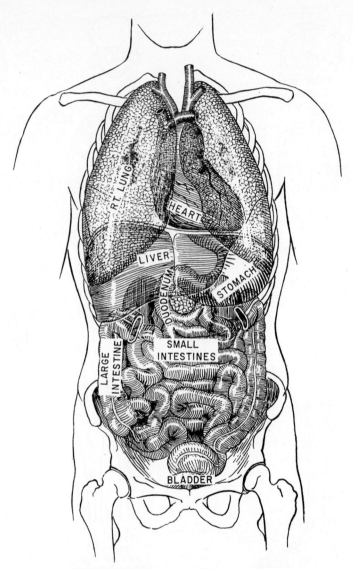

FIG. 11.6. Diagram of arrangement of viscera.

The body musculature, supported from the skeleton by tendons and laced together with a network of loose connective-tissue fibers, forms a secondary supporting structure for the skeleton and joints.   Fat and skin also contain liberal amounts of supporting connective tissue.

In compression, soft tissues resemble water in their mechanical properties but in shear they approximate stiff nonlinear gels with internal losses; therefore they provide considerable damping for vibratory motion.

Within the thoracic cage and abdominal cavity are the visceral organs (Fig. 11.6). They are soft-tissue elements, separately encapsulated to slide freely over each other and supported individually by membranes and suspensory ligaments and collectively by the bone, muscle, and connective tissue surroundings. Their weights range from a fraction of an ounce to several pounds and most of the supporting membranes are readily stretchable. The kidneys are embedded in fatty tissue and enclosed in a sheath of connective tissue which holds them in a depression in the posterior wall of the abdominal cavity. The stomach is supported by the esophagus and by the dome-shaped diaphragm which is a large sheet of muscle separating the chest cavity from the abdominal cavity. The lungs, filled with tiny air sacs, are held in place against the chest wall by a combination of supports including a pressure differential. Considerable support for the viscera also is provided by the diaphragm.

The brain and spinal cord have special protection. The former is surrounded by liquid contained mostly in the spongy subarachnoid space inside a bony box, the skull. The spinal cord runs longitudinally through holes in the vertebrae lined with heavy ligaments to form a tube and is also bathed in liquid.

Liquid in the body consists of: (1) the blood (5 to 6 liters) which is found in the heart, arteries, and veins and capillary bed; (2) the cerebrospinal fluid (100 to 150 cu cm) which surrounds the brain and spinal cord and is also contained within the brain in the ventricular cavities; (3) the interstitial fluid found everywhere in the body as a bathing fluid for all cells and tissues but nowhere in large reservoirs; and (4) liquid contained irregularly in the stomach, intestines, and bladder. Gas occurs in the sinuses, the oronasal cavity, the trachea, the lungs, and often in the stomach and intestines. The latter organs contain variable quantities of solid matter from time to time as well.

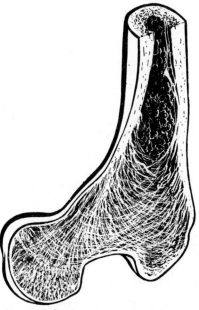

FIG. 11.7. Section of bone (head of femur) showing kinds of bone structure and arrangement of trabeculae for optimum stress resistance along direction of expected loading.

The Mechanical Properties of Cells and Tissues. Cells are the building blocks of all living organisms. Animal (including human) cells vary in size from about 0.0001 to 0.01 in. They may be spherical, irregular, columnar, or flat in shape with a complex internal structure. They contain 60 to 80 per cent water along with salts, carbohydrates, and proteins. There is a nucleus consisting largely of nucleoprotein; inclusion bodies contain enzymes, proteins, and salts. The rest of the cell interior is an aqueous solution, rather viscous but sometimes a gel. Some cells have long thin filaments projecting from them.

Soft tissues consist of densely packed cells held together by interlacing fibers of connective tissue and by intercellular links. Blood is a liquid containing nearly 50 per cent by volume of disklike red blood cells about 0.0003 in. in diameter together with a relatively few irregularly shaped white cells which are generally slightly larger. Bone contains many cells, but embedded in a matrix of calcium salts which give it its hard rigid quality.

The structure of bone is quite complex (Fig. 11.7). There is an outer layer of hard compact bone under which is a layer of looser bone, spongelike in appearance, so arranged as to produce a maximum of resistance to commonly encountered stresses. The marrow of some bones contains blood-forming tissues. Some representative values of the physical properties, which vary considerably, are given in Table 11.1. Few such measurements have been made.

Soft tissues exhibit a wide variety of structures. Striped (voluntary) muscle consists of parallel bundles of long thin cells which can exist in a relaxed or in a contracted state. Control of contraction is provided through nerve fibers which operate on the muscle fibers in small groups. Thus a whole muscle can exhibit graded degrees of

Table 11.1. Physical Properties of Human Bone

Specimens machined from hard bone	Femur	Tibia	Source
Specific gravity...............................	1.96	1.98	14
Young's modulus (compression), psi..............	2.7×10^6	2.8×10^6	14
Compressibility from sound-velocity data.........	5×10^{-6} per atm		15
Acoustic impedance............................	6×10^5 cgs units approx		15
Compressive strength, psi.......................	25,000	26,300	14
Tensile strength, psi...........................	22,000	....	14
Torsional strength, lb-in.......................	450	....	14

contraction even though the individual fibers have only two possible states. Hence the elasticity of muscle can vary readily over a considerable range. Smooth (involuntary) muscle occurs mostly in the walls of the hollow organs such as the stomach, intestines, blood vessels, or other specialized organs. The heart consists of a specialized type of muscle fiber.

Nerve tissue may be primarily cells (gray matter) or fibers (white matter). The latter has an appreciable amount of fat contained in the sheaths of the fibers. Liver, kidney, and other organs each display some peculiarity of cell type, arrangement, and packing. The density of most soft tissues is between 1.0 and 1.2, with fatty tissue having values somewhat less than 1.0. Lung tissue is lighter still because of the air content. A few elastic constants for soft tissues are listed in Table 11.2.

The curve in Fig. 11.8 is a typical example of the nonlinear stress-strain relation found with soft tissues. Estimates of some mechanical parameters of soft-muscle tissue are given in Table 11.3.

Dynamic Characteristics of the Body. In dealing with a structure as complicated as the human body, it is exceedingly useful to have models, or mechanical analogues, which are simple enough to permit easy visualization of major properties. One would like to have linear, passive, lumped parameter networks. Because of the complexity of the body,

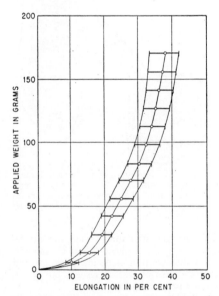

Fig. 11.8. Tension-length curve of normal dog aorta. (*After Pate and Sawyer.*[18]) The horizontal lines are one standard deviation on either side of the mean.

it is necessary to have almost as many models as there are experiments to be performed or situations to be explored. Assumptions of linearity and passivity are justifiable only at the lowest amplitudes; the use of lumped parameters is appropriate only at low frequencies. Exposure of human beings to low-frequency vibration is largely by direct contact with vibrating solids which are often driven strongly enough to produce forced motion of the body. Heavy machinery and vehicles, including tractors and aircraft, are common sources of such vibration. Hand power tools such as pneumatic hammers and drills produce forces large enough to shake the hands, arms, and even bodies of their operators severely. Thus special consideration has to

Table 11.2. Young's Modulus for Soft Tissues at Small Loads

Tissue	Psi	Source
Striped muscle (frog) (relaxed)............	1–2	16
Striped muscle (frog) (contracted).........	5–7	16
Fascia lata (thigh) (man).................	30,000	17
Aortic wall (dog) (longitudinal)............	5–10	18

Table 11.3. Acoustical Properties of Soft Tissue

Property	Value	Source
Sound velocity	1,500–1,600 m/sec	19
Compressibility	4×10^{-5} per atm	19
Shear modulus	0.4 psi	20
Shear viscosity	150 poises	20

be given to the effects of a vibrating solid surface on the hands, arms, feet, or on the entire body in the standing, sitting, prone, or supine positions.

At very low frequencies the body may be considered as a system having an internal frame of rather tightly coupled rigid elements, namely, the bones. The coupling is through the pads of connective tissue and cartilage reinforced by ligaments and muscles. The soft tissues serve as a shunt for transmission of vibration and also as a damping medium. Specific fairly well damped resonances may be expected where tissue masses, tied together, are supported in a springlike manner. A simple mechanical circuit suitable for a standing man for vertical vibration is shown in Fig. 11.9.

The mechanical impedance of a man standing on a vertically vibrating platform has been measured in the range from 0.5 to 100 cps (Fig. 11.10).[21] The phase-frequency curve shows that the body behaves as a unit mass below about 3 cps. There is also a phase reversal which corresponds to a maximum of the impedance amplitude and indicates a resonance. This resonance point is easily observed on a vibration machine and may be related to the phenomenon of a reversal of the phase of the motion of the head with re-

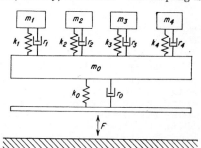

FIG. 11.9. Simplified mechanical analogue for man standing on vertically vibrating platform. m_0 is mass of skeleton and parts rigidly attached thereto. k_0 and r_0 are the stiffness and resistance of the foot-pad structures. The other m, k, and r values represent masses with spring and dashpot attachments to the body frame, e.g., the head and neck, the arm and shoulder, the abdominal viscera, the gluteal and thigh muscles, etc.

spect to the torso. This suggests that possibly the head and neck (or at least the upper vertebral column) act as a mass-spring combination. It has also been noticed that the transient response of the body to the sudden impact delivered during aircraft seat-ejection experiments shows a free oscillation of the vertebral column near

14 cps.   The graph also shows a second phase reversal near 40 cps but with no corresponding hump in the amplitude curve.   The mechanical system responsible for this has not yet been identified.   In any case the apparent effective masses and springs must be expected to change from one part of the frequency range to another.   These data are based on relatively few measurements; and while the general characteristics are likely to be uniform, the numerical values may prove to be rather variable from subject to subject.   It must also be emphasized that changes in mode of excitation or body posture need not necessarily be large in order to yield appreciably different results.   In the case of a man sitting on a vertically vibrating platform, the impedance characteristics do not seem to be very different from those of a standing man, but the first-phase crossover occurs at a slightly higher frequency.[21]

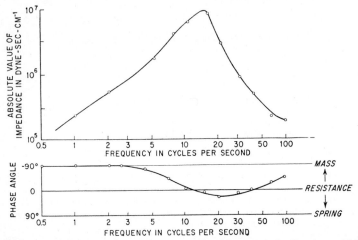

Fig. 11.10. Mechanical impedance of standing man for vertical vibration.   (*After von Békésy.*[21])

The behavior of the chest has been studied by applying oscillating air pressures to the mouth and measuring the motion of the chest and abdominal walls, and by applying alternating pressures to the outside of a body placed in a modified Drinker respirator and recording responses at the mouth.[22]   The data so far indicate that resonant responses do exist.   For excitation at the mouth, the chest and abdominal walls move in phase at 1 to 2 cps with a gradually increasing delay of the lower areas as the frequency increases.   Near 4 cps the whole body motion as measured with a ballistocardiograph is a maximum.   The pressure and flow are nearly in phase near 6 cps.   From 5 to 8 cps the abdominal wall shows maximum response.   In the range from 7 to 11 cps the velocity of the anterior chest wall is in phase with the air pressure at the mouth.

The mechanical impedance of an area of the chest wall has been determined from its response to a vibrating piston applied to the anterior surface.[23,24]   There appears to be zero mechanical reactance near 600 cps.   Whether this figure bears any relation to the internal characteristics of the chest cavity is doubtful.   Possibly the bending of the ribs and the superficial tissues moved thereby are the chief contributing factors.   The resistance values obtained were of the order of 10^4 dyne-sec per cm.

As to the transmission of low-frequency vibration through the body, the motion of the head of a man standing on a vertically vibrating platform has been compared with that of the platform itself in the frequency range from 20 to 140 cps (Fig. 11.11).[7]   Measurements at lower frequencies show a resonance in the 8- to 12-cps range.[21,25]   The peak probably corresponds to that obtained from impedance measurements.   The effectiveness of body tissue as a damping medium is evidently considerable.

This is also indicated by studies on the use of vibrating hand tools.[26] With one device which operates at 40 to 50 cps, it was found that there was a reduction in vibration amplitude of one-third to two-thirds between the tool surface in contact with the palm, where the amplitude was nearly 0.5 mm, and the back of the hand. A further loss occurred between the hand and the elbow, and no vibration was detected at the shoulder. The measurements included observations on the transmission of harmonics of the operating speed up to over 5,000 cps but were not sufficiently precise to detect any special trend with frequency variation.

Another type of study bearing on the low-frequency mechanical properties of the body is related to the ballistocardiograph. This is a device with which the mechanical displacement reaction of the body to the events associated with the heartbeat is recorded. It is of considerable interest to physicians and physiologists as an indicator of the mechanical behavior of the heart and its expulsion of blood into the aorta. With each cardiac impulse the heart contracts, shifts position slightly, and forces blood into the aorta, which makes a 180° turn just above the heart to carry arterial blood down into the torso. Simultaneously, blood is pumped through the pulmonary artery into the lungs for reoxygenation. The cardiac mechanical impulse travels through the body structures to the outside. If the subject lies on a suspended platform, its motion reflects his heartbeat. However, there is considerable distortion of the impulse between the heart and the external body surface. The subjecting of supine individuals to horizontal low-frequency vibration with the head, arms, and legs not in contact with the platform has led to the observation that the body mass resonates at about 3 cps, corresponding to a shear elasticity of the skin of the back of about 140 lb per in. for a 155-lb man and a mechanical "Q" of about 3.[27] In addition, the diaphragm, liver, and other abdominal viscera play some role in the transmission.

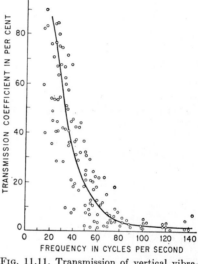

Fig. 11.11. Transmission of vertical vibration through body of standing man from platform to head. Composite for 10 subjects. (*After Coermann.*[7])

Ballistocardiograph records are in effect transient responses of the body system to the internal impulse. It follows that the cardiac impulse itself cannot be seen until the effects of the transmission network are disentangled. Using an equivalent network based on estimates of body and organ characteristics, one can obtain what should prove to be a fairly "pure" cardiac impulse which is very nearly a half sine wave.

The preceding data concern primarily the lowest part of the frequency range. As the frequencies of interest increase, the lumped parameter models become less satisfactory, and it is preferable to treat the body as a complex continuous medium for wave propagation. This is evidently more convenient in relation to exposure of the body to air-borne sound.

Mechanical-impedance measurements have been made using a vibrating piston or a resonant air tube applied to the body surface. This has been done for several regions, over a rather wide frequency range, and with several piston or tube diameters.[20] Figure 11.12 shows some resistances and reactances of the surface of the thigh; Fig. 11.13 shows similar data for the surface of the stomach; Fig. 11.14 gives values for the upper arm. The consistency of the data is very good considering the difficulties of such measurements.

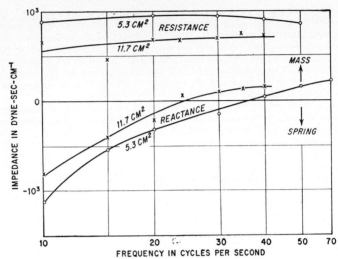

Fɪɢ. 11.12. Mechanical impedance of surface of thigh. Note effect of area of driving piston. (*After von Gierke et al.[20]*)

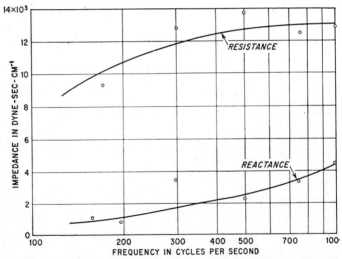

Fɪɢ. 11.13. Mechanical impedance of surface of stomach for driving area of 2.0 cm². (*After Franke.[24]*)

Absorption coefficients for soft-tissue surfaces of the body can easily be calculated from the impedances, but such calculations give only the fractions of energy absorbed when the driven area is as specified.   The absorption per unit area decreases markedly as the driven area increases, and the indications are that only a few per cent of the incident sound energy is absorbed by the body when exposed as a whole to a sound field at low frequencies, the absorption decreasing as the frequency increases.   It should also be noted that these values all refer to the uncovered body surface.   The presence of clothing must be expected to increase the energy absorbed.   This must

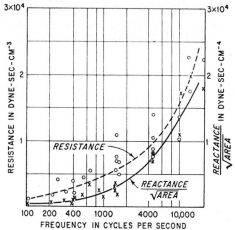

FIG. 11.14. Mechanical impedance of surface of upper arm for several driving areas and methods of measurement. (*After von Gierke et al.*[20])

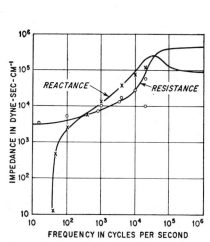

FIG. 11.15. Impedance offered to vibrating sphere of 1 cm diameter by a viscoelastic medium having a volume elasticity of 2.6×10^{10} dynes per sq cm, a shear elasticity of 2.4×10^4 dynes per sq cm, a volume viscosity = 0, and a shear viscosity = 150 dyne-sec per sq cm. Marked values are experimental measurements at body surface. (*After Oestreicher.*[28])

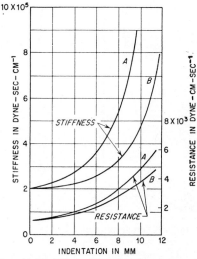

FIG. 11.16. Effect of loading distortion of body surface on measured impedance values for two experimental subjects *A* and *B*. (*After Franke.*[24])

be kept in mind in evaluating the effects of exposure to very intense sound, especially with respect to heating.

The problem of interpreting these impedance data has met with some success. Calculations have been carried out of the mechanical impedance offered to a rigid oscillating sphere embedded in a homogeneous isotropic viscoelastic medium.[28] The results are applicable to surface excitation of the type described above on the basis of the empirical observation that the surface impedance to a piston of given area is about half that of a completely embedded sphere of the same diameter.[20] The agreement is rather good with respect both to values and to frequency characteristics over the range from about 20 to 20,000 cps (Fig. 11.15). Best fit values of tissue parameters agree fairly well with estimates based on other methods. The shear viscosity and shear elasticity of soft tissues given in Table 11.3 were obtained in this way.

As a reminder of the nonlinearity and variability of living tissue, there is shown in Fig. 11.16 the effect of pressing the driving element (rod or tube) against the skin on

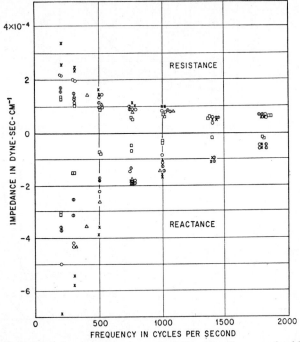

FIG. 11.17. Mechanical impedance of human mastoid surface for several subjects. (*After Franke.*[31])

the impedance components of two different subjects. The general shape of the curves is characteristic of muscle, connective tissue, and many other types of tissue.

The impedance of the head in a sound field is of considerable importance in bone-conduction problems. From observations of the vibration of the head driven by a small receiver it has been found that resonances of the skull occur between 500 and 1,000 cps although impedance measurements of intact subjects show primarily the effect of the soft tissues overlying the bone. The impedance of the human mastoid from 100 to 1,800 cps is shown in Fig. 11.17. Computed values for equivalent mechanical parameters are a compliance of about 10^{-8} and resistance of about 10^4 cgs units in agreement with figures from other sources.[29,31,32] However, the skin over the mastoid process may contribute to the existence of a series resonance in the frequency range from 1,200 to 4,000 cps.[33] Nonlinear effects which in this case bear on the use of bone-conduction receivers are significant here as well (Fig. 11.18).

Cavity resonance occurs in the sinuses and oronasal cavities of the head in the range from 1,000 to 1,500 cps.[34] The sensations are unmistakable and not particularly pleasant but seem to be significant only at sound levels of 150 db or more.

In the ultrasonic frequency range, almost no physical studies have been made on living tissues below several hundred kilocycles per second. Recent developments in the use of high-frequency ultrasound for diagnostic and therapeutic purposes have, however, stimulated considerable effort toward the investigation of the physical properties of tissue at the higher frequencies. Here the wavelength of sound is rather small, about 1.5 mm at 1 megacycle. In this frequency range geometrical acoustics is a better approximation and tissue absorption is appreciable. However, interfaces between soft tissue, bone, and air are important because of localized standing waves set up there. This frequency range is of little present interest in noise-control work,

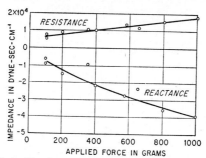

FIG. 11.18. Effect of loading on impedance of mastoid. (*After Franke.*[31])

but some of the studies contribute information as to the general physical properties of tissue. Sound-velocity and acoustic impedance measurements show soft tissues to differ relatively little from water. Absorption measurements indicate that through much of this frequency range the absorption values increase linearly with frequency. This behavior is of considerable theoretical interest in relation to the fundamental structure of tissue and is also found in some high polymers, but no satisfactory explanation has yet been offered. At frequencies above about 10 megacycles per sec, internal losses in tissue become very high. The wavelengths approach cellular dimensions, and internal scattering may be important.

REFERENCES

1. Ackerman, E.: *J. Cellular Comp. Physiol.*, **39**: 167 (1952).
2. Goldman, D. E., and W. W. Lepeschkin: *J. Cellular Comp. Physiol.*, **40**: 255 (1952).
3. von Békésy, G.: *Pflügers Arch. ges. Physiol.*, **236**: 59 (1935).
4. Benox Report, University of Chicago, ONR Project NR 144079, Dec. 1, 1953.
5. von Békésy, G.: *Akust. Z.*, **4**: 316 (1939).
6. Bishop, G. H.: *J. Neurophysiol.*, **12**: 51 (1949).
7. Coermann, R.: *Jahrb. deut. Luftfahrtforschung*, **3**: 111 (1938).
8. Sueda, M.: *Mitt. med. Akad. Kioto*, **21**: 1066, 1357 (1937).
9. Vollmer, E. P., and D. E. Goldman: Unpublished data.
10. Goldman, D. E.: Naval Medical Research Institute Report 1, NM 004 001, Mar. 16, 1948.
11. Dart, E. E.: *Occupational Med.*, **1**: 515 (1946).
12. Guillemin, V., Jr., and P. Wechsberg: *J. Aviation Med.*, **24**: 208 (1953).
13. Ride and Vibration Data, *SAE Spec. Publ.*, SP-6, 1950.
14. Carothers, C. O., F. C. Smith, and P. Calabresi: Naval Medical Research Institute and National Bureau of Standards, Report NM 001 056.02.13, Oct. 6, 1949
15. Theismann, H., and F. Pfander: *Strahlentherapie*, **80**: 607 (1949).
16. Hogben, L. T., and K. F. Pinhey: *Brit. J. Exptl. Biol.*, **4**: 196 (1926).
17. Gratz, C. M.: *J. Bone and Joint Surg.*, **13**: 334 (1931).
18. Pate, J. W., and P. N. Sawyer: Naval Medical Research Institute Report 007 081.10.09, July 27, 1955.
19. Ludwig, G. D.: *J. Acoust. Soc. Amer.*, **22**: 862 (1950).
20. von Gierke, H. E., H. L. Oestreicher, E. K. Franke, H. O. Parrack, and W. W. von Wittern: *J. Appl. Physiol.*, **4**: 886 (1952).
21. von Békésy, G.: *Akust. Z.*, **4**: 360 (1939).

22. Dubois, A. B., A. W. Brody, D. H. Lewis, and B. F. Burgess, Jr.: *Federation Proc.*, **13**: 38 (1954).
23. Bárány, E.: *Acta Med. Scand.*, **111**: 252 (1942).
24. Franke, E. K.: U.S.A.F. Tech. Rept. 6469, April, 1951.
25. Loeckle, W. E.: *Arbeitsphysiologie*, **13**: 79 (1944).
26. Agate, J. N., and H. A. Druett: *Brit. J. Ind. Med.*, **4**: 141 (1947).
27. von Wittern, W. W.: U.S.A.F., WADC Tech. Rept. 52-340, November, 1952.
28. Oestreicher, H. L.: *J. Acoust. Soc. Amer.*, **23**: 707 (1951).
29. von Békésy, G.: *J. Acoust. Soc. Amer.*, **20**: 749 (1948).
30. Franke, E. K.: U.S.A.F. WADC Tech. Rept. 54-24, November, 1954.
31. Franke, E. K.: *J. Acoust. Soc. Amer.*, **24**: 410 (1952).
32. Bárány, E.: *Acta Oto-Laryngol.*, *Suppl.* **26**: 56, 1938.
33. Morton, J. Y.: *J. Acoust. Soc. Amer.*, **25**: 159 (1953).
34. Parrack, H. O., D. H. Eldredge, and H. F. Koster: U.S.A.F., Air Materiel Command, Memorandum Report MCREXD-695-71B, May 24, 1948.

Chapter 12

PRINCIPLES OF VIBRATION CONTROL

CHARLES E. CREDE

Barry Controls Inc.

DEFINITIONS

The following list of definitions gives the meaning of frequently used terms in this and ensuing chapters concerned with the control and measurement of vibration:

Vibration. A particle experiences mechanical vibration if it has a number of reversals of velocity relative to an applicable reference system.

Simple Harmonic Motion. Simple harmonic motion is the projection on a diameter of point P moving around the circumference of a circle with uniform angular velocity.

Frequency. The frequency of a motion is the number of times the motion repeats itself per unit of time.

Period. The time required for the motion to complete one cycle is called the period; it is the reciprocal of the frequency.

Displacement. Referring to the above definition of simple harmonic motion, displacement is the instantaneous value of the distance from the center of the circle to the projected position of point P on the diameter.

Velocity. In simple harmonic motion, velocity is the instantaneous value of the velocity of point P along the diameter. This is the derivative of displacement with respect to time.

Acceleration. In simple harmonic motion, acceleration is the instantaneous value of the acceleration of point P along the diameter. This is the derivative of velocity with respect to time, or the second derivative of displacement with respect to time.

Amplitude. The maximum value of displacement, velocity, or acceleration in simple harmonic motion is designated as the amplitude. Referring to the above definition of simple harmonic motion, the displacement amplitude is the radius of the circle, the velocity amplitude is the peripheral velocity of point P on the circle, and the acceleration amplitude is the centrifugal acceleration associated with the motion of point P on the circle.

Excursion. In the definition of simple harmonic motion, the diameter of the circle is sometimes designated the excursion. This is two times the displacement amplitude, and is sometimes referred to as the peak-to-peak or double displacement amplitude to distinguish from displacement amplitude.

Free Vibration. Free vibration is the vibratory motion which takes place when an elastic system is displaced from its equilibrium position and released.

Forced Vibration. When the vibration results from the application of an external periodic force, it is called forced vibration.

Transient Vibration. Any motion in a vibrating system which occurs during the time required for the system to adapt itself from one force condition to another is called transient vibration.

Steady-state Vibration. After a vibrating system has been acted upon by a definite force condition for a sufficient time, it will follow a definite cycle of events described as steady-state vibration.

Natural Frequency. The frequency of free vibration is called the natural frequency of the system.

Forcing Frequency. The frequency associated with a harmonically varying force or motion acting upon a system is the forcing frequency.

Resonance. When a system is acted upon by an external harmonic force whose frequency equals the natural frequency of the system, the amplitude becomes great and the system is said to be in a state of resonance.

Damping. Any influence which extracts energy from a vibrating system is known as damping.

Phase Angle. If simple harmonic motion is represented by the rotation of a vector through point P, the phase angle of two motions is the angle less than 180° between two vectors rotating at the same angular frequency.

Transmissibility. Transmissibility is defined as the ratio of a resultant displacement or force amplitude to the applied displacement or force amplitude.

Static Deflection. The deflection of the spring in an elastic system resulting from the dead weight of the supported load.

LIST OF SYMBOLS

a = radius
b = damping coefficient
b_c = coefficient for critical damping
d = static deflection
f = frequency, cps
f_n = undamped natural frequency, cps
f_{nc} = undamped natural frequency in a coupled mode, cps
F = force
F_f = Coulomb friction force
F_r = resultant force
g = acceleration of gravity
G = modulus of elasticity in shear
h = height
I = moment of inertia
J = impulse
K = linear stiffness
K_r = rotational stiffness
l = length
m = mass
m_u = unbalanced mass
m_c = mass of crank
m_p = mass of piston
n = number of coils, supports, etc.
t = thickness, time
T = transmissibility, torque
w = width

W = weight
x = linear displacement
y = linear displacement
Y = modulus of elasticity in tension (Young's modulus)
γ = damping ratio = b/b_c
δ = distance
Δ = logarithmic decrement, dimensionless
Δ_d = decrement, db per sec
ϵ = eccentricity
η = ratio of horizontal to vertical stiffness
λ = ratio of height to width
ξ = correction factor, as defined in text
ρ = radius of gyration
τ = shear stress
ϕ = angular displacement
ω = forcing frequency, radians per sec
Sub 0 indicates amplitude; i.e., maximum value of a varying parameter
Sub x, y, z indicates association with coordinate axis of same designation
Single dot indicates first derivative with respect to time
Double dot indicates second derivative with respect to time

STEADY-STATE AND TRANSIENT VIBRATION

In steady-state vibration, the displacement is the distance from center O to the projection of point P on the diameter aa, as shown in Fig. 12.1a. The time history of the displacement is obtained by tracing this projection as the ordinate on a plot having the time coordinate as the abscissa, and is defined by the following equation:

$$x = x_0 \sin \omega t = x_0 \sin 2\pi ft \tag{12.1}$$

where x_0 is the displacement amplitude.   The angular velocity ω of point P is expressed in radians per second, where $\omega = 2\pi f$ and f is the frequency in cycles per second. Expressions for the velocity $\dot{x}$ and acceleration $\ddot{x}$ are obtained by first and second differentiation of Eq. (12.1) with respect to time, yielding the following expressions for velocity and acceleration amplitudes:

$$\dot{x}_0 = 2\pi x_0 f \qquad \ddot{x}_0 = 4\pi^2 x_0 f^2 \tag{12.2}$$

In common engineering practice, x_0 is in units of inches, $\dot{x}_0$ in units of inches per second, and $\ddot{x}_0$ in units of inches per second per second.   The latter is commonly divided by the gravitational acceleration in identical units and thereby expressed dimensionlessly. The relations between these amplitudes and the frequency in steady-state harmonic motion are shown graphically in Fig. 12.2.

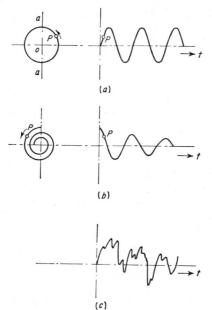

(a)

(b)

(c)

FIG. 12.1. Typical examples of steady-state and transient vibration: (a) Steady-state vibration at a single frequency; (b) damped transient vibration at a single frequency; and (c) irregular, nonperiodic transient vibration.

If the displacement amplitude does not follow a repetitive pattern throughout consecutive time intervals, a transient condition exists.   This may be described by a point moving in a noncircular pattern.   For example, a continuously decreasing displacement amplitude is a common occurrence and may be defined by a point moving along a converging spiral as illustrated in Fig. 12.1b.   The pattern of the decrease is a function of the type of damping and is discussed in detail in the section in this chapter on free vibration of a single-degree-of-freedom system.   In many instances, such vibration may be described by numerical parameters including amplitude, frequency, and a definition of the decay pattern.   In many engineering problems, transient vibration involves no regular pattern, as illustrated in Fig. 12.1c.   When this occurs, it is not possible to describe the vibration by numerical parameters, and it becomes necessary to inscribe the time history of displacement, velocity, or acceleration graphically.

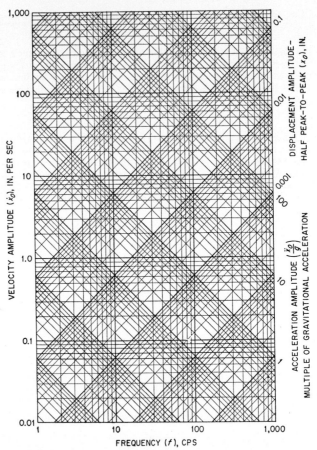

Fig. 12.2. Diagram for harmonic motion showing the relation between frequency, and displacement, velocity, and acceleration amplitudes. (*Crede.*[1])

SINGLE-DEGREE-OF-FREEDOM SYSTEM

Free Vibration. Vibration generally results from the application of a fluctuating force or couple to an elastic system. In the ensuing discussion, the elastic system is represented schematically by the damped single-degree-of-freedom system illustrated in Fig. 12.3. This system consists of a rigid body constrained by frictionless guides to move only in the vertical direction, a massless spring (see the section on *Standing Waves* in Chap. 13 for a discussion of wave effects when the mass of the spring is considered), and a massless damper whose properties will be discussed in detail later. This system is known as a single-degree-of-freedom system because its configuration at any instant can be completely defined by a single coordinate, the height of the body with respect to any reference plane. It is

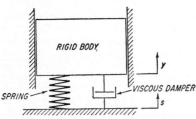

Fig. 12.3. Viscously damped single-degree-of-freedom system.

convenient for mathematical purposes to assume the damper to be viscous; i.e., the force applied by the damper to the body is directly proportional to the velocity of the body with respect to its support and is 180° out of phase with this velocity.

Natural Frequency. In general, a system has a natural frequency for each degree of freedom; the single-degree-of-freedom system illustrated in Fig. 12.3 thus has one natural frequency. The natural frequency may be defined as the number of cycles of vertical oscillation that the system will carry out in unit time if displaced from its equilibrium and permitted to vibrate freely. The expression for the damped natural frequency of the system illustrated in Fig. 12.3, expressed in units of cycles per second, is

$$\frac{1}{2\pi}\sqrt{\frac{Kg}{W}\left[1 - \left(\frac{b}{b_c}\right)^2\right]}$$

where K is the stiffness of the spring in pounds per inch, $W = mg$ is the weight of the body in pounds, g is the acceleration due to gravity in inches per second per second, b is the damping coefficient in pounds per inch per second, and $b_c = 2(KW/g)^{1/2}$ is the

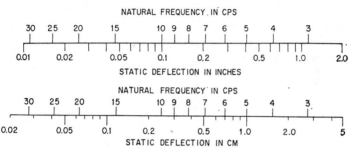

NATURAL FREQUENCY IN CPS

STATIC DEFLECTION IN INCHES

NATURAL FREQUENCY IN CPS

STATIC DEFLECTION IN CM

FIG. 12.4. Relation between natural frequency and static deflection for a linear single-degree-of-freedom system.

value of b for which the damping is critical. A critically damped system returns without oscillation to equilibrium if displaced; i.e., it has no natural frequency of oscillation, as indicated by the substitution of $b = b_c$ in the above expression.

Except in special circumstances, the damping is relatively small, and its influence on the natural frequency may be neglected. Setting the damping coefficient b equal to zero, the system becomes an undamped single-degree-of-freedom system whose natural frequency is given by the following expressions:

$$f_n = \frac{1}{2\pi}\sqrt{\frac{Kg}{W}} = 3.13\sqrt{\frac{1}{d}} \qquad \text{cps} \qquad (12.3)$$

where d is the static deflection of the spring in inches under the weight of the body. The relation between natural frequency and static deflection given by Eq. (12.3) is shown graphically in Fig. 12.4. This relation is valid only if the spring K is linear and if its dynamic and static stiffnesses are equal. The effect of a non-

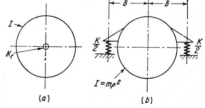

FIG. 12.5. Typical single-degree-of-freedom systems having freedom in rotation about an axis perpendicular to the paper.

linear spring is discussed in the section in this chapter on the free vibration of a single-degree-of-freedom system; differences between static and dynamic stiffnesses arise principally in certain organic materials which are considered in the section on the *General Properties of Materials* in Chap. 13.

A single-degree-of-freedom system may have its degree of freedom in rotation about an axis extending through the center of gravity of the mass of the system. For example, the disk or cylinder shown in Fig. 12.5a may be constrained to move only in rotation about its axis of symmetry normal to the paper. If rotation about this axis is elastically resisted by a torsional spring having a coefficient K_r, the undamped natural frequency in rotation is

$$f_n = \frac{1}{2\pi} \sqrt{\frac{K_r}{I}} \qquad \text{cps} \qquad (12.4)$$

where K_r is in units of pound inches per radian and I is in units of pound inch second squared.

If the torsional spring in Fig. 12.5a is replaced by the two linear springs $K/2$ arranged as shown in Fig. 12.5b, the undamped natural frequency in rotation is given by the following equation:

$$f_n = \frac{1}{2\pi} \sqrt{\frac{K\delta^2}{m\rho^2}} = \frac{1}{2\pi} \frac{\delta}{\rho} \sqrt{\frac{Kg}{W}} \qquad \text{cps} \qquad (12.5)$$

where K is in units of pounds per inch, W is in units of pounds, and ρ is the radius of gyration in inches. Comparison of Eqs. (12.3) and (12.5) shows that the natural frequency in rotation of the system of Fig. 12.5b is the natural frequency in vertical translation multiplied by δ/ρ.

Nonlinear Stiffness. In the expression for natural frequency, Eq. (12.3), the stiffness K is the slope of the force-deflection curve. Where the force-deflection curve

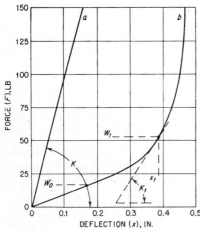

Fig. 12.6. Force-deflection curves for a linear system (a) and a nonlinear system (b).

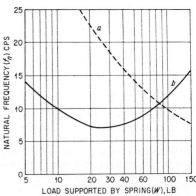

Fig. 12.7. Curves showing relation between natural frequency and supported load for the linear (a) and nonlinear (b) force-deflection curves shown in Fig. 12.6. (*Crede.*[15])

is the straight line a in Fig. 12.6, the stiffness K is a constant. The force-deflection curve may be nonlinear, as shown at b; a weight W_1 applied to the spring then causes a deflection x_1. If the system is now vibrated with a relatively small amplitude, the vibration may be considered to consist of moving a point back and forth along the force-deflection curve a small distance on either side of a vertical line extending through x_1. Inasmuch as no other part of the force-deflection curve becomes involved in this vibration, the natural frequency of the system is determined by its characteristics in the region of the deflection x_1. The slope K_1 of a straight line tangent to the force-deflection curve at the deflection x_1 and the weight W_1 may then be substituted in Eq. (12.3) to obtain the natural frequency. This value of natural frequency applies only for vibration of small amplitude.

If the load applied to the linear spring is increased, the value of W in Eq. (12.3) increases while the value of K remains constant. The natural frequency of the system thus decreases with an increase in the supported load, as indicated by curve a in Fig. 12.7. For relatively small loads applied to system b in Fig. 12.6, a similar result is attained.   For larger loads, the stiffness increases at a faster rate than the load and the natural frequency increases with each addition of load, as indicated by curve b in Fig. 12.7.   The natural frequency represented by the valley of curve b is the minimum that can be attained in a system whose force-deflection curve b has the characteristics shown in Fig. 12.6.

In determining the natural frequency of a nonlinear system, it is important to note whether all the load results from the dead weight of a massive body.   If the load W_1 represents the weight of the supported body, the above calculation of natural frequency is valid for small amplitudes.   The weight of the load may be only W_0, as indicated in Fig. 12.6, and the incremental load between W_0 and W_1 may result from belt pull, for example.   Inasmuch as a deflection x_1 exists, the appropriate value for stiffness is the slope K_1.   The only massive load in the system, however, is represented by W_0.   In the use of Eq. (12.3), then, the value of W_0 must be substituted for W and the value of K_1 for K.

Effect of Damping. If a viscously damped system with less than critical damping is displaced from its equilibrium position and permitted to vibrate freely, the vibration amplitude decreases continuously as shown in Fig. 12.8a and approaches zero asymptotically.   If the damping is greater than critical, however, the system does not oscillate but rather creeps gradually back to the equilibrium position.   The value of damping which divides these two conditions, i.e., the minimum value of the damping coefficient b which can cause a gradual creeping back without oscillation, is critical damping for the system.   It is related to other physical characteristics of the system by $b_c = 4\pi m f_n$ where b_c is in units of pounds per inch per second, m is in units of pound seconds squared per inch, and f_n is in units of cycles per second.

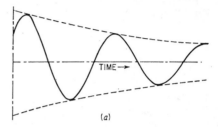

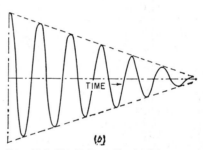

FIG. 12.8. Typical amplitude decay curves for (a) system with viscous damping and (b) system with Coulomb damping.

From a mathematical viewpoint, it is convenient to define damping in terms of critical damping b_c.   This gives the dimensionless damping ratio b/b_c.   In a physical sense, the damping in a system is often evaluated by noting the pattern of decay of free vibration.   Employing the vibration amplitudes at two successive cycles of free vibration, the damping in the system may be defined by the logarithmic decrement.   The logarithmic decrement is the natural logarithm of the ratio of the amplitude at any given cycle of vibration to the amplitude at the succeeding cycle.   Logarithmic decrement Δ is related to the dimensionless damping ratio b/b_c by the following equation:

$$\Delta = \frac{2\pi(b/b_c)}{\sqrt{1 - (b/b_c)^2}} \approx 2\pi \frac{b}{b_c} \tag{12.6}$$

In a lightly damped system, the decrease in amplitude between two successive cycles of vibration may be too small to measure conveniently.   The ratio of vibration amplitudes taken over an interval of several cycles and expressed in decibels may be related to the dimensionless damping ratio b/b_c.   This relation involves the natural frequency of the system and is given by the following equation:

$$\Delta_d = 54.5 f_n \frac{b}{b_c} \quad \text{db per sec} \tag{12.7}$$

where f_n is the undamped natural frequency in cycles per second.

In a viscously damped system, the damping force is directly proportional to the velocity across the damper and acts in a direction opposite to this velocity. This gives the exponential envelope to the decay curve illustrated in Fig. 12.8a. Inasmuch as this envelope approaches zero asymptotically, the vibration theoretically never ceases to exist. In a Coulomb friction-damped system, the damping force is a constant independent of the velocity and acts in a direction opposite to the velocity. In free vibration, the amplitude decreases by a constant increment at each cycle. The envelope of the peaks of the vibratory motion is thus a straight line as illustrated in Fig. 12.8b, and reaches zero after a finite time.

FORCED VIBRATION

Force Excited. The viscously damped single-degree-of-freedom system shown in Fig. 12.3 may be excited in forced vibration by the application of a periodically varying

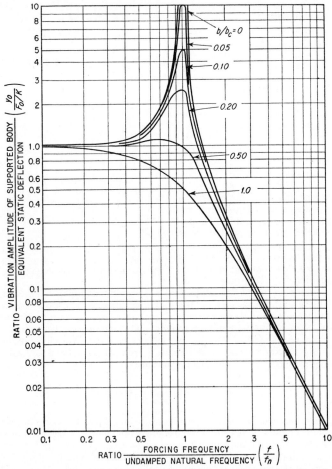

FIG. 12.9. Curves showing ratio of vibration amplitude to equivalent static deflection, as a function of the ratio of forcing to undamped natural frequencies. These curves apply to the viscously damped single-degree-of-freedom system shown in Fig. 12.3 when excited by force $F = F_0 \cos 2\pi f t$ applied to the rigid body.

disturbance, either a force applied to the rigid body or a motion of the support. If the forced vibration results from a periodically varying force $F = F_0 \cos 2\pi f t$ applied to the body, the differential equation of motion of the body is obtained by equating the inertia force to the sum of the externally applied forces. See Eq. (4.43) of Ref. 1. The displacement amplitude y_0 of the viscously damped system is conveniently expressed in dimensionless terms as follows:

$$y_0 = \frac{F_0/K}{\sqrt{[1 - (f/f_n)^2]^2 + [2(f/f_n)(b/b_c)]^2}} \quad \text{in.} \quad (12.8)$$

where F_0 is in pounds, K is in pounds per inch, and the frequency and damping ratios f/f_n, b/b_c are dimensionless. The relation defined by Eq. (12.8) is shown graphically in Fig. 12.9. These curves are not transmissibility curves in the usual sense but rather curves showing the displacement amplitude y_0 associated with the forced vibration of the system.

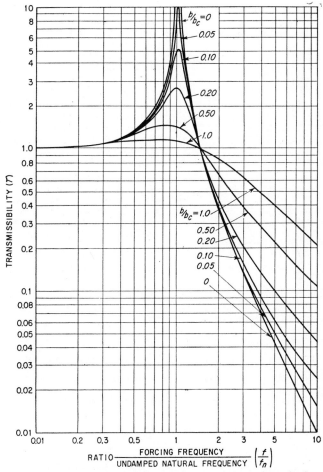

FIG. 12.10. Force and displacement transmissibility curves for a viscously damped single-degree-of-freedom system. Referring to Fig. 12.3, force transmissibility is the ratio of maximum transmitted force to maximum applied force F_0. Displacement transmissibility is the ratio of displacement amplitude y_0 to applied displacement amplitude s_0.

The motion of the rigid body often is of less significance than the proportion of the force which is transmitted through the spring and damper to the support. The two parts of the transmitted force are not in phase and, therefore, must be added vectorially. Force transmissibility is defined as the absolute value of the ratio of the vector sum of the transmitted force amplitudes to the applied force amplitude F_0. The expression for force transmissibility is

$$T = \sqrt{\frac{1 + [2(f/f_n)(b/b_c)]^2}{[1 - (f/f_n)^2]^2 + [2(f/f_n)(b/b_c)]^2}} \qquad (12.9)$$

Figure 12.10 portrays force transmissibility graphically.

Motion Excited. Forced vibration of the system shown in Fig. 12.3 may also be excited by periodic motion of the support as defined by $s = s_0 \cos 2\pi ft$. In this instance, the rigid body is acted upon only by the forces applied by the spring and the damper. Denoting the displacement amplitude of the massive body by y_0, displacement transmissibility is defined as the absolute value of the ratio y_0/s_0. The mathematical expression for displacement transmissibility is identical to the corresponding expression for force transmissibility set forth by Eq. (12.9). The family of curves in Fig. 12.10, therefore, portrays displacement transmissibility as well as force transmissibility.

The transmissibility given by Eq. (12.9) and shown in Fig. 12.10 is a function only of the ratio f/f_n of forcing frequency to undamped natural frequency and the damping ratio b/b_c. The transmissibility reaches a maximum at a frequency ratio of unity when b/b_c is equal to zero and at a frequency ratio always less than unity when the damping ratio b/b_c is greater than zero. The numerical value of the maximum transmissibility, and the frequency ratio at which maximum transmissibility occurs, depend only upon the damping ratio b/b_c. Maximum transmissibility occurs when

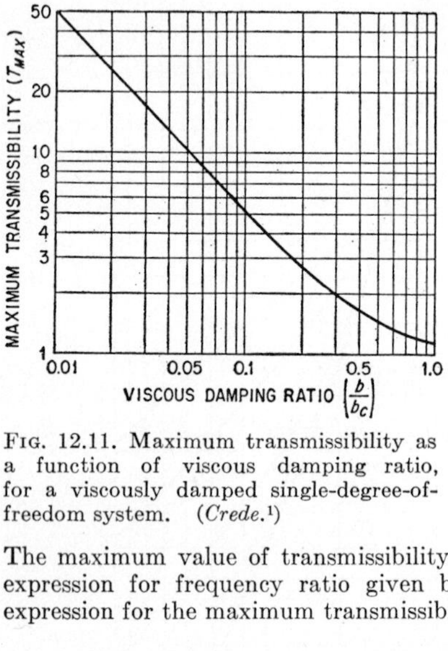

FIG. 12.11. Maximum transmissibility as a function of viscous damping ratio, for a viscously damped single-degree-of-freedom system. (*Crede.*[1])

$$\frac{f}{f_n} = \sqrt{\frac{-1 + \sqrt{1 + 8(b/b_c)^2}}{4(b/b_c)^2}} \qquad (12.10)$$

The maximum value of transmissibility is found by substituting in Eq. (12.9) the expression for frequency ratio given by Eq. (12.10). This yields the following expression for the maximum transmissibility:

$$T_{\max} = \frac{4(b/b_c)^2}{\sqrt{16(b/b_c)^4 - 8(b/b_c)^2 - 2 + 2\sqrt{1 + 8(b/b_c)^2}}} \qquad (12.11)$$

The maximum transmissibility is thus a function only of the damping ratio b/b_c, as illustrated in Fig. 12.11. When the damping ratio b/b_c is equal to 0.1 or less, the maximum transmissibility is defined approximately by the following expression:

$$T_{\max} \approx \frac{1}{2(b/b_c)} \qquad (12.12)$$

SEVERAL-DEGREE-OF-FREEDOM SYSTEM

The single-degree-of-freedom system shown in Fig. 12.3 is adequate for illustrating the fundamental principles of vibration but is a great oversimplification in so far as many practical applications are concerned. Rigid guides for constraining the motion of an elastically mounted mass are not consistent with the requirements in many applications. It is generally necessary to consider freedom of movement in all directions, as dictated by existing forces and motions and by the elastic constraints.

Natural Modes of Vibration. Consider now a symmetrical body supported by identical springs at each of the eight corners and unrestrained by rigid guides, as shown in Fig. 12.12a. This is a six-degree-of-freedom system. It is free to move vertically and horizontally in the plane of the paper and rotationally with respect to an axis normal to the paper. Furthermore, when viewed in a vertical plane normal to the plane of the paper, it has similar freedom of motion horizontally and rotationally. When viewed from above, it is free to rotate with respect to a vertical axis. The system has a natural frequency in each of these six natural modes of vibration, three in translatory modes along three mutually perpendicular axes and three in rotational modes with respect to the same three mutually perpendicular axes. Any vibration may be resolved into components in these modes.

When the resilient supports are located unsymmetrically with respect to the center of gravity of the body, certain translatory and rotational modes of vibration may become coupled. A coupled mode of vibration may be comprised, for example, of a translatory component and a rotational component about an axis through the center of gravity of the body. This may appear as rotational motion about an axis which does not pass through the center of gravity. If the supports are placed at the bottom, as shown in Fig. 12.12b, the vibration in the horizontal translatory mode becomes coupled to vibration in a rotational mode in which the mounted body vibrates in rotation with respect to an axis below the center of gravity of the body. Furthermore, the rotational vibration of Fig. 12.12a becomes coupled to vibration in the horizontal translatory mode whereby the body vibrates with respect to an axis above the center of gravity.

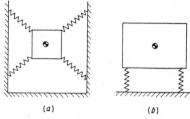

Fig. 12.12. Schematic diagrams of (a) multi-degree-of-freedom system having decoupled natural modes of vibration and (b) multi-degree-of-freedom system having coupled natural modes of vibration.

A body on resilient supports may vibrate in a natural mode simultaneously with but independently of its vibration in other natural modes if the respective modes are decoupled. If the modes are coupled, vibration in one coupled mode cannot occur independently of vibration in another mode that is coupled thereto. Coupling depends upon the stiffness and location of the resilient supports, and on the mass distribution of the supported body. The following test may be applied to a body on flexible supports: If it is desired to determine whether translatory vibration in a particular direction is decoupled, apply a steady force to the body through its center of gravity and in the specified direction. If the body moves in the direction of the force without rotation, translatory vibration in the direction of the force is decoupled from vibration in other modes. The meaning of this test can be illustrated by reference to Fig. 12.12b. When a vertical force is applied to the body along a line extending through the center of gravity, the body moves vertically without rotation. The vertical translatory mode is thus decoupled. A horizontal force through the center of gravity, however, not only displaces the body horizontally but causes it to rotate about an axis below the body. The horizontal and rotational modes are thus coupled and vibration in one of these modes cannot exist independently of vibration in the other mode.

Forced Vibration—Two Planes of Symmetry. One of the most common cases of vibration in coupled modes of a rigid body on elastic supports concerns the system shown in Fig. 12.13. This is an undamped system comprised of a rigid cuboid supported by four springs located adjacent the four lower corners. It is symmetrical with respect to two coordinate vertical planes through the center of gravity of the supported body, one of the planes being parallel with the plane of the paper. Because of this symmetry, vibration in a vertical translatory mode is decoupled from vibration in the horizontal and rotational modes. The natural frequency in the vertical translatory mode is thus given by Eq. (12.3) where the stiffness K is the sum of the stiffnesses K_y in Fig. 12.13, and the analysis of forced vibration of the single-degree-of-freedom system in the section on Forced Vibration in this chapter applies.

Vibration of the system is forced by a periodic force $F = F_x \cos 2\pi ft$ applied in the direction of the X axis at a distance ϵ above the center of gravity and in one of the planes of symmetry. The differential equations of motion for the supported body in the coupled horizontal translatory and rotational modes are as follows:

$$m\ddot{x} = -4K_x x + 4K_x \delta_y \phi + F_x \cos 2\pi ft$$
$$I\ddot{\phi} = 4K_x \delta_y x - 4K_x \delta_y^2 \phi - 4K_y \delta_x^2 \phi - F_x \epsilon \cos 2\pi ft \qquad (12.13)$$

Making the common assumption that transients may be neglected in problems involving forced vibration, the translatory and rotational displacements of the supported body are assumed to be harmonic at the forcing frequency, i.e., $x = x_0 \cos 2\pi ft$ and $\phi = \phi_0 \cos 2\pi ft$. The differential equations of motion, Eqs. (12.13), are then solved simultaneously to give the following expressions for the displacement amplitudes x_0 in horizontal translation and ϕ_0 in rotation:

$$x_0 = \frac{F_x}{4K_y} \frac{A_1}{D} \qquad \phi_0 = \frac{F_x}{4K_y} \frac{A_2/\rho}{D} \qquad (12.14)$$

where
$$A_1 = \left(\frac{1}{\rho^2}\right)(\eta\delta_y^2 + \delta_x^2 + \eta\epsilon\delta_y) - \left(\frac{f}{f_n}\right)^2$$

$$A_2 = \epsilon\left(\frac{f}{f_n}\right)^2 + \eta(\delta_y - \epsilon)$$

$$D = \left(\frac{f}{f_n}\right)^4 - \left(\eta + \frac{\eta\delta_y^2}{\rho^2} + \frac{\delta_x^2}{\rho^2}\right)\left(\frac{f}{f_n}\right)^2 + \frac{\eta\delta_x^2}{\rho^2}$$

In the above equations, η is the dimensionless ratio of horizontal stiffness to vertical stiffness of the isolators, ρ is the radius of gyration of the supported body about an

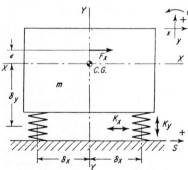

axis through its center of gravity and perpendicular to the paper, f_n is the undamped natural frequency in vertical translation, f is the forcing frequency, δ_y is the vertical distance from the elastic axis of the spring (mid-height if symmetrical top to bottom) to the center of gravity of body m, and the other parameters are as indicated on Fig. 12.13.

Forced vibration of the system in Fig. 12.13 may also be excited by periodic motion of the support in the horizontal direction as defined by $s = s_0 \cos 2\pi ft$. The differential equations of motion for the supported body are as follows:

FIG. 12.13. Elevation view of rigid body on resilient supports located at four corners, and excited by (1) harmonic force $F = F_x \cos 2\pi ft$ applied to supported body in XY plane when $s_0 = 0$ or (2) by motion of support defined by $s - s_0 \cos 2\pi ft$ when $F_x = 0$.

$$m\ddot{x} = 4K_x(s - x - \delta_y\phi)$$
$$I\ddot{\phi} = 4\delta_y K_x(s - x + \delta_y\phi) \qquad (12.15)$$
$$\qquad\qquad - 4K_y\delta_x^2\phi$$

Making the usual assumption that transients may be neglected in problems involving forced vibration, the motion of the mounted body in horizontal translation and in rotation is assumed to be harmonic at the forcing frequency. Thus, $x = x_0 \cos 2\pi ft$ and $\phi = \phi_0 \cos 2\pi ft$. The expressions in Eq. (12.15) may be then solved simultaneously to give the following expressions for the displacement amplitudes, x_0 in horizontal translation and ϕ_0 in rotation:

$$x_0 = \frac{s_0 B_1}{D} \qquad \phi_0 = \frac{s_0(B_2/\rho)}{D}$$

where
$$B_1 = \eta\left(\frac{\delta_x{}^2}{\rho^2} - \frac{f^2}{f_n{}^2}\right) \tag{12.16}$$

$$B_2 = \frac{\eta \delta_y f^2}{\rho f_n{}^2}$$

The other terms which appear in the above equations are defined with reference to Eq. (12.14), as illustrated in Fig. 12.13.

Natural Frequencies. *Two Planes of Symmetry.* In forced vibration, the amplitude becomes a maximum when the forcing frequency becomes equal to the natural frequency. In an undamped system, the amplitude becomes infinite at resonance. The natural frequency or frequencies of an undamped system may thus be determined by writing the expression for the displacement amplitude of the system in forced vibration and finding the forcing frequency at which this amplitude becomes infinite. Expressions for the displacement amplitudes of the system shown in Fig. 12.13 are given by Eqs. (12.14) and (12.16). The denominator of each of these equations includes the expression for D. The natural frequencies of the system shown in Fig. 12.13 in coupled rotational and horizontal translatory modes may thus be determined by equating D to zero and solving for the forcing frequencies. This gives the following expression defining the natural frequencies:

$$\frac{f_{n_c}}{f_{n_y}}\frac{\rho}{\delta_x} = \frac{1}{\sqrt{2}}\sqrt{\frac{\eta\rho^2}{b^2}\left(1 + \frac{\delta_y{}^2}{\rho^2}\right) + 1 \pm \sqrt{\left[\frac{\eta\rho^2}{\delta_x{}^2}\left(1 + \frac{\delta_y{}^2}{\rho^2}\right) + 1\right]^2 - \frac{4\eta\rho^2}{\delta_x{}^2}}} \tag{12.17}$$

where f_{n_c} designates a natural frequency in a coupled rotational and horizontal translatory mode, and f_{n_y} designates the natural frequency in the decoupled vertical translatory mode. The other parameters are defined in connection with Eq. (12.14). Two numerically different values of the dimensionless frequency ratio f_{n_c}/f_{n_y} are obtainable from Eq. (12.17), applicable to the two discrete coupled modes of vibration. Curves computed from Eq. (12.17) are set forth in Fig. 12.14, in which two distinct families of curves appear.

The ratio of a natural frequency in a coupled mode to the natural frequency in the vertical translatory mode is a function of three dimensionless ratios, two of the ratios including the radius of gyration ρ and the dimensions δ_y and δ_x, while the third is the ratio of horizontal to vertical stiffnesses of the elastic supports. In applying the relations set forth in Fig. 12.14, the applicable value of the abscissa ratio is first determined directly from the constants of the system. Two appropriate numerical values are then taken from the ordinate scale, as determined by the two curves for applicable values of δ_y/ρ, and the ratios of natural frequencies in coupled and vertical translatory modes are determined by dividing these values by the dimensionless ratio ρ/δ_x. The natural frequencies in coupled modes are then determined by multiplying the resulting ratio by the natural frequency in the decoupled vertical translatory mode, as calculated from Eq. (12.3). The appropriate value to use for the stiffness K is the sum of the stiffnesses of the elastic supports in Fig. 12.13.

The two straight lines in Fig. 12.14 for $\delta_y/\rho = 0$ represent natural frequencies in decoupled modes of vibration. When $\delta_y = 0$, the elastic supports lie in a horizontal plane passing through the center of gravity of the mounted body. The horizontal line at a value of unity on the ordinate scale represents the natural frequency in a rotational mode corresponding to that illustrated in Fig. 12.5b. The inclined straight line for the value $\delta_y/\rho = 0$ represents the natural frequency of the system in horizontal translation.

One Plane of Symmetry. A rigid body supported by elastic supports with one vertical plane of symmetry has three coupled natural modes of vibration, and a natural frequency in each of these modes. A typical system of this type is illustrated in Fig. 12.15 wherein the system is assumed to be symmetrical with respect to a plane parallel with the plane of the paper and extending through the center of gravity of

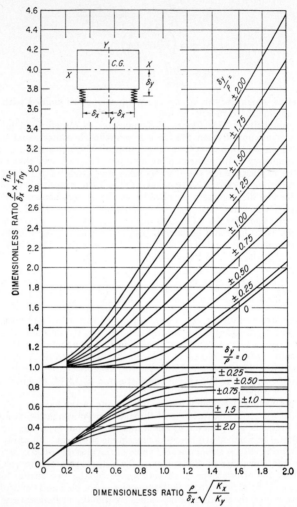

FIG. 12.14. Curves showing ratio of two coupled natural frequencies f_{nc} in XY plane to decoupled natural frequency f_{ny} in translation along Y axis. The stiffnesses of the resilient supports in the X and Y directions are indicated by K_x and K_y, respectively, and the radius of gyration with respect to the Z axis through the center of gravity is indicated by ρ. (*Crede.*[1])

the supported body. Motion of the supported body in horizontal and vertical translatory modes and in the rotational mode, all in the plane of the paper, are coupled. Motion in these three coupled modes is determined by writing three simultaneous equations of motion for the supported body as follows:

$$\begin{aligned}
I\ddot{\phi} &= -\phi(\Sigma\delta_{y_n}{}^2 K_{x_n} + \Sigma\delta_{x_n}{}^2 K_{y_n}) + x\Sigma\delta_{y_n}K_{x_n} - y\Sigma\delta_{x_n}K_{y_n} + T_0 \sin 2\pi ft \\
m\ddot{x} &= -x\Sigma K_{x_n} + \phi\Sigma\delta_{y_n}K_{x_n} \\
m\ddot{y} &= -y\Sigma K_{y_n} - \phi\Sigma\delta_{x_n}K_{y_n}
\end{aligned} \tag{12.18}$$

Care must be taken in deriving the above differential equations of motion to observe the indicated convention of signs, not only for the applied forces and couples, but also for the distances to the elastic supports from the coordinate axes. These distances are taken as positive if upward or toward the right, negative if downward or toward the left. To find the natural frequencies of the system shown in Fig. 12.15, Eqs. (12.18) are solved simultaneously for any one of the coordinate displacements. A typical expression is the following equation for the rotational displacement amplitude ϕ_0:

$$\phi_0 = \frac{T_0[m(2\pi f)^2 - \Sigma K_{x_n}]\,[m(2\pi f)^2 - \Sigma K_{y_n}]}{A(2\pi f)^6 + B(2\pi f)^4 + C(2\pi f)^2 + D} \qquad (12.19)$$

where $A = -Im^2$

$B = m^2(\Sigma\delta_{x_n}{}^2 K_{y_n} + \Sigma\delta_{y_n}{}^2 K_{x_n}) + Im(\Sigma K_{x_n} + \Sigma K_{y_n})$

$C = -m(\Sigma K_{x_n} + \Sigma K_{y_n})(\Sigma\delta_{x_n}{}^2 K_{y_n} + \Sigma\delta_{y_n}{}^2 K_{x_n}) - I\Sigma K_{x_n}\Sigma K_{y_n} + m(\Sigma\delta_{y_n}K_{x_n})^2 + m(\Sigma\delta_{x_n}K_{yn})^2$

$D = \Sigma K_{x_n}\Sigma K_{y_n}(\Sigma\delta_{x_n}{}^2 K_{y_n} + \Sigma\delta_{y_n}{}^2 K_{x_n}) - \Sigma K_{y_n}(\Sigma\delta_{y_n}K_{x_n})^2 - \Sigma K_{x_n}(\Sigma\delta_{x_n}K_{yn})^2$

The expression for each of the coordinate displacement amplitudes x_0, y_0, and ϕ_0 has the same denominator as Eq. (12.19).

This denominator, when equated to zero, gives a cubic equation whose variable is f^2. Three numerically different values of f are thus obtained, which represent the three natural frequencies of the supported body in the three coupled modes of vibration. Inasmuch as the modes are coupled, each mode includes components of motion in vertical and horizontal translation as well as in rotation.

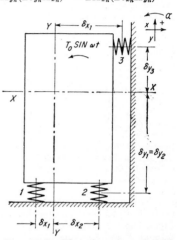

FIG. 12.15. Elevation view of rigid body on resilient supports and having a single plane of symmetry. The system is symmetrical with respect to the XY plane passing through the center of gravity of the body. (*Crede.*[1])

BALANCING OF ROTATING MACHINES

Vibration generally originates in a fluctuating force or couple and becomes evident as an oscillating motion. If the vibration is steady state, it may be reduced by one or more of the following methods:

1. Neutralize the driving force or couple by counterbalancing rotating or reciprocating members.
2. Isolate the driving force or couple, or the motion resulting therefrom, by introducing resilient supports or connections.
3. Counteract the driving force or couple by increasing the damping of structural members or by adding a tuned vibration absorber.

Method 1 is discussed in subsequent paragraphs of this section, and in Chap. 30. Method 2 is discussed in Chap. 13 while method 3, useful primarily to overcome the effects of resonance, is considered in Chap. 14.

In a rotating machine, the vibration results from the centrifugal force that occurs when the principal axis of inertia of the rotating member does not coincide with its axis of rotation. The usual remedy for this condition is the addition of a counterweight to the rotating member. In Fig. 12.16, a shaft and an eccentric disk fixed thereto are indicated by the solid lines. The mass center of the disk is to the right of the shaft axis, and a centrifugal force indicated by the vector F occurs when the shaft is rotated. A second eccentric disk, shown in dotted lines, is added to the shaft with an eccentricity 180° out of phase with that of the solid disk, thereby causing the centrifugal force F'. Designating the eccentricity as the radial distance from the shaft axis to the center of gravity of the disk, the shaft is said to be in static balance if the products of weight and eccentricity for the two disks are equal because the summation of the moments of the gravity forces about the shaft center is zero in all positions of the shaft.

During rotation of the shaft, the centrifugal forces F and F' act in opposite directions and introduce a resultant couple which acts about a transverse axis through the shaft. This couple rotates with the shaft and causes vibration. The combination of shaft with solid and dotted disks, as illustrated in Fig. 12.16, is thus said to be in dynamic unbalance even though in static balance. If dynamic balance is to be achieved, the couple of the centrifugal forces must have a zero resultant. Dynamic balance of the shaft and solid-disk assembly of Fig. 12.16 can be attained only by applying the counterbalance directly to the solid disk, or by adding two counterbalances to the shaft, one on each side of the original unbalanced disk.

In general, a rotating member may be counterbalanced by the application of appropriate balances in two preselected planes. Figure 12.17 illustrates schematically a shaft having unbalanced loads F and F' disposed in planes spaced apart along the axis of the shaft. The unbalanced assembly may be balanced by the addition of weights attached to the shaft and located in planes I and II. The magnitudes and

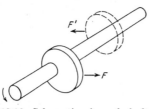

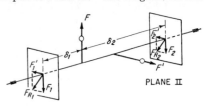

FIG. 12.16. Schematic view of shaft with unbalanced disk shown in solid lines. Addition of disk in dotted lines may achieve static balance but dynamic unbalance.

FIG. 12.17. Diagram showing method for determining magnitude and direction of counterbalances F_{R_1} and F_{R_2} to compensate for initially unbalanced forces F and F'.

locations of these counterbalances are determined from the principle of static equilibrium in planes extending through the shaft and through the unbalanced weights. Equations (12.20) are written by taking a summation of forces in the plane passing through F and a summation of couples in the same plane with respect to the line of action of F:

$$F_1 + F_2 = F \qquad F_1\delta_1 - F_2\delta_2 = 0 \tag{12.20}$$

The forces F_1 and F_2 are determined by solving Eqs. (12.20) simultaneously.

A similar analysis is carried out in a plane extending through the axis of the shaft and through the unbalanced weight F'. By taking a summation of forces and couples in this plane, a pair of equations similar to Eqs. (12.20) are established from which the magnitudes of forces F_1' and F_2' are determined. A similar procedure is followed for each unbalanced weight. The resultants F_{R_1}, F_{R_2} of the components F_1, F_1' and F_2, F_2' are now determined. These resultant forces F_{R_1} and F_{R_2} determine the magnitudes and positions of the counterbalances required to effect a complete static and dynamic balance of the shaft. Balancing machines are available commercially and are in common use in industrial establishments for automatically indicating the required counterbalances for rotating members. They are discussed in detail in Chap. 30.

BALANCING OF RECIPROCATING MACHINES

The machines considered in this section are of the type that effect a transformation of rotational motion to, or from, reciprocating motion. The machine may be driven by either the reciprocating motion or the rotational motion. The essential moving elements of such a machine are a piston, a crank, and a connecting rod. Vibration of the machine may result from the gas pressure applied periodically to the piston, and from the inertia forces associated with the moving parts. The inertia forces and the resultant couples may be substantially balanced in certain types of multicylinder machines but are inherently unbalanced in one- or two-cylinder machines. The gas

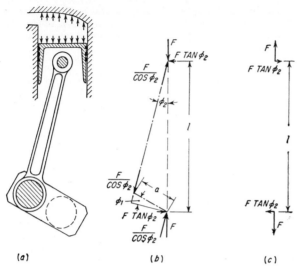

(a)   (b)   (c)

Fig. 12.18. Cross section through a cylinder of an internal-combustion engine, and diagrams showing forces resulting from gas pressure in the engine. (*Crede.*[1])

pressure acting upon the piston reacts on the chassis of the machine in the form of a couple which is transmitted to its support, and cannot be balanced.

The forces and couples resulting from the gas pressure are illustrated by reference to the single-cylinder internal-combustion engine shown in Fig. 12.18a.   The engine is driven by the expanding gas confined between the piston and cylinder head, as indicated by F in Fig. 12.18b.   The reaction to the force F may be resolved into a horizontal force $F \tan \phi_2$ and a force $F/\cos \phi_2$ applied along the line of the connecting rod to form a couple:

$$T_s = \frac{Fa \cos \phi_1}{\cos \phi_2} \qquad (12.21)$$

which tends to rotate the crankshaft.   The force $F/\cos \phi_2$ at the crankshaft bearing is resolved into a vertical component F and a horizontal component $F \tan \phi_2$.

The resultant forces applied to the engine chassis are shown in Fig. 12.18c.   These forces exert a couple upon the engine chassis:

$$T_f = Fl \tan \phi_2 \qquad (12.22)$$

From Fig. 12.18b, $l = a \cos \phi_1/\sin \phi_2$.   Substituting this expression for l in Eq. (12.22):

$$T_f = \frac{Fa \cos \phi_1}{\cos \phi_2} \qquad (12.23)$$

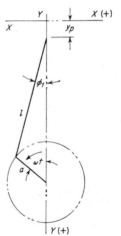

Fig. 12.19. Kinematics of piston, crank, and connecting-rod motion. (*Crede.*[1])

This is identical to T_s, Eq. (12.21), showing that each fluctuation in the magnitude of the couple applied to the crankshaft is reflected at the support for the engine.   It is not possible to eliminate the couple T_f by counterbalancing.

The technique in balancing the inertia forces is discussed with reference to Fig. 12.19. The crank rotates in a counterclockwise direction with constant angular velocity $2\pi f$. The piston is constrained to move along a vertical line and its motion is determined by the crank a and connecting rod l. The uppermost position of the piston is taken as the coordinate reference, and downward displacement y_p of the piston from the reference is considered as positive. The piston displacement is then given by the following expression:

$$y_p = a + l - a \cos 2\pi ft - l \cos \phi_1 \tag{12.24}$$

By writing an expression for ϕ_1, in terms of $2\pi f$, expanding the resultant expression by the binomial theorem, and dropping all terms containing a/l to greater than the second power, the following expression is obtained for y_p:

$$y_p = a \left(1 + \frac{a}{4l}\right) - a \left(\cos 2\pi ft + \frac{a}{4l} \cos 2\pi ft\right) \tag{12.25}$$

Taking the center of coordinates through the uppermost position of the piston, equations that define the vertical and the horizontal components of the crankpin displacement are written as follows:

$$y_c = l + a(1 - \cos 2\pi ft) \qquad x_c = a \sin 2\pi ft \tag{12.26}$$

The connecting rod is assumed to consist of (1) a concentrated mass whose motion corresponds to that of the piston and (2) a second concentrated mass, joined to the first mass by a massless strut, whose motion corresponds to that of the crankpin.

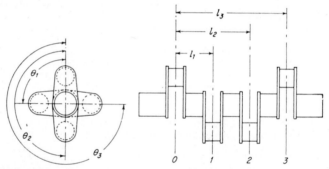

FIG. 12.20. Positions of the cranks on the crankshaft of a typical four-cylinder engine.

Designating the mass of the piston and crankpin (including the assigned portions of the connecting rod) by m_p and m_c, respectively, the vertical component F_y of the inertia force is obtained from the product of these masses and their respective accelerations as determined from double differentiation of Eqs. (12.25) and (12.26):

$$F_y = (m_p + m_c)a(2\pi f)^2 \cos 2\pi ft + m_p a \frac{a}{l} (2\pi f)^2 \cos 4\pi ft \tag{12.27}$$

The horizontal component F_x of the inertia force results only from the rotating mass m_c. Multiplying the second derivative of the second of Eqs. (12.26) by m_c:

$$F_x = -m_c a(2\pi f)^2 \sin 2\pi ft \tag{12.28}$$

The vertical component of the inertia force thus consists of parts having frequencies equal to one and two times the rotational frequency. Higher harmonics, which usually are of negligible magnitude, were excluded when powers of a/l greater than the second were neglected.

The necessary conditions for balancing a multicylinder engine are indicated by reference to Fig. 12.20. The cranks are numbered, and the angular position of each is indicated by the angle θ_n referred to the position of crank 0. The position of each crank along the shaft is indicated by the distance l_n from crank 0. The vertical and horizontal components of the inertia forces for a single cylinder are given by Eqs.

(12.27) and (12.28). The total inertia force for an entire engine is the summation of these equations over the number of cylinders. If the reciprocating and rotating masses m_p, m_c for each cylinder are respectively equal, the following conditions for balance of inertia forces are obtained:

$$\Sigma F_y = 0: \qquad \Sigma \cos \theta_n = 0 \quad \text{and} \quad \Sigma \cos 2\theta_n = 0$$
$$\Sigma F_x = 0: \qquad \Sigma \sin \theta_n = 0 \tag{12.29}$$

In a multicylinder engine, the inertia forces defined by Eqs. (12.27) and (12.28) create couples about horizontal and vertical transverse axes. For convenience, the

Table 12.1. Summary of Inertia Forces and Couples in Four-cylinder Engine

Crank	θ	2θ	$\cos \theta$	$\cos 2\theta$	$\sin \theta$	$l \cos \theta$	$l \cos 2\theta$	$l \sin \theta$
0	0	0	1	1	0	0	0	0
1	180	360	-1	1	0	$-l$	l	0
2	180	360	-1	1	0	$-2l$	$2l$	0
3	0	0	1	1	0	$3l$	$3l$	0
Summation............			0	4	0	0	$6l$	0

couples are taken with respect to axes through the 0 crank in Fig. 12.20. Assuming again that the masses of the piston and crank of each cylinder are respectively equal, the following conditions for balance of inertia couples are obtained:

$$\Sigma l_n F_y = 0: \qquad \Sigma l_n \cos \theta_n = 0 \quad \text{and} \quad \Sigma l_n \cos 2\theta_n = 0$$
$$\Sigma l_n F_x = 0: \qquad \Sigma l_n \sin \theta_n = 0 \tag{12.30}$$

For example, consider a four-cylinder engine whose crank angles, starting at one end, are 0, 180, 180, 0°; and whose cranks are spaced apart equal distances l along the shaft. Table 12.1 is now established in accordance with Eqs. (12.29) and (12.30). It is evident from the table that the primary forces and couples are balanced because $\Sigma \cos \theta = \Sigma \sin \theta = \Sigma l \cos \theta = \Sigma l \sin \theta = 0$. However, $\Sigma \cos 2\theta$ and $\Sigma l \cos 2\theta \neq 0$; the second-order forces and couples therefore are not balanced.

CONTROL OF IMPACT FORCES

Preceding sections of this chapter have referred to means for controlling the vibration of elastic structures acted upon by periodic disturbances. If the exciting force or motion is periodic, a condition of steady-state vibration develops. If the excitation is transient, the response of the elastic structure will also be transient. This section includes a brief discussion of certain types of transient excitation and the control of transient vibration of elastic structures resulting therefrom.

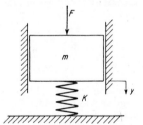

Fig. 12.21. Undamped single-degree-of-freedom system excited by impulsively applied force F.

Impulsively Applied Force. The structure being considered here may be idealized as the undamped single-degree-of-freedom system illustrated in Fig. 12.21. This system is acted upon by a force F which continues only for the period of time $1/2f$, as defined by the following equations:

$$F = F_0 \sin 2\pi ft \qquad (0 \leq t \leq 1/2f)$$
$$F = 0 \qquad (t \geq 1/2f) \tag{12.31}$$

The equation of motion for the body m is written for two time intervals, one for the period during which the force F acts and the other for the period after the force F has ceased to act. The differential equations of motion are as follows:

$$m\ddot{y} + Ky = F_0 \sin 2\pi ft \qquad (0 \leq t \leq 1/2f) \tag{12.32}$$
$$m\ddot{y} + Ky = 0 \qquad\qquad (t \geq 1/2f)$$

The conditions discussed here arise most often when the time $1/2f$ is small. It is then convenient to consider the impulse of the force F. The impulse of a sinusoidally varying force having a duration of a half period $1/2f$ is defined by the following expression:

$$F_0 = \frac{2\pi fJ}{2} \tag{12.33}$$

where the force F is in pounds, the frequency $2\pi f$ is in cycles per second, and the impulse J is in pound seconds.

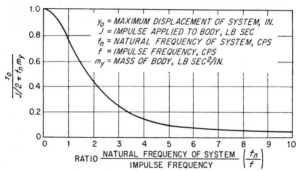

FIG. 12.22. Relation among the several parameters which determine the maximum deflection y_0 of the system illustrated in Fig. 12.21.

The solution of Eqs. (12.32) gives two expressions for the maximum displacement y_0 of the body m in Fig. 12.21, one of the equations being for the time during which the force F is applied and the other being for the time after the force F has ceased to act:

$$\frac{y_0}{J/2\pi f_n m} = \frac{1}{2}\left(\frac{f_n}{f} - 1\right) \sin \frac{2n\pi}{(f_n/f) + 1} \qquad \left(0 \leq t \leq \frac{1}{2f}\right) \tag{12.34}$$

$$\frac{y_0}{J/2\pi f_n m} = \frac{1}{1 - (f_n/f)^2} \cos \frac{\pi f_n}{2f} \qquad \left(t \geq \frac{1}{2f}\right) \tag{12.35}$$

The term n in Eq. (12.34) is a positive integer chosen so as to make the sine term as large as possible while the argument remains less than π. When $f < f_n$, Eq. (12.34) applies; when $f > f_n$, Eq. (12.35) applies. The relations given by Eqs. (12.34) and (12.35) are illustrated graphically in Fig. 12.22.

Assuming the numerical value of the impulse J to be fixed, the above analysis and the resulting curve of Fig. 12.22 suggest several means for minimizing the deflection y experienced by the system:

1. A reduction in the magnitude of the forcing frequency f increases the value of the abscissa parameter, thereby reducing the deflection y of the system. Means for reducing the forcing frequency f are considered in detail in subsequent paragraphs of this section with particular reference to certain common types of metalworking machinery.
2. If the forcing frequency f is required to remain relatively large, the deflection y of the system tends to be great. It may be decreased somewhat by increasing the mass m_y of the system. This is commonly achieved in practical installations by mounting the machine on a massive concrete block so that the inertia of the block counteracts the applied impulse.

The above analysis considers only the deflection at the first cycle of free vibration and refers only to an undamped system.   The maximum deflection of the system is

not materially affected by the addition of damping unless the damping coefficient is relatively great.   The duration of the ensuing free vibration, however, is materially affected by the degree of damping present. The addition of damping to a structure which is subjected to impulsive loading is thus an important means of controlling vibration.   This means is discussed in detail in Chap. 14.

Reduction of Impact Force.   The types of metalworking operations discussed here involve the forming or cutting of metal by dies.   A typical operation in this class is illustrated schematically in Fig. 12.23.   A plate of thickness t to be blanked is placed upon a stationary die and is engaged by a descending punch whose width w_1 is slightly less than the clearance w_2 between the spaced parts of the die.   The portion of the plate between these spaced parts of the die is thus sheared from the body of the plate and moved downward ahead of the punch.

If the punch is designed as illustrated in Fig. 12.23a, all the shearing action occurs simultaneously.   A large force is thus involved, as indicated by the height of the shaded area at the right of the figure.   If

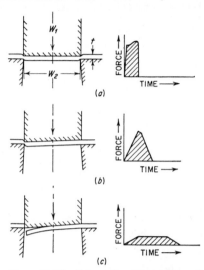

Fig. 12.23.   Schematic illustration of blanking operation, showing the effect of shear angle of the punch.   The force-time diagram for each condition is shown at the right.

the lower face of the punch is slightly inclined, as illustrated in Fig. 12.23b, the shearing action is distributed over a greater part of the stroke.   The maximum force then

endures for a shorter period and the duration of the force is increased, as shown by the shape of the shaded area. A further increase in the angle of the lower face of the punch, as shown at Fig. 12.23c, brings about a pronounced decrease in the magnitude of the force and increase in the duration of the force.   Effectively, this decreases f, with the consequent results shown in Fig. 12.22 on the deflection of the system.

In an operation involving the punching of several holes at one stroke of a press, a similar reduction of total force can be attained by stepped punches, as illustrated in Fig. 12.24.   The punching of successive holes

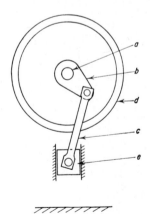

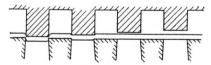

Fig. 12.24.   Illustration of stepped punches for punching several holes at one stroke of a press.

Fig. 12.25.   Schematic diagram of driving mechanism of a typical punch press.

occurs progressively, and not all the punches are operative at a given time.   Where pierced blanks are required, punching and blanking operations frequently are performed in multistage dies.   Perforations are first made in the material; the material is then moved the length of one stage and the piece is blanked around the perforations while first-stage operations are being performed on the following increment of material. It is desirable, where possible, to equalize the work between stages and to keep the strokes in the several stages out of phase to maintain the individual impulses as small as possible.

Punch presses frequently create unnecessary noise because of double impact. Figure 12.25 illustrates schematically the crankshaft a, crank b, connecting rod c, and flywheel d of a typical punch press. A clutch is interposed in the crankshaft between the flywheel and crank. The flywheel rotates continuously, and the clutch is engaged at each stroke to impart motion to the moving head e, or remains engaged for extended periods if the press is equipped with an automatic feed. The metalworking operation is performed as the moving head, generally carrying the punch, approaches its lowermost position. The mass of the moving head tends to accelerate the crank, causing it to get ahead of the flywheel and thereby take up any lost motion in the clutch. One impact results when the punch hits the work, and a second impact occurs in the clutch mechanism an instant later as the flywheel catches up with the crank. A properly equipped punch press of this type is provided with a brake, an air cylinder, or a counterbalance to retard the downward motion of the moving head. By preventing the crank from getting ahead of the flywheel, it is possible to eliminate the second impact. Care in adjusting and maintaining these features of presses will eliminate unnecessary impacts.

Oil is frequently used during metalworking operations to reduce wear on the tools by providing lubrication and sometimes to carry away heat generated by the metalworking operation. This oil also tends to reduce transient vibration resulting from the impulsive application of forces. An oil film between the die and the work tends to cushion the impact, thereby decreasing the magnitude of the forcing frequency f. It also adds damping to the system, thus reducing the duration of the ensuing free vibration.

REFERENCES

1. Crede, C. E.: "Vibration and Shock Isolation," John Wiley & Sons, Inc., New York, 1951.
2. Den Hartog, J. P.: "Mechanical Vibrations," 3d ed., McGraw-Hill Book Company, Inc., New York, 1947.
3. Freberg, C. R., and E. N. Kemler: "Elements of Mechanical Vibrations," John Wiley & Sons, Inc., New York, 1943.
4. Timoshenko, S., and D. H. Young: "Advanced Dynamics," McGraw-Hill Book Company, Inc., New York, 1948.
5. Kimball, A. L.: "Vibration Prevention in Engineering," John Wiley & Sons, Inc., New York, 1932.
6. Timoshenko, S.: "Vibration Problems in Engineering," D. Van Nostrand Company, Inc., Princeton, N.J., 1928.
7. Mindlin, R. D.: *Bell System Tech. J.*, **34** (3–4) (July–October, 1945).
8. Frankland, J. M.: *Proc. Soc. Exptl. Stress Anal.*, **6** (2): 7 (1948).
9. Morse, P. M.: "Vibration and Sound," 2d ed., McGraw-Hill Book Company, Inc., New York, 1948.
10. Stoker, J. J.: "Nonlinear Vibrations," Interscience Publishers, Inc., New York, 1950.
11. Cole, E. B.: "Theory of Vibration for Engineers," Crosby Lockwood & Son, Ltd., London, 1950.
12. Scanlan, R. H., and R. Rosenbaum: "Introduction to the Study of Aircraft Vibration and Flutter," The Macmillan Company, New York, 1951.
13. Manley, R. G.: "Fundamentals of Vibration Study," John Wiley & Sons, Inc., New York, 1942.
14. Bernhard, R. K.: "Mechanical Vibrations," Pitman Publishing Corporation, New York, 1943.
15. Crede, C. E.: *Machine Design*, **26**: 139 (August, 1954).

Chapter 13

VIBRATION ISOLATION

CHARLES E. CREDE

Barry Controls Inc.

ISOLATION OF STEADY-STATE VIBRATION

Vibration isolation concerns means to bring about a reduction in a vibratory effect. A vibration isolator in its most elementary form may be considered as a resilient support for equipment. The function of an isolator is to reduce the magnitude of force transmitted from the equipment to its support or, alternatively, to reduce the magnitude of motion transmitted from a vibrating support to the equipment. The effectiveness of an isolator in bringing about such a reduction is defined by the transmissibility of the isolator system. In the force-excited system, transmissibility is the ratio of the force experienced by the support to the force originating within the mounted equipment. In the motion-excited system, transmissibility is the ratio of the displacement amplitude of the mounted equipment to the displacement amplitude of the support.

Vibration isolation is commonly discussed with reference to a single-degree-of-freedom system constrained to move along a single line or about a single axis. With this one-mass system, the transmissibility becomes smaller than unity when the forcing frequency is greater than 1.41 times the natural frequency of the equipment on the isolators, as illustrated in Fig. 12.10. For smaller values of forcing frequency, the isolators increase rather than decrease the vibration. The principle of vibration isolation is based upon maintaining a frequency relation in which the forcing frequency is greater than 1.41 times the natural frequency.

Although the classical theory of vibration isolation based on a single-degree-of-freedom system indicates the applicable principles, it does not include sufficient practical engineering information to form the basis for design or application of vibration isolators. In practice, the equipment usually is supported by several isolators and has freedom of motion along or about several coordinate axes. This chapter discusses practical aspects of vibration isolation with several degrees of freedom, drawing upon the theoretical treatment set forth in Chap. 12, and includes a discussion of the properties of materials and characteristics of commercially available isolators.

Properties of Mounted Equipment. In a single-degree-of-freedom system constrained to have translatory motion along a single line, only the mass of the equipment and the stiffness of the isolators must be known to determine the natural frequency of the system. When the equipment is free to move along several coordinate axes simultaneously, the natural modes of vibration become coupled, as described in the section on *Natural Modes of Vibration* in Chap. 12. The natural frequencies in these coupled modes then depend not only on the mass of the supported equipment but also on its mass distribution. The latter property is defined by the moment of inertia of the equipment. If the mounted equipment has a simple form, the moment of inertia may be calculated.   If the shape of the equipment is irregular, the calculation becomes laborious, and it may be more practical to measure the moment of inertia, particularly if the equipment is small.   The moment of inertia often may be estimated with satisfactory accuracy for practical purposes.

The moment of inertia of a particle about any axis is defined as $\Delta I = (\Delta m)r^2$ where Δm is the mass of the particle and r is its distance from the axis, measured along a line perpendicular to the axis.   The moment of inertia of a rigid body comprised of a number of discrete particles is the summation of the moments of inertia of the separate particles:

$$I = \sum_{i=1}^{i=n} (\Delta m)_i r_i^2 \tag{13.1}$$

The moment of inertia of a body with respect to a given axis is thus the sum of the moments of inertia of its parts with respect to the same axis.

It is convenient to define a length ρ, designated the radius of gyration of the body. If a body of total mass m has a moment of inertia I, the radius of gyration is defined by the following equation:

$$I = m\rho^2 \tag{13.2}$$

The relation between the radius of gyration about the reference axis and the radius of gyration ρ' about any parallel axis spaced from the reference axis by a distance δ is

$$\rho' = \sqrt{\rho^2 + \delta^2} \tag{13.3}$$

If the weight and size of a rigid body are known, the radius of gyration may be calculated from Eqs. (13.1) and (13.2).   For complex equipment having many components, this is a very laborious procedure which generally is not practical.   If the equipment is available and is small enough to be handled readily, the moment of inertia can be determined experimentally.   In one method of determining moment of inertia, the equipment is suspended as a torsional pendulum with the axis about which the moment of inertia is to be determined arranged in a vertical direction.   The body may be supported by one, two, or three relatively long wires, and the moment of inertia may be calculated from the natural period of oscillation.   In another method, the body is suspended as a compound pendulum with the axis in question oriented horizontally. By employing two lengths of support for the compound pendulum independently and measuring the natural period for each, the moment of inertia may be calculated. Details of these methods for determining moment of inertia are set forth on pages 16–21 of Ref. 1.

If it is impractical to calculate or measure the moment of inertia, an estimating method may be used.   The radius of gyration, being a simple linear quantity, is readily visualized as a measure of mass distribution within the body.   Its meaning is best illustrated by reference to the several typical bodies shown in Fig. 13.1.   For more details, see Ref. 2.

In the thin-walled cylinder whose end view is shown in Fig. 13.1a, the mass is concentrated at the radius a from the axis of symmetry.   The radius of gyration is therefore equal to the radius.   The mass is distributed, however, in the solid homogeneous cylinder shown in Fig. 13.1b; and the radius of gyration is less than the radius, $\rho = 0.71a$.   Several rectangular prisms with various form factors are illustrated in other views of Fig. 13.1.   The radius of gyration for each is indicated with reference to the length of the short side.   These examples may be used in estimating radius of gyration by visualizing the equipment under consideration as having a mass distribution equivalent to that of some regular body whose radius of gyration is known or can be determined.

Isolators for Symmetrical Equipment.   When vibration isolation is considered with respect to a single-degree-of-freedom system having only one possible mode of motion, as discussed in the section on *Forced Vibration of a Single-degree-of-freedom System* in Chap. 12, the concept of transmissibility may be expressed in simple numerical terms.   In most practical systems, the mounted equipment has freedom in several modes of vibration which may exist concurrently.   The displacement at each isolator may thus differ from that at other isolators.   The method of analysis set forth in the section on the *Several-degree-of-freedom System* in Chap. 12 yields numerical values for the vibration amplitude at each isolator and makes it possible to calculate numerically the transmissibility for each isolator location.   Except in special circumstances, it is difficult to justify the time required to make such a calculation.   In general, an acceptable and conservative approach is to select a natural frequency from Fig. 12.10

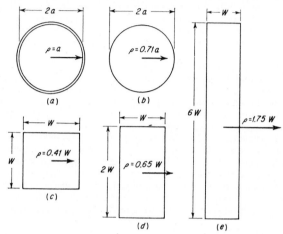

FIG. 13.1. Outlines of representative bodies.   The arrows indicate radii of gyration ρ with respect to axes perpendicular to the paper and passing through the centers of gravity of the respective bodies.   (*Crede.*[1])

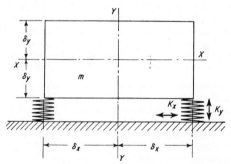

FIG. 13.2. Elevation view of equipment supported upon isolators located at four lower corners.

on the basis of the desired transmissibility, and to design the isolator system to have a maximum natural frequency in any mode not exceeding the selected value.

The most common type of problem in vibration isolation concerns an equipment mounted upon four isolators located beneath the equipment.   This type of problem reduces to its simplest form if the equipment and the isolator pattern may be considered symmetrical with respect to two vertical coordinate planes passing through the center of gravity of the equipment.   Assuming such symmetry, and viewing one face of the mounted equipment as shown in Fig. 13.2, the equipment is free to move vertically, horizontally, and in rotation about an axis perpendicular to the face being viewed.   The motion in certain of the modes may be coupled or decoupled, as explained. in the section on *Natural Modes of Vibration* in Chap. 12.

If the vertical stiffness of each isolator is directly proportional to the dead-weight load which it carries, vibration in the vertical translatory mode is decoupled from vibration in other modes, and the natural frequency is determined by the mass of the mounted equipment and the vertical stiffnesses of the isolators. This natural frequency constitutes a reference for defining the natural frequencies in other modes, using Fig. 12.14. It is necessary in using this figure to know the radius of gyration of the mounted equipment, the locations of the isolators with reference to the center of gravity of the equipment, and the stiffnesses of the isolators in the several coordinate directions. The results obtained are the natural frequencies in the coupled rotational and horizontal translatory modes, presented as a dimensionless ratio involving the natural frequency in the vertical translatory mode. Examples illustrating the use of Fig. 12.17 for the calculation of natural frequencies are given under examples in this chapter.

The above procedure for determining the natural frequencies in coupled modes is generally applicable and represents a rigorous analysis where the assumed symmetry exists. The procedure is somewhat laborious, however, because the dimensionless ratio ρ/δ_x appears in both ordinate and abscissa parameters, and because it is necessary to determine the radius of gyration of the equipment. The relations set forth in Fig. 12.14 may be approximated in a more readily usable form if (1) the mounted equipment can be considered a cuboid having uniform mass distribution, (2) the four isolators are attached precisely at the four lower corners of the cuboid, and (3) the height of the isolators is negligible. The ratio of the natural frequencies in the coupled rotational and horizontal translatory modes to the natural frequency in the vertical translatory mode then becomes a function of only the dimensions of the cuboid and the stiffnesses of the isolators in the several coordinate directions. Results obtained by making these assumptions and substituting in Eq. (12.17) are given by the following equation:

$$\frac{f_{nc}}{f_{ny}} = \frac{1}{\sqrt{2}} \sqrt{\frac{4\eta\lambda^2 + \eta + 3}{\lambda^2 + 1} \pm \sqrt{\left(\frac{4\eta\lambda^2 + \eta + 3}{\lambda^2 + 1}\right)^2 - \frac{12\eta}{1 + \lambda^2}}} \tag{13.4}$$

where $\eta = K_x/K_y$ designates the ratio of horizontal to vertical stiffness of the isolators and $\lambda = 2\delta_y/2\delta_x$ indicates the ratio of height to width of mounted equipment. The relation given by Eq. (13.4) is shown graphically in Fig. 13.3. The curves included in this figure are useful for calculating approximate values of natural frequencies and for indicating trends in natural frequencies resulting from changes in various parameters. The following important trends are worthy of emphasis:

1. Both the coupled natural frequencies tend to become a minimum, for any ratio of height to width of the mounted equipment, when the ratio of horizontal to vertical stiffness K_x/K_y of the isolators is low. Conversely, when the ratio of horizontal to vertical stiffness is high, both coupled natural frequencies also tend to be high. It is thus apparent that, when the vibration isolators are located underneath the mounted body, the generally favorable condition of low natural frequencies is obtained using isolators whose stiffness in a horizontal direction is less than the stiffness in a vertical direction. A low horizontal stiffness may be undesirable, however, in applications requiring maximum stability. A compromise between natural frequency and stability may then lead to optimum conditions.

2. As the ratio of height to width of the mounted equipment increases, the lower of the coupled natural frequencies decreases. The trend of the higher of the coupled natural frequencies depends on the stiffness ratio of the isolators. It is evident that one of the coupled natural frequencies tends to become very high when (1) the horizontal stiffness of the isolators is greater than the vertical stiffness and (2) the height of the mounted equipment is approximately equal to or greater than the width. When the ratio of height to width of mounted equipment is greater than 0.5, the spread between the coupled natural frequencies increases as the ratio K_x/K_y of horizontal to vertical stiffness of the isolators increases.

Isolators for Nonsymmetrical Equipment. In some applications, the center of gravity of the mounted equipment is so eccentric to the pattern of isolators that the assumption of two vertical planes of symmetry discussed above is not justifiable. In other instances, it may be necessary to employ more than four isolators underneath the equipment or to employ additional isolators near the top of the equipment for stabilizing purposes. Assuming the equipment to be symmetrical with respect to a single vertical plane through the center of gravity, the system may be analyzed as a three-degree-of-freedom system having motion in the plane of symmetry. The three differential equations of motion for such a system are set forth in the section on *One Plane of Symmetry* in Chap. 12. If the system meets the test for decoupling set forth in the section on *Natural Modes of Vibration* in Chap. 12, the differential equation of

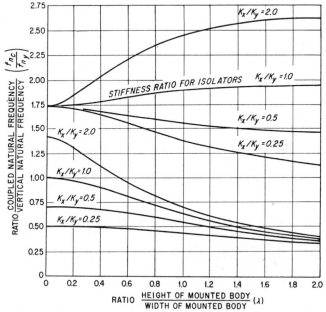

FIG. 13.3. Curves showing ratio of coupled natural frequencies f_{nc} in XY plane to decoupled natural frequency f_{ny} in translation along Y axis for body supported as shown in Fig. 13.2 and having uniform mass distribution. The body is assumed to be a cuboid with the isolators attached precisely at the lower corners. (*Crede.*[1])

motion for the decoupled mode may be omitted, and the remaining two equations may be solved simultaneously for the natural frequencies in the two remaining modes. If the system does not meet the test for decoupling, the three equations of motion must be solved simultaneously to yield three natural frequencies in three coupled modes of vibration. The calculations involved in evaluating the three natural frequencies often require that many significant figures be carried throughout the analysis, thereby making a calculating machine necessary.

When the center of gravity of the mounted equipment in a plan view is not symmetrical with respect to the pattern of isolators, the distribution of the dead-weight load among the isolators is unequal. If the equipment is supported on three isolators, the load carried by each may be determined simply by applying the principles of statics. If four isolators are employed, as shown by the plan view in Fig. 13.4, the analysis becomes considerably more involved because a change in the deflection of any one isolator causes a redistribution of the load among the other isolators.

The following three equations are obtained from a summation of vertical forces and from summations of moments of these forces about two perpendicular horizontal axes:

$$K_1 d_1 + K_2 d_2 + K_3 d_3 + K_4 d_4 = W$$
$$\delta_b K_1 d_1 + \delta_b K_2 d_2 = \delta_a W \tag{13.5}$$
$$\delta_b' K_2 d_2 + \delta_b' K_4 d_4 = \delta_a' W$$

where the subscripts to K and d refer to the isolator designations shown in Fig. 13.4. Assuming the equipment to be rigid, the isolators to be of the same free height, and the supporting surface to be flat and rigid, the following equation defines the rigidity of the mounted equipment:

$$d_1 + d_4 = d_2 + d_3 \tag{13.6}$$

If the four isolators are identical, there is a unique solution for the load carried by each isolator which may be obtained from Eqs. (13.5) and (13.6) by setting each value of stiffness equal to K. This gives the following set of equations defining the load carried by each isolator:

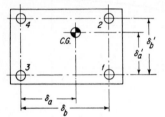

FIG. 13.4. Plan view of equipment supported by four isolators wherein center of gravity of equipment is not located above center of pattern of isolators.

$$\frac{F_1}{W} = \frac{1}{2}\left(\frac{\delta_a}{\delta_b} - \frac{\delta_a'}{\delta_b'} + \frac{1}{2}\right)$$

$$\frac{F_2}{W} = \frac{1}{2}\left(\frac{\delta_a}{\delta_b} + \frac{\delta_a'}{\delta_b'} + \frac{1}{2}\right)$$

$$\frac{F_3}{W} = \frac{1}{2}\left(\frac{3}{2} - \frac{\delta_a}{\delta_b} - \frac{\delta_a'}{\delta_b'}\right) \tag{13.7}$$

$$\frac{F_4}{W} = \frac{1}{2}\left(\frac{\delta_a'}{\delta_b'} - \frac{\delta_a}{\delta_b} + \frac{1}{2}\right)$$

The relations given by Eq. (13.7) are shown graphically in Fig. 13.5, employing the type of presentation first published in Ref. 3. In this figure, the dimensionless ratios δ_a/δ_b and δ_a'/δ_b' are plotted on the horizontal and vertical axes, respectively, while the dimensionless ratio F/W of load carried by each isolator to total load is the parameter of the family of diagonal lines. The isolator locations are designated by the encircled numerals at the four corners, in accordance with corresponding designations in Fig. 13.4. The load carried by each isolator is indicated by the diagonal line, where the appropriate numerical value is determined from the scale on the side of the line facing the particular isolator designation. Negative values indicate that the force on the isolator is upward whereas positive values indicate a downward force.

Example. Assume that the arrangement of equipment and isolators is such that both dimensionless ratios δ_a/δ_b and δ_a'/δ_b' are numerically equal to 0.8. This point is adjacent to the upper right-hand corner of Fig. 13.5. The portion of the load carried by isolator 1 is determined from the diagonal lines extending from lower left to upper right. The applicable numerical values, being on the same sides of the lines as 1, are along the upper and right margins. Interpolating between diagonal lines, isolator 1 is found to carry 25 per cent of the load; i.e., $F_1/W = 0.25$. The load carried by isolator 4 is determined from the same lines, using the coordinate scale along the left and lower margins. Thus F_4/W is also 0.25. The loads carried by isolators 2 and 3 are determined from the opposite set of diagonal lines. For isolator 2, the load as indicated by values extending along the lower and right margins is determined from the ratio $F_2/W = 0.55$. The load on isolator 3 is determined from the same set of diagonal lines, using the scale extending along the left and upper margins. The ratio F_3/W is -0.05; i.e., the force on isolator 3 is an upward force equal to 5 per cent of the weight of the equipment.

It is a requirement in decoupling vibration in the vertical translatory mode that the stiffness of each isolator be proportional to the dead-weight load which it carries. This tends to occur when the static deflections of all isolators are equal. Equations (13.5) define three necessary conditions for static equilibrium, and a fourth may be assumed at will. The fourth condition assumed here is that diagonally disposed isolators between them carry 50 per cent of the weight of the supported equipment.

This eliminates the possibility that a pair of diagonally opposite isolators will be excessively stiff, with the result that the supported equipment tends to pivot about a line connecting these isolators. This assumption gives the following equation:

$$(K_1 + K_4)d = (K_2 + K_3)d \qquad (13.8)$$

Setting $d_1 = d_2 = \cdots = d$ in Eq. (13.5), and solving simultaneously with Eq. (13.8),

$$\frac{K_1}{W/d} = \frac{1}{2}\left(\frac{\delta_a}{\delta_b} - \frac{\delta_a'}{\delta_b'} + \frac{1}{2}\right) \qquad \text{etc.} \qquad (13.9)$$

where the equations are similar to Eq. (13.9).

The relations given by Eqs. (13.9) are also shown graphically by Fig. 13.5, wherein the parameter of the family of diagonal lines is $K/(W/d)$. Figure 13.5 may thus be

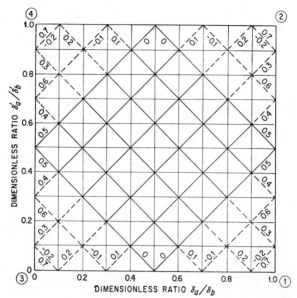

Fig. 13.5. Diagram for determining deflection of isolators and loads on isolators for system shown in Fig. 13.4. If all isolators are of the same stiffness, the proportion of the total load carried by each isolator is indicated by the numerical value on the appropriate diagonal lines. If all isolators experience the same static deflection, the required stiffnesses of the isolators are obtained from the numerical values on the appropriate *solid* diagonal lines.

used to determine the stiffnesses of the respective isolators required to maintain the equipment level. The appropriate scale to use in determining the stiffness of any isolator is that appearing on the same side of a diagonal line as the encircled isolator designation, in accordance with the example in this section. When Fig. 13.5 is employed to determine the stiffnesses required to attain equal static deflection at each isolator, the diagonal lines which are *dotted* must not be used. The dotted lines indicate a value of K greater than $\frac{1}{2}(W/d)$, a condition which is incompatible with the initial assumption that diagonal pairs of isolators between them carry 50 per cent of the weight of the equipment. In the above example, the equipment cannot be mounted to attain equal static deflections because the coordinate point $\delta_a/\delta_b = 0.8$, $\delta_a'/\delta_b' = 0.8$ is in a region of dotted lines.

Isolators for Low-speed Machines. From the known operating frequency of a machine, the natural frequency required of the isolators to attain a desired transmissibility may be determined from Fig. 12.10. This natural frequency must be considered a maximum; it is divided by the ratio f_{n_c}/f_{n_y} obtained from Fig. 12.14 to obtain the maximum acceptable natural frequency in vertical translation. The latter is converted to static deflection by reference to Fig. 12.4. The relatively great static deflection which appears necessary in mounting low-speed machinery introduces many problems.

In general, it is advantageous to maintain the static deflection at a minimum by the application of either of two somewhat different methods as follows:

1. The horizontal distance between isolators may be made relatively great compared with the dimensions of the mounted equipment, thereby setting the natural frequencies in the coupled rotational and horizontal translatory modes either substantially equal to or much greater than the natural frequency in the vertical translatory mode. The high natural frequency then falls above the forcing frequency, and there is no isolation in the common sense of the word. However, there is force reduction in rotational modes of vibration, because the isolators are disposed at the ends of long arms. This approach can be used only for constant-speed machines, because the forcing frequency is interposed between two natural frequencies and variation of the forcing frequency may lead to resonance.

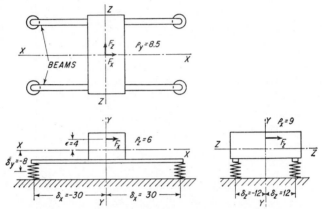

FIG. 13.6. Mounting method in which isolators are placed at ends of long beams extending in direction of short dimension of mounted equipment. (*Crede.*[1])

2. The equipment may be rigidly mounted upon a concrete inertia block which in turn is supported by isolators. The inertia block makes it possible to attain a center of gravity for the machine-and-block combination which is low relative to the machine. The isolators may then be placed in the same horizontal plane as this center of gravity without being above the level of the base of the machine, and the maximum natural frequency may be substantially equal to the natural frequency in vertical translation. The addition of the inertia block is also advantageous in that it increases the mass of the machine and thereby decreases its vibration amplitude. This approach is satisfactory for use with variable-speed machines because all natural frequencies are below any designated operating speed for the machine. The use of a concrete inertia block is often the best solution to the isolation of low-frequency vibration but usually results in a relatively elaborate installation.

The following two examples indicate generally the method of analysis used in the application of isolators and illustrate in the same order the above two procedures for mounting low-speed machinery.

Example 1. The machine to be considered, as illustrated schematically in Fig. 13.6, is relatively long in the direction of the Z axis and relatively narrow in the direction of the X axis. The force that is to be isolated is harmonic at the constant frequency of 8 cps.

It is assumed to result from the rotation of an unbalanced member whose plane of rotation is taken, in the first instance, as a plane perpendicular to the Z axis and, in the second instance, as a plane perpendicular to the X axis. The machine is set upon beams which extend parallel with the X axis and engage the isolators at their opposite ends. The distance between isolators is thus 60 in. measured in the direction of the X axis and 24 in. measured in the direction of the Z axis. The center of coordinates is taken at the center of gravity of the supported body, i.e., at the center of gravity of the machine-and-beams assembly. The total weight of the machine-and-supporting-beam assembly is 100 lb, and its radii of gyration in inches with respect to the three coordinate axes through the center of gravity are $\rho_x = 9$, $\rho_y = 8.5$, $\rho_z = 6$. The isolators are of equal stiffnesses in the directions of the three coordinate axes ($\eta = K_x/K_y = K_z/K_y = 1$).

The following dimensionless ratios are established as the initial step in the solution:

$$\begin{aligned}
\delta_y/\rho_z &= -1.333 & \delta_y/\rho_x &= -0.889 \\
\delta_x/\rho_z &= \pm 5.0 & \delta_z/\rho_x &= \pm 1.333 \\
(\delta_y/\rho_z)^2 &= 1.78 & (\delta_y/\rho_x)^2 &= 0.790 \\
(\delta_x/\rho_z)^2 &= 25.0 & (\delta_z/\rho_x)^2 &= 1.78 \\
\eta(\rho_z/\delta_x)^2 &= 0.04 & \eta(\rho_z/\delta_z)^2 &= 0.561
\end{aligned}$$

The various natural frequencies are next determined in terms of the vertical natural frequency f_{ny}. Referring to Fig. 12.14, the coupled natural frequencies for vibration in a plane perpendicular to the Z axis are determined as follows:

$$\frac{\rho_z}{\delta_x} \sqrt{\frac{K_x}{K_y}} = 0.2 \sqrt{1} = 0.2$$

For $\delta_y/\rho_z = -1.333$, $(f_{nc}/f_{ny})(\rho_z/\delta_x) = 0.19; 1.03$. The signs of the dimensionless ratios δ_y/ρ_z and δ_x/ρ_z require an explanation. According to Eq. (12.17), the natural frequencies are independent of the sign of δ_y/ρ_z. With regard to the ratio δ_x/ρ_z, the sign chosen should be the same as the sign chosen for the radical on the right side of Eq. (12.17). The frequency ratio f_{nc}/f_{ny} then becomes positive. Dividing the above values for $(f_{nc}/f_{ny})(\rho_z/\delta_x)$ by $\rho_z/\delta_x = 0.2$; $f_{nc}/f_{ny} = 0.96$; 5.15.

Vibration in a plane perpendicular to the X axis is treated in a similar manner. It is assumed that exciting forces are not applied concurrently in planes perpendicular to the X and Z axes, and vibration in these two planes is independent. Consequently, the example becomes two independent but similar problems, and similar equations apply:

$$\frac{\rho_x}{\delta_z} \sqrt{\frac{K_x}{K_y}} = 0.75 \sqrt{1} = 0.75$$

For $\delta_y/\rho_x = -0.889$, $(f_{nc}/f_{ny})(\rho_x/\delta_z) = 0.57; 1.29$. Dividing by $\rho_x/\delta_z = 0.75$, $f_{nc}/f_{ny} = 0.76$; 1.72.

The natural frequency in rotation with respect to the Y axis is calculated from Eq. (12.5) as follows, taking into consideration that there are two pairs of springs and that $K_x = K_y$:

$$f_{n_Y} = \frac{1}{2\pi} \frac{\sqrt{\delta_x{}^2 + \delta_z{}^2}}{\rho_y} \sqrt{\frac{4K_y g}{W}} = \frac{\sqrt{(30)^2 + (12)^2}}{8.5} f_{ny} = 3.80 f_{ny}$$

The six natural frequencies are now tabulated:

1. Translatory along Y axis: f_{ny}.
2. Coupled in plane perpendicular to Z axis: $0.96 f_{ny}$.
3. Coupled in plane perpendicular to Z axis: $5.15 f_{ny}$.
4. Coupled in plane perpendicular to X axis: $0.76 f_{ny}$.
5. Coupled in plane perpendicular to X axis: $1.72 f_{ny}$.
6. Rotational with respect to Y axis: $3.80 f_{ny}$.

Considering vibration in a plane perpendicular to the Z axis, the two highest natural frequencies are in the translatory mode along the Y axis and in the coupled mode in which the natural frequency f_{nc} is 5.15 times the vertical natural frequency f_{ny}. In a similar manner, the two highest natural frequencies in a plane perpendicular to the X axis are the natural frequency f_{ny} in translation along the Y axis and the natural frequency $1.72 f_{ny}$ in a coupled mode. The natural frequency in rotation about the Y axis is $3.80 f_{ny}$. The widest frequency increment which is void of natural frequencies is between 1.72 and 3.80 times the vertical natural frequency. This increment is used for the forcing frequency, which is taken as 2.5 times the vertical natural frequency. Inasmuch as the forcing frequency is established at 8 cps, the vertical natural frequency is 8 divided by 2.5, or

3.2 cps. The required vertical stiffnesses of the isolators are calculated from Eq. (12.3) to be 105 lb per in. for the entire machine, or 26.2 lb per in. for each of the four isolators. This results in a static deflection of 0.95 in. if the static and dynamic stiffnesses of the isolators are equal.

Example 2. The following example illustrates the procedure for designing an inertia-block installation. The required weight of the block may first be estimated from the requirement that the isolators be approximately in the same horizontal plane as the center of gravity of the machine-and-block combination, and from limitations on the permissible vibration amplitude of the machine and block as supported by isolators. In the example which follows, the inertia block appears T-shaped when viewed from one end, as shown in Fig. 13.7. This permits the spacing between isolators in both horizontal directions to be selected for optimum conditions and makes effective control of vibration possible. Although the example is based on this type of construction, the procedure is general and may be followed for any design of inertia block.

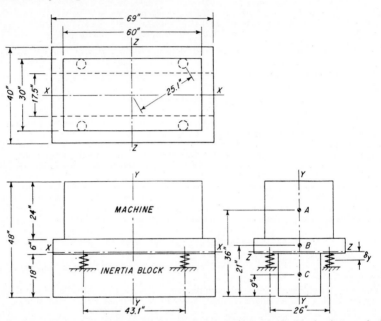

Fig. 13.7. Mounting method in which machine is secured to inertia block whose end view is T-shaped and which is supported by isolators.

The first step is to assume dimensions for the block and to divide the mounted combination into parts which may be assumed regular. This includes the machine A and the parts B and C of the inertia block. The weights of these parts are recorded as item 1, their masses as item 2, and their moments of inertia as item 3 in Table 13.1. The moments of inertia of each part are calculated with respect to the three coordinate axes through the center of gravity, assuming it to be a cuboid of uniform density and using the expression $I = m(l_1{}^2 + l_2{}^2)/12$ where l_1 and l_2 are the length and width of the face perpendicular to the axis about which the moment of inertia is calculated.

The center of coordinates is next taken at the center of gravity of the machine-and-block combination. The height of the center of coordinates is determined with reference to the plane of the lowermost surface of the block by taking the moment of the center of gravity of each part with respect to this reference plane, adding these moments, and dividing by the total mass of the combination. The resultant height of the center of coordinates is set forth as item 4 in Table 13.1, while the distance from this center of coordinates to the center of gravity of each of the three parts is included as item 5. If the distance in item 5 is designated h, the product of mass and h^2 for each of the parts is set forth as item 6. The total moment of inertia of the machine-and-block combination is the sum of quantities for all three parts in items 3 and 6, and is set forth in item 7. The

Table 13.1. Method of Calculating Natural Frequencies of Machine Secured to Concrete Block and Supported by Isolators, as Shown in Fig. 13.7

		Properties with respect to axis		
		X-X (1)	Z-Z (2)	Y-Y (3)
1	Weight of part, lb (A) (B) (C)	800 1,380 1,820	800 1,380 1,820	800 1,380 1,820
2	Mass m of part, lb sec²/in. (A) (B) (C)	2.07 3.58 4.72	2.07 3.58 4.72	2.07 3.58 4.72
3	Moment of inertia of parts, lb in. sec² (A) (B) (C)	258 486 251	720 1,428 2,004	775 1,896 2,004
4	Height of center of coordinates above base	18.6	18.6	
5	Height h from each center of gravity to center of coordinates (A) (B) (C)	17.4 2.4 9.6	17.4 2.4 9.6	
6	mh^2 for part (A) (B) (C)	624 21 491	624 21 491	
7	Total moment of inertia, lb in. sec²	2,131	5,288	4,675
8	Radius of gyration, in.	14.8	22.6	21.2
9	Dimensionless ratios: δ_y/ρ_x [Col. (1)] or δ_y/ρ_z [Col. (2)] ρ_x/δ_z [Col. (1)] or ρ_z/δ_x [Col. (2)]	0.23 0.568	0.15 0.523	
10	$(\rho_x/\delta_z)\sqrt{K_z/K_y}$ [Col. (1)] or $(\rho_z/\delta_x)\sqrt{K_x/K_y}$ [Col. (2)]	0.50	0.46	
11	$(\rho/\delta)(f_c/f_n)$	0.568; 0.442	0.523; 0.440	
12	f_c/f_n	1.00; 0.778	1.00; 0.84	
13	Natural frequency in coupled modes, cps	2.5; 1.94	2.5; 2.1	
14	Natural frequency in rotation, cps			2.6

corresponding radius of gyration as included in item 8 is the square root of the quotient of the moment of inertia in item 7 divided by the sum of the masses in item 2 [see Eq. (13.2)].

The parameter δ_y in Fig. 12.13, the vertical distance from the center of coordinates to the mid-height of the supporting spring, is 3.4 in. for the height of springs contemplated. The two dimensionless ratios δ_y/ρ and ρ/δ are now evaluated using $\delta_y = 3.4$, $\delta = 13$ and

21.55 for vibration in planes normal to the X and Z axes, respectively, and the values for radius of gyration are calculated as item 8. The type of spring contemplated for use here is known to have a ratio of horizontal to vertical stiffness of 0.80. With this assumed value and the values for ρ/δ set forth in item 9, the values for the dimensionless ratios in item 10 are calculated. Entering Fig. 12.14 with these values for the abscissa scale, the values set forth in item 11 are read from the ordinate scale. Two values are available from the ordinate scale for each value on the abscissa scale because there are two curves for the dimensionless ratio δ_y/ρ. The ratios of the natural frequencies in the coupled modes to the natural frequency in the vertical translatory mode, as set forth in item 12, are obtained from item 11 by dividing the respective values by the appropriate values for the dimensionless ratio ρ/δ.

From the stated conditions of the installation, the minimum forcing frequency is 5 cps. To achieve a transmissibility of 0.33 for vertical vibration, a natural frequency of 2.5 cps is required in the vertical translatory mode (see Fig. 12.10). Using the total weight of 4,000 lb for the machine-and-block combination, the required total vertical stiffness of the isolators is calculated from Eq. (12.3) to be 2,600 lb per in., or a unit value of 650 lb per in. for each spring. Using the above value of 0.80 for the ratio of horizontal to vertical stiffness, the horizontal stiffness of each spring is calculated to be 560 lb per in.

The natural frequencies in the coupled modes, expressed in cycles per second, are obtained by multiplying the vertical natural frequency of 2.5 cps by the dimensionless ratios set forth in item 12. The resulting values for the natural frequencies in the coupled modes are set forth in item 13. The natural frequency f_{n_Y} in the rotational mode, with respect to the vertical Y axis, is calculated from Eq. (12.5). This calculation employs the radius of gyration of 21.2 in. set forth in item 8 and the diagonal distance of 25.1 in. shown in Fig. 13.7, and takes cognizance of the four active springs. The resultant natural frequency is set forth as item 14 in Table 13.1.

VIBRATION THROUGH A CRITICAL SPEED

It is inherent in vibration isolation that the natural frequency of the isolator system be lower than the frequency of the forcing vibration. In the starting and stopping of

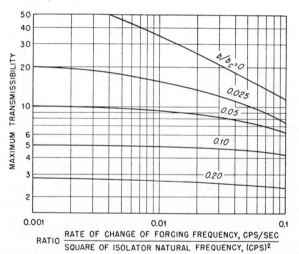

FIG. 13.8. Maximum transmissibility of a single-degree-of-freedom system undergoing forced vibration wherein the forcing frequency varies at a uniform rate through the natural frequency of the system.

the machine, therefore, a condition of resonance must exist momentarily. The relatively great amplitudes commonly associated with resonance do not occur instantaneously but require a finite time to build up. If the forcing frequency is continuously varied as the machine starts or stops, the resonant condition may exist for such a short period of time that only a moderate amplitude occurs at resonance. This problem has been investigated for a linear system in which the forcing frequency varies uniformly through resonance (see Ref. 4), and the results are summarized by the curves in Fig. 13.8. The ordinate in Fig. 13.8 is the maximum transmissibility; the abscissa is a ratio in which the numerator is the rate of change of forcing frequency in cycles per second per second while the denominator is the square of the natural frequency of the isolator expressed in cycles per second. From the curves for various values of the damping ratio b/b_c, it is evident that the rate of change of forcing frequency is of little importance with highly damped isolators but of considerable importance if the isolators are lightly damped.

For example, a machine operating at a frequency of 30 cps is mounted upon isolators whose natural frequency is 10 cps and whose damping ratio b/b_c is 0.025. In starting the machine, the operating frequency increases from zero to 30 cps in 5 sec with a uniform rate of change of frequency. This rate of change is expressed numerically by the quotient of 30 divided by 5, or 6 cps per sec. For a natural frequency of 10 cps, the abscissa parameter is the quotient of 6 divided by 10^2, or 0.06. Entering Fig. 13.8 at 0.06 on the horizontal scale, a value of 9.5 for maximum transmissibility is obtained for the curve $b/b_c = 0.025$. The maximum transmissibility compares with a corresponding value of 20, which occurs with equal damping for steady-state operation at resonance.

ISOLATION OF SHOCK

The application of isolators to alleviate the effects of shock is difficult to discuss, partly because the term "shock" has no definite and accepted meaning. It seems to connote suddenness, either in the application of a force or in the inception of a motion. Because various categories of shock exist, it is not possible to formulate a single procedure that may be used universally in the design and application of isolators.

Two general types of problem are encountered in the application of isolators to reduce shock. In one type of problem, the applied force is of an impulsive nature, with the consequence that a massive member or members acquire additional momentum. The motion associated with this increase in momentum introduces a requirement that the isolator have adequate energy-storage capacity to arrest such motion. In a nonimpulsive application of force, the machine upon which such force acts often acquires a motion temporarily but arrests itself ultimately after experiencing some displacement. The optimum isolator is one which permits such motion while preventing the transmission of excessive force. Such an isolator is not required to have capacity to store energy but only to provide a suitable support for the equipment.

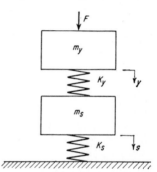

Fig. 13.9. Schematic diagram to illustrate effectiveness of isolator K_y in protecting foundation m_s, K_s from impulsively applied force F acting on mounted machine m_y.

Impulsive Loading. For impulsive loading, the analysis refers to the schematic diagram illustrated in Fig. 13.9. The body m_y represents a machine supported by an isolator K_y which in turn is supported by a foundation represented by the system m_s, K_s. The machine m_y suddenly acquires a downward velocity when acted upon by the impulsively applied force F. This may occur in a forging hammer, for example, where m_y represents the anvil of the machine and its downward velocity results from hammer impact. The effectiveness of the isolator K_y is indicated by a reduced deflection of the spring K_s. Although a complete analysis of this problem becomes too complex to consider in detail here, certain particular cases are discussed in Refs. 1 and 5. A simplified analysis may be carried out by making the following assumptions:

1. The downward velocity of the mass m_y is acquired instantaneously.
2. The isolator K_y is linear within the limits of travel sustained during the shock motion.

3. The natural frequency of the machine and isolator system m_y, K_y is small relative to the natural frequency of the support m_s, K_s.

4. The mass m_y of the machine is negligible relative to the mass m_s of the support.

When the machine is rigidly mounted to the floor; i.e., the isolator K_y in Fig. 13.9 is made infinitely stiff, an expression for maximum deflection s_0 of the foundation may be derived from Eq. (12.35) by letting f approach infinity and substituting $y_0 = s_0$, $m = m_s + m_y$ and $f_n = 1/2\pi \sqrt{K_s/(m_y + m_s)}$:

$$s_0 = \frac{J}{2\pi f_{n_s} m_s \sqrt{1 + m_y/m_s}} \quad \text{in.} \tag{13.10}$$

where $f_{n_s} = 1/2\pi \sqrt{K_s/m_s}$ in cycles per second, m_s is in units of pound second squared per inch, J is the impulse of the force F in pound seconds [see Eq. (12.33)], and s_0 is expressed in inches.

The influence of the mass of the machine may be determined by letting $m_y = 0$ in Eq. (13.10). This gives the following expression for maximum deflection of the foundation:

$$s_0 = \frac{J}{2\pi f_{n_s} m_s} = \frac{J}{\sqrt{K_s m_s}} \quad \text{in.} \tag{13.11}$$

The influence of the mass m_y of the machine in reducing the maximum deflection s_0 of the foundation is obtained from a comparison of Eqs. (13.10) and (13.11). The

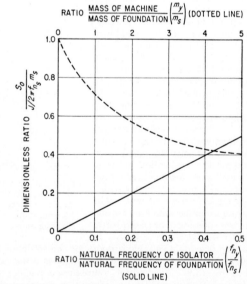

Fig. 13.10. Curves showing effect of means to reduce deflection s_0 of foundation m_s, K_s in Fig. 13.9. The dotted curve applies to the scale on the upper margin and indicates deflection of support with machine rigidly attached thereto wherein mass m_y of machine is varied. The solid line applies to the scale on the lower margin and indicates effectiveness of isolator K_y in reducing deflection of the support. The impulse of the force F is designated by J, and the natural frequency of the foundation by $f_{n_s} = \frac{1}{2\pi} \sqrt{K_s/m_s}$.

result of the comparison is illustrated by the dotted line in Fig. 13.10, wherein unity on the ordinate scale is the dimensionless deflection obtained from Eq. (13.11).

The effectiveness of an isolator is investigated by letting K_y be relatively small in accordance with above assumptions 3 and 4. This creates two independent systems which are uncoupled because m_y is assumed much smaller than m_s. The maximum displacement y_0 of the machine is then determined from the following expression:

$$y_0 = \frac{J}{2\pi f_{n_y} m_y} = \frac{J}{\sqrt{K_y m_y}} \quad \text{in.} \tag{13.12}$$

where m_y is in units of pound seconds squared per inch, f_{n_y} is in units of cycles per second, and J is in units of pound seconds. The permissible motion of the machine under the influence of the impulse J depends largely upon operating conditions. If the machine operates automatically, substantially more over-all motion often is permissible than if manually operated.

When the machine is supported by isolators, assuming $m_y \ll m_s$, the natural frequency of the machine-and-isolator system is $f_{n_y} = 1/2\pi \sqrt{K_y/m_y}$ and the maximum deflection s_0 of the foundation is $s_0 = K_y y_0$ where y_0 is given by Eq. (13.12):

$$s_0 = \frac{J}{2\pi f_{n_s} m_s} \times \frac{f_{n_y}}{f_{n_s}} \tag{13.13}$$

The relation given in Eq. (13.13) is shown by the solid line in Fig. 13.10. Inasmuch as the maximum deflection of the foundation is directly proportional to the natural frequency of the isolator system, the value of s_0 may be decreased by either increasing m_y or decreasing K_y. The latter may be undesirable because it increases the motion of the machine, as indicated by Eq. (13.12). The addition of mass to a machine supported by isolators; i.e., an increase in m_y in Eqs. (13.12) and (13.13), decreases both the deflection of the support and the movement of the mounted machine. This is commonly accomplished by mounting the machine on a concrete block supported by isolators, as illustrated by the forging-hammer foundation shown in Fig. 13.11. The combination of isolators with an inertia block for the machine is an optimum solution to problems requiring energy storage within the isolators where there is an impulsive addition of energy.

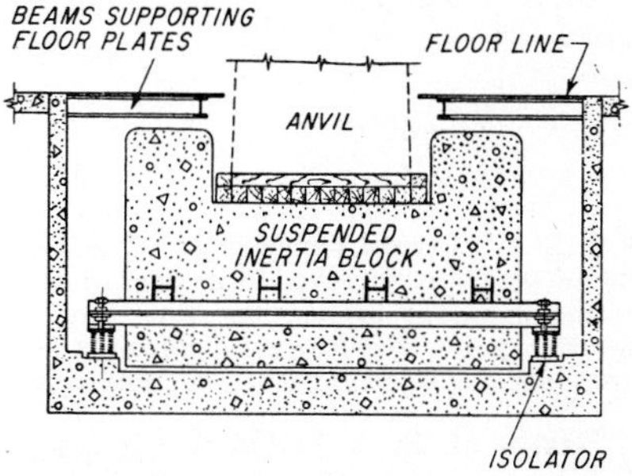

Nonimpulsive Loading. If there is no change in the over-all momentum of the system but only a change in the distribution of momentum within the system, it is

Fig. 13.11. Typical application of inertia block and isolators for supporting a forging hammer. (*Courtesy Korfund Co., Inc.*)

not essential generally that the isolators have energy-storage capacity but rather only freedom to permit motion as dictated by the momentum transformation. In the punch press shown in Fig. 13.12a, for example, the total momentum remains constant. The angular momentum of the flywheel is suddenly reduced during the working stroke, but the angular momentum of the entire press is increased correspondingly. Conversely, the flywheel momentum is increased as its velocity is gradually restored by the motor, and the momentum of the entire press is decreased.

The moment applied to the flywheel by the metalworking operation is indicated by pulses A in Fig. 13.12b, while the moment applied to the flywheel by the motor is indicated by pulses B. An equal and opposite pattern of moments reacts upon the body of the press. Assuming the press to be supported to rotate freely about an axis normal to the paper, its angular position at any instant is indicated by the solid line in Fig. 13.12c. As the press periodically acquires and then loses its velocity, it gains a step of displacement at each cycle, as indicated by the successive angular-displacement increments ϕ in Fig. 13.12a and the time history shown by the solid line in Fig. 13.12c.

If the punch press is supported by isolators, it cannot continue to rotate indefinitely as suggested by the solid line in Fig. 13.12c. The isolators take command of the press after each stroke and restore it to its initial position, as indicated by the dotted line in Fig. 13.12c.   The press is then in its normal position when the next metalworking stroke occurs.   If the isolators are adequate, they interfere but little with the motion of the punch press during the metalworking stroke and permit it to rotate in response to the moments applied during the metalworking operation.   The isolators should have permissible deflection at least as great as suggested by the maximum displacement of the dotted line in Fig. 13.12c, and adequate stiffness to return the press to its normal position before the inception of the next working stroke.

In general, satisfactory isolation will be obtained by noting the duration of the metalworking force as indicated by the width of pulse A and applying isolators accordingly.   If the isolators are selected so that their natural period is substantially greater than the duration of the metalworking force, the effect is similar to maintaining a large ratio of forcing to natural frequency for conditions of vibration isolation. Shock isolation is then attained in a manner somewhat analogous to vibration isolation.

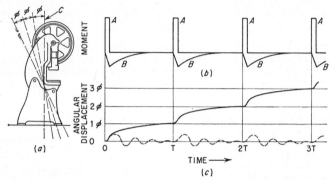

FIG. 13.12. Typical punch press (a) and diagram of its movement under influence of non-impulsive forces involved in its operation.   The curves A and B at (b) indicate the couples acting upon the press.   The solid line at (c) indicates the displacement that the press would experience if freely supported in space, whereas the dotted line indicates the corresponding displacement when supported by vibration isolators.   (*Crede.*[17])

Design of Shock Isolators.   In punch presses and similar machines, the applied forces are periodic though nonharmonic, and care must be taken to avoid a resonant condition.   Isolation generally is assured if the natural period of the isolator system is made great relative to the duration of the metalworking force.   The natural period of the isolator system must not coincide, however, with the period between applications of the metalworking force.   The usual practice is to design the isolator system so that its natural period is greater than the duration of the metalworking force, but smaller than the period between applications of the force.

SPECIAL PROBLEMS IN ISOLATION OF HIGH-FREQUENCY VIBRATION

In the classical theory of vibration isolation upon which the above discussion is based, it is assumed that the resilient element of the isolator is massless and that the support for the isolator is infinitely rigid.   If the frequency of the forcing vibration is relatively low, the assumption leads to a good approximation and the results usually are acceptable for practical purposes.   When the frequency of the forcing vibration becomes relatively high, standing waves tend to occur in the isolator and the transmissibility may become relatively great at the standing-wave frequencies.   Furthermore, resonances may occur in the support for the isolator with consequently large vibration amplitudes.

Standing Waves.   It is difficult to determine standing-wave frequencies in rubber elements of irregular shape by analytical means.   The applicable principles, however, have been demonstrated on the basis of simple rubber elements.   The analysis refers to the system illustrated in Fig. 13.13 and includes a rubber cylinder of mass m_0 and stiffness K_1, a rigid massive support m_2, and a rigid body m_1 arranged to load the rubber cylinder along its axis of symmetry. The expression for transmissibility, as derived in Ref. 6, is

$$T| = \cfrac{1}{\sqrt{\left[1 + \left(\dfrac{B_2}{B_1}\right)^2\right] \sinh^2 \xi_b B_2 + \left(\cos B_2 - \dfrac{B_2}{B_1} \sin B_2\right)^2 + \xi_b \dfrac{B_2}{B_1} \sinh 2\xi_b B_2}}$$

(13.14)

where $B_1 = m_0/m_1$ and $B_2 = (f/f_n)\sqrt{m_0/m_1}$. The forcing frequency in cycles per second is indicated by f, while $f_n = 1/2\pi \sqrt{K_1/m_1}$ is the natural frequency assuming the rubber cylinder to be massless. The damping parameter ξ_b is a function of the viscosity and the velocity of sound in the resilient material of the isolator. For small values of damping and to a first approximation, $\xi_b \approx b/b_c$. A comprehensive discussion of this phenomenon, including a theoretical treatment which is rigorously correct for any degree of damping, is given in Ref. 6.

Transmissibility curves calculated from Eq. (13.14) are shown in Fig. 13.14 for values of the damping parameter ξ_b equal to 0.05 and 0.30, when the ratio of mass of

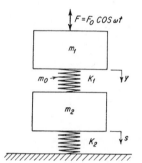

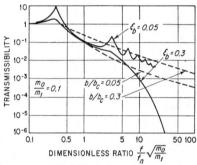

Fig. 13.13. Schematic diagram of systems to show effect of standing waves in isolator K_1 or resilience in support K_2 when mounted equipment is acted upon by force F.

Fig. 13.14. Transmissibility curves for the isolator K_1 in Fig. 13.13 when K_2 is infinitely rigid, and when standing-wave effects are considered in the isolator K_1. The two solid curves are calculated from Eq. (13.14) for the indicated damping ratios and the mass ratio $m_0/m_1 = 0.1$, while the dotted curves are calculated from Eq. (12.9), which neglects effect of mass of isolator.

mounted equipment to mass of resilient element is equal to 10. The ordinate in Fig. 13.14 is dimensionless transmissibility, while the horizontal scale is the product of the dimensionless frequency ratio f/f_n and the square root of the dimensionless mass ratio m_0/m_1. For comparison, classical transmissibility curves as calculated from Eq. (12.9) for a massless resilient element and $b/b_c = 0.05, 0.3$ are shown in dotted lines in Fig. 13.14. It is evident that the effect of the mass of the resilient element is negligible at low values of the forcing frequency. When the forcing frequency becomes greater, the length of the rubber cylinder includes one or more half wavelengths of the forcing frequency and a standing wave develops. A peak then occurs in the transmissibility curve. The heights of successive peaks, as the forcing frequency increases, tend to decrease and the effect of standing-wave resonances ultimately disappears. The analytical result shown in Fig. 13.14, as calculated from Eq. (13.14), has been substantially confirmed by experimental investigations.

The heights of the peaks resulting from standing-wave resonances increase as the damping parameter ξ_b decreases and as the mass ratio m_0/m_1 increases. The peaks are most likely to be high where the resilient element is a metal spring because the damping of metal is relatively small, and the mass is relatively large. For resilient elements made of rubber, the mass ratio m_0/m_1 tends to be small, and the damping parameter ξ_b is substantially greater than that for metal. Referring to Fig. 13.14, the damping parameter $\xi_b = 0.025$ is relatively small for rubber, and the mass ratio $m_0/m_1 = 10$ is relatively large. As a consequence, the upper solid curve in Fig. 13.14 represents approximately the most unfavorable circumstances likely to be encountered with the use of rubber isolators. Most applications using rubber isolators will be somewhat more favorable than this. If metal springs are used and if high transmissibility occurs as a result of a standing-wave resonance, the difficulty often can be eliminated by interposing a pad of rubber in series with the metal spring. Experience shows that this usually eliminates any noticeable peak in the transmissibility curve.

Resilience of Support. The effectiveness of vibration isolators may be decreased by resilience of the foundation. This is illustrated with reference to Fig. 13.13 wherein the system m_2, K_2 is an idealization in lumped parameters of any structure, such as a steel beam. The mounted equipment is represented by the rigid body m_1, and the

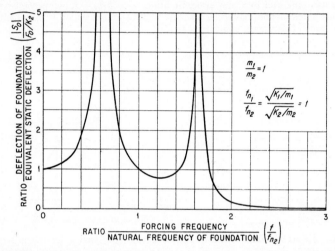

FIG. 13.15. Curve showing ratio of displacement of system m_2, K_2 to equivalent static deflection F_0/K_2, for system shown in Fig. 13.13, as a function of the ratio of the forcing frequency f to the natural frequency $f_{n2} = (1/2\pi)(K_2/m_2)^{1/2}$. These curves are for a mass ratio $m_1/m_2 = 1$, and for a ratio of natural frequencies $f_{n1}/f_{n2} = 1$.

isolator is represented by the massless linear spring K_1. Excitation of the system results from the force F applied to the mounted equipment. If the structure K_2 is infinitely stiff, the foundation is rigid and the previously developed theory for isolators as given by the transmissibility expression [Eq. (12.9)] is applicable. If the structure K_2 is not rigid, the equation for the maximum displacement s_0 of the support m_2, as developed in Ref. 7, is

$$\frac{|S_0|}{F_0/K_2} = \frac{(f_{n1}/f_{n2})^2}{[(m_1/m_2)(f_{n1}/f_{n2})^2 - (f/f_{n2})^2 + 1][(f_{n1}/f_{n2})^2 - (f/f_{n2})^2] - (m_1/m_2)(f_{n1}/f_{n2})^4}$$
(13.15)

where $f_{n1}^2 = 1/4\pi^2(K_1/m_1)$ and $f_{n2}^2 = 1/4\pi^2(K_2/m_2)$, and both branches of the system are undamped. The relation given by Eq. (13.15) is illustrated numerically in Fig. 13.15 for a ratio m_1/m_2 of unity and a ratio f_{n1}/f_{n2} of unity.

The curves of Fig. 13.15 show two resonant frequencies because the system illustrated in Fig. 13.13 is a two-degree-of-freedom system with coupling between the two branches of the system. The vibration amplitude of the foundation tends to become great when the frequency of the forcing vibration equals one of the natural frequencies of the coupled system. The natural frequencies of the system are determined by equating the denominator of Eq. (13.15) to zero. The resulting expression for the two natural frequencies in the coupled modes is as follows:

$$\frac{f_{n_c}}{f_{n_2}} = \frac{1}{\sqrt{2}} \sqrt{\left(1 + \frac{m_1}{m_2}\right)\left(\frac{f_{n_1}}{f_{n_2}}\right)^2 + 1 \pm \sqrt{\left[\left(1 + \frac{m_1}{m_2}\right)\left(\frac{f_{n_1}}{f_{n_2}}\right)^2 + 1\right]^2 - 4\left(\frac{f_{n_1}}{f_{n_2}}\right)^2}}$$

(13.16)

where f_{n_c} represents natural frequencies in the coupled modes and $f_{n_2} = 1/2\pi \sqrt{K_2/m_2}$ is the natural frequency of the foundation considered as a decoupled system. The relation given by Eq. (13.16) for the natural frequencies in coupled modes is shown graphically in Fig. 13.16 for several values of the mass ratio m_1/m_2.

It may be noted from Fig. 13.16 that one natural frequency of the coupled system is always equal to or greater than the natural frequency of the foundation considered as a decoupled system. If the frequency of the forcing vibration becomes equal to this coupled natural frequency, the foundation may be expected to vibrate with relatively large amplitude. An actual structural foundation has distributed mass and, consequently, natural frequencies in many modes. The relations set forth in Fig. 13.16 apply to any one of such natural frequencies, and resonances may occur between the forcing vibration and any one of the natural frequencies of the coupled system. This effect cannot be completely eliminated by isolation because the coupled system has relatively large values of natural frequency, even when the natural frequency f_{n_1} of the isolator branch approaches zero. This may account for the failure of vibration isolators to isolate vibration of relatively high frequency under certain conditions. The use of damping materials to reduce the effect of resilience of the foundation is discussed in some detail in Chap. 14.

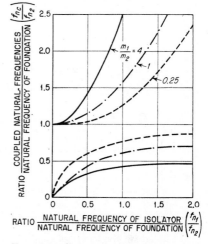

Fig. 13.16. Curves showing the ratio of the coupled natural frequencies f_{n_c} to the natural frequency of the foundation,

$$f_{n_2} = \frac{1}{2\pi} \sqrt{K_2/m_2}$$

in Fig. 13.13, as a function of the ratio of the natural frequencies of the two individual branches of the coupled system. The curves are for three discrete values of the mass ratio m_1/m_2 as indicated.

FLEXIBLE CONDUITS

The advantages attained through the use of vibration isolators may be lost if the mounted machine or equipment is attached to rigid piping, electrical conduit, or shafting. Conduits for supplying electrical power or for conducting fluids should have flexible portions to prevent transmission of vibration. Rubber hose often is preferable but, if the temperature is too great or if chemically active fluids must be transmitted, metal hose or tubing must be used. The properties of flexible metal hose and tubing are discussed in the following paragraphs.

In the installation of flexible conduits, the following design principles are of importance:

1. The conduit should be attached to the mounted machine near the point of minimum vibratory movement. This effects minimum vibration input and ensures minimum transmission of vibration through the conductor. A length of rigid conduit carried by the machine may be desirable to enable the flexible conduit to be attached at point of minimum movement.

2. The other end of the conduit should be attached to the most massive structure available. This tends to reduce the influence of transmitted vibration and makes it possible to employ a more rigid conduit while achieving the desired isolation of vibration.

3. The conduit may be installed with relatively large loops where one end experiences large displacement relative to the other end or where a very low stiffness is required of the conduit. In general, the vibration amplitude is small and the conduit usually may be installed straight. The manufacturers of flexible conduit do not provide data on stiffness which make it possible to determine whether a loop is required for any particular application.

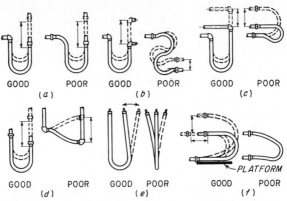

```
GOOD       POOR       GOOD       POOR        GOOD       POOR
    ( a )                 ( b )                  ( c )

GOOD       POOR       GOOD     POOR          GOOD       POOR
    ( d )                 ( e )                  ( f )
```

FIG. 13.17. Diagrams of preferred and nonpreferred arrangements of flexible conductors to distribute movement over the length of the conductor and thereby minimize wear. (*P. H. Geiger.*[16])

4. If a loop is used, the conduit should be arranged so that the vibratory movement is substantially distributed throughout its length. If the movement occurs only adjacent the ends of the conduit, excessive wear resulting from stress concentration at the end connections may shorten the life of the conduit. Figure 13.17 shows a number of preferred arrangements for ensuring distribution of movement throughout the length of conduit.

The oldest type of flexible conduit is the strip-wound hose illustrated in Fig. 13.18. This hose is made from a continuous coil of strip metal and embodies an interlocked construction with a packing wound continuously into the groove in the interlocked joint. Its flexibility is derived from the sliding action at the interlocked joint; its pressuretight qualities are derived from the packing, which is usually asbestos. This type of hose is suitable for containing air, oil, water, and steam but generally is unsatisfactory for handling gases at high pressure or highly volatile substances where the slightest leakage may create a dangerous condition. It is available in diameters from $\frac{1}{2}$ to 6 in. and may be constructed from different alloys depending on service requirements.

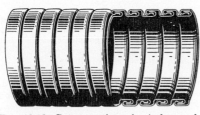

FIG. 13.18. Cutaway view of spiral-wound or interlocked type of flexible metallic hose.

A more modern type of flexible conduit is the corrugated tubing illustrated in Fig. 13.19. It is available with the corrugations having an annular configuration as illustrated in Fig. 13.19*a*, or a helical configuration as illustrated in Fig. 13.19*b*. It is made from seamless, welded, or soldered tubing in diameters from $\frac{1}{8}$ to 4 in., depending upon the materials and styles offered by various manufacturers. Welded tubing in diameters as large as 20 in. is also available in corrugated form. Corrugated conduit is commonly made from bronze, steel, and stainless steel but is also available in a variety of alloys, including Monel, Super Nickel, Everdur, and Inconel. Corrugated seamless or welded tubing is not susceptible to leakage and is therefore satisfactory for containing volatile substances and gases under pressure.

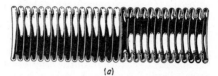

(a)

Flexible conduit is normally obtained from the manufacturer equipped with integral fittings at the opposite ends. Lengths of tubing are available in standard sizes or to custom dimensions determined by the application. Corrugated tubing for pressure lines is normally enclosed within a flexible braid to prevent elongation and ultimate bursting of the tubing, the braid being attached to the end fittings. It is acceptable for use without a braid only for such applications as transmitting air or gas under low pressure.

Data on the stiffness of flexible conduit are not available from the manufacturers.

(b)

Fig. 13.19. Cutaway views of flexible seamless tubing of (a) annular and (b) spiral types.

A considerable background of experience has been accumulated, however, and good recommendations may be obtained regarding specific applications.*

GENERAL PROPERTIES OF RESILIENT MATERIALS

Many different materials are commonly used as the resilient elements of isolators. These may be grouped somewhat arbitrarily as (1) natural and synthetic rubber; (2) metal springs; and (3) a group of miscellaneous materials including, cork, felt, and sponge rubber. Each of these materials has its peculiar advantages and disadvantages. The materials listed in the third group are generally available only in slab form and are used principally to mount machinery. Isolators embodying steel springs and molded-rubber parts, on the other hand, are used generally as component parts of machines as well as for the mounting of machinery.

Steel springs are commonly used where the static deflection is required to be great, where temperature or other environmental conditions make rubber unsuitable, and under some circumstances where a low-cost isolator is required. Molded-rubber parts find wide application because they may be conveniently molded to many desired shapes and stiffnesses, embody more internal hysteresis than metal springs, often require a minimum of space and weight, and can be bonded to metallic inserts adapted for convenient attachment. Although natural rubber is probably used most extensively, synthetic rubbers including Neoprene, Buna-S, and Buna-N see considerable use, the latter being identified by the trade names Hycar, Perbunan, and Chemigum. The additional synthetic rubbers, Butyl and Thiokol, find little use in isolators except where unusual environmental requirements exist.

Natural rubber probably embodies the most favorable combination of mechanical properties, such as minimum drift, maximum tensile strength, and maximum elongation at failure; and it tends to be the least expensive. Its usefulness is restricted somewhat by limited resistance to deterioration under the influence of hydrocarbons, ozone, and high ambient temperatures. Neoprene and Buna-N exhibit excellent resistance to hydrocarbons and ozone, Buna-N being particularly well suited to applications involving relatively high ambient temperatures. Buna-S is used to a considerable extent in vibration isolators. It has few outstanding properties but has become widely available as a result of the government synthetic-rubber program.

* Manufacturers of flexible hose and tubing include: the American Brass Company of Waterbury, Conn.; Flexonics Corporation of Maywood, Ill.; Pennsylvania Metallic Tubing Company of Philadelphia, Pa.; and Titeflex Corporation of Newark, N.J.

Rubber can be coated with lacquer to protect against small or occasional amounts of oil.*

Silicone rubber is a synthetic material which is suitable for applications involving either high or low ambient temperatures at which no other rubberlike material can be used. It shows remarkable stability in important properties over a very wide temperature range, both above and below room temperature. Some compounds of silicone rubber retain their flexibility at temperatures approaching $-100°F$ and are undamaged by exposure to temperatures as high as 400°F. Although the compression set tends to become relatively great at elevated temperature, the stiffness of the material appears to change but little after exposure to high temperature for a considerable time. Tear and abrasion resistance of currently available materials are relatively low. The characteristically low tensile strength and high drift rate introduce limitations for general use in vibration isolators except where the material is loaded lightly. Rapid developments in silicone rubber are currently occurring, and there is promise that more suitable materials will be available in the future.

Felt, cork, and sponge rubber are usually cut from large slabs and used flat, thereby lacking the ready adaptability of rubber parts molded to shape and frequently adhered to metal inserts for easy application. Cork is used frequently to support relatively large concrete foundations. It is a readily compressible material of relatively low modulus which is particularly suited for supporting large concrete blocks because it may completely fill the space surrounding the block. Felt is sometimes used under machinery; its application is convenient because it can be cemented in place and is generally unaffected by oil and other foreign substances. Glass fibers impregnated with a suitable binder† and knitted wire compressed to specified shape and density have been proposed recently to form the resilient elements of vibration isolators. The latter is relatively immune to environmental influences and has seen extensive use in military aircraft. Its use for noise-control purposes has been very limited.

Rubber. The stiffness of a rubber member is a function of (1) the modulus of the material and (2) the size and shape of the member. Modulus is measured indirectly and only approximately by determining the resistance of the material to indentation. The most commonly used instrument is a Shore durometer, which includes a spring arranged to press the end of a truncated cone against the surface of the rubber. The reading is obtained from a scale indicating depth of indentation, a large indentation being indicated by a low durometer number. The softest rubber generally used in isolators is approximately 30 durometer, and the hardest approximately 70 durometer. A reasonably good indication of the relative stiffnesses of dimensionally equal members is obtained from the resistance to indentation as measured by the durometer. The relation between shear modulus and durometer reading is shown in Fig. 13.20 for natural rubber. It is not possible to establish a similar relation for compression modulus, for reasons which are explained below.

In a system having a rubber spring, the natural frequency calculated using the stiffness determined from a static force–deflection test of the spring almost invariably gives a value lower than that experienced during vibration. In other words, the dynamic modulus appears greater than the static modulus. The ratio of moduli seems to be approximately independent of the velocity of strain and has a numerical value generally between 1 and 2. The ratio increases substantially as the durometer increases, as indicated by the data presented in Fig. 13.21 from tests of a number of representative isolators selected at random.

Rubber is a viscoelastic substance. In pure gum form, the elastic properties predominate and the material exhibits minimum damping. It is then capable of sustaining substantial static strain without excessive drift. In compounding, other ingredients are added which generally tend to increase the viscosity and decrease the elasticity. Damping is then increased, but the load-carrying limit without excessive

---

* Lacquers which are available include: Egyptian Lacquer, Egyptian Lacquer Company, New York, N.Y.; Nitroloid Lacquer, Forbes Varnish Company, Cleveland, Ohio; Glyptal Lacquer, General Electric Company, Schenectady, N.Y.; and Ivco Varnish, Impervious Varnish Company, Rochester, Pa.

† See Chap. 19.

drift may be reduced. Harder rubbers thus tend to have greater damping. The applicable value of the damping ratio in rubber depends upon many parameters, including the durometer. Typical values are given in Fig. 13.22 as a function of durometer, using data obtained from the decay rate in free vibration.

Vibration isolators may employ rubber loaded in either shear or compression. When loaded in shear, the rubber member is commonly bonded between two substantially parallel metal faces, and the load is applied parallel to these faces. Rubber has a Poisson's ratio of approximately one-half; i.e., it is substantially incompressible and

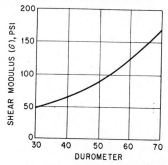

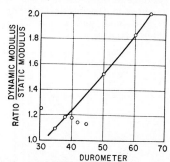

FIG. 13.20. Shear modulus of natural rubber for small deflections, as a function of durometer. (*Crede.*[1])

FIG. 13.21. Relation between dynamic and static moduli of rubber, as a function of rubber durometer. (*Crede.*[1])

changes shape without changing volume. The rectangular face of a rubber element strained in shear thus becomes a parallelogram. The relation between force and deflection of such a rubber element is

$$\frac{F}{S} = G\frac{d}{t}$$

(13.17)

where F = applied force in pounds, S = area of rubber in square inches, G = shear modulus of elasticity in pounds per square inch, d = deflection in inches, and t = rubber thickness in inches. The modulus G is a constant for small strains, and Eq. (13.17)

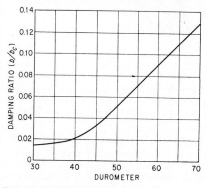

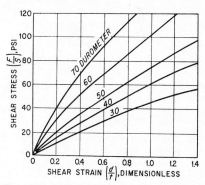

FIG. 13.22. Typical values of damping resulting from internal hysteresis of rubber, as a function of rubber durometer.

FIG. 13.23. Stress-strain curves for rubber in shear. (*Crede.*[1])

thus applies only for small deflections. For large values of strain, the modulus G decreases with increasing strain. This is indicated by the stress-strain curves for shear shown in Fig. 13.23 for rubber of various durometers. The maximum permissible static strain depends somewhat on the degree of drift which is tolerable; conservatively, static strain d/t in shear should not exceed 0.25 to 0.50.

The incompressibility of rubber permits it to deflect under a compressive force only if it is permitted to expand laterally; in the absence of space for lateral expansion, deflection becomes nearly impossible. Any condition that restricts lateral expansion tends to increase the stiffness. Two important factors in this respect are:

1. The conditions at the interface over which the compressive force is applied to rubber. If this interface is perfectly lubricated, lateral expansion of the rubber is unrestricted and occurs uniformly from one loading face to the other. The stiffness in compression is then a minimum. If the rubber is adhered to a rigid member at the interface, lateral expansion cannot take place adjacent to the rigid member, and the stiffness in compression is increased by this restriction of lateral expansion.

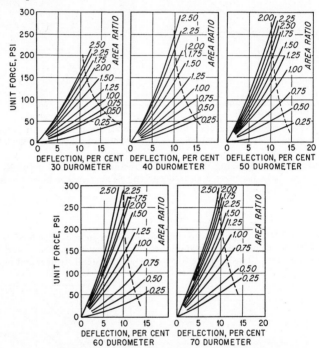

Fig. 13.24. Force-deflection curves for unbonded square rubber pads loaded in compression. Force is in pounds per square inch of load-carrying area, and deflection is in per cent of pad thickness. Area ratio is the ratio of load-carrying area to lateral area available for bulging. (*Courtesy United States Rubber Co.*)

2. The free area available for lateral expansion. A rubber member to which a compressive force is applied has maximum stiffness per unit of load-carrying area when the ratio of free lateral area to load-carrying area is a minimum. The free lateral area may be increased by providing holes through the rubber parallel to the direction of the compressive force, or by selecting a shape whose peripheral area is large.

The above factors are difficult to consider analytically, and empirical methods usually are employed to determine the stiffness characteristics of rubber members loaded in compression. Defining the area ratio of the pads as the ratio of the load-carrying area to the lateral expansion area, it has been observed (see Ref. 8) that square pads whose area ratios are equal deflect the same percentage of their thicknesses when supporting equal unit loads. A series of force-deflection curves for *unbonded* square pads of various durometers is reproduced in Fig. 13.24, the parameter of each family being the ratio of load-carrying area to lateral-expansion area. The stiffness is 15 per cent lower, for the same area ratio, when the length of the pad is twice its width, and 30 per cent lower when the length is ten times the width (see Ref. 9).

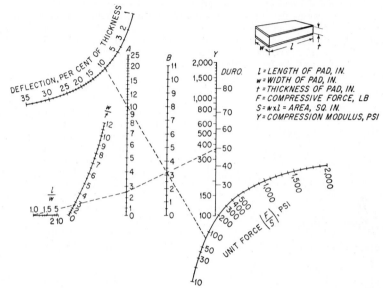

Fig. 13.25. Nomograph for determining relation of force and deflection for *bonded* rectangular rubber pads loaded in compression. A straight line is drawn intersecting the l/w and w/t scales at appropriate values. This determines a value of A, from which a second straight line is drawn to the Y scale. To determine the deflection resulting from any unit force, a straight line is drawn from the force scale to the deflection scale, intersecting the B scale at the same point as the line from A to Y. (*Courtesy United States Rubber Co.*)

Compression pads that are bonded to the rigid members by which the load is applied usually are stiffer than unbonded pads. Research work by the United States Rubber Company has resulted in the nomograph of Fig. 13.25 for determining force-deflection relations of *bonded* pads. The deflection is expressed in percentage of pad thickness, resulting from a unit force expressed in pounds per square inch. The procedure for using the nomograph is set forth in the caption to Fig. 13.25.

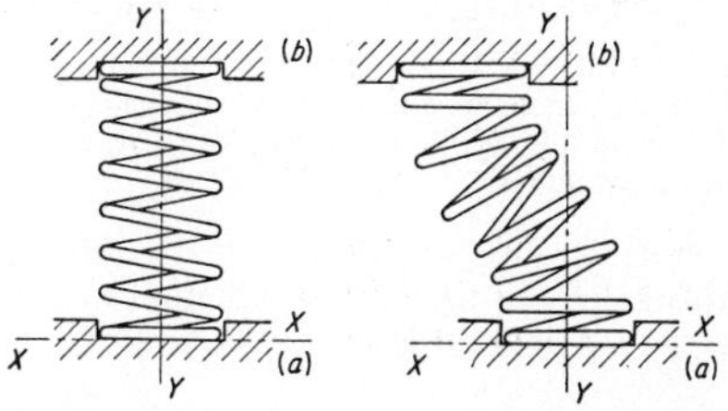

Metal Springs. A typical application of a helical-compression spring as a vibration isolator is illustrated in Fig. 13.26. It is placed between the foundation (*a*) and the mounted equipment (*b*), often with no positive attachment but with pilots to locate the spring. The springs constitute the sole support vertically and

Fig. 13.26. Typical application of helical compression spring as a vibration isolator. The spring is in the undeflected position at the left, and in the laterally deflected position at the right. (*Crede.*[1])

laterally for the mounted equipment. This section includes information on the stiffness of helical springs along vertical and horizontal coordinate axes, actual and allowable stress in springs, and stability of spring-mounted systems.

The stress in a helical spring as a result of a downwardly acting load is primarily shear stress due to torsion of the spring wire. The maximum shear stress is **given by** the following equation:

$$\tau_{\max} = \frac{128Fa_2}{\pi a_1{}^3}\left(\frac{4\xi - 1}{4\xi - 4} + \frac{0.615}{\xi}\right) \quad \text{psi} \tag{13.18}$$

where F = vertical force applied to spring in pounds, a_1 = wire radius in inches, a_2 = mean coil radius in inches, and $\xi = a_2/a_1$ = spring index. The term within parentheses in the above equation is the Wahl correction factor which accounts for the relatively greater stress at the inside diameter of the coil. It is negligible for large values of the spring index, having a value of 1.1 for a spring index of 16, 1.25 for a spring index of 6, and 1.4 for a spring index of 4 (see Ref. 10).

The maximum permissible stress in a helical spring is a function of the minimum stress. The curves of Fig. 13.27 show the value of endurance-stress ranges which may be expected from good-quality helical-compression springs made from various materials. The limiting stress range is read vertically between the line of minimum stress and the lines representing maximum stress. The Wahl correction factor is used in computing the stress. The curves hold roughly for springs having a spring index between 5 and 10. For larger indexes, somewhat lower values of stress range may be expected.

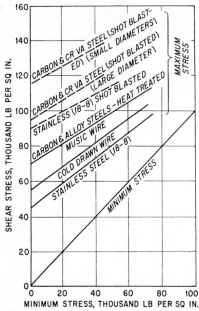

FIG. 13.27. Curves showing maximum working stress in shear for various types of spring material, as a function of the minimum stress. (*A. M. Wahl.*[10])

The stiffness K_y of the spring along the vertical axis is given by the following expression:

$$K_y = \frac{Ga_1{}^4}{16na_2{}^3} \quad \text{lb per in.} \tag{13.19}$$

where G is the shear modulus of the spring material in pounds per square inch, n is the number of active coils, a_1 is the wire radius in inches, and a_2 is the mean coil radius in inches.

If the supported equipment is displaced laterally, the helical spring shown at the left of Fig. 13.26 assumes the position shown at the right. Deflection of the spring in the lateral direction embodies strain of the wire in both torsion and flexure. Results of the analysis of this deflection may be simplified by assuming that the spring is made of steel wire ($G = 11.5 \times 10^6$, $Y = 30 \times 10^6$ psi) having a circular cross section. The stiffness K_x in the lateral direction may then be expressed in terms of the stiffness K_y in the vertical direction as follows:

$$\frac{K_y}{K_x} = 1.44\xi'\left[0.051\left(\frac{h}{a_2}\right)^2 + 0.256\right] \tag{13.20}$$

where h is the working height of the spring, a_2 is the mean coil radius, and ξ' is a correction factor to compensate for the decreased vertical stiffness resulting from the horizontal deflection. The correction factor ξ' is a complicated function of the ratios h/a_2 and d/h. It has been evaluated numerically and is included in the results shown in graphical form in Fig. 13.28.

One of the predominant applications of helical springs is for the isolation of low-frequency vibration. The principal requirement then is for a great static deflection of the spring. If the spring is deflected as shown at the right of Fig. 13.26, the lateral stiffness of the spring may be insufficient to restore the mounted equipment to its initial position. The equipment thus tends to fall sideways as a result of instability. A condition of stable equilibrium exists when a system is in a condition of minimum potential energy. During horizontal deflection of the spring to the position illustrated at the right of Fig. 13.26, the vertical stiffness of the spring decreases because the load is applied eccentrically. If stability is to be maintained, the loss of potential energy due to lowering of the supported equipment must be at least balanced by an increase in strain energy in the spring. The increase in strain energy is greater than the loss of potential energy and the system is stable when the following conditions are met:

$$\frac{K_x}{K_y} \geq 1.20 \left(\frac{d}{h}\right) \qquad (13.21)$$

where d is the static deflection and h is the working height, both in units of inches. This equation is represented graphically by the straight line shown in Fig. 13.29 separating the regions of stability and instability.

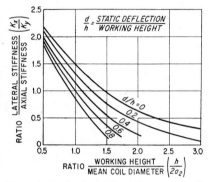

FIG. 13.28. Ratio of lateral to axial stiffness for helical-compression springs, as a function of the ratios of working height to mean coil diameter and static deflection to working height. (*Crede.*[1])

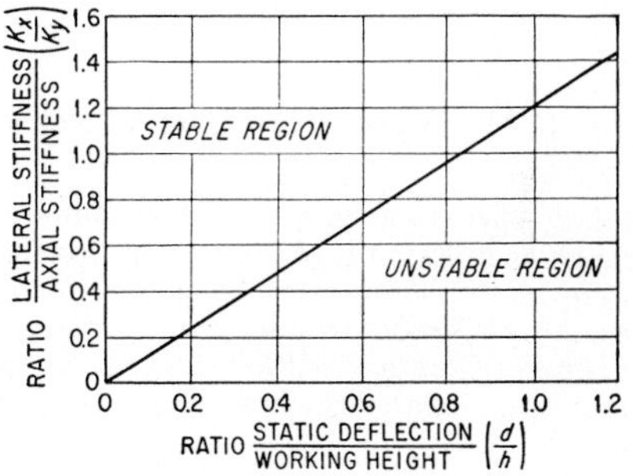

FIG. 13.29. Curve separating stable and unstable regions for a system whose sole support is comprised of helical springs loaded in compression, as shown in Fig. 13.26. (*Crede.*[1])

Other Materials.* *Felt.* Felt is defined by the Felt Association as "a fabric built up by the interlocking of fibers by a suitable combination of mechanical work, chemical action, moisture and heat, without spinning, weaving or knitting. Felt may consist of one or more classes of wool fibers, with or without admixture with animal, vegetable, and synthetic fibers." A distinction is thus made from textile products in which the fibers are drawn into parallelism, spun into yarns, and then interlaced by weaving. The felting process, on the other hand, induces the movement of individual fibers throughout the mass and utilizes the natural crimp and interlocking characteristics of the wool fiber. The result is a well-compacted fibrous material made in a range of thicknesses from $\frac{1}{32}$- to 3-in.

Felt usually is applied for isolation purposes by cutting small pads of the desired area and placing them under the equipment to be supported. Cement is often used to hold the pads in position. The force-deflection curve for a felt pad in compression is fairly linear for deflections as great as 25 per cent of the thickness, but thereafter the stiffness increases rapidly and at 50 per cent deflection is approximately ten times as great as at 25 per cent deflection. This stiffness increase at deflections greater than 25 per cent shows the necessity of exercising care to avoid overloading the felt.

The natural frequency as a function of load for three densities of felt pad 1 in. thick are shown in Fig. 13.30. A decrease in natural frequency occurs as the felt thickness increases, but the stiffness apparently is not inversely proportional to the thickness. For example, an increase in felt thickness from 1 to 4 in. causes a reduction in natural frequency to only 0.66 times the original natural frequency. A decrease to 0.50 times the original natural frequency would be expected.

* See Chap. 19 for data on the stiffness of glass-fiber blankets.

The curves in Fig. 13.30 appear to be substantially horizontal in the extreme right-hand region. A condition thus exists in which the natural frequency cannot be further reduced by an increase in load. The minimum attainable natural frequency is approximately 19 to 26 cps, depending on the density; but the minimum natural frequency corresponding to maximum recommended loading is 25 to 28 cps. This is based on a felt thickness of 1 in.; for a felt thickness of ½ in., data available from

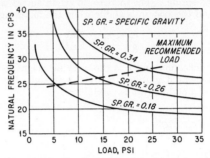

Fig. 13.30. Natural frequency as a function of load for several weights of felt 1 in. thick. (*Crede.*[1])

other sources indicate that the minimum usable natural frequency is 30 cps. Inasmuch as isolation is obtained only for frequencies greater than 1.41 times the natural frequency, felt of ½-in. thickness, for example, may be considered useful only for isolating vibration whose frequency is greater than $30 \times 1.41 = 42.3$ cps.

Cork. Cork as used for the isolation of vibration, shock, and sound is generally in the form of slabs which are made by compressing cork particles under high pressure

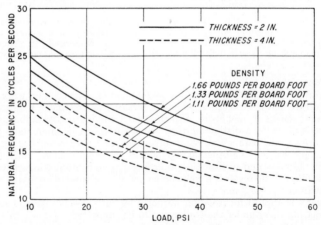

Fig. 13.31. Natural frequencies of several densities of Vibracork as a function of load. The solid lines refer to material 2 in. thick, and the dotted lines to material 4 in. thick. (*Crede.*[1])

and subsequently baking them by means of superheated steam. Cork differs from rubber in that it contains many minute air cells which become reduced in volume as the cork is deflected. The material is thus not an incompressible solid but, on the contrary, has been deflected in compression as much as 24 per cent without exhibiting noticeable lateral expansion. It is applied as slabs loaded in compression by placing the slabs directly under the base of the machine or under an inertia block.

Cork exhibits properties similar to most other resilient materials when loaded in compression and subjected to a great deflection. The stiffness is characterized by a continuing increase as the deflection increases, and a limit is placed upon the minimum natural frequency that is attainable. From a practical standpoint, the maximum load is that which the cork can safely support without being overstressed. The following data on Vibracork, a cork board manufactured by compressing cork particles $\frac{1}{2}$ in. in diameter, were made available by the manufacturer, the Armstrong Cork Company, and first published in Ref. 1. The natural frequency of Vibracork as a function of supported load is shown by the curves of Fig. 13.31.

Cork appears to exhibit peculiar properties that tend to make it less effective as an isolation medium than indicated by the natural frequencies shown in Fig. 13.31. To calculate the transmissibility under steady-state vibration of a system that employs cork as the resilient element, it has been determined empirically that the natural frequencies indicated by Fig. 13.31 should first be multiplied by 1.5. The transmissibility at frequencies greater than the natural frequency may then be determined from Eq. (12.9), using the corrected natural frequency and assuming zero damping. It is desired to determine, for example, the transmissibility of 4-in.-thick Vibracork of 1.66 lb per board foot density, when loaded at 40 psi and subjected to vibration at a frequency of 40 cps. From Fig. 13.31, it is determined that the natural frequency of the system is 14 cps. The corrected natural frequency is then $14.0 \times 1.5 = 21$ cps, and the ratio of forcing frequency to corrected natural frequency is $40/21 = 1.90$. The transmissibility calculated from Eq. (12.9) for a frequency ratio $f/f_n = 1.90$ is 0.38.

The damping ratio b/b_c for cork loaded in compression is approximately 0.06, independent of the density. This corresponds to a transmissibility at resonance of

Table 13.2. Stiffness Data for Sponge Rubber

Designation	Compression Load for 25% Deflection, lb/in.^{2}
10	1 ± 1
11	$3\frac{1}{2} \pm 1\frac{1}{2}$
12	7 ± 2
13	11 ± 2
14	15 ± 2
15	$20\frac{1}{2} \pm 3\frac{1}{2}$

The designation numerals above are prefixed by RN to indicate natural rubber, by RS to indicate a non-oil-resistant synthetic rubber, and by SC to indicate an oil-resistant synthetic rubber.

approximately eight times, which is equivalent to that of rubber in the range of 50 to 60 durometer.

Sponge Rubber. Rubber in its conventional vulcanized state is a substantially incompressible though flexible solid with considerable stiffness. To reduce the stiffness and to introduce certain advantages derived from compressibility, rubber is made with a multiplicity of minute air or gas pockets. Upon application of load, the air or gas is compressed, and the over-all stiffness of the material is thus relatively low. Sponge rubber is available generally in the form of slabs of constant thickness and large area, which can be cut into pads of the required size. It is also occasionally molded as intricate shapes. The stiffness of sponge rubber is defined by an ASTM designation number (see Ref. 11) as set forth in Table 13.2.

DAMPING AND DAMPERS

The principal interest in damping concerns its effect upon transmissibility in forced vibration and shock, and upon the decrement of free vibration. If a system with any arbitrary type of damping is caused to vibrate throughout a frequency range and the maximum amplitude of vibration is noted, the maximum transmissibility is established. A value for the viscous damping ratio b/b_c taken from Fig. 12.11 for this maximum transmissibility is known as the equivalent viscous damping ratio and may be used in any analysis where the ratio b/b_c appears. Where the damping is small, results calculated with the equivalent viscous damping ratio are sufficiently accurate for most practical applications.

Internal Hysteresis. Damping may be obtained either from internal hysteresis of elastic load-carrying elements or from discrete dampers having no intended load-carrying function. Materials with high hysteresis frequently embody other undesirable characteristics, among which one of the most prominent is a tendency to creep or drift excessively under a constant application of load. A few representative values of equivalent viscous damping ratio representing internal hysteresis of typical materials are given in Table 13.3 to indicate the order of magnitude of this property. The

Table 13.3. Equivalent Viscous Damping Ratio for Typical Materials

Material	Equivalent Viscous Damping Ratio b/b_c
Rubber, 30 durometer	0.02
Rubber, 60 durometer	0.08
Steel	0.005

values are only approximate and represent the averages of somewhat diverse values obtained under various conditions of forced and free vibration. They tend to be low rather than high and may increase substantially if there is energy loss as a result of friction between sliding surfaces.

Discrete Dampers. Where adequate damping cannot be attained from internal hysteresis, a discrete damper may be placed in parallel with the elastic load-carrying element. The degree of damping attainable in this manner is practically unlimited, depending only upon the space, cost, and mechanical complexity which can be tolerated. The following paragraphs describe some damping devices which have been used, and point out the limitations of each.

Dashpot. One of the most commonly used damping devices is a dashpot, as shown schematically in Fig. 13.32a. A piston a attached to the mounted body m is arranged to move vertically through the liquid in a cylinder b secured to the support s. If the piston is relatively long, the force required to cause the liquid to flow through the annular space between the piston and the cylinder is approximately proportional to the velocity of the piston in the cylinder. This is viscous damping; some data on

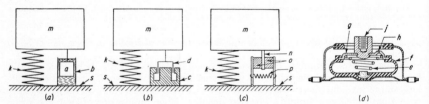

Fig. 13.32. Schematic views of several typical dampers. A dashpot is shown at (a), a magnetic damper at (b), a friction damper at (c), and an isolator embodying an air damper at (d). (*Crede.*[1])

dashpot characteristics are set forth in Ref. 12. If the piston is short and the fluid flows either through the annular space or through apertures in the piston, the damping force tends to be proportional to a power of the velocity.

Magnetic Damper. Damping is also attainable as a result of a current induced in a conductor moving through a magnetic field, using a device which may have any of several different physical embodiments of which one is shown schematically in Fig. 13.32b. A magnet c similar to that used in a dynamic loudspeaker is secured to the support s, and a conductor d attached to the mounted body m moves vertically through the field of the annular air gap. A flow of current is induced in the conductor, and energy is absorbed thereby. The damping force is proportional to the velocity of the conductor moving through the field, although some difficulty may be experienced in maintaining a constant damping coefficient throughout a substantial displacement.

The usefulness of dashpots and magnetic dampers in vibration isolation is limited by several practical considerations. Both types, as commonly constructed, are operative only for motion along a single straight line and their construction is such as to restrict motion in other directions unless a mechanism is added. The dashpot generally requires a packing gland to retain the liquid. The magnetic damper requires either a power source to energize an electromagnet or an excessively large permanent magnet, except for applications wherein the mounted equipment is very light in weight. Both types experience variations in properties as a result of temperature fluctuations, the properties of the dashpot varying because of changes in viscosity of the liquid and those of the magnetic damper because of changes in the resistance of the conductor.

Friction Damper. Damping may be obtained by causing one substantially dry member to slide upon another, using the device illustrated schematically in Fig. 13.32c. A tongue n is attached to the mounted equipment m and is arranged to slide between two blocks o which are forced against the tongue by the tension spring p. The force exerted by the damper in opposition to the vertical motion of the mounted equipment is the product of the normal force and the coefficient of friction between the tongue and blocks. The damping force is nominally a constant, independent of the position or velocity of the mounted body. This type of damping is termed dry friction or Coulomb damping, and is treated analytically in Refs. 13 and 14.

The nominally constant force transmitted by the Coulomb damper may introduce characteristic disadvantages. When the amplitude and the frequency of the vibration are low, the acceleration of the mounted equipment is low and the resultant inertia force may be less than the friction force of the damper. The damper then functions as a rigid connection, and the isolator has no resilience. At frequencies greater than the natural frequency, the relative motion between the support and the mounted equipment tends to become small. The force transmitted by the elastic element thus becomes correspondingly small. The damper, however, transmits a force whose magnitude is independent of the vibration amplitude. This may be relatively great when the vibration amplitude is small and may thus increase the transmissibility at higher frequencies.

Air Damper. An air damper embodied in an isolator is illustrated in Fig. 13.32d. The isolator includes a load-supporting metal spring e located within a rubber bellows f. The rubber bellows and metal cap g combine to form an enclosure which is substantially airtight, except for a small orifice h through the cap. The mounted equipment is attached to the central member j, and its motion in the vertical direction causes the volume within the bellows to change. Air thus flows through the orifice either into or out of the bellows. The work expended in forcing air through the orifice withdraws energy from the vibrating system, thereby providing the desired damping. The viscosity of air varies but little with temperature, and the characteristics of the damper are thus relatively independent of temperature changes.

CHARACTERISTICS OF ISOLATORS

The manufacture and sale of isolators to reduce vibration, shock, and noise have become a well-established business. This is the principal product of several concerns, and an important line in products employing rubber. A complete catalogue of available isolators would be too voluminous for inclusion here. Typical and representative products selected from the catalogues of the respective manufacturers are illustrated in Figs. 13.33 and 13.34, and the characteristics are defined by the numerical values included in Tables 13.4 to 13.6.* To facilitate classification, the isolators are grouped as (1) self-contained rubber isolators, (2) isolators employing coil springs, and (3) pad-like materials. Detailed comments on the different classes are included in the following paragraphs.

Self-contained isolators in which the resilient load-carrying element is natural or synthetic rubber are illustrated in Fig. 13.33. In general, these isolators comprise an integral assembly of rubber and metal parts and are supplied with holes or other means to facilitate mounting to the machinery. Certain of the isolators are symmetrical with respect to a central axis, while others are linear assemblies of either predetermined or indefinite length. A height adjustment to facilitate leveling of

* The list of products may not be complete, nor are the products listed necessarily recommended by the author.

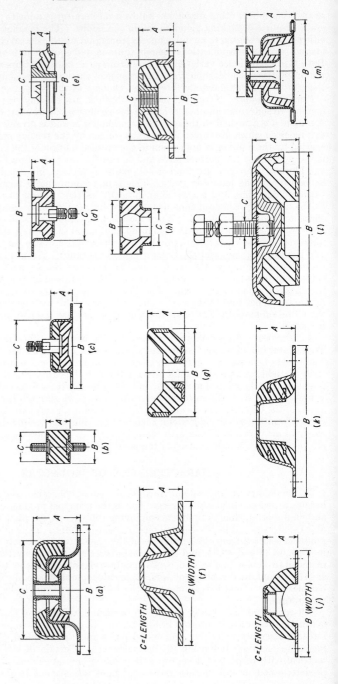

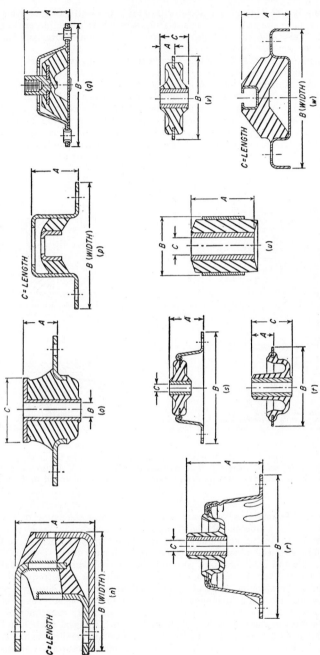

Fig. 13.33. Typical and representative commercially available isolators employing natural or synthetic rubber as the load-carrying element. A vertically extending center line indicates that the isolator is symmetrical with respect to that center line, whereas the lack of such a center line indicates that the isolator has a length of uniform cross section extending perpendicular to the paper. Dimensions, load-carrying capacities, stiffnesses, and names of manufacturers are included in Table 13.4; load and natural-frequency data are summarized in Fig. 13.35.

the mounted machine is a feature of one style of isolator. Over-all and mounting dimensions, load-carrying capacity, and relevant stiffnesses where available are set forth in Table 13.4. This table also includes the name of the manufacturer and the manufacturer's type designation for the isolators illustrated in Fig. 13.33.

Isolators employing coil springs as the resilient load-carrying element are illustrated in Fig. 13.34. The springs are embodied as integral parts of an isolator which includes metal parts having mounting holes for attachment to the mounted machine and to the floor. This type of isolator commonly includes height-adjustment means for leveling the machine, and damping means to compensate for the relatively small damping which is characteristic of coil springs. The over-all size of the isolator increases as the load-carrying capacity increases, the increased size being necessary to accommodate the larger number of springs. Spring isolators are commonly used for the isolation of vibration of relatively low forcing frequency where a great static

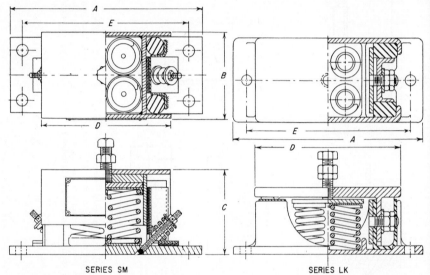

SERIES SM   SERIES LK

Fig. 13.34. Commercially available isolators employing coil springs to carry the load, generally used to isolate vibration of relatively low frequency. Dimensions, load-carrying capacities, stiffnesses where available, and names of manufacturers are included in Table 13.5.

deflection is necessary. Dimensions, load-carrying capacity, and the name of the manufacturer, together with available data on stiffnesses, are included in Table 13.5.

A common method of mounting machinery is simply to interpose a resilient pad between the mounting feet of the machine and the floor. Such pads are available in a wide variety of materials and configurations, generally in pads of large area intended to be cut to smaller pads of the desired size. While such pads are most frequently installed directly under the machine, they are often used in series with spring-type isolators to afford isolation of high-frequency vibration. Pads are usually used in applications where control of natural frequencies is not critical; consequently, available engineering data are not so well documented as with integral rubber and spring isolators. Table 13.6 lists typical pads which are commercially available, together with a description of the pad and the name of the manufacturer. Certain pads are made of unique materials, others of common materials provided with distinctive and functional surfaces, and others are flat pads of common materials. In the latter instance, Table 13.6 supplies references to appropriate sections in this chapter for detailed information.

Table 13.4. Data for Isolators Using Natural and Synthetic Rubber Illustrated in Fig. 13.33

Drawing in Fig. 13.33, manufacturer,[h] and type No.	Max load, lb	Dimensions, in.				Stiffness, lb/in.[f]		
		A (no load)	B		C	Vertical	Normal to paper	Parallel to paper
			Shape	Size				
a (Barry):								
C-1010	25	1 1/8	Square	2 3/8	2 3/8	640*	580*	580*
C-1015	40	1 1/8	Square	2 3/8	2 3/8	1,200*	1,080*	1,080*
C-1035	90	1 1/8	Square	2 3/8	2 3/8	2,250*	2,020*	2,020*
C-1050	125	1 1/8	Square	2 3/8	2 3/8	3,600*	3,250*	3,250*
C-2020	50	1 1/2	Square	3	3	2,250*	2,030*	2,030*
C-2040	100	1 1/2	Square	3	3	3,600*	3,250*	3,250*
C-2060	150	1 1/2	Square	3	3	5,000*	4,500*	4,500*
C-2080	200	1 1/2	Square	3	3	6,400*	5,750*	5,750*
C-2090	350	1 1/2	Square	3	3	8,700*	7,800*	7,800*
C-4100	250	2 1/2	Square	5 1/4	5	5,600*	5,050*	5,050*
C-4135	300	2 1/2	Square	5 1/4	5	8,400*	7,600*	7,600*
C-4200	500	2 1/2	Square	5 1/4	5	10,800*	9,750*	9,750*
C-4300	750	2 1/2	Square	5 1/4	5	16,000*	14,400*	14,400*
C-3125	300	3 9/16	Square	6 7/8	6 1/2	6,400*	5,770*	5,770*
C-3175	400	3 9/16	Square	6 7/8	6 1/2	10,000*	9,000*	9,000*
C-3300	750	3 9/16	Square	6 7/8	6 1/2	13,200*	11,900*	11,900*
C-3500	1,250	3 9/16	Square	6 7/8	6 1/2	27,600*	24,800*	24,800*
b (U.S. Rubber):								
A-300	43-13[a]	3/4	Circular	1	1	430	55	55
A-301	10-5	1/2	Circular	9/16	9/16	145	30	30
B-310	80-30	1 1/4	Circular	1 1/4	1 1/4	450	65	65
C-311	70-30	1	Circular	1 3/8	1 3/8	500	80	80
C-314	95-20	3/4	Circular	1 1/4	1 1/4	375	90	90
A-316	45-10	1	Circular	1	1	440	65	65
B-315	40-	3/4	Circular	1 1/4	1 1/4	600		
A-321	5-3	1/2	Square	3/8	3/8	80	15	15
A-322	4-3	5/16	Square	3/8	3/8	65	15	15
A-323	5-3	9/16	Square	1/2	1/2	70	15	15
44	45-10	1	Circular	1	1	440	65	65
36	125-30	1	Circular	1 1/2	1 3/16	700		
30	110-	1 1/2	Circular	1 5/8	1 3/16	580		
33	150-	1	Circular	1 5/8	1 3/16	950		
c (Firestone):								
DA-1090-30	20	11/16	Circular	2 5/8	1 9/16	150		
DA-1090-40	25	11/16	Circular	2 5/8	1 9/16	200		
DA-1090-50	30	11/16	Circular	2 5/8	1 9/16	250		
DA-1090-60	50	11/16	Circular	2 5/8	1 9/16	370		
DA-1090-70	70	11/16	Circular	2 5/8	1 9/16	550		
d (Firestone):								
DA-1089-30	25	11/16	Circular	2 5/8	1 9/16	220		
DA-1089-40	30	11/16	Circular	2 5/8	1 9/16	265		
DA-1089-50	40	11/16	Circular	2 5/8	1 9/16	335		
DA-1089-60	60	11/16	Circular	2 5/8	1 9/16	460		
e (M-B):								
171.08	0.5	0.30	Square	1 1/4	1	8	8	8
171.15	0.9	0.30	Square	1 1/4	1	15	15	15
171.32	2.0	0.30	Square	1 1/4	1	32	32	32
171.46	2.9	0.30	Square	1 1/4	1	46	46	46
171.68	4.2	0.30	Square	1 1/4	1	68	68	68
172.32	3.2	0.40	Square	1 3/4	1 1/2	32	32	32
172.68	6.8	0.40	Square	1 3/4	1 1/2	68	68	68
1721.0	10	0.40	Square	1 3/4	1 1/2	100	100	100
1721.2	12	0.40	Square	1 3/4	1 1/2	120	120	120
1721.5	15	0.40	Square	1 3/4	1 1/2	150	150	150
1721.8	18	0.40	Square	1 3/4	1 1/2	180	180	180
1731.5	15	0.59	Square	2 1/4	2	150	150	150
1732.6	26	0.59	Square	2 1/4	2	260	260	260
1733.2	32	0.59	Square	2 1/4	2	320	320	320
1733.8	38	0.59	Square	2 1/4	2	380	380	380
1735.6	56	0.59	Square	2 1/4	2	560	560	560
1736.8	68	0.59	Square	2 1/4	2	680	680	680
1738.3	83	0.59	Square	2 1/4	2	830	830	830
17310	100	0.59	Square	2 1/4	2	1,000	1,000	1,000

Table 13.4. Data for Isolators Using Natural and Synthetic Rubber Illustrated in Fig. 13.33 (Continued)

Drawing in Fig. 13.33, manufacturer,[h] and type No.	Max load, lb	A (no load)	B Shape	B Size	C	Vertical	Normal to paper	Parallel to paper
f (Firestone):								
CA-148-40	30[b]	$1\frac{3}{8}$	Rectangle	$4\frac{7}{16}$	e	215[b]		
CA-148-50	45	$1\frac{3}{8}$	Rectangle	$4\frac{7}{16}$	e	320		
CA-148-60	70	$1\frac{3}{8}$	Rectangle	$4\frac{7}{16}$	e	500		
g (Firestone):								
CA363(1)-40	140	$1\frac{3}{16}$	Circular	$2\frac{3}{4}$	....	700		
CA363(1)-50	220	$1\frac{3}{16}$	Circular	$2\frac{3}{4}$	....	1,200		
CA363(1)-60	300	$1\frac{3}{16}$	Circular	$2\frac{3}{4}$	....	1,700		
CA363(1)-70	400	$1\frac{3}{16}$	Circular	$2\frac{3}{4}$	....	2,300		
CA363(2)-40	230	$1\frac{3}{16}$	Circular	$2\frac{3}{4}$	....	1,500		
CA363(2)-50	300	$1\frac{3}{16}$	Circular	$2\frac{3}{4}$	....	2,000		
CA363(2)-60	430	$1\frac{3}{16}$	Circular	$2\frac{3}{4}$	....	2,800		
CA363(2)-70	600	$1\frac{3}{16}$	Circular	$2\frac{3}{4}$	....	4,000		
CA368(3)-40	230	$1\frac{3}{16}$	Circular	$2\frac{3}{4}$	....	1,500		
CA368(3)-50	300	$1\frac{3}{16}$	Circular	$2\frac{3}{4}$	....	2,000		
CA368(3)-60	380	$1\frac{3}{16}$	Circular	$2\frac{3}{4}$	....	2,600		
CA368(3)-70	550	$1\frac{3}{16}$	Circular	$2\frac{3}{4}$	....	3,600		
CA368(5)-40	125	$1\frac{15}{64}$	Circular	$2\frac{3}{4}$	....	760		
CA368(5)-50	185	$1\frac{15}{64}$	Circular	$2\frac{3}{4}$	....	1,200		
CA368(5)-60	250	$1\frac{15}{64}$	Circular	$2\frac{3}{4}$	....	1,700		
h (Firestone):								
CA360(5)-30	60	$1\frac{1}{16}$	Circular	$1\frac{5}{8}$	....	500		
CA360(5)-40	100	$1\frac{1}{16}$	Circular	$1\frac{5}{8}$	No. 6-$\frac{7}{8}$	1,000		
CA360(5)-50	140	$1\frac{1}{16}$	Circular	$1\frac{5}{8}$	No. 7-$1\frac{1}{8}$	1,500		
CA360(5)-60	190	$1\frac{1}{16}$	Circular	$1\frac{5}{8}$	No. 8-$1\frac{7}{64}$	2,000		
CA360(5)-70	250	$1\frac{1}{16}$	Circular	$1\frac{5}{8}$	....	2,750		
i (Firestone):								
CA-244(5)30	150	$1\frac{1}{8}$	Diamond	$3\frac{5}{8}$	$2\frac{1}{4}$	850		
CA-244(5)40	210	$1\frac{1}{8}$	Diamond	$3\frac{5}{8}$	$2\frac{1}{4}$	1,300		
CA-244(5)50	290	$1\frac{1}{8}$	Diamond	$3\frac{5}{8}$	$2\frac{1}{4}$	1,800		
CA-244(5)60	390	$1\frac{1}{8}$	Diamond	$3\frac{5}{8}$	$2\frac{1}{4}$	2,400		
j (Barry):								
262-60	60	$1\frac{21}{32}$	Rectangle	$4\frac{7}{16}$	2	250*	100*	100*
262-100	100	$1\frac{21}{32}$	Rectangle	$4\frac{7}{16}$	2	450*	180*	180*
262-130	130	$1\frac{21}{32}$	Rectangle	$4\frac{7}{16}$	2	650*	260*	260*
262-200	200	$1\frac{21}{32}$	Rectangle	$4\frac{7}{16}$	4	800*	320*	320*
262-260	260	$1\frac{21}{32}$	Rectangle	$4\frac{7}{16}$	4	1,200*	480*	480*
k (Firestone):								
CA-1290-30	900	$1\frac{21}{32}$	Diamond	$6\frac{1}{4}$	....	5,500		
CA-1290-40	1,200	$1\frac{21}{32}$	Diamond	$6\frac{1}{4}$	....	7,500		
CA-1290-50	1,600	$1\frac{21}{32}$	Diamond	$6\frac{1}{4}$	....	10,000		
CA-1290-60	2,000	$1\frac{21}{32}$	Diamond	$6\frac{1}{4}$	....	13,000		
CA-1290-70	2,800	$1\frac{21}{32}$	Diamond	$6\frac{1}{4}$	....	17,000		
l (Barry):								
LM-3-4	400	$1\frac{1}{2}$-$1\frac{7}{8}$	Circular	$4\frac{3}{4}$	$\frac{1}{2}$	5,000*	910*	910*
LM-3-6	600	$1\frac{1}{2}$-$1\frac{7}{8}$	Circular	$4\frac{3}{4}$	$\frac{1}{2}$	6,700*	1,220*	1,220*
LM-3-8	800	$1\frac{1}{2}$-$1\frac{7}{8}$	Circular	$4\frac{3}{4}$	$\frac{1}{2}$	9,200*	1,680*	1,680*
LM-3-11	1,100	$1\frac{1}{2}$-$1\frac{7}{8}$	Circular	$4\frac{3}{4}$	$\frac{1}{2}$	14,000*	2,540*	2,540*
LM-5-11	1,100	$1\frac{5}{8}$-$2\frac{1}{8}$	Circular	$6\frac{5}{16}$	$\frac{3}{4}$	11,500	2,100	2,100
LM-5-20	2,000	$1\frac{5}{8}$-$2\frac{1}{8}$	Circular	$6\frac{5}{16}$	$\frac{3}{4}$	20,000	3,600	3,600
LM-5-27	2,100	$1\frac{5}{8}$-$2\frac{1}{8}$	Circular	$6\frac{5}{16}$	$\frac{3}{4}$	28,000	5,100	5,100
LM-5-42	4,200	$1\frac{5}{8}$-$2\frac{3}{8}$	Circular	$6\frac{5}{16}$	$\frac{3}{4}$	50,000	9,100	9,100
LM-7-35	3,500	$2\frac{5}{8}$-$3\frac{1}{8}$	Circular	$9\frac{1}{2}$	1	31,000		
LM-7-50	5,000	$2\frac{5}{8}$-$3\frac{1}{8}$	Circular	$9\frac{1}{2}$	1	43,000		
LM-7-65	6,500	$2\frac{5}{8}$-$3\frac{1}{8}$	Circular	$9\frac{1}{2}$	1	60,000		
LM-7-100	10,500	$2\frac{5}{8}$-$3\frac{1}{8}$	Circular	$9\frac{1}{2}$	1	90 000		
m (Barry):								
990-3	6	$1\frac{9}{16}$	Square	$2\frac{3}{8}$	$1\frac{9}{16}$	40*	20*	20*
990-5	10	$1\frac{9}{16}$	Square	$2\frac{3}{8}$	$1\frac{9}{16}$	65*	30*	30*
990-7	15	$1\frac{9}{16}$	Square	$2\frac{3}{8}$	$1\frac{9}{16}$	85*	40*	40*
990-10	20	$1\frac{9}{16}$	Square	$2\frac{3}{8}$	$1\frac{9}{16}$	100*	50*	50*
990-15	40	$1\frac{9}{16}$	Square	$2\frac{3}{8}$	$1\frac{9}{16}$	250*	125*	125*
990-20	60	$1\frac{9}{16}$	Square	$2\frac{3}{8}$	$1\frac{9}{16}$	350*	175*	175*
990-30	75	$1\frac{9}{16}$	Square	$2\frac{3}{8}$	$1\frac{9}{16}$	450*	225*	225*

Table 13.4. Data for Isolators Using Natural and Synthetic Rubber Illustrated in Fig. 13.33 (*Continued*)

Drawing in Fig. 13.33, manufacturer,[h] and type No.	Max load, lb	A (no load)	B Shape	B Size	C	Vertical	Normal to paper	Parallel to paper
n (U.S. Rubber):								
201A	215	$2\frac{3}{4}$	Rectangle	$3\frac{7}{8}$	$4\frac{15}{16}$	750		
201C	370	$2\frac{3}{4}$	Rectangle	$3\frac{7}{8}$	$4\frac{15}{16}$	1,250		
200B	900	$3\frac{11}{16}$	Rectangle	$4\frac{1}{16}$	$8\frac{1}{4}$	3,000		
o (M-B):								
516C178	2,670	$1\frac{1}{2}$	Diamond	$7\frac{1}{2}$	$4\frac{1}{2}$	17,800	17,800	17,800
516C147	2,205	$1\frac{1}{2}$	Diamond	$7\frac{1}{2}$	$4\frac{1}{2}$	14,700	14,700	14,700
516C121	1,815	$1\frac{1}{2}$	Diamond	$7\frac{1}{2}$	$4\frac{1}{2}$	12,100	12,100	12,100
516C100	1,800	$1\frac{1}{2}$	Diamond	$7\frac{1}{2}$	$4\frac{1}{2}$	10,000	10,000	10,000
516C83	1,245	$1\frac{1}{2}$	Diamond	$7\frac{1}{2}$	$4\frac{1}{2}$	8,300	8,300	8,300
512C100	1,800	$1\frac{3}{8}$	Diamond	$6\frac{1}{4}$	$3\frac{1}{2}$	10,000	10,000	10,000
512C83	1,245	$1\frac{3}{8}$	Diamond	$6\frac{1}{4}$	$3\frac{1}{2}$	8,300	8,300	8,300
512C68	1,020	$1\frac{3}{8}$	Diamond	$6\frac{1}{4}$	$3\frac{1}{2}$	6,800	6,800	6,800
512C56	840	$1\frac{3}{8}$	Diamond	$6\frac{1}{4}$	$3\frac{1}{2}$	5,600	5,600	5,600
512C46	690	$1\frac{3}{8}$	Diamond	$6\frac{1}{4}$	$3\frac{1}{2}$	4,600	4,600	4,600
510C68	1,020	$1\frac{1}{4}$	Diamond	$5\frac{1}{4}$	$2\frac{3}{4}$	6,800	6,800	6,800
510C56	840	$1\frac{1}{4}$	Diamond	$5\frac{1}{4}$	$2\frac{3}{4}$	5,600	5,600	5,600
510C46	690	$1\frac{1}{4}$	Diamond	$5\frac{1}{4}$	$2\frac{3}{4}$	4,600	4,600	4,600
510C38	570	$1\frac{1}{4}$	Diamond	$5\frac{1}{4}$	$2\frac{3}{4}$	3,800	3,800	3,800
510C32	480	$1\frac{1}{4}$	Diamond	$5\frac{1}{4}$	$2\frac{3}{4}$	3,200	3,200	3,200
508C38	570	$1\frac{1}{16}$	Diamond	$4\frac{3}{4}$	2	3,800	3,800	3,800
508C32	480	$1\frac{1}{16}$	Diamond	$4\frac{3}{4}$	2	3,200	3,200	3,200
508C26	390	$1\frac{1}{16}$	Diamond	$4\frac{3}{4}$	2	2,600	2,600	2,600
508C22	330	$1\frac{1}{16}$	Diamond	$4\frac{3}{4}$	2	2,200	2,200	2,200
508C18	270	$1\frac{1}{16}$	Diamond	$4\frac{3}{4}$	2	1,800	1,800	1,800
507C22	330	1	Diamond	$4\frac{1}{2}$	$1\frac{7}{8}$	2,200	2,200	2,200
507C18	270	1	Diamond	$4\frac{1}{2}$	$1\frac{7}{8}$	1,800	1,800	1,800
507C15	225	1	Diamond	$4\frac{1}{2}$	$1\frac{7}{8}$	1,500	1,500	1,500
507C12	180	1	Diamond	$4\frac{1}{2}$	$1\frac{7}{8}$	1,200	1,200	1,200
507C10	150	1	Diamond	$4\frac{1}{2}$	$1\frac{7}{8}$	1,000	1,000	1,000
p (U.S. Rubber):								
120A1	15	$\frac{3}{4}$	Rectangle	2	1	165		
120A2	30	$\frac{3}{4}$	Rectangle	2	2	330		
120A3	50	$\frac{3}{4}$	Rectangle	2	3	500		
120A6	100	$\frac{3}{4}$	Rectangle	2	6	1,000		
101C1	90	$1\frac{5}{8}$	Rectangle	$4\frac{1}{4}$	$1\frac{1}{2}$	330		
101C3	180	$1\frac{5}{8}$	Rectangle	$4\frac{1}{4}$	3	660		
101C5	310	$1\frac{5}{8}$	Rectangle	$4\frac{1}{4}$	5	1,200		
101C7	430	$1\frac{5}{8}$	Rectangle	$4\frac{1}{4}$	7	1,700		
q (Barry):								
915-25	25	$1\frac{3}{4}$	Diamond	$4\frac{7}{8}$	....	280*	155*	155*
915-40	40	$1\frac{3}{4}$	Diamond	$4\frac{7}{8}$	....	520*	290*	290*
915-60	60	$1\frac{3}{4}$	Diamond	$4\frac{7}{8}$	....	720*	400*	400*
915-90	90	$1\frac{3}{4}$	Diamond	$4\frac{7}{8}$	....	920*	500*	500*
915-150	150	$1\frac{3}{4}$	Diamond	$4\frac{7}{8}$	....	1,320*	730*	730*
915-200	200	$1\frac{3}{4}$	Diamond	$4\frac{7}{8}$	....	2,280*	1,250*	1,250*
r (Lord):								
106 holder	2	$1\frac{37}{64}$	Square	$1\frac{11}{16}$	0.166	11*	11*	11*
106 holder	3	$1\frac{37}{64}$	Square	$1\frac{11}{16}$	0.166	16*	16*	16*
106 holder	4	$1\frac{37}{64}$	Square	$1\frac{11}{16}$	0.166	21*	21*	21*
156 holder	6	$1\frac{13}{16}$	Square	$2\frac{3}{8}$	0.257	50*	50*	50*
156 holder	9	$1\frac{13}{16}$	Square	$2\frac{3}{8}$	0.257	75*	75*	75*
156 holder	13	$1\frac{13}{16}$	Square	$2\frac{3}{8}$	0.257	108*	108*	108*
206 holder	20	$1\frac{63}{64}$	Square	3	0.391	229*	229*	229*
206 holder	30	$1\frac{63}{64}$	Square	3	0.391	379*	379*	379*
206 holder	45	$1\frac{63}{64}$	Square	3	0.391	571*	571*	571*
s (Lord):								
100 holder	1 min[g]	$2\frac{3}{32}$	Square	$1\frac{11}{16}$	0.166	16*	58*	58*
100 holder	4 max	$2\frac{3}{32}$	Square	$1\frac{11}{16}$	0.166	64*	144*	144*
150 holder	2 min	$1\frac{1}{16}$	Square	$2\frac{3}{8}$	0.257	53*	185*	185*
150 holder	12 max	$1\frac{1}{16}$	Square	$2\frac{3}{8}$	0.257	301*	606*	606*
200 holder	10 min	$1\frac{1}{2}$	Square	3	0.391	251*	524*	524*
200 holder	45 max	$1\frac{1}{2}$	Square	3	0.391	1,582*	2,380*	2,380*
200X holder	60 min	$2\frac{5}{16}$	Square	3	0.391	1,710*	2,100*	2,100*
200X holder	90 max	$2\frac{5}{16}$	Square	3	0.391	3,410*	5,010*	5,010*

Table 13.4. Data for Isolators Using Natural and Synthetic Rubber Illustrated in Fig. 13.33 (*Continued*)

Drawing in Fig. 13.33, manufacturer,[h] and type No.	Max load, lb	A (no load)	B Shape	B Size	C	Vertical	Normal to paper	Parallel to paper
t (Lord):								
106 square	2	17/32	Square	1 1/4	27/32	11*	11*	11*
106 square	3	17/32	Square	1 1/4	27/32	16*	16*	16*
106 square	4	17/32	Square	1 1/4	27/32	21*	21*	21*
156 square	6	35/64	Square	1 3/4	3 1/32	51*	51*	51*
156 square	9	35/64	Square	1 3/4	3 1/32	75*	75*	75*
156 square	13	35/64	Square	1 3/4	3 1/32	108*	108*	108*
206 square	20	9/16	Square	2 1/4	1	229*	229*	229*
206 square	30	9/16	Square	2 1/4	1	379*	379*	379*
206 square	45	9/16	Square	2 1/4	1	571*	571*	571*
u (Lord):								
20203	200 min	1 1/2	Circular	2	4 1/64	3,200		
20210	440 max	3 1/4	Circular	2	4 1/64	7,040		
20303	180 min	1 1/2	Circular	2	4 1/64	1,920		
20310	400 min	3 1/4	Circular	2	4 1/64	4,260		
20403	160 min	1 1/2	Circular	2	4 1/64	1,280		
20410	355 max	3 1/4	Circular	2	4 1/64	2,840		
25204	330 min	1 3/4	Circular	2 1/2	4 1/64	5,280		
25211	670 max	3 1/2	Circular	2 1/2	4 1/64	10,720		
25304	285 min	1 3/4	Circular	2 1/2	4 1/64	3,040		
25311	570 min	3 1/2	Circular	2 1/2	4 1/64	6,080		
25404	235 min	1 3/4	Circular	2 1/2	4 1/64	1,880		
25411	475 min	3 1/2	Circular	2 1/2	4 1/64	3,800		
30208	595 min	2 3/4	Circular	3	1 1/64	9,530		
30216	1,145 max	5 1/4	Circular	3	1 1/64	18,320		
30308	595 min	2 3/4	Circular	3	1 1/64	6,347		
30318	1,145 max	5 1/4	Circular	3	1 1/64	12,200		
30408	520 min	2 3/4	Circular	3	1 1/64	4,160		
30418	1,005 max	5 1/4	Circular	3	1 1/64	8,040		
30608	450 min	2 3/4	Circular	3	1 1/64	2,400		
30618	860 max	5 1/4	Circular	3	1 1/64	4,580		
v (Lord):								
100 square	1 min	1 9/64	Square	1 1/4	1 3/32	16*	58*	58*
100 square	4 max	1 9/64	Square	1 1/4	1 3/32	64*	144*	144*
150 square	2 min	1 3/32	Square	1 3/4	5/8	53*	185*	185*
150 square	12 max	1 3/32	Square	1 3/4	5/8	301*	606*	606*
200 square	10 min	1 9/32	Square	2 1/4	1	251*	524*	524*
200 square	45 max	1 9/32	Square	2 1/4	1	1,582*	2,380*	2,380*
200X square	60 min	1 25/64	Square	2 1/4	1 13/16	1,710*	2,100*	2,100*
200X square	90 max	1 25/64	Square	2 1/4	1 13/16	3,410*	5,010*	5,010*
w (Lord):								
J-2170-1	50	1 17/32	Rectangle	4 1/2	1	114*	40*	216*
J-2171-1	100	1 17/32	Rectangle	4 1/2	2	223*	94*	437*
J-2172-1	200	1 17/32	Rectangle	4 1/2	4	458*	300*	933*
J-2173-1	400	1 17/32	Rectangle	4 1/2	8	960*	480*	2,120*

[a] First value is maximum load in compression; second value is maximum load in shear.

[b] Loads and stiffnesses are per inch of length.

[c] Standard lengths are 1, 2, 3, 4, 6, 12, 24, and 36 in.

[d] Height is adjustable within indicated limits.

[e] Insert 6, 7, or 8 from C column.

[f] Asterisk indicates dynamic stiffness; all other stiffnesses are static. Dynamic stiffnesses are approximate but representative; the exact value of the dynamic stiffness is a function of static strain, dynamic strain, temperature, and to some extent, frequency.

[g] The designation "min" indicates minimum load rating in this size; "max" indicates maximum load rating in this size. Intermediate load ratings are omitted to conserve space.

[h] Addresses of manufacturers: Barry Controls Inc., 700 Pleasant St., Watertown, Mass.; Firestone Industrial Products Co., Akron, Ohio; The B. F. Goodrich Co., Akron, Ohio; Lord Manufacturing Co., Erie, Pa.; The M-B Mfg. Co., Inc., 1060 State St., New Haven, Conn.; United States Rubber Co., Ft. Wayne, Ind.

Table 13.5. Data for Isolators Using Coil Springs Illustrated in Fig. 13.34

Manufacturer and type No.	Max load, lb	Dimensions, in.					No. of springs	Stiffness, lb/in.		
								Vertical	Parallel to dimension	
		A	B	C	D	E			A	B
Barry:										
SM1-2.5-AA	250	$7\frac{1}{4}$	$4\frac{1}{4}$	$4\frac{1}{16}$	5	$6\frac{1}{4}$	1	250	800	550
SM1-4-AA	400							575	1,060	810
SM1-5.5-AA	550							875	1,300	1,050
SM1-7.5-AA	750							1,475	1,780	1,530
SM2-5-AA	500	$9\frac{1}{4}$	5	$4\frac{23}{32}$	$5\frac{1}{2}$	$7\frac{3}{4}$	2	500	1,000	750
SM2-8-AA	800							1,150	1,500	1,270
SM2-11-AA	1,100							1,750	1,960	1,900
SM2-15-AA	1,500							2,950	2,950	2,650
SM4-10-AA	1,000	$11\frac{1}{2}$	5	$4\frac{23}{32}$	$7\frac{11}{16}$	10	4	1,000	1,370	1,150
SM4-16-AA	1,600							2,300	2,400	2,150
SM4-22-AA	2,200							3,500	6,830	4,730
SM4-30-AA	3,000							5,900	8,270	6,500
SM6-15-AA	1,500	$13\frac{1}{2}$	$5\frac{1}{8}$	$4\frac{23}{32}$	$9\frac{13}{16}$	12	6	1,500	1,720	1,500
SM6-24-AA	2,400							3,450	6,200	4,650
SM6-33-AA	3,300							5,250	7,780	5,950
SM6-45-AA	4,500							8,850	11,100	8,850
SM9-23-AA	2,300	$13\frac{1}{2}$	$7\frac{1}{8}$	$4\frac{23}{32}$	$9\frac{13}{16}$	12	9	2,200	2,300	2,100
SM9-36-AA	3,600							5,180	7,670	5,870
SM9-50-AA	5,000							7,880	10,300	10,100
SM9-68-AA	6,800							13,300	14,700	12,500
Korfund:										
LK/C 51	75	$6\frac{7}{8}$	$2\frac{1}{2}$	$3\frac{1}{2}$	4	$5\frac{1}{2}$	1			
LK/C 51-B	110									
LK/C 7	150									
LK/C 8	275									
LK/C 9	350									
LK/C 9-0	500									
LK/D 52	150	$9\frac{1}{2}$	5	4	$6\frac{7}{8}$	8	2			
LK/D 52-B	220									
LK/D 10	350									
LK/D 11	600									
LK/D 12	700									
LK/D 12-0	1,000									
LK/E 54	300	$11\frac{3}{4}$	5	$4\frac{1}{8}$	$9\frac{1}{8}$	$10\frac{1}{4}$	4			
LK/E 54-B	440									
LK/E 13	750									
LK/E 14	1,200									
LK/E 15	1,400									
LK/E 15-0	2,000									
LK/F 56	450	$11\frac{3}{4}$	7	$4\frac{1}{4}$	$9\frac{1}{4}$	$10\frac{1}{4}$	6			
LK/F 56-B	660									
LK/F 16	1,150									
LK/F 17	1,900									
LK/F 18	2,500									
LK/F 18-0	3,000									
LK/G 59	675	14	7	$4\frac{1}{4}$	$11\frac{1}{2}$	$12\frac{1}{2}$	9			
LK/G 59-B	990									
LK/G 19	1,700									
LK/G 20	2,800									
LK/G 21	3,500									
LK/G 21-0	5,000									
LK/H 22	5,000	14	7	$6\frac{3}{4}$	$11\frac{1}{2}$	$12\frac{1}{2}$	4-9			
LK/H 23	6,500									
LK/H 24	8,500									
LK/H 25	10,000									
LK/H 26	12,000									

Table 13.6. Descriptions of Pad-type Isolators

Name	Description	Manufacturer
AIR-LOC	Sisal and cork center with vinyl facing on opposite sides	Clark-Cutler-McDermott Co.
Elasto-Rib	Natural cork board with ribbed neoprene facing on opposite sides	The Korfund Co., Inc.
Fabreeka	Neoprene-impregnated fabric	Fabreeka Products Company
Isomode Pad	Neoprene pad with ribs on opposite faces	The M-B Manufacturing Co., Inc.
Keldur	Synthetic material	Beltron Associates, Inc.
Vibraglass	Interlocked and bonded-glass fibers	Glass Fibers, Inc.
Cork	See section on *Cork* in this chapter	Armstrong Cork Company; Mundet Cork Company, Inc.
Felt	See section on *Felt* in this chapter	American Felt Company, The Felters Company, Western Felt Works
Rubber	See section on *Rubber* in this chapter	Widely available from manufacturers and jobbers
Sponge rubber	See section on *Sponge Rubber* in this chapter	Widely available from manufacturers and jobbers

Addresses of manufacturers: Clark-Cutler-McDermott Co., Franklin, Mass.; The Korfund Co., Inc., 48-15 32nd Place, Long Island City, N.Y.; Fabreeka Products Co., 222 Summer St., Boston, Mass.; The M-B Mfg. Co., Inc., 1060 State St., New Haven, Conn.; Beltron Associates, Inc., P. O. Box 128, Brooklyn 10, N.Y.; Glass Fibers, Inc., 1810 Madison Ave., Toledo, Ohio; Armstrong Cork Company, Lancaster, Pa.; Mundet Cork Company, Inc., 7203 Tonnelle Ave., N. Bergen, N.J.; American Felt Company, Glenville, Conn.; The Felters Company, 210 South St., Boston, Mass.; Western Felt Works, Chicago, Ill.

SELECTION AND APPLICATION OF ISOLATORS FOR VIBRATION ISOLATION

This section on selection and application of isolators is, in effect, a guide to the use of the material included in Chaps. 12 and 13. It should not be construed as detailed instructions which make it unnecessary to understand the applicable engineering principles. If a problem is approached in the manner outlined, however, the result should be attained with a minimum of false moves, although considerable engineering judgment may be required in the process.

1. The first step in selecting isolators is to establish the isolator locations and to determine the magnitude of the load carried by each isolator. If the load is uniformly distributed among isolators, the total load is divided by the number of isolators to obtain the unit load. If the load is not uniformly distributed, the load carried by each isolator may be determined using the procedure set forth in the section of this chapter which discusses *Isolators for Nonsymmetrical Equipment.*
2. The nature of the forcing vibration should be defined by determining its frequency, and the magnitudes and directions of the applied forces. Using the minimum frequency of the forcing vibration, a value should be selected for the maximum natural frequency of the isolators, following the principles set forth in the section of this chapter which discusses *Isolation of Steady-state Vibration.* It is neither necessary nor desirable that the natural frequencies be equal in the directions of all coordinate axes. In a reciprocating engine, for example, the forces acting along the crankshaft axis are relatively small. The natural frequencies of the isolator system in this direction need be only small enough to avoid resonance rather than sufficiently small to attain very low transmissibility.
3. It is necessary now to determine the properties of the equipment and isolators. The radius of gyration of the equipment is calculated, estimated, or measured, using the principles set forth in the section on *Properties of Mounted Equipment.*

Calculation of actual isolator stiffnesses is deferred for the moment, but the ratio of stiffnesses along principal axes must be established. Each type of isolator has a characteristic ratio, which may be determined from Tables 13.4 and 13.5 for commercially produced isolators, or calculated from the data in the section on *Properties of Materials* if the isolator is to be assembled from component parts.

4. Using the data assembled by the procedure of the preceding paragraph, the relation between the natural frequency in a vertical translatory mode and the natural frequencies in other modes is established. If the isolators are in the same horizontal plane as the center of gravity of the mounted equipment, vibration in the horizontal and vertical translatory modes may be decoupled. There is then a characteristic natural frequency in each mode, and the ratios of the various natural frequencies to the natural frequency in vertical translation may be established by using the properties of the isolators in Eqs. (12.3) and (12.5).

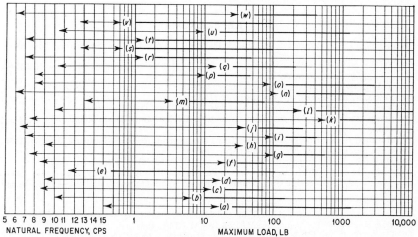

5 6 7 8 9 10 11 12 13 14 15   1   10   100   1000   10,000
NATURAL FREQUENCY, CPS   MAXIMUM LOAD, LB

FIG. 13.35. Summary of load-carrying capacity and minimum natural frequency for isolators shown in Fig. 13.33. Heavy line indicates range of maximum loads, and scale at left indicates natural frequency at maximum load.

5. If the vibration in the various modes is coupled, as explained in the section on *Natural Modes of Vibration* in Chap. 12, the ratio of the natural frequencies in the coupled and vertical translatory modes is determined as follows: If the system is symmetrical, the ratio of the natural frequencies may be determined from the section on *Isolators for Symmetrical Equipment* in this chapter. If the system is unsymmetrical, reference should be made to the section on *Nonsymmetrical Equipment* in this chapter. It is necessary that the greatest natural frequency, as determined in this manner, be set equal to the maximum natural frequency selected by the procedure in Paragraph 2 above. From this maximum natural frequency and the ratio of the natural frequencies in the coupled or uncoupled modes to the natural frequency in the vertical translatory mode, the natural frequency in the vertical translatory mode is determined.

6. The required stiffness of the isolators in the vertical direction is now determined from the required vertical natural frequency (see Paragraph 5) and the unit load (see Paragraph 1). The required stiffness is calculated from Eq. (12.3). A suitable isolator is now selected from Tables 13.4 and 13.5. It is essential to use dynamic stiffness. Tables 13.4 and 13.5 set forth dynamic stiffness where available, as indicated by the asterisk. Other stiffness values are static; they may be converted to approximate dynamic stiffness as indicated in the section

on *Rubber* in this chapter.   It is important that the isolator selected exhibit
the ratio of horizontal to vertical stiffness assumed in Paragraph 3.   If the available isolators include one which is generally suitable but which embodies a somewhat different stiffness ratio, this new ratio should be assumed and the above
calculation repeated to obtain new values of stiffness.   If the required isolator
cannot be found among commercially available isolators, it may be necessary to
design an isolator using the materials whose properties are set forth in the
section on *Properties of Materials* in this chapter.

Data on load-carrying capacity and natural frequency of commercially available
isolators are summarized in Fig. 13.35.   The heavy horizontal lines indicate range
of maximum loads for the series of isolators illustrated in Fig. 13.33.   The minimum
attainable natural frequency for any particular series of isolator, corresponding generally to the maximum load, is indicated by the arrow extending leftward from the
heavy line.   If the load is less than the maximum, the natural frequency can be calculated from the stiffness set forth in Table 13.4.

REFERENCES

1. Crede, C. E.: "Vibration and Shock Isolation," John Wiley & Sons, Inc., New York, 1951.
2. Marks, L. S.: "Mechanical Engineers' Handbook," 5th ed., p. 199, McGraw-Hill Book Company, Inc., New York, 1951.
3. Young, S. E.: *Product Eng.*, February, 1954.
4. Lewis, F. M.: *Trans. ASME*, **54**: 253 (1932).
5. Mindlin, R. D.: *Bell System Tech. J.*, **24** (3, 4) (July–October, 1945).
6. Sykes, A. O.: Navy Department, David W. Taylor Model Basin Report 845, October, 1953.
7. Hamme, R. N.: University of Michigan, Engineering Research Institute, July 31, 1950.
8. Keys, W. C.: *Mech. Eng.*, **59** (5) (May, 1937).
9. Hirshfeld, C. F., and E. H. Piron: *Trans. ASME*, **59** (6): 471 (August, 1937).
10. Wahl, A. M.: "Mechanical Springs," Penton Publishing Company, Cleveland, 1939.
11. Tentative Specification for Cellular Rubber Products, ASTM D798-46AT, issued 1944.
12. Peterson, J. B.: *NACA Tech. Note* 830, 1941.
13. Jacobsen, L. S.: *Trans. ASME*, **52** (APM-52-15), 1930.
14. Den Hartog, J. P.: *Trans. ASME*, **53** (APM-53-9), 1931.
15. Crede, C. E., and J. P. Walsh: *J. Appl. Mechanics*, **14** (1) (March, 1947).
16. Geiger, P. H.: "Noise Reduction Manual," Engineering Research Institute, University of Michigan, 1953.
17. Crede, C. E.: *Machine Design*, **26**: 139 (August, 1954).

Chapter 14

VIBRATION DAMPING

RICHARD N. HAMME

Geiger and Hamme

and

Engineering Research Institute,
University of Michigan

THE FUNCTION AND APPLICABILITY OF VIBRATION-DAMPING MATERIALS

The Mechanism of Damping. The word "damping" has been used loosely for many years to denote any number of noise-abatement procedures. The frequent appearance of almost self-contradictory phrases such as "damp out the sound in the room" and "use sound-damping mounts under the machine" indicates the state of popular confusion among the mechanisms of vibration damping, sound absorption, and vibration isolation.

Energy Dissipation in Solids. From the technical noise-reduction standpoint, it is best to limit the use of the word "damping" to the mechanism of converting the mechanical vibrational energy of solids into the form of heat energy. Then the noise-reduction capacity of damping derives from the fact that, once the mechanical energy is dissipated, it cannot be radiated in the form of air-borne noise. And, once dissipated in the solid, vibrational energy need not be isolated resiliently from radiating surfaces, and the need for absorbing and/or isolating air-borne sound is further reduced.

From the standpoint of elementary physics, this conversion of vibratory energy of a solid into heat can be visualized as a randomization of molecular motion. The gross periodic movement of an assemblage of molecules vibrating in unison is progressively transformed into the fine random motion of thermal agitation. This reduces the concerted movement of molecules at the surface of the solid which would otherwise communicate periodic motion to the surrounding air to be propagated away in the form of sound waves.

The practical importance of making the function of damping clear is demonstrated by the innumerable mistaken applications of sound-absorptive materials (fibrous blankets, etc.) and vibration-isolation materials (rubber, etc.) in purported damping capacity.

Although all materials demonstrate some degree of inherent damping capacity, most materials of any structural integrity (especially metals) require external or surface treatment in order to be deadened sufficiently for noise-reduction purposes. Because the surface movement of the structural material is communicated to the vibration-damping material, the inadequate inherent effects of hysteresis in the live material are supplemented by the higher hysteresis, and the dissipative effects of viscosity, fiber flexure, and internal friction inherent to the deadener, as well as the friction effects at the interface beneath the treatment. The major concern of this chapter is to describe and compare such surface treatments, and to establish their relative effectiveness in contributing practical noise reductions.

There need be no concern about the amounts of heat generated by the use of damping materials in noise control, because the absolute value of the acoustic energies involved is so minute. For example, Lord Rayleigh computed that ten million cornets blowing fortissimo would be required to produce one acoustic horsepower.

Distinct from Mass-stiffness Relations. The noise-reduction effectiveness of damping materials is, to a first approximation, distinct from the mass-stiffness relations upon which depend vibration isolation and the response of a system to given excitation. This should be obvious to everyone familiar with the distinct classical idealizations of stiffness, inertia, and damping by the spring, mass, and dashpot, but the complexity of vibration problems has been known to lead people to odd conclusions, such as "These parts are too stiff and massive for damping to do any good."

Dynamically, springs and masses store energy, rather than dissipate it. When an ideal spring of any form is deflected, the work done in bending it is stored as potential energy and then returned without loss upon its release. Hence adjusting the spring constants of the components of a vibrating system only accomplishes an energy redistribution; so that in practice only the frequency composition of the offending noise is changed. For example, stiffening sheet metal by stamping ribs into it raises its natural frequencies, but it does not make the sheet metal any the less responsive to resonant excitation of panel vibrations at the new natural frequencies.

Similarly, an ideal mass set into motion has stored kinetic energy which is returned without loss as motion ceases. Greater impulsive or periodic force is required to set larger inertias into motion of a given amplitude, but the larger mass delivers more force upon impact or the return stroke. Heavier systems are harder to excite, but their motions persist longer at their low natural frequencies. It is part of the function of vibration-damping materials to relieve the massiveness requirement in quality manufacture, to permit the use of sheet metals where potential excitation would otherwise require heavy castings.

Furthermore, without the help of damping, the possibility of noise reduction is very remote by trying to adjust the mass-stiffness relationships in order to shift the natural frequencies of machinery components. To shift the frequency of a resonance above the limit of audibility requires increased stiffness without compensating increases of mass, and the shift proceeds only as the square root of the stiffness-to-mass ratio. And, alternatively, the shift of a resonance toward lower frequencies usually results in dangerous sacrifice of strength, and simultaneously brings higher harmonics into play.

Hence the mass-stiffness relationships which are so important in vibration isolation become of only secondary importance in vibration damping, the only important qualification being a preference for obtaining fundamental resonances of the highest frequency consistent with good manufacturing practice and economy. This preference arises from the fact that almost all practical vibration-damping treatments perform more efficiently at higher frequencies.

Dynamic-vibration Absorbers. Vibration-damping materials, by virtue of their mechanical hysteresis, etc., resist motion in any direction and during every portion of the cycle of vibration. And, since they provide definite energy losses during each cycle of vibration, their effectiveness varies generally about proportional to frequency. Hence a vibration-damping treatment of given effectiveness in limiting vibration amplitude at a resonance of one frequency will generally be equally effective at neighboring resonances and more effective at higher harmonics.

So-called vibration dampers do exist, however, which depend for their effectiveness upon the generation of a force which is 180° out of phase with the applied force. Such devices consist essentially of a single spring-mounted mass which is attached to the vibrating system at a single point and tuned to the frequency of most prominent excitation. With the resilient mounted machine or the part to which it is attached, the "damper" constitutes an undamped system with two degrees of freedom in which the parameters are so adjusted that the vibration amplitude of one of the masses (the machine or part) goes to zero at one particular chosen frequency. This is most useful when only a single frequency of excitation is involved as in the case of some constant-speed machinery but if speed varies or if other frequencies of excitation exist even at constant speed, the system fails to limit vibration.   Indeed, a single resonance has been replaced by two resonances, one on either side of the tuned frequency.   Speed variation can then result in amplification, so that the "damper" is worse than useless.

Evidently, such devices are not vibration-damping devices in the same technical sense as defined above.   For the lack of better nomenclature, they are now called dynamic vibration absorbers.   Their design and behavior are widely discussed in technical literature, an excellent treatment being found in Ref. 1.

Damping Inherent to Materials and Structures.   All solid materials exhibit the property of mechanical hysteresis to some extent, and the range of variation between different materials and over wide ranges of temperature and stress is enormous. But relatively few homogeneous materials are inherently damped to an extent which would recommend their use in manufacture solely because of this property, except in extraordinary circumstances.   Developments in the next decade may change this picture, but at present the inherent damping of all materials which are usable for machinery and vehicular construction is orders of magnitude lower than the damping that can be obtained by inexpensive vibration-damping treatments.

Admittedly, among the metals, cast iron has appreciably more hysteresis than cold-rolled steel, and lead far more than either.   But even lead, the classic damping metal, is far surpassed on a practical pound-for-pound basis by simple surface constructions designed for the sole purpose of efficient damping.   The use of lead gaskets in fabricating machinery housings and the use of lead end bells on rotating electrical machinery seem ill-advised in the light of present damping technology.   Furthermore, all attempts have failed in measuring reductions in resonant gear noise that can be attributed to inherent damping of the material of the gear wheel, whereas external damping treatments of the web and rim have accomplished significant reductions. Even in the case of the clear resonant "singing" of marine propeller blades, a change from manganese bronze to cast iron was hardly significant in comparison with the improvement attributable to damping by simple frictional attachments.

However, damping is significantly increased by laminating homogeneous layers, provided the lamination interface is not continuously bonded.   For example, two layers of ⅛-in. sheet steel spot-welded together face to face at frequent intervals constitute a much more highly damped plate than would the solid ¼-in. steel plate. On the other hand, continuous lamination by gluing of thin layers of wood into plywood does not accomplish a comparable increase in damping because no mechanism of surface friction has been introduced to supplement the inherent damping.

In most metal structures, nearly all the damping observed can be attributed to the technique of fabrication.   For example, a good weld can be distinguished from a poor one by its effect on the part's ringing after impact; the poorer the joint, the more damping.   Riveted joints generally contribute more damping than welded ones, and bolted joints more than riveted ones.   And even though the effects are not comparable in magnitude with those of special vibration-damping treatments, noise reductions are clearly detectable which can be attributed to damping inherent to fabrication. For example, one automobile manufacturer encountered unprecedented body rumble when he began welding two cross members in the frame instead of bolting them. The damping contributed by bolting the four surfaces together was appreciable, even though the members were fastened securely with ½-in. bolts.

The damping capacities of various metals have been measured with precision by a number of experimental methods (see Ref. 2 for an extensive survey of results and techniques), but no comparable techniques are in use for measuring, or even ranking accurately, the damping capacities of various other structural materials such as glass, wood, and cork.   Nor are there methods in use for quantitative comparison of the damping contributed by different types of fabrication.   Techniques are under development whereby the damping of new materials can be assessed (e.g., high-density fibrous glass boards, aluminum–balsa wood laminates, metal and cardboard honeycomb laminates, etc.) but the lack of such a ranking procedure has not been felt in the past because, with rare exceptions, semiquantitative impact tests have shown that damping inherent to materials and intrinsic to fabrication is inadequate for noise-reduction purposes when the restrictions imposed by manufacture and use are properly observed. At the present state of damping technology it is still undoubtedly best engineering practice to adopt materials and construction to comply with the factors of strength, durability, weight, cost, etc., with a view to obtaining the necessary damping by incorporating into the design the vibration-damping materials and structures specifically developed for that purpose.

Situations Where Damping Is Beneficial. As evidenced by continued research and application of the other techniques of noise reduction, despite the development of extraordinarily effective vibration-damping treatments, high damping is not a cure-all. Its successful use in noise reduction is limited to only those situations where energy dissipation will manifest itself by reduced vibration amplitude at the radiating surface. Such situations are, however, far from rare in practice.

Resonance. Resonance in a mechanical system is a direct consequence of the mass-stiffness relations whereby, at a certain frequency of excitation, a mass and spring can exchange kinetic and potential energy in synchronism, thereby storing energy as it is received, no matter how slowly. If not dissipated somehow, the energy builds up vibration amplitudes out of all proportion to the exciting forces, and resonant components become so prominent in the noise spectrum of the source that they dominate the radiated noise.

If only one, or a few, resonances existed in a machine, they could be avoided by designing so as to provide no excitation forces at the critical frequencies, but, unfortunately, every plate or bar has a large number of natural frequencies which stand in such complicated relation to one another as to be practically impossible to predict except in the simplest geometries.

A practical example of the distribution and relative importance of resonances is shown in Fig. 14.1, where the loudness of resonant tones produced by exciting an automobile door panel is plotted against the frequency of excitation. Obviously, the task of predicting this spectrum of natural frequencies in order to avoid their steady-state excitation would be absurdly difficult.

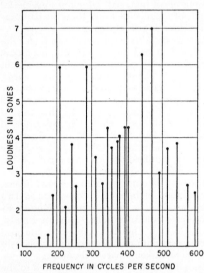

FIG. 14.1. Relative loudness of the natural frequencies of an automobile door panel excited to steady-state resonance by an electromagnet. (*After P. H. Geiger.*[3])

If, now, a steady-state force is generated by the car engine or transmission, it is propagated through the structure to the door panel and radiated very efficiently whenever the forcing frequency corresponds to one of the door's natural frequencies. This situation is the rule rather than the exception with all machines and their housings, because machinery-noise spectra are so rich in discrete forcing components and the response spectra of practical structures are so densely populated with natural frequencies that resonant interaction is bound to occur in practice, especially with machinery of variable speed.

Even when vibration sources are isolated resiliently from radiating surfaces, undamped resonances are excited by the attenuated forces that leak through even the best resilient mounts (see below).

The great effectiveness of vibration-damping treatments in reducing the noise of resonance derives from the fact that the vibration amplitude of most resonating panels is limited in their untreated condition only by the minute inherent damping and by losses due to radiation; i.e., when untreated, the panel amplitude builds up to a level at which energy is radiated at almost the same rate that it is being supplied. And though the energy supply may be minute, the dynamic build-up to efficient radiation will result in loud sound.   The damping treatment is applied to drain off energy fast enough to prevent the dynamic build-up which the mass-stiffness relations favor at resonance.

Figure 14.2 shows what can be accomplished at resonance by application of a commercial deadener to a circular 18-gauge steel panel mounted in rigid clamping rings of 12 in. internal diameter.   The panel was driven through resonance by an electromagnet actuated by an audio oscillator, and the sound pressure level was measured 3 in. away.   A 20-db reduction of resonant sound level is demonstrated, with practically no reduction at frequencies away from resonance.   The downward shift of resonant frequency after application of treatment is due mostly to an increase of the composite mass of the treated panel without compensating increase of stiffness.

In practice, the existence of resonances can be detected by making a slow continuous variation of the speed of a machine from a point considerably below the normal operating range to a point considerably above.   If, as the speed is increased, definite increases in loudness are noted at certain critical speeds (assuming the elimination of standing-wave effects by averaging), this is due either to the excitation of different resonances or to the successive excitation of a single resonance by different exciting components.   When resonances are so prominent that they can be detected by loudness changes in this way, the large amplitude of the resonating part will permit its easy location.

More frequently, however, resonances will manifest themselves during speed change by a change in the quality of the noise emitted as the resonant component appears and disappears.   In discrete-frequency noise spectra measured at different speeds, the existence of resonance is made known by undue prominence of successive noise components as they pass through the fixed frequency of resonance. The possibility must not be overlooked that some resonance may be in evidence at each speed by correspondence of some of the many

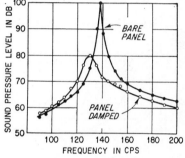

Fig. 14.2. Reduction due to damping of a steady-state panel vibration.   An 18-gauge sheet-metal panel was excited over its resonant range of frequencies by an electromagnet, and the sound pressure level was measured 3 in. away. (*After W. A. Jack.*)

excitation components with any of the large number of natural frequencies possible. This makes the continuously changing character of the noise the only clue to resonance as speed is changed, because total loudness may be comparatively unaffected until the several resonances are eliminated.

It is emphasized also that resonances are excited, and require damping, both when the mechanical-excitation spectrum is continuous, or "white," and when excitation is caused by impinging air-borne sound as in the case of transmission of air-borne sound by housings and partitions.   Quantitative evidence of the effectiveness of damping resonances in both these situations will be presented below.

Direct-impulse Excitation and Shock Excitation.   Whenever a blow is delivered to a solid body of any kind, its natural frequencies are excited and ring out like those of a bell.   The inherent damping or vibration-damping treatment in this case determines both the length of time each tone continues to ring out and, to a lesser extent, the loudness of the initial sound.   Since there is not, in general, an integral relationship between the natural frequencies, the initial sound resulting from the blow will be nonmusical in character, but as decay proceeds the overtones generally disappear more rapidly and the sustained tone of the fundamental mode of vibration persists, especially in simple systems like unconstrained plates and bars.

In sheet-metal structures and housings, the impulse sound of the undamped panel is characterized by what is called "tinniness."   In the consumer's mind, such noise has come to be associated with cheap flimsy construction, so much so that the idea has become a dangerous weapon under the knuckles of competing salesmen. In the enthusiasm of selling, it is seldom pointed out that, under knuckle test, a stronger heavier-gauge sheet metal if untreated would sound considerably tinnier than light sheet metal with even a relatively poor damping treatment concealed behind. For this reason, vibration-damping treatments are used in many commercial products, such as metal furniture and fixtures, even though these products never become serious noise sources on any large scale.

In the case of automobile body panels and similar pressed-steel constructions, the knuckle test is particularly subject to abusive comparisons when the quality of products comes under question. The automotive damping treatment is a multipurpose application required to minimize rain noise on the roof deck, shock noise due to door slamming and road bumps, steady-state resonant excitation as discussed above, and body rumble. The knuckle test does not fairly indicate the effectiveness of a damping treatment in all these respects, except to the ear of an experienced observer. For example, the very mention of the word "tinniness" invariably focuses the observers' attention on the high-frequency resonant components, directly in contradiction to at least half his experience with the blacksmith's anvil and streetcar tracks.

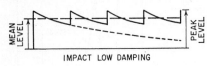

IMPACT LOW DAMPING

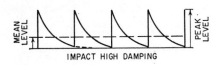

IMPACT HIGH DAMPING

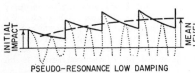

PSEUDO-RESONANCE LOW DAMPING

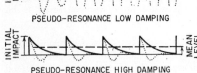

PSEUDO-RESONANCE HIGH DAMPING

Fig. 14.3. Schematics illustrating the influence of damping in reducing the resonant noise of periodic impacts. In the bottom pair of traces, there is assumed to be an integral relation between natural period of vibration and periodicity of impact.

The sustained ringing of an 80-cps tone will not attract his attention during knuckle test unless he is unusually critical. Yet the sustained low-frequency content of the noise is the better criterion for judging the damping effectiveness of the treatment as it bears on the problems of shock and body noise and steady-state excitation of resonances. Evidently also the factor of treatment weight influences the noise of direct impulsive excitation like the knuckle blow or raindrops or pebbles, whereas in the case of shock excitation, such as door slamming and body rumble, only damping affects the noise. The latter is true because when shock is applied to an entire panel the force tending to deflect the panel is proportional to its weight, and its inertia is also proportional to its weight.

Whenever direct impulse or shock excitation becomes recurrent, the noise contribution due to sustained ringing at natural frequencies becomes significant; for example, in office and computing machines and in vehicles on gravel and corduroyed roads. When impulses occur periodically at just the right frequency to contribute energy in phase with vibration already persisting at some natural frequency, a condition of pseudo-resonance develops which ultimately contributes noise levels out of all proportion to the individual impulses involved. The effectiveness of damping in controlling the noise levels produced by these types of excitation is shown schematically in Fig. 14.3.

One type of impulse excitation that is seldom given consideration is that associated with thermal yield in sheet-metal systems, especially the ductwork and piping associated with heating and ventilating systems. With today's thermostatic control, the hot-air ducts are continuously cycling over a temperature range which is wide enough to cause appreciable thermal expansion and contraction of the ductwork. When the inevitable yield points are reached at the duct joints, impulses are communicated to the entire system. The loud noises generated by the flimsy undamped panels occur with maddening irregularity, so that their disturbance factor far exceeds that of the blower in the system.

Vibration Conduction. Quite frequently potential noises do not manifest themselves in the immediate vicinity of the primary source but are propagated as structure-borne vibration to a distant point where they encounter responsive elements which are large enough to be efficient radiators. This situation is especially common in all-metal structures such as seagoing vessels and modern prefabricated buildings. The use of vibration-damping materials in the form of pipe wrappings and flange treatments on girders is of appreciable help in reducing such conduction, but the noise reductions are seldom as dramatic as those obtained by damping the radiating surfaces themselves. The difficulty in using surface damping treatments to limit vibration conduction arises from the variety of different types of conduction waves, some of which do not communicate motion to the surface layer in the direction required for effective dissipation in damping treatments.

Economic Value of Damping Treatments. The economic value of damping arises primarily from the fact that pound for pound the damping of an inexpensive treatment accomplishes a great deal more in limiting the amplitude of steady-state resonances and diminishing the ringing of impulse and shock excitation than do increased massiveness and stiffness of construction. And with the latitude allowed in design by choosing materials and methods of fabrication without regard for inherent damping, the dollar-for-dollar advantage in using a special treatment for damping alone becomes outstanding. Thus the cost savings that can be accomplished in the face of the restrictions of low noise and minimum weight become startling.

An amusing example, but of no small economic consequence, is the household bathtub. The sale of pressed-steel tubs was limited at first by consumer complaints of flimsy construction, not because of structural weakness but because of the noise made by the running water and shower and the occupant's elbows and dropped soap. But the application of a damping treatment surpassed cast-iron construction in providing that feeling of solidity which has apparently come to be so essential to the American's enjoyment of his bath, regardless of his economic status.

More important, though, are the cases where noise and mechanical fatigue must be mitigated without substantial increase of weight, as, for example, in aircraft. The lightweight aircraft soundproofing treatments, though successful in supplementing "weight-law" sound-transmission loss at high frequencies, become transparent at those crucial low frequencies where engine-noise components go into resonance with the fuselage-panel natural frequencies. Efficient damping treatments are now under study which give promise of increasing fuselage attenuations by an average of 8 db or more over the low-frequency range of resonant response, 100 to 250 cps. Such an improvement is comparable with the effect of quadrupling fuselage thickness and weight, which is clearly prohibitive when compared with payload.

MEASUREMENT OF THE EFFECTIVENESS OF DAMPING TREATMENTS

In order to develop and compare practical vibration-damping treatments, a method of measurement had to be devised which would accurately rank a wide variety of materials and structures in order of their noise-reduction effectiveness. The method of test developed and described below, as well as the results upon which most of this chapter is based, are due to two decades of personal research, during which the field of practical vibration-damping treatment was pioneered in conjunction with related research.[3] The "Geiger rating" continues to be the practical gauge of damping effectiveness of surface treatments of all kinds, especially in automotive specifications.

Damping of Treatments and Materials Distinguished. The damping inherent to homogeneous materials, especially metals and alloys, has been the subject of extensive study and precision measurement by various methods involving wires, rods, and bars composed of the material under study.[2] The problem is one of the measurement of one of the inherent properties of a material under various ambient conditions and stresses.

With vibration-damping treatments, on the other hand, the problem is one of measuring its potential effect upon another system, taking into account both the inherent damping of the treatment's components, their mutual interactions, and the effects occurring at the points or surfaces of attachment to the vibrating system. Hence in certain respects the method of measurement must take into account the factors of practical application as well as the technical restrictions of other damping measurements. Only a fraction of the damping treatments available constitute homogeneous adhesive layers, the majority being panel damping treatments of composite structure with special application requirements which profoundly alter their effectiveness. Hence the sampling errors introduced and the complexity of interpreting results make most of the rod and bar methods of measurement inapplicable to practical treatments. The reasons for this will be apparent from a consideration of the technical requirements of the measurements.

Test Requirements for Valid Ranking. Certain requirements are imposed on the measurements by theoretical considerations discussed elsewhere (see Chap. 12). Interpreted in the light of the present test, these include the following restrictions.

Reproducible Undamped Reference System. A simple mechanical system must be devised which is capable of physically accommodating the wide variety of practical panel damping treatments and which is capable of ranking the relative efficiency of the various treatments by their effect on the vibrations of the reference system. Only the steady-state resonant response or else the free vibration of the reference system will be of significance, because it is only under these conditions that damping manifests itself markedly. Hence the reference system must possess an isolated natural frequency of vibration at which it will communicate energy to the damping treatment; i.e., the direction of resonant motion must be essentially perpendicular to the plane of the damping treatment. When vibrating in its resonant mode, the reference system should be essentially undamped in order that the widest possible range of damping will have demonstrable effect. Both the natural frequency and the inherent damping of the reference system should be as insensitive to environmental and uncontrolled changes as possible in order to avoid the necessity for frequent recalibrations and corrections which can only be determined empirically; e.g., correcting for a large shift in natural frequency assumes accurate preknowledge of the damping treatment's frequency characteristic.

Dynamic Massiveness. The selection of an experimental natural frequency essentially establishes the ratio between the equivalent stiffness and the equivalent mass of the reference system at the preferred mode, but another restriction determines the minimum product of the two. Care must be taken that the reference system have sufficient capacity for storing energy to avoid its being overdamped or near critically damped by the most effective of the treatments to be ranked. Otherwise the possibility of distinguishing between high-damping treatments is jeopardized as the system is saturated. Since equivalent stiffness is the less controllable of the two, this requirement amounts to need for dynamic massiveness. Increased mass is also advisable from another point of view; viz., since practical treatments are apt to be more massive than stiff, less natural frequency shift will result from its application to the reference system if the reference system is heavy by comparison.

Dynamic Similarity. In order to rank different treatments accurately, each must be given the same opportunity to perform; i.e., motion must be communicated by the reference system in the same way to any treatment applied.

If each treatment dissipates a definite amount of energy during each cycle of vibration, the same number of cycles per second must be involved in each measurement if the rate of energy dissipation in the reference system is to be the criterion of comparison. Hence either the natural frequency of test must be stable or its shift must be taken into account.

And regardless of the criterion of comparison, whether steady-state resonant amplitude or rate of decay of free vibrations, the mode of vibration of the reference system must be stable; e.g., in the case of flexural vibrations communicated to the panel treatment, there can be no appreciable change in the vibration pattern (i.e., no change in number or migration of nodal lines) unless fortuitously the two amplitude distributions transfer the same vibrational energy from the reference system to the treatment.

With a reference system satisfying the above requirements, the damping effectiveness of different treatments can be ranked by any of several methods based either on excitation of steady-state vibrations at and near resonance or on rate of decay of free vibrations induced at resonance.   The various methods are equivalent and the results can be correlated by simple algebraic transformations as derived elsewhere.   Essentially both methods aim toward a determination of the damping contributed by each treatment as a fraction of that required to critically damp the reference system.   With a constant, even though arbitrary, reference system, these fractions rank the treatments in order of their damping effectiveness.   The choice of method will depend on convenience factors, but the decay-rate method discussed below has the great advantage of insensitiveness to differences in excitation.

Vibration Decay Rate: Thick-plate Test.   *Description of Test Panel.*   The requirements for a suitable reference system for ranking damping treatments by their effect on free vibrations can all be satisfied by a flat cold-rolled steel plate which is 20 in. square and $\frac{1}{4}$ in. thick, provided some care is exercised in the plate's selection, preparation, and suspension.

The practical advantages to selection of a plate of this size are numerous.   Its surface area is great enough to mitigate the effects of sampling errors which tend to be large with some vibration-damping materials.   It is rugged enough to withstand the rough handling of shipment to the manufacturer whose product may require special application or treatment after application.   The natural frequency of its fundamental mode of vibration is 160 cps, a figure selected as most representative of the requirements of the automotive industry, whose early use of panel damping treatments first created the need for a precision ranking method.   The plate's massiveness, nearly 30 lb, avoids the danger of overdamping and minimizes the shift of natural frequency due to application of the treatment.   (The best treatments cause only about 5 per cent of critical damping, and the heaviest treatments in use change the total weight by only about 3 per cent.)   The plate's inherent damping, when properly suspended, is negligibly small and almost independent of temperature change.   It is readily available commercially with adequate homogeneity and thickness tolerance so that, with minimum preparation, several dynamically equivalent panels can be made available for manufacturer's application and aging of several treatments at once in order to study small controlled differences.

In the selection of test panels some must usually be rejected because of inhomogeneities; otherwise it is not possible to adjust the nodal pattern of each plate to obtain the required dynamic similarity.   By careful grinding of the edges of a plate it is possible to adjust somewhat the nodal lines of the fundamental mode of vibration and simultaneously isolate this mode of vibration by shifting all overtones to frequencies considerably above that of the fundamental.   This is important because, if two frequencies are in close proximity, the decay of free vibrations will not be uniformly logarithmic and the decay rate will be difficult to determine accurately.

The suspension of the test panel is designed to accomplish two objectives.   The support points are selected to lie on the nodal lines of the fundamental mode and, if possible, near antinodal positions in the adjacent harmonic modes.   Thus the supports (soft tapered springs tipped with nylon hemispheres, for example) do not interfere with the vibration of the fundamental mode of vibration, and they help damp out the harmonics as rapidly as possible.   When properly suspended, the decay rate of a bare test panel is less than 1.0 db per sec at all temperatures, and the decay envelope becomes logarithmic within a fraction of a second after impact excitation.

Inasmuch as the adjustment of nodal pattern and isolation of fundamental natural frequency place enough restriction on the edge-grinding operation, no attempt is made to adjust the natural frequency of each panel accurately to 160 cps.   Rather a correction is made directly proportional to actual natural frequency, both in accordance with Eq. (12.7) and as verified experimentally with identical treatments on different panels ranging from 131 to 166 cps.

In practice, three different suspensions are used (1) panel vertical; (2) panel horizontal, sample upward; and (3) panel horizontal, sample downward.   Results on the three suspensions are identical for most materials and constructions, except cases where fibrous blankets are septum-loaded by gravity and are pressed differently against the panel in the two possible orientations.

Unless special precautions are taken, erratic results may be obtained in tracing the behavior of low-damping samples as a function of temperature. The difficulties arise because of several causes: failure to control moisture content of the air in the cooled enclosure, resulting in frost deposits which probably affect contact area of the suspension points; insufficient soaking to attain thermal equilibrium of the entire panel and

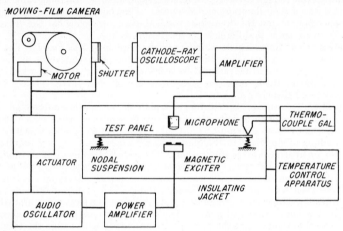

Fɪɢ. 14.4. Schematic block diagram of vibration-damping thick-plate test apparatus. (*After P. H. Geiger.*[3])

sample construction; and possibly a shift of natural frequency and migration of nodal lines with temperature change.

Instrumentation and Measurement. In principle, the experiment requires no more than the accurate measurement of the time in seconds required for the vibration level of the treated panel to decay a specified number of decibels. The instrumentation required to accomplish this simply is shown schematically in Fig. 14.4.

The panel is ordinarily excited by a polarized electromagnet actuated by an audio oscillator which is tuned to the natural frequency of the panel. Under these circumstances only one mode of vibration is excited and the decay is immediately logarithmic once the exciter is de-energized. Of course, the panel can be excited by impact with equally good results provided the decay measurement does not begin until overtones have been damped out.

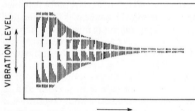

Fɪɢ. 14.5. Vibration-decay curve as traced directly from a moving-film-camera photograph. The horizontal white lines are amplitude reference levels and the vertical white lines are timing marks, as explained in the text. The decay rate represented is 38 db per sec.

The vibration level of the panel is detected as sound by a pressure-sensitive microphone suspended a few inches above the center of the vibrating panel. The decaying signal is amplified and displayed as a horizontal line on a cathode-ray tube, the oscillographic method being one of the many suitable techniques for display and measurement of decay over the short times involved with good damping treatments. A moving-film camera is used to record the decaying trace as a function of time. Figure 14.5 shows one such record obtained. The pairs of white horizontal lines shown on each side of center are the result of opaque calibrating lines marked on the oscilloscope screen. These marks are located carefully so that the sound pressure at the microphone corresponding to the outer pair is accurately e (the base of natural logarithms) times the sound pressure corresponding to the inner pair.   It can be shown that this ratio guarantees optimum accuracy in reading the decay time from the logarithmic decay envelope.   The white vertical marks are the result of a timing signal impressed on the vertical plates of the oscilloscope. The distance between adjacent timing marks represents 0.05 sec.   Recording them eliminates the possibilities of error due to variations in camera-drum speed and differential film shrinkage.

Computed from the record shown in Fig. 14.5, the vibration decay rate of the deadener under test is 38 db per sec at 160 cps.   This represents a contribution of about 0.5 per cent of critical damping of the test panel.   Ranking other vibration-damping treatments with respect to the same arbitrary reference system has resulted in decay rates ranging from 0.5 to 400 db per sec.

For the specification of the damping contribution of treatments ranking as low as 10.0 db per sec and below, the effect of the damping inherent to the bare panel and its suspension must be taken into account.   With each expressed in decibels per second, the arithmetic difference between the decay rate as measured with treatment and the bare-panel decay rate is the actual contribution of the treatment.   This is verified experimentally by altering the damping of the suspension with the same treatment in place and noting the constancy of this difference.

It may be pointed out that the bare-panel oscillograms taken at the same film speed as that used for Fig. 14.5 would be about 18 ft long, indicating the negligible damping of the panel and suspension in comparison with most deadeners when applied in standard thicknesses.

As would be expected from the presence of some frictional damping in a treatment (rather than all being equivalent viscous, see Chap. 12), there is occasional evidence of decay which is not precisely logarithmic.   By varying the reference level above which the decay increment is read, differences in the decay rate can be detected due to nonlogarithmic decay but, surprisingly, the error has never yet been found to be significant compared with the total decay rate measured, except in one case of overdriving a spot-damping frequency-selective deadener, some further properties of which will be discussed in the next section.

Correlation of Results with Other Criteria of Damping Effectiveness.   As obvious as the thick-plate decay-rate measurement now seems, there have been doubts expressed about its general applicability since its development in 1933, the reasoning being that the action of damping treatment on a $\frac{1}{4}$-in.-thick steel plate might be different from the action on sheet metal, for example.   And, of course, the total effect in the two cases is quite different because of differences in both the natural frequency and the dynamic mass involved, the decay rate of any system being dependent on these factors despite constant damping.   For example, despite equality of natural frequency, a given damping treatment will cause more rapid decay of vibrations in a light system than it will in a massive system, not because of different damping action but because the given amount of damping constitutes a greater percentage of critical damping in the lighter system.   This follows directly from the idealized results discussed in Chap. 12 (see *Effect of Damping in a Single-degree-of-freedom System*).

However, in the thick-plate test system, where both natural frequency and mass are sensibly constant, damping treatments are ranked according to their true damping capacity, i.e., according to their ability to contribute toward raising the percentage of critical damping.   And since critical damping is a factor defined in terms of stiffness and mass alone, $c = 2\sqrt{mk}$, two treatments ranked quantitatively on the $\frac{1}{4}$-in. steel plate will be ranked quantitatively the same way on any other size or thickness of panel, the constant conversion factor being determined by stiffness and mass alone. This reasoning is accurate to the approximation that the treatment does not contribute to the stiffness or mass of the panel in varying degrees in the comparison, and that mass and stiffness are interpreted as the dynamic mass and stiffness ordinarily used in idealizing a plate's fundamental mode into a simple spring-mass system of the required natural frequency.

However, reasoning of this kind is not so convincing as experimental correlations between the test method and the actual noise reductions accomplished by treatments of varying effectiveness. A few of the clinching arguments are outlined below, both as demonstrations of the validity of the test method and as evidencing practical application of damping treatments.

Vehicular-noise Measurements and Shock Excitation. The large consumption of vibration-damping materials by the automotive industry required the practical demonstration of the applicability of the test method to ranking automotive deadeners in their relative ability to limit engine- and shock-excited chassis and frame resonances. For this purpose, noise measurements were made inside an automobile running over various kinds of roads at speeds from 20 to 70 mph both at constant speed and under open throttle at various speeds. All the measurements verified the applicability of the test method in that the road measurements ranked the various damping treatments used in the same order of effectiveness as did the laboratory tests.[3] Failure to distinguish in the road tests between the most effective of the damping treatments is clearly attributable to a point of diminishing returns beyond which no increase of damping could manifest itself as noise reduction because body noises were already masked by other noises, such as windage.

Incidentally, this point of diminishing returns was found to vary considerably with placement of the treatment within a single car, and from car to car. On the door panels of one make of car improvement of the treatment decay rate above 12 db per sec yielded no further reductions in running noises, whereas in another make the critical point was reached at 5 db per sec. Yet, on the floor treatment of one of the cars tested, no point of diminishing returns was reached even though treatments were used with decay rates as high as 400 db per sec.*

The noise-reduction effectiveness of vibration-damping treatments has been known to be challenged by experimental "evidence" on frequent occasions in their short history. But, without exception, the evidence arose either from misapplications of the treatment or from misinterpretations of the results. A good example of the latter culminated in the mistaken conclusion that the use of an automotive floor deadener actually increased body rumble. A car with the purported damping layer under the floor carpet was compared with an "untreated" car. The apparently adverse findings were due to the verifiable fact that the carpet laid directly on the metal floor provided more damping than the same carpet isolated from the floor by the purported damping treatment. Hence "treatment" reduced total damping and naturally increased rumble.

Reduction of Steady-state Excitation Levels. That the thick-plate method is valid can be shown further by the existence of a correlation between decay-rate measurements and the levels which build up during steady-state excitation of resonances. One such correlation, remarkable in its quantitative accuracy, is afforded by measurements of sound transmission through circular steel diaphragms of various thicknesses.† With slightly damped diaphragms, resonant excursions of several decibels were noted in the attenuation curves of the fundamental natural frequency and second and third overtones of the panel. The application of damping treatments resulted in increases of attenuation at resonance of precisely the amount predicted from thick-plate decay-rate values when they were adjusted for differences in natural frequency and dynamic mass in accordance with Eqs. (12.7) and (12.8). Such a correlation clearly demonstrates somewhat more than the validity of just the ranking of the effectiveness of damping treatments by the thick-plate decay-rate method.

Good correlations are also found between the computed and experimental suppression of steady-state resonant peaks in the response of mechanically excited two-degree-

---

* These somewhat casual references to quantitative road-test determinations of the relative effectiveness of damping treatments are not meant to imply that such measurements are either easy or economically feasible. The inherent unrepeatability of vehicular-noise measurements dictates extensive sampling and statistical treatment. Indeed, the complexity of these measurements is an important part of the justification for the development of laboratory techniques for ranking vibration-damping treatments.

† Unpublished results of measurements by N. E. Barnett, Engineering Research Institute, University of Michigan.

of-freedom systems with various degrees of damping, where computed results are based on damping ratios deduced from thick-plate decay-rate determinations.[4]

Impulse Excitation: "Tinniness." In so far as damping controls the sound (see below), the thick-plate decay-rate characterizations of panel-damping treatments correlate well with impact-noise studies. When seven identical automobile door panels were each treated with deadeners of different effectiveness, a jury of observers ranked by knuckle test the tinniness of the doors in exactly the order predicted by the measured decay-rate effectiveness of the treatments. More extensive and detailed ranking agreement was obtained when the jury of observers were themselves used in devising and calibrating a "tinniness" meter by which finer discriminations could be made. The tinniness meter is a converted sound-level meter. The plate voltage on the power-output stage is lowered to a value where the tube will overload on the initial impact noise of a measured panel blow, and a slow-acting output meter is used (about 1 sec period, critically damped). Very satisfactory agreement is found between the instrument reading and the jury's subjective judgments of tinniness, and a continuous scale is made available for correlation between damping effectiveness and tinniness.

As suggested above, however, the damping capacity inherent to the treatment is not the only factor which influences tinniness judgments under knuckle impact of automotive door panels. Figure 14.6 is included here to demonstrate the sometimes greater importance of surface density of the treatment. These data were obtained by impact excitation of several door outer panels with various full-area damping treatments having various surface densities and damping capacities. A group of observers independently knuckled and rank-ordered the panels, first on the basis of incremental judgments, and next on the basis of ratio judgments. The individual observer values were then averaged and plotted as shown, relative to the best door, which was arbitrarily assigned a value of 100. Analytical expressions were obtained by least-squares methods for the two curves, yielding the empirical relationships shown on the figure. The fact that thick-plate damping values per se provide essentially no part in the resulting effectiveness by this criterion is shown by the inconsistent scatter of the

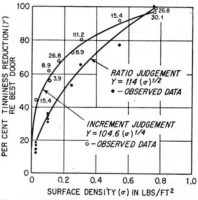

FIG. 14.6. Subjective rating of impact-sound quality of automobile door panels vs. surface density of deadener. Small figures indicate thick-plate ratings of the various treatments in decibels per second. (*After D. C. Apps.*)

thick-plate vibration-decay-rate values specified in the figure for each of the points on the incremental curve. The correlation between decay-rate values and tinniness as discussed previously was obtained using various treatments of closely comparable surface density.

VIBRATION-DAMPING MATERIALS AND STRUCTURES

This section will be devoted to the description of some of the various materials and constructions that are manufactured today for the specific purpose of vibration damping, with mention also of other materials which can be used in this capacity if suitably applied. A tabulation is included of the relative effectiveness of the various classes of materials, and another of manufacturers which are known by the author to supply materials of some of the types described. The damping capacity of all materials will be expressed in terms of the thick-plate decay-rate test described above; i.e., in decibels per second at 160 cps for full coverage of the ¼- by 20- by 20-in. standard test panel, at room temperature unless otherwise specified.

Mastic Deadeners. Mastic deadeners, the most widely used of all materials made solely for the purpose of vibration damping, are supplied in semifluid form for application with a spray gun or trowel. A few are soft enough after drying to indent with the thumbnail, but most of the highly effective compositions are hard and seemingly brittle at room temperatures. Almost all mastic deadeners sold extensively are of asphalt base, either cut-back or emulsion type, with solid content varying from 65 to 85 per cent. Various fillers and fibers are used by different manufacturers. Since high-density granular materials in the mixtures increase their effectiveness, some mastic deadeners are loaded with particles of controlled size. Because of the limited supply of low-cost metal particles, screened sand or marl are ordinarily used for this purpose with some sacrifice of effectiveness. Optimum granule size appears to be dependent on the kind of asphalt and fillers used, as well as on the method used for mixing the final product.

Limitations. Inasmuch as mastic deadeners have been developed primarily for the automotive industry, their damping effectiveness has been sacrificed somewhat to meet the other requirements of this industry; viz., low cost, adherence under severe shock (door slamming, etc.) over a wide temperature range, and ability to stand baking at 300°F soon after spray application without flowing or slipping on even a vertical panel.

Table 14.1. Typical Automotive Specifications for Decay Rate of Mastic Deadeners*

Min decay rate at 70°F, db/sec	Min decay rate over temp. range shown		Air-dry, hr	Bake, hr	At temp, °F
	Decay rate, db/sec	Temp. range, °F			
15	4	0–100	12	0.5	325
9	4	0–100	12	0.5	325
15	4	0–110	...	3	275
11	5	0–110	24	7	225
6†	4	0–110	...	3	160

* All values apply to an application of 0.5 lb per sq ft dry weight.

† Underbody coating, typically designed for high corrosion and abrasion resistance rather than high damping.

Close specifications must also be observed regarding spray rate, abrasion and chemical resistance, and consistency. Some typical specifications for the damping effectiveness of mastic deadeners as required by different automotive manufacturers are shown in Table 14.1.

The wide variability in baking time specified by different manufacturers reflects the fact that the baking is determined by the requirements of the paint to which the deadener performance must conform. Since different paints are used by different manufacturers, a given deadener may not meet the requirements of more than one manufacturer.

Subject to so many restrictions, it is obvious that commercial mastic deadeners will suffer serious limitation outside of automotive use unless specifically reformulated for the differing application. Since the damping effectiveness of mastic deadeners is very sensitive to their baking history, their indiscriminate use at room temperature may result in greatly reduced effectiveness. Most mastic deadeners will ultimately reach their final effectiveness by air drying alone but only after long periods of time, especially in the case of cut-backs where full effectiveness depends on driving off all volatile matter. In one case tested, a mastic deadener reached 90 per cent of its final effectiveness after 5 months of air drying at about 70°F, but another reached only 50 per cent of final value after a year.

Although the appearance of all asphalt-base mastic deadeners is very similar, their damping capacities vary over a remarkably wide range. For applications weighing

0.5 lb per sq ft dry weight, samples have been measured with decay rates as low as 2 db per sec and as high as 32 db per sec. Even the different materials sold by one manufacturer under the same trade name may have widely different mechanical properties and damping capacities. It is particularly important to distinguish the mastics that are manufactured primarily for their corrosion and abrasion resistance, such as automobile undercoatings. These are characteristically low damping.

Hence, in the new application of mastic deadeners, either in production or in experimentation, it is imperative to obtain an efficiency rating on the particular mastic deadener used, especially if any conclusions are to be drawn about the efficacy of damping in a new noise-reduction application. Too often the possibility of damping is thrown out on the basis of an experiment in which the "damping material" used had little or no damping capacity.

Temperature Coefficient. The damping effectiveness of all asphalt-base mastic deadeners shows definite dependence on the temperature. The temperature variations of the decay rate of two typical asphalt-base deadeners are shown in Fig. 14.7.

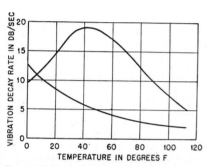

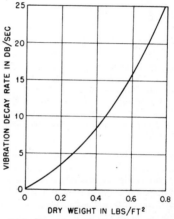

Fig. 14.7. Typical temperature dependences of the damping effectiveness of asphalt-base mastic deadeners, application weight 0.5 lb per sq ft. Materials are available which yield optimum performance at any desired temperature between 0 and 80°F. (*After P. H. Geiger.*[3])

Fig. 14.8. Damping effectiveness of a typical asphalt-base mastic deadener as a function of its application weight. (*After P. H. Geiger.*[3])

The manufacturer can, to a certain extent, vary the composition to shift the temperature of maximum effectiveness; however, no highly effective mastic material has been developed with its optimum performance point above 80°F. Occasionally a mastic deadener is developed which shows two maxima in effectiveness at two different temperatures, but the curves of Fig. 14.7 are typical of the majority of the commercial mastic materials.

Effect of Application Weight. In the application of mastic deadeners, there is considerable advantage in determining regions of large-amplitude panel vibration with a view to concentrating the material there in greater thickness, rather than using the same weight of material for over-all coverage. The reason for this is made clear by Fig. 14.8, where the effectiveness of a typical asphalt-base mastic deadener is plotted as a function of its application weight. The rising characteristic of the curve is such that roughly four times the effectiveness can be obtained by doubling the thickness of the mastic layer. The economy gained by concentrating the treatment into the antinodal vibration areas is obvious then, as discussed in a later section.

Water-soluble Mastic Deadeners. There is at least one non-asphalt-base mastic deadener on the market, which is also furnished in semiliquid form for spray or trowel application. It will adhere to any clean metal surface and will dry in a few minutes, although several days of air drying are required to attain its ultimate effectiveness. It will stand fairly high temperatures and has the great advantage of noninflammability. It is easy to remove in comparison with other mastics because an application need only be soaked a few hours in hot water, even when completely "set," instead of the alternate scrapings and applications of solvent required for removal of asphalt-base deadeners.

The characteristics of the water-soluble mastic can be adjusted over a considerable range by the manufacturer, attaining typical decay rates of 6 to 20 db per sec at room temperature and 6 to 10 db per sec at 150°F. The effect of temperature on the effectiveness of one such water-soluble mastic deadener is shown in Fig. 14.9.

Asphalted Felt. *Description.* Asphalted felts are manufactured by impregnating paper, rag, or asbestos felts of various thicknesses with asphalt in various degrees of

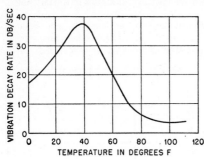

FIG. 14.9. Temperature dependence of the damping effectiveness of a commercial water-soluble mastic deadener. (*After P. H. Geiger.*[3])

saturation. The simplest form is similar to the common "tarpaper" used for building purposes, but most are furnished in greater thicknesses so that the common range of weight is 0.17 to 0.3 lb per sq ft. In most applications the material is cemented to the vibrating surface with an asphalt-base or rubber-base cement, the damping properties being largely independent of the cement used when it is applied in a thin continuous coating. The damping properties of asphalted felts are much less influenced by temperature change than are those of mastic deadeners.

In order to attain greater flexibility, asphalted felts are frequently "needled" by passing the material between rollers which have numerous fine needle points projecting. They are also supplied in "indented" or "waffled" form, the indentations varying widely in shape and size and depth from one material to another. The common range of indentation size is from ¼ to ½ in. in "diameter." Aside from increased flexibility, the indentations of single-ply felts offer no increase in effectiveness, except as used in composite structures as described below.

Table 14.2. Decay Rates on Typical Asphalted-felt Treatments

Description	Decay rate, db/sec (70°F)	Area cemented, %	Weight, lb/ft²
1-ply, plain...................................	1–12	100	0.2–0.4
1-ply, needled...............................	1–6	100	0.2–0.4
1-ply, indented..............................	1–11	100	0.2–0.4
1-ply, indented*.............................	21	None	0.3
Above covered with carpet*.................	85	None	0.7
2-ply, indented + plain......................	6–20	100	0.4–0.6
4-ply, alternate indented and plain...........	20–40	100	0.7–1.0
1-ply, indented, covered with sheet metal.......	400	100	1.0

* For tests made without adhesive, the panel is painted with an automotive floor paint.

Somewhat increased damping effectiveness is available in the form of the multi-ply constructions manufactured, which almost invariably consist of alternate sheets of indented and flat asphalted felt bonded together. Considerably more damping is obtained in the use of multi-ply constructions if the indented rather than the flat side is cemented to the vibrating surface. This difference here represents the first mention of one of the many ways in which different mechanisms of damping can be introduced to supplement that which is inherent to the single bonded damping layer, for, in contrast to mastics, the felts can be applied in any of several different ways.

When cemented uniformly, the damping capacity of the various asphalted felts available varies widely from one product to another because of differences in the fiber base, the amount and kind of asphalt used, and differences in the manufacturing process (see Table 14.2, where the effectiveness of various typical asphalted felts are compared with 100 per cent of their area cemented to the test panel).   But these differences are small compared with those observed between different ways of applying a given material.   As outlined in Fig. 14.10 and below, different mechanisms of damping can be introduced, the effects of which completely dominate the production differences between the materials.

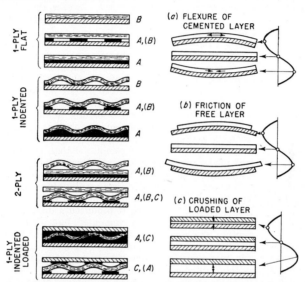

FIG. 14.10. Schematics illustrating some of the mechanisms that come into play with the various applications of asphalted felt.   The crosshatched sections represent the vibrating panel or loading septum, the solid black sections represent cement, and the dashed regions represent asphalted felt.   For each of the treatment sections at the left, there is indicated the damping mechanism at the right which probably contributes most to the treatment's effectiveness.   Compare with Fig. 14.20.

Application.   With single-ply asphalted felts, indented, needled, or plain, cementing is very important, not because of damping properties of the cement but because of the effects of surface friction between the asphalted felt and the vibrating surface.   The poorer the cement from the mechanical standpoint, the greater will be the damping. Indeed, in treating a horizontal surface which is flat enough to assure gravity contact between the surface and the felt over substantially the whole area, the best results are obtained with no adhesive at all.   In other cases, this possibility can be exploited by spot cementing so as to leave the maximum free surface for frictional dissipation.

In cases where an indented felt is surface loaded, for example, covered by a carpet or even by the flat sheet in a two-ply construction, there are two advantages to scant cementing.   First, the load increases the intimacy of contact and enhances frictional effects (see Table 14.2), and second the voids beneath the indentations allow the inertia of the surface load to produce a fiber flexure which further enhances damping (mechanism C in Fig. 14.10).   It is doubly important, then, in the case of composite asphalted indented felt treatments to use cement sparingly enough to avoid filling the indentations.

Use of Loading Septum.   The ultimate exploitation of the effects of surface loading involves the use of a single-ply indented asphalted felt covered with sheet metal.   The felt is cemented to the vibrating surface and the sheet metal is cemented to the felt, in each case with the minimum cement application to avoid filling the indentations. During vibration the inertia of the sheet-metal surface septum makes it tend to stand still, so that the asphalted felt is successively crushed and expanded between the septum and vibrating surface, provided cement has not filled the voids that permit the motion. The fiber flexure that results produces very high damping; indeed, decay rates of 400 db per sec have been obtained with well-indented felt and 26-gauge sheet steel (0.75 lb per sq ft). The best results are obtained with a felt which has rather large indentations, i.e., approximately 15 per foot. The weight per square foot of the loading septum is not critical, the effectiveness of the treatment being somewhat less than proportional to septum weight. It is important, however, that the septum does not communicate with the vibrating surface except through the asphalted-felt layer; otherwise the septum will vibrate in phase with the panel and the inertia lag which crushes the felt will be lost. It is pointed out that septum inertia, not gravitational loading, produces the desired effect: the treatment performs equally well in any position.

Fibrous Blankets. Soft fibrous blankets are not in themselves very effective as vibration-damping treatments, especially if cemented in place. The blanket rides on the vibrating surface with little relative motion between its two surfaces, and, therefore, with little fiber flexure and energy dissipation. However, when a loading septum is used and the blanket is at most spot-cemented in place, the combination ranks with the best of the vibration-damping treatments. Evidently the effect of the septum is similar to that described above with indented asphalted felt; hence, in this case again, the mechanical isolation of the septum from the vibrating surface is important.

Fig. 14.11. Rubber dashpad fasteners used in fastening blanket-septum treatments to sheet-metal surfaces. The fasteners seal up the attachment holes and hold the treatment firmly in place without rigid connection between septum and vibrating panel.

The increase in effectiveness attributable to the use of a septum is indicated by the following figures: A Fiberglas blanket weighing 0.028 lb per sq ft produced a decay rate of 6 db per sec when used alone, not cemented, but, when covered with a septum weighing 0.315 lb per sq ft, the decay rate increased to 95 db per sec. With many lightweight blankets, the decay rate can be roughly approximated as proportional to the total weight of the blanket-septum combination.

Although the kind of fiber and method of bonding have some effect on the blanket's damping capacity, the differences are not pronounced; hence the particular blanket can be chosen on the basis of other considerations. For example, the blanket-septum combination is valuable for its thermal-insulation properties as well as vibration damping, so that thermal conductivity of the blanket may influence its choice. Furthermore, with a loss of only 10 per cent in total inertia, the septum can be perforated and rendered acoustically transparent, so that the sound-absorptive properties of the blanket can be utilized. In this case, the absorption coefficients of the blanket would influence its choice. From the standpoint of vibration damping, suitable blankets are available composed of fibers of glass, cotton, flax, jute, kapok, wood, mineral wool, reclaimed wool, milkweed, etc. Most of these blankets are available in various densities and thicknesses, and some with controlled fiber size.

Inasmuch as the septum serves only as inertia, any material suitable to the other requirements of the application will suffice. For example, sheet metal has the obvious advantage of being fireproof and easily cleaned, but heavily loaded sheet rubber has the sometimes greater advantage of easily conforming to curved and irregular surfaces.

Blanket-septum damping treatments are very advantageous in cases where the sound-transmission characteristics of the treated panels must not be impaired. Their use as the dashpad against the automobile firewall is a good example. The soft blanket helps seal both heat and noise from the openings around the car controls that pass through the dashpad and firewall. Easy removal of the treatment where servicing access is required can be accomplished by the use of rubber fasteners of the kind shown in Fig. 14.11. They have the advantage that they adequately seal the opening through which they are inserted.

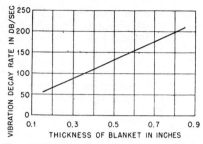

FIG. 14.12. Damping effectiveness of jute blanket septum-loaded with 0.3 lb per sq ft panel board. The curve represents a rough approximation only, other factors besides blanket thickness affecting damping to some extent. (*After P. H. Geiger.*[3])

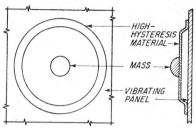

FIG. 14.13. Frequency-selective deadener unit. One of many possible configurations in which a localized mass is supported on high-hysteresis material which is embossed out from the vibrating panel.

Thick-plate decay-rate measurements on automotive-dashpad constructions provide an approximate basis for predicting the damping capacity of blankets as a function of thickness when used with a heavy septum. The relation plotted in Fig. 14.12 was deduced from measurements on jute blankets with a panel-board septum weighing 0.3 lb per sq ft. The approximation is rough because of differences in fiber content and surface character of the blankets, but it is more useful than comparison of blanket weight with its damping because, in the case of a heavy septum, the thickness of a blanket has a greater influence than does its weight.

Frequency-selective Deadener. There is under development at the present time a new type of vibration-damping treatment* which is capable of being broadly tuned to give maximum effectiveness over any desired range of frequencies. Its unique features and potential value in damping very low frequency resonances make it worthy of careful consideration.

Description. The damping unit consists essentially of a sheet of material which has high mechanical hysteresis (the diaphragm) and a concentrated mass (the attached mass) which is supported by the diaphragm in such a way that it is free to vibrate. Figure 14.13 shows one of the many possible configurations. A sheet of damping material, such as asphalted felt, is embossed so that circular portions will stand out away from the vibrating surface to which the sheet is cemented. The free portion constitutes a diaphragm of damping material to which the motion of the vibrating surface is communicated around its entire periphery. If nothing else is done, the material is less effective in damping in this configuration than it would be when laid flat against the vibrating surface, but if a mass is attached at the center of the diaphragm (a lump of loaded asphalt, for example) the effectiveness is remarkably improved. With the inertia concentrated at

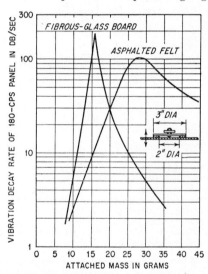

FIG. 14.14. Comparison of the 180-cps damping effectiveness of two 3-in.-diameter frequency-selective deadeners with different diaphragm materials. The vibration-decay rate of the 180-cps plate is plotted against the attached mass on each damper, respectively.

* U.S. Patent No. 2,541,159.

its center, the peripheral edges of the diaphragm follow the panel vibration and the center of the diaphragm tends to stand still, so that considerable flexure is induced in a material with high mechanical hysteresis, with high damping as the result.

By this reasoning, the diaphragm flexure should become more pronounced the greater the attached mass, and the damping capacity of the unit should be nearly proportional to the weight of the concentrated mass. However, if the effectiveness of a given type of diaphragm material is investigated as the attached mass is varied, the results of Fig. 14.14 are typically obtained. On a test plate of given natural frequency (180 cps, in this case) the damping effectiveness, or decay rate in decibels per second, shows a pronounced maximum for a particular weight of attached mass, a sharp maximum in the case of fibrous-glass board as a diaphragm and a broad maximum in the case of an asphalted-felt diaphragm.

In the laboratory, the tuned deadener unit takes the convenient form shown in Fig. 14.15, where a spacer ring of any convenient material communicates the panel vibration to the diaphragm periphery, and the attached mass is made up of interchangeable sets of brass weights. This allows easy experimental changes in both diaphragm material and attached mass.

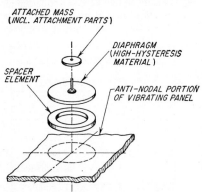

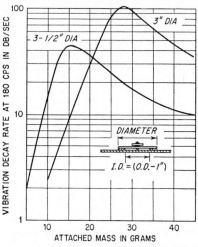

Fig. 14.15. Experimental frequency-selective deadener unit. This laboratory configuration is convenient for experimentation with different diaphragm materials and varying attached mass. The spacer element, serving only to communicate panel vibration to the diaphragm periphery, can be of any convenient stiff material.

Fig. 14.16. Comparison of the 180-cps damping characteristics of two asphalted-felt frequency-selective deadener units of different size. The vibration-decay rate of the 180-cps test panel is plotted against the attached mass on each damper, respectively.

When the damping effectiveness of two identical diaphragms of different diameter is compared as a function of attached mass, the results shown in Fig. 14.16, for asphalted-felt diaphragms 2 and 2½ in. free diameter, respectively, are obtained typically.

It appears from these data that damping effectiveness is a function of both the mechanical hysteresis of the diaphragm material, and the mass-stiffness relations of the mass riding on the diaphragm. However, an idealization of this deadener unit into the simple mass-spring-damper combination of the damped vibration absorber is not possible, because there is no evidence of the steady-state amplifications that are characteristic of tuned absorbers at frequencies somewhat removed from their tuned frequency.

A complete characterization of the damping capacity of a given tuned deadener unit requires the investigation of the vibration decay rate of test panels of different natural frequency, if the test method described above is used so that comparisons with other deadeners can be made directly. In practice square test panels are used with different thicknesses and dimensions, and the decay rates obtained are corrected to compensate for their different dynamic masses.[5]   The results of a complete characterization are shown in Figs. 14.17 and 14.18 for a unit with a 2½-in. free-diameter diaphragm of single-ply asphalted indented felt.   In Fig. 14.17 the damping effectiveness is plotted as a function of the weight of the attached mass at several natural frequencies ranging from 51 to 180 cps, and in Fig. 14.18 the same data are plotted as a function of frequency for several selected values of attached mass.   The particular attached mass that is required to obtain damping of given effectiveness with this same damper unit is plotted against frequency in Fig. 14.19.   The tuning characteristics are such that they cannot readily be predicted from static-stiffness measurements on the diaphragm, the dynamic stiffness apparently being a function of both frequency and amplitude for at least some diaphragm materials.

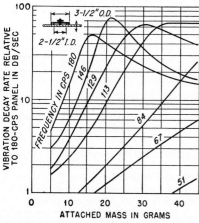

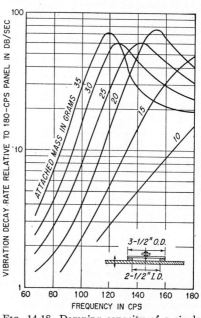

FIG. 14.17. Damping capacity of a single frequency-selective deadener unit fabricated of asphalted felt.   Damping capacity is indicated by the decay rate of the fundamental mode of vibration of various test panels. Decay rates are corrected for differences between the weights of the test panels.   The decay rates of the various panels are plotted as a function of the attached mass on the damper.   Compare with Figs. 14.18 and 14.19.

FIG. 14.18. Damping capacity of a single frequency-selective deadener unit fabricated of asphalted felt.   The vibration-decay rates due to the damper, each corrected for differences in test-panel masses, are plotted against panel natural frequency for various values of the attached mass on the damper.   Compare with Figs. 14.17 and 14.19.

Application.   The great value of the frequency-selective deadener arises from its ability to provide damping at very low frequencies where only massive applications of other vibration-damping treatments can accomplish the same result.   Inasmuch as its tuning characteristic is broad, adequate damping is also provided at all other frequencies provided panel coverage is extensive enough to ensure that all frequencies are communicated to the damper diaphragm.   But if only one damper is used at the antinode of the lowest-frequency mode of the vibrating panel (see next section), some of the higher-frequency modes are apt to remain undamped, not because the damper is incapable of handling them but because their motion is not communicated to the damper diaphragm if the damper happens to be located near one of the nodal lines of the higher-frequency modes.   Where weight economy dictates the use of only one spot damper, this difficulty is easily overcome by using a light continuous treatment (mastic or felt) which damps the high-frequency modes, in conjunction with one damper tuned and positioned to damp out the low-frequency vibrations. In this way a treatment consisting of 0.15 lb per sq ft application of felt in addition to one damper weighing about 1.5 to 2.0 oz is capable of damping a standard ¼- by 20- by 20-in. test panel to the extent that it sounds as dead as white pine under a knuckle blow.

Miscellaneous Deadeners. In addition to the four main classes of vibration-damping treatments and structures discussed above, several other materials have been tried for vibration damping, some successfully and others not. A few are described below by way of completeness and by way of precaution, the more recent developmental advances necessarily being omitted until commercial products are released.

Waterproofed Crepe Paper. When several sheets of waterproofed crepe paper are sewn or spot-cemented together, the resulting blanket has both vibration-damping and sound-absorbing properties. For structures consisting of from 5 to 25 thicknesses of crepe paper, vibration-decay rates have been measured from 5 to 60 db per sec, the latter figure being for a total treatment weight of 0.6 lb per sq ft.

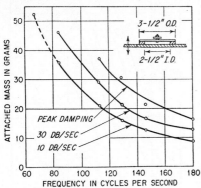

FIG. 14.19. Tuning characteristics of a single frequency-selective deadener fabricated of asphalted felt. The attached mass required to obtain given damping effectiveness is plotted against frequency. Compare with Figs. 14.17 and 14.18.

Waterproofed Pleated Paper. Flat sheets of waterproofed paper can be pleated in any number of ways in order to induce frictional action between pleats during vibration. Obviously, the damping capacity of such a treatment depends markedly on the details of its manufacture and its application.

Laminated Mica. When small thin pieces of sheet mica are cemented together to a thickness of about 0.03 in. with a slow-drying cement, the material is effective for vibration damping when it is fresh, but as it dries out it loses its effectiveness. One such material weighing 0.22 lb per sq ft produced a decay rate of 43 db per sec when first tested, but after 4 months' drying at room temperature, the decay rate of the same material had dropped to 3 db per sec. Despite this progressive failure, mica constructions of this type have been used by the aircraft industry.

Laminated Asbestos Paper. The aircraft industry has also used treatments made up by cementing together thin sheets of hard asbestos-base paper. With such structures decay rates are obtained which range from 1.2 to 6 db per sec; i.e., comparable with mastics and single-ply asphalted felts but with the advantage of fire resistance.

Loosely Felted Fibers. Very pliable fiber blankets are made by loosely felting reclaimed fibers, mostly wool or cotton, and sewing them between sheets of crepe or pleated paper. The blankets conform easily to curved surfaces, but their damping effectiveness depends mainly upon septum loading as do most fibrous blankets and felted materials.

Sheet Asphalt. Heavy sheets of asphalt can be manufactured by applying a layer of asphalt composition to thick paper, and then applying enough talc to prevent the sheets from sticking together during handling and shipment. When applied to a heated metal surface, the asphalt will soften and adhere the assembly firmly in place. As regards vibration damping the material represents little more than a handling variation in the use of asphalt-base mastic deadeners, though less development has been devoted to optimizing their damping properties. They differ in the one important respect that they never harden to the extent that most mastics do, so that they will unbond again when exposed to high temperatures.

Structural Fiber Boards. Attempts have been made to use for vibration damping various fiber boards of the kind used for sheathing and plaster base in the building industry and also the fiber ceiling tiles used ordinarily for sound-absorption purposes. Among those tested in a damping capacity, none is as effective as other materials which are cheaper and easier to apply.

Sponge Rubber. Most attempts to use ordinary sponge rubber as a damping treatment have failed, because the resilient properties that make it so valuable in vibration isolation do not contribute to its damping capacity. Special high-hysteresis rubbers have been compounded, however, but their resilient properties and "feel" are quite different from ordinary sponge rubber. And the damping effectiveness of some of the special high-hysteresis rubbers is extraordinarily sensitive to changes in temperature.

Summary of Vibration-damping Materials and Structures. In the chart of Fig. 14.20, an attempt has been made to collect together the information presented above as regards the relative effectiveness of the commonly used damping materials and structures. Ranking is based solely on 160-cps decay rate at room temperature. It is obvious that the choice of a particular treatment for a given application should

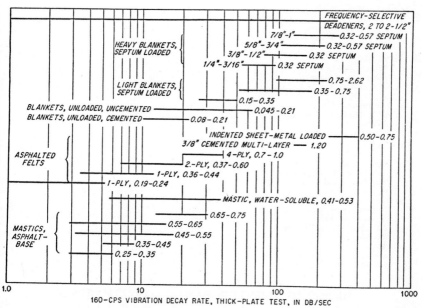

Fig. 14.20. Relative effectiveness of vibration-damping materials and structures. Surface weight of treatment in pounds per square foot shown in parentheses. See text for meaning of ranking criterion.

be governed by numerous other considerations; e.g., cost and weight limitations, temperature dependence, flame resistance, and removability, and particularly the frequencies to be damped, the weight of the panels to be damped, and the area coverage permissible, which are the subjects for discussion in the next part of this chapter.

There are several manufacturers that are known by the writer to be supplying the various types of damping materials discussed above. The reader must not expect too close a correlation between the particular products supplied by these manufacturers and the relative effectiveness of materials as summarized in Fig. 14.20, because data on all their products have not necessarily been included in the figure, and some of the data in the figure apply to products of manufacturers other than those listed.

PARTIAL LIST OF MANUFACTURERS*

1. Mastic deadeners, asphalt base:
   a. Benjamin Foster Company
      4635 West Girard Ave.
      Philadelphia 31, Pa.
   b. Daubert Chemical Company
      4700 South Central Ave.
      Chicago 38, Ill.
   c. Davison Chemical Corporation
      Baltimore 3, Md.
   d. Intercoastal Paint Corporation
      13th St. and Southern Railway
      East St. Louis, Ill.
   e. Minnesota Mining and Manufacturing Company
      Adhesive and Coatings Division
      411 Piquette Ave.
      Detroit 2, Mich.
   f. W. & M. Products Corporation
      13650 Ten Mile Road
      East Detroit, Mich.

2. Mastic deadeners, water soluble:
   a. Mute-Ize Corporation
      3802 Board of Trade Building
      Chicago 4, Ill.

3. Asphalted felt:
   a. Flintkote Company
      Automotive Division
      14201 Schafer Ave.
      Detroit, Mich.
   b. The Ruberoid Company
      307 N. Michigan Ave.
      Chicago 1, Ill.

4. Fibrous blanket materials:
   a. Central Felt, Inc.
      2614 John R. St.
      Detroit 1, Mich.
   b. Detroit Gasket and Manufacturing Company
      12640 Burt Road
      Detroit 23, Mich.
   c. Gustin-Bacon Manufacturing Company
      210 West Tenth St.
      Kansas City 7, Mo.
   d. LOF-Glass Fibers Company
      1810 Madison
      Toledo 2, Ohio
   e. Owens-Corning Fiberglas Corporation
      Newark, Ohio

DESIGN OF VIBRATION-DAMPING TREATMENTS

With the availability and relative effectiveness of vibration-damping materials and structures established, the questions of how much material and where best to put it now arise.

Area Coverage Required. The typical vibration-damping problem is comprised of a complicated panel which has an infinite number of natural frequencies, any of which may be excited by steady-state forces, impulses, or shock. The vibration of the panel at any one of its natural frequencies is characterized by a complex pattern of motion in which irregularly shaped areas vibrate in opposite directions on either side of the so-called nodal lines which constitute the loci of points of zero motion. The points of maximum vibration are called antinodes. When several natural frequencies are excited simultaneously their characteristic vibration patterns are superimposed, so that the nodal lines of one mode of vibration may be set into motion by vibration in another mode. Hence it is only during vibration in a single pure mode that the change of phase encountered in passing a nodal line is precisely 180°.

* Some manufacturers of vibration-damping materials are listed here. The listing is not complete and does not constitute a recommendation of particular products.

Full Coverage. A full coverage of the entire vibrating panel will assure that the motion of every possible vibration mode of the panel will be communicated to the damping material and its energy dissipated. If material is applied in a patch without knowledge or regard for the vibration patterns of high-frequency modes, some of the high-frequency tones are almost certain to remain undamped. For example, if a 10-in.-square patch of damping material or a single frequency-selective spot damper is applied at the center of the ¼- by 20- by 20-in. standard test panel, the so-called edge tones of the plate continue to ring out after a blow is delivered even though the fundamental 160-cps natural frequency is well damped by the treatment at its anti-node. On the other hand, the edge tones of the test panel are of much higher frequency than the fundamental mode so that they are much easier to damp out because of the increasing efficiency of most deadeners with frequency. Hence it would be uneconomical to cover the entire panel with a treatment that was designed to be effective at the low fundamental frequency. The economical and completely satisfactory compromise is the use of a light over-all treatment, which provides adequate damping of high-frequency modes, in conjunction with a supplementary heavy, and preferably tuned, treatment at the antinode or antinodes of the low-frequency vibrations.

Spot Attachment of Damper. The possibility is frequently suggested of attaching a mechanical dashpot of high viscous damping capacity directly at the antinode of the troublesome low-frequency mode. The overriding objection to this idea is the fact that the contact of the dashpot will so alter the vibration pattern of the panel that the attachment point will become a node, so that no motion will be communicated to the dashpot, and hence no damping will be accomplished. The spot damper described above as a frequency-selective deadener is not subject to this objection because it rides on the vibrating panel without working in contact with the stationery environs. It has been demonstrated repeatedly that a spot damper of the latter type does not distort the vibration pattern but rather reduces its amplitude by participating in the motion and internally dissipating the energy. Hence both the frequency-selective spot damper and such highly effective treatments as indented asphalted felt loaded with sheet metal lend themselves nicely to the possibility of antinodal application to serve as the low-frequency supplement to cheaper but less effective over-all treatments designed for high-frequency damping.

Antinodal Treatment. The advantages of antinodal treatment in controlling the lower-frequency vibrations are appreciable even if a frequency-selective deadener is not used. With mastic deadeners, for example, the bulk of the material can be concentrated at the antinodal areas, resulting in two distinct economies: (1) the material that was wasted at and near the nodal lines where it received no excitation and the material that was wasted in overdamping the higher-frequency modes is now concentrated where it is needed; and (2) the increased thickness at the antinodal positions performs more efficiently, per pound of material involved, because of the rising characteristic shown in Fig. 14.8.

The disadvantage to antinodal treatment is the need for a rather elaborate vibration survey to determine the antinode locations. Hence an over-all economy is realized only in cases where a great number of identical items are to be treated. And the adjective "identical" is important because close production tolerances must usually be held in order that the vibration patterns of the panels of the finished product will be sufficiently similar to accommodate the same treatment. Automotive panels correspond very well, but the industry pays a considerable premium on body steel because of the close tolerances specified in composition and thickness.

Fortunately, however, the patterns of the lower-frequency modes, where antinodal treatment is most advantageous, are the patterns least affected by production differences. Hence where there are willingness and need to focus attention on low-frequency antinodes, with higher frequencies damped by a light over-all treatment, an antinodal vibration-damping treatment is practical for nearly every production item.

Design of Antinodal Spot Treatments. The successful application of an antinodal treatment, even in conjunction with an over-all treatment for high frequencies, requires an extensive survey of each panel that is to be damped. The predominant natural frequencies must be identified and their separate antinodes located with fair precision. But the systematic approach to this problem is not so staggering as it seems.

Location of Antinodes: the Nodagraph. The panel in question is excited by a small nonpolarized electromagnet driven by an audio oscillator and power amplifier. No d-c polarizing current is used because it is desirable to have the vibromotive force exerted at double the frequency of the exciting current in order to allow the possibility of eliminating any stray magnetic coupling between the exciter and probe microphone by using an analyzer in the microphone circuit tuned to double the oscillator frequency.

As the oscillator is swept very slowly through the frequency range, the presence of natural frequencies can be easily detected by ear as resonant radiated sound, or detected and measured by a microphone in front of the panel. If the relative amplitudes of the resonances are to be measured with any precision, such as in the case of the automobile-door-panel spectrum shown in Fig. 14.1, care must be taken to average out the variations due to standing waves in the measurement room, but such measurements are seldom necessary because only the frequencies of the very prominent tones are really needed in the design of an antinodal treatment. And only the low-frequency spectrum need be surveyed with any accuracy, the higher-frequency patterns being too complicated for successful antinodal treatment.

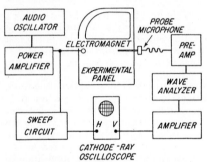

FIG. 14.21. Block diagram of nodagraph. The horizontal sweep circuit is synchronized with the driver voltage so that nodal lines at resonance can be detected by the phase reversal at the probe microphone. (*After P. H. Geiger.*[3])

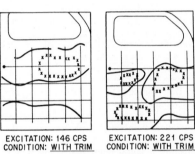

FIG. 14.22. Vibration patterns of automobile door panels as traced from photographs of chalk-nodagraphed doors. Solid lines are nodal lines. *X*'s enclose antinodal areas. Exciter position at dot; excitation frequency as indicated. (*After P. H. Geiger.*[3])

Once the low-frequency spectrum is established, the task of surveying the vibration patterns is started at the lowest-frequency mode, not necessarily at the loudest resonant mode. The reason for this choice is that the application of the spot damper at the antinode of the lowest-frequency mode will invariably reduce the loudness of the higher-frequency modes, but not necessarily the converse.

The vibration pattern is most conveniently surveyed by means of a system called the nodagraph, the block diagram of which is shown schematically in Fig. 14.21. A miniature velocity microphone is connected through suitable amplifiers and a wave analyzer to the vertical plates of a cathode-ray oscilloscope. The horizontal plates are connected to a sweep circuit which is synchronized with the voltage output of the exciting oscillator. The image on the oscilloscope screen is to be one cycle of the sine wave, but since the sweep circuit is synchronized with the exciting voltage, the position of the wave on the screen will be determined by the relative phase of the radiated sound at the microphone.

In practice, the microphone is moved along the vibrating surface at a distance of about $\frac{1}{4}$ in., but this distance is not critical; so the microphone can be hand-held. As the microphone passes a nodal line, the phase of the sound wave shifts 180° and the screen image will reverse suddenly from one side of the horizontal axis to the other. With a piece of chalk in one hand and moving the microphone back and forth with the other, the positions of the phase reversals can be marked down so that the nodal lines can be plotted directly on the panel in a comparatively short time. As regards the location of nodal lines and antinodes, the position of the exciter is not at all critical, inasmuch as any distortions of the resonant nodal patterns are found to be localized in its immediate vicinity.

The vibration patterns of two of the natural frequencies of an automobile door panel are shown in Fig. 14.22 as traced from photographs of the chalk-marked doors. The nodal lines are indicated by the irregular curves drawn as solid lines, and the crosses outline the areas wherein the vibration amplitude exceeds one-half of the maximum. Antinodes are also located accurately enough with the nodagraph because the sound levels registered are surprisingly insensitive to slight variations of the distance between the microphone and panel, provided the distance is roughly $\frac{1}{4}$ in. as judged by eye. Hence the points of maximum amplitude can be located where the effectiveness of the damping treatment will be optimum in reducing the amplitude of this mode of vibration.

Effectiveness of Antinodal Damping Treatments. Repeated nodagraph surveys at each successively higher natural frequency will, with most panels, reveal a fortunate clustering of the antinodes of different modes of vibration. As frequency increases, the antinodal areas become smaller but more numerous; so that the probability of at least one high-frequency antinode falling at or near the position of a low-frequency antinode increases progressively with frequency. This circumstance sometimes permits completely adequate panel damping at all frequencies by the application of only two or three spot treatments, with the surprising result that the sound of knuckle-test excitation becomes far more uniform over the surface than it would in the case of an over-all damping application that damps low frequencies less efficiently than the higher ones.

The savings in total treatment weight that can be effected by a carefully designed spot treatment are indicated by the results of a study of a series of automotive-door-panel treatments. It was found that a spot treatment could be devised with mastic deadeners that was fully as effective as an over-all treatment with a savings of two-thirds in weight. A satisfactory spot-damping treatment for automotive door panels can also be designed which requires only three frequency-selective spot dampers, so that total treatment weight becomes less than 6 oz for a modern tudor door panel.

In most practical applications, however, it is best to regard the antinodal treatments as heavy localizations of damping for control of low-frequency resonances, using a lightweight over-all treatment for control of higher frequencies.

Amount of Damping Material Required. The problem of how much damping material, or how effective a damping treatment, is required in a given application is always best determined experimentally, using a few general rules and simple computations to guide a "trial-and-error" determination.

The effectiveness of the damping treatment required by a given noise-reduction problem is governed by two general considerations. Firstly, how much additional noise reduction can be accomplished by increasing the damping capacity of the treatment; e.g., where is the point of diminishing returns for the given application? And, secondly, how much of a given material, or how heavy must be the loading septum of the treatment, etc., in order to provide the damping capacity required?

The first consideration depends on factors other than damping capacity; indeed, it amounts to an assessment of the relative importance of resonant, as against forced, vibrations in producing the noise in question. If the answer is not obvious from spectrum analysis, the question of how much can be accomplished by damping can best be answered by giving damping a fair chance; i.e., by applying a damping treatment of extreme known effectiveness, regardless of the treatment's ultimate practicality, for the sole purpose of determining the maximum noise abatement that the damping mechanism can contribute. If the noise reduction is found significant enough to exploit, the problem of practicability and economy of treatment can then be attacked systematically with the incentive of guaranteed noise reduction without the tedium and expense of noise reduction "at the source." With only a few trials, using successive treatments of progressively lesser effectiveness, it is easy to locate the point of diminishing returns where the effect of further damping of resonant-noise components is masked by noises from other sources. By this procedure, there is established the minimum of damping capacity that is required of a treatment which will just provide the practical maximum of noise reduction that is attainable by any amount of damping in the given application. Once this is established, the design of a practical treatment can be initiated to take into account the thermal requirements, weight and space factors, and whatever other restrictions may be imposed on the treatment by the specific application.

It is at this point in the treatment design that the relative effectiveness of various damping materials and structures becomes important, but not before this point. One consults Fig. 14.20 as regards the relative effectiveness of various materials only after the magnitude of one's damping requirement is established by trial and error as outlined above. The fact that Fig. 14.20 constitutes no more than a relative ranking of materials and structures with respect to an arbitrary test system of course emphasizes this point. What weight of mastic deadener is required to duplicate the performance of the blanket material that may have been used for convenience in trial and error is a question that can be answered by data of the kind collected in Fig. 14.20, but these data alone cannot specify how much treatment is required by a given noise-reduction job.

Depending, of course, upon the importance of economy of treatment, the following steps might constitute best design procedure. The panel, or panels, which are subject to resonant excitation, either steady-state or impulsive, are first located. If their resonant frequencies are high, damping will be easy and the mere application of a light over-all treatment will constitute the entire treatment design. But if there are low-frequency resonances excited, or if the vibrating elements are massive, the damping treatment requires careful engineering. For maximum economy in large production, the optimum location of treatment is the first step; i.e., in the design of an antinodal spot treatment as outlined above, but where economy is of less importance, over-all coverage constitutes the point of departure even at low frequencies. But in either case, the determination of the amount of material required or the structure to be used, either at antinodes or over-all, requires the initial application of a treatment of extreme effectiveness as described above.

A treatment of effectiveness equivalent to a decay rate of about 150 db per sec in Fig. 14.20, i.e., equivalent to about 2 per cent of critical damping for the thick plate, is a good starting point in the trial-and-error process. For resonances at frequencies lower than 160 cps, which is the reference frequency in Fig. 14.20, the trial treatment must be proportionally more effective; e.g., damping an 80-cps resonance may require a trial treatment of 300 db per sec in the 160-cps decay-rate test. Conversely, however, for panels of lesser massiveness than the test plate, the trial treatment may have proportionally lower decay rates in Fig. 14.20; e.g., a 10-lb sheet-metal panel resonating at 160 cps can be damped to 2 per cent of critical damping by a treatment with a 160-cps decay rate of only 50 db per sec as read from Fig. 14.20. Hence the approximately inverse proportionality between damping effectiveness and effective panel weight, and the direct proportionality to frequency, allows the use of Fig. 14.20 in selecting the trial treatments for use in locating the point of diminishing returns. And once this point is established, the 160-cps decay rate of the optimum trial treatment allows the use of Fig. 14.20 in selecting the equivalent damping materials or structures which may be more suitable to the particular application.

The reader will recognize immediately that the procedures outlined in the preceding paragraphs, involving as they do stepwise noise measurements and decay-rate characterizations, represent treatment design carried to an extreme justified only in large-scale production. However, the laboratory worker and noise-reduction consultant will have no difficulty in abstracting the salient features and approximations that lead to effective damping treatments without extensive measurements.

SOME VALUABLE APPLICATIONS OF VIBRATION-DAMPING MATERIALS

Not all the valuable applications of vibration-damping materials are so immediately obvious as those used in the examples above, and the magnitude of the noise reduction that can be accomplished is not readily appreciated at a glance in some applications. A few outstanding examples, too frequently overlooked, are cited briefly below.

Compliant Machinery Foundations. Resilient mounted machinery is not always set up on the ideally rigid or infinitely massive foundation which is usually assumed to exist in the simple development of resilient mounting theory (see Chap. 12). Responsive resonances sometimes exist in the foundation and associated structure (aboardship, for instance) which are capable of storing the energy that "leaks" through a resilient mount even in the nominally isolated range of frequencies. In the absence of damping, amplifications appear in the transmissibility curves of the mounted system as the foundation resonates with the machinery forces coupled through the mounts (see Chap. 13, *Special Problems in Isolation, Resilience of Support*).

Experimental evidence of the ability of practical vibration-damping treatments to mitigate the effects of foundation resilience is shown in Figs. 14.23 and 14.24. In the first figure, the sound pressure level measured near the ¼-in. steel wall of a motor housing is plotted as a function of motor rotation frequency. The motor was set up on resilient mounts, and its shaft was unbalanced to generate periodic forces along the axis of the mounts. With the housing undamped (solid curve), the sound level peaked

sharply at two frequencies in the range investigated: first at 48 cps, the expected resonance of the motor on its mounts, and second at 150 cps, the fundamental flexural resonance of the housing wall. With the application of a loaded fibrous-

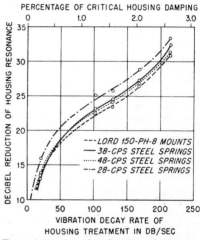

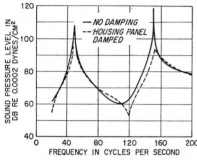

FIG. 14.23. Comparison of sound levels adjacent to a motor housing panel, damped and undamped; off-balanced motor "isolated" from housing by 48-cps resilient mounts; fundamental flexural panel resonance at 150 cps.

FIG. 14.24. Actual reduction of resonant radiated sound from a motor housing as a function of damping capacity of the housing treatment. Motor "isolated" from housing by resilient mounts as indicated.

blanket damping treatment to the housing wall, the sound level at the housing resonance was reduced by more than 20 db (compare dashed curve).

The extent to which the housing resonance was reduced by the application of damping treatments of various degrees of effectiveness is shown in Fig. 14.24, where decibel suppression of the 150-cps peak is plotted against the damping capacity of the treatment. The decay rate specifying the treatment effectiveness is the same rating as used throughout this chapter; hence it will be seen by comparison with Fig. 14.20 that reductions as high as 33 db are attainable in this situation with commercially available vibration-damping treatments. The different curves shown in Fig. 14.24 represent the reductions measured with different sets of resilient mounts under the motor. The effectiveness of panel damping in suppressing housing resonance is seen to be almost independent of resilient-mount stiffness and damping. The reductions measured are entirely consistent with the computed effectiveness of damping in limiting "foundation" amplitude in the equivalent two-degree-of-freedom system. The computed effect of damping on the system response illustrated in Fig. 13.15 is shown in Fig. 14.25 for the cases of extreme "foundation" damping.

Sound Transmission of Aircraft Fuselage. The effectiveness of vibration-damping treatments in enhancing the low-frequency transmission loss through metallic partitions is demonstrated by measurements taken on a section of simulated aircraft fuse-

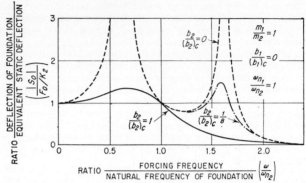

Fig. 14.25. Computed effects of foundation damping as idealized from lumped-parameter system of two degrees of freedom. Compare with Figs. 13.13 and 13.15.

lage. The 5-ft-square specimen consisted of 21 panels of 0.040-in. dural riveted to a frame of simulated ribs and stringers, the panel sizes being chosen so that their fundamental natural frequencies lay equally spaced over the frequency range 100 to 250 cps. Sound-transmission measurements were made by the "two-room" method, determining the attenuation of a diffuse white-noise signal as a continuous function of frequency over the range 60 to 2,000 cps. When frequency-selective deadeners of the kind described above were affixed to each panel and tuned to their respective natural frequencies, increases of attenuation were measured at certain frequencies in the resonant range as high as 16 to 18 db, the increase in the average attenuation over the frequency range 100 to 250 cps was found to be nearly 8 db, and the increase in the average attenuation over the full frequency range 60 to 2,000 cps was found to be 4.4 db. In aircraft, where weight is at a premium and where the soundproofing-blanket treatments fail to provide satisfactory insulation at the low frequencies where engine-noise components prevail, these improvements in fuselage attenuation solely due to damping are very great.

Damping Submerged Systems. The mistaken impression is widespread that metallic panels in contact with liquids are necessarily heavily damped by the liquid. It is true that, if a vibrating plate is submerged, even partially, its vibrations are much more quickly damped out than they would be in air. But experiments have shown that the damping is almost entirely attributable to energy dissipation in the high-velocity reciprocating flow of fluid past the sharp vibrating edges of the submerged portion of the plate. If no edges are exposed to the liquid, as in the case of a floating ship hull or a liquid-filled tank, the plating is nearly as undamped as it would be vibrating in air. Experiments have shown that the capacity of a given vibration-damping treatment to suppress the amplitude of steady-state resonant vibration is nearly independent of the communicating medium, provided only that no vibrating edges are submerged so that the viscosity effects of fluid in shear do not come into play.

REFERENCES

1. Den Hartog, J. P.: "Mechanical Vibrations," 3d ed., p. 112, McGraw-Hill Book Company, Inc., 1947.
2. Potter, E. V.: Damping Capacity of Metals, *U.S. Bur. Mines Rept. Investigations*, 4194, March, 1948.
3. Geiger, P. H.: "Noise-reduction Manual," Engineering Research Institute, University of Michigan, 1953, ONRC N6onr-23219.
4. Hamme, R. N.: "A Preliminary Study of the Effect of Damping in Non-rigid Machinery Foundations," Engineering Research Institute, University of Michigan, Feb. 29, 1952, ONRC N6onr-23219.
5. Hamme, R. N.: Engineering Research Institute, University of Michigan, Oct. 18, 1952, Air Force Contract AF18(600)-56, Wright Air Development Center Tech. Rept. No. 52-328.

Chapter 15

VIBRATION MEASUREMENT

Irwin Vigness, Ph.D.
United States Naval Research Laboratory

INTRODUCTION

Motions of solids may result in the generation and transmission of noise. To deter-mine the source of a noise, and to determine methods for its elimination, it is often necessary to measure these motions. This chapter is concerned with such measurements. It considers vibrational and transient motions, and includes a description of principal types of shock and vibration pickups or electromechanical transducers, methods of calibration, and analyses of records.

Steady-state Vibrations. A steady-state condition of vibration has been defined in Chap. 12 as a continuing motion of a vibrating system that has been acted on by a definite force condition for sufficient time to establish periodic motion. Many quasi steady-state conditions of vibration exist that employ the same techniques and equipments for their measurements as do the steady-state conditions as defined above. Quasi steady-state conditions consist of vibrational motions that exhibit little periodicity but whose average amplitude remains constant over any considerable period of time. The quasi steady-state condition is characteristic of a random noise. Its average amplitude versus frequency spectrum is continuous, although not necessarily constant. Periodic vibrations are characterized by line spectra. Mixtures of these types of vibration may occur. The general title "steady-state vibration" is frequently applied to any of these types of vibration.

The frequency ranges of most importance for structures are those excited by machinery. These commonly extend from a few cycles per second to several thousand cycles per second but there are many cases in which vibrations well outside this range are of interest.

Transient Motions. A transient motion is a disturbance of relatively short time duration which has not reached or has ceased to be steady state. For purposes of instrumentation, at least, it can be considered as resolvable into Fourier components. Fourier, sinusoidal, or harmonic components are synonymous expressions. The more important mechanical transients can usually be described adequately by Fourier components extending from a few to several thousand cycles per second. Instrumentation for the measurement of transient motions that have component frequencies extending from zero to about 10,000 cps is discussed in this chapter.

Vibration Measurement. When the motion of a point is to be measured, a device must be provided with a sensing element which indicates the positions, velocities, or accelerations of the point. This device may be some mechanical system which indicates the resulting motion by means of a mechanical pointer, or it may be a *trans-*

ducer, which is a device capable of absorbing energy from one system and supplying it, usually in a different form, to another system. An *electromechanical transducer* converts energy of mechanical motion into electrical energy, or vice versa. Acousticians generally refer to devices of these types as transducers, whereas many engineers dealing with vibration refer to them as "pickups." Thus a *pickup* is a device which converts mechanical motion to be measured into an electrical, optical, hydraulic, mechanical, or other forms of energy. In conjunction with other equipment, they may be used to measure vibration amplitude, velocity, or acceleration by any of the methods described in the next section. These include various types of meters in association with electronic equipment, mechanical methods, optical techniques, and various combinations of these. Direct optical techniques employing high-speed and streak photography provide simple and excellent methods for observing motion. Stroboscopic methods, in which light pulses of short duration are periodically emitted and used to illuminate an object, can be applied usefully to both transient and steady-state motions. Other techniques varying from interferometric methods to simple light-beam applications make optical techniques of great value to an engineer studying transient and periodic motions of solids.

VIBRATION-MEASURING INSTRUMENTS

Electrical Vibrometers (Vibration Meters). A *vibrometer* is generally considered as a device which indicates amplitude of vibration, while a *vibrograph* provides an oscillographic record of the vibration. Electrical vibration meters are available in which the amplitude of vibration is indicated directly on a meter. A typical unit of this type consists of a pickup, adjustable attenuator, an amplifier, and a direct-reading indicating meter. Such devices are popular because they are simple to operate, portable, and self-contained, and cover a wide frequency-amplitude range (see Fig. 15.1); connections are provided for oscillographic presentation, for a pair of headphones for listening to the vibration being measured, or for connection to a vibration analyzer. Integrating networks are incorporated in the instrument so that either the rms acceleration, velocity, or displacement may be read directly.

Several manufacturers of sound-level meters (see Chap. 16) produce "control boxes" which make it possible to use the pickups in conjunction with their sound-level meters. By means of integrating networks in the control box, voltages can be delivered to the sound-level meter which are proportional to acceleration, velocity, or displacement—the desired response being selected by a switch.

The various types of pickups that are used with such instruments are considered in detail in the next section.

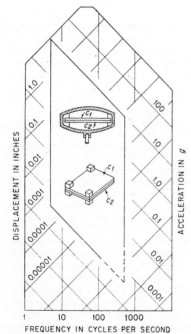

FIG. 15.1. Frequency-amplitude range limits of vibrometer, Type 759-P35, General Radio Co. The inset diagram is a schematic drawing of the pickup.

Mechanical Vibrometers and Vibrographs. Mechanical and mechano-optical vibrometers and vibrographs employ gear trains or mechanical or optical lever arms to magnify the vibratory motions before they are indicated or recorded. These devices are usually held by hand with a projecting probe, or prod, contacting the vibrating surface. The hands and arms constitute a soft-spring system so that, for sufficiently high frequencies, the case remains essentially stationary while the prod drives a gear train or lever arm. A weak spring keeps the prod in contact with the vibrating surface; an upper limit of acceleration amplitude is attained when the prod loses contact with the surface.

Figure 15.2 illustrates how the motion given to a prod by a vibrating surface is used to rock a mirror and thereby actuate an optical lever arm. A light beam reflected

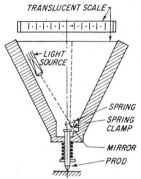

FIG. 15.2. Vibrometer. (*Courtesy of General Electric Co.*)

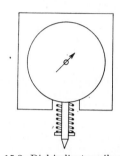

FIG. 15.3. Dial-indicator vibrometer.

from the mirror and focused onto a scale provides an indication of the vibration amplitude. A similar device which mechanically amplifies the motion of the prod can be constructed from a dial indicator, as shown in Fig. 15.3. The cases of these units should be fairly heavy if the units are to be hand-held. Their amplitude and frequency ranges are shown on Fig. 15.4. The light-beam unit is capable of operating to a higher-frequency range because of the smaller mass of the moving parts. The presentation of the frequency-amplitude range of an instrument is frequently given[1] by the method illustrated. The operating range of a unit is within the area bounded by the lines indicating its range limits. Thus the vibrometers illustrated have a low-frequency limit caused by one's inability to hold it steady, a maximum displacement limit set by full-scale deflection, a maximum acceleration limit because of loss of probe contact and strength considerations, a high-frequency limitation because of resonances of instrument parts, and a minimum displacement limit caused by lack of sensitivity.

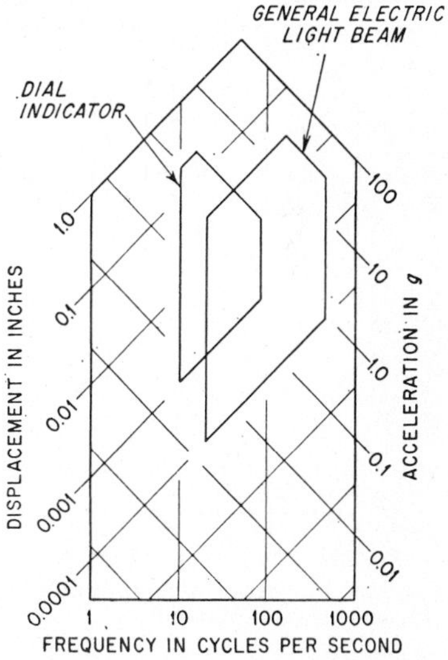

Mechanical vibrographs are illustrated schematically in Fig. 15.5. The instruments contain a moving paper, or film, on which a scribing device records the motions being measured. In Fig. 15.5a the case partakes of the vibration being measured and a mass supported on a soft spring is the stationary reference if the vibration frequencies are sufficiently high. In Fig. 15.5b the mass may be rigidly supported with the prod held against the vibrating surface. Usually, however, the mass is held by hand, the hand support constituting a soft-spring system, with the prod against the vibrating surface. A third method, shown in Fig. 15.5c, is a combination of the systems shown in Fig. 15.5a and b. By clamping the mass to the frame the

FIG. 15.4. Frequency-amplitude range limits of mechanical vibrometers.

system of Fig. 15.5*b* is obtained. If the mass is unclamped and the prod is attached to the case, the unit is equivalent to that shown in Fig. 15.5*a*.

Vibrographs of this more general type are manufactured* in which the records are made by a wire stylus pressing lightly against a celluloid film. A mechanical linkage amplifies the vibratory motion by a factor of about 8, so that amplitudes down to

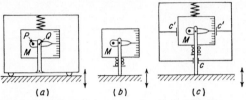

(a)   (b)   (c)

Fɪɢ. 15.5. Vibrographs. Scriber arm pivots on point *P*, attached to mass *M*. Attachment to prod, or case, at point *Q* drives the scriber. In diagram (*c*) the clamps *c* and *c′* may secure the mass and prod to the case.

0.0001 in. can be measured. The groove pressed onto this film is difficult to see unless proper lighting and optical equipment are used. The frequency-amplitude limits of these recorders are illustrated in Fig. 15.6. These units are often supplied with a reed, which is periodically plucked and which scribes a wave train on the edge of the record for a time scale. While the Askania vibrograph[3] and the General Electric recording vibrometer[4] are somewhat less precise than either of these instruments, they are frequently preferred because their records, which are scribed on waxed paper, are more easily visible.

Mechanical-frequency Meters (Reed Gauges). Frequency measurements of vibration mechanical systems frequently are made by the use of resonant mechanical systems.

The sensing elements are usually cantilevered reeds weighted at their free ends whose frequencies are selected to cover a frequency spectrum of interest. A reed vibrometer, shown in Fig. 15.7, contains a reed which is adjustable in length. The end of the reed, which is constrained

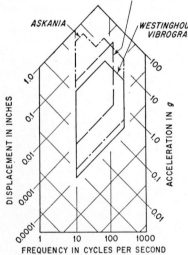

Fɪɢ. 15.6. Frequency-amplitude range limits of mechanical vibrographs.

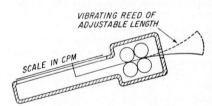

Fɪɢ. 15.7. Reed vibrometer. (*Westinghouse Electric Corp.*)

within the case of the unit, has an extension that is carried through a slot and which indicates on a scale the natural frequency of the reed. The case of the instrument is held against a vibrating surface and the free length of the reed is adjusted until its amplitude is maximum for a fundamental mode of vibration, this frequency being indicated on the scale. This instrument together with the unit shown in Fig. 15.2 make an excellent pair for quick vibration measurements where waveform is not of concern.

* Westinghouse,[2] Cambridge Vibrograph (Ref. 34, p. 336).

The "Frahm" frequency meter[5] consists of a series of cantilever reeds which are accurately tuned to frequencies separated by small increments, generally at half cycle or cycle intervals. These instruments usually have only a small frequency range and are used primarily to determine rotational speeds of machinery. In general, the use of this type of gauge is in the range from about 20 to 500 cps.

Moving Pictures and Streak Photography. The techniques of high-speed moving pictures have been developed so that acceptable results can quickly be obtained by engineers who are well acquainted with the general principles of photography. They are most useful in studying in slow motion the behavior of vibrating equipment under operating conditions. In the most commonly used cameras for this purpose, the photographic image is caused to travel along with the moving film by being diffracted by a rotating plane glass prism.[6,7] Speeds up to 15,000 frames per second can be obtained. Moving-film cameras without shutters can be synchronized with stroboscopic light sources to produce several thousand frames per second.

Photographing an object with a moving-film shutterless camera with ordinary illumination yields streaks which indicate the positions of the more contrasting areas of the image. By some refinements[8] it is possible to obtain time-displacement curves of this type which can include amplitudes up to several inches with accuracies within a few thousandths of an inch and a few hundred thousandths of a second.

Stroboscopes. If a rotating or periodically vibrating body is illuminated by short bursts of light, at time intervals that are about equal to the period of vibration or to some multiple of this period, the body will appear to be stationary or to move slowly. The apparent rate of vibration is equal to the difference between the vibration and the flash frequency. As the flash rate is usually known, this method can be used to determine frequency as well as to observe the details of performance of the moving parts. When vibration amplitudes are measured by means of a traveling microscope illumination by stroboscopic light leads to greater accuracy and ease of measurement.*

A device based on stroboscopic principles is used to determine precisely the frequencies of rotations or vibrations.[9] A pickup device feeds an electrical signal obtained from the source of vibration. This signal fires a group of neon discharge tubes so as to illuminate a group of scanning disks. The speed of rotation of the disks is controlled (to 0.05 per cent) by a tuning fork whose frequency can be varied. By adjusting the tuning fork until certain sectors of the disk appear stationary the vibrational frequency can be determined.

One device has been developed which causes stroboscopic lights to flash at a frequency of about 1 cps less than the frequency of vibration or rotation.[10] It will accomplish this even though the vibrational frequency is changing at a rapid rate. This allows slow motion to be observed under changing conditions where manual control would be impossible.

Interferometers. Light interferometers for the measurement of vibrations have been developed for laboratory applications but are inconvenient to use. An inter-

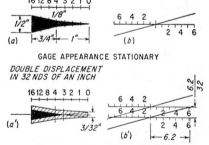

GAGE APPEARANCE STATIONARY

GAGE APPEARANCE DURING VIBRATION

Fig. 15.8. Vibration-amplitude indicator.

ferometer method for calibrating vibration pickups in the frequency range from 250 to 7,000 cps is given in Ref. 11. Another[12] interferometer has been developed for the measurement of the amplitude of acoustic vibration which requires that an optical flat about 1 cm in diameter be attached to the vibrating surface. Amplitudes in the range from 10^{-7} to 10^{-2} in. can be determined with an accuracy of about 10^{-7} in.

Miscellaneous Vibration-indication Techniques. A vibration-displacement indicator, shown in Fig. 15.8a or b, consists of a piece of paper with a figure on one side and mucilage on the other. The indicator is attached to a vibrating structure so

* The General Radio Co. publishes a booklet, "Eyes for Industry," in which uses of the stroboscope are discussed in detail.

that the direction of vibration, in the plane of the indicator, is perpendicular to the long axis of the figure. For frequencies above about 15 cps the figures will appear as illustrated in Fig. 15.8a' and b'. The amplitude of vibration can be noted by observing the location of the apex of the dark portion with respect to the scale printed by the figure, or by the points of intersection, as shown in Fig. 15.8a' and b', respectively. For frequencies below 15 cps measurements become difficult because the eye observes the motion of the gauge rather than the envelope of the motion.

Another method of estimating the vibration amplitude roughly is to hold a pencil firmly by hand and lightly draw a straight line along a smooth section of the vibrating part. The line should be perpendicular to the direction of vibration, which is assumed to be in the plane of the vibrating surface. A paper attached to the vibrating surface is an added convenience.

The amplitude of vibration at a 1g level can be determined by the Bragg "chatter" method, which consists in placing a hard object unsecured onto a vertically vibrating surface.*[13,14] When the acceleration exceeds 1g in a downward direction the object loses contact with the surface and a chattering results. This can be observed visually, audibly, or by means of a pickup attached to the surface. The 1g point can be determined within 1 per cent if a small metal sphere is used as the object and precautions are taken to ensure that the contacting surfaces are clean. The upper frequency limit for this accuracy is several hundred cycles per second.

<h3 style="text-align:center">VIBRATION PICKUPS†</h3>

Accelerometers. An *accelerometer* consists essentially of a mass which is supported seismically with respect to a case and guided to prevent motion in directions other than the seismic direction. (A *seismic system* consists of a mass suspended from a case by a spring. The motion of the mass relative to the case may be damped.) In the operating frequency range of the accelerometer, which is below its resonant frequency, the mass undergoes practically the same acceleration as the body of the accelerometer. The mass exerts on the seismic support a force that is directly proportional to the magnitude of the component of acceleration, and the output is a known function of the force.

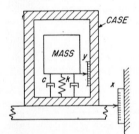

Fig. 15.9. A seismic pickup. The motion of the case is given by x. The relative displacement of the seismic mass with respect to the case is indicated by y. The unit is a linear, damped, single-degree-of-freedom system having a spring constant k and damping factor c.

Instrumentation problems in vibration measurements are generally reduced if measurements at high frequencies and low displacement amplitude are made by acceleration- or velocity-sensitive pickups since for a given displacement the acceleration varies as the square of the frequency and the velocity increases linearly with frequency.

Frequency Range. Pickups should be used only within a specific frequency range in which there exists a simple relation between the motion being measured and the transducer output. A consideration of the following equations of the response of the mass of the pickup to vibrations is helpful in defining the useful frequency range of a seismic-type pickup. Additional limitations may be imposed by the electric circuits employed in conjunction with it. If a seismic-type pickup, shown schematically in Fig. 15.9, is subjected to a displacement

$$x = X \sin 2\pi f t$$

along its sensitive axis then, under steady-state conditions, the relative displacement of the mass with respect to the case is given by

$$y = Y \sin (2\pi f t - \varphi)$$

* g is the unit of acceleration due to gravity. Its value is taken as 386 in. per sec per sec for most vibration work. Acceleration is frequently expressed as multiples of g.

† A compilation of various types of vibration pickups is given in Ref. 15.

The output signals of pickups of this type are proportional to y, or its time derivative; hence a knowledge of the relations between y and x provides information as to the range of frequencies for which there is acceptable mechanical behavior.

Curves showing the ratio Y/X, for a range of frequencies, are given in Fig. 15.10. The undamped natural frequency of the pickup is given as f_n, and the forcing frequency as f. The solution of this problem is given in detail in Ref. 16. Additional information is given in Refs. 17 and 18. (The pickup indicates displacement, or velocity, if the forcing frequency is much higher than the natural frequency.) The deviation of the curves from the unity ordinate value represents the deviation from the calibration factor of the pickup.

It can be seen from Fig. 15.10 that an amount of damping equal to about 0.65 critical will allow the pickup to be used with good accuracy as a displacement or velocity pickup down to a frequency less than 1.5 times that of resonance. When the pickup is to be used for determining transient motions, the damping complicates the interpretation of the records. Undamped pickups are therefore recommended for most shock work.

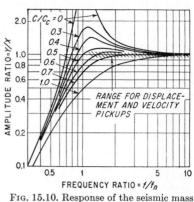

FIG. 15.10. Response of the seismic mass to a steady-state sinusoidal displacement. f_n is the undamped natural frequency and C_c (equal to $2\sqrt{mk}$) is the critical damping resistance.

Curves showing the ratio of Y to the peak value of the forcing vibration, expressed in terms of acceleration, are shown in Fig. 15.11. The maximum acceleration of $\ddot{x}$ is equal to $4\pi^2 f^2 X$. The pickup indicates acceleration when these curves do not deviate appreciably from the unity ordinate value. The amount of deviation represents the

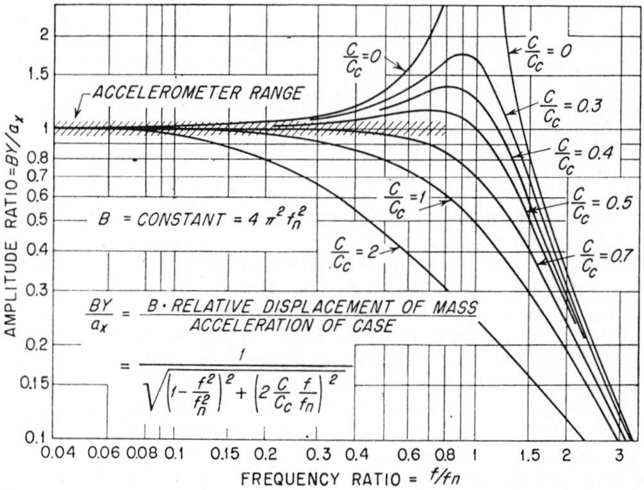

FIG. 15.11. Response of the seismic mass to a steady-state sinusoidal acceleration.

change in the sensitivity factor of the pickup. For undamped accelerometers this error becomes significant for frequencies greater than about a third of the natural frequency. When low-pass filters are used in conjunction with undamped accelerometers the attenuation they introduce may be used to neutralize the resonance amplification. It may then be possible to approach a frequency of about 50 per cent of the resonant value. If about 0.6 critical damping is used, the range of the instrument can be extended to nearer the natural frequency. These results apply to steady-state vibrations and neglect the effects of phase distortion and transient response. Undamped pickups are easily damaged by operation near their natural frequency, and their unfiltered output may overload their amplifier system.

The frequency ranges presented here and in the next section for velocity pickups should be considered only as representative values, for many models of each type are available which have different characteristics. Other factors such as size, internal impedance, and power requirements influence the suitability of a pickup. The limits of minimum amplitude are dependent upon the gain and noise level of associated amplifiers. In particular cases the limits can be extended if more error is tolerated or if more than usual care is taken with associated equipment. The pickups

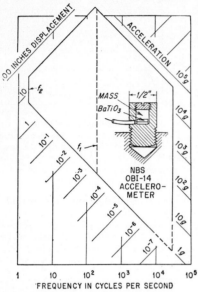

Fig. 15.12. Frequency-amplitude range limits for National Bureau of Standards barium titanate accelerometer OBI-14; f_1 and f_2 are low-frequency limits with 2.2- and 200-megohm impedances, respectively, for a cathode-follower type pre-amplifier.

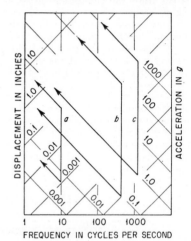

Fig. 15.13. Frequency-amplitude range limits for three models of Statham strain-gauge type accelerometers.

selected for illustration include only a few of the generally available units which cover ranges typical for their types.

Figure 15.12 illustrates the extreme ranges possible with barium titanate accelerometers, the amplitude range extending nearly five decades. By increasing the mass loading of the barium titanate the sensitivity can be increased at the expense of the maximum value of acceleration and frequency. The frequency-amplitude ranges of three models of unbonded strain-gauge wire-type accelerometers are shown in Fig. 15.13. The arrows indicate that the low-frequency response extends to 0 cps. Models having an upper frequency limit of less than a few hundred cycles per second are capable of directly driving sensitive oscillograph galvanometers. The ranges of vacuum-tube type accelerometers are given in Fig. 15.14. All units of this type are capable of very low frequency operation and can drive sensitive oscillograph galvanometers. Figure 15.15 depicts the range of an inductive type which weighs but 4 grams.

Phase Distortion. At very low frequencies the mass and the case of the seismic pickup (Fig. 15.9) vibrate in phase. As the frequency increases the displacement of the mass lags behind that of the case until at resonance the angle of lag is 90° and at very high frequencies it is 180°. The manner in which the phase shift varies for different amounts of damping is shown in Fig. 15.16. If the motion being measured contains several different frequencies, then the motion indicated by the pickup may be distorted because of the change of their relative phase relations. If, however, there is a linear relationship between phase shift and frequency then there will be a constant delay time for the transmittal of all frequencies, and no distortion will result. Figure 15.16 illustrates that there will be very little phase distortion for accelerometers (accelerometers operate at frequencies lower than resonance) if the damping is zero or if it is close to 0.6 or 0.7 critical.

The analysis of the response of the simple instrument shown in Fig. 15.9 was based on a linear differential equation with constant coefficients. This is but an approximation.[19] In a practical instrument the damping is not of a purely viscous type, temperature effects may not be negligible, sensitivity may vary with amplitude, and the pickups may respond to transverse motions. It is important, therefore, that sensitivity curves, obtained under conditions similar to use, be available.

Mounting. The accelerometer mounting must be sufficiently rigid so as to prevent

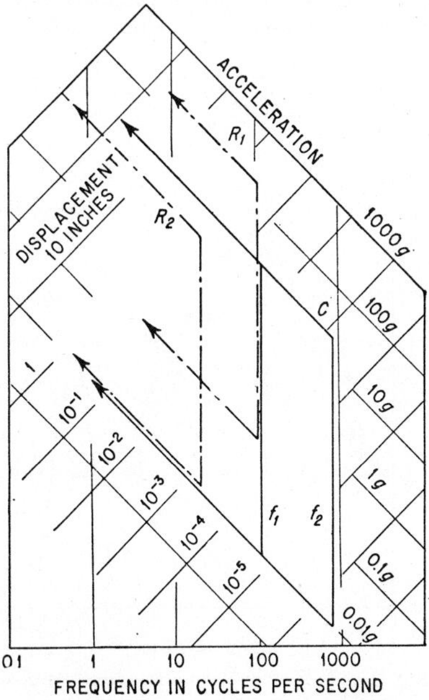

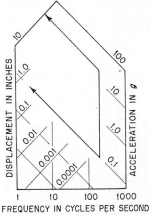

Fig. 15.14. Frequency-amplitude ranges of vacuum-tube type accelerometers. R_1 and R_2 are National Bureau of Standards "Ramberg" types. f_1 and f_2 are for models manufactured by Calidyne.

Fig. 15.15. Frequency-amplitude range of inductive-type accelerometer manufactured by Glenn L. Martin.

appreciable relative motion between the accelerometer and the structure. To indicate an acceleration of $10g$ to within 1 per cent, at a frequency of f cps, the relative motion between the accelerometer and the structure must have an amplitude of less than $1/f^2$, i.e., less than 0.0001 in. at 100 cps and less than 0.00001 in. at 1,000 cps.

Weight. The weight of the accelerometer together with its mounting must be small enough so that the inertia of the accelerometer will not appreciably alter the motion being measured.

Response to Transient Motions. The limitations imposed under the consideration of steady-state conditions apply also to transient conditions. In addition, more stringent specifications are required for the transient case. Studies of the response of the simple system of Fig. 15.9 to various types of transient excitations have been made. The most extensive of these works considers the excitation to be either a force applied directly to the mass, a displacement of the case, or an acceleration of the case.[20] The forms of the excitation have included sinusoidal pulses, combinations of exponential shapes, and many others. No damping is assumed. The case of damping but with fewer pulse shapes is considered in Ref. 21. A typical response of an accelerometer to a triangular acceleration pulse, taken from the latter work, is shown in Fig. 15.17. It was concluded that, to measure the peak acceleration of a triangular or sinusoidal pulse to an accuracy within 5 per cent, an accelerometer must have a natural period less than about one-third of the duration of the acceleration pulse, and a damping constant between 0.4 to 0.7 of critical.

Velocity Pickups. A *velocity pickup* is one which generates a voltage proportional to the relative velocity of two principal elements of the pickup, the two elements frequently being a coil of wire and a source of magnetic field. There are two general types of velocity pickup: (1) The *seismic type*, Fig. 15.9, in which one element is supported seismically from the case so as to form a low-frequency single-degree-of-freedom system, while the other element is integral with the case. Velocity pickups of seismic types operate at frequencies above the natural frequency of the seismic system. The flexibly supported element is essentially stationary* while the case in which it is mounted follows the motion of the structure to which the case is attached. The transducing element provides a signal which is proportional to the relative velocity of the two parts. Since the voltage developed in the coil is proportional to the rate of change of magnetic flux, the voltage will be proportional to the rela-

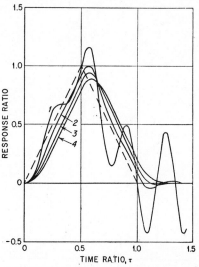

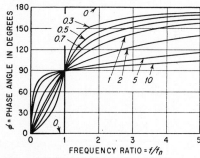

Fig. 15.16. Phase angle

$$\varphi = \tan^{-1}\left[\frac{2Cf/C_c f_n}{1 - (f/f_n)^2}\right]$$

between the vibrations of the seismic mass and exciting sinusoidal vibration.

Fig. 15.17. Response to a triangular pulse of acceleration, dashed curve, of an accelerometer whose natural period is about equal to one-third of the duration of the pulse. Curve (1), damping coefficient zero; curve (2), damping coefficient 0.4 of the critical; curve (3), damping coefficient 0.7 of the critical; curve (4), damping coefficient equal to the critical. (*Taken from Levy and Kroll.*[21])

tive velocity of the two parts. Typical arrangements of the two parts that have been used in velocity pickups are shown in Fig. 15.18. (2) The *probe type*, in which the relative motion between one element and the other is derived from a probe which extends through the case. One end of the probe is attached to the movable element of the pickup and the other end is in contact with the structure whose vibration is to be measured. When hand-held, the case of a probe-type pickup remains essentially fixed in space so that the output voltage depends on the motion of the vibrating structure.

The principle illustrated by Fig. 15.18c and e permits a large relative displacement for given external dimensions. One unit of this type (called the Hartz pickup) weighs about 11 lb and allows 6-in. relative displacement. The amount of damping for large-displacement-type velocity pickups, which are used primarily for shock measurements, is usually of the smallest possible value. An evaluation of the majority of the pickups used for shock measurements, including the above types, is given in Ref. 23.

* There may be considerable deviation from this assumption for liquid-filled velocity pickups.

Even though the velocity type of pickup is relatively large it is frequently used in place of accelerometers. The relatively low impedance and high voltage output of these units account for this popularity. The energy available from these units is often sufficient to operate oscillograph galvanometers directly.

Frequency Range. Velocity pickups are limited in their upper range by local resonances that occur in their parts or in their mounting arrangements. These and other factors relating to frequency response emphasize the importance of reliable calibration curves for the pickup. They should cover the frequency and amplitude range encountered in service. The seismic-type velocity pickup operates in the frequency range above the undamped natural frequency, whereas the operating range of the probe-type pickup is limited to values which permit the probe to maintain contact with the vibrating part. The frequency-amplitude ranges for typical velocity pickups are shown in Fig. 15.19. The measurement of shock motions involving several inches of displacement requires large pickups. Such pickups have been used principally to measure shock motion on structures which are massive, and the pickup can be correspondingly heavy. The first of these pickups to be extensively used was called the "British-type" velocity meter.[22] The magnet assembly is guided on rollers so that it can

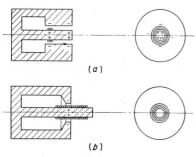

(a)

(b)

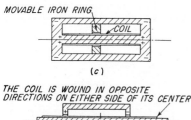

MOVABLE IRON RING

COIL

(c)

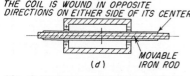

THE COIL IS WOUND IN OPPOSITE DIRECTIONS ON EITHER SIDE OF ITS CENTER

MOVABLE IRON ROD

(d)

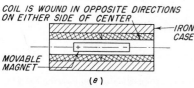

COIL IS WOUND IN OPPOSITE DIRECTIONS ON EITHER SIDE OF CENTER

IRON CASE

MOVABLE MAGNET

(e)

FIG. 15.18. Principles of operation of velocity pickups: (a) short coil in long radial magnetic field; (b) long coil in short radial field; (c) differential magnetic field in long coil; (d) differentially wound coil threaded by a magnetic field; (e) bar magnet in a differentially wound coil.

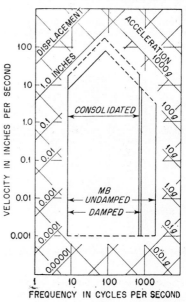

FIG. 15.19. Frequency-amplitude ranges of velocity-type vibration pickups manufactured by *Consolidated* and *MB*.

move only in an axial direction and is supported by springs that give the moving system a natural frequency of about 7 cps in this direction. Displacements up to 3 in. may be measured with a unit of this type which weighs about 40 lb. A velocity pickup is shown on Fig. 15.20, which is essentially a large-scale model of a vibration pickup. The unit accommodates a 3-in. coil travel and weighs 18 lb. The coil swings on one end of an arm which is supported by bearings at the opposite end. The natural frequency of the coil arm is determined by the stiffness of the positioning spring and is usually adjusted to about 3 cps. The output voltage is 9 mv per in. per sec when connected to a 10-ohm load.

Vibration-velocity pickups of small size, weighing about 10 oz but having nearly the same construction as the larger unit shown in Fig. 15.20, are available. Some types are electrically damped to 0.65 of critical by having the coil element wound on a short-circuited aluminum form. Undamped types are also available. These pickups are relatively unaffected by temperature between −50 and 250°F. The natural frequency for most types is about 5 cps, and they have a sensitivity of about 100 mv per in. per sec. The coil has a total clearance of 0.6 in.

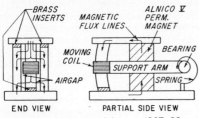

END VIEW   PARTIAL SIDE VIEW

Fig. 15.20. Velocity pickup. (*MB Manufacturing Co.*)

A velocity pickup designed to measure steady-state vibrations can be made relatively small in size. One such pickup is shown schematically in Fig. 15.21. (Its principle of operation is shown in Fig. 15.18*d*.) The unit weighs 10 oz, provides 110 mv per in. per sec velocity, and is liquid-damped about 0.65 of critical.[24] It is usable over a temperature range between 0 and 150°F. Although the total clearance for relative displacement of the magnet is slightly greater than 1 in., the unit is said to be capable of measuring vibration amplitudes having excursions up to 2 in. for horizontal motion. A maximum value of only 1.4 in. is given for vertical vibration because of the static deflections of the magnet from a central position. A linear and integrating amplifier is available from the manufacturer for use with its pickup, which includes an indicating meter calibrated to read average velocity and peak-to-peak displacement.

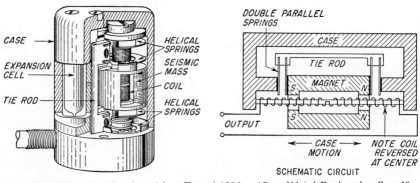

Fig. 15.21. Velocity-vibration pickup Type 4-102A. (*Consolidated Engineering Corp.*[34])

Phase Distortion. There is usually considerable phase distortion for velocity-type or displacement pickups that operate at frequencies higher than resonance. The phase distortion is less for small amounts of damping. The phase angle is not of primary importance for steady-state conditions but must be considered seriously in transient work.

Displacement Pickups. A displacement pickup is a device which generates an output that is a known function of the relative displacement between two elements of the gauge. These pickups are similar in construction and behavior to the velocity pickups of the previous section.

Specifications. Specifications concerning the following points of information are generally of interest to the user of vibration pickups. (For further details see American Standards Association, Method for Specifying the Characteristics of Pickups for Shock and Vibration Measurement, Z24.21, from which these points have been abstracted.)

Purpose of Instrument

TYPE OF MOTION. The nature of the motion to which the pickup will respond, such as: (1) angular, (2) uniaxial, including multiple elements sensitive along orthogonal axes, (3) omnidirectional in a plane, (4) Combinations of the above.

Physical Characteristics

WEIGHT.

OVER-ALL DIMENSIONS.

MOVING-ELEMENT POSITION. The location of the center of gravity of the moving element should be given as it is needed in the calibration of accelerometers on a centrifuge and in other applications where there may be a spatial gradient or a combination of linear and rotational motion in the quantity being measured.

MOUNTING. Method of mounting and the location and size of mounting holes or studs.

CONNECTIONS. Permissible length, weight, shielding, susceptibility to mechanical shock and pressure, and type of connectors between pickup and auxiliary equipment required for use with the pickup.

Environmental Characteristics

TEMPERATURE. The operating temperature range over which the pickup sensitivity and damping do not vary by more than a stated percentage from their rated values. Minimum and maximum storage temperatures.

HUMIDITY. Effect of humidity on the operation of the pickup (where applicable).

SPURIOUS ACOUSTIC RESPONSE. Maximum pickup output for exposure to air-borne sound at a sound pressure level of 100 db or more.

CORROSION.

ATMOSPHERIC PRESSURE. The effect of changing atmospheric pressure on pickup operation.

ORIENTATION.

CASE BENDING.

Principle of Sensing Element. (See detailed treatment in a following section.)

Energy Source

Nature of Output (i.e., whether it is linear, logarithmic, etc., and if it is a voltage, amplitude-modulated carrier signal, or frequency-modulated signal)

Auxiliary Equipment Required

Maximum-motion Limitations. These include motions within a specified accuracy, motions exceeding setting of stops, motions that will damage pickup, and motions exceeding ability to probe to follow motions faithfully.

Minimum-motion Limitation. These include resolving power of potentiometer-type sensing element, sticking, and background noise.

Response and sensitivity. The relationship of output to input, in consistent units, for the operating range.

Frequency range.

Phase shift.

Percentage of critical damping.

Shock response of accelerometers.

Direction of sensitive axis.

Transverse sensitivity.

Equivalent generator impedance.

Effect of electromagnetic fields.

SENSING ELEMENTS

Piezoelectric. Four piezoelectric materials are commonly used as sensing elements: quartz, Rochelle salt, ADP (ammonium dihydrogen phosphate), and barium titanate. Because piezoelectric crystals produce electrical potentials on certain surfaces whenever their dimensions are changed through the application of stress, these materials are commonly used as the sensing elements in accelerometers. The effect of cable capacitance on sensitivity is significant with these elements (see Chap. 16); so it is generally desirable to use a preamplifier connected to the pickup by a short cable. For a complete description of these materials, see Refs. 25 and 26.

Quartz is mechanically an excellent material but its piezoelectric coefficient is relatively low. Quartz-crystal accelerometers have been used successfully, but engineers working in the field generally find this type of unit unsatisfactory because of its high impedance and low energy output.

Rochelle salt is mechanically weak, hygroscopic, and temperature-sensitive but possesses the highest piezoelectrical sensitivity of any known material. Temperatures above 130°F will damage the crystal permanently. (A unit of this type is shown inset in Fig. 15.1.) Accelerations along an axis perpendicular to the crystal faces cause bending of the crystals, which puts one crystal under compression and the other under tension and causes an electrical charge to be developed on the large crystal faces. A pickup of this type should not be subjected to accelerations much in excess of 10*g*, although other types of Rochelle-salt elements may be used up to 5,000*g*.

ADP crystals are more rugged and less temperature-sensitive than Rochelle salt. They are not hygroscopic and will not be damaged by temperatures less than about 200°F. One series of accelerometer-type pickups, suitable for either steady-state or transient conditions and employing ADP crystals, which has been developed will measure accelerations up to about 2,000*g* over a frequency range of 10 to over 10,000 cps, their sensitivites extending to 125 mv per *g* with normal capacity across the crystal.[27]

Barium titanate is unusual among piezoelectric materials in that its sensitive piezoelectric axis is not determined by the crystal orientation but may be made in any arbitrary direction by the application of a polarizing voltage under suitable conditions of temperature. This allows the barium titanate to be cast into shape as a polycrystalline ceramic. The ceramic can be polarized as desired after its manufacture. Rochelle salt, ADP, and barium titanate are all classed as "ferroelectric" materials because of the similarity between their reaction to an electrical field and that of iron to a magnetic field. The analogy is closest, however, for barium titanate, which can be used as a polycrystalline structure and to which impurities are purposely added for improving its piezoelectric properties. At low frequencies relaxation effects may cause nonlinearities if pressures or voltages are applied for more than a few tenths of a second. It is not advisable, without calibrations, to measure amplitudes of frequencies that are less than a few cycles per second.

Some very small and simple compression-type barium titanate accelerometers have been developed by the National Bureau of Standards. One of these units weighs but 3 grams and has a sensitivity of about 2.5 mv per *g* (capacity of 0.001 microfarad); its output is essentially flat from a few to 15,000 cps. Other types capable of measuring to 30,000*g* at frequencies up to 30,000 cps have been described[28–31] (one of which is shown in Fig. 15.12). One of these units uses a barium titanate element to measure the strain on the surface of a structure that is caused to bend because of the acceleration. The barium titanate can be cast between two metal foils with the thickness of the ceramic as small as 0.01 in. This element can be cemented onto a surface and will develop an output charge proportional to the strain of the surface.

Strain-sensitive Resistance Wire. The electrical resistance of a wire changes when it is strained. This change is in part due to its altered dimensions, and in part due to a change of specific resistance.[32] This principle has been applied to a large number of types of transducers, including accelerometers.[33] The basic transducer element is shown in Fig. 15.22*a* and *b*. The mass is constrained by a pair of cantilever leaf springs so that it can move in the direction of the strain-gauge wires. The four sets of wires are wound under tension. When the mass is moved in one direction, with respect to the case, two sets of wires are subjected to increased tension and the other two have their tension relieved. Stops prevent excessive strains. The four sets of wires are connected in a Wheatstone-bridge arrangement, as shown in Fig. 15.22c. An external voltage source is required to activate the bridge, usually of the order of 10 volts. In this manner maximum sensitivity is attained and the unit is insensitive to changes such as temperature, which affect all arms in the same manner.

Strain-gauge accelerometers provide a relatively low signal-output level. Their maximum full-scale output is generally in the order of 50 mv open-circuit. Their

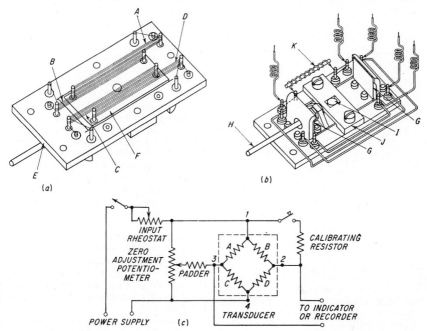

Fig. 15.22. Unbonded-wire strain-gauge type accelerometer. (*Statham.*) (*a*) Wire elements *A*, *B*, *C*, and *D* attached at one end to movable armature *F* and at the other end to the pickup body *E*. (*b*) View of the underside of (*a*) showing armature cantilever springs *G*; motion-limiting stop *I*; trimmer resistance *K*. Probe *H* is attached to the armature when motion is applied externally to the armature. (*c*) A bridge arrangement for using the transducer.

internal impedance is low, however, so that they may be used to drive sensitive oscillographic galvanometer elements directly. Other factors adding to their popularity are a close approximation to linearity with continuous variation of output with input, constancy of calibration, and the fact that much of the large amount of auxiliary instrumentation that has been built for the resistance-wire type strain gauge can be used for amplifying and recording the output of these accelerometers.

The natural frequencies of these accelerometers extend to about 5,000 cps. A damping fluid is usually used which is effective for units having natural frequencies lower than a few hundred cycles per second but which is not easily maintained at the required value for high-frequency units. (Figure 15.13 shows the frequency-amplitude ranges of typical units.)

Commercially available bonded-wire strain gauges may be cemented onto a surface that is put under stress because of an acceleration. With a properly designed accelerometer of this type the indicated strain is proportional to the acceleration. Their natural frequencies extended to about 10,000 cps; generally they are undamped. Most instruments of this type have not become commercially available.

A sensitive, rugged, and convenient displacement pickup that is easily constructed and continuous in its action consists of a flexible beam on which is cemented a pair of bonded-wire strain gauges as shown in Fig. 15.23a. Two or four strain gauges should be used and connected as shown in Fig. 15.23b to cancel undesirable effects causing the same change of resistance in all gauges, such as temperature variations and uniform longitudinal strains, so that the device responds only to strains caused by bending. Gauges on the opposite sides of the beam should be adjacent bridge arms. If only two gauges are used they should be on opposite sides of the beam and external resistors should be used for bridge balance. This device cannot be used to measure motion that might excite the higher modes of vibration of the beam.

Resistive Potentiometer. Resistive potentiometer sensing elements consist of a resistance element such as a wire-wound resistance, a carbon ribbon, or a deposited conducting film. It is possible to produce elements whose outputs are linear, or other functions, of the displacement by properly selecting the form or mandril on which a wire-wound element is wound. These sensing elements are suitable for measuring motions between about 0.1 and several inches with an accuracy of the order of 1 per cent full-scale. Desirable features include high power output, wide range, insensitivity to changes in temperature and humidity, and low internal impedance. A difficulty that is experienced in some applications is that of maintaining proper slider contact. Furthermore, an external voltage source is required to energize the element, which usually has a relatively low resonant frequency. The resolution of wire-wound elements is limited, depending largely on the number of turns and their spacing, being usually better than 1 per cent of full scale.

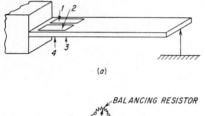

(a)

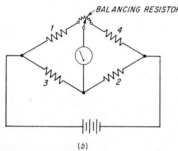

BALANCING RESISTOR

(b)

FIG. 15.23. (a) Cantilever beam with strain gauges for displacement determinations. (b) Bridge circuit.

Numerous potentiometer arrangements exist for displacement and acceleration measurements. Sliding contacts make most of these techniques unsuitable for pickups involving steady-state conditions where wear is an important factor. Such devices are used to measure the displacements associated with shock motions. One such manufactured unit having a travel distance of 5 in. is designed to operate while subject to axial accelerations up to 1,500g and transverse accelerations up to 500g.[35]

Differential Transformer. The principle of the variable differential transformer has been applied to the construction of a number of types of pickups.[36] A schematic diagram of an accelerometer of this type is given in Fig. 15.24a. Units are built having natural frequencies from about 50 to 5,000 cps. They can be excited by frequencies up to 20,000 cps and can be obtained with linear output-displacement ranges from 0.01 in. for the smallest unit to 2 in. for the largest. Damping of about 0.6 of critical value is obtained by the use of a silicone fluid. Accelerometers having full-scale deflections from 10 to 200g are available. Their output varies from 12.5 to 0.13 mv per g per volt of primary input, the lower-frequency units being the more sensitive.

To operate a unit, a source of electrical power at any frequency between 20 and 20,000 cps, and of suitable voltage, is applied to the primary. When the magnetic core is in a central position the voltage generated by the differentially connected secondary is zero. The phase of the output voltage changes by 180° as the iron core passes from one side of center to the other. The frequency of the input voltage should be about ten times greater than the highest component of frequency involved in the measurements. Figure 15.24b illustrates a circuit for use with differential transformers.

Electromagnetic Generating. If a coil is moved relative to a magnetic field, it will create a voltage. This principle is employed in sensing elements which are often used in instruments for measuring velocity. Usually electrodynamic damping can be obtained with considerable stability by utilizing the existing magnetic field which may be created by one or more magnets. For the usual sensing element, the voltage output of the coil may be of the order of 0.1 volt for a velocity of 1 in. per sec. Various arrangements are shown in Fig. 15.18. The principles illustrated in Fig. 15.18b and d can be applied to the measurement of displacement if the magnet utilized is an electromagnet and excited by an alternating voltage. The exciting frequency must be high (by a factor of 10) compared with frequency components of the motions measured; in addition the voltage induced because of the relative velocity of the parts must be small compared with the voltage induced by transformer action.

Desirable features of these sensing elements include high power output, low impedance, good stability, and the fact that no external power source is required if permanent magnets are used. However, they may be relatively bulky and heavy and they have limited displacement range. The effects of external magnetic fields discussed in Chap. 16, *Dynamic Microphones*, also must be considered here.

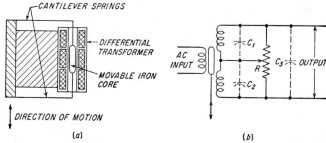

Fig. 15.24. Differential-transformer type accelerometer and circuit arrangement. (*From Schaevitz.*[36])

Electronic (Vacuum Tube). Electronic vacuum tubes may have their output varied by changing the relative position of their elements. Thus the variation in plate-to-cathode spacing in a vacuum tube can be used with a suitable auxiliary circuit to produce an electrical signal. An energizing voltage is required with this sensing means, as well as heating current for the vacuum tube. Such tubes, having a single or double plate, are ordinarily connected in a bridge circuit so that the variation in plate-to-cathode resistance produces an output. Desirable features of this sensing means include high current and voltage output, low internal impedance, a frequency range of about 0 to 1,000 cps, and acceleration levels from about 1 to 500g. However, an external power source is required, damping is difficult to provide, and heat from the tube may be undesirable for some applications.

For example, a diode-type vacuum tube has been constructed in which the plates were supported by cantilever springs so as to give the plate structure a natural frequency above several hundred cps.[37,38] The cathode structure was made comparatively rigid. When the tube was accelerated in a direction perpendicular to the cantilever structure and the plate surface, the distance between the plate and cathode varied with a resulting change in output. For small deflections this deflection and output change is linearly proportional to the acceleration. The pickup is well adapted to measurements of low-frequency (to 30 cps) vibrations. Earlier models are less sensitive and have a higher frequency range, as indicated in Fig. 15.14.

A variety of types of mechanoelectronic transducers has been developed for use primarily as phonograph pickups. These consist of small metal tubes about 1 in. long and ¼ in. in diameter.[39] A rod, supported by a diaphragm at the end of the tube, carries one of the tube elements. Movement of the external end of the rod, perpendicular to its axis, causes a change in relative position of the tube elements. These transducers have been applied as the sensing element of an accelerometer.[40]

Variable Inductance. Here the sensing element consists of one or more coils whose inductance, or mutual inductance, varies as the result of the motion of an armature. It can be used in a bridge, in a differential transformer, and in other arrangements to give an output proportional to an energizing carrier voltage, or to form part of the tank circuit of an oscillator whose frequency variation represents the output. Such sensing elements are usually used for measuring displacements from a thousandth of an inch to several inches, or for measuring accelerations. Desirable features include high output, low impedance, insensitivity to environmental conditions, availability in a variety of ranges, usability in a differential transformer, bridge, and other circuit arrangements. However, an external power supply is required.

Variable-inductance type accelerometers have been used where small weight, good low-frequency response, and high sensitivity have been major considerations. One miniature accelerometer weighs but 4 grams and operates with a 3,000-cps carrier feeding into a bridge circuit.* It has a frequency response flat between 0 and 200 cps, and measures accelerations up to $20g$. Descriptions of various types of pickups employing principles of magnetic induction are given in Ref. 41.

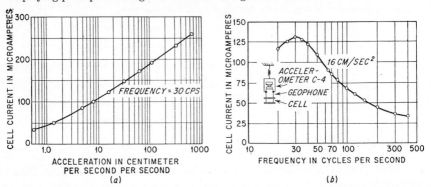

FIG. 15.25. (a) Calibration of electrolytic cell as an accelerometer. Motion applied along axis of cylindrical symmetry. (b) Frequency response of electrolytic cell as an accelerometer. Motion applied along axis of cylindrical symmetry. (R. N. Lane.)

Variable Capacitance. Here the sensing element is that of a capacitance whose magnitude varies with the relative spacing between two or more plates. One plate of the condenser may be the surface to be measured. Thus no mechanical loading of the vibrating surface is involved, a feature which is highly desirable in certain applications. A pair of plates may be used in a bridge arrangement to form a single condenser which is placed in series with a fixed inductance in one arm of the bridge. A voltage is used to energize the bridge whose frequency will give series resonance of this arm. The suppressed carrier output of the bridge, when combined with the energizing voltage in the proper phase relationship and modulated, produces an electrical signal proportional to the relative displacement of the plates.

Condenser-type pickups for vibration measurements are not often used except in the laboratory because of the difficulty in eliminating spurious signals caused by electrostatic pickup and by capacitative changes of elements in the transducer circuit. Extremely sensitive devices of this type can be constructed, detecting displacements down to 10^{-9} in. In one arrangement the capacitor is connected to a frequency-modulated oscillator in such a way that it will in part control the oscillator frequency. The frequency deviations are detected by a discriminator and interpreted in terms of displacement.[42] Such equipment is capable of detecting 1-μin. displacement at frequencies up to 500 kilocycles per sec using a $\frac{1}{16}$-in.-diameter probe.[43]

* Developed by Glenn L. Martin Co.

Several types of seismic pickup have been used in which the displacement of the elements is detected by means of capacity changes in a resonant-bridge carrier system.[44] When unbalance occurs, the amplified output voltage is impressed on a special discriminator circuit in which the direction and magnitude of the unbalance are determined. Capacity changes as small as 0.0001 $\mu\mu$f can be detected.

Condenser-type microphones can be calibrated in terms of pressure by having the microphone and a piston coupled to the same cavity so that the pressure change, caused by imparting a sinusoidal motion to the piston, can be calculated. This scheme can be reversed to allow measurement of displacement. If a calibrated microphone is available and coupled to a cavity containing a vibrating piston, then the amplitude of vibration can be determined. This method has been used for determining the amplitude of vibration machines used as calibrators.[45]

*Electrolytic Cell Accelerometer.** An accelerometer has been developed which utilizes the control of electrons moving in a solution. This device measures the acceleration of the fluid electrolyte through an orifice electrode. A range of 3 decades is achieved in a simple instrument consisting of an electrochemical detector, battery, and microammeter. Figure 15.25a shows the current output of the unit versus acceleration; Fig. 15.25b shows the frequency response of the accelerometer.

AUXILIARY ELECTRICAL EQUIPMENT

Electrical pickups require auxiliary equipment in order that their electrical outputs may be amplified and indicated. This equipment may include oscillographs, filters,

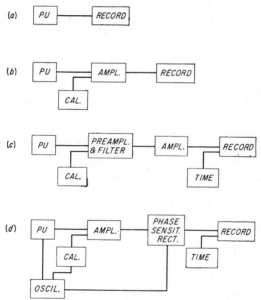

FIG. 15.26. Block diagrams of typical recording systems: (a) low-impedance pickup directly connected to sensitive oscillograph galvanometers; (b) pickups with amplifier; (c) pickups with preamplifier and filter; (d) pickup powered by carrier voltage.

cables, and amplifiers. Other associated equipment is frequently used to provide time and voltage scales by applying impulses at known intervals to some stage in the amplifier circuit and known voltages to the input stage. The latter are considered in a later section of this chapter concerned with calibration.

* Lane, R. N.: *J. Acoust. Soc. Amer.*, **29**: 177 (1957).

Oscillographs. Low-impedance pickups can often supply sufficient power to drive sensitive magnetic oscillographic galvanometers without amplification. Sufficiently sensitive galvanometers are usually resonant below several hundred cycles per second; hence direct coupling of the pickup to the oscillograph is possible only where the upper frequency limit is below several hundred cycles per second. Velocity, strain-gauge, and vacuum-tube-type pickups can be used in this manner. This simple combination is shown in block diagram in Fig. 15.26a.

Direct-writing oscillographs consist of an amplifier and scribing device (Fig. 15.26b) which can give an immediately visible record of the output of a pickup. The frequency range of a typical unit manufactured by Brush Electronics extends from 0 to about 100 cps. Magnetic oscillographs are capable of about 5,000 cps as a practical high-frequency limit. Cathode-ray oscillographs are capable of any desired frequency range.

Filters. For shock measurements low-pass filters are used to eliminate spurious signals caused by accelerometer resonances and signals outside of a desired frequency range (see Fig. 15.26c). When recording systems have a relatively low high-frequency response they act as low-pass filters and render special filters unnecessary. Comparable measurements of accelerations caused by shocks can be made only when systems having the same over-all response frequency are used.

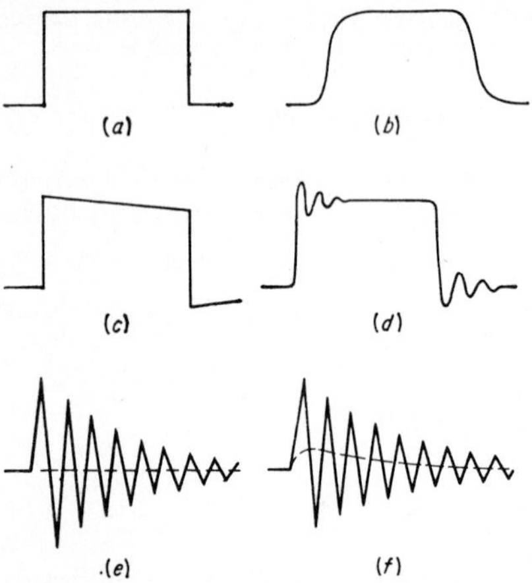

FIG. 15.27. (a) Square wave applied to amplifier; (b) modification caused by high-frequency cutoff; (c) decay caused by lack of low-frequency response; (d) spurious oscillations introduced by "ringing" of electric circuits; (e) damped wave applied to amplifier; (f) zero shift caused by unequal amplification of positive and negative signals.

Cables. The cable that carries the electrical output of a pickup may be subjected to a considerable mechanical shock caused by cable motions or pressure changes. Electrical potentials may be developed between different cable conductors as a result of the shocks. These add to the output of the pickup and produce spurious results which are particularly bothersome when the pickup is a high-impedance source. Unless cables are carefully selected they may provide more output than the pickup. It is good practice in acceleration measurements involving severe shock to determine the signal output when a dummy model is substituted for the accelerometer.

A study of the causes of the cable effect has indicated that the potentials are primarily caused by frictionally developed electrical charges on the surface of the cable dielectric.[46] Separation of the conductor and dielectric under mechanical shock causes the potential change. The cable effect can be largely eliminated by bonding a conductive coating onto the surfaces of the dielectric, which will allow the bound charge to be carried away.[47]

Amplifiers. Electronic amplifiers can be obtained that do not affect the over-all frequency response of the measuring system. Among principal factors of concern in amplifiers are: (1) the frequency range over which its amplification factor is acceptably constant, (2) its linearity with amplitude, (3) the amount of phase distortion, and (4) its sensitivity.

An amplifier of the RC type loses sensitivity at high frequencies principally because of the lower impedance of stray capacities at these frequencies. At low frequencies its sensitivity decreases as electrical charges developed across grid-coupling condensers leak through resistors to cause an appreciable decay in voltage. This decay is appreciable after a time approaching the "time-constant" of the circuit. The same effect occurs when piezoelectric or capacity-type pickups are connected to an amplifier input. The charge developed by the pickup leaks off at a rate inversely proportional to the amplifier input impedance and the parallel pickup resistance. The longest period that can acceptably be amplified generally is less than one-fifth the shortest time constant of the circuit. The time constant of the amplifier input, in this case, is the product of the capacity of the pickup, plus any added parallel capacity, and the effective value of all parallel resistances.

The response-frequency range of amplifiers can be determined by plotting their amplification factor vs. frequency. A quick estimate of the adequacy of their response can be obtained by noting how a square-wave input is amplified. Figure 15.27b and c illustrates how lack of high- and low-frequency response affects a square-wave input shown by Fig. 15.27a. Phase distortion and electrical "ringing" in filters or inductive circuits modify a square wave, as shown in Fig. 15.27d.

Carrier systems are frequently used with resistance- and inductance-type pickups. Most of these systems allow the low-frequency range to extend to 0 cps. The upper-frequency range should be limited to about 15 per cent of the carrier frequency. When the output of a pickup is a modulated carrier-frequency it is necessary to rectify the carrier by means of a phase-sensitive rectifier in order to present the output in terms of an oscillographic record of the motion. A general arrangement for this is shown in Fig. 15.26d.

High-impedance pickups, such as piezoelectric and capacity types, may require pre-amplifiers in their vicinity. Long cables between the pickup and amplifier may result in signal distortion due to voltages induced in the cable, electrical reflections between terminal points, and other losses associated with cable capacity. Preamplifiers are of a cathode-follower type and are designed to present a low output impedance to the following circuit.

In accelerations resulting from explosions and impacts the Fourier components generally increase in amplitude with frequency. This fact imposes a severe requirement on the linearity of the amplifier section that is subjected to the unfiltered signal. Lack of linearity is sometimes made obvious by "zero shifts" (see Fig. 15.27e and f), which can be caused by rectification due to nonuniform amplification of signals of opposite polarity.

CALIBRATION*

An electrical pickup is generally calibrated by subjecting it to a known motion† and determining its electrical output per unit of motion. This ratio is defined as a sensitivity factor. The calibration factor is often taken as the average of sensitivity factors over a given range of frequencies of sinusoidal motions. The output is expressed in terms of units such as volts, amperes, or coulombs; the unit of motion may be displacement, velocity, or acceleration. When sinusoidal vibrations are involved the rms and peak amplitudes are sometimes used. The output of the pickup terminals should be loaded during calibration by specified impedances typical of normal use.

A vibrometer, a vibrograph, or an over-all pickup-indicator system, can be calibrated as a unit by subjecting the proper element to the known motion and observing the deflection of the indicating or recording device. However, since pickups are more stable than their associated amplifiers, calibrations of the two are usually performed separately. The sensitivity of the amplifier-indicator system is frequently checked by applying a known or standard potential to its input, the gain being adjusted to some standard, or other desired value. The pickups themselves are less frequently calibrated. When they are calibrated it is customary to use the same, or similar, amplifiers and recording equipment as are normally used with them.

The principal problems involved in a calibration technique are to obtain a suitable motion and to determine its quantitative description independently. The following general techniques are described here: (1) sinusoidal vibrations of known frequencies

---

* See American Standards Association, "Manual and Specifications for the Calibration of Shock and Vibration," Z24.16.

† Reciprocity methods do not require that the amplitude of the motion be determined.

and amplitudes; (2) sinusoidal vibrations of known frequencies, but reciprocity techniques replace the direct amplitude measurements; (3) a complex motion of known characteristics; (4) a known velocity change in a suitable time interval; and (5) a steady acceleration field of known value.

Sinusoidal Vibration Generators. Vibration generators of sinusoidal motions suitable for calibration purposes are principally electrodynamic, piezoelectric, or mechanical. The mechanical generators include direct drives by linkage systems, reaction types activated by the rotation of unbalanced weights, and systems involving amplification. The principles of these methods are illustrated in Fig. 15.28.

Electrodynamic vibration generators have been developed to a high degree of refinement. Within the frequency range where the amplitude is not appreciably affected by resonances the acceleration vibration amplitude is directly proportional to the armature current. Natural frequencies can be located so as to be not bothersome in the region between about 30 and 2,000 cps. The units are useful beyond these limits, but the amplitude must be directly measured rather than inferred from the armature current. Most commercial vibration generators[48,49] have a separate built-in coil that generates a voltage proportional to the amplitude of vibration, this coil being rigidly attached to the vibration platform. A vibration calibrator with a flat acceleration-frequency response for a given exciting current between 100 and 10,000 cps is described in Ref. 50. The unit is capable of vibrating pickups weighing a few grams to a $20g$ amplitude over this range. A maximum amplitude of about $20g$ is typical for many calibrators of this type.

One manufactured calibration vibrator uses ADP (ammonium dihydrogen phosphate) crystals.[51] This device provides essentially constant displacement as a function of frequency for constant exciting voltages. A maximum amplitude of about 0.0005 in. is provided at frequencies up to 5,000 cps.

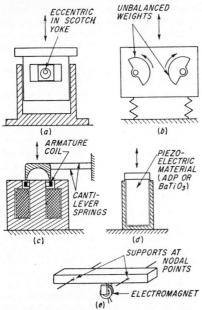

Mechanical vibrators of either the direct-drive or the reaction types, if carefully made, are suitable over the low-frequency range up to about 100 cps. Ball or roller bearings used in such equipment add to the high-frequency "noise" background and may result in inaccurate acceleration calibrations. This noise interferes less with the calibration of displacement or velocity types of units. The amplitude of vibration should be determined by independent measurement at each frequency. Both of these types of machine maintain constant displacement with frequency provided effects of resonances are negligible and if no machine adjustments are made.

Fig. 15.28. Types of vibration generators adopted for calibration purposes.

Resonant-type vibration generators[52] provide very large amplitudes of vibration (over $1,000g$ at 1,000 cps) but suffer from the disadvantage that they are fixed-frequency systems. Although techniques have been devised for varying the frequency they have been inconvenient and of short range.

A free-free resonant-beam calibration technique is illustrated in Fig. 15.28e. Strain gauges are cemented onto the beam and are calibrated so as to provide a convenient measure of high accuracy throughout the full amplitude range.

Calibration of pickups at acceleration amplitudes less than a few g at frequencies above 1,000 cps may involve measurements of displacements in the order of microinches. This has been done using interferometric methods.[11] Other methods described in Refs. 42, 43, 44, and 53 have about the same sensitivity and could be similarly applied. Reference 53 describes a method which involves the change of a mutual inductance in a pickup by the change in proximity to a metallic surface.

Reciprocity Method. Reciprocity techniques for pickup calibration do not require amplitude measurements, but only the measurement of mass, frequency, electric current, and voltage.[54-57] Consequently the accuracy is not limited by the difficulty of measuring small displacement amplitudes at high frequencies.

Three experimental arrangements and sets of measurements, two pickups, and a vibration generator are necessary for the reciprocity technique; these arrangements are shown on Fig. 15.29. At least one of the pickups must be able to act as a vibration generator if proper excitation is applied to its terminals. This is no great handicap as this unit is considered a part of the calibration equipment. A piezoelectric-type accelerometer has been calibrated from 250 to 10,000 cps by this method.[57] A comparison of the interferometric and of the reciprocity methods of calibrating accelerometers is given in Ref. 58.

The low-amplitude high-frequency methods of calibration described are primarily useful for the calibration of pickups which are to be used as standards for calibrating other pickups by a comparison method.

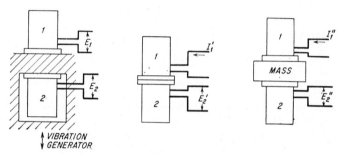

Fig. 15.29. Measurements involved in reciprocity calibrations.

Impact Method of Calibrating Accelerometers. Methods of calibration that impose conditions similar to those encountered in service often reveal factors in the performance not indicated by steady-state methods. Impactive techniques[59] have been developed which allow calibrations to be obtained over an amplitude range from a few to over 30,000g. The accelerometer should be mounted on a metal block of several times the weight of the accelerometer. This unit can then be struck, or dropped, so that the shock is along the sensitive axis of the pickup. The time of the acceleration pulse must be within the response range of the accelerometer, filter, and recording equipment. The pulse time can be lengthened by placing elastic or plastic materials on the striking surface. The superposition of high-frequency local vibrations that do not affect the center-of-mass motion is immaterial.

The following steps are taken in this method of calibration: (1) Record oscillographically the accelerometer output together with an accurate time scale. (2) Place a voltage-calibration scale on the record so that the voltage scale of the accelerometer output can be determined. (3) Measure the area under the acceleration curve in any convenient units. (4) Determine the velocity change of the unit by any independent means.

Let the acceleration pulse be similar to that shown in Fig. 15.30. The area under the pulse corresponds to the velocity change and is equal to

$$V = \int \ddot{x} \, dt$$

where $\ddot{x}$ and t are acceleration and time, respectively, and V is the velocity change. Define the sensitivity factor, which is to be determined,

$$S_1 = \frac{e}{\ddot{x}/g} \qquad \text{or} \qquad S_2 = \frac{q}{\ddot{x}/g}$$

where e is the voltage developed by the accelerometer, q is the charge developed by a piezoelectric-type accelerometer, and $\ddot{x}/g$ is the acceleration magnitude in units of gravity. (It is recommended that the sensitivity of piezoelectric accelerometers be expressed as the electrical charge developed per unit of acceleration, as this unit is independent of the electrical circuitry.)

The ordinate and abscissa scale factors are known and defined as $K_1 = e/y$ and $K_2 = t/x$, respectively. Let $\int y \, dx = A$, where x and y are any convenient units of length and A is the area, expressed in these units, under the curve.

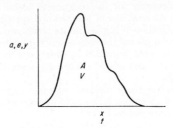

F<small>IG</small>. 15.30. Acceleration pulse.

Substitution in the above equations results in

$$S_1 = \frac{gK_1K_2A}{V} \quad \text{and} \quad S_2 = \frac{gK_1K_2AC_E}{V}$$

where C_E is the electrical capacity (in farads) of the accelerometer plus all effective parallel capacities.

Linear response was assumed in the above derivation. If this assumption is not valid the sensitivity values obtained will vary with the magnitude of the impulse used in the calibration.

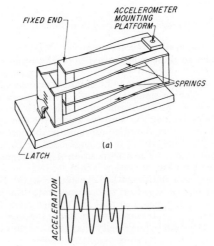

F<small>IG</small>. 15.31. (*a*) Portable accelerometer calibrator; (*b*) waveform at mounting platform.

Plucking Techniques. If a mass is supported by a spring and the mass is slowly forced from its equilibrium position by a known force and suddenly released, the acceleration of the mass can be calculated. For heavy springs, or for beams, the distributed mass gives rise to harmonics which complicate the computations. A portable "pulse" type calibrator,[60] shown in Fig. 15.31, will provide acceleration amplitudes up to about 15g. As the mass containing the accelerometer is accelerated gradually the accelerometer is not shock-excited, and few higher modes are present. The system illustrated has two principal modes of vibration at 12 and 30 cps.

Centrifugal or Gravitational Fields. Accelerometers whose response extends to 0 cps can be calibrated by subjecting them to a constant-acceleration field. The simplest method of calibration for these types of pickup is merely to change the orientation of the pickup in the earth's gravitational field. Any change up to 2g is, of course, obtainable. Steady accelerations up to several thousand g can easily be obtained by means of centrifuges.

ANALYSES

An analysis of a mechanical motion implies a definition of the motion in terms of its more elementary components. A steady-state vibration is conveniently analyzed in terms of its Fourier components but there is no general agreement as to what constitutes an acceptable analysis of a transient motion. Analysis by Fourier series or integral methods will probably provide satisfactory results from the standpoint of noise control. The signal representing the motion may be roughly analyzed frequencywise by being transmitted through various types of low-pass, high-pass, or bandpass filters. Crude analyses are often made by noting the amplitudes and associated frequencies from graphical representations.

Random vibrations of a quasi steady-state type may be measured conveniently by recording their mean-square or their rms values. They may be analyzed and expressed as a frequency spectrum in which the mean-square amplitude per cycle is plotted as a function of frequency. This can be obtained by dividing the output of a sound analyzer, converted to represent the mean-square value of the vibration, by the effective bandpass width of the analyzer. As the rms value can be more conveniently recorded, the spectrum is frequently plotted as the rms amplitude per square root of bandpass width versus frequency. When the amplitude of the vibration has a "normal" or Gaussian distribution, or if the distribution is otherwise known, this type of analysis permits one to determine the probability of occurrence of amplitudes within any given range of magnitudes.[61,62]

Many of the instruments for noise measurement and measuring techniques described in detail in Chaps. 16 and 17 apply to vibration measurement. While mechanical vibrations are observed and generated at frequencies extending into the megacycle region, the range of major interest in noise control extends through the audio down to a few cycles per second. Vibration and sound analyzers are frequently of the same design except that the former may be required to operate down to somewhat lower frequencies.[63,*]

Vibration analyzers can be made to plot the spectrum of the vibration automatically.[64] Figure 15.32 illustrates a vibration spectrum obtained by means of an analyzer.[65,66] A two-channel automatic wave analyzer has been developed which may be used for such analyses.[67] The Vibralyzer and Sona-graph are corresponding instruments used for the analysis of vibrations and sound. They are similar except for a frequency range of 5 to 4,400 cps in the first case and 80 to 8,000 cps in the second and somewhat different filter bandwidths. These instruments provide a three-dimensional Fourier analysis of transient or steady-state signals. Separate graphical recordings are presented of frequency vs. time and of frequency vs. amplitude. Textbooks describe a number of methods for the harmonic analysis of curves.[16]

A transient disturbance consists of motions of relatively short time duration. The transient motions of a single-degree-of-freedom system, if excited by a short impulse, consist of a simple damped train of vibrations. Complicated structures, when excited by short impulses, generally exhibit a nonperiodic noise pattern of decaying amplitude. Perhaps the great variety of motions observable in transients is their most striking characteristic. When a structure is excited by an impact the maximum value of

---

* The General Radio Co. vibration analyzer, Type 762-B covers a frequency range from 2.5 to 750 cps. The GR Type 760-B sound analyzer also can be used for vibration analysis for the frequency range 25 to 7,500 cps (see Chap. 16).

accelerations indicated by an instrument increases with the upper frequency limit of its response.   Very roughly the increase is linear with the response-frequency range. This relation implies that the coefficients of the harmonic components of the acceleration function, on the average, increase linearly with frequency.   It follows that a

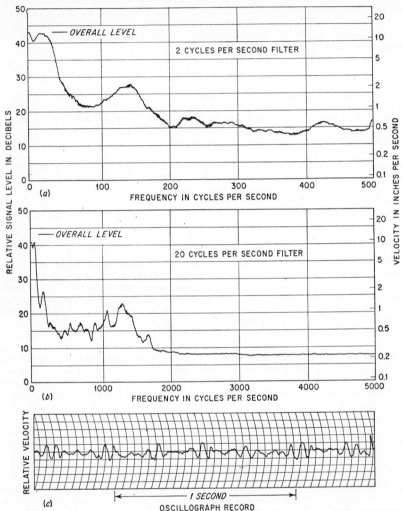

FIG. 15.32. Harmonic analysis of vibration record illustrated in the lower section of the figure.   A Western Electric Type 3A frequency analyzer having a 2-cps bandpass range was used for (a) and 20 cps for (b).   The vibration is on a missile and is largely "noise." (*From C. B. Cunningham, Naval Research Laboratory.*)

velocity function of the same motion would have nearly constant coefficients, and that for a displacement function the coefficients would decrease with frequency.

These observations are of great importance both for measurement considerations and for analysis.   When measurements of acceleration are made, the sensitivity is adjusted so that the maximum value of the record will be close to full scale.   With this adjustment the large-amplitude high-frequency components are readily determined from the record but the small-amplitude low-frequency components become unnoticeable. The low-frequency components, however, may be of as great interest as those of high frequency. Low-pass filters[68,69] are used for two purposes: first, to eliminate components of high frequency so that those of low frequency may be recorded at greater amplitude, and second, to provide an analysis which indicates amplitudes over known frequency ranges.

If comparable acceleration measurements are to be obtained in different laboratories, the frequency-response range must be standardized at definite values. It is also apparent that to express the shock intensity in terms of a peak acceleration is meaningless unless additional information as to the frequency range considered, or other data which will define the impulse or waveform are given.

Data obtained with peak-reading instruments or peak values obtained from analysis of curves often are satisfactory for comparing the intensities of similar shocks and for observing amplitude characteristics of shocks of known waveform. Devices that tabulate the number of times accelerations of given levels have been exceeded may provide suitable information in these cases.

The analysis of oscillographic records by nonautomatic methods is slow and tedious work. Where large-scale efforts are involved it is more efficient to make records that can be electrically reproduced. The electrical signal, corresponding to the shock or vibration motion, can then be analyzed electrically to provide required answers quickly.

REFERENCES

1. Fehr, R. O.: *Gen. Elec. Rev.*, **45**: 695 (December, 1942).
2. Werner, H. C.: *Instruments*, **15**: 83 (March, 1942).
3. Cunningham, C. B.: *Machine Design*, **20**: 133 (January, 1948).
4. General Electric Co., Publication GEC-853.
5. Spencer, J.: *Instruments*, **15**: 128 (April, 1942).
6. Boon, J. L.: *J. Soc. Motion Picture Engrs.*, **43**: 321 (November, 1944).
7. Smith, H. J.: *Bell Labs. Record*, **22**: 1 (September, 1943).
8. Vigness, I., and R. C. Nowak: *J. Appl. Phys.*, **21**: 445 (May, 1950).
9. Stroboconn Operation and Service Manual Mode 6T-4, C. G. Conn, Ltd., Electronics Division, Elkhart, Ind.
10. Slip-Sync Frequency Modifier, Chadwick-Helmuth Co., Monrovia, Calif.
11. Ziegler, C. A.: *J. Acoust. Soc. Amer.*, **25**: 135 (January, 1953).
12. Huntoon, R. D., A. Weis, and W. Smith: *J. Opt. Soc. Amer.*, **44**: 264 (April, 1954).
13. Perls, T. A., and C. W. Kissinger: *Natl. Bur. Standards (U.S.) Rept.* 2390 (see especially p. 18), April, 1953.
14. Hogben, R. S.: Acoustics Group Symposium, p. 132, The Physical Society, London, 1949.
15. "Transducers," Du Mont Laboratories, Inc., Clifton, N.J., 1953.
16. Den Hartog, J. P.: "Mechanical Vibration," 4th ed., McGraw-Hill Book Company, Inc., 1956.
17. Kammer, E. W., and S. Holt: *Proc. Soc. Exptl. Stress Anal.*, **6** (2): 53 (1948).
18. White, G.: *Statham Laboratories Instrument Notes* 2, April–May, 1948.
19. White, G.: "Shock and Vibration Instrumentation," p. 10, American Society of Mechanical Engineers, 1952.
20. Jacobsen, L. S., and R. S. Ayre: *Structural Dynamics Tech. Rept.* 16, Stanford University, January 25, 1952.
21. Levy, S., and W. D. Kroll: *J. Research Natl. Bur. Standards*, **45**: 303 (October, 1950) (Research Paper 2138).
22. Chertock, G.: *Shock and Vibration Bull.* 8, p. 23, Naval Research Lab. Report S-3276 (unclass.), March, 1948.
23. Perls, T. A., and H. L. Rich: David Taylor Model Basin Rept. 720, February, 1951.
24. Consolidated Engineering Corp., *Bull.* CEC-1503, Pasadena, Calif.
25. Cady, W. G.: "Piezoelectricity," McGraw-Hill Book Company, Inc., New York, 1946.
26. Mason, W. P.: "Piezoelectric Crystals and Their Application to Ultrasonics," D. Van Nostrand Company, Inc., Princeton, N.J., 1950.
27. Massa, F.: *Instruments*, **21**: 1013 (November, 1948).
28. Fleming, L. T.: *Instruments*, **24**: 968 (August, 1951).
29. Perls, T. A., and C. W. Kissinger: *Natl. Bur. Standards (U.S.) Rept.* 3299, June, 1954.
30. Dranetz, A. I.: *Natl. Bur. Standards (U.S.) Rept.* 2654, p. 69, August, 1953.

31. Guttwein, G. K., and A. I. Dranetz: *Electronics,* **24**: 120 (October, 1951).
32. Kammer, E. W., and T. E. Pardue: *Proc. Soc. Exptl. Stress Anal.,* **7** (1): 7 (1949).
33. Statham, L.: *Natl. Bur. Standards (U.S.) Circ.* 528, p. 31, February, 1954.
34. Hetenyi, M.: "Handbook of Experimental Stress Analysis," chap. 8, John Wiley & Sons, Inc., New York, 1950.
35. Colvin Laboratories, Pamphlets on Displacement Transducers, Morristown, N.J.
36. Schaevitz, H.: *Proc. Soc. Exptl. Stress Anal.,* **4** (2): 79 (1947).
37. Ramberg, W.: *J. Research Natl. Bur. Standards,* **37**: 391 (December, 1946).
38. Levy, S.: *Proc. Soc. Exptl. Stress Anal.,* **9** (1): 151 (1951).
39. Olson, H. F.: *J. Acoust. Soc. Amer.,* **19**: 307 (March, 1947).
40. Lewis, R. C.: *J. Acoust. Soc. Amer.,* **22**: 357 (May, 1950).
41. Roberts, H. C.: "Mechanical Measurements by Electrical Methods," chap. 5, The Instruments Publishing Co., Inc., Pittsburgh, 1951.
42. Dayton, R. W., and G. M. Foley: *Electronics,* **19**: 106 (September, 1946).
43. Sharaf, H. M.: *Electronics,* **27**: 172 (June, 1954).
44. Cook, George W.: *Electronics,* **26**: 105 (January, 1953).
45. Koidan, W.: *J. Acoust. Soc. Amer.,* **26**: 428 (May, 1954).
46. Perls, T. A.: *J. Appl. Phys.,* **23**: 674 (June, 1952).
47. Burley, J. C.: *Natl. Bur. Standards (U.S.) Rept.* 2654, p. 151, August, 1953.
48. Calidyne Company: Accelerometer Calibrator, *Bull.* 101, Winchester, Mass., November, 1951.
49. Unholtz, K.: The Calibration of Vibration Pickups to 2000 cps., *Bull.* MB Mfg. Co., 1060 State St., New Haven, Conn.
50. Rosenberg, J. D.: *Natl. Bur. Standards (U.S.) Rept.* 2654, p. 85, August, 1953.
51. Massa Laboratories: Summarized Data for Massa Vibration Exciters, Models M-136, M-137, Hingham, Mass.
52. Tyzzer, F. G., and H. C. Hardy: *J. Acoust. Soc. Amer.,* **22**: 454 (July, 1950).
53. Yates, W. A., and M. Davidson: Final Report and Instruction Book, Vibration Calibrator, *Natl. Bur. Standards (U.S.) Rept.* 2112, December, 1952.
54. Trent, H. M.: *J. Appl. Mechanics,* **15**: 49 (March, 1948).
55. Thompson, S. P.: *J. Acoust. Soc. Amer.,* **20**: 637 (September, 1948); *J. Acoust. Soc. Amer.,* **21**: 538 (September, 1949).
56. Camm, J. C.: *Natl. Bur. Standards (U.S.) Rept.* 2651, June, 1953.
57. Harrison, M., A. O. Sykes, and P. G. Marcotte: *J. Acoust. Soc. Amer.,* **24**: 384 (July, 1952).
58. Stowe, E. J.: David Taylor Model Basin Report 786, May, 1954.
59. Conrad, R. W., and I. Vigness: *Proc. Instrument Soc. Amer.,* **8**: 166 (1953). September, 1953.
60. Levy, S., A. E. McPherson, and E. V. Hobbs: *J. Research Natl. Bur. Standards,* **41**: 359 (November, 1948) (Research Paper RP1930).
61. Morrow, C. T., and R. B. Muchmore: *J. Appl. Mech.,* **22**: 367 (1955).
62. Morrow, C. T.: "Shock and Vibration Instrumentation," p. 75, ASME Applied Mech. Div. Conference at Univ. of Ill., June, 1956.
63. Scott, H. H.: *J. Acoust. Soc. Amer.,* **13**: 360 (April, 1942).
64. Bruel and Kjaer: Instructions and Applications of Audio Frequency Spectrometer Type 2109 and Automatic Spectrum Recorder Type 2311, Brush Electronics Company, Cleveland.
65. Cunningham, C. B.: *Proc. Soc. Exptl. Stress Anal.,* **10** (1): 125 (1952).
66. Instruction *Bull.* 1233 and 1234 on Type 3A Frequency Analyzer and 4a Level Recorder, Western Electric Co.
67. Davies Laboratories, Inc.: Automatic Wave Analyzer, *Bull.* 54C, Riverdale, Md.
68. Vigness, I.: *Proc. Soc. Exptl. Stress Anal.,* **5** (1): 101 (1947).
69. Conrad, R. W.: *Natl. Bur. Standards (U.S.) Rept.* 2654, p. 207, August, 1953.

Chapter 16

INSTRUMENTS FOR NOISE MEASUREMENTS

Arnold Peterson, Sc.D.

General Radio Company

Per V. Brüel, D.Sc.

Brüel & Kjaer

INTRODUCTION

After the type of noise measurement to be made has been determined, the instruments to be used are selected. This chapter aids in that selection by describing the functions and characteristics of many instruments for measuring noise.

Because of the variety of information that is needed and because of the variety of conditions encountered, many different types of instrument are used in noise measurements. Almost all these instruments depend on a microphone to transform acoustical noise into an electrical signal so that electronic instruments can be used to measure

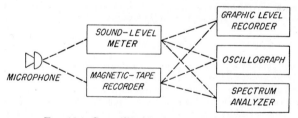

Fig. 16.1. Generalized instrumentation setup.

some characteristics of the signal or to store the signal for later measurements. A generalized instrumentation setup to illustrate this situation is shown in the block diagram of Fig. 16.1. The commonly used measuring instruments are separated here into classes labeled "sound-level meter," "magnetic-tape recorder," "graphic-level recorder," "oscillograph," and "spectrum analyzer."

In the diagram, the microphone is connected either to a sound-level meter or to a magnetic-tape recorder. The sound-level meter is used if the sound pressure level of a noise is to be measured directly, and the magnetic-tape recorder stores the noise signal for future measurements or for future reference. The other instruments shown in the diagram supplement the sound-level meter measurement. The graphic-level recorder gives a graphic record of sound pressure level as a function of time, the oscillograph delineates the waveform of the noise signal, and the spectrum analyzer is used to measure the band-pressure level in different frequency bands. More detailed descriptions of the functions and characteristics of these instruments are given later in this chapter, and their actual use in measurements is covered in the following chapter.

Although these components of a measuring system are shown as separate units, a number of their functions may be combined into one instrument. A sound-level meter, for example, is normally equipped with a particular microphone; and instruments have been built that include a microphone, a sound-level meter, and a spectrum analyzer. Nevertheless, even in these combined instruments, provision is commonly made for the use of different types of microphones, and output circuits are often included so that other measuring instruments can be connected to yield supplementary information about a noise.

Sometimes a sound-level meter is not used, and a microphone is connected directly to a sensitive analyzer. Or, an electronic amplifier may amplify a signal from the microphone for measurement by a spectrum analyzer. A particular measurement may be made by a number of different setups, and the one chosen depends in many instances on the equipment available. But since the sound-level meter has been specifically designed for acoustic measurements, it is usually found to be the most satisfactory basic instrument for noise measurements.

Since the selection of a suitable microphone is necessary in almost all noise-instrumentation setups, a detailed discussion of microphones is given first. The functions and characteristics of instruments are then discussed. The sound-level meter is the first instrument described, and subjective noise meters also are discussed. Auxiliary instruments, consisting of graphic-level recorders, oscillographs, spectrum analyzers, impact meters, and magnetic-tape recorders, are also described.

Much of the reliability of a measurement depends on how the instruments are used. For example, the operating levels must be set so that the instruments do not overload; but, at the same time, when a spectrum is to be analyzed, the operating level should not be set so low that noise inherent in the instrument obscures some parts of the noise to be measured. In other words, one must be thoroughly familiar with an instrument to make full use of its capabilities. For instance, one can then decide what results are characteristic of the noise being measured and what results are seriously limited in reliability by the instruments and how they are used. The material in this chapter will help the reader become familiar with the capabilities of various instruments; but, in addition, a thorough study of the literature supplied by the manufacturer of a particular instrument is essential. Similarly, practice in the use of an instrumentation setup is necessary, particularly with some exploration and analysis of the effects of various settings of the controls on the measurement results.

MICROPHONES

A microphone converts a sound into an electrical wave.[1] Ideally, the electrical wave should be an exact replica of the sound wave with a certain scaling factor, called response or sensitivity. In a given measurement, for example, if an instantaneous sound pressure of 1 microbar is reproduced as 1 mv in an electric circuit, then an instantaneous sound pressure of minus $\frac{1}{2}$ microbar must be reproduced as minus $\frac{1}{2}$ mv. In addition, the measuring system should not disturb the sound field, and the response should not vary with time or with ambient conditions.

Practical microphones only approximate this ideal, but for many measurements the approximation is good enough. In addition, corrections can sometimes be made for departures from the ideal.

Characteristics. How closely a microphone approximates the ideal is indicated by its characteristics, of which the following are important ones: response or sensitivity (scaling factor), variation of response with frequency and with ambient conditions, directivity, nonlinear distortion, impedance, transient response, disturbing effect, size, ruggedness, and inherent noise level. The relative importance of each characteristic depends on the requirements of the measurement system.

Response. The response of a microphone is the ratio of its electric output to the acoustic input. The electric output is commonly given in volts, or decibels re 1 volt, at the output terminals with no electric load on the microphone. The acoustic input is almost always given in terms of the sound pressure at the microphone converted to a reference of 1 microbar (74 db re 0.0002 microbar) or 10 microbars (94 db). (The 10-microbar reference is used mainly for sound-system or public-address microphones.) The sound pressure is commonly the free-field sound pressure at the microphone location without the microphone being in the sound field. The resultant response should then strictly be called the *free-field voltage response* of the microphone.

The response of a microphone for a sine-wave pressure variation having a frequency of 1,000 or 400 cps is commonly called the *sensitivity* or output level. Sound-level meters are calibrated to be used with a microphone of a particular sensitivity, and the indicated sound pressure level must be corrected for a microphone of different sensitivity.

High sensitivity is often a desirable characteristic for a microphone. Because of the great versatility of electronic amplifiers, sensitivity is not generally a dominant factor in determining the usefulness of a microphone for noise measurements. Low sensitivity is often accepted in the design of a microphone in order to obtain improvements in other characteristics, such as stability, response vs. frequency, and ability to operate at high sound levels. Microphones of low sensitivity, however, are often more difficult to use because extraneous effects, for example, solid-borne vibrations and noise and hum in electronic circuits, can then become particularly troublesome.

Response vs. Frequency. A microphone's response is limited in many ways. One of the more important limitations is that the electric output does not faithfully follow the acoustic input if the instantaneous sound pressure varies at a very rapid rate. Furthermore, some microphones are not able to follow slow variations in instantaneous sound pressure. How well a microphone responds to such sound waves is generally indicated by its response vs. frequency characteristic. This characteristic shows the relative response of the microphone for a sine-wave pressure variation as the frequency of the sine wave is changed. Some typical characteristics for commercial microphones are shown in Fig. 16.2.

Directivity. The response of a microphone also varies with direction of arrival of the sound wave. Some microphones are intentionally made to have very little response to sounds arriving from certain directions. Such units are called *directional microphones*, and they are used to some extent in noise measurements. But most microphones are built to be *omnidirectional* (nondirectional). For sounds having frequencies below 1,000 to 2,000 cps, they respond essentially equally for all directions of sound incidence; but at higher frequencies, the size of any microphone becomes comparable to the wavelength of the sound, and some directivity is apparent even in the so-called omnidirectional microphone. This effect is illustrated by the characteristics of several types of commercial microphones given in Fig. 16.2.

The variation in response with the angle of incidence of a sound wave is called the *directivity pattern* and is ordinarily given graphically in a polar diagram. The directivity pattern is generally symmetrical about an axis perpendicular to the microphone diaphragm but is different for different frequencies. As shown in Fig. 16.2, it is necessary to show patterns for a series of frequencies to obtain a sufficiently descriptive picture of microphone behavior.

The directivity pattern is important when a measurement is made in free-field or nearly free-field conditions close to a source of noise. When measurements are made at a distance from a source in a reverberant room, the field tends to be diffuse. It is assumed then that the microphone characteristic that applies is a *random-incidence* one, which is an average response obtained on the assumption that all angles of incidence of sound are equally likely. In practice, for omnidirectional microphones, the random-incidence response is found to be very similar to the response for an angle of incidence at about 70° from the axis perpendicular to the microphone diaphragm.*

When a microphone is placed in a small chamber, the distribution of sound pressure on the microphone diaphragm is different from the distribution that occurs in a free field. This behavior is of most importance in certain calibration techniques where the chamber is made so small that even at high frequencies the pressure is reasonably uniform throughout the chamber. The applicable response here is called the *pressure response* of a microphone. It is rarely used directly in noise measurements, but

* When one of the larger microphones is used, an angle of 65° is recommended.

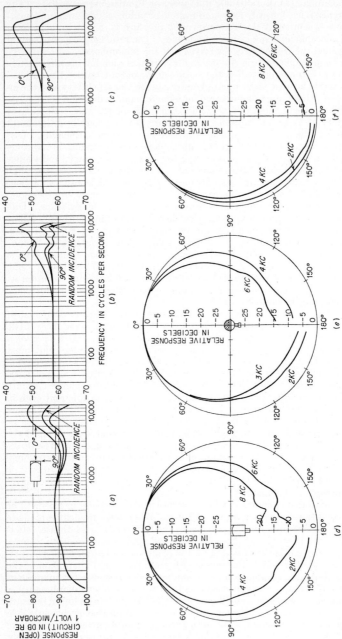

Fig. 16.2. Typical response vs. frequency characteristics and directional characteristics on polar diagrams of some microphones that have been widely used in noise measurements. (*a*) and (*d*) are for an Altec-Lansing Type 633-A Dynamic Microphone (originally Western Electric 633-A). (*b*) and (*e*) are for a Shure Type 98-98 Rochelle-salt microphone. (*c*) is for a Brüel & Kjaer Type 4111 Condenser Microphone (including cathode follower preamplifier). (*f*) is for a Western Electric Type 640-AA Condenser Microphone (see Fig. 16.3 for its response vs. frequency). The directional characteristics are essentially cylindrically symmetrical about the axis of the microphone labeled 0°–180°, so that only one side of the characteristic is given for the indicated frequencies. These directional characteristics are taken from J. R. Cox, Jr.: "Physical Limitations on Free-Field Microphone Calibration," Sc. D. Thesis, Massachusetts Institute of Technology, Cambridge, Mass., 1954.

response curves at various angles of incidence in a free field are sometimes derived from the pressure response by the application of corrections that have been determined for the particular type of microphone by previous measurements. A pressure-response curve and a free-field-response curve for a particular microphone are shown for comparison in Fig. 16.3.

Nonlinear Distortion. As the amplitude of a sound-pressure wave is increased, the output of a microphone increases correspondingly. At a sufficiently high sound level, however, the microphone output will no longer increase proportionately to the sound pressure; and it is then said to be *nonlinear*. This effect is usually a gradual departure from linearity, and a certain amount of it can be tolerated. The common measure of nonlinearity is harmonic distortion in the output when a sine-wave signal is applied. The tolerable level in noise measurements is usually 4 to 5 per cent harmonic distortion. But for some applications less than 1 per cent may be desired; and, on the other hand, for high sound-level measurements even 10 to 20 per cent may be accepted. Fortunately, microphones used for noise measurements ordinarily have less than 1 per cent distortion for all sound levels up to about 120 db.

One limiting aspect of nonlinearity is actual damage to the microphone at high sound levels. When noise of very high intensity may be encountered, it is important to know at what level this damage point is.

Impedance. Microphones of different types vary greatly in electrical impedance, which is basically a ratio between voltage and current. It is of significance in determining how a microphone should be connected to a given instrument and what effect such connection has on the over-all response of the combination. Thus a microphone of high impedance should not ordinarily be connected directly to an instrument having a low-impedance input because of the large loss in sensitivity that will result. Furthermore, the impedance

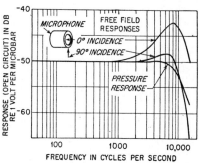

Fig. 16.3. Response vs. frequency of a Western Electric Type 640-AA Condenser Microphone, showing the behavior for sounds arriving along the axis and perpendicular to the axis of the microphone, as well as the pressure response.

of a microphone varies over the normal frequency range so that care must be taken that the connection does not introduce an unwanted change in response vs. frequency. For example, many microphones are, at the electrical terminals, electrical capacitors which may be relatively low impedances at high audio frequencies but high impedances at low audio frequencies. Such microphones are commonly connected to instruments having very high input impedances, so that impedance variations do not result in serious losses in response at low frequencies. Even so, the response of the combination is often limited at low frequencies by the relative impedance of the microphone and the instrument.

The manufacturer of a microphone normally supplies information about the impedance. The manufacturer of measuring equipment also supplies this information, and he specifies microphones that are generally to be used with the equipment.

Inherent Noise. A combination of a microphone and electronic amplifier generates an electrical noise signal, which is produced by thermal agitation in the microphone and input circuit of the amplifier and by noise generated in the amplifier stages. This noise sets a lower limit to the acoustical noise level that can be measured by the combination.

Effects of Ambient Conditions. The response of a microphone varies with temperature, humidity, and atmospheric pressure. Of these, ordinarily the most important is the variation with temperature. A knowledge of the temperature coefficient of response of a microphone is therefore desirable, particularly if the microphone is to be used at temperatures appreciably different from ordinary room temperatures. The temperature coefficient of response may be different at different frequencies, so that, when the ultimate in accuracy is desired, the response vs. frequency characteristic should be taken for the operating temperature.

Certain types of crystal microphones show appreciable variation of impedance with temperature, and the variation may affect the over-all response. This behavior is discussed further in the section on *Crystal Microphones*.

The effects of humidity are sometimes important in measurement microphones, and they are described in the sections on *Condenser Microphones* and *Crystal Microphones*.

Ordinary changes in atmospheric pressure that occur near sea level do not generally affect significantly the response of a microphone. Changes in atmospheric pressure as great as those experienced in military aircraft, however, can cause significant changes.

Basic Types. Microphones* can be classified into three broad groups: (1) pressure microphones, which respond to the sound pressure at the microphone; (2) velocity or pressure-gradient microphones, which respond to a difference in pressure at two closely spaced points; this difference is ordinarily proportional to particle velocity; and (3) microphones that are a combination of the first two classes, that is, their responses are functions of both pressure and particle velocity. The latter two types are directional; and they are used only occasionally in noise measurements; so that they will be described briefly as directional microphones after a description of various pressure microphones.

Condenser Microphones (Capacitor Microphones). A condenser microphone[2] is an electrical capacitor formed by a thin diaphragm, exposed to sound waves, and a back plate or perforated electrode (see Fig. 16.4). The diaphragm may be of stainless steel, of an aluminum alloy, of gold-coated glass or quartz, or of nickel. Sound pressure forces the diaphragm to move with respect to the back plate, with a resulting change in capacitance. This change in capacitance produces a signal that is proportional to sound pressure when a polarizing voltage is applied to the capacitor through a very high resistance.

The condenser microphone has been developed to a very high degree. Some models have been so carefully designed and tested that they are regarded as *laboratory standard* microphones.[†,3] Periodic calibration of such a standard is desirable, naturally, in order to be sure that something unusual has not happened to it. A slow drift in response with time is usually observed, with condenser microphones generally becoming more sensitive as they age.

Very small condenser microphones have been made to have a good response to high frequencies, as shown in Fig. 16.5, and a very small disturbing effect on a sound field.

---

* The following representative list of companies that make microphones used for sound measurements is not necessarily complete and the microphones are not necessarily recommended by the authors (the companies listed under sound-level meters also regularly supply microphones of different types with calibrations for sound measurements): In the United States, Altec Lansing Corp., Beverly Hills, Calif. (condenser, dynamic); Atlantic Research Corp., Alexandria, Va. (barium titanate); Brush Electronics Co., Cleveland, Ohio (Rochelle salt, barium titanate, condenser); Chesapeake Instrument Corp., Shadyside, Md. (barium titanate); Electro-Voice, Inc., Buchanan, Mich. (dynamic, Rochelle salt); Gulton Manufacturing Corp., Metuchen, N.J. (barium titanate); Kellogg Switchboard & Supply Co., Chicago, Ill. (condenser); Massa Laboratories, Inc., Hingham, Mass. (ADP); Radio Corporation of America, Camden, N.J. (ribbon); Shure Brothers, Inc., Chicago, Ill. (Rochelle salt, barium titanate); Tibbetts Industries, Inc., Camden, Maine (Rochelle salt); Western Electric Company, New York, N.Y. (condenser). In Europe, Brüel & Kjaer, Naerum, Denmark (condenser); Rohde & Schwarz, Munich, Germany (condenser); Ronette Piezoelectric Industry, N.V., Amsterdam-W, Netherlands; Siemans & Halske, Munich, Germany (condenser); Standard Telephone & Cables, London, England (dynamic); Telefunken, Berlin, Germany (condenser).

† In particular, the Western Electric 640-AA is designed to have a very good, smooth, response vs. frequency characteristic and, even more important, to be stable in response over long periods of time. As a result of careful testing of each unit and experience over many years, they have been found, in general, to be stable enough to use as standards for comparison calibration purposes. Other models of microphones have also been developed to the point that they are used as standards, but the background of experience with them is not so great or so long as it is for the W.E. 640-AA.

Small condenser microphones with stiff diaphragms have been built for measurement of high sound pressure levels. Not only do they have comparatively low distortion at high levels, but they also can have an exceptionally uniform response vs. frequency characteristic. They have, however, the disadvantage of low sensitivity.

A condenser microphone is reversible, so that it can be driven as an electrostatic loudspeaker. This feature and its smooth response vs. frequency characteristic make a stable condenser microphone particularly desirable for absolute calibration of response by the reciprocity method, which is described later.

A condenser microphone has a very high impedance, particularly at low frequencies. For example, a common value of capacitance for a condenser microphone is 50 $\mu\mu f$, which is a capacitive reactance of 160,000,000 ohms at 20 cps. They are used, ordinarily, only with an amplifier stage with as short as possible connections to the microphone, in order to keep the impedance of the amplifier input as high as possible. Such an amplifier mounted close to the microphone is termed a *preamplifier*. If it is desired to have the main bulk of instrumentation at some point remote from the location of

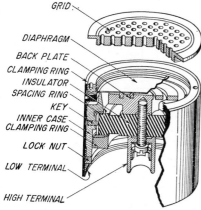

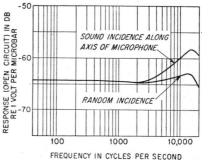

Fig. 16.5. Response vs. frequency of an Altec Type 21BR-180 Condenser Microphone. The upper curve is for sound incident along the axis of the microphone, and the lower curve is an averaged response assuming all angles of incidence are equally likely.

Fig. 16.4. Sectional view of the Western Electric 640-AA Condenser Microphone. The protecting grid is removable. (*Courtesy of Bell Laboratories Record.*)

a microphone, a connecting cable is then used after the preamplifier and not between microphone and amplifier.

Owing to the high impedance of a condenser microphone, the preamplifier must be exceptionally good in order to keep the inherent noise level at a reasonable value. Other characteristics also depend on preamplifier performance. Thus, in order to have a good response, the input impedance of the preamplifier must be exceptionally high at all frequencies.

The high impedance of a condenser microphone also makes it particularly susceptible to troubles from electrical leakage caused by high humidity. If leakage is relatively slight, the only symptom may be an increase in background noise. Severe conditions may render the system inoperable. Ordinarily, however, these troubles can be avoided by keeping the microphone at a sufficiently higher temperature than ambient so that no appreciable leakage occurs. This higher operating temperature is normal when a preamplifier is supplied by power from an a-c line, because of the comparatively high power taken by a-c operated vacuum tubes. Such a condition is not usual with portable battery-operated preamplifiers, however, and separate heating of the microphone may be desirable.

Crystal Microphones (Piezoelectric Microphones). Crystal microphones[4] use piezoelectric materials, for example, Rochelle salt, ammonium dihydrogen phosphate (ADP), and prepolarized barium titanate, which have the property of producing electrical charges on the surface when the material is strained. The most widely used microphone of the crystal type includes a diaphragm connected mechanically to crystal elements of Rochelle salt, as shown in Fig. 16.6. When the diaphragm is forced to move by sound pressure, the crystal elements are strained, and a voltage is produced by piezoelectric action.

The characteristics of a crystal microphone are highly dependent on the properties of the piezoelectric materials used in it. Rochelle salt is the most widely used crystal because of its large piezoelectric effect, high capacitance, and low cost. Its most serious disadvantage is that the Rochelle salt is irreversibly changed at a temperature of 55.6°C (132°F), and the maximum safe operating temperature is 45°C (113°F). The temperature coefficient of response of the microphone itself is not usually large, being, for example, of the order of 0.03 db per °F. But the capacitance of a Rochelle salt crystal varies markedly with temperature. If a long cable is used between the microphone and an amplifier, a large variation in response with temperature of the microphone will then result, as shown in Fig. 16.7. The response vs. frequency characteristic is not affected under those conditions, however, so that only an overall correction to response needs to be made.

Exposure of an unprotected Rochelle salt crystal to a relative humidity of greater than 84 or less than 30 per cent will result in gradual destruction of the crystal. The Rochelle salt elements used

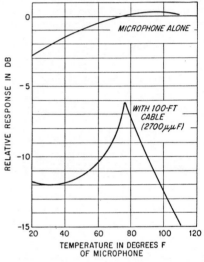

FIG. 16.7. Relative response vs. temperature of a Rochelle-salt microphone (upper curve is for microphone alone; lower curve, for microphone with 100 ft of cable attached).

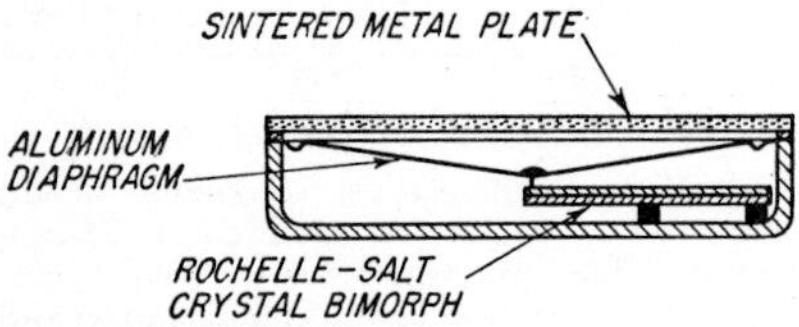

FIG. 16.6. Simplified diagram showing the basic elements of a Rochelle-salt microphone.

in modern measurement microphones are so well sealed, however, that they are ordinarily unaffected by extremes of humidity. Prolonged exposure to extremes should be avoided, however.

Experience with many Rochelle salt crystal microphones over long periods has shown that they are, generally, stable in response, provided they are carefully handled, and avoiding exposure to high temperatures is particularly important. As is true for any measurement microphone, the response should be periodically checked to ensure that the unit has not been damaged.

Crystal microphones using barium titanate are a more recent development. Barium titanate is produced in many forms with various additives to obtain certain desired characteristics. This versatility of the material is useful, but it means that a definite catalogue of characteristics is not possible.

The piezoelectric activity of barium titanate is high, but a microphone using barium titanate is ordinarily 10 to 20 db less sensitive than a microphone of similar acoustical and electrical characteristics using Rochelle salt. Barium titanate is not so readily damaged by exposure to high temperature as is true for Rochelle salt. A common upper temperature limit for barium titanate is over 100°C (212°F). Some preparations of barium titanate, however, have a high temperature coefficient of capacitance and some variation of response with temperature. An aging effect in the piezoelectric sensitivity of barium titanate also occurs. The sensitivity ordinarily decreases with time, with most of the change occurring in the first month after the barium titanate is made piezoelectric.

Barium titanate is being used particularly in hydrophones (microphones for water-borne sound), and these hydrophones can in general also be used for acoustic noise measurements. They are ruggedly built and low in sensitivity for air-borne sound, so that they are mainly useful at high sound levels.

Ammonium dihydrogen phosphate (ADP) is a stable piezoelectric crystal that is used in some measurement microphones. It is not so active as Rochelle salt, and it has a much lower capacitance for a given structure; but the crystal alone can stand temperatures up to 125°C (257°F). It is therefore ordinarily used only when the desired operating temperature makes it impossible to use Rochelle salt.

One particular microphone using ADP is made up of a stack of crystals in a small cylindrical stainless-steel housing. The front plate of the housing contacts the crystals through a thermal-isolation plate. When a sound wave strikes this plate, a compression and expansion of the crystals results, and a voltage is developed. The rugged construction of the microphone makes possible its use at the extremely high sound levels of 200 db. But it is low in sensitivity, so that special precautions must be taken to avoid the generation of electrical signals by the microphone as a result of mechanical vibration of the microphone.

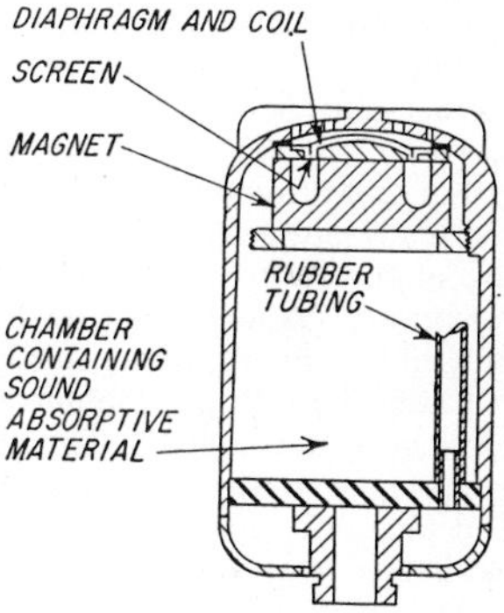

FIG. 16.8. Simplified cross-sectional drawing of a dynamic microphone.

The capacitance of the ADP microphone is stable, and long cables can be used to connect it to a sound-level meter, provided the sensitivity is corrected for the effect of cable capacitance. The use of long cables between the microphone and the instruments used to measure high-level sound permits operating the instruments outside the high-level sound field. This precaution is important in avoiding serious troubles from microphonics in amplifier tubes.

Dynamic Microphones (Moving-coil Microphones).
A dynamic microphone[5] consists of a thin diaphragm of aluminum or plastic to which is fastened a coil projecting into an annular gap in a magnetic structure, as shown in Fig. 16.8. When the diaphragm moves, a voltage is induced in the coil.

Dynamic microphones have been developed to the point that they are rugged and stable. The temperature coefficient of response is usually small, although it varies with frequency. The electrical impedance is low so that the microphone can be connected to an amplifier through a long cable without appreciable effect on response.

An electrical transformer is customarily used at a sound-level meter or amplifier to step up the voltage from the dynamic microphone before it is applied to the amplifier. This transformation is possible because of the low impedance of the microphone and the high impedance of the amplifier. Over-all sensitivity then is comparable with the better crystal microphones.

Because of the coil in the microphone, it is particularly susceptible to pickup of extraneous alternating magnetic fields, such as are present near power transformers, motors, and other electrical devices. The transformer used with the microphone may be similarly affected unless it is well shielded.

The response of a typical dynamic microphone falls off at low frequencies, as shown in Fig. 16.2. Only comparatively large microphones of this type have been made to respond to frequencies as low as 25 cps with only a moderate drop in response. At high levels the maximum distortion in this type of microphone is most serious at low frequencies.

Directional Microphones. A wide variety of directional microphones have been developed.[6] One group of directional microphones depends on a guiding structure or a reflecting structure, such as a parabolic reflector, to bring sound waves from a certain direction into focus at the point where a microphone is placed. In order for such a structure to be highly directional, its size must be many times the wavelength of the lowest-frequency sound of interest. Because of that requirement, such parabolic reflectors are limited in practice to use where high-frequency sounds are of primary interest.

Similarly one type of directional microphone depends on the phase velocity of sound guided in a tube or tubes. The tubes must be long compared with the wavelength of the sound in order to obtain any appreciable directivity. This requirement is one way of stating that the directivity varies with the frequency of the sound.

In contrast to the above, a ribbon microphone[6] can be constructed that has a figure-8 directivity pattern that is remarkably independent of frequency over the audio range. Such a microphone is not highly directional, but its directional properties can be helpful in some noise measurement problems. A ribbon microphone is closely related to the dynamic microphone, because it is a ribbon conductor in a magnetic field. The ribbon is both a conductor and a diaphragm which is exposed to a sound field in back as well as in front. This symmetry accounts for the figure-8 pattern.

A number of microphones can be combined, or delay networks can be used with a simple-element microphone, to obtain a directional characteristic. Some of these have found particular application as close-talking microphones for use in a noisy environment, but they have not been developed for use in noise measurements.

For measurement of apparatus noise in situations where background noise is serious, some advantage can be obtained by using such directional microphones. One measure of the suppression of background possible with such microphones is the ratio of maximum response to that for randomly incident sound. For the figure-8 pattern of a ribbon microphone, this ratio on an energy basis is 3:1, or about 5 db.

Calibration of Microphones. Many different methods of microphone calibration have been developed. The most widely accepted absolute calibration method is the reciprocity method,[7] which is used generally for calibrating standard microphones. But most microphones are calibrated by a substitution method[8] in which a previously calibrated reference microphone is used as a standard of comparison. These two general methods are described in some detail. Other devices used for calibration are, for example, a pistonphone,[9] an electrostatic actuator,[10] a Rayleigh disk,[11] and a thermophone.[12]

Reciprocity Calibration. The reciprocity calibration depends on the use of at least two microphones, one of which is reversible, that is, one of the microphones must be able to operate as a loudspeaker. The calibration is then obtained in terms of the characteristics of the space in which the measurements are made.

The first step is to obtain the relative response of the two microphones a and b. This step is readily carried out by placing first one microphone in a sound field and measuring its output voltage, then replacing that microphone by the second and measuring its output voltage. The relative response M_a/M_b is then given by the ratio of the two output voltages, where M_a and M_b are the responses of the two microphones as the ratio of the open-circuit voltages produced by the microphones to the sound pressures at the diaphragms.

The reversible microphone is then used as a sound source, driven by an electric current I_a with the other microphone being in the sound field, and its output voltage e_b is measured. The product of the two microphone sensitivities is then proportional to the ratio e_b/I_a, with the factor of proportionality being a function of the characteristics of the space in which the measurement is made. With the relations M_a/M_b and M_aM_b both known, the absolute responses of each of the two microphones can be found.

A number of important precautions must be taken in making such a calibration. For example, in each measurement the same type of response must apply. That is, if it is made in a free field at a certain angle of incidence, that angle should be used throughout, even for the microphone used as a source. The voltages measured should be corrected to be open-circuit voltages. The influence of the microphones on the space and on each other should be negligibly small or taken into account.

In order to simplify some of these precautions, it is customary to make the reciprocity calibration in a small closed chamber called a coupler, using three identical microphones. The chamber is made sufficiently small so that a pressure-response characteristic will be obtained. The basic proportionality is then given by the formula

$$M_a M_b = \frac{2\pi f V}{\gamma P_0} \frac{e_b}{I_a}$$

where γ = ratio of specific heats of the gas in the coupler
$\quad$ P_0 = ambient pressure, newton per sq m
$\quad$ f = frequency, cps
$\quad$ V = volume of coupler, cu m

The volume should include the contribution made by the microphone as a result of the motion of its diaphragm.

It is possible to set up such a measurement to obtain response vs. frequency as an end result. The basic process involved here is to record each measured value as a function of frequency. A diagram of such a setup is shown in Fig. 16.9.

Substitution Method. Standard microphones can be accurately calibrated at a number of laboratories that have extensive facilities for such purposes, for example, at the National Bureau of Standards in Washington, D.C., or the National Physical Laboratory in Teddington, England. A measurement of the relative response of such a microphone and of the microphone to be calibrated will then give a correction to be applied to the response of the standard to obtain the response of the unknown.

This relative response is usually obtained in an anechoic chamber (free-field conditions) in the following way: A pure tone is produced by a loudspeaker in the chamber. One of the microphones is placed at some distance from the source. Its output is measured. That microphone is then replaced by the second microphone, with great care being taken that all conditions are similar. Its output is measured. The ratio of the two outputs corrected to open-circuit conditions is the desired relative response.

In this type of measurement also many precautions must be taken to ensure obtaining an accurate measurement at high frequencies. A minimum of disturbing

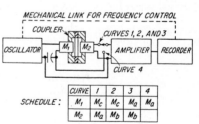

Fig. 16.9. Diagram and typical response characteristics of a setup for determining reciprocity calibrations of three microphones as a function of frequency. Four different response vs. frequency characteristics are taken with the microphones used according to the arrangement shown in the schedule.

elements, such as supporting members, should be in the chamber. Sometimes it may be necessary to apply acoustical treatment to such structures to reduce the effect on the sound field. A very good loudspeaker must be used in order to avoid peculiar distortions of the sound field.

Insert-voltage Technique. In any method of microphone calibration it is convenient to express a developed voltage in terms of the open-circuit voltage of the microphone. The equivalent open-circuit value is ordinarily obtained by a substitution method known as the "insert-voltage" technique.[13] This technique is also used for obtaining an electrical response of a system connected to a microphone with the microphone as the impedance for the source. A typical circuit is shown in Fig. 16.10.

The technique consists of inserting a known voltage in series with the microphone. This voltage is ordinarily small and is developed across a precision resistor having a resistance small compared with the other impedances in the circuit. In the circuit shown, this resistor is labeled as 10 ohms.

The known voltage is obtained from an oscillator, voltmeter, and calibrated attenuator system, and the procedure is as follows: The oscillator source is turned off, and an acoustical wave is applied to the microphone. The indication of the meter is noted. The acoustical wave is turned off, and the oscillator is turned on and set to

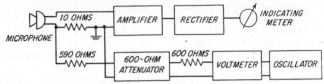

FIG. 16.10. Typical circuit arrangement for using the insert-voltage technique to obtain the electrical response of a system with the microphone as the source impedance. In this circuit the microphone impedance is large compared to 10 ohms.

the same frequency and wave shape (usually sine wave) as the acoustical wave. The attenuator supplying the insert resistor is adjusted until the noted indication of the meter is again obtained. The voltage appearing across the insert resistor is then the desired equivalent open-circuit voltage.

The circuit is shown for an unbalanced grounded system at the amplifier and oscillator, and care must be taken that the microphone system is not also grounded in order to ensure that the insert resistor is not shunted by a low-impedance path.

SOUND-LEVEL METER

The sound-level meter[14] is a sensitive electronic voltmeter used to measure the electrical signal from a microphone. It is calibrated in sound pressure level for use with a particular microphone, which is ordinarily attached to the instrument. It is constructed according to the principle shown in the simplified block diagram of Fig. 16.11. The electrical signal from the microphone is amplified sufficiently so that,

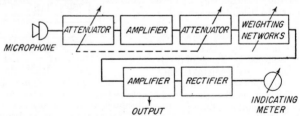

FIG. 16.11. Simplified block diagram of sound-level meter, showing the principal elements. The arrangement is only indicative, since it is customary to separate the attenuator into at least two sections placed at different points in the instrument, and the weighting networks may be placed directly after the microphone.

after conversion by means of a rectifier to direct current, it can deflect an indicating meter. An output connection that can supply the amplified signal to another instrument for analysis is also ordinarily provided. An attenuator controls the over-all amplification of the instrument, and the response vs. frequency characteristic is controlled by electrical circuits called weighting networks. These elements of the sound-level meter are now described.

Amplifier. The amplifier in a sound-level meter must satisfy many requirements. It must have a large available gain in order to measure the signal from a microphone in a quiet location. It should have a wide frequency range; usually it is made of the order of 20 to 10,000 or 20,000 cps, although the frequency range from about 50 to 6,000 cps is the range of greatest interest in noise measurements. The background noise and hum level should be low. It should be stable in gain.

Since the indication on the meter is proportional to the gain of the amplifier, it is particularly important that the gain be maintained at the proper value. A drift in gain will result in an error in indication of the sound level. For that reason most instruments are supplied with devices for checking and adjusting the gain to the original calibrated value, even though the drift in modern stabilized amplifiers is small.

The most widely used sound-level meters have a battery-powered amplifier. Since these batteries wear out with use and with age, it is customary to include battery-checking circuits in the instrument.

Attenuators. Sound-level meters are used for measuring noises that are of widely different level. Some range of level is covered by the relative deflection of the indicating meter. The rest of the range is covered by an adjustable attenuator, which is an electrical resistance network inserted in the electronic amplifier to produce a certain decrease in the signal level. To simplify the calculation of level, it is customary to have the attenuator adjustable in steps of 10 db. Some instruments have

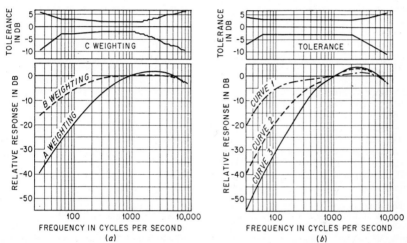

Fig. 16.12. Response vs. frequency of the weighting networks specified in the ASA Z24.3-1944 American Standard on Sound-Level Meters and the DIN 5045-1942 German Standard.

been built with less than 10-db steps in order to reduce the range to be handled by the indicating meter.

Weighting Networks. The response vs. frequency characteristic of a sound-level meter is controlled by electrical weighting networks, and the response curves for some particular networks have been standardized in the United States and Europe (see ASA Z24.3, BS661, and DIN 5045). One of these networks is called C weighting, and it is intended to provide uniform response over the frequency range from 25 cps to 8,000 cps. Some such networks in the electronic circuit are sometimes made to compensate for the response of particular microphones so that the net response is uniform (flat) within the tolerances allowed by the standards. The C weighting is used when the sound pressure level is to be measured, and it is also used, generally, when the sound-level meter supplies a signal to an auxiliary instrument for analysis.

The networks called A and B weighting have a response that decreases with decreasing frequency, as shown in Fig. 16.12. These responses approximate two of the equal-loudness contours for pure tones; the A weighting corresponds to the 40-db contour and the B weighting to the 70-db contour. Readings taken using these responses are weighted *sound levels* in decibels, *not* sound pressure levels.

Although the network responses correspond to particular loudness contours for pure tones, they do *not* give the loudness level of complex tones. Therefore, in the

United States weighted levels are expressed in decibels, *not* in phons, the unit of loudness level.

Metering System.   After the signal from the microphone is amplified in accordance with the setting of the attenuators and weighting networks, it is used to drive a metering circuit. This metering circuit indicates a value that is a characteristic of the wave applied to it. The standards on sound-level meters specify that the rms (see Chap. 2) value of the wave should be indicated. This requirement corresponds to adding up different components of a noise on an energy basis.

The rms value is not always the value that is desired, and then other instruments are used. For example, an oscillograph displaying the complete character of a wave or a peak meter indicating the maximum instantaneous value may be used.

But for many noise measurements, the rms value is a useful indication of the general noise amplitude, and the standards specify a test which is used to check that instruments are operating as rms meters for many practical purposes. This test compares indications obtained with a single sine wave and with a combination of two equal-amplitude sine waves of non-harmonically-related frequencies. If the meter is operating on an energy or rms basis, the indication for the combination of the two sine waves will be 3 db more than for a single wave equal in amplitude to either of the two signals. If the meter is a true peak meter, then the difference is 6 db. If the meter is a rectified-average type, the difference is 2 db. Further characteristics of metering systems of different types are given later in this chapter.

Most sound-level meters are built to be portable, and the bulk, fragility, and expense of true rms meters are avoided by use of a metering system that approximates an rms value within the tolerances allowed by the standards. These systems often use rectifiers operated at low current densities so that the output of the rectifier is nearly proportional to the square of the input. The average value of the output as indicated on a d-c meter will then be nearly proportional to the rms value of the input.

The indicating instrument on a sound-level meter cannot follow the instantaneous variations in sound pressure; instead it presents a running average of the rectified output of the metering circuit. The averaging time is determined by the meter ballistics (sometimes appreciably modified by the electric circuit). In the ASA standards, the speed of response is specified by the following requirements:

The deflection of the indicating instrument for a constant 1,000-cycles sinusoidal input to the sound-level meter shall be equalled by the maximum deflection of the indicating instrument for an input to the sound-level meter consisting of a pulse of 1,000-cycle power which has the same magnitude as the constant input and a time duration lying between 0.2 and 0.25 sec.

The deflection of the indicating instrument for a constant 1,000-cycle sinusoidal input to the sound-level meter shall not be exceeded by more than 1.0 decibel by the maximum deflection of the indicating instrument obtained upon the sudden application of the constant input.

In addition to this standardized speed of response, a number of sound-level meters include a slower response that is about one-fourth normal speed. This slower response is helpful in obtaining an average value for the reading of a noise that fluctuates over a range of 4 db or more.

The range of the indicating instrument is made greater than 10 db in order to cover the full range of levels between attenuated steps. It is common practice to label the full-scale value as +10 db; so that, when operating from 0 to +10 db, the indicated level is added directly to the setting of the attenuator to obtain the sound level. Usually the scale on the instrument is marked for levels at least 6 db below the 0 reference mark.

Output.   Most sound-level meters include an output connection that supplies an electrical signal that is the amplified output of the microphone signal. This output is used to supply a signal to other instruments, for example, graphic-level recorders, oscillographs, or spectrum analyzers. It is now widely recognized that, in order for this output to be of greatest usefulness, it should be an accurate reproduction of the microphone wave with a minimum of nonlinear distortion and inherent noise. Some early sound-level meters, however, supplied an electrical output wave that was seriously distorted by the rectifier system of the metering circuit. The rectifiers are now ordinarily disconnected if the output is taken from the metering circuit, or the output and the metering circuit are sufficiently isolated so that they have little influence on each other.

The output level is usually of the order of 1 volt when the indicating meter is deflected to a full-scale value. This output is adequate to drive most analyzers and graphic-level recorders. The maximum output before serious nonlinear distortion begins is ordinarily about 10 db above this level. This overload capacity is included to take care of waves that have a large peak value but only a moderate rms value. But it can sometimes be used for increased signal output. The overload capacity is seriously affected by the condition of batteries and tubes or transistors.

The inherent noise level at the output is important when the signal is to be analyzed. Over most of the range of a sound-level meter, the inherent noise level is ordinarily 30 db or so below the output level at full scale. This range is adequate for many measurements, but for some noises even more range is desirable and information on a particular instrument type can be obtained from the manufacturer. The actual range can usually be checked reasonably well as part of the step of analysis. Briefly, the procedure is as follows: the microphone is disconnected and replaced by an equivalent impedance. (Sometimes replacement is not necessary, but shielding of the microphone connector is ordinarily essential.) The output is then analyzed to find the inherent electrical-noise level. The noise is a function of the attenuator setting; so that the measurement should be made of the setting used in the measurement of the acoustical noise.

A knowledge of the two limits, overloading and inherent noise level, will permit one to set the attenuator controlling the amplifier so that the maximum useful range is obtained for analysis or recording.

Commercially Available Sound-level Meters. Sound-level meters are made by many different companies.* Most of the instruments are similar in many electrical characteristics, as outlined above, because they are generally built to conform closely with existing standards. The portable battery-operated instrument ordinarily is supplied with a Rochelle-salt diaphragm-type microphone, which can generally be replaced by a different type of microphone for those applications where the regular microphone is not suitable. Some of the a-c line powered instruments are supplied with condenser microphones.

A typical range of sound level covered directly is 40 to 130 db or more. This range can usually be extended upward by the use of special microphones. The lower limit is often set by the inherent noise in the system. An appreciable extension to lower levels is ordinarily possible only for limited frequency ranges by spectrum analysis.

Noise-survey Meters. Some simplified instruments[15] have been developed for making preliminary surveys of noise conditions. These devices have been made small and light in weight, but they include most of the features of the basic sound-level meter. In order to obtain extreme portability, the measurement range is usually less than that of the larger instrument, no output connection is ordinarily provided, and the accuracy and stability are usually less than those of the sound-level meter.

Subjective Noise Meters. Noise is of especial concern because of its effects on the hearing mechanism. An early type of noise measurement was a substitution method based on this effect of noise.[16] Thus a reference sound is produced and adjusted in level until it is judged to have the same effect as the noise being measured. Such a technique has an obvious validity; and in the hands of an expert, it can be

* The following representative list of companies that make sound-level meters is not necessarily complete and the instruments are not necessarily recommended by the authors: In the United States, General Radio Co., Cambridge, Mass.; Hermon Hosmer Scott, Inc., Cambridge, Mass.; Mine Safety Appliances Co., Pittsburgh, Pa.; Techno Instrument Co., Los Angeles, Calif. In England, Dawe Instruments, Ltd., London; Standard Telephones & Cables, London. In Germany, Rohde & Schwarz, Munich; Siemens & Halske, Munich. Sound pressure levels can also be measured by equipment made by the following companies, although no specific sound-level meter according to current standards is manufactured as a unit: Brüel & Kjaer, Naerum, Denmark (Brush Electronics Co., Cleveland, Ohio); Western Electro-Acoustic Laboratory, Los Angeles, Calif.

used with success on certain applications.   But it has so many limitations for field use that it is now rarely used.   Some of the problems encountered in using a subjective measurement are as follows: All the difficulties involved in making psychoacoustic judgments are present, and for general validity the measurement should be made with a large number of subjects.   A judgment of loudness is the only one usually attempted, and loudness is not ordinarily an effect that is the motivation for making the measurement.   Since annoyance is usually related to loudness, however, it can be a useful measure for comparing related types of noise.   It obviously cannot be used in the field to estimate the damaging effect of noise—a nondestructive type of test is preferable.   The measurement by subjective means takes a comparatively long time.   Consequently, it cannot be used for transient noises or for noises that vary greatly in level with time.   Subjective measurement is not generally useful in deciding on effective and efficient noise-control measures.

OSCILLOGRAPHS

The indicating instrument on a sound-level meter shows only one characteristic of a noise wave—the sound level.   For many noises it is approximately the rms value that is indicated.   But it gives no information about the wave shape.   That is, one cannot tell from the indication on the instrument whether a sound wave is a sine wave, a flat-topped type, a peaked wave, or a wave having a random distribution of amplitudes (a random noise).   Furthermore, impact sounds are of such short duration that the indicating instrument cannot respond quickly enough to yield a good measure of the impact.

When one desires to know more about the wave shape, it is possible to use a cathode-ray oscillograph (oscilloscope).[17]   The indicator on this instrument is a cathode-ray tube similar to a television tube.   The electron beam in the tube is ordinarily deflected by a sweeping signal so that the trace on the screen moves at a uniform rate in a horizontal direction (called x axis).   This procedure results in a horizontal linear axis. When the trace reaches the edge of the screen, the sweeping signal quickly returns it to the beginning, and the pattern is repeated.   A signal to be displayed is applied so as to produce a deflection of the trace in the vertical direction (called y axis).   The combined motion results in a display of the instantaneous amplitude of the wave as a function of time.   This display can be photographed to yield a permanent record.

Many varieties of cathode-ray oscillographs are available.   For acoustic measurements, it is desirable to select one whose response vs. frequency is uniform down to direct current; the high-frequency response on almost all cathode-ray oscillographs extends well beyond the audible frequency range.   The phosphor on the screen should be of the long-persistence type, and a sweep as slow as 2 sec for one horizontal sweep is sometimes useful.

Some of the relatively small oscillographs are desirable for field use, but one with a 5-in. screen is ordinarily used when the display is to be photographed.

Other types of oscillographs[18] are also available, and many of them are used in vibration work (see Chap. 15).   Some of them are described briefly in the section on *Recorders* in this chapter, because their response vs. frequency characteristic is not good enough for oscillographic use on acoustic noise problems.   Here the term "oscillograph" is applied to an instrument used for displaying the instantaneous value of a wave as a function of time or some other variable.   The term "recorder" is applied to an instrument used for making a permanent record of some characteristic, for example, the rms value, of a wave as a function of time or other variable.   These distinctions cannot always be clearly maintained, and the classification of some instruments becomes an arbitrary matter.

METERING SYSTEMS

Introduction.   An oscillographic display of a wave is difficult to use in rating a noise because it is difficult to assign numbers to the display.   It is possible to calibrate the deflection system so that the instantaneous peak value can be determined, but this value can be obtained more readily by a peak meter, as will be explained shortly. It is also possible to obtain some measure of the time scale of the noise, and this factor is also considered later.

Although the peak value is a useful measure of a noise, it is not often the value that investigators desire. The question, what is the best single measure of a noise, then naturally arises. The obvious answer is that there is no best single measure, and even when the question is made more specific by indicating that an objective measure of loudness is desired, for example, no definite answer can yet be given.[19] It is widely

Table 16.1. Characteristics of Various Wave Shapes—Rectified Average and Half-wave Peak in Terms of RMS Value of Wave

Wave shape	Rectified average, db	Half-wave peak, db
SINE WAVE	−0.91	+3.0
Random noise	−1.96	Infinite
SQUARE WAVE	0	0

RECTANGULAR WAVE	ΔT:T		
	1:5	−2.0	±6
	1:10	−4.4	±9.5
	1:20	−7.2	±12.8

accepted that the amplitude or level of a noise is very important, but no general agreement on the particular measure of the amplitude that is to be used has been reached.

The main reason for the lack of agreement is that there are so many aspects to the effect of noise on the hearing mechanism that the problem is only partially understood at present. A contributing factor is that, although many feel the rms value would be a good compromise measure, metering based on rectified average or peak has a number of important practical advantages. Furthermore, there is some indication that a measure that is between rms and peak is a better objective measure of some psychoacoustic effects.

Fortunately, for some types of waves, the differences among the measures are not great (see Chap. 2). Thus the rms value of a sine wave is only 3 db less than the peak value, and the rectified average is 3.9 db less than the peak. On an absolute basis for any wave, the larger of the two half-wave peak values is always higher and the rectified average is always lower than the rms value. Additional relative values are shown in Table 16.1 for some representative wave shapes, and for convenience these are expressed in terms of the rms value. The term "square wave" is used to describe a wave that has a constant positive value for a certain time, and then abruptly changes to an equal negative value for the same length of time for each cycle. Similarly, "rectangular waves" have a constant positive value for a short time and then a constant negative value for a longer time for each cycle, such that the product of the positive value and its duration is equal in magnitude to the similar product of the negative value and its duration. This requirement ensures that the wave has no d-c component. The ratio given for the wave is the duration of the positive wave compared with the duration of the whole cycle.

In order to reduce the differences to still lower values on common wave shapes, it is customary to calibrate a meter to indicate the rms value of a sine wave even though it may not be an rms meter. When such a calibration is used, the indication of the meter on different wave shapes will be as shown in Table 16.2. It is assumed that

Table 16.2. Relative Indications (in Decibels) of Different Types of Meters for Various Wave Shapes (All Meters Calibrated To Indicate RMS Value of Sine Wave)

Wave shape	Type of meter		
	RMS	Rectified average	Half-wave peak
Sine wave	0	0	0
Random noise	0	-1.05	$+1$ to $+9$
Square wave	0	$+0.91$	-3.0
Rectangular wave			
$\Delta T : T = 1:5$	0	-1.1	$+3$ -9
$\Delta T : T = 1:10$	0	-3.5	$+6.5$ -12.5
$\Delta T : T = 1:20$	0	-6.3	$+9.8$ -15.8

the metering systems are accurately rms, rectified average, or half-wave peak, except for the peak meter on random noise. A truly random noise has a finite probability of exceeding any value so that a true peak meter should tend to an infinite indication. In actual practice, for a number of reasons, the practical peak meters indicate a value that is ordinarily 1 to 9 db above rms, as shown in the table.

Metering systems are often not exactly of a simply defined type. As mentioned before, the usual metering systems in sound-level meters are basically rectified-average types, but they are operated in a region of the rectifier characteristic where they tend to approach rms values for simple waves. Fortunately, there is little error introduced by assuming that the indication for most steady noises is an rms one.

The possible variations in indication on different waveforms with different types of meters make it highly desirable to know what type of metering system is used in any instrument. This information is normally supplied by the manufacturer. Tests can also be made by the user with sine waves, random noise, and rectangular waves (pulses) to determine the behavior of the metering system. Some of the common methods of converting an a-c signal wave to a deflection on an indicating instrument are described in the following section.

Conversion to D-C Measurement. Most systems for indicating a characteristic of an alternating wave depend on converting it to a direct current. The direct current is then used to operate a sensitive d-c indicating instrument (meter). The two basic reasons for general adoption of this process are: first, some simple means for converting an a-c wave to a d-c wave are available, and second, the permanent-magnet moving-coil instrument (D'Arsonval instrument) for direct current can be made accurate, stable, rugged, sensitive, small, light in weight, low in cost, and comparatively fast acting. No instrument for direct operation from alternating current combines so many useful features.

As its name implies, a permanent-magnet moving-coil instrument[20] includes (see Fig. 16.13) a movable coil, to which a pointer is attached, mounted in a magnetic field produced by a permanent magnet. It operates because of the force produced on the coil current in a magnetic field. This basic mechanism is also used in recorders of various types, and it is sometimes called a "motor" because of the similarity of its action to that of a d-c motor.

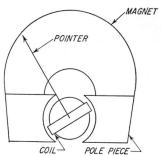

Fig. 16.13. Simplified drawing of the mechanism of a permanent-magnet moving-coil instrument.

The alternating wave is commonly converted to a direct current by a thermocouple, a bolometer bridge, or a rectifier, which are described here briefly.

Thermocouples. The operation of a thermocouple[21] depends on the heat generated in a resistance wire. This heat is transferred to a thermocouple junction whose electrical output is indicated by a d-c meter. This system has the important advantage that it responds to the rms value of the current in the resistance wire. It has the following disadvantages: low sensitivity, easy burnout, drift with ambient temperature, limited reading range, fragility, and slow response. Some of these disadvantages can be overcome by a number of methods, but usually at the expense of added complexity, bulk, and weight. Some of the simple methods of protecting against burnout also limit the useful rms range to waves having relatively low peak to rms values.

Bolometer. The bolometer bridge[22] also depends on the heat generated in a resistive element whose resistance varies markedly with temperature. This resistance is commonly used as one arm in a d-c resistance bridge. The d-c unbalance current caused by the change in resistance as current from an a-c wave is passed through it is used as a measure of the current flowing in the resistance element. This system is also an rms metering system* and some of the disadvantages of the thermocouple are more readily avoided here. Again, however, the system ordinarily becomes so bulky and complex in order to get a reliable and accurate device that it is only rarely used in acoustic measurements.

Rectifiers. An alternating current is readily converted to a direct current by means of rectifiers,[23] which are either vacuum-tube or semiconductor diodes. These depend for their rectifying action on a difference in resistance to flow of current in one direction compared with that in the opposite direction. Rectifiers are used in a variety of circuits, common ones being full-wave bridge circuits and peak circuits. The characteristics of these circuits depend on details of the circuit and the operating levels, which are discussed in the following sections.

LOW-LEVEL RMS OPERATION. When a rectifier circuit is operated at a very low voltage level, the rectification efficiency is very low. In other words, the d-c output compared with the a-c input is lower than at high levels. This effect results from the fact that, at very low levels, the rectifier resistance is nearly the same for either

---

* For waves having frequencies so low that the bolometer resistance element changes appreciably in value during the period of the low frequency, the system departs from being a true rms meter.

direction of current flow. The rectification then comes from a second-order effect. This effect produces a d-c output proportional to the square of the input voltages, and the rectifier operates as an rms type of device.[24] The maximum level at which this square-law behavior persists is ordinarily only a fraction of a volt per rectifier junction. By careful selection of the rectifiers or by using a complicated electronic system, it is possible to extend this upper limit. The lower limit is usually set by noise, drift, and variations with temperature. Thus the total dynamic range that can be covered on an rms basis is ordinarily severely limited.

RECTIFIED AVERAGE. If the voltage across the rectifier junction is made sufficiently high, the current flow in one direction is usually many times that in the other direction. For example, in a type 1N34A germanium rectifier at a voltage of 1 volt, the current is about 8 ma for one direction of application (called the forward direction) and about 4 μa for the opposite direction (called the reverse direction). This high ratio of conductivity of over 1,000:1 is not unusual. For some types of diode rectifiers, such as silicon-junction and vacuum-tube diodes, the ratio can be even higher. At these voltage levels, then, in many circuits, diodes can be considered as switches that close when the voltage across them is in one direction and that open when the voltage reverses.[25]

Under the above conditions, when a rectifier is connected in series with a suitable resistor and sensitive d-c instrument, the result is a half-wave average indicating instrument. It is called "half-wave" because only that part of the wave that is in the direction to produce current flow through the rectifier is measured. The rest is

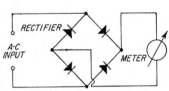

FIG. 16.14. Schematic for full-wave rectifier bridge circuit for a rectified-average meter.

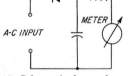

FIG. 16.15. Schematic for peak-responding type of metering circuit.

blocked off by the high impedance of the rectifier in the reverse direction. If the series resistor is made appreciably larger than the resistance of the rectifier in the forward direction, the current flow in the indicating meter will be linearly related to the voltage of the applied wave in the forward direction. The average value of the current flow as indicated by the instrument will then be a measure of the rectified average of the applied wave.[26]

If it is desired to obtain the rectified average on the basis of both halves of a wave, a full-wave bridge circuit, shown in Fig. 16.14, is commonly used.

Rectified-average metering circuits can readily be built to cover directly a wide range of signal levels; they can be made stable, relatively insensitive to temperature changes, reasonably accurate, sensitive, and low in cost. These characteristics are so important that this type of circuit is widely used for noise-measuring instruments.

PEAK RECTIFIERS. If a rectifier is connected in series with a capacitor, as shown in Fig. 16.15, the voltage across the capacitor will tend to approach the peak value of an applied voltage wave.[27] It will not reach the true peak value because no rectifier is perfect and because some of the charge on the capacitor may be lost in the process of measuring the voltage on the capacitor. Nevertheless, such peak rectifiers can be made so that for many wave shapes they measure very close to the peak value, for example, within 1 db. That statement does not hold for random noise, however, as explained previously.

Peak rectifiers are widely used for electrical measurements because they can readily be built to have characteristics that are essentially independent of the frequency of an applied voltage wave over an extremely wide frequency range. Such a feature is not so important for the limited range of frequencies of interest in acoustic noise measurements, however. Other important features are uniformity and stability, with considerable freedom from the effects of changes in ambient temperature.

Impact Noise Meters. Some specialized instruments have been developed for measuring impact sounds.[28] These are based on peak metering circuits* and are intended to simplify the measurement that must ordinarily be done with a cathode-ray oscillograph. They use an amplifier of very low output impedance to drive a rectifier charging a capacitor in a fraction of a millisecond to the peak value of the impact. This maximum level is stored electrically for many seconds in the capacitor, and the level is indicated on an electrometer voltmeter system. At the same time that the peak capacitor is charged, a type of time-averaged value is obtained by using a longer charging time for a second rectifier-capacitor system driven by the amplifier. The difference in level between the peak value and the time-averaged value is a measure of the duration of the impact.

RECORDERS

The metering system of a sound-level meter usually operates an indicating meter. If a permanent record or a continuous monitoring of the level is desired, the indicating instrument is often replaced or supplemented by a recorder. Recorders of many different types have been developed,[29] but the one most commonly used in noise measurements is the graphic-level recorder, which is described first. Many other recorders have been developed, particularly for the fields of industrial process control,

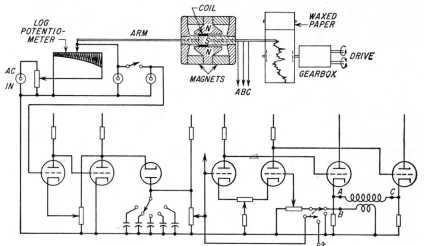

Fig. 16.16. Simplified schematic of a graphic-level recorder that uses a movable coil in a magnetic field.

vibration measurement, geophysical exploration, and electrical measurement. The moving-coil recorder is one of these that is sometimes adapted for noise measurements, and it is described also.

Graphic-level Recorder. A graphic-level recorder is a recording voltmeter with a logarithmic scale.† It is usually a servo-system, and one type[30] works according to the principle shown in Fig. 16.16. The signal voltage connects to a resistance-voltage divider, called a potentiometer, and the voltage from it is amplified and converted to a d-c voltage proportional to some characteristic, rms, rectified average, or peak

---

* The following representative list of manufacturers of impact meters is not necessarily complete and the instruments are not necessarily recommended by the authors: General Radio Co., Cambridge, Mass.; Hermon Hosmer Scott, Inc., Cambridge, Mass.

† The following representative list of manufacturers of graphic-level recorders is not necessarily complete and the recorders are not necessarily recommended by the authors: Brüel & Kjaer, Naerum, Denmark (Brush Electronics Company, Cleveland, Ohio); Radiometer, Copenhagen, Denmark; Rohde & Schwarz, Munich, Germany; Siemens & Halske, Munich, Germany; Sound Apparatus Company, Sterling, N.J.

of the signal wave.   This d-c voltage is amplified and used to drive a movable coil in a strong magnetic field.   The coil is mechanically coupled to the movable arm on the potentiometer and also to a pointer which traces a record on paper.

The voltage supplied to the movable coil is balanced against a fixed reference voltage.   If the d-c voltage produced by the signal is less than the reference voltage, there is a net current in the coil which results in a force tending to move the potentiometer arm.   The system is connected so that the direction of the force drives the arm so as to increase the voltage from the signal until a balance is reached.   Conversely, if the d-c voltage produced by the signal is too great, the system will move in the opposite direction until a balance is reached.

The position of the potentiometer arm and, correspondingly, that of the pointer are then measures of the applied signal wave.   If the potentiometer is arranged so that the voltage division follows a logarithmic relation to position, the scale on the recording paper can be uniformly divided for level in decibels.

The recording paper moves at a uniform rate in a direction perpendicular to the motion of the pen.   The combination of uniform motion of the paper in one direction and tracing of voltage level in a perpendicular direction by the servo-controlled pointer produces a recording of voltage level as a function of time in rectangular coordinates.   The scales of the coordinates are determined by paper speed and potentiometer range.   The paper speed is selected by adjustment of a gear train between the driving motor and the paper drum drive.   A number of interchangeable potentiometers are available so that the voltage-level range can be set to 10, 25, 50, or 75 db, for example.   The servo-system even makes possible a recording with a response vs. frequency that changes with level.   Potentiometers that include the variations in response with level of the equal-loudness contours, for example, have been built.

The graphic-level recorder, when connected to the output of a sound-level meter and properly set for sensitivity, records sound pressure level as a function of time.   It can also be used to record other variables.   For example, if it is connected to the output of a spectrum analyzer and if the analyzer is tuned over its range as a function of time, the recording will be an analysis of the input to the spectrum analyzer.

In one version of this type of graphic-level recorder, control of the speed and dynamic characteristics of the recording pointer is obtained by the use of a small auxiliary coil mounted beside the driving coil.   The voltage induced in this coil as it moves is fed back into the servo-loop to effect the desired control.

The moving elements are made light in weight, a powerful magnetic field is used, and a substantial driving coil with high gain in the servo-loop is used so that high speed of recording is possible.   For example, in one version, the full scale of the potentiometer can be covered in $\frac{1}{20}$ sec.   When a wide-range potentiometer is used, the recorder is then fast enough to record the variation in level of many transient sounds.

Other types of graphic-level recorders have been developed.   One of the early types, the principle of which is shown in Fig. 16.17, uses a special electromagnetic clutch to control the transfer of motor-drive rotation to linear motion of the slider on the potentiometer.[31]   These clutches form part of a servo-loop that includes the potentiometer, an amplifier, and rectifiers.

A number of graphic-level recorders use peak-type rectification exclusively in order to simplify some of the circuits.   When this is done, it is desirable to know how much above the rms value it indicates for a random noise compared with a sine wave.   Then the recorded measurements can be more easily interpreted and compared with data taken by other instruments.

Moving-coil Recorder.   One important type of recording instrument is a moving-coil recorder (see Fig. 16.18).   It is a comparatively powerful type of permanent-magnet moving-coil instrument carrying, instead of an indicating pointer, a lightweight pen that writes on recording paper.   These recorders are normally made to have a deflection that is directly proportional to current so that they do not indicate level in decibels on a uniform scale.   Any rectifier system that is used with the recorder must be included in the final calibration on the recording paper.

Because many of the high-speed moving-cell recorders require a high current in order to give appreciable deflection, power amplifiers are usually provided with the recorders in order to make them sensitive enough for general applications.

One version of the moving-coil recorder is the "inkless" recorder, which includes the basic movement of a permanent-magnet moving-coil instrument. It can be a unit of high sensitivity, however, since the mechanism does not require the coil to drive a marking pen. Instead, the recording is obtained by a mechanical arrangement

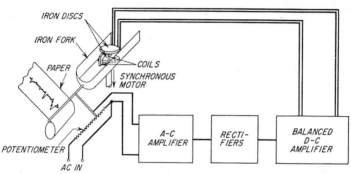

Fig. 16.17. Simplified schematic of a graphic-level recorder that uses a magnetically operated clutch.

that periodically presses the indicating pointer onto the recording paper through interposed carbon paper or ribbon (see Fig. 16.19). The recording obtained will be a series of points, which represent periodic samplings of the deflection of the indicator. The sampling rate is not very rapid, a maximum of two per second, but for recordings over long periods of time, this rate is ordinarily entirely adequate. This type of recorder has the advantages of high sensitivity, of relatively low cost, and of comparatively light weight. Because of these features, it has frequently been driven from a sound-level meter by a simple amplifier and rectifier system in order to record noise for long periods of time.

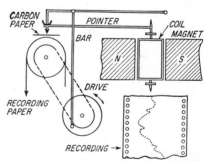

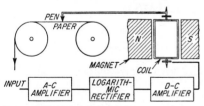

Fig. 16.18. Simplified sketch of moving-coil recorder.

Fig. 16.19. Simplified sketch of inkless recorder. The section of a recording shown in the lower right illustrates the discontinuous recording process.

Amplifiers that have a logarithmic relation between input and output are sometimes used with these linear recorders, and the recording charts are then uniformly divided for level.[32] Ordinarily, the logarithmic relation is obtained in a signal amplifier before rectification, and the amplifier is intended for use with sine-wave signals only. When the amplifier is used with signals of different wave shapes, the relation between input and output may no longer be accurately logarithmic. Then the system may be seriously limited in accuracy for recording of noise, because signals of wave shapes different from a sine wave are the common ones.

MAGNETIC-TAPE RECORDERS

Description.   A magnetic-tape recorder[33] is a device for storing an electrical signal.*
It stores the signal as variations in the magnetic state of finely divided iron oxide
particles coated on one side of a plastic tape.   As shown in Fig. 16.20, it consists of
the following basic units: a tape-transport mechanism, a magnetic recording head, a
reproducing head, an erasing head, a bias oscillator, amplifiers, and electrical equaliz-
ing networks.   Reels are used for convenience in storing and handling the tape, which
may be hundreds to thousands of feet long even though usually only ¼ in. wide and
of the order of 0.001 in. in thickness.

The tape is placed on the recorder so that it goes by the magnetic heads with the
coated side toward them.   It slides across very small gaps in the magnetic cores of
the heads as it is pulled by a capstan drive of the transport mechanism from one reel
to another.   The tape speed is usually 30, 15, 7½, or 3¾ in. per sec.

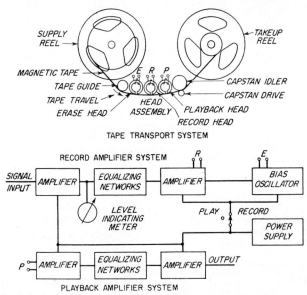

FIG. 16.20. Basic elements of a magnetic tape recorder.

The electrical signal to be recorded is amplified and also passed through an electrical
network to emphasize the high-frequency energy in the signal.   The amplified signal
is then applied to the recording head along with a strong signal from the bias oscillator,
which usually operates at a frequency of 100 kc or higher for a high-quality recorder.

The bias oscillator signal is used to improve the linearity of this recording system
that uses nonlinear magnetic materials for recording.   This technique is so successful
that, in a properly adjusted high-quality recorder, the range of linear operation can
be well over 50 db.

Before any section of the tape is recorded, it slides along the erase head, which is
excited by high-frequency energy from the bias oscillator.   This operation demag-
netizes the magnetic particles on the tape so that any previously recorded signal is

* Hundreds of different models of magnetic-tape recorders have been produced.   Most
of these are intended for use in noncritical applications, such as voice or music recording
in the home.   Some of the better recorders in this class have been used successfully in
noise-control applications.   But for general noise work, a recorder in the professional or
studio class is to be preferred, as explained in the section on *Characteristics*.

erased. When the recorded signal is to be reproduced, the bias oscillator is turned off so that no erasure will occur as the tape moves past the heads.

As the tape slides by the gap in the magnetic core of the reproducing head, a voltage is induced in the winding on the core because of the magnetized state of the particles on the tape. This induced voltage is amplified, and the relative gain as a function of frequency is modified by electrical networks to yield an over-all response vs. frequency that is reasonably uniform over the audio range. This over-all response is the ratio of input voltage of the recording amplifier to the output voltage of the reproducing amplifier.

Characteristics. Although high-quality magnetic-tape recorders are entirely satisfactory for many applications in noise-control problems, their characteristics are not ideal. Some of the limitations are considered here under the following headings: response vs. frequency, flutter, inherent noise and hum, distortion, print through.

Response vs. Frequency. The uniformity of response vs. frequency for a tape recorder is determined by tape speed, magnetic-gap length, gap alignment, nature of head and tape contact, type of tape, equalization, and amplifier response. Recorders using tape speeds of 15 in. per sec are usually adjusted to be within about 3 db in response from 50 to 15,000 cps, and some with tape speeds of $7\frac{1}{2}$ in. per sec also achieve that response. Since it is easier to maintain good high-frequency response at the higher tape speed, the higher speed is generally to be preferred.

Flutter. The tape does not slide by the magnetic gaps at an absolutely uniform speed, and the reproduced signal is then modified by fluctuations in the relative time scale. If a pure tone is recorded, these fluctuations produce a variation in output frequency that is called *flutter* (sometimes "wow"). Unless such fluctuations are very small, they are audible when certain types of sounds are reproduced. They can also make it difficult or impossible to use narrow-band analyzers in searching for discrete components in the recorded sound, and this factor is discussed later in this chapter. For general application to noise recordings, therefore, only the better-quality tape recorders should be used. Then it is possible to obtain and maintain over long periods flutter values less than about $\frac{1}{4}$ per cent, which is ordinarily satisfactory.

When tape recorders are used in the field, it is sometimes necessary to use a storage battery and a converter to supply power to the recorder. Again, this system must be very good in order to keep undesired fluctuations in tape speed to a minimum.

Inherent Noise and Hum. The inherent noise in a magnetic-tape recorder depends on many factors, such as amplifier design and adjustment, bias oscillator distortion, stray magnetic fields, and type of tape used. A spurious signal from the power line, called "hum," may also contribute an inherent noise unless care is taken in the design of the recorder, particularly in magnetic shielding of the reproducing head. Some of the noise in a recorder may appear only when a signal is present. But, in general, the noise level in a high-quality magnetic-tape recorder is satisfactory for most noise-recording applications.

Distortion. The maximum level at which essentially linear operation of recording exists is set by such factors as type of tape used, bias oscillator signal, amplifier operation, equalization, and the distribution as a function of frequency of the energy of the signal to be recorded. This distortion level sets an upper limit and the inherent noise level sets a lower limit to the range of signal levels that can be handled satisfactorily. This range is sometimes called *dynamic range;* and in a high-quality tape recorder, it is 50 db or more, which is adequate for most noise-recording purposes.

The distortion limit may vary appreciably with frequency because of the equalization systems used. When a recorder that uses a tape speed of $7\frac{1}{2}$ in. per sec is equalized to give good response to 15 kc, the dynamic range at the higher frequencies may be appreciably less than for a recorder using a tape speed of 15 in. per sec.

Print Through. Adjacent turns on a reel of recorded tape may affect each other by reason of the magnetized state of the particles. Some transfer of recording may occur so that "echoes" appear. "Echoes" of both positive or negative delay can obviously occur, and the process by which they are produced is sometimes called "print through." The level of these "echoes" can ordinarily be held to less than the inherent noise if the recorded level is always kept below the distortion point, if exposure of the recorded tape to magnetic fields is avoided, and if the tape is not exposed to high temperatures. Such precautions are particularly important if thin tape is used.

Binaural Recording. Some magnetic-tape recorders can record simultaneously two separate signals on the same tape. By the separate recording of the output of two microphones spaced 6 to 8 in. apart, it is possible to simulate a two-ear listening condition. The signals can then be reproduced separately to the two earphones of a headset with an improvement in realism compared with a single-channel pickup. Such a recording may be useful if subjective judgments of the noise are to be made.

Closed Loop of Tape. The recorded tape may be cut up into samples that contain only the noise under study. These can then be spliced to form closed loops so that the noise can be reproduced repeatedly to facilitate extensive measurements of the recorded signal.

SPECTRUM ANALYZERS

As explained in Chap. 2, one important measure of noise is the distribution of energy over the frequency spectrum. The process of determining this distribution is called *analysis* or *spectrum analysis*, and instruments used for analysis are called *analyzers*,[34] *spectrum analyzers*, or *frequency analyzers*.

An analyzer* is basically an electrical filter set or system and a sensitive electronic voltmeter which indicates the relative energy passed by the filter set. The elements may be separate or combined into a complete instrument. An analyzer is usually named according to the type of filter used. Thus, if an analyzer has a set of filters passing octave bands (see Chap. 2), it is called an octave-band analyzer.

The filter is designed to reduce the level of the noise components having frequencies outside the desired passband relative to the level of the components having frequencies in the passband. This selective action of the filter depends on electrical responses or impedance variations as a function of frequency among the combinations of inductors (coils), capacitors, and resistors used as the elements of the filter. When sufficient numbers of these elements are properly designed in combination, highly selective filters can be constructed. Different passbands in a single analyzer are obtained by different combinations of element values as a switch is turned or as one or more adjustable elements in the filter are tuned.

Selective filters can also be constructed using only two kinds of electrical elements, for example, resistors and capacitors. It is common then to use electronic amplifiers as part of the filtering system, and the response of the filter depends on the gain in the amplifier. Such a system is called an *active filter;* and a filter having only resistors, inductors, and capacitors is called a *passive filter*. Although amplifiers are ordinarily included in analyzers, the filter system in the analyzer is not then an active filter unless the amplifier is a part of the filter, as stated above.

One type of active filter used in sound analysis has an electric null circuit in a negative feedback loop of an amplifier,[35] as illustrated schematically in Fig. 16.21. The amplifier has uniform gain over a wide frequency range, and the elements of the null circuit are adjusted so that it greatly attenuates a signal component of one particular frequency. All other signal components having frequencies not in the vicinity of the frequency of the null are passed by the null circuit without appreciable change.

* The following representative list of companies that make analyzers used for sound measurements is not necessarily complete, and the analyzers are not necessarily recommended by the authors: In the United States, Allison Laboratories, Puente, Calif.; Brush Electronics Company, Cleveland, Ohio; General Radio Company, Cambridge, Mass.; Gertsch Products, Inc., Los Angeles, Calif.; Kay Electric Co., Pine Brook, N.J.; Hermon Hosmer Scott, Inc., Cambridge, Mass.; Hewlett-Packard Company, Palo Alto, Calif.; Panoramic Radio Products, Inc., Mount Vernon, N.Y.; Techno Instrument Co., Los Angeles, Calif.; Western Electro-Acoustic Laboratory, Los Angeles, Calif. In Europe, Brüel & Kjaer, Naerum, Denmark; Dawe Instruments, Ltd., London, England; Muirhead & Co., Ltd., Beckenham, Kent, England; Radiometer, Copenhagen, Denmark; Rohde & Schwarz, Munich, Germany; Siemens & Halske, Munich, Germany.

As a result of such a response characteristic, the gain of the amplifier is essentially unchanged at the null frequency, and at other frequencies the gain is reduced. The net response is that of a bandpass filter, having a bandwidth determined by the response of the null network and the gain of the amplifier. In this way, a bandwidth of only 2 per cent is achieved in a commercial instrument, even though only resistors

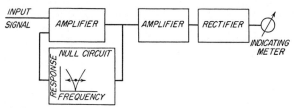

FIG. 16.21. Block diagram of analyzer using an electrical null circuit in a negative feedback loop.

and capacitors are used. In addition, instruments have been built that are tunable down to a frequency of 2.5 cps, which is impractical with a passive filter of reasonable bulk.

Octave-band Analyzers. Octave-band analyzers generally use the following series of octave passbands: 75 to 150, 150 to 300, 300 to 600, 600 to 1,200, 1,200 to 2,400, and 2,400 to 4,800 cps. The lower and upper ends of the audio spectrum are usually filled in with a low-pass* filter with a cutoff at 75 cps and a high-pass* filter with a cutoff at 4,800 cps. This series has been standardized in the United States (ASA Z24.10-1953). A typical set of response curves for such a set of filters is shown in Fig. 16.22. These curves show graphically how the audio range is divided into eight bands.

Another common series of octave bands is the following: 50 to 100, 100 to 200, 200 to 400, 400 to 800, 800 to 1,600, 1,600 to 3,200, and 3,200 to 6,400 cps. Some analyzers include both sets of bands, and some are continuously adjustable to cover the full audio range.

Half-octave and Third-octave Analyzers. When an octave-band analysis of a noise is not sufficiently detailed, analysis with narrower bands is usually tried. These bands may be a half octave or third octave in width or even narrower. The third-octave analyzer bands are ordinarily centered on a preferred number series, standardized in many countries, namely, 1, 1.25, 1.6, 2, 2.5, 3.15 (3.2), 4, 5, 6.3, 8, and this series multiplied by any integral power of 10.

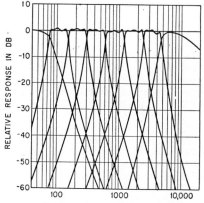

FIG. 16.22. Response vs. frequency of the eight filters in an octave-band filter set.

Narrow-band Proportional Bandwidth Analyzers. Analyzers with passbands that are even narrower than one-third octave are also used, particularly if a measurement of discrete components is desired. The narrower the passband, the more clearly defined do the discrete components become in the analysis (see Chap. 2). When the level of certain components only is desired, it may be of considerable advantage to use an analyzer having very narrow passbands, particularly if components having frequencies that are nearly the same must be distinguished. Furthermore, use of a

---

* The term "low-pass" is used to designate a filter that passes signals of frequency lower than the cutoff frequency, and similarly, a "high-pass" filter passes signals of frequency higher than the cutoff.

narrow-band analyzer often makes possible accurate measurement of the frequency of a component which may be an exceptionally useful clue in tracking down the source of noise. For example, the frequency can then sometimes be related to shaft speeds, rate of meshing of gear teeth, or blade or slot frequencies (see Chaps. 23, 25, 27, and 30).

Analyzers having bands narrower than third-octave bands are ordinarily made continuously tunable. In other words, controls are provided so that the center frequency of the passband can be adjusted to any frequency within the range of the instrument.

Constant-bandwidth Analyzers. Another type of analyzer has a constant bandwidth in cycles per second, and it is made tunable over the audio range by the heterodyne principle. The elements of a typical heterodyne analyzer are shown in Fig. 16.23, as a mixer, oscillator, filter, and electronic voltmeter. The noise signal is transformed in the electronic mixer stage so that the frequencies of all the noise components are increased by an amount equal to the frequency of the oscillator signal supplied to the mixer. The transformed signal is then passed through the highly selective filter, for example, a filter, centered at 50,000 cps, whose bandwidth is 10 cps. The output of the filter is measured by means of the sensitive electronic voltmeter. If, for example, the oscillator is set to a frequency of 49,000 cps, the noise-signal components in the range from 995 to 1,005 cps will be passed by the filter and indicated by the voltmeter. The oscillator tuning dial is usually calibrated in terms of the frequency of the incoming signal that will pass through the filter.

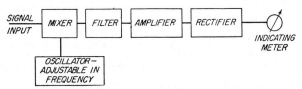

FIG. 16.23. Basic elements of a heterodyne analyzer.

The selectivity of the heterodyne analyzer is determined by the characteristics of the fixed filter. In some instruments, this fixed filter is a highly selective one using quartz-crystal filter elements, in others it is a series of inductor-capacitor filters. These inductor-capacitor filters in some instruments are made more selective by the use of electronic feedback.

For noise analysis, it is generally desirable to have a passband that is 25 to 50 cps wide, or a choice of bandwidths is even more useful.

Limited Attenuation—Effective Bandwidth. The ideal filter or analyzer is ordinarily assumed to have a uniform transmission or response characteristic for signals having frequencies within the passband and no response outside the passband. Actual systems only approximate this ideal. The response in the desired passband is ordinarily uniform enough for most practical purposes, but the response outside the passband is not zero. In other words, there is a contribution to the output of a filter from all components of the signal. The filter is designed to reduce the unwanted contributions as much as practical. How well this is done in any given filter can be judged by plotting a graph of the filter response characteristic.

This response characteristic is used to help interpret the results of analysis. It will show, for example, whether or not a strong component is determining the level in the frequency range near it. In the example of Fig. 2.12, the component at 120 cps is obscuring the analysis from 100 to 150 cps, and the observed values are in effect a type of response curve of the analyzer over the range of 100 to 150 cps.

A similar result is obtained for analyzers having discrete bands. Thus a strong component in one band can be rejected in an adjacent band only by the attenuation at the component frequency. The attenuation sets a limit to the range in level that can be measured on an analyzer. For example, if an analyzer has a maximum rejection of 30 db, the total range of component levels that can be observed is only 30 db, which is inadequate for many noise analyses.

If the sound energy is distributed essentially continuously in frequency, the concept of effective bandwidth[36] is sometimes used to take into account the contribution to the output of the filter from the components outside the nominal passband. The effective bandwidth is ordinarily calculated from a graphical plot on arithmetic paper of the filter response vs. frequency. The response is plotted in terms of the square of the ratio of the relative output voltage at a given frequency to the maximum relative output voltage (see Fig. 16.24). The area under this normalized curve is then the effective bandwidth of the filter.

For most modern analyzers, the effective bandwidth is only slightly greater than the quoted nominal bandwidth. This nominal width is ordinarily the difference between the two frequencies at which the response is 3 db less than the maximum response in the passband.

Separation of Components. The limitations of an analyzer in distinguishing individual components of a noise can be seen from the following simple examples. For an octave-band analyzer, the fundamental and the second harmonic component could ordinarily be readily distinguished if they were each at the center of successive bands. But they could be at either end of one band, and then the level of the two components would not be clearly defined. Measurements in adjacent bands, however, could help to separate the two. The second and third harmonic component

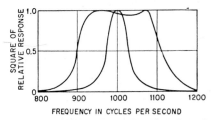

Fig. 16.24. Characteristics of two different filters plotted to show the square of the relative response vs. frequency. The area under each of the curves is then the effective bandwidth of each. Measurements of the areas in the figure show the wider one to have an effective bandwidth of 224 cps, and the narrower one, 70 cps.

would on the average be very likely to occur in the same octave band, so that in general they could not be distinguished. On such a basis, we could rate the octave-band analyzer as being able to distinguish a fundamental and a second harmonic. On a similar basis, a half-octave analyzer can distinguish the second and third harmonic, and a third-octave can distinguish the third and fourth harmonic component. As a further example, if it is desired to distinguish the ninth and tenth harmonic components, it would be desirable to use an analyzer having a passband of less than 10 per cent total width.

The ability of a constant-bandwidth analyzer to distinguish components depends on the difference in frequency between the components and not on the ratio of frequencies. If such an analyzer is capable of separating a 30-cps component and its 60-cps second harmonic, it should also be able to separate the 75th and 76th harmonics at 2,250 and 2,280 cps. Of course, it is assumed that these components are present at a sufficient level to be observed.

Fluctuating Frequency. The noise from many devices, for example, rotating machinery, has components whose frequencies vary appreciably with time. This instability of frequency is a factor limiting the narrowness of the band that can be used to obtain an accurate value of the component level. That is, if the frequency varies so that part of the time during the measurement it lies outside the relatively uniform passband, the indicated average level will be lower than the true level. This variation in frequency is often relatively the same for the majority of the components of a noise. That is, if a 30-cps component fluctuates in frequency by 0.1 cps, it would be common for the component in that same noise that has a frequency of 300 cps to fluctuate by 1 cps. In such a situation, a proportional-bandwidth analyzer would have the same limiting bandwidth for any component. If the passband is wide enough for the 30-cps signal, it is also wide enough at 300 cps.

When a recorded signal is being analyzed, flutter in the recording system will produce a fluctuation in the frequency of the noise components. This fluctuation will ordinarily be less than 0.1 to 0.2 per cent on a high-quality tape recorder, and for most analyzers, such a fluctuation can be tolerated.

The tolerable percentage fluctuation for an analyzer of constant bandwidth will vary with the frequency of the component. Thus a 0.2 per cent fluctuation at 5,000 cps would be too much for a 4-cps band, but it would be acceptable at 500 cps.

Hum Pickup. Analyzers that use inductors in the filter may be susceptible to pickup of extraneous voltages, called hum. This hum may be induced in the inductors by the magnetic field of electric equipment, such as motors and transformers. Hum pickup can be reduced by magnetic shielding of the inductors and by certain designs for the inductors. When hum is picked up, it can often be reduced also by reorienting the equipment.

Recording and Displaying the Output of an Analyzer. As discussed in the section on *Recorders*, the output of an analyzer is frequently recorded on a graphic-level recorder. The position of the recording paper is synchronized with the setting of the analyzer so that a graphic record of the analyzed signal is obtained.

The operation of tuning the analyzer to give this record may lead to erroneous results if an attempt is made to sweep through the analyzer range at too rapid a rate.[37] This situation arises because a selective filter cannot change its output instantaneously as the input changes. That is, it takes a finite time for a filter to reach a steady output when a signal is suddenly applied to it; and, similarly, when a filter is tuned to a different frequency it takes time for the output of the filter to reach a new steady value. Unless the filter is highly selective, however, these response times of the filter are very short.

This problem of response time when switching or tuning is completely avoided in some recording analyzers in the following way: Separate filter networks are used for each desired passband, for example, for each third octave from 40 to 16,000 cps.[38] These filters are all supplied simultaneously with the noise signal. Then the outputs of the filters are connected in succession to the recorder to yield the graphic record of the analysis. Since the noise is always present at the filter, there is no switching build-up time to limit the rate of sampling.

This technique cannot be applied to a continuously tunable analyzer, however. Such an analyzer must be tuned at a rate slower than a certain critical value if accurate results are to be obtained.[39] This critical value is approximately the square of the bandwidth in cycles per second. For example, an analyzer with a bandwidth of 4 cps should be tuned more slowly than 16 cps per second.

Some analyzers display the output of the filter system as a deflection of the beam in the vertical direction in a cathode-ray tube.[40] The horizontal deflection is made proportional to the frequency to which the analyzer is tuned, so that the analysis is displayed on the cathode-ray-tube screen. The frequency traverse is ordinarily quite rapid, so that fine resolution of detail is not achieved.

Even more elaborate display systems have been developed. In one instrument, for example, frequency and time are displayed as the two rectangular axes of the screen and the spot brightness is made proportional to the amplitude of the analyzed output.[41]

ADDITIONAL INSTRUMENTS

The instruments described earlier in this chapter are those generally used for noise measurements. Other instruments have also been used, and some of them are enumerated in this section. As noise-measuring instruments are more widely used, some of these additional instruments may develop into important tools for noise control.

An autocorrelator has been applied to determine the energy of sound in various frequency bands.[42] This equipment is so complicated that it is still basically a research tool.

An instrument that supplies a noise for masking another noise, for example, an impact sound, has been developed to rate such noises on a psychoacoustic basis.[43] This instrument avoids some of the problems of earlier subjective meters; so that it is more readily used as a measuring tool.

Instruments for measuring acoustic power flow have been developed.[44] Such instruments have a limited dynamic range and are still research tools rather than field instruments.

Frequency meters have been used to measure the dominant frequency in a sound or a filtered sound.[45] Many such instruments are available, but no significant use of them has been made in noise control because analyzers have been found to be satisfactory for frequency measurement.

Methods for determining the time distribution of energy in a sound have been developed.[46] These can be applied to measure the probability distribution of amplitude levels of the over-all noise, or they can be applied to noise analysis.

REFERENCES

1. de Boer, J.: *Philips Tech. Rev.*, **5**: 140 (1940).
   Amos, S. W., and F. C. Brooker: *Electronic Eng.*, **18**: 109, 136 (1946).
   Olson, H. F.: "Elements of Acoustical Engineering," 2d ed., Chap. 8, D. Van Nostrand Company, Inc., Princeton, N.J., 1947.
   Beranek, L. L.: "Acoustic Measurements," Chap. 5, John Wiley & Sons, Inc., New York, 1949.
   British Broadcasting Corporation: "Microphones," Iliffe & Sons, London, 1951.
   Peterson, A. P. G., and L. L. Beranek: "Handbook of Noise Measurement," 3rd ed., p. 41, General Radio Co., Cambridge, Mass., 1956.
2. Veneklasen, P. S.: *J. Acoust. Soc. Amer.*, **20**: 807 (1948).
   Hilliard, J. K.: *Electronics*, **26**: 160 (November, 1953).
   Houdek, J. F., Jr.: *J. Audio Eng. Soc.*, **2**: 234 (1954).
3. American Standards Association: American Standard Z24.8-1949.
   Hawley, M. S.: *Bell Labs. Record*, **33**: 6 (1955).
   Cook, R. K.: *Acustica*, **4**: 101 (1954).
4. Massa, F.: *J. Acoust. Soc. Amer.*, **17**: 29 (1945).
   Brush Electronics Company: "Piezotronic Technical Data," Cleveland, Ohio, 1953.
   Medill, J.: *J. Acoust. Soc. Amer.*, **25**: 864 (1953).
   Mason, W. P.: *J. Acoust. Soc. Amer.*, **27**: 73 (1955).
5. Wente, E. C., and A. L. Thuras: *J. Acoust. Soc. Amer.*, **3**: 44 (1931).
6. Mason, W. P., and R. N. Marshall: *J. Acoust. Soc. Amer.*, **10**: 206 (1939).
   Marshall, R. N., and W. R. Harry: *J. Acoust. Soc. Amer.*, **12**: 481 (1941).
   Coile, R. C.: *J. Soc. Motion Picture Engrs.*, **51**: 298 (1948).
   Beaverson, W. A., and A. M. Wiggins: *J. Acoust. Soc. Amer.*, **22**: 592 (1952).
   Clark, M. A.: *J. Acoust. Soc. Amer.*, **25**: 1152 (1953).
   Wiggins, A. M.: *J. Acoust. Soc. Amer.*, **26**: 687 (1954).
7. Cook, R. K.: *J. Research Natl. Bur. Standards*, **25**: 489 (1940)
   MacLean, W. R.: *J. Acoust. Soc. Amer.*, **12**: 140 (1940).
   Olson, H. F.: *RCA Rev.*, **6**: 36 (1941).
   Foldy, L. L., and H. Primakoff: *J. Acoust. Soc. Amer.*, **17**: 109 (1945); **19**: 50 (1947).
   DiMattia, A. L., and F. M. Wiener: *J. Acoust. Soc. Amer.*, **18**: 341 (1946).
   McMillan, E.: *J. Acoust. Soc. Amer.*, **18**: 344 (1946).
   Carstensen, E. L.: *J. Acoust. Soc. Amer.*, **19**: 961 (1947).
   Buchmann, G.: *Funk und Ton*, **1**: 30 (1947).
   Rudnick, I., and M. N. Stein: *J. Acoust. Soc. Amer.*, **20**: 818 (1948).
   American Standards Association: Z24.4-1949, Pressure Calibration of Laboratory Standard Pressure Microphones, New York.
   Beranek, L. L.: "Acoustic Measurements," Chap. 4, John Wiley and Sons, Inc., New York, 1949.
   Wathen-Dunn, W.: *J. Acoust. Soc. Amer.*, **21**: 542 (1949).
   Hawley, M. S.: *J. Acoust. Soc. Amer.*, **22**: 56 (1950).
   Terry, R. L., and R. B. Watson: *J. Acoust. Soc. Amer.*, **23**: 684 (1951).
   Nielsen, A. K.: *Acustica*, **2**: 112 (1952).
   Holle, W., and G. Latzel: *Funk und Ton*, **7**: 109 (1953).
   Simmons, B. D., and F. Biagi: *J. Acoust. Soc. Amer.*, **26**: 693 (1954).
   Biagi, F., and R. K. Cook: *J. Acoust. Soc. Amer.*, **26**: 506 (1954).

8. American Standards Association: American Standard Z24.11-1954.
9. Glover, R., and B. Baumzweiger: *J. Acoust. Soc. Amer.*, **10**: 200 (1939).
10. Ballantine, S.: *J. Acoust. Soc. Amer.*, **3**: 319 (1932).
11. Beranek, L. L.: "Acoustic Measurements," p. 148, John Wiley & Sons, Inc., New York, 1949.
    West, W.: *Proc. Phys. Soc. (London) B*, **62**: 437 (1949).
    King, A. J., and C. R. Maguire: *Acustica*, **1**: 123 (1951).
    Dadson, R. S., and E. G. Butcher: *Acustica*, **4**: 103 (1954).
12. Beranek, L. L.: "Acoustic Measurements," p. 161, John Wiley & Sons, Inc., New York, 1949.
13. Hawley, M. S.: *J. Acoust. Soc. Amer.*, **21**: 183 (1949).
    Beranek, L. L.: "Acoustic Measurements," pp. 132, 601, John Wiley & Sons, Inc., New York, 1949.
14. Tweeddale, J. E.: *J. Acoust. Soc. Amer.*, **12**: 421 (1941).
    Huber, P., and J. M. Whitmore: *J. Acoust. Soc. Amer.*, **12**: 167 (1940).
    King, A. J., R. W. Guelke, C. R. Maguire, and R. A. Scott: *J. Inst. Elec. Engrs. (London)*, **88** (II): 163 (1941).
    Deutscher Normenausschuss: Messgerät für DIN-Lautstärken, DIN 5045, 1942.
    American Standards Association: American Standard Z24.3-1944.
    Scott, H. H., H. Chrystie, and E. G. Dyett: *Proc. Nat. Electronics Conf.*, **4**: 33 (1948).
    King, A. J.: *Phys. Soc. (London)*, **125** (1949).
    Holle, W.: *Funk und Ton*, **3**: 367 (1949).
    Gross, E. E., Jr.: *Gen. Radio Exp.*, **26**: 1 (March, 1952).
    Zeller, W., and E. Ebert: *Arch. tech. Messen*, **V55-5**: 177 (1955).
15. Peterson, A. P. G.: *Gen. Radio Exp.*, **26**: 1 (April, 1952).
16. Barkhausen, H.: *Z. tech. Phys.*, **7**: 599 (1926); *Z. VDI*, **71**: 1471 (1927).
    Churcher, B. G., and A. J. King: *Nature*, **138**: 329 (1936).
17. Rider, J. F., and S. D. Uslan: "Encyclopedia on Cathode-ray Oscilloscopes and Their Uses," John Francis Rider, Publisher, Inc., New York, 1950.
18. Harris, F. K.: "Electrical Measurements," p. 621, John Wiley & Sons, Inc., New York, 1952.
19. Stevens, S. S.: *J. Acoust. Soc. Amer.*, **27**: 815 (1955).
20. Harris, F. K.: "Electrical Measurements," Chap. 5, John Wiley & Sons, Inc., New York, 1952.
21. Köhler, J. W.: *Arch. tech. Messen*, **J712-4** (October, 1938).
    Hermach, F. L., and E. S. Williams: *J. Research Natl. Bur. Standards*, **52**: 227 (1954).
    Wechsung, H.: *Arch. tech. Messen*, **J712-5**: 19 (January, 1954).
22. Hickin, E. M.: *Wireless Engineer*, **23**: 308 (1946).
    Montgomery, C. G.: "Technique of Microwave Measurements," Chap. 3, McGraw-Hill Book Company, Inc., New York, 1947.
    Terman, F. E., and J. M. Pettit: "Electronic Measurements," 2d ed., Chap. 2, McGraw-Hill Book Company, Inc., New York, 1952.
23. Sahagen, J.: *Proc. IRE*, **19**: 233 (1931).
    Harris, F. K.: "Electrical Measurements," p. 418, John Wiley & Sons, Inc., New York, 1952.
24. Grondahl, L. O., and P. H. Geiger: *J. AIEE*, **46**: 215 (1927).
25. Beranek, L. L.: *Electronics*, **12**: 14 (July, 1939).
26. Beranek, L. L.: "Acoustic Measurements," Chap. 11, John Wiley & Sons, Inc., New York, 1949.
27. Beranek, L. L.: "Acoustic Measurements," Chap. 11, John Wiley & Sons, Inc., New York, 1949.
    Terman, F. E., and J. M. Pettit: "Electronic Measurements," 2d ed., Chap. 1, McGraw-Hill Book Company, Inc., New York, 1952.
28. Peterson, A. P. G.: *Noise Control*, **2**: 46 (March, 1956).
29. Drysdale, C. V., and A. C. Jolley: "Electrical Measuring Instruments," part 2, chap. 3, D. Van Nostrand Company, Inc., Princeton, N.J., 1924.
    Stanton, G. T., and J. E. Tweeddale: *J. Acoust. Soc. Amer.*, **3**: 371 (1932).
    Keinath, G.: *Arch. tech. Messen*, **J031-1** (February, 1933).
    Wente, E. C., E. H. Bedell, and K. D. Swartzel, Jr.: *J. Acoust. Soc. Amer.*, **6**: 121, 1935.
    Kübler, A., and K. Boesel: *Siemens-Z.*, **27**: 246 (1953).
    Schneider, J.: *Rohde & Schwarz Mitt.*, **6**: 390 (1955).
30. Brüel, P. V., and U. Ingard: *J. Acoust. Soc. Amer.*, **21**: 91 (1949).
31. von Braunmühl, H. J., and W. Weber: *E.N.T.*, **12**: 223 (1935).
32. Mayo, C. G., and D. G. Beadle: *Electronic Eng.*, **23** (4): 462 (1951).
    LeBel, C. J., and J. Y. Dunbar: *J. Acoust. Soc. Amer.*, **23**: 559 (1951).

Hunt, F. V., and J. F. Hersh: *Rev. Sci. Instr.*, **26**: 829 (1955).
33. LeBel, C. J.: "Fundamentals of Magnetic Recording," Audio Devices, Inc., New York, 1951.
Apps, D. C.: *J. Acoust. Soc. Amer.*, **24**: 660 (1952).
Camras, M.: Magnetic Recording, *Convention Record, IRE*, part 3, p. 16, 1953.
Jorysz, A.: *Tele-Tech*, **13**: 54 (July, 1954).
Begun, S. J.: *Elec. Eng.*, **73**: 1115 (1954).
Schmidbauer, O.: *Funk und Ton*, **8**: 341 (1954).
34. Moore, C. R., and A. S. Curtis: *Bell System Tech. J.*, **6**: 217 (1927).
Hall, H. H.: *J. Acoust. Soc. Amer.*, **7**: 102 (1935).
Arguimbau, L. B.: *Gen. Radio Exp.*, **13**: 1 (December, 1938).
Electronics, **16**: 100 (July, 1943).
Beranek, L. L.: "Acoustic Measurements," Chap. 12, John Wiley & Sons, Inc., New York, 1952.
Fant, C. G. M.: *J. Acoust. Soc. Amer.*, **22**: 449 (1950).
Wulfsberg, K. N.: *J. Acoust. Soc. Amer.*, **22**: 847 (1950).
Peterson, A. P. G.: *Gen. Radio Exp.*, **26**: 1 (September, 1951).
Peterson, G. E., and G. Raisbeck: *J. Acoust. Soc. Amer.*, **25**: 1157 (1953).
Scott, H. H., and D. von Recklinghausen: *J. Acoust. Soc. Amer.*, **25**: 727 (1953).
American Standards Association: American Standard Z24.10-1953.
American Standards Association: American Standard Z24.15-1955.
Richard, J. D., Jr., P. F. Smith, and F. H. Stephens: *IRE Trans. on Audio*, **AU-3**: 37 (1955)
Martin, W.: *Rohde & Schwarz Mitt.*, **6**: 353 (1955).
35. Scott, H. H.: *J. Acoust. Soc. Amer.*, **11**: 225 (1939).
36. Beranek L. L.: "Acoustic Measurements," p. 569, John Wiley & Sons, Inc., New York, 1949.
Young, R. W.: U.S. Navy Electronics Laboratory, San Diego, Calif., May, 1955, PB118036.
37. Schuck, O. H.: *Proc. IRE*, **22**: 1295 (1934).
38. Brüel & Kjaer: *B & K Tech. Rev.*, No. 4, p. 3, October, 1953.
39. Hok, G.: *J. Appl. Phys.*, **19**: 242 (1948).
Barber, N. F.: *Electronic Eng.*, **21**: 175 (1949).
Marique, J.: *Proc. IRE*, **40**: 945 (1952).
40. Feldman, E. F.: *Tele-Tech*, **14**: 78 (October, 1955).
41. Koenig, W., H. K. Dunn, and L. Y. Lacy: *J. Acoust. Soc. Amer.*, **18**: 19 (1946).
Riesz, R. R., and L. Schott: *J. Acoust. Soc. Amer.*, **18**: 50 (1946).
Dudley, H., and O. O. Gruenz, Jr.: *J. Acoust. Soc. Amer.*, **18**: 62 (1946).
Potter, R. K., G. A. Kopp, and H. A. Green: "Visible Speech," D. Van Nostrand Company, Inc., Princeton, N.J., 1947.
Gruenz, O.: *Bell Labs. Record*, **29**: 256 (1951).
Peterson, G. E.: *J. Acoust. Soc. Amer.*, **26**: 406 (1954).
42. Fano, R. M.: *J. Acoust. Soc. Amer.*, **22**: 546 (1950).
Goff, K. G.: *J. Acoust. Soc. Amer.*, **27**: 223 (1955).
43. Hardy, H. C., F. G. Tyzzer, and H. H. Hall: *Noise Control*, **2**: 38 (1956).
44. Clapp, C. W., and F. A. Firestone: *J. Acoust. Soc. Amer.*, **13**: 124 (1941).
Schultz, T. J.: *J. Acoust. Soc. Amer.*, **26**: 936(A) (1954).
Baker, S.: *J. Acoust. Soc. Amer.*, **27**: 269 (1955).
45. Hunt, F. V.: *Rev. Sci. Instr.*, **6**: 43 (1935).
Young, R. W., and A. Loomis: *J. Acoust. Soc. Amer.*, **10**: 112 (1938).
Kent, E. L.: *J. Acoust. Soc. Amer.*, **14**: 175 (1943).
Scott, H. H.: *Gen. Radio Exp.*, **20**: 1 (February, 1946).
Beranek, L. L.: "Acoustic Measurements," Chap. 6, John Wiley & Sons, Inc., New York, 1949.
46. Fontanellaz, G., and E. Wey: *Tech. Mitt. PTT*, **32**: 87 (1954).

Chapter 17

NOISE MEASURING TECHNIQUES

H. H. Scott

Hermon Hosmer Scott, Inc.

INTRODUCTION

This chapter covers the techniques generally employed in the measurement and analysis of air-borne sound with commercial types of noise measuring equipment. Other chapters provide details on specialized techniques for certain applications. In Chap. 16 the various instruments available for noise measurements are described in detail. In all cases the instruction books supplied by the manufacturers of the measuring equipment must be consulted for details concerning the proper operation of each instrument, including checking of battery voltages, calibration, and any other aspects of operation peculiar to each particular model.

The simplest noise measurements are those of over-all sound level and require only the sound-level meter. If the sound field is relatively diffuse,* such readings will not depend significantly upon microphone angle. However, when the sound being measured impinges upon the microphone from a definite direction—particularly when higher-frequency components form an appreciable portion of the spectrum, the readings will depend upon the angle of incidence. Then the directional characteristics of the microphone and the environment must be taken into consideration.

In many cases a measurement of sound pressure level does not provide sufficient information for the problem at hand. Then the noise must be analyzed to determine its spectral distribution or the frequency of the important components. Analyzers for this purpose may be grouped in two classes. The first contains adjustable electrical filters or filter sets dividing the audio spectrum into a series of octave, half-octave, or third-octave bands. The second, used for more specialized applications, contains continuously tunable narrow-band analyzers which allow more exact measurement of the frequency and level of individual components of the sound. Analyzers are generally operated in conjunction with sound-level meters and may be either manual or automatic in operation. Automatic operation of an analyzer which provides a permanent record of the results is obtained through the use of a level recorder that may be an inherent part of the analyzer or a separate accessory. (Level recorders are also used to measure noise levels as a function of time.)

Where it is inconvenient or impractical to make all desired analyses of a noise on the spot, the noise may be recorded on magnetic tape and analyzed later with any of several of the available types of analyzers. The magnetic-tape recording also provides a permanent record of the noise which may be listened to later for aural evaluation or subjected to further types of analysis.

* A sound field is said to be completely diffuse when the pressure is everywhere the same and waves are traveling in every direction with equal probability.

In evaluating the total noise power radiated by a source, measurements of over-all acoustic power are also needed.

Special techniques and instrumentation are required in dealing with intermittent or impact noises which have high-level peaks which are of so short a duration that the standard sound-level meter will not provide a satisfactory indication. Oscilloscopes which operate in conjunction with sound-level meters, and special peak-reading noise meters are used for this purpose.

The wide variety of equipment available for noise measurement makes possible the choice of apparatus suitable for a wide range of applications. Questions of portability, accuracy, required frequency and level ranges, and the degree of resolution required in analyses are factors which generally determine the final choice of instruments for any particular application.

SOUND PRESSURE LEVEL MEASUREMENTS

Sound Pressure Level and Sound Level. From Eq. (2.16) sound pressure level is related to sound pressure by

$$L_p = 20 \log_{10} \frac{p}{p_0} = 20 \log_{10} \frac{p}{0.0002} \quad \text{db}$$

where p is the rms sound pressure in microbars (dynes per sq cm) and p_0 is the rms value of the reference pressure, which is 0.0002 microbar. Sound pressure level measurements are usually obtained from readings of a sound-level meter, although other combinations of calibrated microphones, amplifiers, and indicating instruments are sometimes employed. The characteristics of the rectifier in the indicating instrument are important in determining the indicated level. For example, if the indicating instrument on the sound-level meter provides a true rms reading, the measurement is one of rms sound pressure.

As indicated in Chap. 16, sound-level meters are equipped with weighting networks which alter the frequency response, mainly by attenuating the lower frequencies. Measurements made with these weighting networks do not therefore indicate true sound pressure levels, but *weighted* sound pressure levels, referred to simply as *sound levels*.

Choice of Microphones. For most sound-level measurements the microphone usually supplied with a sound-level meter, a bimorph-crystal of Rochelle salt which is driven by a diaphragm exposed to the sound waves, is well suited. However, for special applications, as noted below, other types of microphones may prove more satisfactory.

Measurements at High Temperature. The maximum temperature to which a Rochelle-salt microphone can be exposed without permanent damage is 132°F (55.6°C); a safe upper limit is about 113°F (45°C). Therefore, when sound-level measurements are made at high temperatures, condenser, dynamic, or ceramic microphones, some of which are designed to operate at temperatures as high as 167°F (75°C), are sometimes used. High temperatures (or extremely low temperatures) also affect the life of the batteries in sound-level meters.

Measurements at Varying Temperatures. The microphone calibrations that are supplied with a sound-level meter, or which may be obtained from the manufacturer, are normally made at room temperature. Actually, microphone sensitivity varies with temperature, although under normal circumstances this variation may be negligibly small. For example, Fig. 17.1 shows the variation in response of a Rochelle-salt microphone as a function of temperature. Note that when the microphone is connected directly to a sound-level meter the variation is relatively small. However, when the microphone is connected by means of a long cable, the variation is quite significant. This variation is a result of the change of the capacity of the crystal with temperature.

The temperature coefficient of sensitivity of a typical condenser microphone system is about −0.04 db per °F. For the dynamic microphone the variation depends on frequency—over much of the frequency range the variation is of the order of 1 db for a 50°F change in temperature.

Effects of Humidity. As indicated in Chap. 16, Rochelle salt may be permanently damaged if exposed to excessively high humidities, i.e., above about 85 per cent. For this reason the Rochelle-salt crystals in microphones of this type are given a protective coating. For the same reason, when the microphone is continuously exposed to excessively high humidities, another type of microphone may be selected. Dynamic microphones are relatively unaffected by high humidities.

While a condenser microphone unit is not damaged by high humidities, its operation may be as a result of leakage across the condenser. The heat of the vacuum tubes in the condenser microphone preamplifier is sometimes utilized, therefore, to keep the temperature of the microphone above that of the surroundings.

Cable Extensions. As noted in Fig. 17.1, when a long cable is employed with a Rochelle-salt microphone, a correction must be made for the sensitivity—the correction varying with temperature. This is discussed under the topic *Sound-level Corrections* below. If a long cable, say 100 ft, is used between a dynamic microphone and the input transformer of a sound-level meter, no correction is necessary (the cable should be shielded and twisted). For this reason, dynamic microphones are sometimes used where the microphone must be placed at a long distance from the instrument.

Very High Sound Levels.[1] Most microphones, including Rochelle-salt units, are not designed to operate with sound-level meters at sound levels in excess of 140 db. Above this level, especially designed crystal, magnetostriction, condenser, or ceramic microphones may be employed.* In sound fields of high level, it is usually necessary to insulate the instruments used in conjunction with the microphone against the high levels to avoid microphonics. In order to reduce the effects of microphonics on the signal-to-noise ratio, it may be advantageous to introduce an additional attenuator (pad) in the circuit of a sound-level meter. The added pad may also make it possible to extend the use of the sound-level meter, with the Rochelle-salt microphone with which it is supplied, to higher levels.

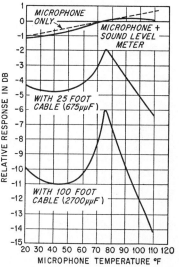

Fig. 17.1. Variation in the response of a Rochelle-salt microphone as a function of temperature for various lengths of cable between the microphone and sound-level meter to which it is connected.

Figure 17.2 shows one recommended installation of an ADP-crystal microphone in the wall of a chamber. Note that it is carefully isolated from solid-borne vibration by means of a resilient support.

Response Characteristics. The Rochelle-salt microphone supplied with the usual sound-level meter has excellent sensitivity, being able to measure sound levels as low as 24 db. Its low-frequency response is excellent, as shown in Fig. 16.2b. On the other hand, it will be noted in this figure that its characteristics at high frequencies are not as good as those of some microphones of the dynamic or condenser type—the latter

---

* For example, the Massa Model M-141B standard microphone, which is of the ADP-crystal type, is rated at 200 db. The Altec condenser microphone Type 21-BR-180 may be used for levels up to 150 db with distortion less than 1 per cent and at levels up to 170 db with distortion below 10 per cent. Microphones for use at very high levels of the barium titanate type are available from the Atlantic Research Corp., Brush Electronics Co., Chesapeake Instrument Corp., and Gulton Mfg. Co.; The Harris Transducer Co. has a magnetostriction unit available.

being the best. However, the condenser microphone (together with its preamplifier) is not so suitable for low-level noise measurements as either the Rochelle-salt microphone or the dynamic microphone because of its relatively high self-noise which is equivalent to a sound pressure level of about 35 db. While the sensitivity of the usual dynamic microphone is good, and its noise level is low in the absence of stray magnetic fields, it is susceptible to hum pickup, as discussed in a section which follows.

Direction of Arrival of Sound at the Microphone. *Randomly Incident Sound.* Since the typical sound-level meter is adjusted so that its frequency response most nearly approaches the design objective for sounds of random incidence, it follows that no corrections are necessary for the directional characteristics of the microphone when the noise which impinges upon the microphone is randomly distributed with respect to angle of incidence. A simple check by rotating the microphone in a plane through its normal axis will generally indicate whether or not such a condition exists; if it does, the reading will not vary. This condition generally obtains when measurements are made in a large reverberant room at a distance from the source so that the sound field is relatively diffuse.

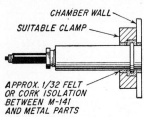

CHAMBER WALL

SUITABLE CLAMP

APPROX. 1/32 FELT OR CORK ISOLATION BETWEEN M-141 AND METAL PARTS

FIG. 17.2. Diagram of recommended installation of the Massa standard microphone model M-141B in the wall of a chamber. This microphone may be used in temperatures up to 167°F (75°C). (*Courtesy of Massa Laboratories, Inc.*)

Unless otherwise specified, sound-level meters are so adjusted that the over-all frequency response is closest to the design objective for sounds of random incidence. For the average microphone the random response closely approximates the response of the microphone at an angle of incidence of about 70°.

Direct Sound from a Source. Noise measurements that are made in a room containing a considerable amount of absorption, or in a reverberant room very close to the source, or measurements made outdoors are primarily of the sound coming directly from the source.

Most microphones, including common Rochelle-salt, piezoelectric, dynamic (moving-coil), and condenser types, have diaphragms which are substantially flat (although in some cases slightly conical or slightly curved) and are symmetrical around a *principal axis* which is perpendicular or normal to the average plane of this diaphragm. This axis is also referred to as the 0° *axis* and is used as the reference in measuring angles of azimuth to define the directional characteristics. Directional characteristics of such microphones are generally plotted in terms of angle of incidence between the 0° axis and the direction of propagation of the sound wave. An angle of 90° of azimuth, also referred to as parallel or grazing incidence, occurs when the direction of sound propagation is parallel to the average plane of the diaphragm. Since the diaphragm is actuated by sound pressure, the high-frequency response will vary as a function of the angle of incidence (see Figs. 16.2 and 17.3). Therefore, it is desirable to make measurements of direct sound at an angle of incidence for which the free-field calibration is known, as for instance the angle when the response closely approximates the random response. Ninety degrees also is a frequently used angle. When the background level is comparatively high, a better signal-to-noise ratio may be obtained by using 0° where the sensitivity is higher.

If the angle of incidence of the sound being measured is, for example, at 70°, the microphone should be rotated around an axis coinciding with the direction of propagation of the sound to detect any variations caused by extraneous high-frequency sound reaching the microphone at 0° incidence. This sometimes occurs if high-frequency sounds are reflected by nearby objects and reach the microphone at the 0° angle at which it is most sensitive to high frequencies. When the microphone is rotated, if there is any noticeable variation in the sound-level meter reading the lowest reading should be considered as correct, since under those conditions there is a minimum of error as a result of the reflection. This rotation is practical only when the microphone is used on an extension cable or when the sound-level meter itself is entirely behind the diaphragm of the microphone and is shaped so as to minimize interference patterns.

One precaution should be observed in rotating the microphone as described above. If strong standing waves are present, which are most likely to be encountered at low frequencies, nulls may occur which may be confused with the minimum reading, as mentioned above, when the microphone is rotated if the microphone position is changed appreciably or if other conditions are changed which modify the standing-wave pattern. Such a standing-wave pattern can be detected by moving the microphone toward or away from the source of sound to determine whether any regularly spaced series of maximum and minimum levels exists.

Use of Weighting Networks. Sound-level meters generally are equipped with weighting networks which adjust the frequency response, mainly by attenuating the lower frequencies, as indicated in Chap. 16.

C Network. The *C* network of the sound-level meter provides the closest practical approach to over-all flat response—that is, equal response of the sound-level meter to sounds of all frequencies within its frequency range. If the sound-level meter is built to standards such as those established by the American Standards Association the frequency response will be within defined limits.[2]

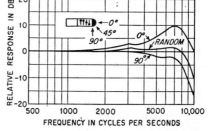

FIG. 17.3. Directional characteristics of a typical sound-level meter microphone. (See Fig. 16.2 for other similar characteristics.) The random response is essentially the same as the response at about 70° azimuth. In most cases the exact angle is not critical and a relatively flat response can be obtained at any angle between 60 and 75°.

Furthermore, although the human ear does not respond equally to all frequencies at low intensities, it approaches this type of response at high sound levels. Therefore, the *C* network is used for all measurements at high sound levels (85 db or higher). Since a reading with the *C* weighting represents a measurement of the actual physical sound pressure level this network is used in all cases where the sound is to be analyzed. Because of their physical significance, such readings are usually taken as a matter of good engineering practice even when other measurements are made with other networks.

A and B Networks. While the sound-level meter is a pressure-actuated device, weighting networks are provided to adjust the frequency response, mainly by attenuating the lower frequencies to approximate the equal-loudness contours of the human ear. However, since the ear does not function as a simple frequency-weighted sound-pressure indicator but has a much more complex response, one's aural estimate of a sound and the weighted sound pressure level (i.e., the sound level) will not always be in agreement. This is particularly true in the case of intermittent and impact noises and other sounds having short-time peaks of very high levels.

The greatest low-frequency attenuation is provided in the *A* network, while the *B* network provides an intermediate degree. These networks have been known, respectively, as the "40- and 70-db networks" because of their resemblance to the equal-loudness contours for the ear at these levels. *Always record the weighting-curve designation as well as the decibel readings when measuring sound level.*

Where weighting networks are used, the following level ranges are suggested for use of the various networks:

Sound-level Range, db	Weighting Network
Under 55	A
55–85	B
Above 85	C (flat response over range of instrument)

Strict use of this table is not always possible. For example, because of strong low-frequency components, a sound may read 84 db on the *B* network and 86 db on the

C network.   In such cases it is usually best to record data with both networks and use the arithmetic average of the two readings.

Normally, the A and B networks are not used for measurements at levels higher than those indicated in the above table.   However, there is one exception.   When noise, for reasons of convenience, is measured close to the source at a high level, the A or B network may be used if data are required concerning the levels at some distance from the source.   For example, a high-intensity sound source may cause annoyance at a distant point where the resulting level will be under 55 db.   Measurements made close to the source to determine the efficiency of any noise-reducing changes may then be made with the A network since such measurements would be more nearly indicative of aural evaluation of the sound at the distant point where the level would be below 55 db.   Similarly, if the resulting sound level at the distant point is between 55 and 85 db, the B network may be used.   However, this procedure should be used with caution since measurements close to a source are not necessarily related by the "inverse-distance law" given in Eq. (2.24) because of the radiation pattern of the source and other factors.

Speed of Indicating Instrument.   In general, shaped pole pieces are used in the indicating-instrument movements of level meters in order to obtain a scale which is substantially linear in decibels.   Therefore, the ballistic characteristics of the indicating instrument are not constant over its entire range of movement.   This sometimes results in a difference between readings on adjacent attenuator settings where one reading is taken at the upper end of the instrument scale and another reading is taken at the lower end of the scale.   Where such a difference is noticed, it is desirable to use the lower attenuator setting, which gives deflection at the high end of the scale, since the ballistic characteristics are more closely controlled over that portion of the scale.

Fast Speed.   The normal dynamic characteristics of the indicating instrument of the sound-level meter are similar to those adopted for volume-level measurements in recording and radio broadcasting and have proved satisfactory for sounds of an essentially continuous nature.   This speed, also called the "fast" speed, is such that the indicating instrument attains its final reading in approximately 0.2 sec and is unsuitable for measuring shorter sound pulses.   Individual impact noises are not indicated satisfactorily by this meter, and the results on intermittent sounds may also be in error if the time duration of the sound pulses is short compared with the repetition time.

Slow Speed.   For many purposes, where the sound level is fluctuating widely, some sort of averaging is often required.   Therefore, most sound-level meters also have a *slow* meter speed, the slower action of which provides an averaging effect that is helpful in measuring sounds of essentially continuous character but varying in amplitude.   For a noise pulse of 0.5 sec duration, such a meter will read 2 to 6 db low.   It is not satisfactory for measuring intermittent sounds.

Reading the Sound-level Meter.   The sound-level meter reading is the sum of the attenuator settings and the reading of the indicating instrument.   With some sound-level meters there is more than one attenuator and the reading of all must be added together.   The instructions of the manufacturer should be followed closely to obtain the correct over-all reading.

If the meter readings fluctuate widely in a reasonably regular manner the readings may be recorded giving both minimum and maximum values, for example, 72–76 db.   On the other hand, if the readings remain relatively steady with only occasional increases or decreases, the preferred method of recording the data is in terms of an arithmetic average plus or minus the occasional deviations, for example, as 74 ± 2 db.

Sound-level Corrections.   *Ambient-noise Correction.*   The sound-level meter reads the total sound level impinging upon the microphone diaphragm, i.e., the ambient acoustic noise plus the noise source being measured, together with other background noises.   The effects of ambient noise often may be much greater than would be assumed as a result of listening.   In general, it is possible to turn off the source of sound being measured or to interrupt the operations which cause the sound.   A separate measurement can then be made of the ambient noise including also any other internal background noise, as will be discussed later.   This can be used to correct the over-all sound-level reading, which includes both the sound level of the total background (ambient and electrical) noise and the sound level of the noise to be measured. Figure 17.4a shows the value of the correction to subtract from the sound-level meter reading to correct for background noise. It will be noted that, if the background noise level is more than 10 db below the sound being measured, there is seldom any practical need to correct for it. If the difference is less than 3 db the noise being measured is actually at a lower level than the background noise and the accuracy of the measurement, even with background-noise correction, will be reduced.

The solid line of Fig. 17.4a is based upon the assumption that both the background noise and the additional noise being measured have a random amplitude distribution and in practice provides satisfactory results in most noise problems. In the *special case* where the noise being measured approaches a sine wave *and* the meter rectifier is an average type,[4,5] the correction approaches the broken line in Fig. 17.4b. In

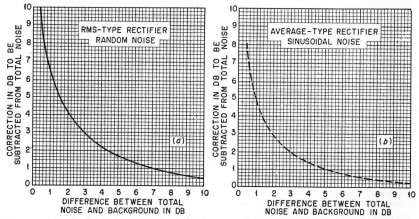

Fig. 17.4. (a) Correction for ambient background level in terms of the difference between the total noise (including the one being measured) and the ambient noise. The solid line indicates the correction for conditions usually approached in practice where both noises are essentially random in character, and the rectifier characteristic is of the rms type. This is the correction curve recommended for the usual type of noise measurement. (b) Correction for the special conditions where the noise being measured is essentially sinusoidal in character, and the rectifier is linear.[3,4]

practice, conditions usually fall somewhere between these two curves but generally close to the solid line. Figure 17.4a is recommended except where conditions clearly indicate otherwise.

Information on the summation characteristics of the indicating meter can be obtained from the manufacturer or the meter can be measured. With a meter having an average-type rectifier, then, the broken line should be used when measuring single tones. This condition will be encountered mainly if the sound-level meter is being calibrated on a pure tone or if pure-tone measurements are being made on a loudspeaker. Most noises commonly encountered will not be pure tones.

Internal-circuit Noise. The circuit elements in the sound-level meter such as vacuum tubes and resistances will generate a certain noise level which limits the lowest level at which the sound-level meter can be used. With the usual type of piezoelectric microphone such noise will seldom be serious when measuring levels above 35 or 40 db, but at lower levels it may introduce an appreciable error into the measurements.

This noise can easily be checked in a location where the ambient-sound level and magnetic fields are sufficiently low so that no reading results from them by merely substituting for the microphone a dummy impedance, as described under *Hum Pickup*. Any residual reading of the meter, then, results from internal-circuit noise for which a correction can be made in exactly the same manner as for *ambient noise,* given above.

Microphonic Noise. While most manufacturers of sound-level meters select and age the vacuum tubes to reduce microphonics to negligible proportions, it should be remembered that any vacuum tube may become microphonic with age or abuse. Microphonic tubes can be detected by listening with headphones while the case of the sound-level meter is rapped. This, however, is a particularly sensitive test and few meters will evidence no ringing noise under these conditions. If, however, any result- ing ringing noise produces meter deflections well below the levels to be measured, the microphonic response can be considered as negligible.

When there is evidence that microphonic response in a sound-level meter may produce errors, the meter should be immersed in the sound field being measured with the microphone disconnected, preferably replaced by a dummy impedance, as described under *Hum Pickup.* Any deflection of the indicating instrument under these condi- tions other than that caused by hum, as previously mentioned, will be the result of microphonic tubes or other internal-circuit noise. Unless such a deflection is at least 10 db below the noise to be measured, it must be corrected for in the same manner as ambient noise.

Hum Pickup. Strong alternating magnetic fields surrounding electrical equipment may induce hum pickup in sound-level meters. Dynamic microphones, moving coil, and the transformers associated with them, are the units most commonly affected by this type of interference, although the instrument itself may pick up hum. For this reason, piezoelectric or condenser microphones are generally preferred for measure- ments close to electrical machinery.

To test for hum pickup excluding the microphone, the microphone should be dis- connected and the reading of the sound-level meter noted. If the reading is the result of hum pickup it will vary considerably as the position or orientation of the meter is changed. Generally, for this check the connector on the sound-level meter from which the microphone has been disconnected should be shielded. If the connector is a relatively small jack, a coin held over it in contact with the metal shield will be satisfactory. If the connector is somewhat larger, a suitable metal disk or plate may be employed. For the most critical applications where hum pickup may be very serious, the preferred procedure is to replace the microphone by a shielded dummy impedance while checking for hum. This impedance should be a capacitance of the normal internal impedance of the microphone (0.0025 μfd for the usual piezoelectric microphones), and for dynamic microphones a resistance equal to the nominal imped- ance of the microphone. This dummy impedance must be shielded and equipped with a plug to connect to the microphone jack on the sound-level meter. If a position for the meter can be found in which hum pickup is 10 db or more below the noise to be measured, and which position fulfills also the acoustical requirements of the measure- ment with regard to microphone placement, hum pickup by the instrument may be neglected.

The above procedure checks only hum pickup within the sound-level meter circuits and the input transformer if one is present. A dynamic microphone itself may pick up hum magnetically. This is easily checked if the interfering magnetic field is not associated with the noise being measured—that is, if the magnetic field and the noise are not radiated by the same source. It is then generally possible to turn off the noise source. With the microphone connected to the sound-level meter the reading of the meter will then indicate the induced hum plus any background noise. Listening with headphones will enable the user to determine the approximate makeup of the interference. Also, the hum interference can be balanced out by the proper orienta- tion of the microphone in the magnetic field. The microphone may then be used in this position of minimum hum pickup provided that position is otherwise satisfactory from an acoustical standpoint.

The situation is more difficult when the noise to be measured cannot be turned off without disturbing the magnetic field. Listening with headphones will give consider- able information, and if a change in orientation of the microphone produces a signifi- cant reduction in the reading of the meter, accompanied by a reduction of hum as heard in the headphones, an orientation of the microphone giving the minimum or negligible interference should be used provided such orientation is satisfactory otherwise from an acoustical standpoint.

Preferred practice where magnetic pickup is a problem is to use a microphone other than the moving-coil type and one which does not require an input transformer. The usual Rochelle-salt piezoelectric microphone is generally entirely satisfactory in such applications.

When a continuously tunable analyzer is used it is possible to correct the resulting analysis for the hum pickup provided the hum and the desired noise do not have important components at the same frequencies. An analyzer tunable in steps can also be used to advantage if similar precautions are taken.

Cable Corrections. A cable correction is not generally necessary with dynamic microphones unless the cable is extremely long. The same is generally true with condenser microphones since the output of the preamplifier associated with the microphone is generally low impedance and intended to feed a cable of reasonable length. However, the common piezoelectric microphone has a capacitive internal impedance which, together with the capacitance of the cable, forms a voltage divider which results in an attenuation that increases with the capacitance of the cable. Furthermore, the internal capacitance of the microphone is a function of temperature; hence the correction will vary with temperature. It is given by the following formula:

$$\text{Cable correction} = 20 \log \left(1 + \frac{C_1}{C_2} \right) \quad \text{db}$$

where C_1 is the capacitance of the cable and C_2 is the capacitance of the microphone at the particular temperature.

Figure 17.5 shows typical characteristics of the common type of piezoelectric microphone and also the correction for common cable capacitances in terms of temperature.

Another way of obtaining the proper cable correction for any given set of conditions is simply to measure a fairly steady sound, both with and without the cable. The only precaution that must be taken in this case is to make sure that the measurement without the cable is not influenced by the sound-level meter case.

Standing Wave Correction. When a sound wave is reflected back toward the source from a large surface such as the wall of a room, alternate addition and cancellation may occur, resulting in a series of maxima and minima in sound level as the microphone is moved along a line between the source and the reflecting surface. The resulting patterns are called *standing waves*. This effect is most pronounced when the noise source is essentially sinusoidal in character; with complex waves it may be entirely unnoticeable because of the averaging effect resulting from the many components.

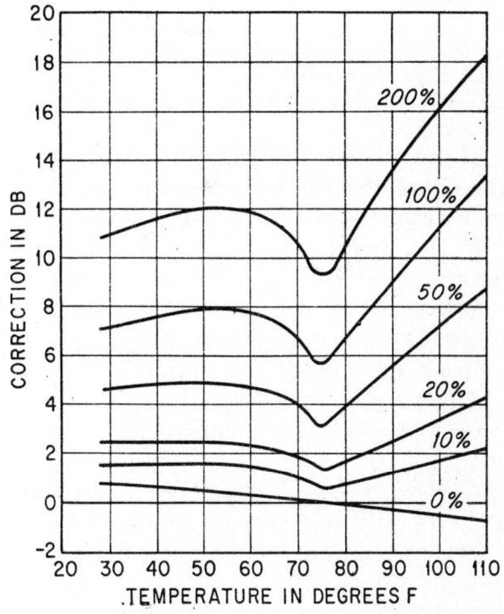

To check for standing waves, move the microphone back and forth along a direct line passing through the sound source. If a series of maxima and minima are observed

Fig. 17.5. Typical cable correction as a function of temperature for piezoelectric microphone. Percentages refer to ratio of cable capacitance to microphone capacitance at 77°F.

and the difference between the maxima and minima is less than 3 db, use the arithmetic average of the maxima and minima of the proper sound level. If the spread is greater than 3 db, the mean sound level should be considered as 3 db below the maximum sound level.

Correction for Rectifier Characteristics.   For greatest accuracy, the characteristic of the rectifier used to drive the indicating instrument of the sound-level meter must also be considered since it influences the rule of combination by which the various components of the noise are combined to provide a single meter reading.   The ASA standard specifies that the sound-level meter shall be calibrated to read correctly the rms value of a complex waveform.   However, most sound-level meters utilize, to drive the indicating instrument, a rectifier which is more nearly linear than square law, and hence the summation of the various rectified components tends to approach an average rather than an rms value.

The difference between a true rms meter and an average meter is approximately 1 db on a random-type waveform.   However, since the rectifier meters in general use are not absolutely true-average devices, the actual difference is of the order of 0.8 db.   A correction of 0.8 db should be included in sound-level measurements, therefore, depending upon how the sound-level meter was originally calibrated, which information may be obtained from the manufacturer or his instruction literature.

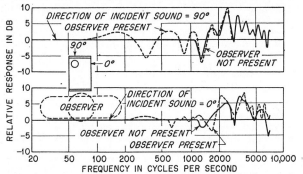

Fig. 17.6. The effect on the frequency response of using the microphone mounted directly on a rectangular sound-level meter with and without an observer present in a free field.[6]

If the meter was originally calibrated to read correctly with random noise the rectifier characteristic may be neglected except when measuring pure tones, under which conditions 0.8 db should be subtracted from the readings.

If the meter was originally calibrated to read correctly with pure tones, 0.8 db should be added to the reading for practically any type of noise other than a pure tone.

Effects of Sound-level Meter Case or Nearby Objects on Meter Readings.   It is generally undesirable to have the microphone mounted in a relatively large flat surface such as one side of the sound-level meter case since diffraction effects produce errors which are not easily predictable.   In most sound-level meters an attempt has been made to reduce the effects of the meter case by raising the microphone above the case or by making the case of such size and dimension that it is entirely behind the microphone diaphragm.   The latter condition closely approaches the results obtained with a completely separated microphone.

Most manufacturers of sound-level meters which are enclosed in rectangular cases of substantial size will provide information concerning the effects of reflections from the case.   In general, it is desirable to hold the meter so that no large plane surface is directly perpendicular to the direction of propagation of the sound being measured or parallel to any large nearby reflecting surface.

At lower frequencies the body of the operator may also affect the readings to some degree.   To minimize this effect, it is desirable that the operator not hold the meter directly between himself and the source of sound or hold the meter too close to his body.   Preferably the meter should be several feet from the operator, who should stand to one side of a line passing through the sound source and the microphone.   Figure 17.6 shows the typical effects produced by the proximity of the observer and by the surfaces of a rectangular sound-level meter case.[6]

Where there is any question of interference by diffraction from the meter case, the use of an extension microphone is recommended. The microphone extension also makes possible the taking of sound-meter readings where it is sometimes impossible or impractical to use the microphone attached directly to the meter case, particularly if it is of the larger type.

Effect of Environment on the Measurements. *Room Measurements.* When a noise source is measured in a room, the microphone will receive acoustic energy which has traveled directly from the source and also energy which has struck the boundaries of the room and has been reflected, perhaps many times, before arriving at the point of measurement. The closer the microphone is to the source, the greater will be the ratio of direct to reflected sound. Graphs showing this ratio are given in the following chapter. After one has receded a distance from the source equivalent to several times the largest dimension of the source, the sound level drops off roughly at a rate of 6 db per doubling of distance until the reflected sound becomes dominant. Then it approaches a constant value. Corrections for standing waves are given in a preceding section. It is recommended that the points of measurement that are selected be at a distance such that the level is, on the average, at least 8 db higher than the level at more distant points from the sound-producing apparatus where the reflected sound pressure dominates. The actual test distance varies with the source being measured, since it is desirable that the test distance be large compared with the dimensions of the source. For this reason, different test codes specify different test distances, for example, a typical value being 3 ft.

Measurements Outdoors. This case is discussed in detail under *Sound Power Measurements.* Here it is important that meteorological effects be taken into account. The absorption of sound in air, wind and inhomogeneities in the atmosphere all affect the sound level that will be produced at some distance from the source. In addition, wind produces an additional source of noise at the microphone itself.

WIND NOISE. When microphones are used outdoors or under other conditions where there is appreciable movement of air, extraneous signals may be generated in the microphone as a result of this air movement. With some microphone types the passage of air through the grille will cause a whistling or a hissing noise. In some microphones the grille is backed by very thin fabric to minimize this noise. The movement of air may also cause a low-frequency popping noise as a result of low-frequency (subsonic) changes in the air pressure on the microphone diaphragm.

Where it is not possible to keep the microphone out of the air current, it is possible to construct a wind screen for the microphone of very thin fabric over a wire or wooden frame. The fabric should be chosen for low porosity (for high attenuation to air currents), and low density (for low attenuation to high-frequency noises). Various thin silk or synthetic fabrics will meet these requirements (see *Wind Screens*, Chap. 27).

Where the interference is not severe, a thin silk handkerchief held over the microphone is generally adequate. For better screening the wind screen should be considerably larger than the microphone. Spherical wind screens having diameters of a foot or more are not unusual. In extreme cases, two layers of fabric with a space between will provide better attenuation than one layer, and the wind attenuation improves as the separation between the layers is increased.

The effectiveness of the wind screen can generally be checked quite easily by listening with headphones to the output of the sound-level meter to note the absence of the typical wind-noise type of interference. The effect of the wind screen on the transmission of noise frequencies can be checked by making typical noise measurements (and analyses) with and without the wind screen under conditions where no wind is present. With most lightweight fabrics it will be found that the sound attenuation in the wind screen is negligible.

Calibration of Sound-level Meters. Sound-level meters are calibrated by the manufacturer to the highest practical degree of accuracy. Since most microphones have the smoothest response in the range from 200 to 1,000 cps, the over-all response of the sound-level meter most closely approaches its design objectives in that range. The original calibration made by the manufacturer is based upon the free-field response of the instrument to noise of random incidence; it may be made with either wideband noise or a series of individual sinusoidal tones, or it may be made by any other method providing the required accuracy.

If the manufacturer's instructions are followed regarding setting of battery voltages and/or internal calibration controls, the usual sound-level meter can be relied upon for approximately 1 year provided it does not sustain damage. Unless means are at hand for checking the over-all calibration at intervals, however, the sound-level meter should be returned to the manufacturer for recalibration at least once per year, or whenever the unit has been subjected to abnormal abuse such as dropping.

Electrical Calibration. The so-called "electrical calibration" of a sound-level meter is simply a check of the over-all gain of the amplifier. Calibrators of this type are supplied as accessories for sound-level meters, or they may be built in as an inherent part of the instrument. Since such a check does not include the microphone, it is possible for the calibration of the over-all system to be off even though the electrical system checks satisfactorily. However, most microphones supplied with sound-level meters are highly stable and do not require frequent recalibration if they are not abused. Nevertheless, as a general precaution some sort of acoustic calibration check is also desirable.

Acoustical Calibration. EXTRA MICROPHONE. The simplest means of checking the sensitivity of the microphone on a sound-level meter is through the use of a spare microphone of similar characteristics. If the spare microphone is used only for calibration checks and is not subject to abuse or damage, merely substituting it for the sound-level meter microphone will indicate whether the latter has change in sensitivity. Therefore, the combined use of an extra microphone with an electrical calibrator gives an over-all check which is satisfactory for most purposes.

ACOUSTIC CALIBRATORS. Where frequent checks must be made on the sensitivity of the over-all acoustical-electrical system, an *acoustic calibrator* may be employed. This is a device which produces a fixed sound pressure in an enclosure that is designed to fit over the microphone of a sound-level meter. Usually the sound pressure is generated by a small stabilized loudspeaker of rugged design; in a few calibrators a purely mechanical sound source has been used. The acoustic calibrator offers the advantage of convenience plus the fact that the calibration checks will always be made with the same type of signal, thus eliminating slight differences due to signal waveform or frequency characteristics. The simplest electrically driven calibrators operate on a single frequency and may be driven from any pure-tone oscillator. In other types of calibrators the frequency characteristic is flat over an appreciable range so that a wideband noise signal may be used; for such calibrators a special noise generator is available.

Sound-level Meter Output Circuit. Some sound-level meters incorporate two separate output stages, one for driving the indicating instrument incorporated in the sound-level meter itself, and one for driving auxiliary equipment such as a recorder, headphones, or an oscilloscope. In others a single output stage performs both functions, and certain provisions are made to eliminate the effects of the internal indicating instrument on the readings of the auxiliary equipment. The manufacturer's instructions concerning this point should be carefully followed.

Use of Headphones. Most sound-level meters have an output jack to which a pair of headphones can be connected. The unaided human ear, by means of binaural effects, is able to separate sounds in space and thus allows the listener to focus his attention upon the sounds which he wants to hear. However, with the earphones the binaural effect is lost and the listener hears all the noise which is being indicated by the sound-level meter. With headphones a skilled user is able to obtain additional information concerning the sound, to determine those components which are most prominent, and to form some idea of the relative importance of the background noise. Also, careful listening with headphones will often allow the user to determine whether or not further analysis is necessary.

Summary of Sound-level Measurement Data to Be Recorded

1. Noise source being measured, including pertinent statistical information.
2. A description of the environment where the source is located, including the position of the source.

3. Operating conditions for which measurements were made.
4. Pertinent meteorological data, if important.
5. Location of the microphone, including angle of orientation of the microphone, with respect to the source.
6. Equipment used for making the measurements: name, make, type, and serial number.
7. Description of background noises and their sources.
8. Applied corrections.
9. Weighting network.
10. The data obtained together with the range of variation, standard deviation, or a more complete statistical description.
11. Speed of the indicating instrument: *slow* or *fast*.

TECHNIQUES IN THE USE OF THE SOUND ANALYZER

The sound-level meter by itself indicates only the over-all sound level, weighted or unweighted, within the range of frequencies to which the instrument responds. For noise studies concerned with causes of noise and possible methods of reducing it, to evaluate its effects on speech interference, and to calculate loudness, more information is required. In particular, some sort of analysis is desirable to give information as to the relative level of noise in various frequency bands or the level of the highest components. Choice of analyzing equipment depends upon the character of sound and the use to be made of the final data.

Octave and Fractional-octave Filters. The most common type of sound analyzer is the bandpass filter, which is available in numerous forms. The general performance characteristics such as minimum number of cutoffs and passbands have been standardized (see Chap. 16).

Octave Bands. The octave-band analysis is the simplest and most common type of analysis, and requires a minimum of time. Such an analysis may be made on a simple octave-band analyzer, or many analyzers capable of more elaborate analysis are also adapted for octave-band measurements.

The simplest sound analyzer includes a series of one-octave bands ranging from 75 to 4,800 cps, a band containing all frequencies below 75 cps, and another for those above 4,800 cps.[7] In general, such an analyzer is equipped with an indicating instrument similar to that on the sound-level meter, and the analyzer input cable connects directly to an output jack on the sound-level meter. It is necessary to adjust the analyzer sensitivity so that when the filters are out of the circuit the reading on the over-all sound is the same as that of the sound-level meter. Thereafter, individual readings can be obtained for each octave band by turning the range selector.

When the level in any octave band is unusually low, an auxiliary gain control or attenuator on the analyzer generally provides additional sensitivity. *Caution:* Do not turn up the sensitivity of the sound-level meter itself to obtain low-level readings on the analyzer. This will overload the output stage of the sound-level meter and cause a serious error. The only exception to this is on special combined sound-level meters and analyzers, in which case the manufacturer's instructions should be followed closely.

The sound level in any band is the sum of the readings of the attenuators of the sound-level meter, the auxiliary attenuator on the analyzer, and the indicating instrument on the analyzer. Reading the analyzer is accomplished in exactly the same manner as reading the sound-level meter, except that the readings of the indicating instrument on the analyzer are used. The passband control of the analyzer is adjusted sequentially to each of the octave bands and the reading is noted. The attenuator on the analyzer, which increases the over-all sensitivity, is adjusted to obtain a satisfactory on-scale reading in each octave band, but during the analysis the attenuator on the sound-level meter is not changed.

In general, the additional sensitivity available on the analyzer does not increase the over-all range of the sound meter except on individual bands. The internal noise in the sound-level meter circuits will limit the use of the extra sensitivity for wideband measurements and will also limit the accuracy to which a low-level band can be measured. With a true "white" noise, the reading on adjacent octave bands will increase by 3 db per band as the bands are switched toward the higher frequencies. This will often give some clue as to the type of noise being measured in a series of adjacent octave bands—that is, whether it is more or less randomly distributed or composed of discrete frequency components. For very low level measurements correction can be made for the background noise in the same manner as was previously described for over-all noise measurements.

Figure 17.7 shows a typical analysis as made on an octave-band analyzer.* This gives a general idea of the character of the sound. It will be noticed that the highest sound level for this particular sound occurs in the octave between 1,200 and 2,400 cps.

Half-octave Bands. For many types of noise survey the octave-band readings are sufficient, but there are many instances where a greater degree of "resolution" in the analyses is desirable. For example, it may be known that a certain harmonic of a machine speed falls near a given frequency, which may, however, be close to the edge of one of the octave bands. Under these conditions, high amplitude of this harmonic would increase the reading in the next adjacent octave band, leaving considerable doubt as to whether that particular harmonic was actually the cause of the reading. With narrower bands it is easier to identify the individual harmonics since not just one but two or more passbands will be available in each octave. For this reason, filter-type analyzers are manufactured with half-octave bands, which doubles the resolution as compared with an octave-band analyzer.

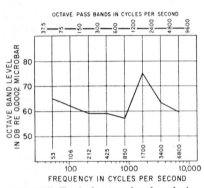

FIG. 17.7. Typical octave-band analysis.

If the energy in a given octave band is divided at the half-octave point, the sound level in the lower half octave will be 3.8 db and that in the upper half octave 2.3 db below the level in the entire octave band. (These values are calculated by dividing the octave band into two half octaves, one containing 0.414 and the other containing 0.586 times the energy in the octave band.) For white noise a half-octave band analysis usually will average 3.1 db below an octave-band analysis. The above figures are for a theoretically perfect bandpass characteristic, i.e., one with a flat top and vertical sides. This, of course, is never encountered in practical instruments, where the difference may be 0.2 to 0.3 db less.

Necessarily, an increase in the number of bands increases the complexity (but not necessarily the size) of the equipment. Choice between such units depends mainly upon the "resolution" required and the maximum acceptable degree of complexity of the equipment. Figure 17.8 shows half-octave band analysis, of the same noise plotted in Fig. 17.7. It will be noted that considerably more detail is available in the low-frequency region, indicating the presence of strong individual components—in this case fundamentals and harmonics of 60 cps. With half-octave bands, the reading on a "white" noise will increase 1.5 db per half octave as the tuning of the analyzer is switched to higher frequencies.

Other refinements are possible which extend the usefulness of the filter-type analyzer, particularly for fractional-octave bands. In some models the range extends above and below the limits set by the standards, thus allowing analysis at higher and lower frequencies. This is very important, particularly in some machinery-noise applications. Such points are also shown in Fig. 17.8, indicating appreciable energy below 37.5 cps.

* Special sound-analysis paper of the type shown for plotting octave-band, half-octave band, and third-octave band data is available from the Codex Book Co., Inc., Norwood, Mass.

Third-octave Bands. An analyzer with third-octave bands provides half again the resolution of the analyzer with half-octave bands, and again the choice between these units depends upon a balance between the desired resolution and the acceptable complexity of the equipment. Figure 17.9 shows the same noise as in Figs. 17.7 and 17.8 plotted in third-octave bands.

In those regions where the noise is essentially "white" in character, the level per band (for a perfect bandpass characteristic) averages 4.9 db below the level in the equivalent octave band. For a true white noise the analysis would slope upward as the frequency is increased at a rate of 1 db per third-octave band. If any given octave of white noise is divided into three third-octave bands the levels in these bands are, respectively, in order of increasing frequency, 5.9, 4.9, and 3.9 db below the level in the entire octave band. In practical instruments these differences will be somewhat lower than the above theoretical values for perfect passbands.

The operation of a third-octave analyzer is the same as the half-octave analyzer, and the same advantages apply. Where the half-octave analyzer provides 100 per cent improvement in resolution over the simple octave analyzer the third-octave unit provides an additional 50 per cent more resolution over the half-octave unit. When considering a third-octave analyzer, it is desirable to investigate also the possibility of a continuously tunable analyzer, as described later.

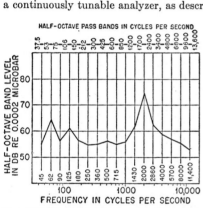

FIG. 17.8. Typical half-octave band analysis of same noise shown in Fig. 17.7.

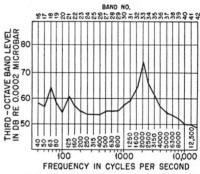

FIG. 17.9. Typical third-octave band analysis of same noise shown in Figs. 17.7 and 17.8.

Adjustable Bandwidth. The upper and lower filter cutoff frequencies of some analyzers are independently adjustable so that bandwidths of a fractional octave, one octave, or more may be used. This allows choice of the bandwidth to depend upon the problem at hand. A wide bandwidth can be used, for instance, in room-noise applications where a high degree of resolution is not required. The narrower bands may be used for machinery-noise problems to provide greater separation of machine rotational harmonics than is possible with single-octave bandwidths.

Adjustable-bandwidth analyzers offer another advantage. A white noise (one having a constant spectrum level, i.e., equal amounts of energy per cycle bandwidth), if measured with an analyzer having passbands in octaves or fractions of octaves (or otherwise proportional to the center frequency of the passbands) will have a slope increasing with frequency at the rate of 3 db per octave. The actual reading in any band will depend upon the bandwidth.

With a true "white-noise" spectrum, the reading on adjacent half-octave bands will differ by 1.5 db, the higher level being on the higher-frequency band. If, when measuring a true white noise, on a half-octave band, therefore, the higher cutoff is increased by one-half octave, the level will theoretically increase approximately 3.8 db. If the lower cutoff is decreased one-half octave the reading will increase theoretically 2.3 db.

The above figures are all based upon theoretically perfect, i.e., square-topped passbands, which are never encountered in actual instruments. In typical commercial instruments the additional reading on white noise when another half-octave band is added to the half-octave band reading will be 0.2 to 0.3 db lower than the figures given above. Generally a rough calculation will show whether the change in meter reading with change in passband can be accounted for by evenly distributed or unpitched noise or whether it is the result of one (or occasionally more) strong individual component within a given band. (Listening with headphones will also provide considerable information of this sort to the skilled observer.) For example, it will be noted that in Fig. 17.8 the half-octave bands from 53 to 75, 106 to 150, and 1,700 to 2,400 cps read only slightly (much less than 3.1 db) lower, respectively, than the octave bands from 37.5 to 75, 75 to 150, and 1,200 to 2,400 cps in Fig. 17.7. This slight change in reading with bandwidth indicates that the greater portion of the noise in those particular half-octave bands is composed of strong single components or narrow groups of components encompassed entirely within the respective half-octave bands. In this case the low-frequency peaks encountered in those bands correspond to the fundamental and first harmonic of 60 cps which gives a clue as to their origin. Similarly, the location of a high-frequency component can be deduced from other mechanical characteristics of the machine being measured. This illustrates a typical use of adjustable bandwidth.

General Characteristics of Octave- and Fractional-octave Band Analyzers. The octave or fractional-octave bandpass type of analyzer has an important advantage. When the power in all the bands is added together, the total power includes all components of the sound, including unpitched noise and random components. With this type of analysis, therefore, the user is able easily both to account for all noise over the entire spectrum and to determine what the level may be in any particular frequency-band range. This is particularly important where the noise contains a relatively large proportion of unpitched noise. This addition is readily accomplished by the use of Fig. 2.17 or by converting the decibel level in each band to relative power level (see *Decibel Table,* Appendix 2.2), adding the power levels and converting back to decibels with the same table.

Since no bandpass analyzer has a perfectly ideal bandpass characteristic with a perfectly flat top and straight sides, errors will be introduced under certain conditions. For example, when the spectrum being measured slopes at steep angles this error increases as the bandwidth increases so that, in general, passbands wider than one octave are not generally recommended unless the spectrum being measured has a very gradual slope. To some extent, however, slight rounding of the corners of the transmission band compensates for lack of perfect cutoff beyond the band. There seems to be little need for concern over this type of error if bands as narrow as one-half octave are employed.[8]

The lack of perfect cutoff beyond the band results effectively in slightly broadening the bandwidth of the filter and consequently in a higher reading of the analyzer than predicted by theory. This is most evident at the lowest percentage bandwidth settings where the reading of the analyzer meter may possibly be up to 1 db higher than predicted. However, this effect is normally compensated for by a somewhat higher insertion loss of the bandpass filter. This is particularly true if independent low-cutoff and high-cutoff filters are "ganged" to act as bandpass filters. The foregoing is applicable when random noises are analyzed. When strong frequency peaks are encountered, the cutoff characteristic beyond the passband of the filter determines the influence of these strong frequency peaks on the reading of the analyzer meter when the frequency region outside the region of strong peaks is analyzed.

Operation of all bandpass-type analyzers is essentially similar. Care must be taken to follow the manufacturer's instructions regarding attenuator settings and battery checks to ensure the highest possible accuracy.

Continuously Tunable Narrow-band Analyzers. Continuous-frequency analyzers are used for measuring the frequency of individual components of the noise. Whereas the usual octave or fractional-octave analyzer accepts a band no less than one-third octave, the continuously tunable narrow-band analyzers may accept a band of $\frac{1}{30}$

octave or, in the case of the constant-bandwidth type, a band of a few cycles per second. With such analyzers, the various discrete frequency components of a sound may be selected individually and their amplitude and frequency measured with a high degree of precision. Such analyzers provide greater resolution in the analysis than any wideband analyzer but with an accompanying increase in measurement time, depending upon the complexity of the sound being analyzed. When a level-recording mechanism is included, either as an accessory or as a part of the analyzer, any inconveniences involved in analyzing a complicated waveform are reduced. Also, by use of magnetic-tape recording the noise waveform may be stored for analyzing at a more convenient time. Because of the narrow passband, the continuous analyzer is not generally used for measurements of unpitched noise although, particularly with a level-recording mechanism, this type of noise can be analyzed with the continuous type of analyzer.

Where exact identification or measurement of discrete frequency components is required, the continuously tunable analyzer is useful. In general either the constant-percentage or the constant-bandwidth unit will be satisfactory if the fundamental frequency of the components is constant, or if exact measurement of their amplitude is of secondary importance compared with the requirement for exact measurement of frequency. However, if the frequency of the components "warbles" significantly, the constant-percentage analyzer will be most accurate. The resolution of the constant-percentage analyzer usually is better at low frequencies and that of the constant-bandwidth type at high frequency. The continuously variable analyzer generally is considered as a complement to rather than a substitute for the octave or fractional-octave analyzer.

Constant-percentage Bandwidth. With the constant-percentage-bandwidth type of analyzer, the bandwidth (in cycles per second) varies automatically with the tuning of the analyzer to remain a constant percentage of the center frequency to which the analyzer is tuned. In this respect, the constant-percentage analyzer is similar to the fractional-octave analyzer, except that the fraction of an octave represented by the passband is very narrow, a typical bandwidth being of the order of $\frac{1}{30}$ octave.[9]

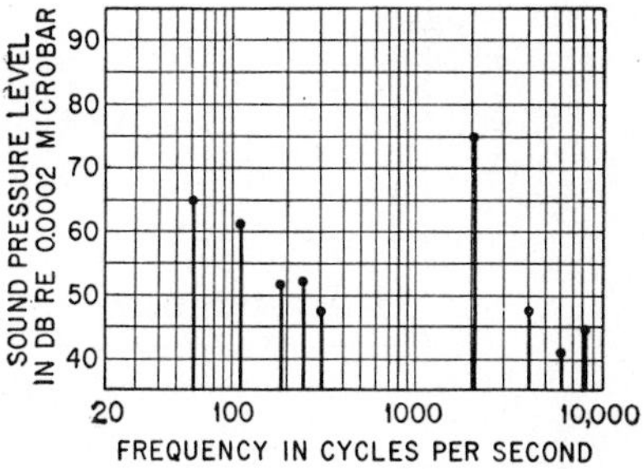

The connections of a continuous analyzer

FIG. 17.10. Typical analysis made manually with constant-percentage bandwidth analyzer.

to a sound-level meter are similar to those of the bandpass analyzer. The analyzer generally connects directly to the output circuits of the sound-level meter and provision is made for adjusting the sensitivity to correlate with the sound-level readings. This is usually accomplished with a single calibration tone which may be obtained from either an electric or an acoustic calibration system associated with or attached to the sound-level meter. The readings of such an analyzer therefore may be indicated directly in decibels.

Some analyzers of this type are equipped also with a percentage scale. When this is used, the sensitivity of the analyzer is generally adjusted for a reading of 100 per cent on the strongest component in the noise and the other components are measured in terms of a percentage of this maximum value. This is in accord with the generally established procedure for analyzing electrical waveform. A typical analysis of a noise comprised mainly of discrete-frequency components is shown in Fig. 17.10. The constant-percentage-bandwidth analyzer is well suited for analyzing machinery noises of this type which are composed mainly of discrete-frequency components but which may be frequency-modulated by slight speed variations in the machine under test. With a constant-percentage-bandwidth analyzer, frequency modulation of the entire noise will result in a constant reduction in the reading for all components (but will not affect their relative amplitudes). This effect is shown in Fig. 17.11.

With the constant-percentage analyzer, as with the octave and fractional-octave passband analyzers (which are really wideband constant-percentage analyzers), a "white" noise will be measured as a spectrum level sloping upward 3 db per octave as the frequency is increased.

Constant Bandwidth. Another type of continuously tunable analyzer operates on the heterodyne principle and provides a bandpass characteristic which remains constant (in cycles per second) as the analyzer is tuned from one end of the frequency spectrum to the other. In some instances, provision is made for adjusting the width of the passband, either in steps or continuously, but the passband does not maintain automatically the constant-percentage relationship to the center frequency as in the case of the constant-percentage bandwidth analyzer.

With a constant-bandwidth analyzer any frequency modulation of the components may result in errors in measurement of the relative amplitude of the components. Figure 17.11 shows the effect on a fixed-bandwidth analysis of a frequency-modulated signal such as is often encountered in measuring machinery noises.[9] This error may be serious under some conditions.

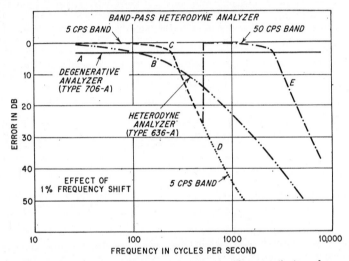

Fig. 17.11. Comparison of error in constant-percentage (degenerative) analyzer and constant-bandwidth (heterodyne analyzer) resulting from a given amount of frequency modulation. (*Scott.*[9])

On the other hand, for noises having components of highly constant fundamental frequency the usual continuous analyzer provides better discrimination outside of the passband than the usual constant-percentage bandwidth analyzer. The usual constant-bandwidth analyzer also covers the entire audio-frequency spectrum on a single turn of the dial, which is not the case with most constant-percentage bandwidth analyzers. For these reasons the constant-bandwidth analyzer has many important uses, particularly where level recorders are used, because of the ease of coupling such a device to a level recorder to provide automatic analyses. With a constant-bandwidth analyzer, "white" noise will provide a constant indication regardless of the frequency to which the analyzer is tuned.

Comparisons of Different Analyzer Types. Figure 17.12 shows a comparison of typical analyzer response characteristics including constant bandwidth, constant-percentage bandwidth, and the octave and fractional-octave types.[10] It will be seen that the type of analyzer should preferably be chosen on the basis of the general type of noise to be analyzed. If the noise, like most noises, contains both discrete frequencies and random noise, and the necessary information consists mainly of the approximate position in the audible spectrum of the greatest portion of the noise, then an octave or fractional-octave analyzer is indicated. As a practical matter, more octave-band analyses are probably made than any other type. For increased resolution and versatility, the half-octave or the third-octave analyzer is indicated, and such an analyzer is particularly useful if it can also be used as an octave-band analyzer for those applications where the additional resolution is not required. The frequency range of the analyzer must also be taken into consideration.

Precautions. Whenever an analyzer or other device is connected to the output of a sound-level meter the operator should notice whether or not the addition of this unit changes the reading of the sound-level meter. If it does affect the reading, the analyzer sensitivity should be standardized with the sound-level meter reading with a given sound or test signal that existed *before* the analyzer was plugged in. Even more important, if the indicating-meter rectifier in the sound-level meter is connected directly to the output circuit driving the analyzer, distortion introduced by the rectifier may affect the analyzer readings. To avoid this, some sound-level meters include an auxiliary output stage for driving the analyzer independently of the sound-level meter indicating instrument. Other models have provision for switching off the internal indicating instrument while an analyzer or other device is being used.

In all cases, however, the narrow passband of the usual continuously tunable analyzer makes manual analysis of un-pitched noise tedious since the instrument must be tuned relatively slowly to obtain average readings of the indicating instrument because in any narrow passband the instantaneous fluctuations of random noise are quite large. For this reason, continuously tunable analyzers are generally used for measuring the frequency of individual components in a noise in addition to over-all measurements made with

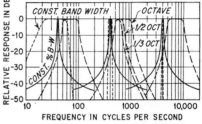

FIG. 17.12. Comparison of response curves of typical sound analyzers having constant bandwidth, constant-percentage bandwidth, octave, and fractional-octave bandwidth. (*W. B. Snow.*[10])

octave or fractional-octave analyzers which include all the components. When the continuously tunable analyzer is used with a level recorder, however, the recorder generally sweeps the tuning across the noise spectrum at a predetermined constant rate, thus providing a more dependable measurement of the random noise than can easily be obtained by manual operation.

Use of Weighting Networks to Improve Analyzer Accuracy. Although as a general rule the *C* weighting network should be used for all noise analyses, it is sometimes advantageous to employ the other networks. If the noise spectrum slopes upward at a high rate as the frequency is reduced below 1,000 cps, use of the *B* or *A* weighting networks will tend to flatten the spectrum, thus resulting in less possible error from the effect of the spectrum slope. Also, it is possible that the range of levels contained in a sound actually exceed the maximum attenuation in the bandpass filters so that, for example, a high-level low-frequency sound will cause noticeable readings on higher-frequency bands. In this case again, use of the *B* or *A* weighting networks to reduce the over-all level range to be measured on the analyzer will improve the accuracy of the results by flattening the spectrum to be measured.

If a weighting network is used during the analysis the resulting data should be corrected for the difference in response between that network and the *C* network which can be obtained from Fig. 16.12. For this purpose, with octave or fractional-octave analyzers, it is generally satisfactory to correct each band for the difference between the two response curves at the center frequency of the band. This will increase the level of the low-frequency components in the analysis to their proper relationship with respect to the higher-frequency components.

Operation at 0° Incidence. If an analyzer is to be used so that the over-all results can be corrected for abnormal high-frequency response, the directional characteristics of the microphone may be utilized to advantage by operating at 0° of incidence where the microphone is most selective directionally to high frequencies and then correcting, by means of the analysis, for the excess of high-frequency response. This, however, is seldom necessary except where very bad reflections are encountered.

Use of Level Recorders with Analyzers. Level recorders are often used with sound analyzers to provide permanent records of levels vs. time or of noise analyses. When the level recorder is properly coupled to a continuously tunable analyzer, automatic analyses may be performed and the combination has certain further advantages in the measurement of unpitched noise. Before using a level recorder with sound-measuring

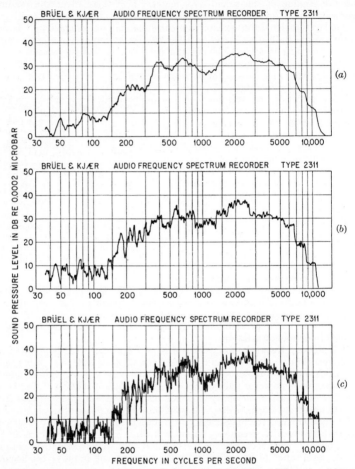

FIG. 17.13. Spectrograms of noise from a lathe, taken with three different writing speeds of the level recorder: (a) 50 db per sec; (b) 200 db per sec; and (c) 700 db per sec. (*Courtesy of Brüel and Kjaer.*)

equipment, the sensitivity of the level recorder should be adjusted so that the readings correlate with those of the sound-level meter or analyzer. This is most easily accomplished with a calibration tone or electrical signal applied to the microphone or input circuit, respectively, of the sound-level meter and the sensitivity of the level recorder adjusted so that maximum reading is obtained when the indicating instrument on the sound-level meter or analyzer reads full scale. The same precautions should be observed as mentioned earlier with respect to coupling an analyzer to a sound-level meter. If the level recorder is connected directly in parallel with a rectifier-type indicating instrument, nonlinearity in the rectifier characteristic may affect the readings of the level recorder.   Most sound-level meters and analyzers provide for this either by incorporation of a separate output tube to drive auxiliary equipment or by means for disconnecting the rectifier meter from a circuit when driving auxiliary equipment such as the level recorder.   Level recorders are generally available with various dynamic ranges.   For the average application, a 40- or 50-db range is most satisfactory.   However, lower or higher ranges can be used where required.

The effect of writing speed of the level recorder is shown in Fig. 17.13, which represents the analysis of noise from a lathe.   The noise source is identical in the three spectrograms, but the writing speed of the recorder in (a) was 50 db per sec; in (b) the speed was 200 db per sec; and in (c) the speed was 700 db per sec.   The slow writing speed has the effect of considerably smoothing the curve which is obtained.

In general, a simple battery or acoustical calibration check before and after the run is sufficient.   If only battery checks are made they can later be correlated with acoustical checks in the laboratory to determine the extent of any sensitivity drift. If battery adjustments are provided on the sound-level meter, readjustment of these at intervals during the test will generally maintain normal accuracy.   If the measurements cover a number of hours the batteries should be checked at intervals or, if practical, the sound-level meter may be calibrated acoustically.

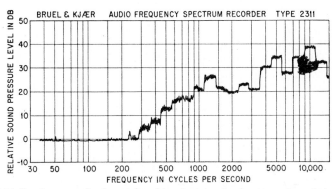

Fig. 17.14. Spectrogram of noise produced by air streaming from a system of pipes.   These data were obtained with a third-octave analyzer.   (*Courtesy of Brüel and Kjaer.*)

Octave or Fractional-octave Bandwidth Analyzers.   In general, two types of recordings may be made with a high-speed level recorder in conjunction with a band analyzer: (1) The level in a given band, or a series of bands, as a function of time.   Such an acoustical analysis of a motor scooter is shown in Fig. 31.47.   In general, if recordings of level vs. time are required for a series of bands, the analysis is made from a magnetic-tape recording which is repeated.   This type of analysis is usually carried out where the noise spectrum changes as a function of time.   (2) When the noise spectrum to be analyzed is fairly constant in level a record may be obtained of the level in each band by merely switching the analyzer from one band to another in succession.   In such use the recorder is connected to the output of the analyzer and the sensitivity is adjusted as previously described.   The analyzer is then operated a given length of time on each band.   The normal procedure is to start with the lowest-frequency band, stepping upward at equal time intervals of, say, 2 or 5 sec.   Switching of the analyzer band may be accomplished mechanically or by hand.   This provides a record, as shown in Fig. 17.14, which shows the spectral analysis of noise produced by air streaming from a system of pipes.   A third-octave analyzer was used to obtain these data. The normal switching transients provide ample separation of the bands.   Such a chart not only provides a permanent record of the analysis but also allows better averaging of the level in each band than can normally be obtained by merely observing the swing of the pointer of the indicating instrument.

Continuously Tunable Analyzer. Some continuously tunable analyzers and level recorders are built as a single instrument. In others the manufacturers provide the coupling equipment and proper chart forms. In either case, the sensitivity of the level recorder should be adjusted as mentioned previously, but in addition, the chart drive and tuning dial of the analyzer must be synchronized. Because of possible backlash in the coupling units it is generally best to let the drive mechanism drive both the chart and the tuning dial up to the starting point for the analysis (generally the lowest frequency on the calibration) and make any adjustment necessary so that these points coincide exactly on the dial and on the chart. When the equipment is all turned on the level recorder will automatically chart the complete analysis of the sound. When a level recorder and analyzer are sweeping across the audio spectrum, white noise, or random noise, will of course be plotted in a random and irregular manner, the number of variations depending upon how slowly the analyzer is driven. If there is any question in studying the final analysis as to whether an indicated peak represents a single-frequency component or a random variation, the analysis should be repeated and the two charts compared.

In the constant-percentage analyzer the bandwidth in cycles per second increases proportionately with the center frequency as the tuning dial is driven over the audio spectrum. A white noise which has a flat spectrum level will appear with an upward

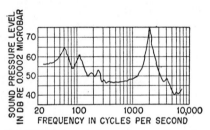

FIG. 17.15. Recorded spectrogram of a noise analyzed with a constant-percentage bandwidth analyzer.

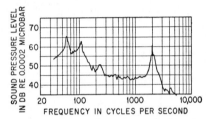

FIG. 17.16. Recorded spectrogram of a noise analyzed with a constant-bandwidth analyzer. This is the same noise whose spectrogram is shown in Fig. 17.15.

slope, increasing with frequency at the rate of 3 db per octave. With this type of analyzer any frequency modulation of single-frequency components will cause a reduction in reading, generally small, which is constant over the entire range. Figure 17.15 shows a typical analysis made with a constant-bandwidth analyzer.

The constant-bandwidth analyzer operates in exactly the same manner as the constant-percentage analyzer when used with a level recorder, except that the drive mechanism for the analyzer can be simpler since the entire range of the constant-bandwidth analyzer is generally available on a single turn of the dial. Figure 17.16 shows a typical analysis made in this manner. Since the analyzer has a constant bandwidth, regardless of the frequency to which it is tuned, a white or random noise will appear as a flat spectrum level but with random variations resulting from the variations in the noise with time. A comparison of Figs. 17.15 and 17.16 shows the typical differences between constant-percentage and constant bandwidth analyzers.

Use of Magnetic-tape Recorders in Noise Analysis. It is often inconvenient to analyze various types of noises at the time or place of their origin. A magnetic-tape recorder provides a convenient means of "storing" the noise for analysis at a later time. Any broadcast-quality tape recorder is adequate for noise analyses. Some tape recorders offer a choice of various speeds, each having a different over-all response vs. frequency characteristic. The frequency response of the tape recorder will affect the over-all recorded level. It is therefore necessary that the tape-recorder frequency range be at least equal to or exceed that of the sound-level meter used for noise measurements. This will result in a speed of either 7½ or 15 in. per sec being used.

It is also important that the tape recorder have a fairly high signal-to-noise ratio

(45 db or better). The internal background noise of the tape recorder, either as recorded or as originating from the playback amplifier, will give an indication of signal as read on the analyzer.

For recording of noises and sounds, the tape recorder should be connected to the output of the sound-level meter. Since most sound-level meters have an output impedance of 5,000 ohms or higher, it is recommended that the *bridging input* of the tape recorder be used. When playing back the recorded signal the normal *line* output should be connected to the input of the analyzer.

On actual field use, various types of noise will be encountered. They can be classified into two broad categories. First, there is the fairly continuous noise such as that made by rotating machinery, steam, or airplane exhausts. This type of noise has a fairly low peak-to-average ratio. If the tape recorder has a recording-level indicator such as a VU meter, the recording of such noise can be made without introducing any frequency components due to overload of the tape recorder if the VU meter reads between −5 and 0 db on its scale. This is true particularly if the VU meter sensitivity is set according to standard recording practice, where a sine-wave signal of +10 db or "VU" would result in a recording with about 2 or 3 per cent distortion. Therefore a VU-meter reading of −5 to 0 db or "VU" will result in negligible overload of the tape.

The second type of noise frequently encountered is intermittent noise of high peak-to-average amplitude distribution. This type of noise is found most frequently with impact-type machinery and gunshots. Because of the time constant of the VU meter, the tape and probably even some stages of the sound-level meter are likely to be overloaded as a result of the peaks. It is difficult to forecast the actual peak level of the noise. For this purpose it is often most useful to make several recordings, the first one being with the VU-meter reading somewhere near mid-scale and then an additional two or three recordings with the sound-level meter attenuators set to levels which are 10, 20, and even 30 db higher. The first recording is likely to overload the tape, whereas the second and later recordings will give a more accurate recording of the impulse noise. It should be remembered that in each case the over-all signal-to-noise ratio of the recording will be degraded in steps of 10 db. A few experiments will usually be adequate to obtain the best possible recording level for the best possible signal-to-noise ratio without overload of either the sound-level meter circuits or the tape itself.

It cannot be expected that commercially available tape recorders will have a constancy of gain comparable with that of a sound-level meter or analyzer. Therefore, it is important that an over-all noise-level reference be established when a recording is made. This can be done in several ways—one of them is to note the over-all reading of the sound-level meter in decibels (sound pressure level) along with a notation of the source of noise, microphone location, microphone orientation, etc.

For example, if an over-all sound pressure level of 86 db is being recorded the playback gain control of the tape recorder, when analyzing the noise at a later time, should be adjusted so that the analyzer will read 86 db in the over-all (for example, 20- to 20,000-cps) position. If the analysis is then performed in, say, octave bands, the over-all sound pressure level in each band can then be read from the meter of the analyzer if the decibel attenuator control on the analyzer is manipulated according to the manufacturer's instructions.

A second method of noting the over-all sound pressure level and the other pertinent data is to announce these data and to record this announcement on the tape. In this case there is no danger that the measurement records and the tape can become mixed because of some unforeseen circumstances.

A tape recording can be analyzed by playing it once and analyzing the recording during the playback time of the tape. This is entirely similar to analyzing noises in the field without the use of a tape recorder. The same type of fluctuations in level will be observed as in the field with the addition of possibly up to $\pm\frac{1}{2}$ db caused by the irregularities in the sensitivity of the tape. These over-all level variations can be reduced by taking a section of the tape lasting from $\frac{1}{2}$ sec to perhaps 10 or 20 sec in length and splicing the two ends of the tape together, forming a tape loop. This loop can be played over and over and can be analyzed at leisure. With a well-made tape recorder this tape loop can be played perhaps several thousand times before any degradation can be observed.

Analyzing the recorded sound by making a tape loop is the best method to determine the frequency distribution of an intermittent noise, particularly if there are only a few discrete noise pulses recorded.

When analyzing a tape loop, "kicks" of the analyzer meter usually are observed just at the time when the splice passes the playback head of the tape recorder as a result of a discontinuity in the magnetic medium at the splice. These pulses should be disregarded as meaningful data. If the meter of the analyzer is used in the *slow* position, it is usually advisable to use a fairly long tape loop so that the transient due to the tape splice will have disappeared by the time the analyzer meter is read.

The frequency response of the tape recorder will affect the analysis of the noise which is recorded, necessitating a correction for the recorder. One way is to measure the frequency response of the tape recorder, using a sine-wave signal. The sine-wave response of the tape recorder then should be averaged over the various frequency bands used for analysis. For example, if the tape-recorder response decreases from 0 to -2 db between 2,400 and 4,800 cps, a -1 db correction figure may be used for this particular frequency band.

A rapid way of determining the relative frequency response of a tape recorder is to record white noise and to analyze both the noise-generator output and the tape-recorder playback output with the type of analyzer used for sound measurements. The over-all wideband reading of the analyzer for both the generator noise and the recorded noise should be adjusted to 0 db. Then the difference in level between the generated and recorded noise is the decibel correction for the tape recorder. With a tape recorder useful for this type of noise-analysis work this correction should be less than ± 3 db in the frequency range of interest.

When using a narrow-band analyzer for the measurement of the various frequency components it is important that the tape speed of the recorder remain constant during the recording and analyzing process. In this case a tape recorder with very low wow and flutter should be used. Otherwise the recorded signal is subject to frequency modulation of an extent which will introduce serious errors in the analyzer reading This is particularly true if a steady-state noise from a piece of rotating machinery or transformer is to be recorded and analyzed.

Sound-analysis Data to Be Recorded. In addition to the data that would normally be recorded for sound-level measurements which have been indicated earlier, the following data should be recorded when making sound analyses:

1. Applied correction in decibels for each frequency band, or at each frequency.
2. Description and characteristics of analysis equipment, including level recorder and tape recorder.
3. A corrected plot of the measurements.

THE MEASUREMENT OF TRANSIENTS

Classification of Transient Noises. Conventional sound-level meters are designed primarily for the measurement of steady-state noises, but since they are used to measure fluctuating noises, the ballistic characteristics of the indicating instrument have been selected with a view toward obtaining satisfactory readings for such sounds. However, in practice it has been found that the differences between aural evaluation of a sound and its level as measured with a conventional sound-level meter increase as the sound departs from a true steady-state type or as the ratio of the peak-to-rms value of the waveform increases (see Chap. 2 for a discussion of *Ratio of Peak-to-rms Values*). This condition exists mainly for intermittent or impact-type noises which consist of transient pulses of noise, either repeated or as individual noises.

Intermittent noise may be interrupted or modulated steady-state noise or it may be a series of impact noises or other transients repeated at regular and irregular intervals. If its rms value is constant but the ratio of peak to rms increases, the noise becomes noticeably louder to the ear, although the sound-level meter reading will not change. In such cases it would appear that the ear is more affected by the instantaneous peak power than by the average power so that the greater the peak-to-rms value the louder and more annoying the sound becomes even though its rms value as read on a conventional sound-level meter may not change.

Peak readings of noise are usually desirable when there is a large peak-to-rms value, but it is not always easy to determine when this is the case. For sine waves the ratio of peak to rms is 3 db, while for a white noise the ratio may be 6 to 10 db. When the ratio is greater than 10 db the noise is generally of a transient or recurrent transient nature. The usual humming, rumbling, and swishing noises associated with well-designed rotating machinery seldom contain high peak-to-rms ratios. At the other extreme, high peak-to-rms noises are produced when one object strikes against another as in a drop hammer, by explosive-type sounds, and by sharp rattles and clanging sounds. A rough but useful criterion is: the less "musical" a sound is, the more likely it is to have a very high peak-to-rms ratio. When this ratio is very high, as in the case of a single gunshot, the reading of a sound-level meter is usually not significant, since the time duration of the peak is much too short to provide a meaningful meter deflection.

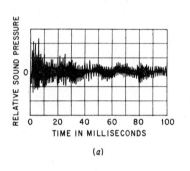

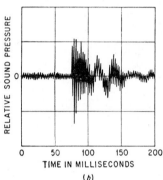

FIG. 17.17. Oscillographic records of impact noises. (*a*) Noise from a single strike of a punch press doing a simple forming operation. The peak level recorded is 120 db. (*b*) Impact noise from a drop hammer. (*A. P. G. Peterson.*[12])

If many sources of intermittent sound are present in a large room, the total noise will tend to have a more or less normal peak-to-rms ratio (except in the immediate vicinity of the sources) provided the sources are operating at random, i.e., are not synchronized. The operator of any large single machine which is a source of impact noise is normally so close to his machine that its noise output will produce a peak in his vicinity which is far above the average sound level in the room. Therefore, when one wishes to measure the characteristics of the noise to which an operator is exposed, it is particularly important that the microphone be placed in his usual operating position.

Figure 17.17 shows oscillographic records of two typical types of impact sounds. In (*a*) the microphone was placed 4 ft from a punch press doing a simple forming operation. The instantaneous peak of 120 db is reached 5 msec after impact. Note that there is a very rapid initial rise, reaching a level of 119 db within 1 sec after impact. The envelope of the decay is very approximately exponential in nature. The random nature of individual peak amplitudes is apparent and the wave is dissymmetrical. In Fig. 17.17*b* the oscillogram is that produced by noise from a 1,800-lb drop hammer in an open field. The microphone was 24 ft from the hammer. Again the initial rise is very rapid and the maximum level obtained is 119 db. In this case there is a low-frequency variation having a period of 25 msec (40 cps) which is caused by the ringing of the hammer. When the microphone was placed close to the hammer, the oscillogram tended to appear more like Fig. 17.17*a*—the difference in shape at the two positions resulting from appreciable attenuation in air of the high-frequency components as compared with the attenuation of the low frequencies, which is relatively slight.

The decay time constants of impact sounds are usually between about 10 and 250 msec.* In general, the relative energy in the various bands decays at different rates. For example, Fig. 17.18 shows the decay time constant in different octave bands of noise from a small punch press stamping out blanks.

In practical problems certain irregularities in waveform will be encountered which result from reflections in the surrounding space as well as from the machine characteristic itself. Such irregularities are generally considerably lower than the initial peak of the impact sound.

Use of the Oscilloscope for Peak Readings. The cathode-ray oscilloscope provides a useful means for observing transient or intermittent noises, particularly if a long-persistence screen is used.

Calibration of Oscilloscope. An oscilloscope, connected to the output jack of a sound-level meter, may be calibrated with a sinusoidal source of audio power. This source may be fed into the sound-level meter either acoustically with a loudspeaker or acoustic calibrator, or electrically with an electric calibrator or other coupling to the input circuits of the sound-level meter. The exact level is not important, but it is desirable that the waveform, as observed on the oscilloscope, be close to true sinusoidal.

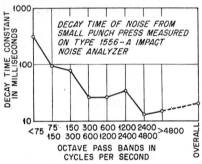

FIG. 17.18. The time constant of analyzed noise from a punch press. (*A. P. G. Peterson.*[12])

First adjust the sound-level meter controls and the amplitude of the calibrating signal so that full-scale deflection is obtained (usually + 10 db) on the indicating instrument of the sound-level meter.

Next, check to determine whether the indicating instrument on the sound-level meter affects the waveform viewed on the oscilloscope; this may be done by switching the indicating instrument out of the circuit (generally by switching to an *A* battery check position). If the waveform is affected, disconnect the indicating instrument while observing the waveform. Some sound-level meters have a separate vacuum-tube stage for the "output-jack" connection, in which case the indicating instrument will not affect the observed waveform. Hence in such sound-level meters this step need not be taken.

Finally, calibrate the face of the oscilloscope, as follows: Adjust the oscilloscope controls for a convenient deflection that corresponds to a full-scale reading of the indicating instrument. The divisions on the oscilloscope screen are linear, in contrast to those on the scale of the indicating instrument on the sound-level meter, which are logarithmic since decibels are proportional to the logarithm of voltage or sound pressure. For convenience it is desirable to calibrate the face of the oscilloscope directly in decibels. Such a scale is easily determined by use of the *Decibel Table* given in Appendix 2.1. For example, if a given oscilloscope deflection is equivalent to a meter reading of +10 db or a sound level of 90 db, half that deflection on the oscilloscope screen will be 6 db lower, or 84 db; 0.316 times that deflection will be 10 db lower, or 80 db. The total level is the sum of the attenuator readings plus the reading of the calibrated deflection on the oscilloscope face. This procedure, which has been widely used because of its simplicity, calibrates the oscilloscope in terms of an equivalent sine wave. In other words, the peak values as read from the oscilloscope are given in terms of the rms value of a waveform having the same peak value. These readings are actually 3 db below the true peak value of the waveform; to obtain the true instantaneous peak 3 db should be added to the readings.

* The time constant is the time required for the wave to drop 8.7 db in level from its initial value.

When the oscilloscope is calibrated for use with a sound-level meter it is desirable to mark the controls of the oscilloscope or tape them for the calibrated position so that they will not be accidentally moved during the measurements.

Reading the Oscilloscope. In using the oscilloscope with a sound-level meter care should be taken not to operate the oscilloscope or the sound-level meter in a region where either is nonlinear. If deflections show sharp "clipping" at a certain amplitude, either the sound-level meter or the oscilloscope itself is overloading. If the fault is with the oscilloscope, the control should be readjusted. If the sound-level meter is overloaded, it should be operated on the next higher attenuator setting. This ensures freedom from waveform distortion caused by the sound-level meter output circuit. (The usual sound-level meter meeting ASA standards has an overload point at least 10 db above full-scale reading, which is equivalent to approximately three times the voltage of full-scale deflection.)

Photography of Oscilloscope. Various types of cameras are available for photographing oscilloscope patterns so that permanent records can be made of waveforms. Some cameras are of the "self-developing" variety, which are particularly convenient for this purpose. Continuous-film cameras are also available for use where a continuous recording is required.

Peak-noise Indicators (Impact-noise Analyzers) (also see Chap. 16). Although the oscilloscope permits actual observation of waveform, it is inconvenient for use as a peak-measuring instrument in that it is somewhat bulky, it generally requires a-c power lines, and the required calibration procedure is time-consuming. So-called "peak-noise indicators" or "impact-noise analyzers" have been developed to simplify the procedure of measuring peak sound pressure levels.[11,12] Such a device is connected to the output of the sound-level meter and is used in place of, or in conjunction with, the regular indicating instrument which measures, in effect, rms values. These battery-operated devices are relatively small and can be used by operators having little training.

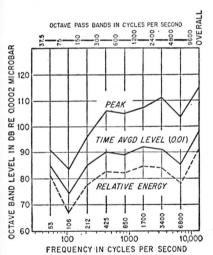

FIG. 17.19. The results of an octave-band analysis of the noise from a single impact of a punch press as measured by an impact-noise analyzer on the output of an octave-band analyzer. (*A. P. G. Peterson.*[12])

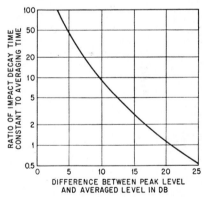

FIG. 17.20. Chart showing the relations between the ratio of the peak to averaged value and the time constants of an impact and of the circuit. (*A. P. G. Peterson.*[12])

Operation. Peak-noise indicators (impact-noise analyzers) usually are connected to a sound-level meter in the same manner as other accessories or they may be used with some types of octave- or fractional-octave band analyzers. For example, Fig. 17.19 shows the results of an octave-band analysis of noise from a single impact of a punch press which was obtained with an impact-noise analyzer connected to the output of an octave-band analyzer. The upper curve shows the measured peak levels in the various bands; the middle curve is the time-average level when a time constant of 0.01 was used; the bottom curve shows the computed relative energy in the various bands.

Storage in the electric circuits is sufficiently long so that peak readings can be taken directly for most impulses by merely observing the maximum deflection of the meter, indicating the maximum sound pressure level reached by the noise. Another characteristic which can be measured is the "time-average level," which is a measure of the level maintained over a period of time. As indicated in Fig. 17.20, the difference between the peak level and the averaged level is a measure of the time duration of the wave. Assuming impact noise to be approximately exponentially decaying random noise, this relationship gives the impact decay time in terms of the ratio between the decay time and the time used in obtaining the average level.

In general, to conform with the usual oscilloscope readings, the peak-noise indicator is calibrated in terms of the rms value of an equivalent peak value. If true peak values are required, the readings should be increased by 3 db.

Analysis of Transients and Intermittent Sounds. There are many methods of mechanically analyzing a waveform from an oscillogram such as may be photographed from the screen of an oscilloscope. However, electrical methods which employ various types of wave analyzers are usually far more convenient and rapid. Direct electrical analysis generally requires repetitive waveform.

While various recording methods may be used to obtain a repetitive signal of the waveform to be analyzed, magnetic tape is by far the most convenient since it may be cut and spliced in the form of a loop to repeat the wave at regular intervals. The electrical signal can then be analyzed by any of the methods covered earlier. When magnetic-tape recorders are used to record waveforms of high peak-to-rms ratios, the waveform should be observed on an oscilloscope before and after recording to ensure that overloading in the recorder has not altered the waveform. If clipping or other high-level distortion is apparent the recorder must be operated at a lower level.

If an oscilloscope is not available, the same test may be made with a peak-reading noise meter. Here, since the waveform cannot be seen, checks should be made with both a sinusoidal signal and an impulsive noise. The same difference in readings between these two signals should exist when the recording is played back as when the original recording was made. If that is not the case, overloading is occurring in the magnetic-tape recorder. The "VU meters" incorporated in many magnetic-tape recorders are quite similar in dynamic characteristics to the indicating instruments on standard sound-level meters; they should not be relied on to indicate high peak levels.

Interpretation of Analysis. In interpreting an analysis made of sound recorded on a tape loop it should be remembered that certain components in the result are introduced by the repetition tape loop itself and have no physical counterpart in the original sound. For a given tape speed, repetition rate depends on the length of the loop. In general, the actual tape-loop repetition rate will be below the range of the analyzing equipment. When transient sounds are analyzed the loop should be long enough to allow decay of the noise practically to zero. The analysis then will show accurately the energy distribution of the noise as a function of frequency.

SOUND POWER MEASUREMENTS

The following methods are used in the measurement of the sound-power output of a source:

1. *Free-field Method.* Sound-pressure measurements are made in a free field at a fixed distance from the source in various angular directions. From these data one can determine the power flowing in various angular directions from the source. By integrating over all angles, the total power is obtained.

2. *Reverberant-field Method.* Sound-pressure measurements are made in a highly reverberant room where diffuse conditions are approximated. Then the sound pressure level is approximately the same everywhere in the room (except very close to the source). Since the sound pressure level and the total power output of the source are related under these conditions, the latter may be obtained.

3. *Semireverberant-field Method.* The sound power of a source frequently must be measured under actual operating conditions which are neither free-field nor reverberant conditions. Under these circumstances, the sound power may be calculated very approximately from mathematical relationships in terms of measurements of the sound pressure in the room generated by the source; a more accurate determination may be made if the room is "calibrated" by means of another source whose power output has been previously measured accurately by the free-field method. This method is not so accurate as either of the above methods, which are described in detail and which are recommended.

In all the above procedures measurements of sound power may be made in contiguous octave, half-octave, or third-octave bands. The total power can then be computed by adding the powers contributed from all bands by means of Fig. 2.17. Alternatively, the total power may be determined directly by measurements of over-all sound pressure levels. However, the former method, which employs filters, provides additional useful engineering data.

Free-field Method. From Eqs. (2.22a) and (2.22b), the sound-power level in decibels (re 1 picowatt) of a simple source (i.e., one that radiates uniformly in all directions) is given by

$$L_w = L_p + 20 \log_{10} r + 0.6 \qquad \text{dbp} \qquad (17.1)$$

where L_p is the sound pressure level at a distance of r feet from the source.

If the distance r is measured in meters, then the sound-power level in decibels is given by

$$L_w = L_p + 20 \log_{10} r + 10.9 \qquad \text{dbp} \qquad (17.2)$$

These formulas may be used to determine the sound power W of a source since the sound power is related to sound-power level by

$$\begin{aligned} L_w &= 10 \log W/10^{-12} \qquad \text{dbp} \\ &= 120 + 10 \log_{10} W \qquad \text{dbp} \end{aligned} \qquad (17.3)$$

where L_w is the sound-power level expressed in decibels re 10^{-12} watts (1 picowatt) and W is the power of the source in watts.

In determining the sound pressure level, the free-field plane-incident wave calibration of the microphone should be used. To obtain the best possible signal-to-noise ratio it is desirable to use the microphone at normal incidence (0°) so as to obtain an increased sensitivity. In this case, calibration curve at this angle should be employed, and the microphone should be so oriented during the measurements. The microphone itself should be connected to the sound-level meter by a cable in order to minimize diffraction effects, or a correction should be included for the effects of the case of the sound-level meter in the sound field.

In the free-field method of determining the sound power of a source, measurements must be made under conditions where the reverberant field is negligible. In the above equations a simple source of sound power was assumed. If the source does not radiate uniformly in all directions, the power flowing across an imaginary sphere or hemisphere drawn around the source can be determined by dividing the spherical surface into a number of divisions and measuring the power across each one, the power being determined from measurements of sound pressure level over a suitably chosen array of points. When the source to be measured is in the center of a free-field (anechoic) room the array of points would be in the form of a sphere surrounding the source. On the other hand, it is frequently necessary to measure the power output of a source which is mounted on a concrete surface or on the ground in the open air, away from any other reflective surfaces. Under these conditions, the array of points at which measurements would be made would be a hemisphere and slightly different formulas would be employed to calculate the sound power of the source.

Measurements in a Free-field Room. When measurements of sound power are made in an enclosed space, the absorption coefficients of the bounding surfaces should be sufficiently high, and there should be an absence of reflecting surfaces other than those of the machine under test, so that essentially free-field conditions exist. The volume of the enclosure must be sufficiently large so that the microphone may be placed in the far radiation field of the machine under test.

MICROPHONE POSITIONS. The microphone should be placed at a distance not less than twice, and preferably five times the largest dimension of the machine under test, and in any case, not less than 3 ft from the source. Furthermore, to ensure that the microphone is in a region of the free-field room where free-field conditions actually exist, the microphone should never be closer than a distance of $\lambda/4$ from the walls of the enclosure, where λ is the lowest frequency to be measured.

If a source of sound whose power to be measured is a perfect spherical radiator, then it is only necessary to measure the sound pressure level at one distance from the source to determine the power. However, since most sources have a nonuniform radiation pattern, the power must be determined at an array of points which provides information on the power per unit area flowing in various directions. The more nonuniform the radiation field, the greater the number of points at which measurements should be

Table 17.1. Coordinate Positions on the Surface of a Unit Sphere in Terms of Cartesian Coordinates (x, y, z) with the Origin at the Source, for a 20-point Array. The Averaging Constant $N = 13$ db

x	y	z
0	0.93	0.36
0	0.93	−0.36
0.58	0.58	0.58
0.58	0.58	−0.58
0.93	0.36	0
0.36	0	0.93
0.36	0	−0.93
0.93	−0.36	0
0.58	−0.58	0.58
0.58	−0.58	−0.58
0	−0.93	0.36
0	−0.93	−0.36
−0.58	−0.58	0.58
−0.58	−0.58	−0.58
−0.93	−0.56	0
−0.36	0	0.93
−0.36	0	−0.93
−0.93	0.36	0
−0.58	0.58	0.58
−0.58	0.58	−0.58

made. For greatest accuracy with a highly directive source, a 20-point array is recommended. The positions of the 20 points are given in Table 17.1. If a more uniform source is to be measured, or if less accuracy is required, a 12-point or 8-point array, whose positions are given in Tables 17.2 and 17.3, respectively, may be used.

CALCULATION OF SOUND POWER. In Eqs. (17.1) and (17.2) the sound-power level of a simple source is given in terms of the sound pressure level measured at a distance r from the source. When the source is directional, its power output may be calculated conveniently from measurements of sound pressure level on an array of points located on an imaginary sphere surrounding the source. From these measurements it is possible to compute an "average" sound pressure level $\bar{L}_p$ which would exist if the actual source were replaced by a point source of equal sound-power output. Then the radiated power may be computed from the average power $\bar{L}_p$ relationships similar to those of Eqs. (17.1) and (17.2):

$$L_w = \bar{L}_p + 20 \log_{10} r + 0.6 \qquad \text{dbp} \qquad (17.4)$$

where $\bar{L}_p$ is the average sound pressure level from a source at a distance of r ft. The

Table 17.2. Coordinate Positions on the Surface of a Unit Sphere in Terms
of Cartesian Coordinates (x, y, z) with the Origin at the Source, for a
12-point Array.   The Averaging Constant $N = 10.8$ db

x	y	z
0	0.89	0.45
0.53	0.72	−0.45
0.85	0.28	0.45
0.85	−0.28	−0.45
0.53	−0.72	0.45
0	−0.89	−0.45
−0.53	−0.72	0.45
−0.85	−0.28	−0.45
−0.85	0.28	0.45
−0.53	0.72	−0.45
0	0	1
0	0	−1

Table 17.3. Coordinate Positions on the Surface of a Unit Sphere in Terms
of Cartesian Coordinates (x, y, z) with the Origin at the Source, for
an Eight-point Array.   The Averaging Constant $N = 9$ db

x	y	z
0	0.82	0.58
0	0.82	−0.58
0.82	0	0.58
0.82	0	−0.58
0	−0.82	0.58
0	−0.82	−0.58
−0.82	0	0.58
−0.82	0	−0.58

corresponding equation when the distance is measured in meters is

$$L_w = \bar{L}_p + 20 \log_{10} r + 10.9 \qquad \text{dbp} \qquad (17.5)$$

The average sound pressure level $\bar{L}_p$ may be computed from measurements made at an array of points in the following way: Each sound pressure level measurement corresponds to a value of power per unit area flowing across an imaginary sphere.   Therefore, to obtain the average power per unit area, and hence the average sound pressure level on the surface of the sphere:

1. Combine all the level readings on a power basis by means of Fig. 2.17.   This may be done by combining the readings at the first two points (for example, if each had a reading of 80 db, then the combined level from Fig. 2.17 would be 83 db) and then combine this new value with the reading taken at the third point, etc.
2. Subtract from total combined levels obtained in (1) an "averaging constant" N which depends on the number of points at which measurements were made.   The values of N for measurements in an enclosure are given in Tables 17.1 to 17.3.

SAMPLE CALCULATION.   Suppose measurements are made in a spherical array consisting of 12 points whose relative coordinates are given in Table 17.2.   Measurements are made 20 ft from the source.   The following values of sound pressure level are obtained in the band from 150 to 300 cps: 87, 85, 82, 81, 81, 80, 80, 80, 81, 82, 82, and 85 db.   If these readings are all combined by the use of Fig. 2.17, the combined level is 93.6 db. From Table 17.2, the value of the averaging constant N that must be subtracted from the combined level is 10.8 db. Therefore, the average sound pressure level $\bar{L}_p$ is 82.8 db re 0.0002 microbar.

Substituting this average value of $\bar{L}_p$ in Eq. (17.4), the sound-power level in the 150- to 300-cps band is 109.4 dbp, i.e., 109.4 db re 1 picowatt. If the total sound-power output of the source is desired, similar measurements would be made in each of the bands and the total power level would be obtained by combining levels by means of Fig. 2.17.

Measurements Outdoors. When measurements are made outdoors, away from any reflective surfaces other than the ground on which the source is mounted, or if the source is in an enclosure having highly absorptive boundaries except for a concrete floor, then measurements of sound pressure level on the surface of an imaginary hemisphere surrounding the source may be used to compute the power output of the source. Measurements above a reflecting plane are sometimes required, even where a free-field room is available, because the machine to be measured may be too heavy to be suspended or its power-output characteristics may be altered when it is not resting upon a solid foundation as in its normal operation.

Table 17.4. Coordinate Positions on the Surface of a Unit Hemisphere in Terms of Cartesian Coordinates (x, y, z) with the Origin at the Source, for a 12-point Array. The Averaging Constant N = 10.8 db

x	y	z
0	0.93	0.36
0.58	0.58	0.58
0.93*	0.36	0
0.36	0	0.93
0.93*	−0.36	0
0.58	−0.58	0.58
0	−0.93	0.36
−0.58	−0.58	0.58
−0.93*	−0.36	0
−0.36	0	0.93
−0.93*	0.36	0
−0.58	0.58	0.58

* Subtract 3 db from the measured levels at these points to provide a power weighting factor of $\frac{1}{2}$ at these points.

MICROPHONE POSITIONS. Measurements should be made in the far radiation field of the machine under test. Therefore, the microphone should be placed at a distance not less than twice, and preferably five times the largest dimension of the machine under test, and in any case, not less than 3 ft from the source. Furthermore, if the effective source height over the ground plane is appreciable, the microphone positions near the ground plane should be at least $4h^2/\lambda$ from the source, where h is the effective height of the source and λ is the wavelength of the sound of the highest frequency to be measured. (This is done to place the microphone beyond the zone of successive maxima and minima near the ground which results from the interference between the source and its image.)

In order to eliminate errors due to pressure doubling, the microphone position should be at least several inches above the ground plane.

As in the case of the measurement of the sound power of a source in a free-field room, the more highly directional the source, and the greater the accuracy required, the greater will be the number of measurement points in the hemispherical array around the source. In Tables 17.4, 17.5, and 17.6, recommended positions are given for 12-, 6-, and 4-point arrays. The averaging constant N, which must be subtracted from the total combined levels to obtain the average sound pressure level $\bar{L}_p$ on the surface of the imaginary hemisphere, is given in each of the tables.

Table 17.5. Coordinate Positions on the Surface of a Unit Hemisphere in Terms of Cartesian Coordinates (x, y, z) with the Origin at the Source, for a Six-point Array. The Averaging Constant $N = 7.8$ db

x	y	z
0	0.89	0.45
0.85	0.28	0.45
0.53	−0.72	0.45
−0.53	−0.72	0.45
−0.85	0.28	0.45
0	0	1

Table 17.6. Coordinate Positions on the Surface of a Unit Hemisphere in Terms of Cartesian Coordinates (x, y, z) with the Origin at the Source, for a Four-point Array. The Averaging Constant $N = 6$ db

x	y	z
0	0.82	0.58
0.82	0	0.58
0	−0.82	0.58
−0.82	0	0.58

When measurements outdoors are made at distances greater than 100 ft, it is generally necessary to correct for atmospheric conditions (see Chap. 3).

If the machine whose power is being measured has a radiation pattern which is circularly symmetrical about an axis parallel to the ground plane in the frequency range of interest, one may omit measurements at microphone positions other than those near the ground plane and compute the average sound pressure level accordingly.

CALCULATION OF SOUND POWER. Where measurements are made over an imaginary hemispherical surface above a hard reflective surface, the power output of the source may be computed from the average sound pressure level $\bar{L}_p$ on the surface of this hemisphere from the following relationships:*

$$L_w = \bar{L}_p + 20 \log_{10} r - 2.4 \quad \text{dbp} \quad (17.6)$$

where L_w is the power level of the source in decibels relative to 1 picowatt (10^{-12} watt); r is the distance in feet of the surface of the hemisphere from the effective center of the source. If the distance is measured in meters, the above formula becomes

$$L_w = \bar{L}_p + 20 \log_{10} r + 7.9 \quad \text{dbp} \quad (17.7)$$

Reverberant-field Method. A perfectly diffuse sound field is said to exist in a room in which the sound pressure level is everywhere the same and the sound waves travel in every direction with equal probability. These conditions are approximated in large reverberant rooms, as noted below. Then according to Eq. (18.3) the sound-power level in decibels of the source (re 10^{-12} watt) L_w is related to the average sound pressure level in the room $\bar{L}_p$ by the equation

$$L_w = \bar{L}_p + 10 \log_{10} a - 16.4 \quad \text{dbp} \quad (17.8)$$

where a is the total absorption in the room in "sabins" (i.e., square-foot units) which is obtained by multiplying the total area of each surface in the room by its respective absorption coefficient [see Eq. (18.2)].

* See the footnote to Eq. (3.3) regarding the limitations to which these relationships are subject.

If the total absorption in the room is expressed in square meters, then the corresponding equation giving the sound-power level in decibels of the source in the room is

$$\bar{L}_w = L_p + 10 \log_{10} a - 6.1 \qquad \text{dbp} \qquad (17.8a)$$

The above equations assume that the absorption of sound by air in the room is negligible. At higher frequencies, particularly at certain values of relative humidity, this approximation is inaccurate. If the effects of air absorption are included, Eq. (17.8) then becomes

$$L_w = \bar{L}_p + 10 \log_{10} (a + 4mV) - 16.4 \qquad \text{dbp} \qquad (17.9)$$

where a is the total absorption in the room in sabins, m is the attenuation coefficient for air given by Fig. 17.21, and V is the volume of the test room in cubic feet.

It should be emphasized that the above equations apply only when "diffuse" conditions exist throughout the test room; then the sound pressure level will be very nearly uniform throughout the room. The degree of diffusion is a function of the room dimensions, its shape and absorption, and the character of the noise itself. Thus the

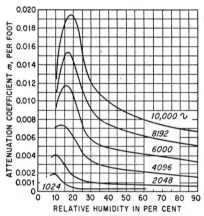

FIG. 17.21. Values of the attenuation coefficient m as a function of relative humidity for different frequencies. See Eq. (17.9). For the measurement of relative humidities below about 35 per cent a standard sling psychrometer is recommended. In any case direct-reading instruments of at least ±5 per cent accuracy are recommended. (*V. O. Knudsen and C. M. Harris.*[13])

degree of diffusion is dependent on N, the number of normal modes of vibration which are excited, given approximately by the following relationship:

$$N = [(4\pi f^2 V/c^3) + (\pi f A/2c^2)]\Delta f \qquad (17.10)$$

where A = total surface area of room, and where Δf is the bandwidth of the noise in cps, or, in the case of a very wideband noise, it may be taken as the bandwidth of the sound analyzer being used. The minimum frequency for which a reasonable state of diffusion exists can be calculated from Eq. (17.10) by assuming that N should be at least equal to 20 for a bandwidth Δf. As might be deduced from Eq. (17.10), broadband noise tends to be more uniformly diffused than pure tones. Hence, where strong pure tones are present, it may be necessary to use many measurement points in order to obtain a good space average. This may be accomplished by moving the microphone along a circular arc through the room, and using specially designed equipment to obtain an integrated average level. Thus in order to obtain diffuse conditions in the test room three factors must be considered:

1. *Volume of Test Room.* The minimum volume that the test room must have depends on the lowest frequency at which measurements will be made—the lower the test frequency, the larger the volume of the test room.

2. *Absorption of the Test Room.* In order for diffuse conditions to prevail, the absorption in the test room must be small enough so that the sound waves will undergo many reflections before decay. This condition will obtain when the average absorption coefficient is not greater than 5 or 6 per cent, i.e., the total number of units of absorption in the chamber (including air absorption) should not be greater than about 5 or 6 per cent of the total wall areas of the test room.

3. *Shape of the Test Room.* The frequency distribution of the normal modes of vibration of the test room will depend on its relative proportions.[14] Some rooms have nonparallel walls with irregular boundary surfaces to improve the diffusion within the test room. In others having a rectangular shape, diffusing columns may be introduced or large rotating vanes may be used to improve the diffusion. In a rectangular test room it is important that the ratios length to width, length to height, and width to height are all different. The proportions used may depend on the volume and available space. The proportions 1:1.25:1.6 or 2:3:5 are frequently employed.

The values of L_w may be computed for all frequency bands of interest by: (1) measuring the average sound pressure level $\bar{L}_p$ in the test room, and (2) determining the total absorption in the test room—including the effect of air absorption, where it is significant.

Measurement of the Average Sound Pressure Level. Since measurements are to be made in a diffuse field, the *random-incidence* response of the microphone should be used. Because the sound pressure levels in the test chamber will be higher nearer the walls, corners, and edges than throughout the rest of the room, to avoid appreciable errors the microphone should be placed at least $\frac{3}{4}\lambda$ away from the corners and edges of the chamber and at least $\lambda/4$ from the walls, where λ is the wavelength of the lowest frequency of interest.[15]

Furthermore it is recommended that the microphone be no closer than one major dimension of the noise source under test, and in any case no closer than 3 ft from the nearest surface of the source. As indicated in the above formulas, the *average* sound pressure level must be obtained. This average should be carried out over a space of at least one wavelength and may be obtained by swinging the microphone from a cord or employing some other means for moving the microphone through space. (It is important that no signal be generated by the device for moving the microphone.) Similar measurements should be carried out in three or four other microphone positions and the results averaged. The number of positions required to obtain accurate results depends somewhat on the width of the spectrum of the sound source. For example, if the sound source has strong discrete frequencies, more positions will be required. Thus if the range exceeds 12 db the field is too nonuniform to obtain accurate results; if the range is 6 to 10 db, a value of 3 db less than the maximum value should be taken; if the range is less than 6 db, simply use the average value.

The sound source under test usually is some type of machine, and it should be mounted under its normal operating conditions and position in the room. If no such condition exists, the machine should be placed at least $\frac{3}{4}\lambda$ from the corners and edges and at least $\lambda/4$ from the walls of the room (with no major surface of the machine parallel to a nearby wall), where λ is the wavelength corresponding to the lowest frequency of interest.

The case may arise where the room is not sufficiently large to permit the placement of the microphone within the limits indicated above. If the room is large enough so that no room surface is less than one major machine dimension away from the nearest major surface of the machine, the average sound pressure level in the room may be obtained by measuring the sound pressure level in each of the four corners on the floor, averaging these values, and subtracting 9 db from the average in the corners; this figure is equivalent to the average sound pressure level in the central portion of the room.

Determining the Total Absorption in the Test Room. The total absorption in the test room may be determined in three ways:

1. *From Reverberation-time Measurements.* A warble tone or a band of thermal noise is produced in the room long enough for a steady state to be reached. The time interval required for the level to decay 60 db is determined with a high-speed graphic-level recorder. This time, defined as the reverberation time, is related to the total absorption in the room by Eqs. (18.6) and (18.7).

2. *From Calculations Based on Absorption Coefficients.* The total absorption may be computed directly from Eq. (18.2), merely by multiplying each surface in the test room by its respective absorption coefficient and obtaining the sum. However, the required absorption coefficients are not always accurately known.

3. *By Means of Calibrated Sound Source.* If a sound source has had its power output measured accurately, then if it is placed in the test chamber and the average sound pressure level is measured, Eq. (17.9) may be used to solve for the term $10 \log_{10} (a + 4mV)$. Since this quantity is a constant for the same conditions, an unknown source may then be placed in the test room and the sound-power level may be determined directly from Eq. (17.9) if the average sound pressure level $\bar{L}_p$ is measured.[16] If the source which is used in the calibration procedure is calibrated in a free field, the source should be placed in the test room in such a way that it radiates substantially the same power in the test room as it did in the free field.

Reporting Sound-power Measurements. It is recommended that the following information be included in reporting measurements:

1. *Machine under Test.* A description of the device measured, its operating conditions, mounting conditions, and its location in the test room during the tests.

2. *Description of the Test Room.* A description of the test room, including its volume, boundary surfaces, total absorption, and the temperature and relative humidity at the time of the measurements.

3. *Equipment.* A description of the equipment used in the tests, including name, manufacturer, type, and serial number, together with any information regarding the calibration of this equipment.

4. *Measurements.* A description of the microphone positions, the sound pressure levels obtained at each of the microphone positions for each of the frequencies or bands of frequencies used, together with the range of variation of time or space averages used.

5. *Data Presentation.* Compute both the sound power in watts and the sound-power level in decibels, and plot these data on standard graph paper available for the purpose; include information on standard deviation for the measurements.

REFERENCES

1. Peterson, A. P. G.: *Noise Control*, **2**: 20 (January, 1956).
2. American Standard Z24.3-1944, American Standards Association, New York.
3. Pomper, V. H.: "Noise Simplified," Hermon Hosmer Scott, Inc.; also *Safety Maintenance and Production*, **107**: 54, 60 (1954).
4. Bennett, W. R.: *J. Acoust. Soc. Amer.*, **15**: 164 (1944); *Bell System Tech. J.*, **12**: 228 (1933).
5. Beranek, L. L.: "Acoustic Measurements," John Wiley & Sons, Inc., New York, 1949.
6. Peterson, A. P. G., and L. L. Beranek: "Handbook of Noise Measurement," General Radio Company.
7. American Standard Z24.10-1954, American Standards Association, New York.
8. Young, R. W.: "Effective Bandwidths of Filters Used for Noise Measurement," unpublished.
9. Scott, H. H.: *J. Acoust. Soc. Amer.*, **11**: 225 (1939).
10. Snow, W. B.: *Noise Control*, **1**: 16 (May, 1955).
11. Scott, H. H.: "Intermittent Sound Measurement, A Challenge," Encyclopedia of Instrumentation for Industrial Hygiene, University of Michigan, 1956.
12. Peterson, A. P. G.: *Gen. Radio Exp.*, **30**: 1 (February, 1956).
13. Knudsen, V. O., and C. M. Harris: "Acoustical Designing in Architecture," John Wiley & Sons, Inc., New York, 1950.
14. Morse, P. M.: "Vibration and Sound," p. 395, 2d ed., McGraw-Hill Book Company, Inc., 1948.
15. Waterhouse, R. V.: *J. Acoust. Soc. Amer.*, **27**: 247 (1955).
16. Hardy, H. C., H. H. Hall, and L. G. Ramer: *Trans. Inst. Radio Eng.* PGA, **10**: 14 (1952).

Chapter 18

ACOUSTICAL MATERIALS

Hale J. Sabine

The Celotex Corporation

ABSORPTION OF SOUND

Introduction. Acoustical materials and structures may be described for purposes of noise reduction as those which have the property of absorbing a substantial fraction of the energy of sound waves which strike their surface. They may be used in four ways: (1) as surfacing for walls and ceilings, (2) as individual suspended units, (3) as linings for barriers and enclosures used for confining the noise of specific sources, and (4) as linings to reduce noise transmission through ducts or small passages. The last-named application is discussed in Chap. 27. Data on sound-absorptive materials used at high temperatures and in high-velocity air streams are given in Table 34.3 and Fig. 34.26, respectively.

Generally speaking, the primary function of acoustical materials in noise control is to counteract the undesirable effects of sound reflection by the hard, rigid, interior surfaces which they cover or replace. As will be explained more fully in later sections, excessive room reflection may increase the annoyance experienced by room occupants because of noise in several ways, namely, by increasing the sound pressure level, by prolonging noise through reverberation, and by causing noise to spread with little attenuation throughout a room.

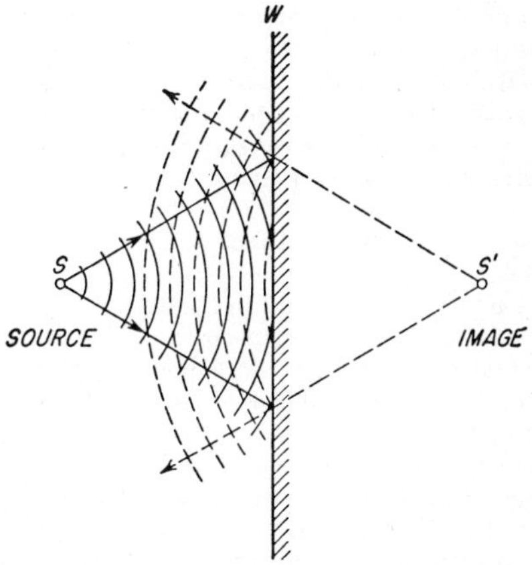

Since acoustical materials are used as finished surfaces in many types of rooms, such as offices, schools, hospitals, restaurants, industrial plants, or any enclosed

Fig. 18.1. Reflection of sound waves from a plane surface.

area in which the occupants are exposed to noise, they must satisfy in varying degree a number of structural and architectural requirements. Some of the properties which merit consideration aside from high sound absorptivity are appearance, decorative effect, light reflectivity, maintainability, durability, and flame resistance.

Reflection and Absorption of Sound Waves. When a sound source is in operation, sound waves travel outward in all directions radially from the source. When the sound waves encounter an obstacle or surface, such as a wall, their direction of travel is changed; in other words, they are *reflected*. Figure 18.1 illustrates the reflection of waves originating at the sound source S from a large plane wall W. The curved solid lines represent a train of waves spreading outward in the directions indicated by the solid arrows. The curved dotted lines and arrows illustrate the behavior of the waves after they have been reflected by the wall. As indicated in this figure, the reflection of sound from a surface large in comparison with the wavelength follows the same laws as the reflection of light from a plane mirror. Two facts are apparent: (1) the direction of travel of the reflected sound makes the same angle with the wall as that of the incident sound; (2) the reflected sound waves travel in the same manner as they would if they had originated at the "image" S' of the sound source. This image source is located the same distance behind the wall as the real source is in front of the wall, just as in the case of a light image in an ordinary mirror.

If the reflecting surface is completely impervious to air and perfectly rigid, there will be no loss of energy due to reflection, and the reflected wave will produce the same pressure at any given point as it would have if the image source S' had the same power output as the true source S. However, no physical surface is a perfect reflector, but will either be set in motion by pressure of the incident sound waves or, if it has a porous structure, will allow continued travel of the waves within the body of the material. If either of these processes results in the setting up of frictional forces or in the transmission of sound waves into free space on the opposite side, the reflected waves will have less energy than the incident waves, and we say that part of the incident energy is *absorbed* by the surface.

Rating of Absorption of Materials. *Sound Absorption Coefficient.* The fraction of the energy absorbed when a sound wave is reflected from it is called the *sound absorption coefficient* (also termed *acoustic absorptivity*) of the material, and may vary from 1 or 2 per cent to nearly 100 per cent for various materials. The absorption coefficient of a material depends on the nature of the material itself, on the frequency of the sound, and on the angle at which the sound wave strikes the surface of the material.

Noise Reduction Coefficient. Since the coefficient of every material varies with the frequency of the sound it is common practice to list the coefficients of a material at the six frequencies, 125, 250, 500, 1,000, 2,000, and 4,000 cps.* Some testing laboratories measure and publish coefficients for frequencies above and below this range. In comparing materials for noise quieting applications, the *noise reduction coefficient* (NRC) is commonly used. This is the average, usually stated to the nearest multiple of 0.05, of the coefficients at the four frequencies 250, 500, 1,000, and 2,000 cps.

Coefficients of General Building Materials. Interior finish materials such as concrete, hard plaster, glass, masonry, wood, and hard flooring materials are sufficiently rigid and non-porous as to be nearly perfect reflectors, having sound absorption coefficients generally of less than 0.05. Thick porous materials may have coefficients of 0.50 to 1.00.

Carpets, drapes, and upholstered furniture provide a useful degree of sound absorption by virtue of their porosity. The absorptivity of carpeting depends on a number of factors, including pile height, weight, the type of backing, and the thickness and material of the underlay.[1] In most types of carpeting, the absorptivity rises with frequency and generally reaches high values in the high-frequency region. A typical carpet with a 40-oz underlay has a noise reduction coefficient of about 0.50 to 0.55. The absorptivity of drapes varies widely, depending on their weight and amount of gather. The absorptivity is increased, particularly at low frequencies, by spacing the drapes out a few inches from the wall. Upholstered furniture as well as the clothing of persons may add an appreciable amount of absorption to a room. Representative absorption values for the above are listed in Table 18.1.

Variation in Absorptivity with Angle of Incidence. The absorption coefficient of any material varies considerably with the angle of incidence of the sound waves. When materials are used for room surfacing, which is their most common function, they are normally exposed to sound waves incident at many different angles more or less randomly distributed. For this reason, published coefficients of commercial materials

* Some laboratories list absorption coefficients for materials at frequencies of 128, 256, 512, 1,024, 2,048, and 4,096 cps. These values are, for practical purposes, identical with the corresponding values at 125, 250, 500, 1,000, 2,000, and 4,000 cps.

are generally determined by the reverberation-chamber method. This is basically an integrating method in which sound waves strike the test sample from many directions simultaneously. The coefficient is calculated from the measured effect of the sample on the sound field in the chamber, and the result thus obtained is considered to be an average value for all angles of incidence. This coefficient is termed the "random incidence," or "chamber" coefficient α as distinguished from the "normal-incidence" coefficient which applies to the case of sound waves striking the surface perpendicularly and is measured by a different method. Coefficients referred to in the following pages

Table 18.1. Sound Absorption Coefficients of Building Materials

Material	Coefficients		
	125 cps	500 cps	2,000 cps
Brick wall, painted.............................	0.01	0.02	0.02
Same, unpainted................................	0.02	0.03	0.05
Carpet, unlined.................................	0.05	0.25	0.60
Same, 40 oz hair-felt underlay...................	0.10	0.60	0.80
Fabrics:			
Light, 10 oz per sq yd, hung straight............	0.04	0.11	0.30
Medium, 14 oz per sq yd, draped...............	0.07	0.49	0.66
Heavy, draped, 18 oz per sq yd, draped.........	0.14	0.55	0.70
Floors:			
Concrete or terrazzo..........................	0.01	0.02	0.02
Wood...	0.05	0.03	0.03
Linoleum, asphalt, rubber or cork tile on concrete..		0.03–0.08	
Glass..	0.03	0.03	0.02
Marble or glazed tile...........................	0.01	0.01	0.01
Plaster, gypsum or lime, smooth finish on tile or brick	0.01	0.02	0.04
Same, on lath..................................	0.02	0.03	0.04
Plaster, gypsum or lime, rough finish on lath........	0.04	0.06	0.05
Wood paneling..................................	0.08	0.06	0.06

Absorption of furnishings and occupants. Values are given in sabins (square-foot units of absorption) per person or per object of furnishing

Occupants, seated, depending on character of seats, etc.	1.0–2.0	3.0–4.3	3.5–6.0
Chairs, metal or wood..........................	0.15	0.17	0.20
Desks..	0.9*	1.0*	1.1*

Complete tables of coefficients of the various materials that normally constitute the interior finish of rooms are given in Ref. 23. This list, adapted by permission from Acoustical Materials Association *Bull.* 17, 1957, is useful in making simple calculations of noise reduction in rooms.
    * Author's estimate.

and in other published literature may be taken as random-incidence values unless specifically stated otherwise.

There is unfortunately no fixed or exact relation between the normal and random-incidence coefficient for various materials. In other words, two materials having the same normal-incidence coefficient will not necessarily have the same random-incidence values. The relation will vary depending on the physical properties, thickness, and mounting conditions. However, it may be stated to a very rough approximation that random-incidence values are twice the normal-incidence values in the low range, higher by 0.25 to 0.35 in the middle range, and approximately equal in the high range.

Reduction Due to a Single Reflection. Occasionally one wishes to determine the decrease in sound pressure level due to a single reflection from the surface of an acoustical material. To arrive at this exactly it is necessary to know both the angle of incidence under consideration and the absorption coefficient for that particular angle

α_θ. The decrease in sound pressure level is given by

$$10 \log_{10} \frac{1}{1 - \alpha_\theta} \quad \text{db per reflection}$$

If the value of α_θ is not known, the random incidence coefficient α may be substituted as an approximation.

General Properties of Sound-absorptive Materials.[2–8] In order for the surface of a material to absorb sound energy it is necessary (1) that the surface be relatively transparent to sound waves, and (2) that means be provided for the vibratory energy of the waves to be more or less completely transformed into heat energy by friction. (The case where sound is "absorbed" by passing through an acoustically transparent surface directly into free space is excluded here.) Acoustical transparency* may take the form of the exposed surface of a highly porous material, a perforated board or sheet used as a facing over a porous material, a light flexible air-impervious membrane, or integral mechanical perforations or fissured openings into the body of a porous material, the external surface of which may be impervious. All these except the porous surface act as a positive or mass-series acoustic reactance and therefore show decreasing transparency with increasing frequency. If 4,000 cps is taken as the highest frequency for which effective sound absorption is desired, it can be stated very approximately that a perforated surface should have not less than about 10 per cent open area, and an impervious membrane should have a mass of not more than about 0.01 gm per sq cm.

The frictional element which accounts for the dissipation of sound energy most commonly takes the form of a layer of highly porous material at least ½ in. thick, in which the pores must intercommunicate throughout. The pores may be formed by felted mineral or vegetable fiber, by the interstices between small granules, or by a foamed composition in which the solidified bubbles open into each other throughout the structure. When a sound wave enters a porous material the amplitude of vibration of the air molecules is progressively damped out by friction against the surfaces of the fibers or particles forming the pore structure. This friction acts as an acoustic resistance whose value depends on the resistance of the material to direct air flow, or *flow resistance*, and only slightly on the frequency. Flow resistance is defined as the ratio of the pressure drop across a sample of material to the velocity of air passing through it; it is expressed in rayls (dyne-sec per cu cm). Generally speaking, the flow resistance must be held within certain limits in order to develop maximum absorption. If it is too high, sound waves cannot readily enter the material, and if too low, there is not sufficient friction encountered to dissipate a high proportion of sound energy. The optimum value of acoustic resistance varies with frequency and with the thickness and method of mounting of the material.

The flow resistances of a number of porous materials commercially available in the form of mineral fiber blankets and boards are shown in Fig. 18.2.[9] The value of flow resistance is a function of the thickness and density of the material, fiber diameter, percentage of binder, and the average orientation of the fibers with respect to the direction of air flow.[10] The effect of moderate compression on the flow resistance can be estimated from the inset chart. Some porous materials which are employed as sound-absorptive treatment are used in combination with a covering of perforated metal, cloth, or wire screen for protection. If the flow resistance of this covering is not too high, e.g., less than 10 rayls, the sound-absorptive efficiency of the structure will not be affected.

A third element which governs sound absorption, principally in the low-frequency range, is the total depth of the air volume between the face of the material and the rigid backing surface behind it. This volume includes both the air in the pores of the material and any air space between the material and its backing. The latter may vary in practice from zero, when the material is secured directly to a rigid backing, to several feet in the case of suspended acoustical ceilings. When the total depth of the air volume is less than about one-fourth wavelength, it acts as a series-negative or stiffness acoustic reactance, whose value increases with decreasing frequency and

* "Acoustical transparency" is a descriptive term intended to denote the relatively free passage of sound through the exposed surface of a material.

decreasing depth of air volume. The low-frequency absorption coefficient of any material, accordingly, will start to drop off with decreasing frequency at a frequency determined by the total depth of the air volume. While this "turnover" frequency is not at all sharply defined and varies considerably with different materials, it may be determined very approximately by the relation

$$f = \frac{c}{2d}$$

where f is the turnover frequency in cycles per second, and d is the total depth of air volume. Where d is expressed in inches, the turnover frequency f is approximately $f = 500/d$. It will be seen that a depth of at least 4 in. is necessary to maintain high absorption at low frequencies. This relation will also explain the characteristically low absorptivity at 125 and 250 cps of materials of $\frac{1}{2}$ to 1 in. thickness when mounted directly on a solid backing.

Acoustical materials in general, therefore, display a peaked absorption-frequency curve, the shape of which is determined at low frequencies largely by the depth of the air volume, in the peak region by the flow resistance and at the high frequencies by

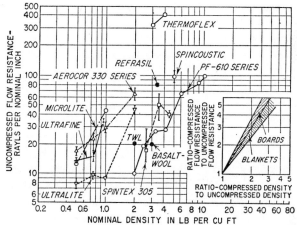

FIG. 18.2. Flow resistance of various acoustical materials, showing spread of data. The effect of compression on the flow resistance is shown on the inset chart. (*S. Labate.*[9])

the amount of surface opening. If the air volume is very deep, and the surface very open, the curve will be flat over a wide frequency range, and the absorption coefficient can be adjusted by choice of flow resistance of the material. A further description of the general properties of conventional sound-absorptive constructions is given in Chap. 22.* Technical information on the use of *resonators* in walls to provide sound absorption is given in Chap. 21; in general this type of absorber is used to provide absorption in a selected frequency range.

COMMERCIAL ACOUSTICAL MATERIALS[12]

Types of Acoustical Materials. Commercial acoustical materials used as continuous surfacing for walls or ceilings of rooms may be classified in several ways,

---

* Another type of sound absorber employs the principle of wave cancellation (for an application of this principle in noise reduction see *Sound Cancellation* in Chap. 29). An *electronic sound absorber* has been developed which consists of a microphone, amplifier, and loudspeaker connected so that, for an incident sound, the sound pressure at the microphone is reduced by as much as 10 to 25 db over a frequency range of three octaves in the low-frequency portion of the spectrum.[11] However for practical reasons this type of absorber has but limited application.

depending on the physical and structural properties under consideration. The large majority of materials which find practical use for noise quieting purposes are included in four major groups. These may be described as (1) tiles and boards, (2) materials for plastic application, (3) special acoustical assemblies, and (4) acoustical roof decks.

Tiles and Boards. An acoustical tile or board may be described as an integral rigid self-supporting material furnished in prefabricated units of a definite size and thickness. The distinction between tiles and boards is one of size only. Unit sizes commonly range from 12 by 12 in. to 24 by 48 in., with larger and smaller sizes available in some products. Thicknesses range in general from ½ to 1¼ in. The many products available in tile or board form differ widely in composition and surface characteristics, with corresponding differences in properties other than sound absorption, such as appearance, architectural style, cleanability, paintability, light reflectance, flame resistance, and the method of application desired. The Acoustical Materials Association has classified tiles and boards manufactured by its members according to appearance and composition into eight types, as follows (see Appendix 18.1):

Type I, Regularly Perforated Cellulose Fiber Tile. Wood or cane fiber board with regularly spaced integral surface perforations.

Type II, Random Perforated Cellulose Fiber Tile. Same, except perforations are of random spacing and diameter for decorative effect.

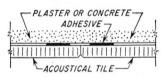

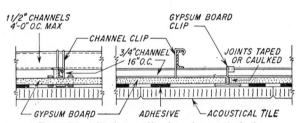

Fig. 18.3. Adhesive application of acoustical tile.

Type III, Slotted Cellulose Fiber Tile. Same, except surface slotted instead of perforated.

Type IV, Fissured or Textured Cellulose Fiber Tile. Same, except surface openings are an irregular fissured or textured pattern instead of mechanical perforations, for decorative effect.

Type V, Perforated Mineral Fiber Tile. Rock wool or glass wool board with integral surface perforations.

Type VI, Fissured Mineral Fiber Tile. Same, except surface openings are an irregular fissured pattern, for decorative effect.

Type VII, Textured or Smooth Mineral Fiber Tile or Board. Same, except no large openings appear on surface. Access of sound to interior of tile is by surface porosity.

Type VIII, Membrane-faced Mineral Fiber Tile or Board. Same, except surface is covered with a light, flexible, air-impervious, relatively sound-transparent membrane, for appearance and cleanability.

The above descriptions refer only to materials that are manufactured currently by member companies of the Acoustical Materials Association. Further classifications could be added to cover other combinations of surface appearance and composition, or materials now on the market which have a granular or foamed structure and surface texture.

Application of Acoustical Tiles and Boards. One of the principal advantages of acoustical tile is its adaptability to a number of installation and construction methods

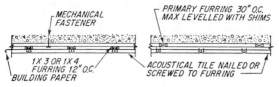

WOOD FURRING TO CONCRETE

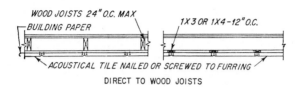

DIRECT TO WOOD JOISTS

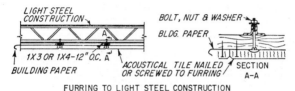

FURRING TO LIGHT STEEL CONSTRUCTION

FIG. 18.4. Application of acoustical tile to wood furring.

in both new and existing buildings. All acoustical tiles may be applied by means of approved acoustical adhesives to surfaces of plaster, concrete, and gypsum board which are in proper condition. A tile size of 12 by 24 in. is generally the largest that is recommended for adhesive application. All cellulose fiber and some mineral fiber tiles and boards of any size may be nailed or screwed to wood furring on proper spacing or to a wood ceiling or roof deck, and may also be screwed to a suspended gypsum-board backing.

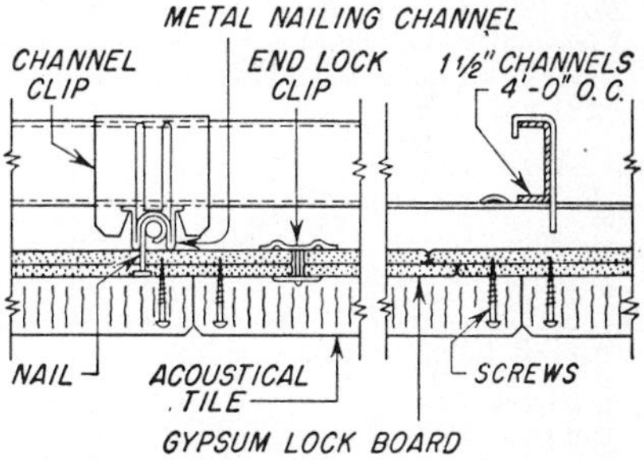

Most tiles and boards may be installed as a complete suspended ceiling by means of metal members which either engage slots in the edges of the tile or are exposed. The maximum unsupported span of tile or boards which is allowable depends on the deflection characteristics of the particular material used, especially with respect to high humidities.

A number of mechanical suspension systems are available which permit the combination of sound-absorptive ceiling surfaces with lighting, air conditioning,

FIG. 18.5. Screw application of acoustical tile to double gypsum board.

and sometimes radiant-heating elements in any desired arrangement. The systems having exposed suspension members generally provide easier removal of acoustical tile or board from the under side where access to the space above is desired.

These various methods of erection are illustrated in Figs. 18.3 to 18.7.

Sound-absorption Characteristics. The effects of thickness and method of mounting on the absorption-frequency characteristics and the noise reduction coefficients of two types of acoustical tile are shown in Figs. 18.8 to 18.12. The materials shown are Type I, regularly perforated cellulose-fiber tile, and Type VI, fissured mineral fiber tile, which are two of the most widely used types of tile product. Each graph indicates the average of the coefficients of from three to nine materials of the same type, thickness, and method of mounting, but of different manufacture. The curves show the peaked frequency characteristics common to materials having perforated or fissured openings in an otherwise impervious surface. The methods of mounting are those used by the Acoustical Materials Association and are shown in Appendix 18.1; for example:

Mounting No. 1. Spot-cemented to a rigid surface, with ⅛-in. air space.
Mounting No. 2. Nailed to 1- by 3-in. furring strips, 1³⁄₁₆-in. air space.
Mounting No. 7. Supported on metal suspension system.

FIG. 18.6. Erection of acoustical tile by concealed metal suspension system.

FIG. 18.7. Erection of acoustical tile by exposed metal suspension system.

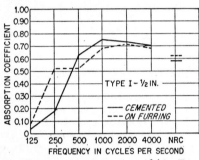

FIG. 18.8. Average absorption of ½-in. Type I (regularly perforated cellulose fiber) acoustical tile on cemented and furred mountings. (*AMA Bulletin.*[16])

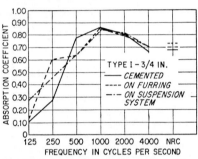

FIG. 18.9. Average absorption of ¾-in. Type I acoustical tile on cemented, furred, and suspension system mountings. (*AMA Bulletin.*[16])

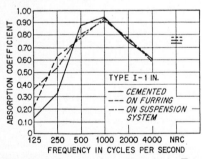

FIG. 18.10. Average absorption of 1-in. Type I acoustical tile on cemented, furred, and suspension system mountings. (*AMA Bulletin.*[16])

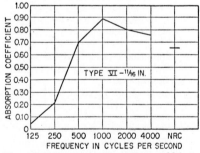

FIG. 18-11. Average absorption of 1¹⁄₁₆-in. Type VI (fissured mineral fiber) acoustical tile on cemented mounting. (*AMA Bulletin.*[16])

The effect of thickness increase within the comparatively narrow range shown is seen to increase the absorption mainly at the three frequencies 250, 500, and 1,000 cps, with negligible effect outside of this range. Mounting the materials over an air space increases the absorption markedly at 250 cps and to some extent at 125 cps for the deeper air spaces provided by the No. 7 mounting.   There is also a characteristic decrease in absorption at 500 cps for all air-space mountings, but little or no change at higher frequencies.

More complete data on the effect of air spaces have indicated that materials having an internal structure such as to allow sound to penetrate easily through the back surface into the air space exhibit greater changes in absorption with increasing air-space depth, particularly at low frequencies, than materials with a relatively impervious back surface.   However, most materials show no significant changes in absorption as the air space is increased beyond about 8 in. to the limit of 16 in. placed on the series of tests.

Maintenance.   Practically all acoustical tiles used for noise-reduction purposes are furnished with surfaces having high light reflectance of the order of 0.70 to 0.80. In most installations it is desired to maintain the light reflectance close to its initial value, preferably by standard washing or repainting procedures carried out as often as may be required without damaging the surface or impairing the sound absorptivity of the material.   Some tile products are available with washable factory-applied paint finishes.   Type VIII materials, having a decorative membrane surfacing, are most easily maintained by

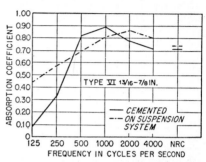

FIG. 18.12. Average absorption of $1\frac{3}{16}$- and $\frac{7}{8}$-in. Type VI acoustical tile on cemented and suspension system mountings.   (*AMA Bulletin*.[16])

washing.   With most materials, however, the common maintenance procedure employed in practice is that of repainting.

The so-called "paintability" of an acoustical material, which for practical purposes means the degree to which its original light reflectance can be restored by painting relative to an accompanying loss of sound absorption, depends essentially on the means originally provided for sound waves to penetrate the surface of the material, and the effect of successive paint coatings in restricting this means of access to the interior. The types of acoustical tile having virtually complete and unqualified paintability are those having integral mechanical perforations or slots, represented by Types I, II, III, and V in the classification.   These materials are initially furnished with an impervious factory paint coating which permits sound to enter only through the perforations. Additional paint coatings therefore have no effect on sound absorption unless a considerable number of the perforations are actually covered over.   The perforations in all products now on the market are purposely made large enough that this is very unlikely to occur in normal painting procedures, or even with a large number of successive paint coatings.   It may be stated, therefore, that integrally perforated materials can be repainted an indefinite number of times by any standard brush, spray, or roller-coating method, without impairing their sound absorption.

Fissured materials, included in Types IV and VI, have potentially high paintability, but some precautions must be observed.   Like the integrally perforated materials, these types also have an impervious factory-applied paint coating covering the surface between the fissured openings.   However, the fissures characteristically exhibit a wide variation in size and depth, even within a single tile unit, and additional paint coatings will tend to close over the smaller and shallower openings.   If the material contains the normal proportion of large, deep fissures, the closing of the smaller ones will have a negligible effect on sound absorption.   If care is taken in successive paint applications to avoid filling the larger fissures and to confine the paint to the flat surfaces between them, the paintability of these types will approach that of the integrally perforated materials.

Materials similar to those in Type VII, which have no large surface openings but which depend entirely on the surface porosity of the material itself for sound absorption, have limited paintability.   They are normally furnished with a factory paint coat which is applied heavily enough to produce satisfactory initial light reflectance but in such a way as to form a porous painted surface. Special precautions, however, as to the type and method of application of additional paint coatings must be taken to avoid sealing the surface, with resulting loss of sound absorption. The manufacturer of the particular material of the type under consideration should be consulted as to recommended paints and application techniques.

Flame Resistance. The flame-resistant properties of acoustical materials are an important consideration in many cases. Since acoustical materials in general come under the classification of interior finish rather than structural members or components, their behavior as regards spread of flame along the surface is usually of the most direct concern. Two methods of test designed to rate materials comparatively as to surface flame spread are currently in accepted use. In both of these, a controlled flame is applied to the test sample at a fixed point and the extent and rate of the resulting flame spread, if any, are measured. In one method,[13] materials are rated by an A, B, C, D classification defined arbitrarily in the test method, and in the other[14] they are given numerical ratings with the characteristics of red oak taken as a comparative standard.

Materials for Plastic Application. This designation refers to acoustical materials which are applied in a wet state by trowel or by spraying to form continuous unbroken surfaces of any desired thickness. The troweled materials, known as acoustical plasters, are furnished as a mixture of dry ingredients to which water is added on the job. Most plasters are composed of an aggregate of perlite or vermiculite and a binder which is usually gypsum. The voids between the particles of the aggregate provide the porosity required for sound absorption. In other types a foaming agent is used to create a porous structure. Acoustical plasters are normally applied to a brown coat of regular plaster as a base in new construction but may also be applied to existing solid surfaces of plaster, concrete, etc., either directly or after application of a bonding coat of asphalt emulsion. Application is generally in two or more coats to a thickness of ½ in., using essentially standard plastering methods, although spray methods are coming into greater use. It is usually recommended that the plaster be given a float finish rather than a trowel finish to avoid sealing the surface. Some plasters require stippling with a rice-straw brush to develop the required surface porosity. Perforating of the wet surface with a nail block is also recommended for most materials, principally as a means of increasing paintability rather than initial absorption. Since acoustical plasters in general depend on the application technique as well as on their formulation for their sound-absorptive properties, it is essential that manufacturers' instructions on both mixing and application be followed explicitly for the expected results. Plasters which are not perforated at the time of application depend entirely on surface porosity for sound absorption and therefore have limited paintability. The perforated plasters may be painted more heavily without loss of absorption. In any case, the manufacturer's specific recommendations on painting should be followed. Cleaning by wallpaper cleaner or vacuum brush is commonly recommended.

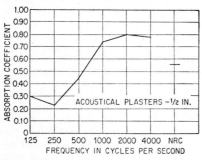

FIG. 18.13. Average absorption of ½-in. acoustical plasters. (*Compiled from data published by manufacturers.*)

The absorption coefficients averaged for 10 acoustical plasters, as published by the manufacturers,[15] are shown in Fig. 18.13. These tests include more than one type of plaster or finish for a single manufacturer, but are for ½-in. thickness throughout. The high values of absorption at 125 cps are probably due to the fact that the test panels are usually constructed to permit a considerable air space behind the material or its backing.

Acoustical plasters are used for noise-reduction purposes where extremely high sound absorption is not required and where architectural and structural requirements indicate the substitution of a sound-absorptive plaster for regular hard plaster.

Sprayed-on materials, except for acoustical plasters applied by spray methods, have mineral fiber, or a mixture of mineral and asbestos fiber, as their dry ingredient, which is mixed with a quick-setting binder and adhesive during the spraying process by means of a special gun. They differ from acoustical plasters principally in that they are considerably softer, can be built up to greater thicknesses, usually 1½ in. as a maximum, and can be applied directly to metal lath as well as to a variety of solid surfaces. Their loosely compacted fibrous structure affords extremely high sound absorption, particularly when applied to metal lath over an air space. Noise reduction coefficient values of 0.80 and higher have been published for ½- and ¾-in. thicknesses applied in this way. These materials are useful chiefly where the combined functions of high sound absorption and thermal insulation are needed. The latter property also renders these materials effective for fire protection of steel beams, joists, roof decks, and other structural members.

Special Acoustical Assemblies, Porous Materials, and Blankets. This group is intended to include materials and systems which cannot be conveniently classified under tiles or materials for plastic application. The most widely used single type of product in this group is that designated as Type IX by the Acoustical Materials Association, perforated metal pans with mineral fiber pads. As illustrated in Fig. 18.14,

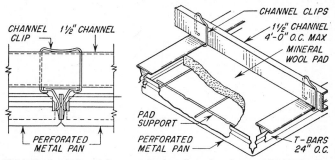

Fig. 18.14. Perforated metal pan and mineral-wool pad assembly (AMA Type IX).

this assembly consists of a 12-in. by 24-in. pan of perforated steel or aluminum, with upturned flanges which snap into special spring-steel T bars. The sound-absorptive element is a pad of mineral wool, usually 1¼ in. thick and wrapped in lightweight flameproofed paper to prevent sifting of small particles. The pad is placed in the pan during installation and is held away from direct contact with the pan by a spacer grid, the main purposes of which are to facilitate repainting and washing operations and to afford maximum sound absorption. The pan is given a high-quality baked-enamel finish which makes it particularly suitable to installations where frequent washing is necessary. The pans supplied by different manufacturers are perforated in a variety of patterns to provide various architectural and decorative effects. This system finds its widest application as a complete suspended acoustical ceiling of high sound-absorbing efficiency, which is easily removable and can be coordinated flexibly with lighting and air-conditioning facilities. Its principal use is in office areas, particularly in new buildings. The absorption coefficients averaged for seven products of this type are shown in Fig. 18.15. The air spaces used in the test mountings were of approximately 1-in. depth. Further tests have shown that deeper air spaces produce a large increase in the 125-cps coefficient, with comparatively small changes in the values at higher frequencies.

Several other varieties of metal surface suspended acoustical ceilings are available. One type consists of large sheets of corrugated perforated steel or aluminum which are self-supporting in one direction and supported by exposed metal members in the other direction. A lightweight blanket of glass wool is laid on top of the corrugated metal to provide sound absorption. In another type, a ribbed metal sheet having slit perforations is supported by an exposed metal suspension system on 2-ft spacing in both directions, and has a glass-wool blanket adhered to the back side during manufacture. A third variation utilizes 12-in.-square perforated pans with the flanges formed to fit special suspension members. All these types have high sound-absorptive efficiency, but the exact values will vary to some extent depending on the perforation pattern, the density and thickness of the absorbent element, and the air space behind it.

Another subgroup of special acoustical assemblies is listed by the Acoustical Materials Association as Type X, perforated asbestos board panels with mineral-fiber pads. This classification is better described as a method of acoustical construction than as an acoustical material or assembly. The construction normally consists of the erection of 2- by 2-in. or 2- by 4-in. wood studs or ceiling joists between which a blanket of mineral wool or glass wool is placed. The studs are cross-furred with secondary wood strips to which facing sheets of perforated asbestos-cement board are secured. Alternatively, an all-metal furring system may be used. The facing sheets are usually $\frac{3}{16}$ in. thick with $\frac{3}{16}$-in. perforations on $\frac{1}{2}$-in. centers. The absorptive element may

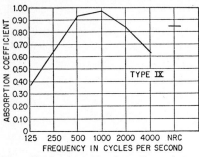

FIG. 18.15. Average absorption of perforated metal pan and mineral-fiber pad assembly. (*AMA Bulletin.*[16])

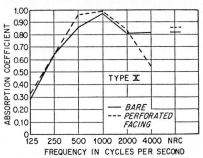

FIG. 18.16. Absorption of typical 2-in. mineral-fiber blanket on solid backing, with and without perforated facing. (*AMA Bulletin.*[16])

be any of a number of mineral- or glass-wool blankets of various thicknesses and densities, depending on the absorption-frequency characteristics desired. The chief function of the asbestos-cement board is to provide a rigid, durable, acoustically transparent surface of good appearance, which is also incombustible and unaffected by extreme moisture conditions. Where various of these requirements are unimportant, other facings such as perforated hardboard, metal lath, or even poultry wire are sometimes used. The latter two facings usually have the effect in comparison with perforated facings of increasing the absorption above 2,000 cps and decreasing the values at 500 and 1,000 cps.

The absorption coefficients of a typical assembly using a 2-in.-thick blanket on a solid backing, with and without a perforated asbestos-cement board facing,[16] are shown in Fig. 18.16. As pointed out previously, the low-frequency absorption is governed chiefly by the thickness of the blanket and the depth of the air space behind it. Low frequency absorption also increases up to a certain point with increasing airflow resistivity of the blanket material. This property in turn increases with compaction of the fiber structure and with increasing fineness of the fiber. For a given fiber fineness the compaction will be indicated by the density of the blanket. However, since blankets of different manufacture may have widely different fiber fineness, their density alone furnishes no basis of comparison of their sound absorptive properties. Increasing the airflow resistivity of a blanket tends to reduce the high-frequency absorption before the low-frequency absorption reaches its maximum value. The net result is to obtain a more uniform absorption-frequency characteristic with decreased absorption at the high frequencies.

Acoustical Roof Decks. Acoustical materials may be used as an integral part of a roof structure in one-story buildings such as industrial plants, schools, and certain types of residential construction, where the under side of the roof deck forms the exposed ceiling surface of the room below.   The three most common types of acoustical roof deck are (1) form board for a poured gypsum deck, (2) perforated-steel roof-deck panel with absorbent element, and (3) structural insulating roof slabs.

Acoustical form boards for poured gypsum decks are essentially acoustical tiles in special sizes and thicknesses which are supported by steel subpurlins on 24- to 32-in. spacings in place of the usual nonacoustical form boards.   The gypsum roof deck is poured onto the acoustical form to a thickness of 2 to 3 in.   The sound absorption of currently available products of this type ranges from 0.55 to 0.70 in noise reduction coefficient.

The second type of acoustical roof deck listed above consists of a standard ribbed or hollow steel roof-deck panel which is modified by having the lower surface perforated and a mineral-wool absorptive element laid over the perforated surface, with a wire spacer grid inserted.   One type of structure is illustrated in Fig. 18.17.   Roof insulation and built-up roofing are installed over the steel deck in the standard manner. Sound absorption coefficients range from 0.65 to 0.85 noise reduction coefficient, depending on the depth of air space available in the particular structure used and on the type of absorbent element.

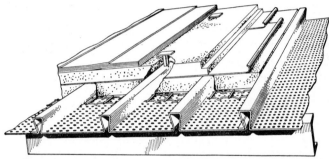

Fig. 18.17. Sound-absorptive steel roof-deck assembly.   (*Courtesy of Detroit Steel Products Co.*)

Structural insulating roof slabs, as the name implies, are large sheets of heat-insulating material sufficiently thick and rigid that they can be used alone as a complete roof deck with the usual roofing applied directly to the top side.   Some of these materials are formed of wood excelsior pressed with a cement binder into a rigid slab, and are sufficiently porous to provide effective sound absorption when their lower surface is left exposed.   Sound absorption coefficients in thicknesses up to 3 in., as normally used for a roof slab, range from 0.70 to 0.85 in noise reduction coefficient.

Suspended Absorbers.[17]   This is the general name given to a class of acoustical materials and structures which are suspended as individual units from the ceiling of a room instead of being erected as a continuous ceiling or wall surface.   They commonly take the form either of flat sheets or "baffles" of absorptive material hung vertically in continuous rows, or of hollow boxlike units suspended singly.   Either type has its principal application in areas where a directly applied or suspended over-all ceiling treatment of the conventional type is impractical for one reason or another, such as the obstruction of piping, ductwork, etc.

The sound absorptivity of suspended absorbers is usually stated as the number of sabins of absorption furnished by each one.   This figure increases with the spacing of the absorbers, and approaches a constant value at wide spacings.   As the spacing increases, however, the total number of absorbers which can be installed in a given area decreases correspondingly, and the over-all effect of the absorbers in that area likewise decreases.   The effectiveness of absorbers suspended below a given ceiling area in comparison with over-all treatment on the same area can be determined by dividing the number of sabins furnished by each absorber by the area of ceiling taken up by each absorber.   The resulting "equivalent-ceiling absorption coefficient" of the absorbers is a measure of their effectiveness in the area and is directly comparable with the coefficient of a continuous ceiling treatment in the same area.

Baffles.   A typical suspended absorber of the baffle type now on the market consists of a mineral fiber board 2 ft by 4 ft by 1½ in. thick, covered with a thin impervious washable plastic membrane which is light enough to transmit sound waves readily over most of the frequency range.   The baffles are suspended in continuous rows from steel wires or cables stretched between walls or ceiling beams.   The spacing varies from 2 to 6 ft, and the rows may run in either one or two directions.   The sound-absorption characteristics as a function of spacing are shown in Fig. 18.18, where the sabins per baffle and the equivalent ceiling absorption coefficient are plotted against the spacing of continuous rows of 2- by 4-ft baffles hung in one direction with the long dimension horizontal.   The absorption figures are noise reduction coefficient values.   The absorption vs. frequency characteristics of the baffles for two spacings are shown in Fig. 18.19.

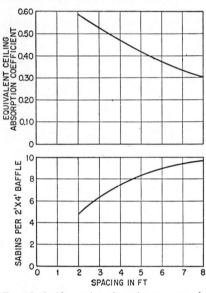

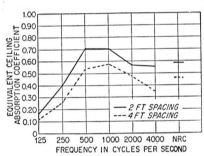

FIG. 18.18. Absorption of continuous rows of 2- by 4-ft baffle-type suspended absorber as a function of spacing. Absorption is averaged from 250 to 2,000 cps. (*Courtesy of Owens-Corning Fiberglas Corp.*)

FIG. 18.19. Absorption vs. frequency characteristics of 2- by 4-ft baffle-type suspended absorber for two spacings. (*Courtesy of Owens-Corning Fiberglas Corp.*)

Unit Absorbers.   Figure 18.20 gives data for one type of suspended unit absorber which is commercially available.   These consist of hollow boxes of perforated metal with a lining of sound absorptive material which are suspended singly at any desired spacing.   The absorption vs. frequency characteristics of these units in terms of sabins per absorber and equivalent ceiling absorption coefficient are shown as a function of frequency.   These data were determined with the absorbers suspended on 4-ft spacing in both directions.   Their efficiency in sabins per absorber remains constant for wider spacings, but the equivalent ceiling absorption coefficient drops as the ceiling area per absorber increases.   With closer spacings the efficiency in sabins per absorber decreases somewhat and the equivalent ceiling absorption coefficient increases, but not in proportion to the number of absorbers in a given area.

Another type of absorber is manufactured in the form of a hollow double cone of 14 in. diameter formed of low-density molded wood pulp.[18]   Its absorption characteristics as a function of frequency and spacing are shown in Figs. 18.21 and 18.22.   Since these absorbers are of considerably smaller size than the foregoing type, the absorption furnished by each one is proportionally less.

Absorbent Lined Barriers and Enclosures.   In many cases, particularly in large industrial areas, the transmission of noise in a given direction or from a specific noise source is effectively blocked by erecting a barrier or part-height partition in the path of the directly transmitted sound.   Any person on the same side of the barrier as the

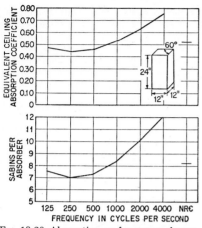

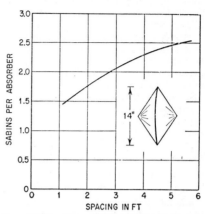

FIG. 18.20. Absorption vs. frequency characteristic of illustrated suspended unit absorber on 4-ft spacing in square array. (*Courtesy of Bolt, Beranek, and Newman.*)

FIG. 18.21. Absorption of illustrated suspended unit absorber as a function of spacing. Absorption is averaged from 250 to 2,000 cps. (*Courtesy of Johns-Manville Research Center.*)

noise source, such as the operator of the noisy machine in question, will receive more instead of less noise as a result of erecting the barrier, because of reflection from it. This is shown in Fig. 18.23. The source side of the barrier should obviously be covered with as efficient a sound-absorptive surface as possible. Baffles or barriers are sometimes mistakenly used in the arrangement shown in Fig. 18.23 in an effort to reduce the noise heard by a person stationed on the same side of the barrier as the machine. It must be remembered that when a new surface is erected in a comparatively open space it will produce reflection of sound waves which would otherwise have con-

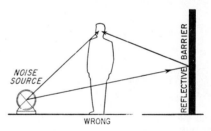

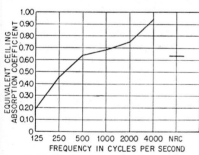

FIG. 18.22. Absorption vs. frequency characteristic of suspended unit absorber shown in Fig. 18.20. Spacing is 20 in. in square array. (*Courtesy of Johns-Manville Research Center.*)

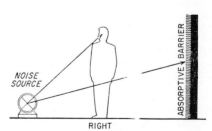

FIG. 18.23. Use of absorptive treatment on the source side of a noise barrier.

tinued to travel outward toward more distant surfaces. If this reflection reaches the ear it will add to the level of the noise which arrives at the ear directly from the source. The best that can be done is to keep the reflected component to a minimum by using highly absorptive materials on the new surfaces. The same principle holds in the construction of partial enclosures such as open-sided booths around noisy machines. These effectively block off noise from persons outside the enclosure, but the level inside is never less than before.

Close-fitting housings around noise sources, with no operator inside, should also be lined with absorptive material, but for a somewhat different reason. In this case, the confinement of sound by a reflective interior surface would greatly increase the sound pressure level inside the enclosure and would therefore require a heavier structure to reduce the noise to the desired level outside.

Special structural panels having a perforated metal facing backed by mineral-wool absorptive element on one or both sides are available from several manufacturers in modular unit sizes for use in constructing absorbent lined partitions, shields, booths, etc. Acoustical tiles, boards, or blankets of the various types described heretofore may also be used as linings against backing surfaces of gypsum board, plywood, or sheet metal in constructing shields and enclosures to specified dimensions.

CALCULATION OF NOISE REDUCTION

Multiple Reflection in a Closed Room.[19] The progress of a sound wave in a closed room may be illustrated schematically by the diagrams of Fig. 18.24. These figures represent a horizontal section of a room 24 by 40 ft having plane sound reflecting walls; a sound source is located at S. The solid circle represents the "front" of a single sound wave, and the dotted arrowed lines indicate the directions in which it is traveling. Figure 18.24a shows the wave front $\frac{1}{200}$ sec after it has left the source S and shows that no reflections from the walls have yet taken place. Figure 18.24b shows

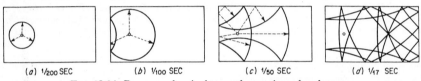

    (a) $\frac{1}{200}$ SEC   (b) $\frac{1}{100}$ SEC   (c) $\frac{1}{50}$ SEC   (d) $\frac{1}{17}$ SEC

FIG. 18.24. Progress of a single sound wave in a closed room.

the wave front $\frac{1}{100}$ sec after the start of the wave. The wave front has now traveled twice as far as in the first figure, and part of it is being reflected from the nearest end wall. In Fig. 18.24c a total time interval of $\frac{1}{50}$ sec has elapsed since the sound has left the source. Reflections from the side walls, and also double reflections from the end and side walls, are taking place, as shown by the arrows. In Fig. 18.24d about $\frac{1}{17}$ sec after the start of the wave, the reflection pattern is quite complicated. The original wave front, which started out as a circle, is now broken up into a large number of segments, all traveling in different directions through the room. In addition to the segments shown in this figure there would also be segments of the original wave front which had been reflected by the floor and ceiling, but which cannot be shown on a horizontal section.

It is seen that almost immediately every part of the room is filled with reflected sound waves traveling in many different directions. There are two effects of this multiple reflection which have a direct bearing on noise control.

Tne first effect is the increase in sound pressure caused by reflections. If a continuous sound is made, a listener in any part of the room will not only receive the sound waves which come directly to his ear from the sound source but will also hear all the reflected waves. Thus the combined pressure of the direct and reflected sound at his ear will be greater than that of the direct sound alone.

If the absorption coefficient of the interior surfaces is low, as in a room finished entirely in hard plaster, concrete, and glass, which have coefficients of less than 5 per cent, the reflected sound waves will lose very little energy at each reflection and will build up the total sound pressure to a value far above that of the direct sound alone.

The second effect of multiple reflections is reverberation. From Fig. 18.24 it is apparent that, while the sound source is operating, the room becomes filled with reflected sound waves. If the source is stopped at any given moment, these reflected waves will not simply cease to exist at that moment but instead will continue to travel back and forth between the room surfaces. At each successive reflection thereafter, each wave will lose a fraction of its energy by absorption, and the sound pressure in the room will gradually diminish. If a listener is in the room, the reflected waves strike his ear in such rapid succession that he usually does not hear them as distinct repetitions of the original sound. Instead, he hears the original sound being drawn out or prolonged after the source is stopped, and steadily dying out until it becomes inaudible. This prolongation of sound is called *reverberation*.

If all the interior surfaces of a room are of materials with low absorption coefficients, such as plaster, concrete, or glass, the sound pressure will diminish only slightly at each reflection, and the total sound pressure level in the room will decrease at a slow rate.

These two effects of multiple reflection are illustrated by the hypothetical example shown in Fig. 18.25, which represents the loudness of reflected sound heard by an observer in the room shown in Fig. 18.24 when a single source is started and stopped. It is assumed that the room is otherwise very quiet and that the acoustic power of the source is constant and is arbitrarily chosen so as to produce the indicated loudness.

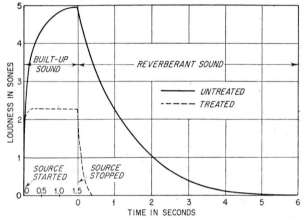

Fig. 18.25. Loudness of built-up and reverberant sound before and after acoustical treatment of a highly reflective room.

The solid line, drawn for the case of highly reflective interior surfaces having an average absorption coefficient of 0.03, shows the loudness building up to a value of 5 sones immediately after the source is started and dying out slowly as reverberation after the source is stopped. The dotted line shows the effect of introducing sufficient acoustical treatment into the room to increase the average absorption coefficient of the room surfaces to 0.30. The built-up sound reaches a loudness of only 2.3 sones and dies out almost immediately after the source is stopped. Thus, in general, reducing the sound pressure of reflected waves by absorption has the two basic effects of (1) lowering the loudness to which the sound builds up while the source is producing acoustic energy, and (2) increasing the rate at which the reverberant sound dies out after the source is stopped.

Level of Direct Sound. When a sound field is set up in a closed room by a single steady omnidirectional source, the total sound pressure level at any given point in the room may be considered to be the logarithmic sum of the pressure level of the sound which travels directly from the source, and the pressure level of the reverberant sound due to all the sound waves which arrive at the same point after one or more reflections from the room surfaces. The pressure level of the direct sound depends only on the power of the source and its distance from the point of observation. It is not affected by any characteristics of the room whatever, assuming there are no large obstructions in or near the path of direct sound, and it therefore has the same value at a given distance that it would have in the open air with the room boundaries entirely removed. According to Eq. (2.22a) the sound pressure level of the direct sound L_d for a non-directional source is*

$$L_d = 10 \log_{10} W - 20 \log_{10} r + 119.4 \qquad \text{db} \qquad (18.1)$$
$$ = L_w - 20 \log_{10} r - 0.6 \qquad \text{db}$$

where W is the acoustic power of the source in watts, L_w is the power level of the source in db re 10^{-12} watt, and r is the distance from the source in feet.

If the distance r from the source is expressed in meters, Eq. (18.1) becomes

$$L_d = L_w - 20 \log_{10} r - 10.9 \qquad \text{db} \qquad (18.1a)$$

From the above equations it can be shown that the sound pressure level decreases 6 db with each doubling of distance from the source, or 20 db with each 10-fold increase in distance (see Chap. 2). For a directional noise source, the level at a distance r should be obtained from Eq. (2.22).

Level of Reflected Sound. The sound pressure level of the reflected sound, due to the accumulation of multiple reflections from a steady sustained source of acoustical power, will be nearly uniform throughout a room if it is of fairly regular proportions (i.e., where the longest floor dimension is not more than about five times the ceiling height) and if the source contains no strong discrete frequency components. In this case the steady-state sound pressure of the reflected sound will be determined by the point at which the rate of energy loss by absorption at the room surfaces equals the rate at which sound energy is supplied by the source. Thus the level will vary inversely with the total sound absorption in the room. This total absorption is represented by the symbol a and is obtained by multiplying the area of each room surface by its absorption coefficient, taking the sum of these products, and adding the absorption supplied by furnishings, equipment, and persons in the room. Thus

$$a = \Sigma \alpha_i S_i = \alpha S \qquad (18.2)$$

The unit of absorption is the *sabin* ("square-foot unit") in the English system of units. One sabin is defined as the equivalent of 1 sq ft of perfectly absorptive surface. For example, a surface of 100 sq ft having a coefficient of 0.65 has an absorption of 65 sabins. In countries employing the metric system, the corresponding unit is the *square meter* of absorption. From the total absorption in a room, the "average absorption coefficient" α is calculated by dividing the total absorption a by the total interior room-surface area S.

For a source of acoustic power W, the average sound pressure level of reflected sound L_r in a room of fairly regular proportions depends only on the total absorption a and not on the distance from the source. If a is expressed in sabins

$$L_r = 10 \log_{10} W - 10 \log_{10} a + 136.4 \qquad \text{db} \qquad (18.3)$$
$$ = L_w - 10 \log_{10} a + 16.4 \qquad \text{db}$$

where L_w is the power level re 10^{-12} watt.

If the total absorption is expressed in square meters, then the formula corresponding to Eq. (18.3) is

$$L_r = 10 \log_{10} W - 10 \log_{10} a + 126.1 \qquad \text{db} \qquad (18.3a)$$
$$ = L_w - 10 \log_{10} a + 6.1 \qquad \text{db}$$

It should be emphasized that Eq. (18.3) is derived on the assumption of the diffuse distribution of sound in the room, a condition that usually obtains only when the average absorption coefficient α is small, when there are nonuniformities at the boundary in absorption or geometrical configuration, and when many frequencies are present.

The relation of the reflected sound pressure level L_r to the acoustic power of the source W and the room absorption a is shown graphically in Fig. 18.26.

* A characteristic impedance of 40.8 rayls is assumed in the formulas given in this chapter.

Level of Direct-plus-Reflected Sound. The total sound pressure level $L_d + L_r$, being the logarithmic sum * of the levels of the direct and reflected sound, will be only slightly higher than the level of the larger component, by an amount never exceeding 3 db. An example of the relation of the total sound pressure level to distance from the source and to room absorption is shown by the curves of Fig. 18.27, which is drawn for the case of a single source having a power of 0.0115 watt, i.e., a power level of 100.6 dbp. This value, which is chosen simply for convenience, produces a sound pressure level of the direct sound of 100 db at a distance of 1 ft, as may be noted by substitution in Eq. (18.1). For a source of any other acoustic power W, the values of sound pressure level read from the curves are simply raised or lowered by $10 \log (W/0.0115)$ db. These curves indicate that at a point very close to the source the direct sound will furnish the largest component of the total level, and on moving away from the source the level

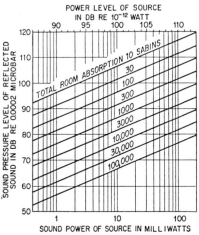

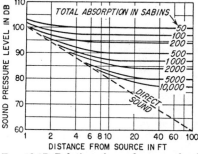

FIG. 18.26. Relation of pressure level of reflected sound in a reverberant room to acoustic power of source and room absorption. (*After R. W. Young.*)

FIG. 18.27. Relation of sound pressure level of a diffuse sound field in a regularly proportioned room due to a single omnidirectional source of 0.0115 watt acoustic power to distance from the source in a room having a total absorption a.

will drop off. If the sound in the room is essentially diffuse, at a certain distance a point will be reached where the direct sound is much less than the reflected sound, and at all distances beyond this point the total level will be practically equal to the reflected level alone and will therefore remain essentially constant. The distance in feet from the source at which this takes place depends only on the absorption in the room according to the approximate relation $D = 0.5 \sqrt{a}$. As the room absorption increases, the rate of drop-off of the total level approaches that of the direct sound alone, as indicated by the dotted line.

Relation of Reflected Sound Pressure Level to Room Absorption. According to Eq. (18.3) the reflected sound level due to a source of given acoustic power will decrease as the logarithm of the room absorption increases. If two rooms have absorptions of a_1 and a_2 and if the sound in the room is diffuse, then the difference in reflected level set up in the two rooms by the same source will be approximately

$$\text{Reduction} = 10 \log_{10} \frac{a_2}{a_1} \quad \text{db} \quad (18.4)$$

This relationship is shown graphically in Fig. 18.28. Since from Eq. (18.2) the absorption depends directly on the total surface area S, the above equation indicates

---

* The logarithmic sum L in decibels of two quantities L_1 and L_2, also in decibels, is

$$L = 10 \log \left(\log^{-1} \frac{L_1}{10} + \log^{-1} \frac{L_2}{10} \right) \quad \text{db}$$

The sum also may be obtained graphically by the use of Fig. 2.17.

that, if two rooms are surfaced with materials having the same average absorption coefficient α, a given source will set up a higher level of reflected sound in the smaller room. If one room has four times the surface area of the other, for instance, the reflected level will be 6 db lower. The practical point here is that the noise level from a single machine can be reduced to some extent simply by moving it into a larger room of the same average absorption coefficient.

Equation (18.4) also applies to the more typical case where the room absorption is increased by adding absorptive material to the room surfaces. In this case, the surface area S remains the same, but the *average* absorption coefficient α is increased. Thus Eq. (18.4) indicates the reduction in level of reflected sound that may be expected when the total absorption in a room is increased from a_1 to a_2. Equation (18.4) also may be written, for this case, as

$$\text{Reduction} = 10 \log_{10} \frac{\alpha_2}{\alpha_1} \quad \text{db} \qquad (18.5)$$

The amount of reduction depends quite critically on the total absorption before treatment a_1, especially when this total is very low. This means that the more reflective the room before treatment, the larger the reduction obtainable with a given amount of treatment. Very large reductions may be obtained in a relatively bare room by covering all room surfaces, including the floor, with material having a coefficient of over 0.90.* Reduction of reflected sound to this extent, however, is generally

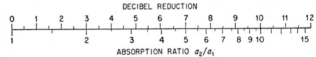

FIG. 18.28. Reduction in sound pressure level of reflected sound in a regularly proportioned room, in which diffuse conditions prevail, due to increasing the total absorption from a_1 to a_2.

required only in special acoustical test rooms. For most noise reduction purposes, the covering of all wall and ceiling surfaces is the maximum practical amount of treatment, in which case an average coefficient α_2 of 0.80 is about the highest obtainable; and for ceiling coverage only, the maximum value of α_2 is about 0.40.

As an example, consider an office space 20 by 50 ft by 10 ft high, having the conventional sound-reflective interior surfaces and the usual number of desks, furnishings, and occupants. We shall calculate the effect of acoustical treatment of the ceiling on the reflected sound level. The first step is to determine the absorption a_1 of the room before treatment, as follows, using the data of Table 18.1:

Floor, linoleum,	1,000 sq ft at 0.03 =	30 sabins
Ceiling, plaster,	1,000 sq ft at 0.03 =	30 sabins
Walls, plaster and glass,	1,400 sq ft at 0.03 =	42 sabins
Total surface S =	3,400 sq ft	
Desks, 15 at 1.0 sabins each		= 15 sabins
Occupants, seated, 15 at 4.0 sabins each		= 60 sabins
Miscellaneous		= 5 sabins
Total absorption before treatment a_1		= 182 sabins

If the entire ceiling area is treated with a material having an absorption coefficient of 0.70, covering a plaster surface having a coefficient of 0.03, the net added coefficient of the treatment will be 0.70 − 0.03 = 0.67. The absorption added to the room therefore will be 1,000 sq ft at 0.67 = 670 sabins. The above figures then become

Total absorption after treatment a_2 = 182 + 670 = 852 sabins

From Eq. (18.4), the reduction in reflected sound pressure level effected by the ceil-

* Note that, in the derivation of Eq. (18.4) (or in similar alternate expressions), diffuse conditions are assumed. Such will not be the case for very large values of α, and the formula may not apply.

ing treatment is approximately

$$\text{Reduction} = 10 \log \frac{a_2}{a_1} = 10 \log \frac{852}{182} = 6.7 \text{ db}$$

Relation of Total Sound Level to Room Absorption. Since the level of combined direct and reflected sound depends on both the room absorption and the distance from the source, the reduction in total level due to adding absorption will likewise depend both on the increase in absorption and on the distance from the source. As shown in Fig. 18.27, the reduction in total level at points remote from the source will be the same as the reduction in reflected level as given by Eqs. (18.4) or (18.5). At closer distances from the source, the direct sound will predominate, and the reduction in total level will become smaller. For example, if the room absorption a is increased from 50 to 500, as would result from acoustically treating the ceiling of a room approximately 15 ft by 20 ft by 13 ft high, the total level will be reduced 10 db at all distances more than about 10 ft from the source. At closer distances the reduction will diminish to 7 db at 3 ft and 3 db at 1 ft. In a larger room, in which a is increased from 500 to 5,000, the reduction in total level will again be 10 db, but only at distances greater than about 30 ft from the source, diminishing to 3 db at 3 ft. As a general rule, therefore, the greater the absorption of a room the greater is the distance from the source at which a given increase in absorption will be fully effective in reducing the total sound level. This distance is given approximately by

$$D = \frac{\sqrt{a_2}}{2}$$

where a_2 is the total room absorption after the increase.

Multiple Noise Sources. If a number of noise sources are present in a room instead of the single source considered heretofore, the relationships of direct, reflected, and total sound pressure levels are changed to some extent. If *it is assumed* as before *that the room is of fairly regular proportions and that essentially diffuse conditions prevail,* the pressure level of the reflected sound will still be uniform throughout the room and will have the value given by Eq. (18.3) except that W is the sum of the power outputs of all the noise sources. Thus, for example, the reflected sound pressure level due to four typewriters in a room is 6 db higher than the reflected level due to one typewriter.

The reduction in reflected sound pressure level due to increasing the room absorption will be the same for any number of equal or unequal sources as it is for a single source as given by Eqs. (18.4) or (18.5).

The level of combined direct and reflected sound from unequal sources at positions where the direct sound from one or more sources is not negligible cannot be computed unless the power and distance of each source are known. The direct sound from all the sources combined, at a given point of observation, is most conveniently determined, if their separate powers and distances are known, by calculating the sound pressure level of each from Eq. (18.1) and combining the levels according to Fig. 2.17. This level is then combined to the reflected level due to all the sources, as obtained from Eq. (18.3) to give the total level of the direct plus reflected sound. It is a more common situation, however, for multiple sources to be essentially equal in power output, in which case the relationships of direct, reflected, and total sound level to distance and room absorption can be determined more simply and without knowing the power of each source. This is illustrated by the following example:

Suppose there are six noise sources each having a power of 0.0115 watt which are at respective distances from the point of observation of 5, 7, 8, 10, 12, and 15 ft. Calculate the pressure level of combined direct and reflected sound (1) for a room absorption of 100 sabins and (2) with the absorption increased to 1,000 sabins. From Eq. (18.1) (or from Fig. 18.27, which is drawn for a single source having this power) the direct sound level from each source is

Distance, ft	5	7	8	10	12	15
Direct level, db	86	83	82	80	78	76

The total direct level is the logarithmic sum of the individual direct levels and is 89.8 db.

According to Eq. (18.3), the reflected level for any given room absorption with six equal sources instead of one will be raised by $10 \log_{10} 6 = 7.8$ db. For an absorption of 100, therefore, the reflected level due to six sources of 0.0115 watt each is equal to 104.8 db. The combined direct and reflected level at the specified point of observation will be 89.8 db added logarithmically to 104.8 db, which is 104.9 db, according to Fig. 2.17.

With the absorption a increased from 100 to 1,000, or 10 times, the reflected level according to Eq. (18.4) is reduced 10 db to 94.8 db.

It must be noted that the power of 0.0115 watt (i.e., a power level of 100.6 dbp) for each source is arbitrarily chosen. For any other power levels all sound pressure levels would be raised or lowered accordingly, and the reduction of 8.9 db in combined level due to acoustical treatment would remain the same. It must also be remembered that the reduction of 8.9 db takes place only at the particular position chosen. At a point closer to any one of the sources the reduction would be less, and at points more distant than 5 ft from the nearest source the reduction would be greater and would approach 10 db, the reduction in reflected level, as a limit. Generally speaking, the sources nearest to the point of observation, rather than the more distant ones, largely govern the level of direct sound in relation to reflected sound, and determine how closely the reduction in combined level at that point approaches the reduction in reflected level.

Extended Floor and Ceiling—Single Source.[20] In all the discussion heretofore *it has been assumed that the pressure level of the generally reflected sound is essentially uniform throughout the room*, both before and after treatment. This is found experimentally to be approximately true when the noise in the room is essentially random in character and when neither of the floor dimensions is more than about five times the ceiling height. It has been observed that in rooms having floor dimensions very large in comparison with the ceiling height the reflected level does not remain uniform but drops off continuously with increasing distance from the source clear to the limits of the room. Noise level readings made in such rooms both before and after ceiling treatment correspond closely to the values that would be expected if the walls were nonexistent and multiple reflection took place only between the floor and ceiling. The problem has not yet been studied sufficiently to determine just how large the floor dimensions must be in relation to ceiling height for wall reflections to become negligible, but indications are that the ratio is of the order of five to ten times.

A series of calculations based on geometrical analysis of multiple reflection between infinitely extended floor and ceiling surfaces, with no wall reflection, has been made to indicate approximately the behavior of noise and the effect of acoustical treatment in very large, comparatively low-ceilinged rooms. Some further simplifying assumptions have been made which should not cause appreciable errors, namely:

1. The absorption coefficient of the floor is assumed constant at 0.02, which is a typical value for hard flooring materials.
2. The noise source and the observer's ear are both midway between the floor and ceiling. This is approximately true in practice for ceiling heights up to about 15 ft.
3. The absorption coefficients of the floor and ceiling are independent of the angle of incidence of the sound. This is not true, but the calculations involve a summation over many angles which minimize errors inherent in this assumption.

As in the previous example, a single noise source is assumed, which emits steady continuous noise at an acoustic power of 0.0115 watt which produces a sound pressure level of 100 db at 1 ft from a point source. Figure 18.29 shows the calculated levels of direct and reflected noise under the conditions assumed above for a ceiling height cf 10 ft and for ceiling absorption coefficients of 0.02, 0.50, and 1.00. These three values would represent, respectively, an untreated ceiling of hard material, a low-efficiency acoustical treatment, and 100 per cent efficient treatment. In the latter case, there will of course be no ceiling reflection and therefore no multiple reflection

The reflected noise for this case is due simply to the single reflection from the floor, which at considerable distances from the source becomes essentially equal to the directly transmitted noise.

The curves of reflected pressure level differ from those in Fig. 18.27 for the case of a regularly proportioned room in the following ways: First, the sound pressure level of the reflected sound does not remain constant regardless of distance from the source but starts to drop off at a distance of about half the ceiling height. For a highly reflective ceiling, the final slope of the curve with respect to distance is essentially that of a cylindrical wave front, namely, 10 db per 10-fold increase in distance. Second, the reflected noise for the highly reflective ceiling condition is always below the direct noise at all distances from the source of less than about six-tenths of the ceiling height, which for a 10-ft ceiling is 6 ft. For the regularly proportioned room with all surfaces reflective, however, it is quite possible for the reflected sound to exceed the direct sound at only 1 ft from the source, as shown by the top curve of Fig. 18.27. Third, acoustical treatment does not lower the reflected level by a fixed amount

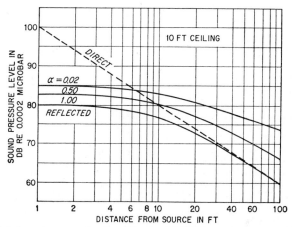

Fig. 18.29. Relation of pressure levels of direct and reflected sound to distance from source and absorption coefficient α of 10-ft ceiling, assuming negligible wall reflection, due to single source of 0.0115 watt acoustic power. Coefficient of floor taken as 0.02.

dependent only on the change in absorption, as given in Eq. (18.4), but the reduction increases continuously with distance from the source. For the 10-ft ceiling height shown in Fig. 18.29 the reduction in reflected level due to raising the ceiling coefficient from 0.02 to 1.00 ranges from about 5 db at 1 ft from the source to about 14 db at 100 ft, with larger reductions at greater distances. For intermediate ceiling coefficients, the reductions appear to be closely proportional to the coefficient at all distances.

Figure 18.29 may be used for any other ceiling height simply by diagonally shifting the group of curves of reflected level parallel to the line representing direct level, so that the horizontal component of the shift equals the change in ceiling height. For an increased height, the shift would be to the right. For a source of different output, the vertical scale may be shifted correspondingly, as before.

Since total levels are of more practical concern than reflected or direct levels alone, these are shown in Fig. 18.30 for a ceiling height of 10 ft. In the case of total levels, the variation in the effect of acoustical ceiling treatment with distance from the source is even more marked. At 3 ft, the reduction due to 100 per cent efficient treatment on a 10-ft ceiling is only 1 db, but it increases up to about 12 db at 100 ft.

It will be noted that the total level for 100 per cent ceiling absorption remains 3 db higher than the direct level at considerable distances from the source. This is due to the single floor reflection mentioned previously. The curves for total level may be shifted for different ceiling heights in the same manner as for Fig. 18.29.

Extended Floor and Ceiling—Multiple Sources. For the case of multiple noise sources in a large low-ceilinged room, the direct, reflected, and total noise levels at a given point depend on the output of each source, the distance of the point of observation from each source, the ceiling height, and the ceiling absorption coefficient. The levels for any set of conditions involving multiple sources may be calculated by combining the levels for a single source given in Figs. 18.29 and 18.30, after shifting these curves as necessary for different ceiling heights and source outputs.

A fairly typical situation involving multiple sources is that of a large bank of machines spaced fairly uniformly and having essentially similar noise-output characteristics, such as a spinning or weave room or a screw-machine department. Some calculations that have been made for an idealized case of this type are shown in Fig. 18.31. It is assumed that the point of observation is at the exact center of a bank of 100 machines spaced equally in both directions and each having a power level of 100.6 dbp, i.e., producing a steady noise output of 100 db at 1 ft, as in the previous

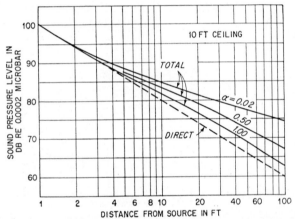

Fig. 18.30. Relation of pressure levels of direct and total sound to absorption coefficient α of 10-ft ceiling and distance from source, assuming same conditions as for Fig. 18.29.

examples. The observation point is equidistant from the four center machines of the bank, so that its distance from each of them is 0.707 times the machine spacing. The levels shown are of the combined direct and reflected sound from the entire bank of machines for a reflective and a totally absorptive ceiling.

Figure 18.31 shows that, as would obviously be expected, the levels due to multiple sources are higher than for a single source for the same distance from the nearest source, but it also shows that the reduction due to treatment is considerably greater. For instance, the reduction at the center of the bank of machines for 10-ft spacing and 10-ft ceiling height is 5.6 db as against only 2 db for a single machine at the same distance. Figure 18.31 also illustrates very clearly the advantages to be gained by spacing machines as widely as possible, both in lowering the levels, with or without ceiling treatment, and in increasing the effectiveness of ceiling treatment.

Relation of Noise Reduction to Frequency. Frequency has an effect in determining noise reduction with acoustical treatment. Office, industrial, and home noise in general covers a wide range of frequencies and specific noises may differ greatly in the distribution of their energy with respect to frequency. It has also been pointed out that acoustical materials vary in absorptive efficiency over the frequency range. It follows, therefore, that the over-all reduction of a typical broad-band noise by acoustical treatment will depend on both the frequency spectrum of the original noise and the absorption frequency characteristic of the acoustical material, and that both of these must be known in order to calculate the over-all reduction.

The energy distribution of noise within buildings has been measured in an extensive survey.[21] The results show that, in general, the spectra of reflected sound are very similar if a number of noise sources are present, as would be the case in a typical business location: typewriters and other office equipment, voices, footsteps, noise transmitted to the office from the outside, etc. The shape of this spectrum is shown in Fig. 18.32. The over-all reading on a sound-level meter which corresponds to the spectrum, using the A weighting network, shown is 50 db. In general, a higher noise level will result in the curve's position being shifted up or down, but the shape of the spectral distribution will remain approximately the same. The data of Fig. 18.32, which is given in terms of sound pressure spectrum level, can be converted to corresponding spectra in terms of octave, half-octave, or third-octave values by the use of Fig. 2.14.

In all the foregoing formulas and examples for computing noise reduction, it has been tacitly assumed that only a single frequency or a narrow frequency band within which both the noise energy distribution and the absorption coefficient are essentially

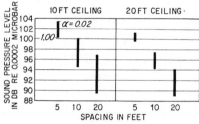

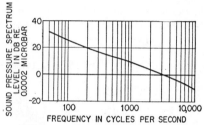

Fig. 18.31. Pressure level of combined direct and reflected sound in center of bank of 100 sources as related to spacing of sources, ceiling height, and ceiling coefficient α. Each source has acoustic power of 0.0115 watt. Floor coefficient taken as 0.02. Wall reflection assumed negligible.

Fig. 18.32. Average-room noise spectrum. (*Hoth.*[21])

uniform is being considered. In practice, these requirements are met with sufficient accuracy by considering octave wide bands of the noise together with the published absorption coefficients which are listed at octave intervals. The procedure for calculating over-all reduction of pressure level of reflected sound is as follows:

1. Determine by measurement (or best possible estimate) the sound pressure level in each octave band of the reflected noise before treatment.
2. Determine the over-all reflected pressure level before treatment by measurement or by adding logarithmically the octave-band levels.
3. Calculate from Eq. (18.4) the reduction in level of the reflected sound for each octave band using the value of absorption coefficient published for the single frequency within that band. For the commonly used scale of divisions in commercial octave-band frequency analyzers, the corresponding coefficient frequencies are as follows:

For Octave-band Frequencies	Use Coefficient at Frequency
Below 150 cps	125 cps
150–300	250
300–600	500
600–1,200	1,000
1,200–2,400	2,000
2,400–4,800	4,000
Above 4,800	4,000

4. Add logarithmically the reduced values of reflected-sound level in each octave band to obtain the over-all reflected level after treatment.
5. The reduction in over-all reflected level is the difference between the over-all reflected-sound levels before and after treatment, as calculated by (2) and (4), respectively.

To illustrate these steps, assume that the reflected level of noise in an untreated room is 80 db in all octave bands, a frequency distribution which is fairly typical of many types of noise. Suppose that the room is treated with an acoustical material 1 in. thick applied directly to existing surfaces. Representative coefficients of such a material and mounting are as follows:

Frequency, cps..................	125	250	500	1,000	2,000	4,000	NRC
Absorption coefficient..........	0.20	0.40	0.85	0.90	0.80	0.70	0.75

If it is further assumed that the average coefficient of the room surfaces before treatment is 0.05 at all frequencies, and that 40 per cent of the total room surface is treated, the calculated reduction in reflected sound pressure level at each frequency, and the computation of the over-all reduction are as shown in the following table:

Octave band, cps	Octave-band level L_p before treatment, db	Calculated L_p reduction, db	Octave-band level L_p after treatment, db
0–150	80	3.9	76.1
150–300	80	6.7	73.3
300–600	80	8.2	**71.8**
600–1,200	80	11.1	68.9
1,200–2,400	80	10.3	69.7
2,400–4,800	80	9.5	70.5
Above 4,800	80	9.5	70.5
Over-all	88.4		80.6

The over-all reduction is 88.4 − 80.4 = 8.0 db.

Noise Reduction Coefficient. The term noise reduction coefficient (abbreviated NRC) was defined earlier as the simple average of the coefficients of an acoustical material at the four frequencies 250, 500, 1,000, and 2,000 cps, expressed to the nearest multiple of 0.05. It is intended only as a simple means of obtaining an approximate rating of the relative effectiveness of different materials in reducing noise.

The noise reduction coefficient has also been used for making approximate calculations of reduction in over-all pressure level of reflected sound. Such calculations are necessarily more or less in error, first, because the four frequencies included in the noise reduction coefficient do not cover the entire range of noise frequencies, and second, because the use of an average of absorption coefficients for these calculations is invalid. However, the error becomes small as the absorption coefficient becomes more nearly constant with respect to frequency. Referring to the example in the above section, the calculated reduction in over-all reflected sound pressure level based on the NRC value of 0.75 would be approximately 10 db, as compared with the value of 8.0 db calculated from the octave-band analysis.

Reverberation. Reverberation contributes to the total amount of noise existing in a room over a period of time, since it produces audible prolongation of noise during those intervals in which no noise is actually being emitted by the source. Its effect is commonly measured in terms of *reverberation time*, which is defined as the number of seconds required for the sound pressure level of the generally reflected sound to die out over a range of 60 db after the source is stopped. For example, the reverberation time for the decay curve shown in Fig. 18.33 is 1.8 sec. The reverberation time t_{60} depends only on the volume of the room V and the total room absorption a, according to the formula

$$t_{60} = \frac{0.049V}{a} \quad \text{sec} \tag{18.6}$$

where V is expressed in cubic feet and a is in sabins. The corresponding formula in metric units is

$$t_{60} = 0.161 \frac{V}{a} \quad \text{sec} \tag{18.6a}$$

where V is expressed in cubic meters and a is the absorption in square meters. Equation (18.6) is an approximation to the general formula

$$t_{60} = \frac{0.049V}{-2.30S \log (1 - \alpha)} \quad \text{sec} \tag{18.7}$$

where α is the average coefficient of absorption of the total absorptive area S [see Eq. (18.2)]. For values of α of less than 0.30, Eqs. (18.6) and (18.7) agree within 20 per cent.[*]

For some purposes it is useful to determine the rate at which the reverberant sound dies out. This is given by the relation

$$\text{Rate of decay} = \frac{60}{t_{60}} \quad \text{db per sec}$$

For example, the rate of decay of the decay curve shown in Fig. 18.33 is 33 db per sec.

Equations (18.6) and (18.7) indicate that the reverberant sound in a room of given size can be made to die out more rapidly by increasing the average absorption coefficient α with the addition of

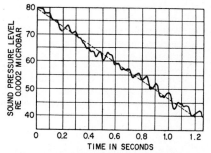

Fig. 18.33. A high-speed level record showing how the sound pressure level in a room decays with time. Since the sound decays 40 db in 1.2 sec, the reverberation time (i.e., the time to decay 60 db) is 1.8 sec.

acoustical material. It can also be shown that, if two rooms of different size have the same average absorption coefficient, that is, if they are finished with the same materials, the level of reflected sound due to a given steady source will build up to a lower value in the larger room but will die out more slowly.

PRACTICAL CONSIDERATIONS[22]

Subjective Effects of Acoustical Treatment.[†] The benefits in increased comfort resulting from acoustical treatment of an office, a restaurant, a hospital corridor, an industrial area, or any other space having highly reflective interior surfaces and nonabsorbent furnishings are almost invariably greater than can be accounted for by the reduction of noise level alone. The reason for this is probably that the reduction of excessive reflection not only reduces the level of the reverberant sound, with correspondingly lessened stimulation of the ear, but by greatly altering the time and space distribution of sound in the room it produces marked changes in the quality or character of the noise, which are interpreted by the ear and brain as substantial reductions in

[*] If air absorption in the room is important, as it will be at high frequencies or in very large rooms, then a term $4mV$ should be added to the total absorption a, where V is the volume in cubic feet and m is the attenuation coefficient given in Fig. 17.21.

[†] Since controlled tests to evaluate subjective effects, such as those discussed here, are difficult to set up, quantitative experimental data have not been obtained; the observations which are noted here concerning these effects are based upon practical experience.

annoyance. Based largely on study of the reactions and comments of the occupants of rooms before and after treatment, the various physical and psychological factors involved may be analyzed as follows:

1. When any sound or noise is produced in a highly reflective room, its sound pressure is immediately magnified many times to a level which is interpreted by the ear as being unnaturally and unnecessarily loud, and therefore annoying.
2. Since the sound pressure due to a given noise source is maintained by multiple reflection at a uniformly high level throughout the room, the noise from distant sources, such as typewriters or machines at the other end of the room, is very nearly as loud as that from nearby machines. This may be termed the *spreading effect* of noise and constitutes a second element of annoyance in that sources far removed from the listener are heard at a loudness which is unnecessarily high in relation to their distance. The transmission of noise in untreated corridors is an excellent example of this situation.
3. The fact that generally reflected sound strikes the ear from many different angles at once makes it impossible to judge the direction and distance of the original source with normal accuracy. This together with the feeling due to the same cause of being immersed in noise very probably contributes to the sense of uneasiness and distraction so often experienced.
4. When noise sources are of an intermittent or impact nature, as typified by many machine operations and activities, the presence of excessive reverberation is responsible for a considerable degree of annoyance due to the unnecessary prolongation of an originally disagreeable noise stimulus after the original sound has stopped. In the case of short sound impulses, furthermore, the sensation of loudness depends considerably on the duration of the sound as well as on its sound pressure, so that an impact sound, such as the click of a typewriter or the stroke of a punch press, will seem much louder to the ear when sustained by reverberation than when the sound is cut off immediately in the absence of reverberation. It is noted in practice that in large untreated rooms the characteristically long reverberation time is frequently the most obvious feature of the general impression of noisiness.

All the above factors contribute in varying amounts to the over-all feeling of confusion observed in a nonabsorptive room and described by the average person as the disagreeable "ringing" or "roaring" quality of all sounds produced in such a room. In many cases, of course, some of these effects may actually interfere directly with working operations. Activities which depend on verbal or telephone communication are especially subject to disruption by the effects of reverberation and spreading both on speech sounds and on background noise which may be present. Sometimes the ability to hear and locate the sources of particular sounds accurately is an important factor in machine operation, and interference with this function by excessive sound reflection becomes serious.

After adequate acoustical treatment is installed, the loudness of all reflected sound in the room is substantially decreased. The reduction in over-all sound pressure level effected by acoustical treatment is not necessarily an index of the reduction in loudness. For the most usual noise spectra the over-all loudness reduction will be governed largely by the reduction in level of the components above about 200 cps. Consequently, high absorbing efficiency is more important in the frequency range above 200 cps than for lower frequencies, and a drop in low-frequency absorption causes no serious loss in the over-all effectiveness of treatment as judged by the ear.

With the accompanying reduction of the spreading effect of noise, distant sources in the room are much less apparent to the ear in relation to those nearby. Considering the spreading effect from a different aspect, the sound pressure observed in moving away from a single source continues to drop off over a greater distance before reaching a constant level. The impression is now that of being able to escape the noise from a given source by moving away from it, instead of having the noise "follow" one throughout the room in the reflective condition.

It becomes much easier to judge the location of individual noise sources with increased absorption, because of the reduction in the pressure of the sound reaching the ear by reflected paths.

As a result of the reduction in reverberation time, all sounds are cut off sharply after they are produced, and the amount of noise audible as prolongation becomes negligible.

Probably the most frequently cited benefit of acoustical treatment, aside from generally increased comfort, is the marked improvement in speech intelligibility in the presence of impact sources. The results apparently are much greater than can be expected from similar reductions in steady background noise, particularly at very high levels, and are explainable by the fact that the reduction in reverberation makes it possible to talk "between" noise peaks instead of above them. See Chap. 9 for a detailed discussion.

Consideration of all the above effects of acoustical treatment has led to the general use of the term "sound conditioning." The analogy to air conditioning is apparent when it is remembered that in the latter instance comfort depends not only on cooling the air but also on proper control of humidity and circulation.

The degree of annoyance due to reflected sound and the corresponding relief afforded by acoustical treatment are governed to some extent by the type and distribution of noise sources in the room and the location of the occupants with respect to them. The most noticeable contrast brought about by treatment is obtained under conditions where the effects of reflected sound are most obvious to the ear beforehand. Thus, for example, excessive reverberation is more noticeable with intermittent or impact sources than with steady sources, and the spreading effect is most apparent when sources are widely spaced or when a few sources having high power output or easily distinguishable frequency characteristics tend to override the noise of other sources in the area. At the other extreme, the condition least favorable to effective correction by treatment is the presence of a multiplicity of identical, continuous, steady, closely spaced noise sources, with the listener in close proximity to one or more of them. In this case, it is difficult or impossible for the ear to differentiate the generally reflected sound from that which is transmitted directly from the nearest sources, and removal of the reflected sound by absorption is not readily noticeable. Fortunately, most situations encountered in practice tend to the more favorable combination of factors.

Required Amounts of Treatment. The treatment required for satisfactory noise control in a given room must be proportioned to the size and shape of the room in such a way that the effects of sound reflection (i.e., sound pressure level build-up, reverberation, and spreading) are unobjectionable, but the extent of treatment should be kept within practical and economical limits. This can be accomplished satisfactorily in the great majority of practical cases by use of the following working rule, which is based on extensive experience:

Rule 1. The total absorption in sabins in any room should be between 20 *per cent and* 50 *per cent of the total interior surface area in square feet.* In other words, the average absorption coefficient α should be between 0.20 and 0.50. The 20 per cent limit generally requires treatment of at least the entire ceiling, or its equivalent area, and the 50 per cent limit can be reached by treating all the ceiling and at least half the wall areas with highly efficient material. Choice of the exact amount of absorption within the 20 to 50 per cent working range is not subject to hard-and-fast rules. In general, however, the lower part of the range is suitable for rooms having floor dimensions large in comparison with the ceiling height and for noise sources of moderate sound power and wide spacing, while the upper part of the range should be used where the ceiling height is relatively large. If the type and distribution of noise sources in a new space are not yet known or are subject to change, it is advisable to provide for an amount of treatment lying in the upper part of the range in order to anticipate all possible conditions.

When treatment is being used to correct an existing noisy condition in an occupied space, it is important not only to arrive at a total amount of absorption lying within the range given in Rule 1 but to ensure that the added absorption is sufficient to produce a satisfactory improvement over the previous condition, as judged by the ear. A measure of this change is provided by the *absorption ratio* a_2/a_1 where a_1 is the total number of sabins in a given room *before* treatment and a_2 is the number of sabins after treatment. The absorption ratio is simply the number of times the absorption in a room is increased by treatment. A second working rule, also based on experience, may be stated as follows:

Rule 2. To produce a satisfactory improvement in an existing room, the total absorption after treatment should be between three and ten times the absorption before treatment.

An absorption ratio of 3 is about the least which is recognized by the ear as an appreciable change in the over-all effects of reflected sound under average conditions, while a 10:1 increase in absorption in the average room corresponds to the point where sound reflection is so greatly reduced that further addition of absorption approaches a point of diminishing return as far as the ear is concerned and therefore tends to become uneconomical.

Rule 1 should always be used as a check on Rule 2 when considering treatment for an existing room. For example, a room before treatment might contain unusually reflective surfaces such as hard concrete and glazed tile and very few furnishings, so that the absorption would come to only 2 per cent, say, of the total surface area. If the absorption were increased ten times, in accordance with the upper limit of Rule 2, the total absorption would still be only 20 per cent of the room area, which is the lower limit for the required absorption given by Rule 1. In such a case it would probably be advisable to increase the absorption by more than 10 times, which in view of the very small amount of original absorption would not involve an excessive amount of treatment. This would bring the total absorption farther within the range of 20 to 50 per cent of the room area, with a correspondingly more satisfactory reduction of sound reflection. The contrast between the before and after conditions would be greater than usual, but only because the "before" condition was so much worse than usual because of the abnormally low original absorption.

In applying the above rules, it is sufficiently accurate to use noise reduction coefficient (NRC) values for estimating required amounts of treatment.

Acceptable Noise Levels. In various types of room there is an upper limit as to the noise level that will be generally acceptable. In such cases many aspects of noise control must be considered, one of these being the amount of sound-absorptive material within the room. A tabulation of acceptable noise levels is given in Table 27.1.

Measurement of Over-all Noise-level Reduction. It is often desired to make before-and-after readings of noise level with a sound-level meter to measure the effect of acoustical treatment in a given room or to compare actual results against those predicted by calculations. Conducting tests for the latter purpose with any degree of scientific precision is far from a simple procedure and requires careful attention to all factors entering into the test conditions. These include:

1. The room must be of regular enough proportions and of low enough average absorption, after treatment, that the assumptions of good sound diffusion on which the calculations are based are valid. A test for this condition is to find some distance from a single source beyond which the measured sound level remains constant, on the average, clear to the boundaries of the room.

2. Since the calculations refer only to the reflected sound, while sound-level measurements record the combined direct and reflected sound, readings must be taken at distances far enough from the source that the directly transmitted component is negligible in comparison with the generally reflected level. The required distance can be checked by noting whether the level due to a single source remains constant with increasing distance. The use of a single source near one end of the room rather than distributed multiple sources will obviously make this and the foregoing condition easier to fulfill.

3. The noise source must have the same acoustic output after treatment as before. This can be checked by taking readings close enough to the source, say, 1 or 2 ft that the reflected sound is negligible in comparison with the direct sound. Test sources consisting of a white-noise generator feeding a loudspeaker, a mechan-

ically actuated wideband noise generator, or a recording of wideband noise, are satisfactory from the standpoint of ease of reading and reproducibility.

4. Both the calculations and the measurements must be made at single frequencies or narrow bands of frequencies.   As pointed out above, the reduction calculated from the noise reduction coefficient of the acoustical material is only approximate and may be in considerable error if the absorption-frequency characteristic of the material differs widely from the spectral distribution of a particular noise source.   Narrow frequency bands are much preferable to fixed single frequencies for uniformity of readings, because of the tendency to average out the point-to-point fluctuations caused by the interference pattern.   Octave or half-octave bands of noise, obtained by the use of filters either with the signal source or with the sound-level meter, are satisfactory for practical purposes.

If before-and-after measurements are made simply on a spot-check basis to compare average noise levels due to the actual noise sources normally present in the room, it will be found in general that agreement with theoretical predictions is only approximate and that measured reductions will be less than calculated values in about the degree that the test conditions listed above are not strictly complied with.   It has been observed that at test positions close to a single source or in the midst of closely spaced sources, where the directly transmitted sound is large in comparison with the reflected sound, the measured effect of treatment in reducing the over-all level is much less than at locations which are far enough from any single source so that the reflected sound is the major component of the total energy.

If the noise is due to a number of varied or randomly intermittent sources, as in a machine shop, the resulting irregular fluctuations of noise level may be so much larger than the expected reduction due to the treatment that it may be impossible to obtain even an approximate measured comparison of before-and-after conditions.

REFERENCES

1. Harris, C. M.: *J. Acoust. Soc. Amer.*, **27**: 1077 (1955).
2. Morse, P. M., R. H. Bolt, and R. L. Brown: *J. Acoust. Soc. Amer.*, **12**: 217 (1940).
3. Beranek, L.: *J. Acoust. Soc. Amer.*, **19**: 556 (1947).
4. Sabine, H. J.: *J. Soc. Motion Picture Engrs.*, **49**: 262 (1947).
5. London, A.: *J. Acoust. Soc. Amer.*, **22**: 263 (1950).
6. Sabine, H. J.: *J. Acoust. Soc. Amer.*, **22**: 387 (1950).
7. Harris, C. M., and C. T. Molloy: *J. Acoust. Soc. Amer.*, **24**: 1 (1952).
8. Ingard, U., and R. H. Bolt, *J. Acoust. Soc. Amer.*, **23**: 535 (1951), also Ingard, U.: *J. Acoust. Soc. Amer.*, **26**: 151 (1954), and Ingard, U.: *J. Acoust. Soc. Amer.*, **26**: 289 (1954).
9. Labate, S.: *Noise Control*, **2**: 15 (January, 1956).
10. Nichols, R. H., Jr.: *J. Acoust. Soc. Amer.*, **18**: 866 (1947).
11. Olson, H. F., and E. G. May: *J. Acoust. Soc. Amer.*, **25**: 1130 (1953).
12. Complete technical data on products manufactured by member companies are listed in the current *Bulletin of the Acoustical Materials Association*, 335 E. 45th St., New York 17, N.Y.   Price 50 cents.   Further data on these and other products may be found in the Architectural File published by Sweet's Catalog Service, Division of F. W. Dodge Corporation, New York.
13. Federal Specification SS-A-118-b, for sale by the Superintendent of Documents, Washington, D.C., price 10 cents.
14. ASTM Tentative Method E-84-50-T, Fire Hazard Classification of Building Materials. Obtainable from American Society for Testing Materials, 1916 Race St., Philadelphia, Pa.
15. Data obtained from Architectural File, Sweet's Catalog Service, 1954.
16. Acoustical Materials Association *Bull.* 16, 1956.
17. Cook, R. K., and P. Chrzanowski: *J. Acoust. Soc. Amer.*, **17**: 315 (1946).
18. Olson, H. F.: *RCA Rev.*, **7**: 503 (1946).
19. Excerpted from "Less Noise, Better Hearing," published by The Celotex Corporation, Chicago, 1950.
20. The following two sections are excerpted from Sabine, H. J.: The Use of Acoustical

Materials in the Control of Industrial Noise, *Proc. Third Annual National Noise Abatement Symposium*, vol. 3, Oct. 10, 1952.
21. Hoth, D. F.: *J. Acoust. Soc. Amer.*, **12**: 499 (1941).
22. Excerpted from "Less Noise, Better Hearing," published by The Celotex Corporation, Chicago, 1950.

The following books are primarily concerned with acoustical materials and architectural acoustics:

23. Knudsen, V. O., and C. M. Harris: "Acoustical Designing in Architecture," John Wiley & Sons, Inc., New York, 1950.
24. Brüel, P. V.: "Sound Insulation and Room Acoustics," Chapman & Hall, Ltd., London, 1951.
25. Ingerslev, F.: "Acoustics in Modern Building Practice," The Architectural Press, London, 1952.
26. "Less Noise, Better Hearing," The Celotex Corporation, Chicago, 1950.
27. Zwikker, C., and C. W. Kosten: "Sound Absorbing Materials," Elsevier Press, Inc., New York, 1949.

The following book is of historical interest in the field:

28. Sabine, W. C.: "Collected Papers on Acoustics," Harvard University Press, Cambridge, Mass., 1927.

Appendix 18.1.   Summary Tables

For convenience, materials in these tables, which are adapted from Acoustical Materials Association Bulletin 17, are grouped irrespective of the name of the producer.   Knowing the general appearance, composition, method of installation, and acoustical efficiency desired, the various materials meeting these specifications can be easily located.

Because appearance and composition are often the primary consideration, each table (except Type XII materials) contains materials which are essentially similar:

Thickness. In each table, except for Type XII, materials are arranged by thickness. Unless otherwise indicated by footnotes, the thickness given is the nominal thickness of the material as designated by the producer.   Actual thickness may vary slightly from the nominal according to the producer's own manufacturing specifications.

Light Reflection (Lt. Ref.). All light reflection values listed are from tests conducted at the Association's official laboratory with a type of reflectometer known as the "Baumgartner Sphere" and described in the *Transactions of the Illuminating Engineering Society*, **33**: 379 (1938).   Average samples are selected by laboratory personnel from factory-painted material submitted for sound absorption tests.   Each value listed is the average of five tests on three different samples.   The light reflection value given is for a finish designated as "white."

Summary Tables contain letters indicating light reflection values of newly manufactured material in ranges as follows:

> a—.75 or more
> b—.70 to .74 inclusive
> c—.65 to .69 inclusive
> d—.60 to .64 inclusive

Illuminating engineers indicate no need for more definite values than given in the above ranges since the aging of paint surfaces or the accumulation of dust or dirt will reduce light reflection by .10 or .20.

Flame Resistance (see text).   Many of the materials listed have been tested for flame resistance by the Association's official laboratory using a method essentially like that described in Federal Specification SS-A-118b.

The Federal Specification establishes specific criteria by which materials may be classified from "A" to "D," depending on their performance in the test.   No specific terms are given to describe these classes but materials classified as "A" are usually considered as "incombustible" and those classified as "D" as "combustible."   Classes "B" and "C" represent materials of intermediate flame resistance.   No class "B" materials are currently produced by Association members.

For the flame resistance tests for which ratings are shown, materials were mounted by bolting them directly to an asbestos-cement board panel.

The indiscriminate use of terms such as "fire proof," "fire-resistant," "flameproof," "fire-retardant," "slow-burning," etc., in specifications has created confusion among architects, consumers, and the public. By adopting the letter designation for various degrees of flame resistance, as determined by a recognized standard test method, the Association hopes to aid the architect in specifying the type of material required.

Type of Mounting Used in Conducting Sound Absorption Tests

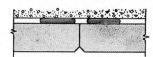

1. CEMENTED TO PLASTER BOARD WITH 1/8-IN. AIR SPACE. CONSIDERED EQUIVALENT TO CEMENTING TO PLASTER OR CONCRETE CEILING

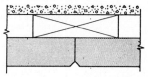

2. NAILED TO 1-BY 3-IN. WOOD FURRING 12 IN. O.C. UNLESS OTHERWISE INDICATED

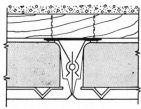

3. ATTACHED TO METAL SUPPORTS APPLIED TO 1-BY 3-IN. WOOD FURRING

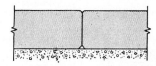

4. LAID DIRECTLY ON LABORATORY FLOOR

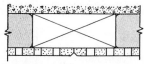

5. FURRED 1 IN., FURRING 24 IN. O.C., 1 IN. MINERAL WOOL BETWEEN FURRING

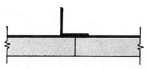

6. ATTACHED TO 24 GAUGE SHEET IRON, SUPPORTED BY METAL ANGLES

7. MECHANICALLY MOUNTED ON SPECIAL METAL SUPPORTS

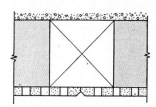

8. FURRED 2 IN., FURRING 24 IN. O.C., 2 IN. MINERAL WOOL BETWEEN FURRING

Type I Materials. Regularly Perforated Cellulose Fiber Tile
All tile 12 in. by 12 in. unless otherwise noted

Thickness, in.	Mounting No.	NRC spec. range	Material	Producer	Lt. ref.	Flame res. Note 3
½	1	.45–.55	Fir-Tex Perforated	Dant & Russell, Inc.	a	C, D
	1	.55–.65	Acousti-Celotex Type C-1	The Celotex Corp.	a	C, D
			Acoustifibre	National Gypsum Co.	a	C, D
			Auditone Perforated	United States Gypsum Co.	a	C, D
			Cushiontone	Armstrong Cork Co.	a	C, D
			Fibretone	Johns-Manville Sales Corp.	a	C, D
			Flintkote Acoustical Tile Type RS	Pioneer Div., The Flintkote Co.	a	C, D
			Simpson Acoustical Tile Type S-1	Simpson Logging Co.	a	C, D
	2	.50–.60	Fir-Tex Perforated	Dant & Russell, Inc.	a	
	2	.60–.70	Acousti-Celotex Type C-1	The Celotex Corp.	a	
			Acoustifibre	National Gypsum Co.	a	
			Auditone Perforated	United States Gypsum Co.	a	
			Cushiontone	Armstrong Cork Co.	a	
			Fibretone	Johns-Manville Sales Corp.	a	
			Flintkote Acoustical Tile Type RS	Pioneer Div., The Flintkote Co.	a	
			Simpson Acoustical Tile Type S-1	Simpson Logging Co.	a	
	7	.50–.60	Acoustifibre	National Gypsum Co.	a	
⅝	1	.60–.70	Acousti-Celotex Type C-2	The Celotex Corp.	a	C, D
			Acoustifibre	National Gypsum Co.	a	C, D
			Cushiontone	Armstrong Cork Co.	a	C, D
			Flintkote Acoustical Tile Type RS	Pioneer Div., The Flintkote Co.	a	C, D
			Simpson Acoustical Tile Type S-2	Simpson Logging Co.	a	C, D
	2	.65–.75	Acousti-Celotex Type C-2	The Celotex Corp.	a	
			Acoustifibre	National Gypsum Co.	a	
			Cushiontone	Armstrong Cork Co.	a	
			Flintkote Acoustical Tile Type RS	Pioneer Div., The Flintkote Co.	a	
			Simpson Acoustical Tile Type S-2	Simpson Logging Co.	a	
	7	.65–.75	Acousti-Celotex Type C-2	The Celotex Corp.	a	
			Cushiontone	Armstrong Cork Co.	a	
			Fir-Tex Perforated	Dant & Russell, Inc.	a	
	7	.60–.70	Acousti-Celotex Type C-2 (Note 4)	The Celotex Corp.	a	
¾	1	.65–.75	Acousti-Celotex Type C-9	The Celotex Corp.	a	C, D
			Acoustifibre	National Gypsum Co.	a	C, D
			Auditone Perforated	United States Gypsum Co.	a	C, D
			Cushiontone	Armstrong Cork Co.	a	C, D
			Fibretone	Johns-Manville Sales Corp.	a	C, D
			Fir-Tex Perforated	Dant & Russell, Inc.	a	C, D
			Flintkote Acoustical Tile Type RS	Pioneer Div., The Flintkote Co.	a	C, D
			Simpson Acoustical Tile Type S-3	Simpson Logging Co.	a	C, D
	2	.70–.80	Acousti-Celotex Type C-9	The Celotex Corp.	a	
			Acoustifibre	National Gypsum Co.	a	
			Auditone Perforated (Note 2)	United States Gypsum Co.	a	
			Cushiontone	Armstrong Cork Co.	a	
			Fibretone	Johns-Manville Sales Corp.	a	
			Fir-Tex Perforated	Dant & Russell, Inc.	a	
			Flintkote Acoustical Tile Type RS	Pioneer Div., The Flintkote Co.	a	
			Simpson Acoustical Tile Type S-3	Simpson Logging Co.	a	

Type I Materials. Regularly Perforated Cellulose Fiber Tile *(Continued)*

Thick-ness, in.	Mount-ing No.	NRC spec. range	Material	Producer	Lt. ref.	Flame res. Note 3
	7	.65–.75	Acousti-Celotex Type C-9 Acoustifibre Cushiontone Fir-Tex Perforated Simpson Acoustical Tile Type S-3	The Celotex Corp. National Gypsum Co. Armstrong Cork Co. Dant & Russell, Inc. Simpson Logging Co.	a a a a a	
	7	.65–.75	Acousti-Celotex Type C-9 (Note 4)	The Celotex Corp.	a	
1	1	.70–.80	Acousti-Celotex Type C-8 Acoustifibre Cushiontone Fibretone Flintkote Acoustical Tile Type RS Simpson Acoustical Tile Type S-5	The Celotex Corp. National Gypsum Co. Armstrong Cork Co. Johns-Manville Sales Corp. Pioneer Div., The Flintkote Co. Simpson Logging Co.	a a a a a a	C, D C, D C, D C, D C, D C, D
	2	.75–.85	Acousti-Celotex Type C-8 Acoustifibre Cushiontone Cushiontone (Note 1) Fibretone Flintkote Acoustical Tile Type RS Simpson Acoustical Tile Type S-5	The Celotex Corp. National Gypsum Co. Armstrong Cork Co. Armstrong Cork Co. Johns-Manville Sales Corp. Pioneer Div., The Flintkote Co. Simpson Logging Co.	a a a a a a a	
	7	.60–.70	Acoustifibre	National Gypsum Co.	a	
	7	.70–.80	Acousti-Celotex Type C-7 Cushiontone	The Celotex Corp. Armstrong Cork Co.	a a	
	7	.70–.80	Acousti-Celotex Type C-7 (Note 4)	The Celotex Corp.	a	

Note 1. Tile size 24 in. by 24 in.
Note 2. Tile size 24 in. by 48 in.
Note 3. Materials rated as C, D are available with factory-applied paint finish which gives them the C rating and also a standard paint finish which gives a D rating.
Note 4. 6 in. wide, exposed, unperforated suspension members, spaced 30 in. on centers or 54 in. on centers. Tile size 12 in. by 24 in. for C-7 only.

Type II Materials. Random Perforated Cellulose Fiber Tile

Perforations vary in diameter and spacing. All tile 12 in. by 12 in. unless otherwise noted.

Thickness, in.	Mounting No.	NRC spec. range	Material	Producer	Lt. ref.	Flame res. Note 2
½	1	.50–.60	Acousti-Celotex Type CR-1	The Celotex Corp.	a	C, D
			Acoustifibre Random Pattern	National Gypsum Co.	a	C, D
			Auditone Random Perforated	United States Gypsum Co.		C, D
			Cushiontone Full Random	Armstrong Cork Co.	a	C, D
			Fibretone Variety Drilled	Johns-Manville Sales Corp.		
			Flintkote Acoustical Tile Type MS	Pioneer Div., The Flintkote Co.		C, D
			Simpson Acoustical Tile Type S-1-S	Simpson Logging Co.	a	C, D
	2	.55–.65	Auditone Random Perforated	United States Gypsum Co.		
			Cushiontone Full Random	Armstrong Cork Co.	a	
			Fibretone Variety Drilled	Johns-Manville Sales Corp.		
	7		Flintkote Acoustical Tile Type MS	Pioneer Div., The Flintkote Co.		
			Simpson Acoustical Tile Type S-1-S	Simpson Logging Co.	a	
	7	.50–.60	Acoustifibre Random Pattern	National Gypsum Co.	a	
⅝	1	.55–.65	Acousti-Celotex Type CR-2	The Celotex Corp.	a	C, D
			Acoustifibre Random Pattern	National Gypsum Co.	a	C, D
			Flintkote Acoustical Tile Type MS	Pioneer Div., The Flintkote Co.		C, D
			Simpson Acoustical Tile Type S-2-S	Simpson Logging Co.	a	C, D
	2	.60–.70	Flintkote Acoustical Tile Type MS	Pioneer Div., The Flintkote Co.		
			Simpson Acoustical Tile Type S-2-S	Simpson Logging Co.	a	
	7	.60–.70	Acousti-Celotex Type CR-2	The Celotex Corp.	a	
¾	1	.60–.70	Acousti-Celotex Type CR-9	The Celotex Corp.	a	C, D
			Acoustifibre Random Pattern	National Gypsum Co.	a	C, D
			Auditone Random Perforated	United States Gypsum Co.		C, D
			Cushiontone Full Random	Armstrong Cork Co.	a	C, D
			Fibretone Variety Drilled	Johns-Manville Sales Corp.		
			Flintkote Acoustical Tile Type MS	Pioneer Div., The Flintkote Co.		C, D
			Simpson Acoustical Tile Type S-3-S	Simpson Logging Co.	a	C, D
	2	.65–.75	Acousti-Celotex Type CR-9	The Celotex Corp.	a	
			Acoustifibre Random Pattern	National Gypsum Co.	a	
			Auditone Random Perforated (Note 3)	United States Gypsum Co.		
			Cushiontone Full Random	Armstrong Cork Co.	a	
			Fibretone Variety Drilled	Johns-Manville Sales Corp.		
			Flintkote Acoustical Tile Type MS	Pioneer Div., The Flintkote Co.		
			Simpson Acoustical Tile Type S-3-S	Simpson Logging Co.	a	
	7	.60–.70	Acousti-Celotex Type CR-9	The Celotex Corp.	a	
			Acoustifibre Random Pattern	National Gypsum Co.	a	
			Cushiontone Full Random	Armstrong Cork Co.	a	
			Simpson Acoustical Tile Type S-3-S	Simpson Logging Co.	a	
	7	.60–.70	Acousti-Celotex Type CR-9 (Note 1)	The Celotex Corp.	a	

Type II Materials. Random Perforated Cellulose Fiber Tile (*Continued*)

Thickness, in.	Mounting No.	NRC spec. range	Material	Producer	Lt. ref.	Flame res. Note 2
1	1	.60–.70	Acoustifibre Random Pattern	National Gypsum Co.	a	C, D
	1	.70–.80	Acousti-Celotex Type CR-8	The Celotex Corp.	a	C, D
			Cushiontone Full Random	Armstrong Cork Co.	a	C, D
			Flintkote Acoustical Tile Type MS	Pioneer Div., The Flintkote Co.		C, D
	2	.65–.75	Acousti-Celotex Type CR-8	The Celotex Corp.	a	
			Acoustifibre Random Pattern	National Gypsum Co.	a	
			Cushiontone Full Random	Armstrong Cork Co.	a	
			Flintkote Acoustical Tile Type MS	Pioneer Div., The Flintkote Co.		
	7	.65–.75	Acousti-Celotex Type CR-8	The Celotex Corp.	a	
			Cushiontone Full Random	Armstrong Cork Co.	a	
	7	.55–.65	Acoustifibre Random Pattern	National Gypsum Co.	a	

Note 1. 6 in. wide, exposed, unperforated suspension members, spaced 30 in. on centers or 54 in. on centers.

Note 2. Materials rated as C, D are available with factory-applied paint finish which gives them the C rating and also a standard paint finish which gives a D rating.

Note 3. Tile size 12 in. by 24 in.

Type III Materials. Slotted Cellulose Fiber Tile
All tile 12 in. by 12 in. unless otherwise noted

Thickness, in.	Mounting No.	NRC spec. range	Material	Producer	Lt. ref.	Flame res. Note 2
¾	1	.60–.70	Auditone Slotted	United States Gypsum Co.	a	C, D
	2	.65–.75	Auditone Slotted (Note 1)	United States Gypsum Co.	a	

Note 1. Tile 12 in. by 24 in.

Note 2. Materials rated as C, D are available with factory-applied paint finish which gives them the C rating and also a standard paint finish which gives a D rating.

Type IV Materials.   Textured or Fissured Cellulose Tile or Board
All tile 12 in. by 12 in. unless otherwise noted

Thick-ness, in.	Mount-ing No.	NRC spec. range	Material	Producer	Lt. ref.	Flame res.
½	1	.50–.60	Econacoustic	National Gypsum Co.	a	
⁹⁄₁₆	1	.55–.65	Simpson Forestone	Simpson Logging Co.		C
	2	.60–.70	Simpson Forestone	Simpson Logging Co.		
¾	1	.60–.70	Simpson Forestone	Simpson Logging Co.		C
	2	.65–.75	Simpson Forestone	Simpson Logging Co.		
	7	.55–.65	Simpson Forestone Simpson Forestone Ceiling Board (Note 2)	Simpson Logging Co. Simpson Logging Co.		
1¼	1	.35–.45	Corkoustic (Note 1)	Armstrong Cork Co.	a	C
	7	.35–.45	Corkoustic (Note 1)	Armstrong Cork Co.	a	

Note 1.   Tile 11½ in. by 11½ in.
Note 2.   Board 23¾ in. by 47¾ in.

Type V Materials. Perforated Mineral Fiber Tile
All tile 12 in. by 12 in. unless otherwise noted

Thickness, in.	Mounting No.	NRC spec. range	Material	Producer	Lt. ref.	Flame res.
½	1	.55–.65	Acousti-Celotex Type M-8	The Celotex Corp.	a	A
			Fiberglas Acoustical Tile Type PRW	Owens-Corning Fiberglas Corp.	a	A
			Fiberglas Acoustical Tile Type PRWR	Owens-Corning Fiberglas Corp.	a	A
			Minatone	Armstrong Cork Co.	a	A
	2	.60–.70	Minatone	Armstrong Cork Co.	a	
⅝	1	.60–.70	Acousti-Celotex Type M-1	The Celotex Corp.	a	A
			Acousti-Celotex Type M-1 (Note 5)	The Celotex Corp.	a	A
			Fiberglas Acoustical Tile Type PRW	Owens-Corning Fiberglas Corp.	a	A
			Fiberglas Acoustical Tile Type PRWR	Owens-Corning Fiberglas Corp.	a	A
			Minatone	Armstrong Cork Co.	a	A
	2	.65–.75	Minatone	Armstrong Cork Co.	a	
	7	.65–.75	Acousti-Celotex Type M-1 (Note 2)	The Celotex Corp.	a	
			Fiberglas Acoustical Tile Type PRW	Owens-Corning Fiberglas Corp.	a	
			Minatone	Armstrong Cork Co.	a	
			Minatone (Notes 1 and 3)	Armstrong Cork Co.	a	
	7	.75–.85	Fiberglas Acoustical Tile Type PRWR	Owens-Corning Fiberglas Corp.	a	
	7	.65–.75	Acousti-Celotex Type M-1 (Notes 2 and 4)	The Celotex Corp.	a	
¾	1	.60–.70	Fiberglas Acoustical Tile Type PRW	Owens-Corning Fiberglas Corp.	a	A
			Fiberglas Acoustical Tile Type PRWR	Owens-Corning Fiberglas Corp.	a	A
	7	.70–.80	Fiberglas Acoustical Tile Type PRW	Owens-Corning Fiberglas Corp.	a	
			Fiberglas Acoustical Tile Type PRWR	Owens-Corning Fiberglas Corp.	a	
⅞	1	.70–.80	Minatone	Armstrong Cork Co.	a	A
	7	.80–.90	Minatone	Armstrong Cork Co.	a	
1	1	.70–.80	Acousti-Celotex Type M-2	The Celotex Corp.	a	A
	7	.70–.80	Acousti-Celotex Type M-2 (Note 2)	The Celotex Corp.	a	
			Acousti-Celotex Type M-2 (Notes 2 and 4)	The Celotex Corp.	a	

Note 1. Tile size 24 in. by 24 in.
Note 2. Tile size 12 in. by 24 in.
Note 3. Tile size 24 in. by 48 in.
Note 4. 6 in. wide Acousti-Line exposed metal suspension systems members spaced 30 in. or 54 in. on centers or 3 in. wide Acousti-Line members spaced 27 in. or 51 in. on centers.
Note 5. Perforated 296 holes per square foot, $\frac{3}{16}$, $\frac{7}{32}$, and $\frac{1}{4}$ in. diameter, random pattern.

Type VI Materials. Fissured Mineral Fiber Tile
All tile 12 in. by 12 in. unless otherwise noted

Thick-ness, in.	Mount-ing No.	NRC spec. range	Material	Producer	Lt. ref.	Flame res.
¾	1	.65-.75	Acoustone F	United States Gypsum Co.	a	A
			Celotone	The Celotex Corp.	a	A
			Permacoustic	Johns-Manville Sales Corp.	a	A
			Simpson Fissured Mineral Tile	Simpson Logging Co.	a	A
			Travacoustic	National Gypsum Co.	a	A
			Travertone	Armstrong Cork Co.	a	A
	7	.75-.85	Acoustone F	United States Gypsum Co.	a	
			Celotone	The Celotex Corp.	a	
			Celotone (Notes 1 and 2)	The Celotex Corp.	a	
			Permacoustic	Johns-Manville Sales Corp.	a	
			Simpson Fissured Mineral Tile	Simpson Logging Co.	a	
			Travacoustic	National Gypsum Co.	a	
			Travertone	Armstrong Cork Co.	a	

Note 1.   Tile size 12 in. by 24 in.
Note 2.   6 in. wide Acousti-Line exposed metal suspension system members spaced 30 in. or 54 in. on centers or 3 in. wide Acousti-Line members spaced 27 in. or 51 in. on centers.

Type VII Materials. Textured or Smooth Mineral Fiber Tile or Board

All tile or board 12 in. by 12 in. unless otherwise noted

Thick-ness, in	Mount-ing No.	NRC spec. range	Material	Producer	Lt. ref.	Flame res.
½	1	.50–.60	Fiberglas Acoustical Tile Type TMW	Owens-Corning Fiberglas Corp.	a	A
⅝	1	.60–.70	Crestone (Striated)	Armstrong Cork Co.	a	A
			Fiberglas Acoustical Tile Type TMW	Owens-Corning Fiberglas Corp.	a	A
	7	.60–.70	Crestone (Striated)	Armstrong Cork Co.	a	
			Crestone (Note 1)	Armstrong Cork Co.	a	
	7	.80–.90	Fiberglas Acoustical Tile Type TMW	Owens-Corning Fiberglas Corp.	a	
¾	1	.65–.75	Fiberglas Acoustical Tile, Stria	Owens-Corning Fiberglas Corp.	a	A
			Fiberglas Acoustical Tile Type TMW	Owens-Corning Fiberglas Corp.	a	A
			Fiberglas Fresco Acoustical Tile	Owens-Corning Fiberglas Corp.	a	A
			Motif'd Acoustone (Striated) Pattern No. 19	United States Gypsum Co.	c	A
			Striatone	The Celotex Corp.		A
	2	.70–.80	Fiberglas Acoustical Tile Type TXE (Note 1)	Owens-Corning Fiberglas Corp.	a	A
	7	.70–.80	Motif'd Acoustone (Striated) Pattern No. 19	United States Gypsum Co.	c	
	7	.80–.90	Fiberglas Acoustical Tile, Stria	Owens-Corning Fiberglas Corp.	a	
			Fiberglas Acoustical Tile Type TMW	Owens-Corning Fiberglas Corp.	a	
			Fiberglas Acoustical Tile Type TXE (Note 1)	Owens-Corning Fiberglas Corp.	a	
			Fiberglas Ceiling Board (Note 2)	Owens-Corning Fiberglas Corp.	a	A
			Fiberglas Stria Ceiling Board (Note 2)	Owens-Corning Fiberglas Corp.	a	A
			Fiberglas Fresco Acoustical Tile	Owens-Corning Fiberglas Corp.	a	
1		.70–.80	Fiberglas Acoustical Form Board (Note 3)	Owens-Corning Fiberglas Corp.		
1¼	7	.85–.95	Fiberglas Ceiling Board (Note 4)	Owens-Corning Fiberglas Corp.	a	A
			Fiberglas Stria Ceiling Board (Note 4)	Owens-Corning Fiberglas Corp.	a	A
1½		.80–.90	Fiberglas Acoustical Form Board (Note 3)	Owens-Corning Fiberglas Corp.		
2		.85–.95	Fiberglas Acoustical Form Board (Note 3)	Owens-Corning Fiberglas Corp.		

Note 1. Tile size 24 in. by 24 in. Furring 24 in. on centers.
Note 2. Board size 24 in. by 48 in.
Note 3. Board size 32 in. by 36 in. Board was mounted for test by setting in 2 in. thickness of gypsum for 1 in. thick board and in ½ in. thickness of gypsum for 1½ in. and 2 in. thick boards.
Note 4. Board size 48 in. by 48 in.

Type VIII Materials.   Membrane-faced Mineral Fiber Tile or Board
Unit size 12 in. by 12 in. unless otherwise noted

Thickness, in.	Mounting No.	NRC spec. range	Material	Producer	Lt. ref.	Flame res.
¾	1	.60–.70	Fiberglas Sono-Faced Acoustical Tile Center Units	Owens-Corning Fiberglas Corp.	c	A
	1	.30–.40	Fiberglas Sono-Faced Acoustical Tile Border Units	Owens-Corning Fiberglas Corp.	d	A
	7	.70–.80	Fiberglas Sono-Faced Acoustical Tile Center Units	Owens-Corning Fiberglas Corp.	c	
	7	.20–.30	Fiberglas Sono-Faced Acoustical Tile Border Units	Owens-Corning Fiberglas Corp.	d	
	7	.70–.80	Fiberglas Sono-Faced Ceiling Board Center Units (Note 1)	Owens-Corning Fiberglas Corp.	d	A
	7	.30–.40	Fiberglas Sono-Faced Ceiling Board Border Units (Note 1)	Owens-Corning Fiberglas Corp.	d	A

Note 1.   Size of units 24 in. by 48 in.

Type IX Materials.   Perforated Metal Pans with Mineral Fiber Pads
All units include pan and pad and are 12 in. by 24 in. in size unless otherwise noted

Thickness, in.	Mounting No.	NRC spec. range	Material	Producer	Lt. ref.	Flame res.
1¼	7	.60–.70	Steelacoustic (Note 1)	The Celotex Corp.	b	A
1⅜	7	.50–.60	Panelcoustic (Note 2)	National Gypsum Co.	b	A
1⅝	7	.60–.70	Panelcoustic (Note 2)	National Gypsum Co.	b	A
2	7	.85–.95	Corrutone (Note 3)	United States Gypsum Co.		A
2½	3	.80–.90	Acousteel	The Celotex Corp.	b	A
			Acoustimetal	National Gypsum Co.	b	A
			Arrestone	Armstrong Cork Co.	a	A
			D & R Acoustical Metal Pan	Dant & Russell, Inc.	b	A
			Flintkote Perforated Metal Acoustical Tile	Pioneer Div., The Flintkote Co.		A
			Perfatone	United States Gypsum Co.	a	A
			Random Acoustimetal	National Gypsum Co.	b	A
			Sanacoustic, Type KK	Johns-Manville Sales Corp.	a	A
			Sanacoustic, Spincoustic Pads	Johns-Manville Sales Corp.	a	A
			Simpson Metal Acoustical Units	Simpson Logging Co.		A
	3	.55–.65	Acoustimetal, 50-50 Pattern (Note 4)	National Gypsum Co.	b	A
			Sanacoustic, Type KK, 50-50 Pattern (Note 4)	Johns-Manville Sales Corp.	a	A
2⅝	7	.75–.85	Panelcoustic (Note 2)	National Gypsum Co.	b	A

Sound-absorption values of these materials are dependent on the specific combination of metal pan and pad tested.   Other pads than those specified by the producer for use with his pans may give radically different results.

Note 1.   Size of units 24 in. by 24 in.   Pad laminated to metal facing.
Note 2.   Size of units 24 in. by 48 in.
Note 3.   Metal pan corrugated.   Unit size 24 in. by 24 in.
Note 4.   Half of pans perforated and half unperforated.

Type X Materials. Perforated Asbestos-board Panels with Mineral Fiber Pads
Thickness includes perforated facing and pad. Unit size 24 in. by 24 in.

Thickness, in.	Mounting No.	NRC spec. range	Material	Producer	Lt. ref.	Flame res.
$1\frac{3}{16}$	5	.65–.75	Transite Acoustical Panels	Johns-Manville Sales Corp.	b	A
$1\frac{7}{16}$	Note 1	.70–.80	Perforated Asbestos Board Gold Bond Perforated Asbestos Panels	United States Gypsum Co. National Gypsum Co.		A A
$2\frac{3}{16}$	8	.75–.85	Asbestos Board Panel	Armstrong Cork Co.		A
$2\frac{3}{16}$	8	.80–.90	Transite Acoustical Panels	Johns-Manville Sales Corp.	b	A
$3\frac{3}{16}$	Note 1	.70–.80	Asbestos Board Panel Perforated Asbestos Board Panel	Armstrong Cork Co. The Celotex Corp.		A A

Note 1. See producer's literature for description of special mounting.

Type XI Materials. Sound Absorbent Duct Lining*

Thickness, in.	Mounting No.	NRC spec. range	Material	Producer	Lt. ref.	Flame res.
$\frac{1}{2}$	6	.55–.65	Airacoustic Q-T Ductliner	Johns-Manville Sales Corp. The Celotex Corp.		A A
1	6	.65–.75	Airacoustic Q-T Ductliner	Johns-Manville Sales Corp. The Celotex Corp.		A A
			Aircoustat Absorbers	Industrial Sound Control, Inc.		

* Values of absorption coefficient vs. frequency are given in Chap. 27.

Type XII Materials.   Special Acoustical Panels and Materials

Producer	Material	Description	NRC spec. range	Flame res.
Fenestra Incorporated	Fenestra Acoustic Panels	Perforated, structural steel ceiling and roof panels with glass fiber absorbent pads. See producer's table for details		
	Type AD		.80–.90	A
	Type C		.80–.90	A
	Type D	Flat plate down	.75–.85	A
	Type Holorib		.70–.80	A
	Type AD and Std. AD		.60–.70	A
	Type C and Std. C		.60–.70	A
	Type D and Std. D	Flat plate down	.50–.60	A
	Type TAC-AC and TAC-T		.55–.65	A
	Type TAC-T and Three TAC-AC		.60–.70	A
The E. F. Hauserman Co.	Acoustic Ceiling	3-in.-thick panels, perforated steel face, unperforated steel back, filled with mineral fiber and plaster wallboard	.80–.90	A
	Acoustiwall	2¾ in. thick. Similar to above	.75–.85	A
Industrial Sound Control, Inc.	Sound Metal Acoustical Panels	Hollow steel panels filled with mineral-fiber pads		
	Type A-3PP	3½ in. thick. Both faces perforated		A
	Type F-4PS	4 in. thick. One face perforated		A
	Type A-6PS	6 in. thick. One face perforated		A
Johns-Manville Sales Corp.	Spincoustic	Mineral wool blanket. 1 in. thick	.70–.80	A
	Spincoustic	Same as above. 2 in. thick	.85–.95	A
Owens-Corning Fiberglas Corp.	Fiberglas Sonocor Metal Pan Filler Batts	Absorbent pads for perforated metal pans	.80–.90	
Simpson Logging Co.	Simpson Acoustical Roof Slab	2-ft by 8-ft structural slab, t and g joint long edges, perforated exposed surface	.50–.60	C

Producers' literature should be consulted for further information.

Chapter 19

CONTROL OF SOLID-BORNE NOISE

Fritz Ingerslev, Ph.D.

Royal Technical University, Copenhagen, Denmark

Cyril M. Harris, Ph.D.

Columbia University, New York

INTRODUCTION

One of the problems in architectural acoustics that has increased in severity in recent years has been that of controlling the transmission of solid-borne energy which is imparted to building structures by impacts or by steady vibration.

Such energy may be transmitted throughout a building to surfaces which are set in motion and radiate noise. The problem of controlling structure-borne noise has increased in multiple dwellings, office buildings and industrial plants for two reasons: (1) Due to the tremendous increase in labor-saving devices and machinery which makes our working and living areas more pleasant; for example, air conditioners, washing and drying machines, business machines, etc. This increase in mechanization with its concomitant potential noise sources frequently has outweighed advances in the technology of machinery noise control. (2) Many of the newer types of building constructions are actually much poorer in their ability to provide insulation against solid-borne noises than were their earlier counterparts.

How Noise Is Transmitted in Buildings. Noise in buildings may originate from sources in air, from impacts or vibration which is communicated directly to the building structure, or from a combination of both. Then it may be transmitted throughout the building by any, or a combination, of a number of mechanisms—some of which are illustrated in Fig. 19.1. Several paths are shown by which sound may be transmitted from one room to another. Along certain paths the transmission may be entirely through the air, as, for example,

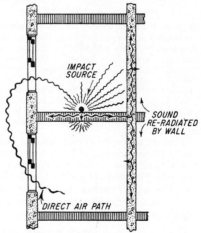

Fig. 19.1. Schematic sectional diagram of a building illustrating some of the mechanisms by which sound may be transmitted from one room to another.

along a ventilation duct into an adjacent room; along other paths the sound which originates in air may force into vibration an entire wall or ceiling, be transmitted to the structure as solid-borne energy, and then be reradiated as sound from a surface which is forced into vibration (these mechanisms are described in the next chapter).

Mechanical energy may be imparted directly to a building structure and then be transmitted through the structure to some other part of the building where a surface is forced into vibration—thereby radiating sound. This chapter is concerned with the control of such solid-borne noise. In general, the methods described here are designed for the control of solid-borne noise, although some of the techniques which are employed to provide good impact-sound insulation also provide excellent air-borne sound insulation.

Figure 19.1 illustrates the basic mechanism by which solid-borne noise is propagated. In this case an object is dropped on the floor, causing it to vibrate. Thus the floor itself is set into vibration and becomes a radiator of air-borne sound, producing noise in the room below. The force which is applied to the floor is of short duration—referred to as an impact force, which results in transient vibration of the floor. Solid-borne noise also may result from the application of a steadily oscillating force, such as a motor which is off-balance. Note that some of the solid-borne energy is propagated along the floor itself to the side walls of the room below, causing them to radiate sound. Thus solid-borne noise may be propagated by many paths.

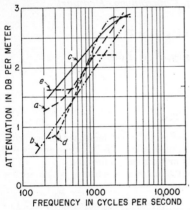

FIG. 19.2. Attenuation of solid-borne sound, measured in rows of buildings having various constructions and differing in plan and section: (*a*) blocks of hollow bricks; (*b*) concrete slabs containing brick chips; (*c*) hollow pumice stones; (*d*) and (*e*) concrete, containing brick chips, filled in. The attenuation in (*a*) to (*d*) was measured in the horizontal direction; (*e*) was measured in the vertical direction. (*Kuhl and Kaiser.*[1])

Table 19.1. Attenuation of Longitudinal Waves

	db/100 *ft*
Iron	0.3–1
Brickwork	0.5–4
Concrete	1.0–6
Wood	1.5–10

Solid-borne noise frequently arises from footsteps, the dragging of chairs or other pieces of furniture across an uncarpeted floor, the slamming of doors, water hammer in pipes, or the starting and stopping of pumps and motors. The magnitudes of peak vibratory power from such sources which are transmitted to the building structure are usually quite large. Furthermore, as indicated in Table 19.1 and Fig. 19.2, the attenuation of solid-borne noise in building materials is usually quite small. Therefore, solid-borne noise sources should be isolated from the building structure wherever it is possible to do so. The methods described in Chap. 13 are applicable to the isolation of many such mechanical sources. In this chapter various floor finishes and "floating" floor constructions are described which provide considerable improvement in the insulation of impact sounds and steadily oscillating forces.

RATING OF FLOOR CONSTRUCTIONS

A number of possible methods might be employed to compare the relative merit of partitions as regards their solid-borne sound insulation. The method which has been widely adopted throughout the world makes use of a device that can produce a steady series of impacts on a floor (this is the surface to which solid-borne energy is usually imparted). Then the steady-state sound pressure levels in octave (or fractional-octave) bands are measured in the room below, or in some other room in the building.

Such devices are usually referred to as *tapping machines.* Suppose a tapping machine is placed on the floor of a room as shown in Fig. 19.3. The room in which it is placed is defined as the *source room;* the room in which measurements are made is called the *receiving room.*

Impact-sound Level. If a tapping machine is set into operation on the floor of a building, the sound pressure level in octave (or fractional-octave) bands can be measured in various locations in this building; this level, defined as the *impact-sound level,* may be used to characterize the merit of a floor in reducing impact noise. Thus the lower the impact-sound level in a room below a floor on which a standard tapping machine is operated, the better the floor. Typical data of this kind are shown in Fig. 19.4 which gives laboratory measurements of the impact-sound level per octave band in a room beneath a concrete floor before and after the placement of a rug on the floor. Note the considerable improvement at high frequencies. This is typical of the insulation that may be provided by resilient floor finishes.

Impact-sound Level in Distant Rooms. Solid-borne energy originating from impacts produces noise not only in the receiving room, directly below the floor set into vibration by the impacts, but also in more distant rooms. This transmission has been studied, by means of a tapping machine, in buildings with reinforced-concrete and wood-joist floors. The average impact-

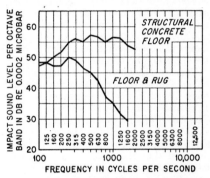

FIG. 19.4. Impact-sound level measured in a room directly below a concrete slab floor using a tapping machine constructed in accordance with international specifications. Noise spectra are shown for the tapping machine striking the bare concrete floor, and the concrete floor when covered by a rug.

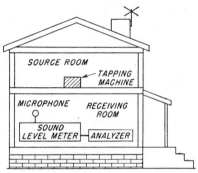

FIG. 19.3. Schematic sectional diagram of a building showing test setup for impact-sound measurements.

sound levels measured in the two types of buildings were about the same in the room directly below the tapping machine but very different in rooms situated at a considerable distance from the tapping machine. The noise level in the building with wood-joist floors was more than 20 db lower than the level in the building with concrete floors. This pronounced difference is due to the fact that solid concrete floors are homogeneous and continuous from room to room, while wood-joist floors are not homogeneous and are interrupted between rooms. In the case of wood-joist floors there also is an important difference between the materials used for floors and for walls.

Impact-sound Insulation. Impact-sound levels have no physical significance in themselves; they are useful in comparing data taken by different laboratories only when a tapping machine having the same characteristics is employed by the various laboratories. (For this reason a standard tapping machine is being adopted—see the following section.) Therefore another method of rating the merit of a floor with regard to its ability to isolate impact noise is used: its *impact-sound insulation,* which represents the improvement in decibels vs. frequency that the floor construction provides over another one that is arbitrarily selected as a standard of reference. The impact-sound insulation is obtained by subtracting two sets of measurements: (1) the impact-sound level in the receiving room when the tapping machine strikes the test floor, from (2) the impact-sound level in the receiving room when the tapping machine strikes the "reference floor." In all cases, when data are presented the floor which has been selected as the reference for comparison should be specified. Thus comparative values for various floating floor constructions and floor finishes reported in this chapter are rated in these terms. It should be noted that a positive value of impact-noise insulation represents an *improvement* over the reference floor.

IMPACT-SOUND MEASUREMENTS

As indicated in the preceding section, the impact-sound level in a room depends on the characteristics of the tapping machine that is used in the measurements. A consideration of such devices will indicate that the character of the impact that is produced depends upon such factors as the mass and height of the weight that falls, the type of material of which the hammerhead is fabricated, the length of time that the hammerhead remains in contact with the floor when it strikes, and the radius of curvature of the hammerhead. In order that impact-sound measurements by different laboratories be comparable, the tapping machines which they use should have the same physical characteristics and the same procedure should be employed in computing the impact-sound levels obtained from measurements employing these machines. For this reason an international code for field and laboratory measurements of impact-sound insulation is now being considered for adoption and it forms the basis for the method now in widespread use, which is described below.

Tapping Machines. The international code states that the tapping machine shall be constructed in accordance with the following specification: It shall have five hammers placed in line, the distance between the two end hammers being about 16 in. It shall give 10 impacts per second. The mass of each hammer shall be 500 grams. The free drop of a hammer shall be $1\frac{5}{8}$ in. The hammerhead which strikes the floor shall be of brass and shall have a diameter of $1\frac{1}{4}$ in.; the surface of the hammerhead shall be spherical, with a radius of about 20 in. The driving mechanism shall be so designed that the hammers are lifted out of contact with the floor approximately 0.05 sec after they have fallen the $1\frac{5}{8}$ in. These specifications are such that, when operating on a test floor, this tapping machine produces a sound level in the room directly below the floor sufficiently high and continuous to make accurate measurements possible.*

Measurement of Impact-sound Level. In the measurement of impact-sound level, the tapping machine is placed on the floor to be tested and set into operation. Then, the sound pressure level in the receiving room, i.e., the impact-sound level, is determined. Various factors, in addition to the construction of the floor itself, which may affect the measured value of the impact-sound level are: 1) The position of the tapping machine on the floor being tested; 2) The method of determining the average sound pressure level in the receiving room (the average level will depend upon the number of microphone positions and their locations within the room), and; 3) The absorption in the room in which the sound level is measured.

Position of the Tapping Machine. The impact-sound level in a room is not independent of the position of the tapping machine on the floor of the room above. In testing floors in most dwellings, three positions of the tapping machine on the floor will yield a fairly representative result if the sound pressure level in the receiving room is measured at a number of microphone positions and the average computed from these data. Since there may be some variation in impact level with positions due to

---

* There is considerable difference between the character of the impacts produced by footsteps and those produced by hammerheads in a tapping machine. A few measurements have been made to indicate the extent of correlation between the impact-sound insulation measured using these two sources of impacts.[10] The improvement provided by a floating floor resting on a resilient mineral-wool blanket proved to be approximately the same. However, the correlation was rather poor when measuring the improvement provided by coconut matting laid on the concrete floor. This difference may be due to the fact that the compression of the coconut matting produced by a hammerhead is much higher than the compression produced by a shoe.

inhomogeneities in floor construction, the positions of the tapping machine on the floor should be chosen, taking this factor into consideration.

Determination of Impact-sound Level from Measurements. In determining the impact-sound level in a room, measurements of sound pressure level are first made at a number of positions. These data are obtained in octave (or fractional-octave) bands. The average sound pressure level $\bar{L}_p$ in any band is then obtained from the following relation

$$\bar{L}_p = 10 \log_{10} \left[\frac{p_1^2 + p_2^2 + p_3^2 + \cdots + p_n^2}{np_0^2} \right] \quad \text{db}$$

where p_1, p_2, p_3, . . . p_n are the sound pressures in microbars measured at n different positions in the receiving room (in general three to six microphone positions are used); p_0 is the reference sound pressure of 0.0002 microbar. For purposes of comparison of data from various sources, it is convenient if all data are expressed in terms of the impact-sound level in octave frequency bands. Thus if measurements are made in bands of less than one octave wide they may be converted to corresponding octave band measurements as follows: If measurements are made in third-octave bands, add 4.9 db; if measurements are made in half-octave bands, add 3.1 db. For example, the data of Fig. 19.4 were measured in third-octave bands; then 5 db (i.e. 4.9 db rounded off to the nearest db) was added to each of the plotted points in order to express these data in terms of impact-sound levels in octave bands.

Effects of Room Absorption on Impact-sound Level Measurements. The impact-sound level which is measured in the receiving room depends on the absorption in the room, varying inversely with the total absorption. Since field measurements are made in both furnished and unfurnished buildings it is desirable for comparative purposes to adjust the results so that they correspond to levels that would have been obtained had the receiving room contained a standard amount of absorption. This *adjusted* impact-sound level, L_i, is defined by the relation

$$L_i = \bar{L}_p - 10 \log_{10} \frac{a_0}{a} \quad \text{db}$$

where a is the total absorption in the receiving room, and a_0 is the reference standard absorption of 108 sabins (square-foot units), i.e., 10 sq m, which is approximately the total absorption in an average living room. For example, if the receiving room has a total absorption of 5 sq meters instead of 10, then 3 db should be subtracted from the sound level measured in the receiving room to obtain the adjusted impact-sound level.

Adjustment to a reference absorption provides a basis for comparing the impact-sound levels measured under different conditions of absorption in the receiving room. (However, note that this does not make possible a direct comparison between the results of field and laboratory measurements, because of flanking transmission.) *Unless otherwise stated, all impact-sound level data presented in this chapter are the adjusted values.*

Average Values. Note that the impact-sound level per octave band varies with frequency. It is frequently convenient to employ an average value, obtained by averaging the levels in the various frequency bands—usually those centered between about 125 and 1,600 cps. It is the average over this frequency and that is used in this chapter, unless otherwise specified, although there has been no standard established which specifies the range over which an average is to be taken. It should be noted that if the octave band levels vary considerably with frequency, an average figure may not be especially meaningful since the average value will depend on the range over which it is taken.

Laboratory and Field Measurements. Impact-sound measurements are of two types: (1) laboratory measurements, which are carried out under idealized conditions, and (2) field measurements, which are made in building. Suppose a tapping machine is placed on a floor of a dwelling as shown in Fig. 19.3. When set into operation, it will cause the floor and hence the ceiling below it to vibrate and therefore radiate sound from the ceiling into the room below. In addition, some of the energy will be transmitted along the floor structure to adjacent wall partitions. Thus, it may travel to the walls of the room below, cause them to vibrate, and radiate sound in the room below. The transmission of sound from one room to another by some path other than the panel under test is called *flanking transmission*. Since flanking transmission can often be the limiting factor in controlling the propagation of impact noise from one room to another, it must be reduced to insignificance if we wish to evaluate the merit of a floor construction. Therefore, in laboratory measurements of impact-sound insulation, the test panel is isolated so that impact noise will be transmitted only by the panel itself. Only under such test conditions we may rate a series of different floor constructions in a manner which should depend upon the floor construction alone. Such measurements are termed *laboratory measurements*.

Because flanking transmission is usually difficult, if not impossible, to predict within desired engineering accuracy, it is frequently desirable to obtain information on full-scale floors in typical building constructions which include the effects of flanking so that these constructions may be compared with each other. Such measurements in buildings which include the effects of flanking transmission are called *field measurements*.

According to the international code for laboratory measurements, it is recommended that the size of the test partition be approximately 10 sq m. The minimum volume of the receiving room should be at least 50 cu m, although a minimum volume of 100 cu m is desirable. The sound transmitted by any indirect path shall be small compared with the sound transmitted through the test floor. The edge conditions of the test floor shall be as near practical conditions as possible. The sound field in the receiving room shall be as diffuse as possible. The determination of the impact-sound level in octave bands is rather difficult at low frequencies since the sound field is far from being diffuse. Because of this, measurements much below 100 or 125 cps are inaccurate in dwellings with rooms of normal size. An upper limit of 1,600 or 3,200 cps is set by the difficulty of measuring very low impact-sound levels in octave frequency bands in the receiving room at higher frequencies when testing a "good" floor.

For field measurements the receiving room may be any room in the building—not necessarily the room directly below the floor being tested. It is, however, in most cases of greatest interest to know the impact-sound level in the room directly below the floor being tested, as the room which usually has the highest value of the impact-sound level. The impact-sound levels given in this chapter are, unless otherwise stated, the impact-sound levels in rooms directly below the floors tested.

BUILDING CONSTRUCTIONS FOR CONTROLLING IMPACT NOISE

This section describes building constructions that have been especially designed for controlling impact noise and gives the results of experimental measurements on these as well as on ordinary building constructions. *Additional data concerning impact-sound insulation are given in the following chapter, together with corresponding data for air-borne sound insulation.** A discussion of "acceptable" impact-sound insulation is given in Chap. 40.

Bare Concrete, Hollow-block, and Wood-joist Floors. Comparative measurements made on floors of reinforced concrete, hollow-block or the filler-joist type, show that these floors differ little in their ability to provide insulation against impact sounds. Their effectiveness depends partly on the thickness of the floor and partly on its density. The dependence on thickness and density is not simple, as both the velocity-amplitude and the wavelength for the bending waves depend on these quantities. (See *Theoretical Considerations*, below.) However, an increase in thickness and density usually improves the insulation. Data also indicate that a hollow-block floor may be poorer than a corresponding reinforced-concrete floor. Measurements in buildings show that average impact-sound level below a bare con-

---

* Comprehensive field studies have been carried out in England by the Building Research Station, Garston, Herts., and in the Netherlands by the Research Institute for Public Health Engineering TNO, The Hague, Netherlands.

crete floor having an area of about 150 to 250 sq ft and a weight of 30 to 60 lb per sq ft is 70 to 75 db.   Curve 1 in Fig. 19.5 is typical of the impact-sound level measured in octave bands in the room directly below a floor of hollow-clay blocks having no floor finish.   It will be noted that there is relatively little variation with frequency. Poor insulation against impact noise at high frequencies is characteristic of such floors. In contrast curve 2 shows the impact-sound level below a wood-joist floor which shows a pronounced decrease with increasing frequency above about 500 cps; this decrease in impact-sound level is equivalent to an improvement in impact-sound insulation with respect to hollow-clay blocks.

Resilient Floor Finish on Concrete Floors.   The effectiveness of a concrete floor in isolating impact noise in buildings can be increased if a resilient floor finish is laid on the floor.   Materials such as linoleum, rubber, tile, cork tile, asphalt, and carpets are beneficial.   From the standpoint of impact-sound insulation, a thick and highly resilient floor finish rates very high.   When choosing an appropriate floor finish many nonacoustical factors must be considered which often call for a finish which is undesirable from the noise-control standpoint.   It is sometimes possible to meet both

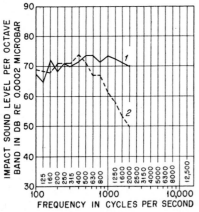

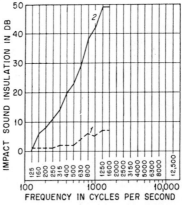

FIG. 19.5. Impact-sound level vs. frequency measured in the rooms directly below two floors, (1) a floor of hollow-clay blocks without a floor finish, and (2) a wood-joist floor.

FIG. 19.6. Impact-sound insulation provided by two different types of floor finish on a concrete floor: (1) ⅛-in. linoleum, and (2) ⅜-in. Wilton carpet.

requirements by using a floor finish composed of a hard upper layer and a resilient lower layer, e.g., linoleum and a soft fiberboard, respectively.

Usually a floor finish reduces the solid-borne vibration transmitted to the building structure by the impact; on the other hand it may increase the noise level in the same room where the impacts are produced, as indicated in the next section.

Figure 19.6 shows the impact-sound insulation provided by ⅛-in. linoleum (curve 1) and ⅜-in. Wilton carpet (curve 2) *laid on a concrete floor.*   The "average" improvements were 3 and 24 db, respectively.   Other results are illustrated in Figs. 19.7 and 19.8, which show the improvements obtained with various floor coverings on a concrete slab and on a wood floor, respectively.   If the same materials were laid on a different floor, such as a wood-joist floor, quite different results would be obtained.

Because of the effects of compression of the resilient material in the immediate area of impact, the relative improvements which are obtained may not necessarily be the same for different sources of impact.   Nevertheless such information is useful in obtaining a relative rating of various materials.

Additional data are given in Table 19.2, which tabulates the average impact-sound insulation for several floor finishes laid on bare concrete.

Floating Floor Constructions.   A *floating floor* is one which rests on the structural floor but is separated from it by a resilient support such as a resilient "chair" or a mineral-wool blanket, for example, see Fig. 19.9 (also see Fig. 19.17). It is one of the most practical means of obtaining high impact-sound insulation in building construction. *It is important in any floating-floor construction that the resilient element nowhere be shorted by a rigid mechanical connection.* (For example, Fig. 19.14c shows an example of poor construction practice because the floating floor has been short-circuited by nails through the flooring into the joists.) Particular attention must be

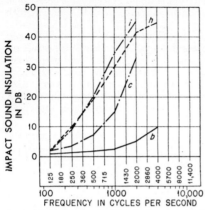

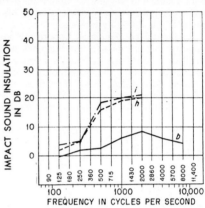

FIG. 19.7. Impact-sound insulation provided by different types of floor finish on a concrete floor: (b) linoleum on felt paper, (c) cork linoleum, ¼ in. thick, (h) "looped uncut pile" carpet, (i) coconut matting. (*Kasteleyn and van den Eijk.*[3])

FIG. 19.8. Impact-sound insulation provided by different types of floor finish on a wooden floor: (b) linoleum, ³⁄₃₂ in. thick, (h) "unlooped uncut pile" carpet, (i) coconut matting. (*Kasteleyn and van den Eijk.*[3])

paid to electric ducts, service pipes, and skirtings to avoid a solid connection between the structural floor and the floating floor. Service pipes should be wrapped in some material such as bitumen felt, where they pass through the floating floor. Ordinary skirtings will short-circuit the resilient layer, and precautions must be taken to prevent this. If the floor finish is a material such as cork tile, rubber tile, or linoleum, a wood skirting with a chamfered lower edge may be used. If a hard floor finish such as

Table 19.2. Average Values of Impact-sound Insulation Provided by Various Floor Finishes Laid on Bare Concrete

Finish	*Impact-sound Insulation, db*
Linoleum, ⅛ in.	3
Rubber tile, ⅛ in.	5
Asphalt, ⅞ in.	5–7
Parquet flooring on battens	7
Cork tile, ⁵⁄₁₆ in.	10
Wilton carpet, ⅜ in.	24
⁵⁄₃₂-in. linoleum on ¼-in. hard cork tile	6
⁵⁄₃₂-in. linoleum on ¼-in. soft cork tile	14
⁵⁄₃₂-in. linoleum on ½-in. soft cork tile	16
⁵⁄₃₂-in. linoleum on ½-in. soft fiberboard	18

jointless concrete is used, a strip of felt or building paper should be placed between the floating parts and the skirting. In general, the insertion of an elastic layer between any two elements of a building construction will provide an improvement in the insulation of solid-borne noise.

Glass-fiber blankets are sometimes used as the resilient element in floating-floor constructions because of their chemical inertness, resistance to moisture, and vibration-damping properties. Figure 19.10a shows the amount by which a resin-bonded glass-fiber blanket will be deflected if a vertical load is applied to the horizontal blanket.   The deflection depends on the density of the blanket; data are given for various blanket densities from 2 to 20 lb per cu ft.   These data are plotted in another way in Fig. 19.10*b*, which shows the deflection of the blanket as a function of blanket density for lines of constant loading.   The deflection should not exceed the line *A-A*, or the initial resilient properties of the material will be altered.

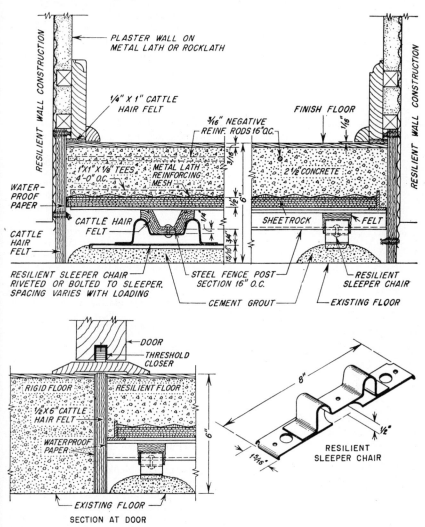

Fig. 19.9. Illustration of a floating-floor construction.   Reinforced-concrete slab "floats" on resilient chairs made of steel.   (*Courtesy of United States Gypsum Co.*)

In floating floor constructions, the velocity-amplitude of the structural element is approximately constant at low frequencies and decreases inversely as the square of the frequency at high frequencies.   The lower the rigidity of the elastic layer the lower will be the natural frequency of the system and the lower will be the vibration amplitude at high frequencies.   This reduction in vibrational energy at high frequencies is offset by the risk of an increase in noise transmission, at low frequencies.   This shift in frequency of the transmitted energy from the high-frequency range to the low-frequency range is of practical importance since the efficiency of radiation in the low-frequency range is less than that in the high-frequency range; also the ear is less sensitive at low frequencies.

Concrete Screeds Floating on Concrete Floors. Floating floors using concrete screeds may be highly effective in insulating impact noises. For example, Fig. 19.11 shows one such construction of a floating floor on a concrete structural floor. The construction shown consists of a layer of resilient material 1 in. thick laid out on the bare structural floor, care being taken to avoid gaps between the adjoining strips of the resilient material so that concrete will not pour through these gaps and short-circuit the resilient material. For this purpose a waterproof building paper with the edges overlapping 3 in. to keep the concrete from getting through will suffice. A 1½-in.-thick concrete screed is then poured on chicken wire, which is used for reinforcement. The resilient layer must be turned up along the walls to prevent contact between screed and walls. Table 19.3 shows some results of measurements on floating floors using concrete or asphalt screed. The impact-sound insulation obtainable when there is a heavy load on the asphalt screed may be less than the values given above, especially when resilient blanket is used. A greater improvement in the impact-sound insulation of concrete screed resting on a soft fiberboard can be obtained by reducing the stiffness of the resilient layer. By coating the underside of soft fiberboard with cork granules before laying it on the structural floor[5] an improvement in the impact-sound insulation of 16 db is obtained.

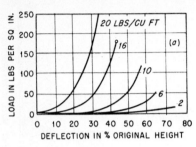

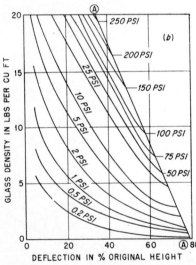

FIG. 19.10. (*a*) Deflection of a resin-bonded glass-fiber blanket vs. applied load. These data are given for various blanket densities. (*b*) Deflection of a resin-bonded glass-fiber blanket vs. blanket density for lines of constant loading. The deflection should not exceed line *A–A*. (*S. Musikant*.[4])

Wood Floors Floating on Concrete Structural Floors. The effectiveness of a concrete floor in insulating impact noise can be improved by wood flooring laid on the concrete, but an even greater improvement is obtained if the wood floor rests ("floats") on blankets, strips, or pads of a resilient material, such as mineral-wool, 1 to 1½ in. thick, laid on the bare structural floor as shown in Fig. 19.12.

Figure 19.13 shows the impact-sound level as a function of frequency below a concrete floor. Curve 1 was measured below a 3½-in.-thick bare reinforced-concrete floor; curve 2 was measured when boarding was laid on battens resting on pads of an extremely soft fiberboard on the concrete floor. The impact-sound level decreases rapidly at high frequencies, which is characteristic of a good floor.

A technique for the further increase of the impact-sound insulation is the placing of sand on the structural concrete floor between the battens which carry the floating floor. The thickness of the sand should be less than the height of the battens.

Table 19.4 gives the results of laboratory measurements of the average impact-sound insulation for various types of wood flooring on a concrete structural floor.

Table 19.3. Average Impact-sound Insulation Provided by Concrete or Asphalt Screed Floating on a Bare Concrete Floor

Construction	*Impact-sound Insulation, db*
1½-in. concrete screed resting on ½-in. soft fiberboard..............	10
1½-in. concrete screed resting on 1-in. granulated cork.............	10
1½-in. concrete screed on 1-in. resilient blanket...................	24
1-in. asphalt on ½-in. soft fiberboard............................	15
1½-in. asphalt on 1-in. mineral-wool blanket......................	27

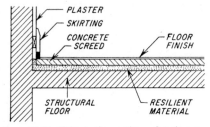

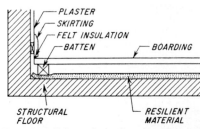

FIG. 19.11. Schematic section, showing a floating concrete screed on a concrete structural floor.

FIG. 19.12. Schematic section, showing wood floor floating on concrete structural floor. The wood floor is on 2- by 2-in. battens which rest on a mineral-wool blanket.

The following conclusions can be drawn from these data:

1. The impact-sound insulation depends on the resilient material separating the battens and the structural floor.   For example, the average relative values for no material, cork strips, and mineral-wool strips, are 7, 10, and 15 db, respectively. The insulation increases with increasing resilience.   Results of other measure-

Table 19.4. Average Impact-sound Insulation Provided by Types of Wood Flooring on a Bare Concrete Floor

Material	Additional load, lb per sq ft	Impact-sound insulation, db
Parquet flooring on battens....................	0	7
Parquet flooring on battens resting on 1½-in. cork strips.......................................	0	10
Parquet flooring on battens resting on 1-in. mineral-wool strips............................	12	15
Parquet flooring (without battens) on 2-in. dry sand...	0	11
Parquet flooring (without battens) on 2-in. dry sawdust......................................	12	21
Parquet flooring (without battens) on ¾-in. glass-silk blanket....................................	0	27
Parquet flooring (without battens) on ¾-in. glass-silk blanket....................................	12	22
Parquet flooring (without battens) on 1-in. glass-silk blanket....................................	12	21

ments show that blankets of such materials as mineral wool provide about the same insulation.   Accurate information is not available on the extent to which various resilient materials become less resilient with time, but this is a factor which should be considered and should be obtained from the manufacturer of the material that is used.

2. A ¾- or 1-in. resilient blanket provides about the same insulation although a

1-in. blanket of the same material is less apt to compress and short-circuit the floating structure.

3. A floor without battens provides considerably higher insulation than a floor with battens. This is due to the higher loading of the resilient material when battens are used. A value of 15 db was measured for a parquet flooring on battens resting on 1-in. mineral-wool strips, and 21 db for the same floor without battens resting on 1-in. glass-fiber blanket.

4. The measurements show the effect of loading a light floor which rests on resilient material. For example, the average impact-sound insulation below parquet flooring (without battens) on a ¾-in. glass-fiber blanket is 27 db with no load, and 22 db with an additional load of 12 lb per sq ft. Usually the values obtained in a building are not quite so high as those obtained in the laboratory because of short circuiting of the resilient intermediate layer which often occurs in practice. Furthermore skirtings and ducts carrying service pipes will reduce the effectiveness of the construction.

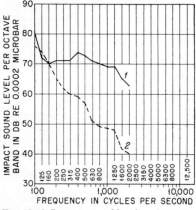

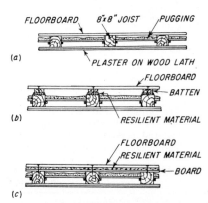

FIG. 19.13. Impact-sound level vs. frequency in rooms directly below: (1) a 3½-in.-thick bare reinforced-concrete floor, and (2) a wood flooring attached to battens which rest on pads of soft fiberboard; this structure floats on the concrete structural floor of (1).

FIG. 19.14. Three types of wood-joist floors: (a) an ordinary construction, (b) a floating-floor construction, and (c) a floating-floor construction that has been incorrectly built—nails pierce the resilient material and "short-circuit" the resilient material.

Floating Wood-joist Floors. Figure 19.14 shows three types of wood-joist floors. The first (a) is an ordinary wood-joist floor; the second and third are floating constructions, (b) being a good construction, and (c) a poor construction. In the two latter cases the floor boards are nailed to battens which are separated from the joists by a resilient layer. *The nails should not pass through the resilient layer as shown in (c).*

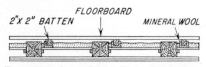

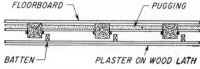

FIG. 19.15. A wood-joist floor with battens resting on mineral-wool strips.

FIG. 19.16. False ceiling carried on independent joists.

The average impact-sound level beneath a wood-joist floor having an area of about 150 to 250 sq ft and filled with clay used as pugging* is usually about 65 to 70 db. A

---

* Pugging (British terminology): materials used to pack the space under finish floor to improve sound insulation by providing additional mass at low cost and by additional damping.

characteristic curve for the impact-sound level as a function of frequency in a room below such a wood-joist floor construction is shown as curve 2 in Fig. 19.5.

The characteristic distinction between solid-borne sound below a wood-joist floor and a concrete floor appears in the high-frequency range, where the impact-sound level is considerably higher below the concrete floor than below the wood-joist floor. Figure 19.15 shows a wood-joist floor, having the boards nailed to special battens resting on mineral-wool strips laid out on trays.

Effect of Floor Finish on Noise Level in Source Room.   Thus far the discussion in this chapter has pertained to noise production in rooms other than that in which the solid-borne sound is produced.   It is not always realized that *a floor construction which assures a low noise level in the other rooms of a building does not necessarily assure a low noise level in the room in which the solid-borne vibration is produced.*   For example, consider a floating wood floor which is laid on a bare concrete structural floor; the noise in the room where the impacts are produced may be greater for the wood floor than for the bare concrete—however, the noise produced in distant rooms may be less for the wood floor than for the bare concrete because much less energy is transmitted to the building structure.

Table 19.5. The Sound Pressure Level Produced in the Same Room as the Tapping Machine*

The values are given in decibels referred to the level produced by the tapping machine on bare concrete.

	125 cps	250 cps	500 cps	1,000 cps	2,000 cps	4,000 cps	Average db
¾-in. wood floor on 2 by 3 battens...	+8	+27	+14	+10	+3	−1	+10
Same, with rock-wool fill...........	+10	+15	+11	+6	+3	−2	+7
Bare concrete.......................	0	0	0	0	0	0	0
³⁄₁₆-in. hard board on ¼-in. Celotex..	−3	+1	−1	0	−2	−5	−2
⁵⁄₃₂-in. asphalt tile...................	−1	+3	0	−2	−6	−8	−2
³⁄₁₆-in. rubber tile..................	−1	+2	−1	−3	−5	−8	−3
Heavy carpet (no pad)..............	−2	−1	−3	−7	−7	−5	−4
½-in. cork tile....................	−3	0	−7	−4	−6	−8	−5
⅛-in. asphalt-saturated felt.........	−5	−2	−3	−4	−8	−9	−5
½-in. asphalt-saturated Celotex......	−4	0	−4	−5	−8	−10	−5
³⁄₁₆-in. linoleum on felt.............	−3	−3	−6	−9	−9	−12	−7

* After Lindahl and Sabine.[6]

The influence of floor finishing on the sound produced in the room itself is measured in the following way: A tapping machine is placed on a floor covered with various floor finishings.   The effective sound pressure level then is measured in octave bands. Table 19.5 shows the results of some measurements of the sound pressure level in a room; the noise is produced by striking the concrete floor with a tapping machine (1) when the floor is bare, and (2) when various floor finishes are placed on the concrete structural floor.   A positive value indicates that striking that floor finish produces a higher sound level than striking the bare concrete; a negative value indicates an improvement over the bare concrete by the number of decibels indicated. These data show that an elastic layer between the source of impacts and the structure floor can produce a marked decrease in the noise level in the source room.   Similar results are given in References 7 and 8.

Ceiling Constructions.   Two types of ceiling construction, which will reduce the radiation of sound waves from floors set into vibration by impacts, are discussed below: the false ceiling and the suspended ceiling.   Such ceilings reduce the noise level *only* in the room where they are used, by decreasing the radiation from the ceiling treated; no reduction is obtained in other rooms in the building having an ordinary ceiling.   Furthermore they do not reduce the radiation of sound from the side walls which results from flanking transmission (see the following section).   On the other hand, they improve the insulation not only for impact sound but for air-borne sounds as well.

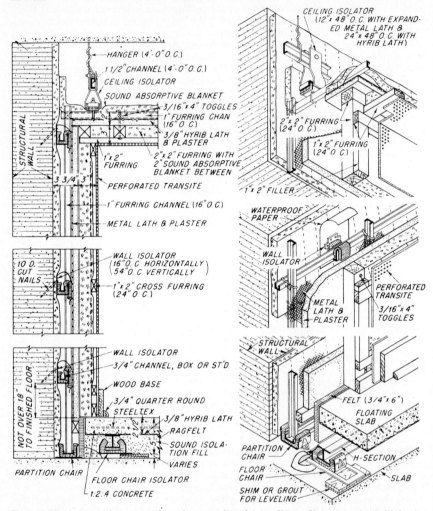

FIG. 19.17. A type of construction often employed in radio studios where both high air-borne and solid-borne sound insulation is required.   This is obtained by a floating-floor construction, a suspended ceiling, and a wall construction in which the interior surface is connected to the structural wall in a non-rigid manner.   In this construction the interior surface consists of a perforated board, backed with a sound-absorptive mineral-wool blanket which provides high sound absorption in the room.   The sound insulation against noises of outside origin is obtained principally through the use of the resilient construction. (*Courtesy of Johns-Manville Sales Corp.*)

False Ceiling.   False ceilings are ceilings which are independent of the floor-ceiling structure.   For example, Fig. 19.16 shows a false ceiling carried on independent joists.

Suspended Ceiling.   Suspended ceilings are ceilings which are hung from the structural floor by wire suspension or resilient hangers.   Figure 19.17 shows a type of construction sometimes employed in radio and recording studio.

Figure 19.18 shows an example of plaster on wood lath which is suspended from a concrete floor by means of a resilient clip.   The noise reduction obtained using this construction is usually not so high as that obtained with a fully suspended ceiling. Best results are obtained if the points of contact with the structural floor are as few as possible.

Ceilings with High Critical Frequencies.   The effectiveness of a false or a suspended ceiling, or of an isolated wall construction, can be increased by using an interior finish panel having a high *critical frequency.**   This will result in a low radiation efficiency for the structure.   Minimum energy will be radiated from a heavy panel that is flexible.   It can be obtained, for example, by providing the ceiling (and the walls)

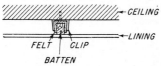

FIG. 19.18. A semi-suspended ceiling of plaster on wood lath on the underside of a concrete floor.

with a covering consisting of lightweight panels, nailed to lath, which are plastered on the surface facing the room; this covering has a low bending stiffness compared with its mass, and thus a high critical frequency (see Chap. 20).

The critical frequency of panels having a high bending stiffness, for example, plywood, can be increased by cutting slits in it.   This slitting diminishes the bending stiffness without altering the mass per unit area significantly.   It is also possible to use a thin supporting panel and increase the weight by fixing heavy strips to the panel.

Wall Insulation.   The general principles of impact-sound insulation outlined above for the insulation of floor and ceiling constructions also apply to walls.   An example of effective wall insulation is given in Fig. 19.17.   See Chap. 20 for further details.

THEORETICAL CONSIDERATIONS

Excitation of Vibration in Building Structural Elements by Impacts.   Vibration in building structural elements may be propagated as longitudinal-, transverse-, or bending-type waves.   Bending waves are of considerable importance in the transmission of solid-borne noise.   The velocity amplitude of the bending waves caused by the impact of a mass striking a building structural element, especially a floor, at low frequencies is approximately independent of frequency and is inversely proportional to the mechanical impedance of the building structural element at the exciting point; at high frequencies (usually above the frequencies of interest in solid-borne noise control) it is inversely proportional to the frequency.   The lighter the striking mass and the higher the mechanical impedance of the building structural element, the higher will be the frequency at which this decrease occurs.

Recent laboratory measurements in a concrete bar show that the attenuation values for longitudinal and bending waves are about the same.[1]   (Some attenuation measurements for longitudinal waves in samples of building materials are given in Table 19.1.)   The attenuation which is measured in actual building structures is considerably higher than that which is obtained in the laboratory, and depends on frequency. This is partly due to loss at nonrigid connections between different parts of the building structure, and partly to dispersion and reflection of energy where there are changes in cross-sectional areas, materials, and other discontinuities in the building structure.

Floating Floors.   According to theory, the impact-sound insulation which can be obtained from the use of a floating floor at frequencies very much greater than the resonant frequency f_n is[9]

$$\Delta L_p \cong 40 \log \frac{f}{f_n} \qquad \text{db} \qquad\qquad (19.1)$$

---

* See Chaps. 20 and 22 for a discussion of *critical frequency.*

where ΔL_p is the insulation in decibels and f_n is the natural frequency of a floating floor on a resilient layer, given by $(1/2\pi)(k/m)^{1/2}$; k is the dynamical stiffness of the resilient layer per unit of area of floating floor, and m is its surface mass per unit area. The dynamical stiffness is determined primarily by the properties of the resilient layer and the stiffness of the air enclosed between the floating floor and the structural floor. Neither the impact mass nor the properties of the structural floor nor the flexural stiffness of the floating floor form part of this simplified expression for the reduction.

Elastic Layer between Structural Elements. Another possible method of obtaining a considerable increase in attenuation of the vibration transmitted from one building structural element to another is by the insertion of an elastic layer between the two elements. When the thickness of the intermediate layer (of negligible damping) is small compared with the wavelength and both parts of the interrupted building structural elements extend infinitely, the attenuation for longitudinal waves is given by

$$20 \log \frac{\pi l_2 Y_1}{\lambda_1 Y_2} \quad \text{db} \tag{19.2}$$

where Y_1 and Y_2 are Young's moduli of the interrupted structural elements and the resilient layer, respectively, l_2 the thickness of the resilient layer, and λ_1 the wavelength of longitudinal waves in the interrupted element.[9] The attenuation increases with increasing thickness of the resilient layer and with increasing frequency. The assumptions of the expression are *not* fulfilled in actual building construction. However, the expression permits one to estimate whether significant insulation will occur. For example, $1\frac{3}{16}$-in.-thick cork $(Y_2 = 3.10^8 \text{ g cm}^{-1} \text{ sec}^{-2})$ inserted in a concrete pillar or wall according to the above expression provides an attenuation of 7 db at 100 cps and 27 db at 1,000 cps.

The attenuation for bending waves when interrupting a structural element by a resilient layer computed under similar conditions is characterized partly by a frequency f_t of total transmission (damping is neglected) occurring in the low-frequency range, and partly by an attenuation which for frequencies from $2f_t$ to $4f_t$ is determined by

$$30 \log \frac{f}{f_t} \quad \text{db} \tag{19.3}$$

For a resilient layer at a corner, e.g., between a ceiling and its supporting walls, theory indicates that the attenuation for bending waves is characterized by two frequencies of total insulation, if damping is neglected. These frequencies occur in the low-frequency range.

REFERENCES

1. Kuhl, W., and H. Kaiser: *Acustica*, **2**: 179 (1952).
2. International Standards Organization, Technical Committee 43, "Field and Laboratory Measurements of Airborne and Impact Sound Transmission in Buildings," 1957 draft.
3. Kasteleyn, M. L., and J. van den Eijk: Report No. 22, Publication No. 56, Technical Physics Service, T.N.O., The Hague, December, 1954.
4. Musikant, S.: *Prod. Eng.*, **25**: 166 (February, 1954).
5. Gösele, K.: *Gesundheits Ingenieur*, **75**: 20 (1954).
6. Lindahl, R., and H. J. Sabine: *J. Acoust. Soc. Amer.*, **11**: 401 (1939).
7. Ingerslev, F.: "Acoustics in Modern Building Practice," Architectural Press, London, 1950.
8. Gösele, K.: *Veroffentl. Forschungsgemeinschaft Bauen und Wohnen*, **11** (1951).
9. Cremer, L.: Department of Scientific and Industrial Research, London, England. Sponsored Research in Germany, Report No. 1 Series B.
10. Gösele, K.: *Gesundheits Ingenieur*, **70**: 66 (1949).

Chapter 20

TRANSMISSION OF NOISE THROUGH WALLS AND FLOORS

RICHARD K. COOK, PH.D., AND PETER CHRZANOWSKI

National Bureau of Standards, Washington, D.C.

INTRODUCTION

The sound insulation provided by internal walls and floors, and by the exterior walls and roof of a building, is an important factor in the control of noise. Internal noises may originate from speech, music, plumbing, footsteps, or machinery in the building. Noises external to a building might be the sounds from street traffic, industrial operations, or aircraft.

Transmission of noise into a room of a building can take place in several ways: (1) by air-borne sound passing through the walls or floor structures in a manner described in the next section, (2) by the transmission of vibration in the building structure caused by mechanical vibration or impacts imparted directly to it; this vibration may cause a surface such as a wall or floor to vibrate and to radiate sound, and (3) entirely through the air, for example, by the entry of sound through open windows, doors, and the ducts of ventilating systems. In this chapter we consider only item (1) and part of item (3); item (2) is discussed in Chap. 19, and the control of ventilation system noise is discussed in Chap. 27.

MECHANISM OF SOUND TRANSMISSION

Air-borne sound is transmitted through a wall in the following way: Sound waves incident on one side of a wall exert a fluctuating pressure on it. As a result, the wall vibrates like a diaphragm and radiates sound into the space on the opposite side; this occurs to some extent even in the case of a massive wall—for example, one constructed of 8-in. thick concrete. For most practical constructions, the heavier the partition the smaller will be its amplitude of vibration and, therefore, the greater the sound insulation it will afford. Fortunately, from the standpoint of noise control, the transfer of energy from an air-borne sound wave to the much denser material in any useful wall construction is low. Only a small fraction of the energy in the incident sound waves is transformed into vibrational energy of the wall and then radiated as sound on the far side of the wall. The major portion is either reflected or absorbed at the surface on the side exposed to the sound. Most of the remainder is dissipated within the material and structural members of the wall, although for a simple wall, constructed of a panel of nonporous, homogeneous material and rigidly clamped at the edges, the fraction of the energy which is absorbed at the surface or dissipated within the material is insignificant.

A surprisingly large difference between the sound levels on the opposite sides of the wall is necessary for good insulation. Even if the average level difference is 40 db, a listener on the quieter side may readily hear and understand loud speech on the other side of the wall.

For example, consider a panel that is an edge-clamped sheet of gypsum wallboard. At middle audio frequencies, such a panel will reflect about 95 per cent of the sound energy incident on it. Most of the remaining 5 per cent of the incident sound energy will be transmitted to the opposite side, so that there will be a loss of about 13 db in the sound that is transmitted through the panel. This is the order of magnitude of sound transmission actually found by measurement for walls of this type, which, since the sounds of loud speech can be easily heard and understood on the quiet side, do not provide adequate sound insulation.

USE OF ACOUSTICAL MATERIALS FOR SOUND INSULATION PURPOSES

Laboratory experiments show that acoustical materials that are applied to a partition that is a poor sound insulator usually are not effective except in the case of certain lightweight constructions. Putting on a single layer of almost any commonly available acoustical material will reduce the sound energy transmitted by less than 5 db. Much more effective results can be obtained by a large increase in mass or the construction of a double wall. Although porous materials are frequently good absorbers of sound, they usually provide little acoustic insulation for a partition.

RESONANCE

Most walls when struck will vibrate for a shorter or longer time at their own natural frequencies. When the sound incident on a wall is of the same frequency as one of the natural frequencies of the wall, the wall will resonate and vibrate at a much larger amplitude than at other frequencies. The result will be that a proportionally larger part of the incident sound will be transmitted so that the air-borne sound insulation will be poorer at this frequency. The insulation will be particularly low at the lowest natural frequency.

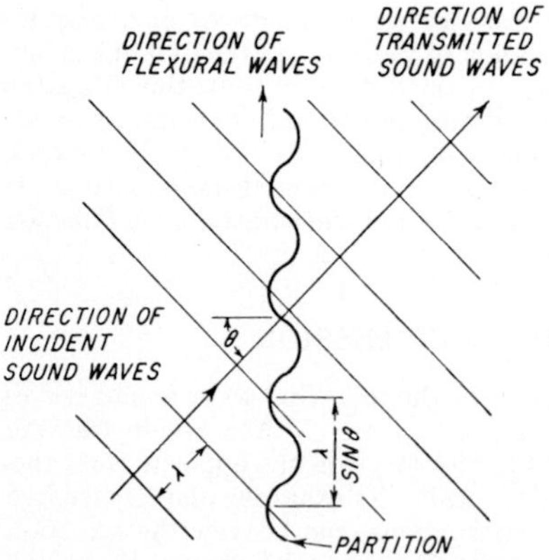

FIG. 20.1. For certain angles of incidence of sound waves, the *coincidence effect* may be responsible for low values of transmission loss for a partition. The amplitude of flexural waves in the above partition has been exaggerated.

If effects of resonances are to be avoided, it is desirable to have the lowest natural frequency as low as possible. This condition can be met by partitions of large mass and small stiffness. Another way to reduce resonance effects is to make the walls so stiff that the lowest natural frequency is above the limit of audibility, but with ordinary building construction materials it is impractical or impossible to do this.

Coincidence Effect. An effect analogous to resonance occurs when a thin homogeneous partition, constructed of material with low damping, is set into flexural vibration by plane sound waves incident on the partition at an oblique angle. At certain frequencies the phases of the incident sound waves will "coincide" with the phases of vibration of the panel in such a way as to transmit an abnormally high fraction of the incident sound. Let λ be the wavelength of the sound waves whose normal to the wavefronts forms the angle θ with the normal to the partition as indicated in Fig. 20.1. At a certain angle of incidence, the wavelength of the flexural wave in the partition is such that the pressure crests in the sound wave coincide with the crests in the flexural wave.   This occurs when the wavelength in the partition is $\lambda/\sin\theta$, and when it does, the sound insulation of the partition is greatly reduced.

The velocity of a flexural wave in a thin panel is proportional to the square root of the frequency.   Thus the coincidence effect occurs only at frequencies greater than a certain critical frequency, f_c, which is the frequency at which the flexural wave velocity just equals the velocity of sound in air.   For a given material, f_c is inversely proportional to the thickness of the panel.

The coincidence effect may occur in actual building partitions, but because of studding, discontinuities, and damping in partitions, its effects can usually be neglected. Furthermore the sound wave fields in rooms are usually more or less random; this too reduces the influence of the coincidence effect because only a small fraction of the sound energy is incident at the correct angle.   Wall constructions of homogeneous concrete made with a lightweight aggregate, having a thickness of 1 to 3 in., or thin homogeneous partitions will have a critical frequency in the range of audibility. Hence, they may provide poor sound insulation at certain frequencies.   The coincidence effect can be reduced by the use of very stiff and thick walls or by heavy walls with small stiffness.

DEFINITION OF TRANSMISSION LOSS

A quantitative measure of the air-borne sound insulation of a structure is called the *sound-transmission loss*, which is defined as the number of decibels by which sound energy which is randomly incident on a partition is reduced in transmission through it. It is abbreviated as *T.L.*

In normal use a wall or floor construction has air-borne sound incident upon it from many different directions.   For example, a person speaking in a room may direct the sound waves of his voice at some particular angle at a given wall, but the sound waves reflected from the other walls and objects in the room will be incident on the wall at different angles.   Therefore transmission loss is defined and measured for the condition of random sound incidence, that is, when sound waves are incident upon a wall with equal intensities and from all directions over a hemisphere on the "loud" side.

Sounds of low frequency can be transmitted much more easily through a building partition than can high-frequency sounds.   This is a matter of common observation which is discussed from the theoretical point of view in Chap. 22.   Because of this variation with frequency, measurements of transmission loss are made at a number of frequencies.   A knowledge of the frequency dependence of the transmission loss of the partition, together with the frequency distribution of the noise to be insulated, is essential for scientific noise control.   On the other hand, it is sometimes convenient to denote an "average" insulating value of a partition by a single number, even though an average value does not indicate this frequency dependence and depends on the method of averaging.   A number frequently used in the United States is the average value of the transmission losses measured at the nine frequencies: 125, 175, 250, 350, 500, 700, 1,000, 2,000, and 4,000 cps.   The *average* transmission loss is implied when a single number is given in this Handbook for the sound transmission loss of a construction.   In Europe, measurements are made at 16 test frequencies at one-third octave intervals in the range between 100 and 3,200 cps.   The average transmission loss for these 16 frequencies is about 2 db less than for the nine frequencies specified above.

Suppose a plane wave of sound is incident on a partition.   A certain fraction of the energy will be transmitted through the structure.   This fraction will vary with frequency and the angle of incidence.   At a given frequency, the fraction which represents the average over all angles of incidence is defined as the transmission coefficient τ. The transmission loss is related to τ by the formula

$$T.L. = 10\log_{10}\frac{1}{\tau}\quad\text{db}\quad\quad\quad (20.1)$$

For example, if a wall transmits very little sound energy its value of τ will approach zero; in contrast, a wall that transmits almost 100 per cent of the energy which strikes it will have a transmission coefficient approximately equal to unity.

The *sound insulation data* given in Appendix 20.1 lists values of transmission loss for representative types of wall and floor constructions. Figure 20.2 shows transmission losses for various types of partition constructions which illustrate principles of sound insulation.

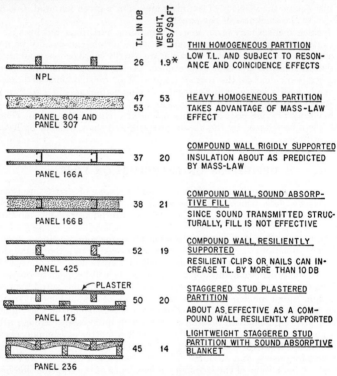

	T.L. IN DB	WEIGHT, LBS/SQ FT	
NPL	26	1.9*	THIN HOMOGENEOUS PARTITION LOW T.L. AND SUBJECT TO RESONANCE AND COINCIDENCE EFFECTS
PANEL 804 AND PANEL 307	47 53	53	HEAVY HOMOGENEOUS PARTITION TAKES ADVANTAGE OF MASS-LAW EFFECT
PANEL 166 A	37	20	COMPOUND WALL RIGIDLY SUPPORTED INSULATION ABOUT AS PREDICTED BY MASS-LAW
PANEL 166 B	38	21	COMPOUND WALL, SOUND ABSORPTIVE FILL SINCE SOUND TRANSMITTED STRUCTURALLY, FILL IS NOT EFFECTIVE
PANEL 425	52	19	COMPOUND WALL, RESILIENTLY SUPPORTED RESILIENT CLIPS OR NAILS CAN INCREASE T.L. BY MORE THAN 10 DB
PANEL 175	50	20	STAGGERED STUD PLASTERED PARTITION ABOUT AS EFFECTIVE AS A COMPOUND WALL RESILIENTLY SUPPORTED
PANEL 236	45	14	LIGHTWEIGHT STAGGERED STUD PARTITION WITH SOUND ABSORPTIVE BLANKET

* SUPERFICIAL WEIGHT OF SHEET (I.E. EXCLUDING STUDDING)

FIG. 20.2. Various types of partition constructions which illustrate principles of sound insulation. The numbered panels correspond to those listed in the tables of Appendix 20.1. The panel labeled NPL is from Ref. 10.

MEASUREMENT OF AIR-BORNE SOUND TRANSMISSION LOSS

Laboratory Measurements. The standard laboratory method of measuring airborne sound transmission loss is based upon the definition of τ given above. A specimen of the wall under test is placed in an aperture between two test rooms which are acoustically insulated from one another (see Fig. 20.3). Only the wall under test transmits sound from the source room to the receiving room. A random sound field is created in the source room by means of loudspeakers radiating a narrow band of frequencies. The sound which is transmitted through the test wall gives rise to a random sound field in the reverberant receiving room whose sound level is determined by the sound power entering and by the total absorption in this room. The sound levels in the two rooms are measured with microphones. Hence, the transmission coefficient τ and the sound transmission loss $T.L.$ of the test wall may be deduced from the following formulas:[1]

$$|p_2|^2 = \frac{\tau S}{a} |p_1|^2 \tag{20.2}$$

where S = area of the test wall, a = total number of sound absorptive units in the receiving room, $|p_1|^2$ = mean squared sound pressure in the source room, and $|p_2|^2$ = mean squared pressure in the receiving room. Then:

$$T.L. = L_1 - L_2 + 10 \log_{10} \frac{S}{a} \quad \text{db} \qquad (20.3)$$

where $L_1 = 10 \log_{10} |p_1|^2$, and $L_2 = 10 \log_{10} |p_2|^2$.

For example, in the transmission test chambers of the National Bureau of Standards, the wall to be tested is constructed as a panel about 7 ft high by 6 ft wide which fills the aperture between the source and receiving rooms. Panels for floor and ceiling constructions are about the same size. A random sound field is established in the source room by means of a rotating array of loudspeakers which radiate a narrow band of frequencies. The center frequency of the band can be adjusted anywhere between 125 cps and 4,000 cps. Nine test frequencies are generally used. The sound levels L_1 and L_2 in Eq. (20.3) are measured by several microphones which have been carefully located in each of the source and receiving rooms. Further details of the method of measurement that is used are given in a tentative recommended standard published by the American Society for Testing Materials.[2] Methods have been developed at the National Bureau of Standards for the measurement of sound transmission loss as a

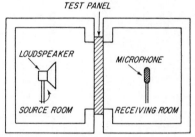

FIG. 20.3. Mounting of a partition test panel between two rooms for a sound transmission loss test. (Not to scale.)

continuous function of frequency in which the results are plotted automatically.[3] These results are reported in the form of curves.

Field Measurements. A number of European laboratories have made "field measurements" of transmission loss in actual building constructions following the basic principle of laboratory measurements. A random sound field is established in the source room and the average sound pressure levels are measured in the source room and an adjacent receiving room. From these data and the absorption in the receiving room, the transmission loss for the partition, which is common to the two rooms, may be determined. It should be noted that the value which is computed depends not only on the characteristics of the common partition, but on other factors as well. In contrast to laboratory measurements, where sound is transmitted from one room to an adjoining room only through the partition under test, in field measurements sound energy may pass from one room to another by many paths. The transmission through paths other than that through the common partition is defined as *flanking transmission*. In field tests the above method of transmission measurements between adjoining rooms has been extended to include the transmission of sound between any two rooms in a building, even though they may have no common partition.

The results of field measurements are sometimes given as average *sound pressure level differences*, defined as the difference between the average sound pressure levels in the source room, L_1, and the receiving room, L_2. The difference is a function of the total absorption in the receiving room. In order to provide a standard basis for comparison of field measurements made in various buildings, the level difference may be "normalized" by a correction term which takes into account the absorption in the receiving room, a, relative to a standard absorption, a_0. Thus, the normalized level

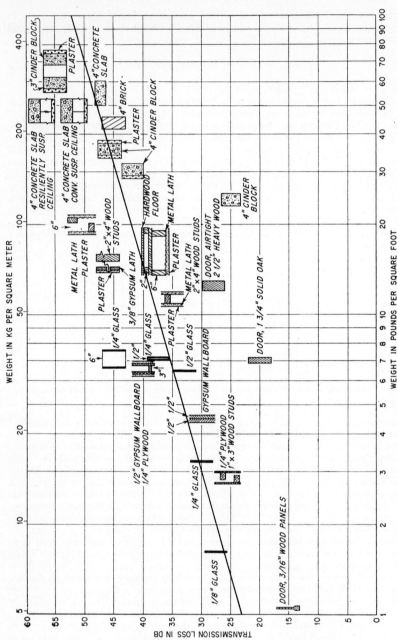

Fig. 20.4. The mass law relation between average sound transmission loss and mass per unit area of partition. For additional data see Appendix 20.1.

difference is given by

$$D_N = L_1 - L_2 + 10 \log_{10} \frac{a_0}{a} \quad \text{db} \tag{20.4}$$

where a_0 is 10 sq meters of absorption.*

HOMOGENEOUS PARTITIONS

One of the simplest types of wall constructions is a nonporous, homogeneous partition having the same physical properties throughout. Typical examples of homogeneous partitions are brick walls, concrete walls and floors, solid concrete block or gypsum block walls, solid plaster partitions, etc. An example of a nonhomogeneous partition is the stud wall with plasterboard and plaster on either side, commonly found in building constructions in the United States.

At a given frequency, the transmission loss for a homogeneous partition increases with the mass per unit area. Although the theory presented in Chap. 22 shows that the increase should be 6 db for each doubling of the mass per unit area, experiments show that this increase in average transmission loss is nearer 4.4 db. This empirical law is called the "mass law," and is represented by the straight line shown in Fig. 20.4. The empirical formula corresponding to the straight line is

$$T.L. = 23 + 14.5 \log_{10} m \quad \text{db} \tag{20.5}$$

where m is the mass of the partition in lb per sq ft. If m is expressed in kg per sq meter, then Eq. (20.5) becomes

$$T.L. = 13 + 14.5 \log_{10} m \quad \text{db} \tag{20.5a}$$

It is apparent that the average transmission losses of each of the various homogeneous partitions represented in the diagram follow this empirical law reasonably well, regardless of the material of construction.

The sound insulation of a partition is much greater at high frequencies than at low frequencies. According to theory, the transmission loss of a homogeneous partition should increase by 6 db with each doubling of frequency; but this theoretical result does not agree with experimental measurements. Figure 20.5 gives

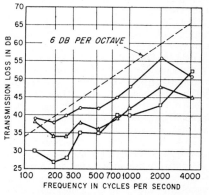

Fig. 20.5. Variation of transmission loss with frequency for three partitions. The dotted line has a slope of 6 db per octave. The panels, whose numbers correspond to those listed in the tables of Appendix 20.1, are:

○ = Panel 236, staggered wood studs with gypsum wall board.

△ = Panel 304, hollow gypsum block, plastered.

□ = Panel 166A, steel studs and metal lath, plastered.

(*National Bureau of Standards.*[9])

the comparison for several partitions. Generally, the transmission loss increases more slowly than 6 db per octave below 1,000 cps and increases at about the theoretical rate above this frequency, but there are many exceptions to this. Resonances and coinci-

* According to the Building Research Station in England, the reverberation time in furnished dwellings is very nearly independent of volume and of frequency and is approximately 0.5 sec. On this basis, they have computed the normalized level difference from the equation

$$D'_N = L_1 - L_2 + 10 \log_{10} \frac{t_{60}}{0.5} \quad \text{db}$$

where t_{60} is the reverberation time of the receiving room. The difference D_N usually differs from the transmission loss by less than 3 db. The results of some field measurements of level differences in dwellings are shown in Figs. 20.10 through 20.13.

dence effects discussed above may cause the values of transmission loss to be exceptionally low near some frequencies.

NONHOMOGENEOUS SINGLE-WALL PARTITIONS

The wall and floor-ceiling constructions in many types of buildings do not have the homogeneous character described in the preceding section. Such nonhomogeneous walls and floors are of various types. Consider, for example, the sound insulation of a wood-stud construction with plasterboard and nonporous plaster on the two faces of the studding. This is a type of wall construction frequently used in America. The mechanism of transmission through such a partition may be described as follows: Sound waves incident on one plastered face of the partition cause it to vibrate. The vibrations are transmitted mechanically to the studs and through them to the second plaster face which vibrates in turn and radiates sound. It is difficult to calculate or to estimate, on other than an empirical basis, the transmission loss of such a construction. About the only general observation that can be made is that the transmission loss is equal to or greater than that for a homogeneous partition having the same mass per unit area.

For the case where the plasterboard is nailed to the studs, the transmission loss is about the same as that given by the mass law (see Fig. 20.4). However, the insulation can be substantially improved without an increase in mass by making use of special nails or resilient clips for holding the plasterboard (or metal lath) onto the studding. With some spring-clip fastening systems, as in Panel 420, it is possible to obtain a transmission loss about 10 db greater than for a similar construction where ordinary lathing nails are used, as in Panel 148 (see Appendix 20.1). Consistent with adequate mechanical strength, the lath should be attached to the studs at as few points as possible if maximum sound insulation is to be provided; this will reduce the coupling between the plaster faces and the studs.

In stud walls having plasterboard nailed to the studs, practically all of the sound is transmitted through the studs themselves. Experiments show that inserting sound-absorptive material into the space between the studs provides little improvement in sound insulation, unless the material added contributes appreciably to the mass of the panel or to the damping of the studs. This does not apply to staggered-stud constructions, which are discussed below.

Another common nonhomogeneous wall construction is a masonry wall with furring, and plasterboard and plaster on the outer faces of the furring. The results of measurements show that the average transmission loss for such walls can be considerably greater than that for a homogeneous wall of the same mass. The tables in Appendix 20.1 show that by furring out a masonry wall, the average transmission loss can be increased by as much as 5 db for an increase in mass of less than 15 per cent, as is illustrated by Panels 85 and 82.

NONHOMOGENEOUS DOUBLE-WALL PARTITIONS

An effective way of obtaining a large amount of sound insulation for a given weight per unit area is by means of a double-wall construction. One type is the staggered-stud construction, e.g., Panel 235, which requires two separate sets of studs. Each set carries one of the wall leaves. There is no mechanical connection between the two sets of studs except, of course, at their common support. The average transmission loss for such a construction can sometimes be greater than that for a homogeneous partition having three times the mass per unit area. The sound insulation can be further improved somewhat by weaving an absorbent blanket between the two sets of staggered studs; this benefit is obtained for lightweight constructions only. The basis for the improvement resulting from the addition of an absorptive blanket appears to come from the fact that a substantial portion of the sound energy is absorbed in the blanket as the sound is transmitted from one side of the partition to the other through the air space between the two leaves.

The transmission loss of a double wall increases as the separation of the two parts of the double wall increases, provided the distance between them is less than a wavelength, for, according to theory, the combined transmission loss of two leaves (neglecting flanking transmission) should be the sum of the transmission losses for the separate leaves, when the distance between them is much greater than the wavelength of the transmitted sound. Full advantage cannot be taken of this spacing effect because only small separations, 2 in. to 4 in., are practicable in most building constructions. Improvements resulting from the use of resilient clips, stud staggering, and increased spacing between the wall leaves may be greater for large walls than for relatively small panels of a size such as those which are measured in the laboratory.

USE OF GRANULAR FILL FOR AIR-BORNE SOUND INSULATION

Sand and other materials such as crushed brick and tile chips may be used to increase the sound insulation of building partitions and floors.[4,5] When such a material is used in a thin layer, it acts as an added mass element and to some extent also as a friction element, and so helps to attenuate the sound transmission. This increase in attenuation is greater at higher frequencies and increases with the thickness of layer. Fine sand spread on a floor to a thickness equivalent to 10 per cent of the weight of the floor slab, or about 1 to 2 in. thick, has been found to be effective.

A similar damping effect occurs when the cavities in hollow-tile walls and floors are filled with granular material. The greatest improvement is obtained with tiles having large cavities when the cavities are filled with a mixture of fine sand and sharp-edged rubble. The use of materials such as sawdust also provides such an improvement.

SOUNDPROOF ROOMS AND STUDIOS

"Soundproof" rooms (in which the noise level is very low) are required for some purposes, as for example in radio studios or audiology clinics. Not only must great care be exercised in selecting the location, but also considerable attention must be paid to the details of construction of such rooms. A single-wall construction will suffice for many purposes. Where the utmost in sound insulation is required, a double-wall construction should be used.

The walls of a soundproof room can be constructed of masonry—brick or tile—with plaster on each side. Fitted with a good door, such a room can be expected to show an over-all transmission loss of over 40 db. If the foundation on which the room is to be placed is subject to vibration, the room should be supported on vibration-isolation pads or "chairs." The interior wall surfaces should be treated in accordance with the principles given in Chap. 18 to reduce the level of any noise generated within the room.

A highly effective soundproof room, with a transmission loss of 60 or more db, can be achieved by a double-wall masonry construction having an air space 3 to 6 in. wide between the two walls. Extreme care must be taken during construction to make certain no objects fall into the air space to form a mechanical tie between the walls. Otherwise, a large part of the improvement with the double-wall construction will be lost.

Masonry-type soundproof rooms have a number of disadvantages. They cannot be moved easily to another location; in the event that they must be dismantled, they have almost no salvage value; construction and removal of such rooms are accompanied by dirt; and vibration-isolation support may be difficult to achieve. To overcome the objections to masonry construction, demountable soundproof booths having steel-panel type wall constructions have been designed. In one type the booths were constructed with the panels shown in Fig. 20.6.

DEMOUNTABLE PARTITIONS

Modern office, industrial, and other types of large buildings are frequently designed in such a way that large rooms can be subdivided on demand into smaller working areas by means of demountable partitions. Such partitions, now commercially available, are constructed usually of metal panels in modular widths. Whenever it is desired to rearrange the partition layout, the panels are unbolted, moved to their new location and fastened together again.

The design for demountable partitions should be based on the general sound-insulation principles for other types of constructions. These principles are illustrated in Fig. 20.6. The panels consist of two sheets of steel with composition board cemented on their inner faces.[6] The space between the steel panels contains a rock-wool blanket. The over-all thickness of the panels is 3 in. and the weight is 7 lb per sq ft.

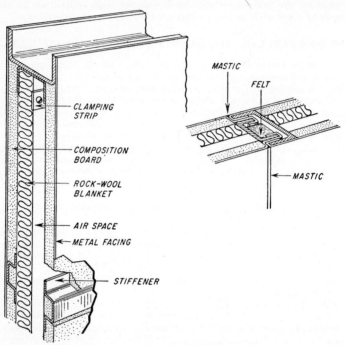

MASTIC

FELT

CLAMPING STRIP

COMPOSITION BOARD

ROCK-WOOL BLANKET

AIR SPACE

METAL FACING

MASTIC

STIFFENER

Fig. 20.6. Construction of a demountable metal partition which provides higher sound insulation than that given by the mass law.   (*W. S. Gorton.*[6])

They provide approximately the same sound transmission loss as a 31 lb per sq ft hollow-tile wall with ¾-in. plaster on both sides. Other types of panels are available which have one or both exterior faces perforated and backed with sound absorptive material.

FOLDING PARTITIONS

Commercially available accordion-pleated type folding partitions, which fold or collapse to the sides of a room, provide a simple means of dividing a room into smaller areas. However, while they achieve visual privacy, the sound insulation they provide is almost always inadequate because of the lightweight constitution of such partitions, as well as because of the cracks at the edges, which can transmit a substantial amount of sound energy.

Thus, if sound insulation is an important requirement where a folding-type partition is contemplated, the transmission loss required should be specified in advance of installation. If the specified transmission loss value cannot be met with any of the available folding partitions, other types of partitions should be employed. In judging the sound-insulating capabilities of competitive partitions, preference should be given to nonporous partitions of the greater weight per square foot. The installation should provide the minimum communicating air leakage around the edges of the partition.

WINDOWS

The sound insulation provided by a window structure is more difficult to estimate than the insulation of a wall, since it is more dependent on the physical dimensions of the window. Window dimensions are usually of such a size that the lowest natural flexural frequencies of the glass pane in a window may be higher than some of the standard frequencies at which measurements are made. Therefore, the average transmission loss may depart noticeably from the mass law.

Few test data are available on the average transmission losses of various window constructions. The best estimate for a window of known mass per unit area is that obtained from the "mass law." For a twelve-light double-hung window, for example, the average mass per unit area should be based on the weight of the entire sash. The mass law can be used also to estimate the transmission loss of several layers of glass separated by small air spaces (less than $\frac{1}{2}$ in.). For windows with two layers of glass separated by a relatively large air space ($\geqq$ 1 in.), the average transmission loss is estimated to be about 3 db greater

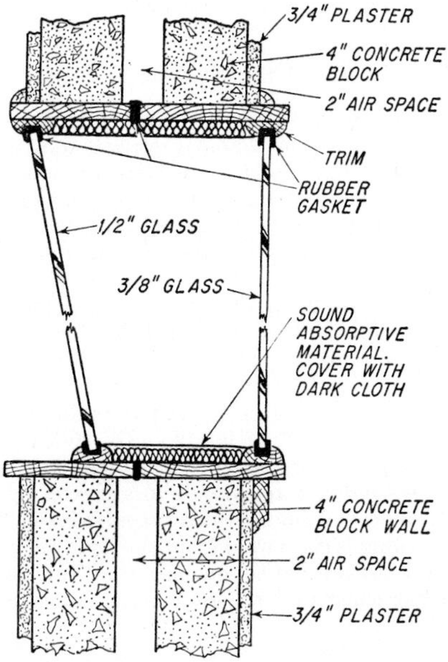

Fig. 20.7. Double-window construction designed to provide high sound insulation.

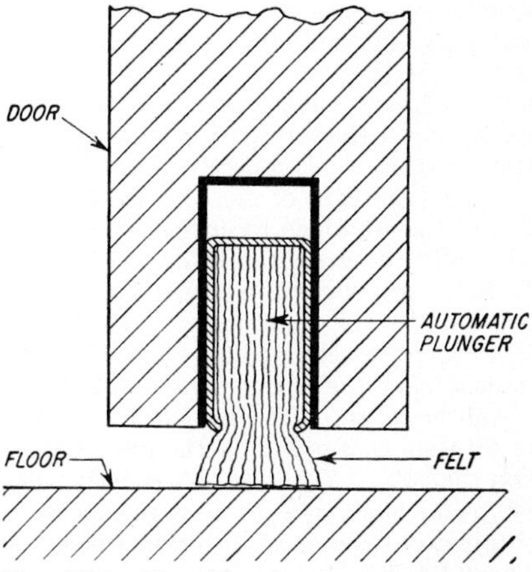

Fig. 20.8. Movable plunger which seals a door threshold automatically when the door is closed. Such devices reduce the leakage of sound under a door.

than the mass-law value, provided the two layers of glass are structurally insulated from one another as, for example, by mounting one layer in each of the two leaves of a double-wall partition, or by mounting the panes in a resilient material such as rubber. Sound absorptive material placed around the periphery of the air space may improve the insulation (see Fig. 20.7). Some benefit may be obtained by selecting panes of different sizes or thickness so that their resonant frequencies will differ.

When a window is open, it has a transmission loss approximately equal to zero, i.e., a transmission coefficient approximately equal to unity at all frequencies.

DOORS

The transmission loss of a closed door is best estimated from the mass law shown in Fig. 20.4. However, this insulation can be achieved only if the closed door is carefully sealed at the edges, particularly at the threshold. For this reason, where very good sound insulation is required, threshold closers such as that shown in Fig. 20.8 are used. Also, rubber gaskets are installed to fill all cracks at the other edges of the door.

Since the insulation of a door increases with mass, solid-core doors have greater transmission loss than hollow-core doors of the same thickness.

The transmission of sound through a threshold crack of known dimensions can be estimated from the "small-openings theory" given below. The additional sound insulation obtained by carefully sealing the door is illustrated by Panels 612 and 613.

Values of transmission loss greater than that given by the mass law can be obtained by the use of double doors. If the two doors are separated by a short passageway, sound absorptive material applied to the walls and ceiling in the passageway will further improve the insulation. For double doors separated by at least 3 in., the average transmission loss is estimated to be at least 5 db greater than the mass-law value based on a mass equal to the total weight of the two doors. For the two doors separated by a passageway having sound absorptive material on the walls and ceiling, the transmission loss will be further improved by at least 5 db, although results of measurements for such a construction are apparently not available. The seal of the doors around the periphery must be as carefully done as for a single door.

FLOOR-CEILING CONSTRUCTIONS

The same principles apply for the air-borne sound insulation of floor-ceiling constructions as for walls. However, floors are subjected to mechanical impacts due to footsteps, dropped objects, movement of furniture, etc. Special consideration must be given to the control of impact noise in the design of a building (see Chap. 19), since a floor-ceiling construction can be a good insulator for air-borne sound, and yet be wholly unsatisfactory with respect to the transmission of impact noise; an example of this is a 4-in. thick concrete slab (Panel 804).

The advantages of nonhomogeneous construction for good air-borne sound insulation can be obtained by proper selection of the ceiling construction, provided that, as is usually the case, the ceiling is not required to support loads other than its own weight. An example is Panel 706 which is the floor-ceiling counterpart of the staggered-stud walls discussed earlier. The floor is on one set of joists, and the ceiling is on a separate set of joists staggered with respect to the floor joints. The average transmission loss of this panel is 14 db greater than that predicted by the mass law.

Another example is Panel 705. It also has an average transmission loss greater by 14 db than that given by the mass law, but a somewhat higher impact sound insulation than Panel 706. In this construction the ceiling is supported from the floor joists by means of screw-eyes and wire loops. Useful amounts of sound insulation can be obtained with some of the other suspended-ceiling constructions listed in the tables of Appendix 20.1.

POROUS PARTITIONS

Partitions made of porous masonry materials, such as pumice block, cinder block, and clinker block, provide little sound insulation. If the pores in the material are interconnected, sound can propagate through the air in the pores from one side to the other. Such partitions provide less insulation than that predicted by the mass law. Thus Panel 311, made of pumice and portland cement blocks, has an average transmission loss of only 20 db, which is 26 db less than predicted by the mass law.

Plastering one or both faces of a porous partition to make it impervious to the flow of air will prevent sound transmission through the pores. This is seen in the results of measurements on Panel 312, which is the same as Panel 311 except for ½ in. of plaster on one side. The average transmission loss of 44 db for the pumice block plastered on one side is an improvement of 24 db over Panel 311, and comes close to the mass-law value of 47 db. Painting the porous surface with two layers of cement paint will also provide improved insulation.

Porous blankets of rock wool or glass wool are unsuitable as sound insulators. The transmission loss in decibels of such a porous material is proportional to its thickness, whereas for a homogeneous nonporous partition the transmission loss increases as the logarithm of the mass. While it is possible to select a porous partition thick enough for its transmission loss to be as great as that given by the mass law, it will be unusually thick.   Thus rock wool of density 5 lb per cu ft, the average transmission loss of which is 2.2 db per in., will have its average transmission loss equal to 35 db for a 16-in. thickness.   This is the same as the mass-law value, since the 16-in. thickness corresponds to 7 lb per sq ft area density of the blanket.

SMALL OPENINGS

The sound insulation of a well-designed wall, for example, one having a transmission loss of 50 db, can be vitiated easily by an opening in it even though the opening may be so small as to escape notice.   The opening may be a crack around a loose-fitting window or door.   The cracks need not be very large.   A $\frac{1}{16}$-in. crack around a door will lower the sound-insulation value of the door considerably.   Imperfectly sealed openings for pipes, conduits, and wiring also can cause annoying sound leaks.

For a large partition having only a moderate amount of insulation, say 40 db, larger openings can be tolerated.   For example, a circular hole of 1-in. diameter in a partition 15 ft by 10 ft, whose transmission loss is equal to 40 db, will reduce the sound insulation by less than 2 db.

The following calculations for shapes of openings which might be encountered in buildings indicate the magnitude of the effect of small openings.

Holes.   A circular or square hole of area A in a thin plane wall whose thickness is small in comparison with the hole's maximum dimension will have a transmission coefficient $\tau \approx 1$, i.e., a transmission loss approximately 0 db for all frequencies.[7] Thus the transmission loss for open windows and doors is 0 db over the entire audio-frequency range.

Slits.   A slit is an opening whose length is large in comparison with the wavelength of sound and the slit width.   Suppose the slit is in a plane wall of thickness t.   Figure 20.9 shows the transmission coefficient τ for perpendicularly incident sound waves of various frequencies, where $A = bl$ is the area of the slit.   Suppose the crack (along the width of the door) is 36 in. long, 2 in. thick (the door thickness), and $\frac{1}{2}$ in. wide. We can imagine the floor on either side of the door to be an infinite plane reflector which will make the effective crack width twice as great, i.e., $b = 1$ in.   Figure 20.9 shows that τ varies with frequency.   For example $\tau = 1.0$ at 200 cps; $\tau = 0.3$ at 1,000 cps; and $\tau = 0.15$ at 4,000 cps.

The value $\tau = 0.3$ represents a suitable average for speech frequencies.   Therefore, the transmittance (see the next section) for the above slit is $\tau A = \tau bl = 10.8$ sq in.   Suppose the slit is below a door which is 7 ft × 3 ft having an average transmission loss of 26 db; the door will have a transmission coefficient equal to 2.5×10^{-3}.   Thus, the door will have a

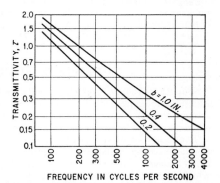

FREQUENCY IN CYCLES PER SECOND

Fig. 20.9.   Transmission coefficients τ for slits of width b in a wall of 2-in. thickness as a function of frequency.   Curves are for slits long in comparison with sound wave-length.   (*After F. Ingerslev and A. K. Nielsen.*[7])

transmittance equal to 7.6 sq in. so that more sound energy will be transmitted under the door than through it.   The effective transmission loss of the door and threshold-crack combination will be about 22 db.

TRANSMISSION LOSS OF A COMPOSITE WALL

The fundamental formula for determining the transmission loss of a single uniform wall is given by Eq. (20.2).   The sound power entering the receiving room is directly proportional to the transmittance τS which appears in the formula.   When a wall is constructed of parts having differing transmission coefficients τ_1, τ_2, τ_3, etc., and corresponding areas S_1, S_2, S_3, etc., then the total sound-power transmittance of the composite wall is

$$\bar{\tau}S = \tau_1 S_1 + \tau_2 S_2 + \tau_3 S_3 + \text{etc.} \tag{20.6}$$

where S is the total area of the wall, and τ is now the average transmission coefficient of the entire wall. Therefore the over-all transmission loss for a composite wall is $T.L. = 10 \log_{10} (1/\bar{\tau})$.

Example. Suppose there is a wall 15 ft long and 9 ft high between two offices having an average transmission loss of 45 db. This provides satisfactory insulation for speech sounds and the usual sources of office noise, e.g., typewriters, telephone bells, etc. A door opening 3 ft × 7 ft is to be made in the wall, and a door weighing 75 lb is to be installed. What will be the over-all transmission loss of the wall-door combination?

The door weighs 3.6 lb per sq ft, and its transmission loss, calculated from the mass-law Eq. (20.4), is 31 db. The following table shows the details of the calculation for the net transmission loss:

	$T.L.$, db	τ	S, sq ft	τS, sq ft
Wall..........	45	3.16×10^{-5}	114	36×10^{-4}
Door..........	31	7.95×10^{-4}	21	167×10^{-4}

Total transmittance $\bar{\tau}(S_1 + S_2) = 203 \times 10^{-4}$. Therefore $\bar{\tau} = 1.50 \times 10^{-4}$, and the net transmission loss of the wall-door combination is T.L. $= 10 \log_{10} (1/\bar{\tau}) = 38$ db.

Suppose the door is not sealed around the edges when it is closed; there is a threshold crack under it. The method and data for including the effect of a threshold crack on insulation calculations have been discussed in the preceding section on *Small Openings*. The transmission loss of the wall-door combination will be reduced to less than 35 db if there is a threshold crack of about $\frac{1}{2}$ in. under the door.

DESIGN OF SOUNDPROOF ROOMS

Soundproof rooms, in which the noise level must be very low so that acoustical activities and measurements are not interfered with, are frequently needed. Typical acoustical situations requiring a soundproof room are measurement of auditory threshold, radio and television studios, and recording studios.

The design of a soundproof room must accomplish two things. First, it must provide sound-insulating walls so that very little sound energy is transmitted into the room from outside. Second, it should provide for the absorption of any sound energy which gets into the room, the absorption usually being accomplished by acoustical materials applied to the walls and ceiling.

The formula connecting the noise level outside, L_1; the noise level inside, L_2; the total transmittance of the walls (including doors and windows), $\bar{\tau}S$; and the total absorption inside the room, a, is

$$L_2 \text{ (inside)} = L_1 \text{ (outside)} + 10 \log_{10} \frac{\bar{\tau}S}{a} \quad \text{db} \tag{20.7}$$

This is obtained from Eq. (20.2).

In practice, the greatest noise reduction that can be achieved in a room by the use of absorbent materials is about 5 db. Therefore if the noise level is caused by sound transmitted into the room from outside, any reduction needed which is greater than about 5 db must be achieved by means of improved insulation of the walls, floor, and ceiling.

Example: Design of an Audiometer Booth. Suppose a booth is to be constructed in which audiometric measurements of threshold are to be made. It is to be located on the floor of an assembly room in a factory, where the over-all noise level is 70 db. A tentative design has been chosen.   What will the estimated noise level be inside the booth?

The booth is to be 13 ft long × 8 ft wide × 8 ft high, and will have a 3 ft × 7 ft door and a 2 ft × 3 ft window.   The walls are to be of a staggered-studs construction (see Panel 175) and the ceiling and roof are to be on separate sets of joists, staggered (see Panel 706).   The door is to weigh 7 lb per sq ft, and the window will have two $\frac{1}{4}$-in. thick glass panes separated by a 6-in. air space.

The calculation of the noise level will be made for the band of frequencies, 300 to 600 cps, for which the octave band noise level outside the booth is $L_1 = 61$ db.   The average transmission loss of the walls and roof-ceiling construction in this band is 50 db.   The transmission loss of the door, estimated from the mass law, Eq. (20.5), is 35 db.   The window has an estimated transmission loss of 38 db.   The table shows the details of the calculation for the total transmittance:

	$T.L.$, db	τ	S, sq ft	τS, sq ft
Walls and ceiling........	50	10^{-5}	413	4.1×10^{-3}
Door..................	35	3.16×10^{-4}	21	6.6×10^{-3}
Window..............	38	1.58×10^{-4}	6	0.9×10^{-3}

Total transmittance $\bar{\tau}S = 11.6 \times 10^{-3}$.   The walls and ceiling of the booth are finished with acoustical material, mineral-wool blankets with perforated asbestos-board facing, which has an absorption coefficient of 0.85 and, therefore, a total absorption $a = 351$ sq ft.   Therefore, the estimated noise level in the booth, for the 300 to 600 cps band, is $L_2 = L_1 + 10 \log_{10} (\bar{\tau}S/a) = 16$ db.

The estimated noise levels in other frequency bands would be calculated in a similar manner.   Values of transmission loss and absorption coefficients corresponding to the frequency bands being computed would have to be used.   In order to decide whether or not the estimated noise levels in the booth would be low enough to allow auditory threshold measurements to be made, the criteria of acceptability for noise levels in audiometric booths are used (see Chap. 6).   The criterion for the 300 to 600 cps band requires the level to be 23 db or less, and the estimated level is 16 db.   The proposed booth design, for this frequency band, is therefore acceptable.

REFERENCES

1. Buckingham, E.: *Nat. Bur. Standards* (U.S.) *Sci. Papers* **20**: 193 (1925).
2. Recommended Practice for Laboratory Measurement of Air-borne Sound-Transmission Loss of Building Floors and Walls, *ASTM, Pub. No.* E 90-55 (1955).   [Also printed in *J. Acoust. Soc. Amer.* **23**: 686 (1951).]
3. Waterhouse, R. V., and R. K. Cook: *J. Acous. Soc. Am.* **27**: 967 (1955).
4. Kuhl, W., and H. Kaiser: *Acustica*, **2**: 179 (1952).
5. Schmidt, H.: *Acustica*, **4**: 639 (1954).
6. Gorton, W. S.: *J. Acoust. Soc. Amer.* **17**: 236 (1946).
7. Ingerslev, F., and A. K. Nielsen: On the Transmission of Sound Through Small Apertures and Narrow Slits, *Acoustical Laboratory of the Danish Academy of Technical Sciences Pub. No.* 1 (1944).
8. Purkis, H. J.: Unpublished data, Building Research Station, Garston, Watford, Herts, England.
9. Sound Insulation of Wall and Floor Constructions, Staff of Sound Section, *Nat. Bur. Standards* (U.S.) *Report No. BMS* 144 (February, 1955), and *Supplement* (February, 1956).
10. Aston, G. H., The Sound Insulation of Partitions, National Physical Laboratory, London (1948).
11. Knudsen, V. O., and C. M. Harris, "Acoustical Designing in Architecture," John Wiley and Sons, Inc., New York, 1950.
12. Ingerslev, F., "Acoustics in Modern Building Practice," Architectural Press, London. 1952.

Appendix 20.1. Sound Insulation Data

Field Measurements. Results of field measurements of air-borne and impact sound level in various dwellings are shown in Figs. 20.10 to 20.13. The measurements were made in various apartment buildings by the Building Research Station, England.[8]

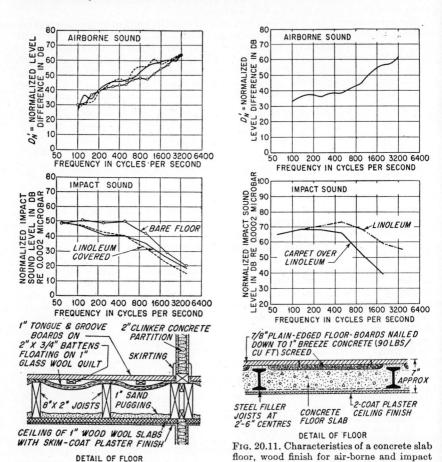

FIG. 20.10. Characteristics of a floating floor on wood joists with pugging for air-borne and impact sound. These data are normalized using a reference value of 0.5 sec reverberation time instead of 10 sq meters of absorption. See footnote to Eq. (20.4) and Chap. 19. (*Building Research Station.*[8])

FIG. 20.11. Characteristics of a concrete slab floor, wood finish for air-borne and impact sound. These data are normalized with a reference value of 0.5 sec reverberation time instead of 10 sq meters of absorption. See footnote to Eq. (20.4) and Chap. 19. (*Building Research Station.*[8])

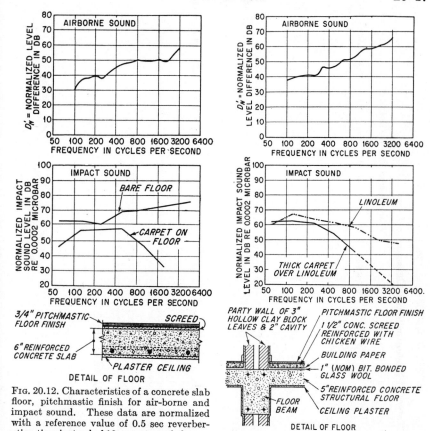

FIG. 20.12. Characteristics of a concrete slab floor, pitchmastic finish for air-borne and impact sound. These data are normalized with a reference value of 0.5 sec reverberation time instead of 10 sq meters of absorption. See footnote to Eq. (20.4) and Chap. 19. (*Building Research Station.*[8])

FIG. 20.13. Characteristics of a floating floor on a concrete slab, pitchmastic finish for air-borne and impact sound. These data are normalized with a reference value of 0.5 sec reverberation time instead of 10 sq meters of absorption. See footnote to Eq. (20.4) and Chap. 19. (*Building Research Station.*[8])

Laboratory Measurements. The data given in the following tables represent measurements of transmission loss made in the Sound Laboratory at the National Bureau of Standards, Washington, D.C.[9] Similar data have been obtained by the National Physical Laboratory in England.[10] Many of the British results have been summarized in the literature.[11] Details of special constructions which may be useful in sound insulation are available.[11,12]

APPENDIX 20.1

Tables of Sound Insulation Data

					Transmission loss, in decibels*								
Description of partition		Thickness, in.	Weight, lb/sq ft	Average, 125–4,000 cps	125 cps	175 cps	250 cps	350 cps	500 cps	700 cps	1,000 cps	2,000 cps	4,000 cps
NBS panel No.	Construction												
	Single sheets of prefabricated material												
605	Glass fiberboard	2	5.3	**30**	27	25	23	25	27	29	34	39	41
606	Steel sheet, fluted, 18 gage	....	4.4	**24**	30	20	20	21	22	17	30	28	31
232	Asbestos board, corrugated, stiffened horizontally by a 2- X 8-in. wood beam	....	7.0	**34**	33	29	31	34	33	33	33	42	39
	Multiple sheets of prefabricated material												
528	Gypsum wallboard, two ½-in. sheets cemented together, joints wood-battened	1	4.5	**30**	24	25	29	32	31	33	32	30	34
522	Gypsum wallboard, four ½-in. sheets cemented together, fastened together with sheet-metal screws, dovetail-type joints paper-taped	2	8.9	**37**	28	35	32	37	34	36	40	38	49
428	Gypsum wallboard, combination of panel 522 and panel 528 separated by spring clip and channel system	4	13.4	**41**	36	32	32	38	40	42	45	46	56

* Except for those panels which are designated by an asterisk, the values of transmission loss are measured at 128, 192, 256, 384, 512, 768, 1024, 2048, and 4096 cps; the average is for 128 to 4096 cps. However, these values are essentially the same as at the frequencies listed.

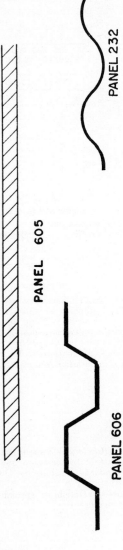

PANEL 605

PANEL 606

PANEL 232

PANEL 528

PANEL 522

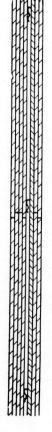

PANEL 428

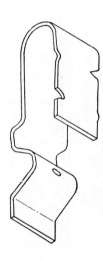

PANEL 428

Description of partition					Transmission loss, in decibels								
NBS panel No.	Construction	Thickness, in.	Weight, lb/sq ft	Average, 125–4,000 cps	125 cps	175 cps	250 cps	350 cps	500 cps	700 cps	1,000 cps	2,000 cps	4,000 cps
	Solid built-up partitions												
602	Wood-shaving (portland-cement binder) board core, 2 in. thick, 3/4 in. gypsum plaster on both sides	3½	16.0	**33**	31	33	25	31	31	29	32	41	42
603	Same as panel 602 except core 5 in. thick	6½	28.0	**36**	26	34	33	36	34	35	38	42	49
604	Wood-shaving (portland-cement binder) board core, two 3 in. sheets with waxed-paper vapor seal between them, 5/8 in. gypsum plaster on both sides	7¼	20.9	**36**	32	33	30	33	35	35	36	42	52
504	Gypsum-lath core, 3/8 in. thick, 13/16 in. gypsum plaster on both sides	2	16.8	**37**	38	36	27	32	35	32	36	46	54
506	Like panel 504 except 1 1/16 in. gypsum plaster on both sides	2½	19.7	**39**	38	32	32	32	35	36	39	49	55
512	Like panel 504 except 1 5/16 in. gypsum plaster on both sides	3	25.4	**40**	39	36	32	34	35	40	42	48	53
521	Gymsum-lath core, 1/2 in. thick, 3/4 in. perlite-gypsum plaster on both sides	2	10.9	**37**	32	38	36	37	34	34	31	41	47
515	Gypsum-lath core consisting of two 3/8 in. sheets of gypsum lath clamped together, 7/8 in. gypsum plaster on both sides	2½	18.1	**41**	40	38	37	40	41	40	37	44	52
513	Like panel 515 except lath separated by 1/8-in. felt-pad spacers, 13/16 in. gypsum plaster on both sides	2½	17.9	**42**	43	40	37	38	39	40	37	45	56
509	Gypsum-lath and fiberboard core, 1/2 in. fiberboard held by spring clips between a sheet of 3/8 in. and a sheet of 1/2 in. gypsum lath, 1/4-in. air space between fiberboard and lath on each side, 1/2 in. gypsum plaster on outer lath faces	2⅞	15.9	**47**	36	41	41	44	47	49	48	53	62

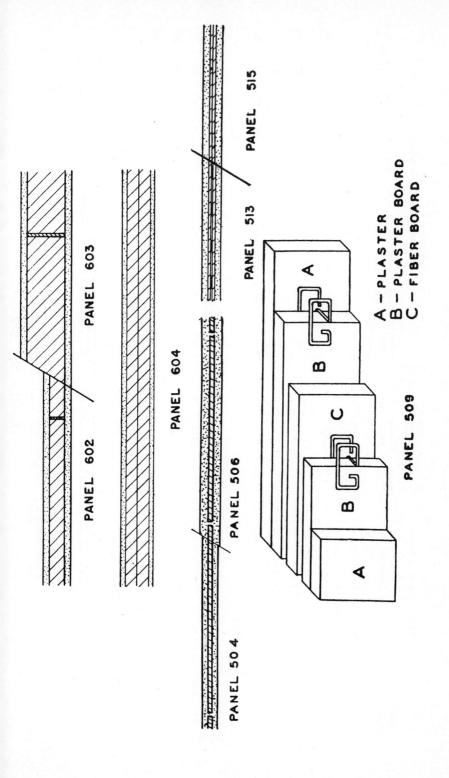

PANEL 603

PANEL 602

PANEL 515

PANEL 513

PANEL 604

PANEL 506

PANEL 504

A
B
C

PANEL 509

A — PLASTER
B — PLASTER BOARD
C — FIBER BOARD

Description of partition | Transmission loss, in decibels

NBS panel No.	Construction	Thickness, in.	Weight, lb/sq ft	Average, 125–4,000 cps	125 cps	175 cps	250 cps	350 cps	500 cps	700 cps	1,000 cps	2,000 cps	4,000 cps
	Solid built-up partitions (continued)												
525	Expanded metal-lath core, lath attached to 3/4-in. steel channels, 22 in. o.c., perlite-gypsum plaster both sides	1½	7 4	**33**	28	36	32	31	29	29	30	38	41
526	Expanded metal-lath core, perlite-gypsum plaster on both sides	2	8.8	**33**	37	35	20	26	31	29	32	41	45
527	Like panel 526 except sanded gypsum plaster on both sides	2	13.1	**38**	35	38	28	37	34	36	40	48	50
154	Expanded metal-lath core, lath paper-backed, attached to 3/4-in. steel channels, 16 in. o.c., gypsum plaster on both sides	2	....	**40**	38	37	34	33	36	36	41	48	56
	Masonry partitions												
307	Brick, common	12	121	**53**	45	49	44	52	53	54	59	60	61
80	Brick, common, 5/8 in. gypsum plaster on both sides	9¼	97	**51**[a]	...	...	48	...	49	...	57	59	70[b]
85	Brick, laid on edge, 5/8 in. gypsum plaster on both sides	3½	31.6	**42**[a]	...	...	40	...	37	...	49	59	59[b]
82	Brick, laid on edge, ½ in. gypsum plaster applied to 3/8 in. gypsum lath on 13/16- × 2-in. furring, 16 in. o.c. and wired to brick, on both sides	4½	36.5	**52**[a]	...	...	52	...	47	...	56	54	58[b]

a Average of 256, 512, and 1024 cps values.
b Measured at 3,100 cps instead of 4,000 cps.

20–22

PANEL 525

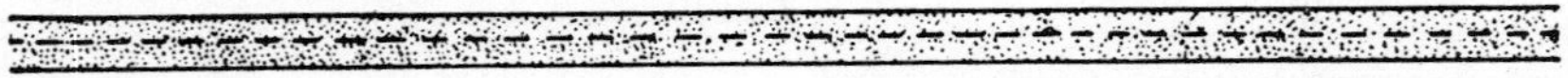

PANELS 526. 527

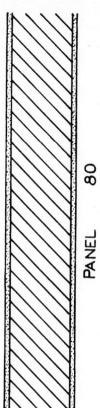

PANEL 154

PANEL 80

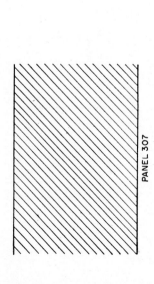

PANEL 307

PANEL 85

PANELS 82

Description of partition

Transmission loss, in decibels

NBS panel No.	Construction	Thickness, in.	Weight, lb/sq ft	Average, 125–4,000 cps	125 cps	175 cps	250 cps	350 cps	500 cps	700 cps	1,000 cps	2,000 cps	4,000 cps
	Masonry partitions (continued)												
144	Cinder block, hollow, 4 in. × 8 in. × 16 in., ⅝ in. gypsum plaster on both sides	5¼	35.8	**46**	36	37	37	41	44	47	51	55	62
145	Cinder block, hollow, 3 × 8 × 16 in., ⅝ in. gypsum plaster on both sides	4¼	32.2	**45**	34	36	36	40	42	45	51	57	64
140	Clay tile, hollow, 4 × 12 × 12 in., ⅝ in. gypsum plaster on both sides	5¼	27.5	**38ᵃ**	31	...	31	...	36	...	47	50	58
303	Clay tile, hollow, 4 × 12 × 12 in., ⅝-in. vermiculite-gypsum plaster on both sides	5¼	25.2	**38**	29	34	38	35	36	36	39	48	51
308	Concrete block, hollow, 8 × 8 × 12 in. and 4 × 8 × 16 in.	12	79	**49**	47	49	43	43	46	50	53	54	56
155	Glass brick, 3¾ × 4⅞ × 8 in.	3¾	....	**41**	30	36	35	39	40	45	49	49	43
304	Gypsum tile, hollow, 3 in. thick, ½ in. gypsum plaster on both sides	4	21.8	**39**	38	34	34	38	36	39	42	48	45
305	Gypsum tile, hollow, 4 in. thick, ½ in. gypsum plaster on both sides	5	23.4	**43**	37	42	42	41	38	42	45	49	49
301	Gypsum tile, hollow, 3 in. thick, ⅝-in. fibrous acoustic material sprayed on one side, ¾ in. gypsum plaster on both outer surfaces	5⅛	27.5	**42**	40	35	32	36	34	40	44	52	64
311	Lightweight aggregate, pumice and portland-cement tile, hollow	12	38.7	**20**	13	17	16	20	22	19	20	25	30
312	Like panel 311 except ½ in. gypsum plaster on one side only	12½	43.2	**44**	34	41	40	40	43	44	45	50	59
313	3- × 12- × 30-in. hollow gypsum blocks. On one side ½-in. sanded gypsum plaster; on other side resilient clips, spaced 18 in. o.c. vertically and 16 in. o.c. horizontally, held vertical ¾-in. metal channel 16 in. o.c., expanded metal lath and ⅞ in. of sanded gypsum plaster	....	27	**46**	38	40	37	40	44	48	51	56	59
317	Same as panel 313 except 4- × 12- × 30-in. gypsum blocks were used	....	31	**50**	45	44	44	47	50	53	55	56	59

ᵃ Average of 256, 512 and 1024 cps values.

20–24

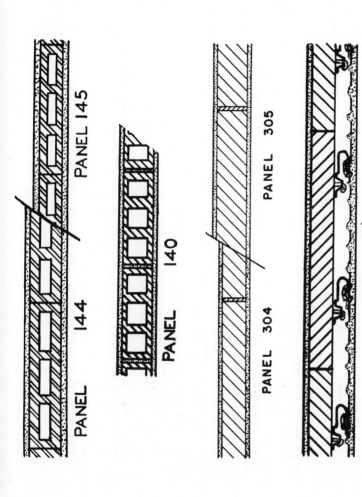

PANEL 145

PANEL 144

PANEL 140

PANEL 305

PANEL 304

PANEL 313/317

Description of partition | Transmission loss, in decibels

NBS panel No.	Construction	Thickness, in.	Weight, lb/sq ft	Average, 125–4,000 cps	125 cps	175 cps	250 cps	350 cps	500 cps	700 cps	1,000 cps	2,000 cps	4,000 cps
	Masonry partitions (continued)												
314	3- × 12- × 30-in. hollow gypsum blocks. On one side ½-in. sanded gypsum plaster; on other side resilient clips, stapled 16 in. o.c. horizontally and vertically, held ⅜-in. gypsum lath and ½ in. of sanded gypsum plaster	....	24	**49**	42	41	43	46	48	51	53	56	60
318	Same as panel 314 except 4- × 12- × 30-in. gypsum blocks were used	....	26	**50**	43	41	42	46	52	52	56	55	61
315	3- × 12- × 30-in. hollow gypsum blocks. On one side ½ in. of sanded gypsum plaster; on other side resilient clips (same as clips of panels 313 and 317 above) stapled 24 in. o.c. horizontally, held ¾-in. horizontal metal channels and ½-in. long-length gypsum lath wire-tied to the channels, and ¾ in. of sanded gypsum plaster	....	27	**48**	48	43	41	43	47	48	44	55	62
316	3- × 12- × 30-in. hollow gypsum blocks. On one side ½ in. of sanded gypsum plaster; on other side slotted resilient metal runners, placed horizontally 25 in. o.c., ½-in. long-length gypsum lath wire-tied to the runners, ¾ in. of sanded gypsum plaster	....	26	**47**	41	40	40	43	46	44	46	58	61
319	Same as panel 316 except 4- × 12- × 30-in. gypsum blocks were used	....	26	**48**	41	41	40	43	49	49	49	57	62
	Wood-stud partitions												
211	Plywood, ¼ in., glued to both sides of 1- × 3-in. studs, 16 in. o.c.	3	2.5	**24**	16	16	18	20	26	27	28	37	33
212	Same as panel 211 except ½-in. gypsum wallboard nailed to each face	4	6.6	**40**	26	34	33	40	39	44	46	50	50
214	Plywood, ¼ in. glued to opposite sides of 1- × 3-in. staggered wood studs, 16 in. o.c. in each leaf, 4-in. air space	4	2.9	**26**	14	17	20	23	28	30	33	40	30

215	Same as panel 214 except ½-in. gypsum wallboard glued to both plywood faces	5	7.0	**46**	40	37	39	45	48	50	51	54	55
216	Plywood, ¼ in., glued to opposite sides of two sets of 2- × 2-in. wood studs, 16 in. o.c., inner sides of studs spaced 1 in., two sheets ½-in. gypsum wallboard inserted in 1-in. space	4¾	8.0	**35**	18	25	29	31	32	37	42	49	51
217	Plywood, ¼ in., glued to opposite sides of 2- × 2-in. wood studs, 16 in. o.c., inner sides of studs spaced ¼ in., one sheet ¼-in.-plywood inserted between studs, paper-backed mineral wool inserted in air spaces	4	5.2	**37**	20	31	31	35	37	41	41	49	50
218	Plywood, ¼ in., glued to outer surface of 2- × 2-in. wood studs 16 in. o.c., ½-in. gypsum wallboard nailed to inner surfaces of studs, 1-in. air space between gypsum wallboards	5¾	7.4	**39**	27	24	29	33	37	42	46	55	55

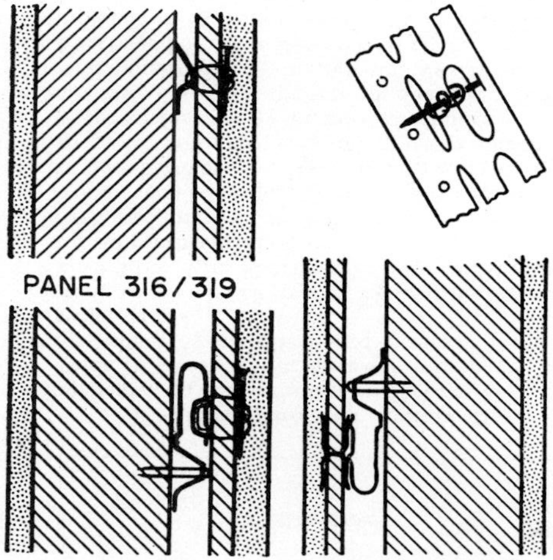

PANEL 211 / PANEL 212 / PANEL 214 / PANEL 215

PANEL 216

PANEL 218

PANEL 217

PANEL 316/319

PANEL 315

PANEL 314/318

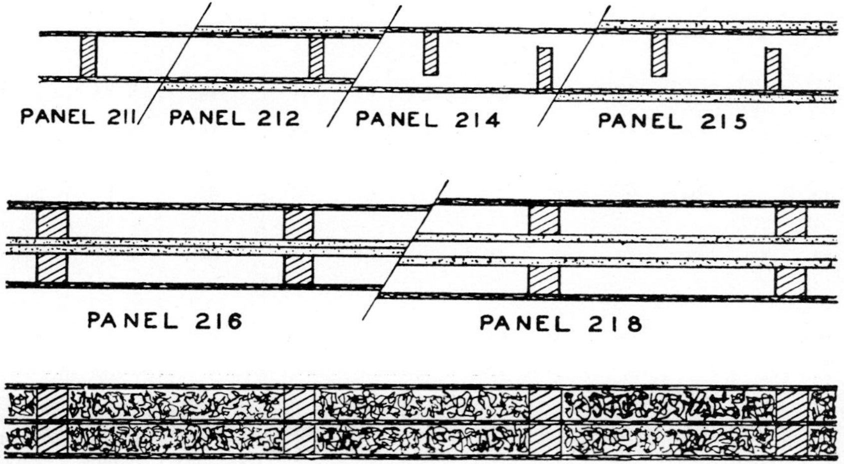

Description of partition

Transmission loss, in decibels

NBS panel No.	Construction	Thickness, in.	Weight, lb/sq ft	Average, 125–4,000 cps	125 cps	175 cps	250 cps	350 cps	500 cps	700 cps	1,000 cps	2,000 cps	4,000 cps
	Wood-stud partitions (continued)												
219	Fiberboard, ¾ in., on outer surfaces of 2- × 2-in. studs 16 in. o.c., inner sides of studs spaced 2 in., one sheet ½-in. fiberboard inserted loose between studs	7	6.2	**43**	28	29	28	39	40	43	48	62	68
220	Similar to panel 219 except ¾ in. fiberboard replaced by ½ in. fiberboard, ½ in. gypsum plaster on outer surfaces	7½	14.3	**52**	42	48	48	51	49	51	55	54	73
206	Fiberboard, dense, on both sides of 2- × 4-in. wood studs 16 in. o.c., fiberboard joints at studs	4½	3.8	**32**	16	19	22	32	28	33	38	50	52
207	Like panel 206 except fiberboard ¾ in., soft type	5	4.3	**33**	21	18	21	27	31	32	38	49	53
205	Like panel 206 except ½ in. gypsum plaster on outer surfaces of ½-in. soft fiberboard	5½	12.6	**41**	28	27	31	38	41	44	46	47	66
213	Panel 205 plus auxiliary wall on one side. Added wall consisted of ½-in. gypsum plaster on ½-in. fiberboard on 2- × 2-in. studs, 16 in. o.c.	10	18.2	**51**	41	46	44	49	50	51	52	56	72
162	Lime plaster, ½ in., on wood lath on both sides of 2- × 4-in. wood studs, 16 in. o.c.	5¼	15.6	**42**	27	27	36	38	41	44	50	55	60
163	Gypsum plaster, ½ in., on wood lath on both sides of 2- × 4-in. wood studs, 16 in. o.c.	5¼	15.1	**36**	32	29	18	34	33	40	37	40	58
201	Like panel 163	5¼	17.1	**38**	35	32	24	37	34	32	37	45	61
164	Lime plaster, ⅞ in., on expanded metal lath on both sides of 2- × 4-in. wood studs, 16 in. o.c.	5¼	19.8	**44**	26	34	41	40	44	49	52	56	58
165	Gypsum plaster, ⅞ in., on expanded metal lath on both sides of 2- × 4-in. wood studs, 16 in. o.c.	5¼	20.0	**39**	31	26	34	32	38	44	43	45	61

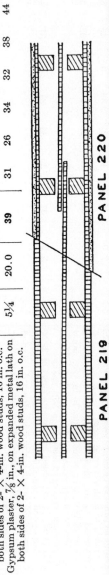

PANEL 219

PANEL 220

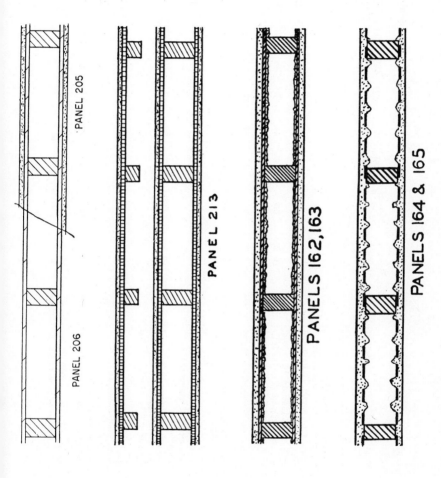

PANEL 205

PANEL 206

PANEL 213

PANELS 162,163

PANELS 164 & 165

20-29

Description of partition

Transmission loss, in decibels

NBS panel No.	Construction	Thickness, in.	Weight, lb/sq ft	Average, 125–4,000 cps	125 cps	175 cps	250 cps	350 cps	500 cps	700 cps	1,000 cps	2,000 cps	4,000 cps
	Wood-stud partitions (continued)												
228	Gypsum plaster, ¾ in., on expanded metal lath on both sides of 2- × 4-in. wood studs, 16 in. o.c.	5	18.1	**39**	29	28	28	38	38	43	45	46	54
174	Gypsum plaster, ¾ in., on paper-backed metal lath on both sides of 2- × 4-in. studs, 16 in. o.c.	5	12.6	**35**	30	27	25	31	34	37	38	38	54
175	Gypsum plaster, ¾ in., on expanded metal lath on opposite sides of staggered 2- × 4-in. wood studs, 16 in. o.c.	6¾	19.8	**50**	44	47	47	48	47	50	50	52	63
224	Gypsum wallboard, ½ in., on both sides of 2- × 4-in. wood studs, 16 in. o.c.	4½	5.9	**35**	20	22	27	35	37	39	43	48	43
225	Gypsum wallboard, two ⅜-in. sheets cemented together, on both sides of 2- × 4-in. wood studs, 16 in. o.c.	5	8.2	**38**	27	24	31	35	40	42	46	53	48
235	Gypsum wallboard, two ½-in. sheets cemented together, on opposite sides of staggered 2- × 3-in. studs, 16 in. o.c.*	5½	11.0	**43***	42	40	39	40	45	42	45	41	53
236	Gypsum wallboard, ½ in. on opposite sides of staggered 2- × 4-in. wood studs, 16 in. o.c. Wood-fiber wool blanket, 0.9 in. thick, stapled to studs in one set*	5½	13.8	**45***	39	38	40	42	42	45	48	56	51
148	Gypsum plaster, ½ in., on ⅜-in. gypsum lath on both sides of 2- × 4-in. wood studs, 16 in. o.c.	5¼	15.2	**41**	33	28	31	35	39	44	46	47	66
202	Gypsum plaster, ½ in., on ⅜-in. gypsum lath on both sides of 2- × 4-in. wood studs, 16 in. o.c.	5¼	15.0	**35**	33	24	24	30	28	38	36	42	59
203	Vermiculite-gypsum plaster, ½ in., on base similar to that for panel 202	5¼	9.6	**33**	27	24	20	31	27	36	36	38	55
204	Vermiculite-gypsum plaster, ⅞ in., on ⅜-in. gypsum lath on both sides of 2- × 4-in. wood studs, 16 in. o.c.	6	12.9	**37**	31	25	22	34	31	38	38	46	66

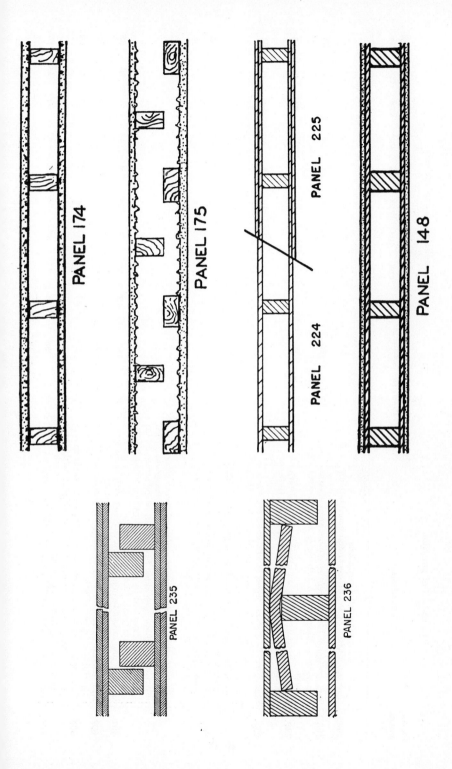

PANEL 174

PANEL 175

PANEL 224

PANEL 225

PANEL 148

PANEL 235

PANEL 236

Transmission loss, in decibels

NBS panel No.	Construction	Thickness, in.	Weight, lb/sq ft	Average, 125–4,000 cps	125 cps	175 cps	250 cps	350 cps	500 cps	700 cps	1,000 cps	2,000 cps	4,000 cps
	Steel-stud partitions												
166A	Gypsum plaster, 7/8 in., on expanded metal lath on both sides of 3¼-in. metal studs, 16 in., o.c.	5	19.6	**37**	30	27	28	35	35	40	40	43	53
166B	Same as panel 166A except space between plaster faces was filled with 5.2 lb/cu ft mineral-wool bats	5	21.1	**38**	34	35	31	34	40	38	39	40	52
229	Gypsum plaster, ¾ in., on expanded metal lath wired to both sides of 3¼-in. steel studs, 16 in. o.c.	4¾	19.1	**40**	40	34	29	41	37	42	40	48	53
237	Staggered 2- × 4-in. wood studs, each set 16 in. o.c. and spaced 8 in. o.c. with ½-in. offset from the other set. On each side ⅜-in. plain gypsum lath and ½ in. of gypsum vermiculite plaster.*	....	4.1	**40**	36	37	33	39	42	40	42	41	51
238	Same as panel 237 except air space filled with vermiculite fill. Density of fill was 6.3 lb/ft³ or 1.8 lb/ft² of panel area.	....	12.9	**47**	37	37	37	42	49	49	50	52	66
	Partitions using special nails and spring clips NOTE: Panels 401 to 423: ½ in. gypsum plaster on ⅜-in. gypsum lath on each side of 2- × 4-in. wood studs, 16 in. o.c. Lath fastened by nails and clips described below. Approximate panel thickness: 5¼ in.												
401	Head of nail imbedded in felt and covered with sheet iron; ¾-in. felt pad between stud and gypsum lath		13.6	**41**	19	30	34	38	39	44	46	52	63
402	Nail similar to that of 401; no felt pad between stud and perforated gypsum lath		15.8	**42**	29	36	34	38	40	43	46	50	66
403	Nail head consisting of a ring of steel rod integral with nail itself; similar to that of panel 405 but without cardboard; perforated gypsum lath used		15.9	**39**	23	29	30	36	39	39	41	48	62
404	Same as 403, except solid gypsum lath was used.		14.5	**38**	23	25	33	36	37	43	43	44	62

Description of partition

20–32

	15.2	**39**	27	26	34	38	39	42	43	44	61
	14.8	**40**	31	31	31	36	39	43	45	48	62

405 Nail head consisting of a ring of steel rod integral with nail itself; corrugated cardboard and expanded metal-lath strip applied to head of nail; gypsum board held snugly against the stud

406 Ordinary nail with head encased in expanded metal-lath square; metal lath girdling the expanded metal-lath square; gypsum lath snug against studs

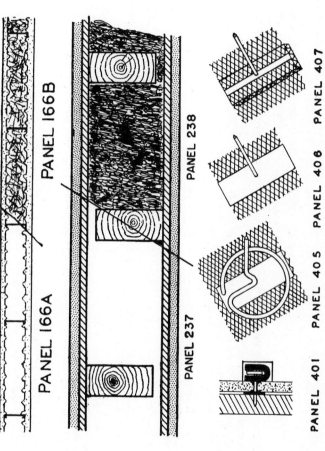

PANEL 166A PANEL 166B

PANEL 237 PANEL 238

PANEL 401 PANEL 405 PANEL 406 PANEL 407

Description of partition

Transmission loss, in decibels

NBS panel No.	Construction	Weight, lb/sq ft	Average, 125–4,000 cps	125 cps	175 cps	250 cps	350 cps	500 cps	700 cps	1,000 cps	2,000 cps	4,000 cps
	Partitions using special nails and spring clips (continued)											
407	Ordinary nail with head encased in corrugated cardboard, and expanded metal-lath square encompassing the cardboard but not touching nail; gypsum lath snug against studs	14.4	**41**	29	33	32	36	40	46	45	50	63
408	Ordinary nail with head enclosed in corrugated cardboard, metal strap girdling the cardboard square but not in contact with nail; gypsum lath loose against studs, approximately 3/32-in. of play	14.8	**42**	34	31	32	39	40	45	45	51	64
409	Nail similar to that of panel 401; gypsum lath snug against studs	15.2	**42**	31	33	35	36	39	44	47	50	64
410	Ordinary nail with head encased in thin cardboard, expanded metal-lath square over cardboard which was highly compressed	13.6	**43**	31	32	33	41	42	47	48	48	65
411	Nail similar to that of panel 410, but head of nail was encased in felt and then covered by an expanded metal-lath square; lath snug against studs	14.3	**43**	32	33	31	37	41	47	48	50	66
412	Same nail as in panel 411; 1/4-in. felt pad between stud and gypsum lath	14.0	**47**	36	38	37	42	45	51	53	54	68
413	Clip as shown in sketch	12.4	**42**	26	32	37	41	42	46	47	44	62
414	Similar to clip used in panel 413 except that resilient member was added to clip	14.1	**46**	39	41	40	46	43	45	46	48	63
416	Clip as shown in sketch. Clip gave 1/8-in. space between stud and lath	14.9	**44**	37	38	39	40	42	45	45	49	66
417	Clip as shown in sketch. Clip gave 1/8-in. space between stud and lath	15.5	**44**	29	38	38	42	40	47	44	49	66

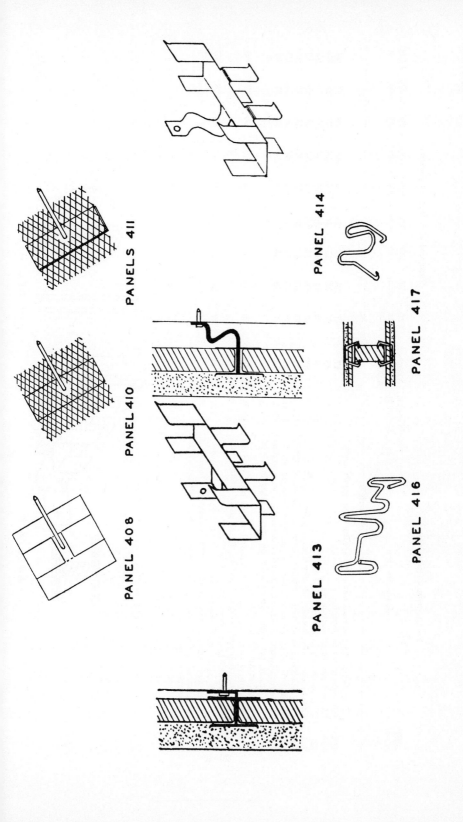

PANEL 408

PANEL 410

PANELS 411

PANEL 413

PANEL 414

PANEL 416

PANEL 417

Description of partition

NBS panel No.	Construction	Weight, lb/sq ft	Average, 125–4,000 cps	Transmission loss, in decibels								
				125 cps	175 cps	250 cps	350 cps	500 cps	700 cps	1,000 cps	2,000 cps	4,000 cps
	Partitions using special nails and spring clips (continued)											
418	Clip as shown in sketch	14.3	**47**	41	44	42	44	45	48	48	49	62
419	Clip as shown in sketch	15.1	**45**	37	33	37	44	44	48	48	52	63
420	Clip as shown in sketch	13.1	**52**	46	44	46	46	54	57	57	50	62
421	Clip as shown in sketch. Stiffer than clip for panel 420	13.1	**52**	43	48	45	56	54	57	57	49	59
422	Clip as shown in sketch. Stiffer than clip for panel 421	13.1	**52**	45	45	46	56	54	57	58	48	62
423	Similar to panel 420 except plaster aggregate was perlite	11.9	**51**	38	40	45	52	54	56	56	51	64
425	Gypsum plaster, ⅝ in., on expanded metal lath wire tied to ¼-in. metal rods. Rods held by spring clips on 2- × 4-in. studs, 16 in. o.c.	19.1	**52**	47	50	48	51	52	54	54	51	61
429	Gypsum plaster, ¾-in., on expanded metal lath tied to ¼-in. steel rods. Rods tied to metal clips. Clips fastened to 3¼-in. steel studs, 16 in. o.c.	19.0	**55**	50	52	52	59	55	56	56	52	60
438	2½ × ½-in. steel trusses used as studs 16 in. on centers. On each side resilient clips held ⅜-in. gypsum lath and ½ in. of gypsum vermiculite plaster; edges of lath held by other clips	9.0	**36**	27	26	28	32	39	41	44	38	49

PANEL 419

PANEL 418

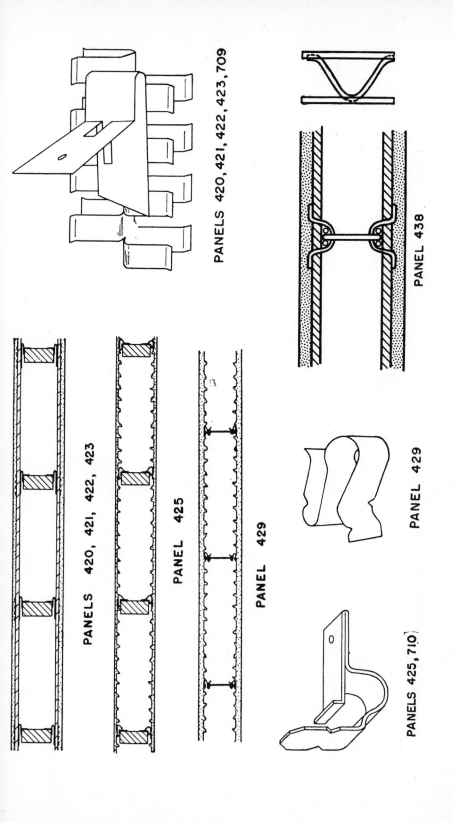

PANELS 420, 421, 422, 423, 709

PANEL 438

PANELS 420, 421, 422, 423

PANEL 425

PANEL 429

PANEL 429

PANELS 425, 710

Description of partition

Transmission loss, in decibels

NBS panel No.	Construction	Weight, lb/sq ft	Average, 125–4,000 cps	125 cps	175 cps	250 cps	350 cps	500 cps	700 cps	1,000 cps	2,000 cps	4,000 cps
	Wood-joist floors											
701	Joists 2 × 8 in. 16 in., o.c. Floor: 1-in. pine subfloor, 1-in. pine finish floor. Ceiling: ½ in. fiberboard, ½ in. gypsum plaster	14.3	**45**	23	28	34	44	47	52	55	54	69
702	Same as panel 701 except floor. Floor: 1-in. pine subfloor, ½ in. fiberboard, 1- × 3-in. sleepers, 16 in. o.c.; 1-in. pine finish floor	16.2	**50**	30	30	37	47	50	52	57	65	79
703	Same as panel 701 except added 1- × 3-in. furring, 16 in. o.c., ½-in. fiberboard, ½ in. gypsum plaster to ceiling	19.0	**45**	31	28	32	43	45	49	48	54	79
704	Same as panel 701 except ceiling was ½ in. fiberboard, 1- × 3-in. furring, 16 in. o.c., ½ in. fiberboard, ½ in. gypsum plaster	15.9	**47**	24	32	38	43	49	50	56	58	77
705	Same as panel 701 except ceiling. Added second ceiling of 2- × 2-in. wood joists, 16 in. o.c., ½ in. fiberboard, ½ in. gypsum plaster. Second ceiling suspended 4 in. below original ceiling by screw eyes and wire loops 36 in. o.c., 2- × 5- × 5-in. fiberboard pads between second ceiling joists and original ceiling plaster	20.3	**56**	46	44	50	53	55	57	56	63	75

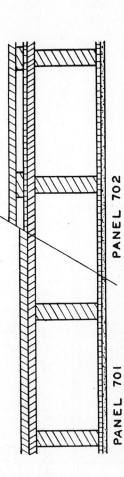

PANEL 701   PANEL 702

20–38

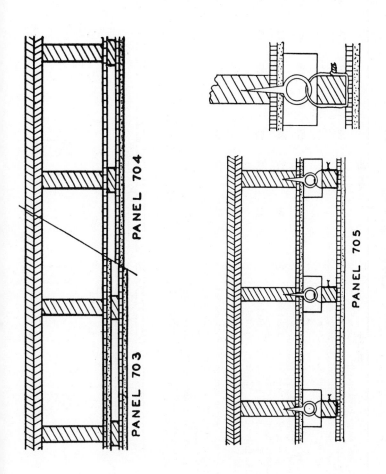

PANEL 704

PANEL 703

PANEL 705

Transmission loss, in decibels

NBS panel No.	Construction	Weight, lb/sq ft	Average, 125–4,000 cps	125 cps	175 cps	250 cps	350 cps	500 cps	700 cps	1,000 cps	2,000 cps	4,000 cps
	Wood-joist floors (continued)											
706	Same as panel 702 except old ceiling removed, added 2- × 4-in. joists, 16 in. o.c., ½ in. fiberboard, ½ in. gypsum plaster (air space set by 10-in. dimension of 2- × 10-in. frame)	16.7	**54**	48	**50**	**49**	**51**	50	52	54	58	75
707	Joists 2 × 8 in., 16 in. o.c. Floor: 1-in. pine subfloor, 1-in. pine finish floor. Ceiling: ¾ in. fiberboard	9.6	**40**	22	**28**	**31**	38	40	41	44	55	62
708	Same as panel 707 except ceiling was ½ in. fiberboard, ¾-in. fiberboard facing	15.8	**42**	31	**23**	**30**	40	40	44	47	56	68
709	Joists 2 × 10 in., 16 in. o.c. Floor: Pine subfloor, building paper, 1³⁄₁₆-in. pine finish floor. Ceiling: Gypsum lath held by spring clips (same as used in panel 420), ½ in. gypsum plaster	....	**49**	42	**41**	**40**	**47**	48	52	51	56	68
710	Same as panel 709 except ceiling consisted of expanded metal lath held on ¼-in. rods and spring clips (as in panel 425), ¾ in. gypsum plaster	....	**51**	42	44	**45**	**47**	48	52	53	59	68
180A	Joists 2 × 6 in. Floor: Wood subfloor, 2 × 2 in. sleepers, 16 in. o.c., hardwood finish floor. Ceiling: Expanded metal lath, ¾ in. gypsum plaster	16.3	**38**	35	23	24	32	34	39	42	50	62

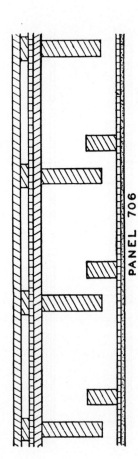

PANEL 706

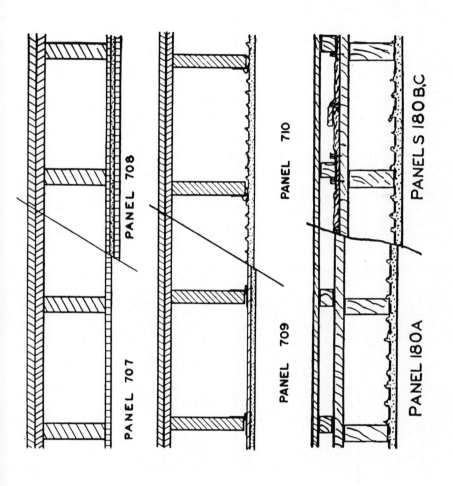

PANEL 707

PANEL 708

PANEL 709

PANEL 710

PANEL 180A

PANELS 180 B,C

Description of partition
Transmission loss, in decibels

NBS panel No.	Construction	Weight, lb/sq ft	Average, 125–4,000 cps	125 cps	175 cps	250 cps	350 cps	500 cps	700 cps	1,000 cps	2,000 cps	4,000 cps
	Wood-joist floors (continued)											
180B	Same as panel 180A except ½-in. wood-fiber blanket laid on subfloor, and 2- × 2-in. sleepers held down with special clips	16.6	**50**	32	37	38	46	48	52	55	65	76
180C	Same as panel 180B except blanket was 1 in. thick	16.7	**50**	35	38	37	48	49	52	55	64	75
180D	Same as panel 180A except sleepers supported on ½- × 6-in. strips of wood fiberboard and held down with special clips. Strips of 1-in. wood-fiber blanket laid between sleepers	16.7	**50**	37	38	39	47	48	52	55	63	75
180E	Same as panel 180D except sleepers held in position by metal strips over ½- × 2½- × 2½-in. wood fiberboard pads	16.6	**46**	32	32	33	41	44	49	52	60	72
180F	Same as panel 180E except wood-fiber wool blanket was 1 in. thick	16.7	**49**	30	36	36	46	48	51	54	63	75
711	2- × 10-in. wood joists 16 in. o.c., cross braces with 1-× 3-in. wooden bridging strips bisecting length of panel. On ceiling side ½-in. gypsum wall-board, joints filled and taped; on floor side ¾-in. subflooring, rosin paper, and floating floor consisting of ½- × 2-in. fiberboard 16 in. o.c., trapezoidal sleepers (1⅛ in. wide at top, 2 in. at bottom, 1⅝ in. thick) 16 in. o.c., 2⁵⁄₃₂-in. oak flooring	11.4	**37**	30	20	29	30	37	40	42	50	56
712	Same as panel 711 except air space in floating floor filled with vermiculite fill. Density of fill was 7.8 lb/ft³ or 1.2 lb./ft² of panel area.	12.6	**38**	24	21	30	33	40	41	46	52	58

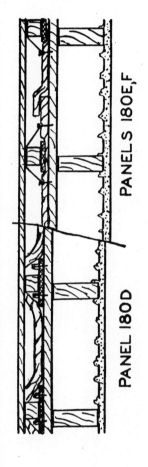

PANEL 180D PANELS 180E,F

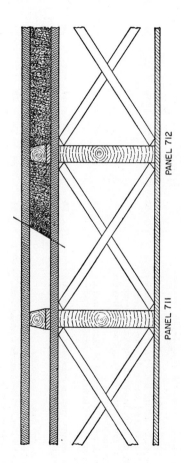

PANEL 711 PANEL 712

Description of partition   Transmission loss, in decibels

NBS panel No.	Construction	Weight, lb/sq ft	Average, 125–4,000 cps	125 cps	175 cps	250 cps	350 cps	500 cps	700 cps	1,000 cps	2,000 cps	4,000 cps
	Steel-joist floors											
137	Open web 8-in. steel joists, 20 in. o.c. Floor: 3-in. thick wood-shaving board (portland-cement binder) clipped to joists, ½ in. concrete, ¼ in. linoleum cemented to concrete. Ceiling: 1-in. thick wood-shaving board clipped to joists, ½ in. gypsum plaster	....	**53**	31	51	44	46	52	55	58	64	74
137A	Same as panel 137 except floor consisted of high-rib metal lath, 2½ in. concrete, ¼ in. linoleum cemented to concrete	....	**54**	37	46	47	48	52	56	59	65	75
137B	Same as panel 137A except ceiling consisted of high-rib metal lath attached to joists, ¾ in. gypsum plaster	....	**55**	40	41	48	51	54	59	66	63	72
	Concrete-slab floors—no joists											
804	Concrete slab, reinforced, 4 in. thick	53.4	**47**	37	33	36	44	45	50	52	60	67
805	Same as panel 804 except 1 in. concrete made with asphalt-water emulsion added on floor side	63.9	**51**	38	38	40	44	49	52	56	66	72
801	Same as panel 804 except ¾ in. furring, expanded metal lath, and ⅞ in. gypsum plaster added on ceiling side	62.2	**43**	39	38	39	39	39	40	42	50	60
802	Same as panel 801 except added 3/32 in. mastic, ¾ in. parquet floor	65.7	**49**	43	44	44	43	44	48	52	58	66
803	Same as panel 801 except floor. Floor: 3/32 in. mastic, ½ in. fiberboard, 3/32 in. mastic, ¾ in. parquet floor	67.0	**48**	41	42	39	44	44	45	50	62	69
	Doors											
182	Heavy wooden door, approximately 2½ in. thick, special hardware, rubber gasket around sides and top, drop felt at sill	12.5	**30**	30	30	30	29	24	25	26	37	36

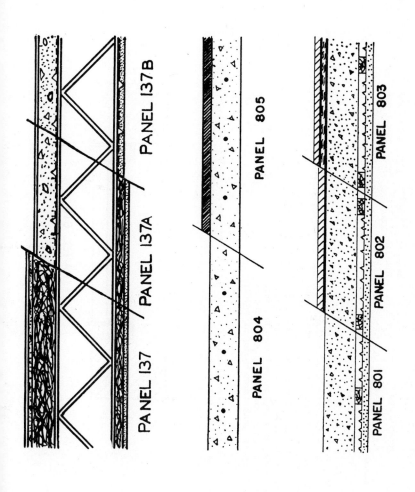

PANEL 137 PANEL 137A PANEL 137B

PANEL 804 PANEL 805

PANEL 801 PANEL 802 PANEL 803

Description of partition | Transmission loss, in decibels

NBS panel No.	Construction	Weight, lb/sq ft	Average, 125–4,000 cps	125 cps	175 cps	250 cps	350 cps	500 cps	700 cps	1,000 cps	2,000 cps	4,000 cps
	Doors (continued)											
612	Wood door, 3 ft × 7 ft, 2½ in. thick; door faces of ¼-in. hardwood panels; door hung in split frame with felt inserts; frames insulated from each other with hair felt; mounted in 12-in. brick wall. Two tubular gaskets formed a double seal around both sides and top of door, felt at sill*	6.8	35*	29	33	33	32	36	34	34	31	40
613	Same as panel 612, except edges of door sealed with plaster*	6.8	40*	32	38	38	35	39	38	42	49	53
616	3- × 30- × 84-in. wooden door, of special soundproof construction; sponge-rubber gasket around sides and top, approximately ½-in. square cross section, chamfered on hinge side; and a sponge-rubber drop closure at bottom of door.	7	32	31	27	32	30	33	31	29	37	41

* Except for those panels which are designated by an asterisk, the values of transmission loss are measured at 128, 192, 256, 384, 512, 768, 102 2048, and 4096 cps; the average is for 128 to 4096 cps. However, these values are essentially the same as the frequencies listed.

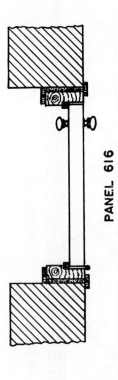

PANEL 616

Chapter 21

ACOUSTICAL FILTERS AND MUFFLERS

Don D. Davis, Jr.

National Advisory Committee for Aeronautics

INTRODUCTION

Filter Requirements and Basic Principles. In noise-control work, the need for an acoustic filter usually is encountered when it becomes necessary to transport air or other gases from one place to another through a duct or tube. If one of the requirements of the duct installation is that the transmission of noise through the duct be held to a minimum, then some acoustic device must be inserted in the duct. For example, in an air-conditioning system, an acoustical requirement is that the conditioned air be distributed and exhausted without allowing noise that may be generated at blowers, at the conditioning unit, or in flowing through the ducts, to enter the air-conditioned rooms. These requirements can be met only by inserting some acoustical attenuating device in the ducting itself.

One of the problems encountered in the installation of internal-combustion engines is that of reducing the intake and exhaust noise to acceptable values. This may be accomplished by inserting mufflers in the intake and exhaust ducting to attenuate the pressure pulsations before they reach the surrounding atmosphere.

In some cases, the acoustical problem is not to reduce noise that annoys or endangers people, but to reduce pressure pulsations that endanger engineering structures. In gas-pipe lines, for example, if pressure pulsations reach excessive magnitude, the life of the pipe is reduced and the pipe may even fail. The acoustical problem here is to prevent excessive pressure pulsations in the pipe line.

The acoustical problems in the above examples are similar in principle. A harmonic analysis of the flow in the duct, in any of these problems, would show pulsating or alternating-current flows at several different frequencies superimposed on an average direct-current flow of gas. The acoustical problem is to impede the alternating-current flow as much as is practical, while at the same time allowing the direct-current flow to pass. The type of filter that will satisfy these requirements is a low-frequency pass filter with a cut-off frequency below the lowest alternating-current frequency that is present in the duct. The majority of filter problems that are encountered by noise-control engineers entail the design of this type of filter; hence, low-pass filters are emphasized in this chapter. A nonacoustical requirement—that the static-pressure drop in the duct not be excessive—often influences the type and size of filter employed.

Two general principles are employed in obtaining the filtering action. (1) *Absorption:* The transmission of sound energy can be reduced by absorbing a large part of the incident energy inside the duct (see Chap. 27). Sound-absorptive structures sometimes meet practical difficulties in application in ducts where the temperature or velocity in the duct is very high. (2) *Reflection:* When a sound wave traveling through a duct arrives at a discontinuity where the acoustical impedance is either

21–1

much higher or much lower than the characteristic impedance of the duct, only a small fraction of the acoustical energy can flow through the discontinuity. The rest of the energy goes into a reflected wave that originates at the discontinuity and travels back toward the source. Thus, the transmission of sound energy can be reduced by inserting appropriate discontinuities in the duct, even though these discontinuities may not actually absorb any of the energy. This chapter considers only those filters that employ the principle of reflection. Reflective acoustical filters are most effective at low frequencies in contrast to sound-absorptive structures which are usually most effective at high frequencies. (Limitations on the attenuating range of particular filter configurations are discussed later in this chapter.)

Factors That Influence Sound Transmission. According to theory, the physical behavior of an acoustical filter is assumed to be adequately represented by linear differential equations. As a result of this basic assumption, the theory indicates that the intensity of the sound transmitted through the duct system, at any frequency, is directly proportional to the intensity at the acoustical inlet to the duct. Other factors that influence the sound transmission are the duct configuration, the filter and its location, and the configuration and location of the duct outlet. The quantitative interrelationships among these factors are discussed in the following sections.

The noise output may also be affected by the steady gas flow in the duct: (1) The steady flow may actually generate noise when it impinges on discontinuities in the system. (2) The steady flow may affect the transmission characteristics of the filter-duct combination.

Linear theory, which is employed in this chapter, makes these important basic assumptions: (1) that the sound pressures are small in comparison with the average static pressure in the system, and (2) that the particle-velocities are small relative to the velocity of transmission of sound waves in the system. In certain filter systems, one or the other of these assumptions is violated; it is important to recognize, in engineering practice, that although the filter theory may still be quite useful in such cases, numerical attenuation calculations may be inaccurate. An example of such a system is the exhaust pipe of an internal-combustion engine, where peak sound pressures of the order of one-third to one-half of the static pressure have been measured.[1]

PARAMETERS USED TO DESCRIBE FILTER CHARACTERISTICS

Impedance, Transmission, and Reflection Factors. A filter installation is shown schematically in Fig. 21.1. The magnitude of the incident wave at the inlet is signified by A_1. The complex number B_1 represents both the magnitude and phase (with respect to A_1) of the reflected wave at the inlet. Similarly A_2 and B_2 represent the magnitude and phase (with respect to A_1) of, respectively, the transmitted wave at the outlet of the filter and the wave reflected back to the outlet from the next discontinuity beyond the filter outlet.

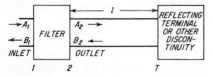

Let the rms value of the sound pressure at the inlet be given by $p_1 = A_1 + B_1$. Then the volume current will be given by:

Fig. 21.1. Schematic diagram of a filter installation.

$$U_1 = \frac{A_1 - B_1}{Z_{01}}$$

where Z_{01} is the characteristic acoustical impedance $\rho_o c / S_1$ of the inlet duct. The *impedance* at the inlet, looking toward the filter, is

$$Z_1 = \frac{p_1}{U_1} = Z_{01} \frac{A_1 + B_1}{A_1 - B_1} \tag{21.1}$$

The complex ratio between the reflected pressure and the incident pressure is called the *reflection factor R* of the filter. It is related to the impedance by the following equation:

$$R_1 = \frac{Z_1/Z_{01} - 1}{Z_1/Z_{01} + 1} \tag{21.2}$$

If Z_1 is infinite, then the reflection factor is 1; if Z_1 is zero, $R_1 = -1$ (full strength reflection 180° out-of-phase with A_1). If, however, $Z_1 = Z_{01}$, there is no reflection.

It is often useful to work with the reflection factor that is found when the filter is terminated with the characteristic impedance Z_{02}. In this case, there is no reflected wave in the outlet duct ($B_2 = 0$). The reflection factor of the filter for this case is the *characteristic reflection factor* R_{01}. This is related to the reflection factor R_1 with a reflecting terminal by the equation:

$$R_1 = R_{01} + \frac{R_T T_{01} T_{02} e^{-ik2l}}{1 - R_T R_{02} e^{-ik2l}} \qquad (21.3)$$

Where $k = 2\pi f/c = \omega/c$, l is the length of duct between the filter outlet and the next discontinuity, R_T is the reflection factor at this discontinuity, R_{02} is the characteristic reflection factor at end 2 of the filter when sound is sent in end 2 and end 1 is terminated in the characteristic impedance Z_{01}. The symbols T_{01} and T_{02} signify characteristic transmission factors for sound entering at ends 1 and 2 respectively, and with the opposite end terminated with the characteristic impedances Z_{02} and Z_{01} respectively. It is assumed that there is no energy absorption in the duct between the filter and the next discontinuity.

The *transmission factor* of the filter shown in Fig. 21.1 is defined as the complex ratio of the transmitted pressure to the incident pressure. Thus:

$$T_1 = \frac{A_2}{A_1} \qquad (21.4)$$

It is related to the characteristic transmission factor T_{01} for sound entering at 1 by:

$$T_1 = \frac{T_{01}}{1 - R_T R_{02} e^{-ik2l}} \qquad (21.5)$$

The transmission factor T_{02} is related to T_{01} by:

$$T_{02} = T_{01} \frac{Z_{01}}{Z_{02}}$$

If there is no energy absorption in the filter:

$$|R_{01}|^2 = |R_{02}|^2$$

In this case, the reflection factors are related to the transmission factors by:

$$1 - |R_{01}|^2 = |T_{01}|^2 \frac{Z_{01}}{Z_{02}} = |T_{02}|^2 \frac{Z_{02}}{Z_{01}}$$

If the inlet and outlet duct areas are equal, $Z_{02} = Z_{01}$ and $T_{01} = T_{02}$. Thus, the preceding equations are simplified somewhat. Further simplification occurs if the filter is symmetrical, for then $R_{01} = R_{02}$.

Transmission and Reflection Factors for Multi-section Filters. The transmission and reflection factors for a complicated filter can be obtained by starting at the termination and working back through the filter, applying Eqs. (21.3) and (21.5) to each section of the filter in turn. The quantities that must be known are the reflection factor at the termination, the characteristic reflection and transmission factors of each section of the filter, and the lengths and cross-sectional areas of the ducts between adjacent sections of the filters. If the terminating impedance Z_T is the known quantity, the reflection factor of the termination can be computed from Eq. (21.2) as follows:

$$R_T = \frac{Z_T/Z_0 - 1}{Z_T/Z_0 + 1} \qquad (21.6)$$

As a specific example of this method, consider the problem of determining the transmission and reflection factors for a loss-free filter built up of two identical and symmetrical sections terminated without reflection. The filter is shown schematically in Fig. 21.2. The areas of the connecting ducts are equal. The characteristic reflection and transmission factors for a single section, referred to inlet and outlet terminals at 2 and 3 or 5 and 6, are given by:

$$R_{01} = R_{02} = R_0' \qquad T_{01} = T_{02} = T_0'$$

These factors can be referred to inlet and outlet terminals at 1 and 4 or 4 and 7 as follows:

$$R_0 = R_0' e^{-ikl} \qquad T_0 = T_0' e^{-ikl}$$

The transmission factor for the first section is then:

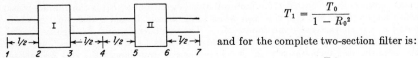

$$T_1 = \frac{T_0}{1 - R_0^2}$$

and for the complete two-section filter is:

FIG. 21.2. Schematic diagram of a two-section filter.

$$T = \frac{T_0^2}{1 - R_0^2}$$

The reflection factor at 1 is:

$$R = R_0 + \frac{R_0 T_0^2}{1 - R_0^2} = R_0 \left(1 + \frac{T_0^2}{1 - R_0^2} \right)$$

Let the characteristic transmission factor be written $T_0 = De^{i\delta}$, where D is a real number giving the magnitude of T_0 and δ is the phase angle. If the transmission factors for filters of one, two, three, and four identical loss-free symmetrical sections terminated without reflection are given by $T_n = D_n e^{i\delta_n}$ where the subscript refers to the number of sections, the values of D_n and δ_n are:[2]

One section:

$$D_1 = D$$
$$\delta_1 = \delta$$

Two sections:

$$D_2 = \frac{D^2}{\sqrt{D^4 + 4(1 - D^2) \cos^2 \delta}}$$

$$\delta_2 = \arctan \left[\frac{2 \cos^2 \delta}{2 \cos^2 \delta - D^2} \tan \delta \right]$$

Three sections:

$$D_3 = \frac{D^3}{\sqrt{D^4 - 8 \cos^2 \delta (1 - D^2)(D^2 - 2 \cos^2 \delta)}} \qquad (21.7)$$

$$\delta_3 = \arctan \left[\frac{4 \cos^2 \delta - D^2}{4 \cos^2 \delta - 3D^2} \tan \delta \right]$$

Four sections:

$$D_4 = \frac{D^4}{\sqrt{D^8 + 16 \cos^2 \delta (1 - D^2)(D^2 - 2 \cos^2 \delta)^2}}$$

$$\delta_4 = \arctan \left[\frac{8 \cos^4 \delta - 4D^2 \cos^2 \delta}{8 \cos^4 \delta - 8D^2 \cos^2 \delta + D^4} \tan \delta \right]$$

If the filter consists of a very large number of identical sections, the transmission factor for a single section approaches that for a single section of a filter that is built up of an infinite number of identical sections. This will be called the image transfer factor $F = |F|e^{i\varphi}$. The transfer factor for n sections of the infinite filter is $F_n = |F|^n e^{in\varphi}$. The relationship between the image transfer factor and the characteristic transmission factor is given in the following equation:

$$F = |F|e^{i\varphi} = \frac{\sqrt{\dfrac{\cos\delta + D}{\cos\delta - D}} - 1}{\sqrt{\dfrac{\cos\delta + D}{\cos\delta - D}} + 1}$$

The magnitude and phase angle of the transmission factors for two-, three-, and four-section filters are plotted against δ, with D as a parameter, in Figs. 21.3, 21.4, and 21.5.[2] The image transfer factor $|F|e^{i\varphi}$ is plotted in the same manner in Fig. 21.6.[2] The magnitudes are plotted to a logarithmic scale. The auxiliary linear scale at the right gives the transmission loss in decibels. Observation of these figures shows that the characteristics of the finite filters are quite different from those of an equal number of chambers of an infinite filter, especially near the ends of the stop bands where the

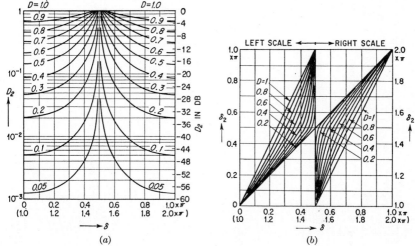

Fig. 21.3. Transmission factor for two-section filters. (a) Magnitude D_2; (b) Phase angle δ_2. (*Lippert.*[2])

transmission loss is low. Also, at the middle of a stop band $|F_n| \approx \frac{1}{2}D_n$. The practical consequence of this approximate relation is that at the middle of a stopband the transmission loss for a finite filter, terminated without reflection, will be about 6 db less than the transmission loss computed for an equal number of chambers of an infinite filter. When using the infinite-filter equations as a basis for filter design, this fact should be taken into account. Wherever it is practical to do so, however, a filter built up of only a few identical sections should be treated as a finite filter.

Insertion Loss and Transmission Loss. An obvious way to judge the effectiveness of a filter is to compare the sound pressure levels at a specified point with and without the filter in the system. The difference between the two sound pressure levels, in decibels, is the *insertion loss J* due to the filter. It is important to recognize that the insertion loss is not a unique property of the filter; it depends also on the source and terminating impedances and the location of the point at which the insertion loss is determined (see Chap. 22). As a result, it is not practical to present general curves for the insertion loss of filters of various types; separate calculations are normally required for individual cases.

The *transmission loss T.L.* gives the relationship between the energy in the incident wave at the inlet and the energy in the transmitted wave at the outlet. Referring to

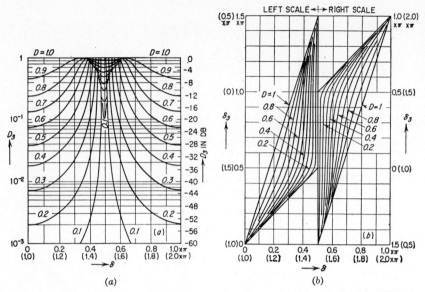

FIG. 21.4. Transmission factor for three-section filter. (a) Magnitude D_3; (b) Phase angle δ_3. (*Lippert.*[2])

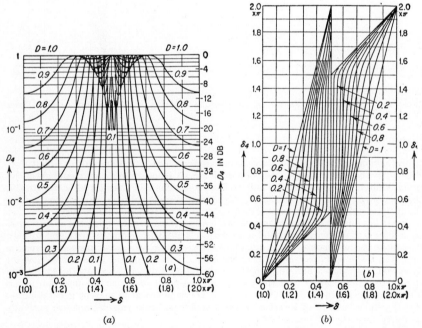

FIG. 21.5. Transmission factor for four-section filter. (a) Magnitude D_4; (b) Phase angle δ_4. (*Lippert.*[2])

the symbols used in Fig. 21.1:

$$T.L. = 10 \log_{10} \frac{|A_1|^2 \, Z_{02}}{|A_2|^2 \, Z_{01}} = 10 \log_{10} \frac{1}{1 - |R_1|^2} \quad \text{db} \qquad (21.8)$$

Note that the transmission loss does not depend on the source impedance, although it does depend on the terminating impedance. The characteristics of acoustical filters are often presented in the form of transmission-loss curves calculated for the special case of a reflection-free termination ($R_T = 0$). For instance, the db scale at the right of Figs. 21.3 to 21.6 gives the transmission loss for these filters.

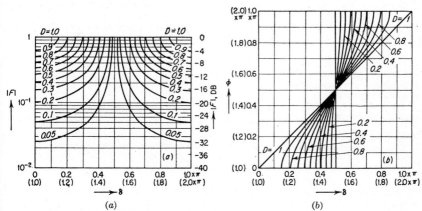

FIG. 21.6. Image-transfer factor for one element of an infinite filter. (a) Magnitude $|F|$; (b) Phase angle φ. (Lippert.[2])

Two methods of determining the transmission loss are apparent here. One method is to determine the ratio $\dfrac{|A_1|^2}{|A_2|^2}$ directly from the acoustical equations or from the filter impedances (using the methods of electrical network theory). An alternative method is to determine the characteristic reflection or transmission factors of the individual sections of the filter and then to combine them by the methods described earlier in this section.

IMPEDANCE OF FILTER ELEMENTS

This section considers the impedance of several of the acoustical elements that are used in filters. Wherever applicable, characteristic transmission and reflection factors are given.

Abrupt Area Change in Tube Terminated without Reflection (Fig. 21.7). At the junction:

$$Z_1 = \frac{1}{m} Z_{01} \qquad (21.9)$$

$$R_{01} = -\frac{m - 1}{m + 1} \qquad (21.10)$$

$$T_{01} = \frac{2}{m + 1} \qquad (21.11)$$

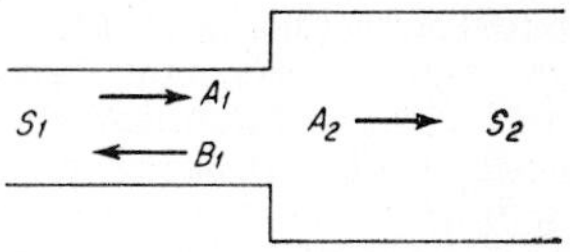

FIG. 21.7. Abrupt area change in tube terminated without reflection.

where $m = S_2/S_1$.

These equations are based on the consideration of only plane waves in the ducts. The boundary conditions of continuity of pressure and of volume current are satisfied at the discontinuity. The detailed boundary condition of zero normal velocity at the surface of the solid part of the juncture is not satisfied; this can only be done by the use of higher modes of vibration in the vicinity of the juncture. The exact solution shows that the effect of those higher modes can be represented by a positive reactance in series with the ducts at the juncture.[3] In practice, experience has shown that the approximate Eqs. (21.9) to (21.11) give satisfactory results in the design of expansion-chamber filters for noise control.

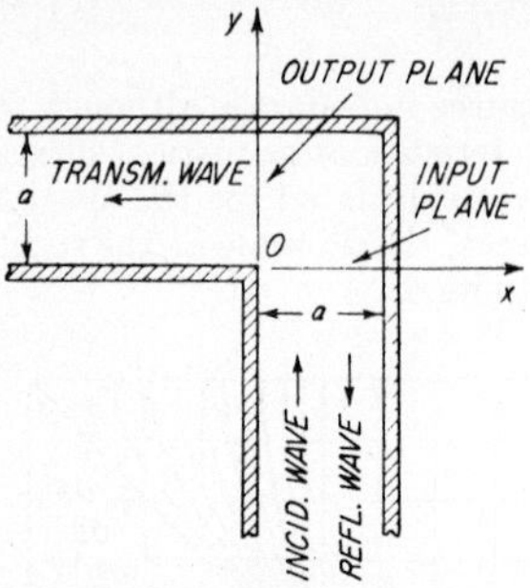

Right-angled Bend in Tube of Square Cross Section. Figure 21.8 shows a right-angled bend in a tube of square cross section, with the direction of propagation of the incident, reflected, and transmitted waves indicated. The input and output reference planes are also shown. This problem has been solved by computing the impedance ratios of an equivalent circuit by a step process.[4] The results of the first step (zero-order approximation) of this calculation are:

Fig. 21.8. A right-angled bend in a tube of square cross section showing coordinates and position of input and output planes. (*Lippert.*[5])

$$\frac{Z_{11} \mp Z_{12}}{Z_0} = -j\left(\cot\theta \mp \frac{1}{\theta}\right)$$

where $\theta = ka$, a is the width of the conduit, and $k = 2\pi f/c$. Z_{11} and Z_{12} are the components of the impedance matrix for the equivalent circuit ($Z_{22} = Z_{11}$ due to symmetry).

The characteristic reflection and transmission factors for this approximation are:[5]

$$R_0 = Ce^{i\gamma}$$

where

$$C = \frac{1 - \dfrac{1}{\theta^2} + \cot^2\theta}{\sqrt{\left(1 + \dfrac{1}{\theta^2} - \cot^2\theta\right)^2 + 4\cot^2\theta}} \tag{21.12}$$

$$\gamma = \pi + \arctan\left[\frac{2\cot\theta}{1 + \dfrac{1}{\theta^2} - \cot^2\theta}\right]$$

and

$$T_0 = De^{i\delta}$$

where

$$D = \frac{2}{\theta\sqrt{\left(1 + \dfrac{1}{\theta^2} - \cot^2\theta\right)^2 + 4\cot^2\theta}} \tag{21.13}$$

$$\delta = -\arctan\left[\frac{1 + \dfrac{1}{\theta^2} - \cot^2\theta}{2\cot\theta}\right]$$

Figures 21.9 and 21.10 show the magnitude and phase angle, respectively, of the reflection and transmission factors as a function of θ/π. The solid curves are computed from Eqs. (21.12) and (21.13) and the dashed curves, with circled test points, are from experimental measurements.[5] These curves indicate that the equations predict the reflection and transmission factors with accuracy sufficient for most filter-design work. It has been shown[5] that the accuracy is improved if the second order approximation of Ref. 4 is used. Values read from the experimental curves of Figs. 21.9 and 21.10 can be used in design work, subject to two restrictions if the theory of loss-free filters is to be used. These restrictions are:

$$C^2 + D^2 = 1$$

$$\gamma - \delta = \mp\frac{\pi}{2}$$

These equations are very nearly satisfied by the experimental results, thus indicating that the losses in the bend are negligible. Note that from Fig. 21.10, $\gamma - \delta \approx 3\pi/2$, which is equivalent to $-\pi/2$, since a phase shift of $3\pi/2$ is indistinguishable from a phase shift of $-\pi/2$ in a steady-state vibration.

The physical interpretation of these results is that the bend acts as a low-pass filter. At low frequencies, where the wavelength is very large compared to the duct width, there is little reflection and the transmission is high. As the frequency increases until λ approaches $2a$, the reflection increases until the transmission is reduced nearly to zero. This does not mean, however, that the transmission will remain zero at higher frequencies. This theory is based on the free propagation of only plane waves in the tube. Although higher modes are excited in the corner, they do not propagate freely

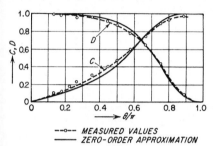

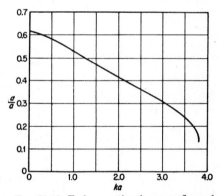

--o-- MEASURED VALUES
——— ZERO-ORDER APPROXIMATION

--o-- MEASURED VALUES
——— ZERO-ORDER APPROXIMATION

Fig. 21.9. The measured magnitudes and the zero-order approximation of C and D for the right-angled bend of Fig. 21.8 as a function of θ/π. (*Lippert.*[5])

Fig. 21.10. The measured phase angles and the zero-order approximation of γ and δ for the right-angled bend of Fig. 21.8 as a function of θ/π. (*Lippert.*[5])

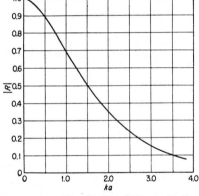

Fig. 21.11. Magnitude of the reflection coefficient at the open end of an unflanged circular pipe. (*Levine and Schwinger.*[6])

Fig. 21.12. End correction for an unflanged circular pipe. (*Levine and Schwinger.*[6])

at low frequencies, but are attenuated without energy loss in the tube. When the frequency rises to the value for which $\lambda = 2a$, however, free propagation of the first unsymmetrical higher-order mode is possible; and at $\lambda = a$, free propagation of the first symmetrical higher-order mode can occur. Thus, Eqs. (21.12) and (21.13) should be regarded as valid only for values of θ less than π.

Open End of Tube. A rigorous solution for the reflection coefficient at the open end of an unflanged circular pipe is available.[6] The magnitude of the reflection coefficient $|R|$ is plotted in Fig. 21.11 as a function of ka, where a is the tube radius. The phase shift can be determined from Fig. 21.12, which is a plot of α/a as a function of ka. The reflection coefficient is:

$$R = -|R|e^{-2ik\alpha}$$

For the small values of ka that are most often encountered in filter design $|R| \approx 1$ and $\alpha \approx 0.613a$. With these approximations, the reflection coefficient becomes:

$$R \approx -e^{-2ik\alpha} = -e^{-1.23ika} \qquad (21.14)$$

It is often convenient in filter calculations to add an end correction $\alpha = 0.613a$ to the true length of the tube and assume a reflection coefficient of -1 at the end of the lengthened tube. This produces the same result mathematically as Eq. (21.14). Although Eq. (21.14) gives the conditions inside the tube with sufficient accuracy for small values of ka, it cannot be used in determining the transmitted sound energy, because the assumption of total reflection ($|R| = 1$) corresponds to zero transmission. The transmitted-sound energy for unit incident-wave energy in the tube is:

$$1 - |R|^2$$

where the exact values of $|R|$ must be used. The impedance at the open end of the actual tube is given by:

$$\frac{Z}{Z_0} = \frac{1 + R}{1 - R} \qquad (21.15)$$

In the case of a circular tube with an infinite flange, the end correction, for small values of ka, is about $\alpha = 0.82a$ (Ref. 7, Sec. 307 and Appendix A). The reflection coefficient at the end of the tube is approximately:

$$R = -e^{-2ik\alpha} = -e^{-1.64ika}$$

Further information on the impedance of flanged circular tubes for larger values of ka may be found in Refs. 8 and 9.

Open Tube of Finite Length. Figure 21.13 is a diagram of a tube of finite length, open at the end. If the reflection factor at the open end is R_2, the reflection factor inside the tube at the reference plane 1 is:

$$R_1 = R_2 e^{-2ikl}$$

If an approximation of the type given in Eq. (21.14) is permissible:

$$R_1 = -e^{-2ik(l+\alpha)} \qquad (21.16)$$

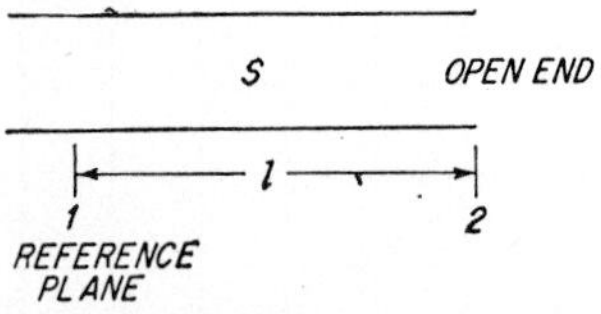

Fig. 21.13. Diagram of a tube with an open end.

where α is the end correction, which has the value $0.613a$ for a circular unflanged open end.

The impedance at 1 can be calculated from the reflection factor R_1 by using Eq. (21.15). Using Eq. (21.16) for R_1 the impedance is:

$$\frac{Z}{Z_0} = i \tan k(l + \alpha) \qquad (21.17)$$

Equations (21.16) and (21.17) can also be used in the case of a circular open tube with a flange at the end if the value of α is taken as $0.82a$.

If the tube is sufficiently short with respect to the wavelength of the sound so that $\tan k(l + \alpha) \approx k(l + \alpha)$ the impedance can be approximated by:

$$\frac{Z}{Z_0} = ik(l + \alpha) \qquad (21.18)$$

$$Z = i\rho_o \omega \frac{l + \alpha}{S}$$

where S is the cross-sectional area of the tube.

Orifice. It is difficult to predict the impedance of an orifice or a group of orifices in a filter because the orifices are in walls of finite thickness; the walls are bounded rather than infinite; they often are not plane; and in many cases there are several orifices so that there is interference between the flow fields of the orifices. Furthermore, if the sound intensity is high, there will be jet flow through the orifice, and the orifice impedance becomes a function of the acoustic velocity in the orifice.

The impedance of an orifice (neglecting the resistive component) is:

$$Z = i\rho_o\omega/c_o \tag{21.19}$$

where c_o is the conductivity of the orifice. In the case of a circular orifice in an infinite plane of zero thickness, the conductivity is $2a$, where a is the radius of the orifice.[7] It is assumed here, and in what follows, that $a \ll \lambda$. If the ratio a/λ exceeds about 0.1, errors of 10 per cent or greater are possible in orifice reactances, computed from these equations.

In the case of an orifice in a wall of finite thickness, the orifice resembles a short tube, open at both ends, and flanged at both ends. The impedance can be written in a form similar to that of Eq. (21.18), except that an end correction is required at both ends. Thus:

$$Z = i\rho_o\omega\frac{l + 2\alpha}{S} \tag{21.20}$$

Comparison of this equation with Eq. (21.19) shows that the conductivity is $S/(l + 2\alpha)$.

In the case of a circular orifice, as l goes to zero, c_o becomes $2a$; therefore, $\alpha = \pi a/4$. On the other hand, if l is sufficiently long, $\alpha = 0.82a$. These statements can be expressed in the following inequality:

$$0.785a \leq \alpha \leq 0.82a \tag{21.21}$$

which gives the upper and lower bounds on the value of α for an orifice with an infinite flange. In Eq. (21.20), as in Eq. (21.18), it is assumed that l is considerably less than λ. *If not, the orifice must be treated as a tube*, using an equation similar to Eq. (21.17), namely:

$$Z = i\frac{\rho_o c}{S}\tan k(l + 2\alpha) \tag{21.22}$$

where the end correction is applied to both ends of the tube, because both ends are open.

The values of α given in Eq. (21.21) are for circular orifices. In the case of an elliptical orifice in an infinitely thin plate, the conductivity is:[7]

$$c_o = 2\sqrt{\frac{S}{\pi}}\left[\frac{\pi}{2\sqrt{\cos\psi}\,K(\sin\psi)}\right]$$

where S = area of ellipse; $\sin\psi = e$, eccentricity of ellipse; and K = complete elliptic integral of the first order. For a circle, $\sin\psi = 0$, the part in brackets is unity, and $c_o = 2(S/\pi)^{\frac{1}{2}} = 2a$. The end correction for an elliptical orifice in a thin plate is, for one end:

$$\alpha = \sqrt{\frac{S}{\pi}}\frac{\pi}{4}\left[\frac{2\sqrt{\cos\psi}\,K(\sin\psi)}{\pi}\right] \tag{21.23}$$

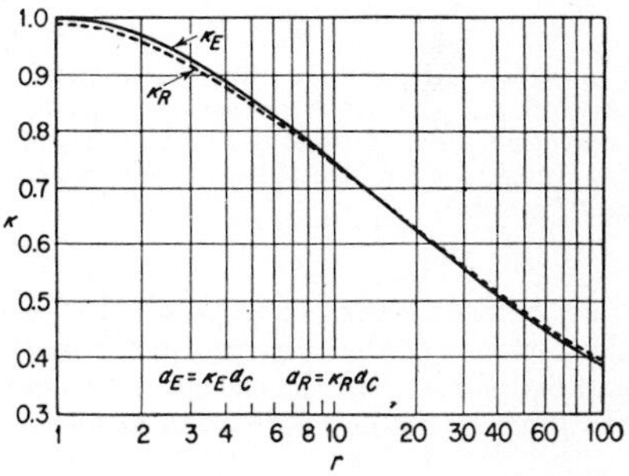

Let the part in the brackets be signified by κ_E, let α_E = end correction for elliptical orifice, and α_C = end correction for circular orifice of the same area.

$$\alpha_E = \kappa_E\alpha_C$$

Fig. 21.14. Correction factor to account for the influence of orifice shape on the end correction for elliptical and rectangular orifices in infinite baffles.

The quantity κ_E is plotted in Fig. 21.14 as a function of r, the ratio of the length of the major axis of the ellipse to that of the minor axis. Because the computation is for an orifice in an infinitely thin baffle, the end correction given in Eq. (21.23) is lower than for the case of a baffle of finite thickness.[7]   In the latter case, it would probably be more accurate to apply the correction factor κ_E to the circular-tube end correction $0.82(S/\pi)^{1/2}$.

In the case of a square or rectangular orifice, the reactance has been computed[10] assuming constant normal velocity in the opening.   This gives values of end correction that are too high, so it is advisable to write the end correction in terms of that for a circular orifice of equal area.   Thus, for a thick baffle:

$$\alpha = 0.82(S/\pi)^{1/2}\kappa_R$$

where κ_R is the ratio between the rectangular-orifice and circular-orifice end corrections, as given by the equations of Ref. 10.   The quantity κ_R is also plotted in Fig. 21.14, as a function of r, where in this case r is the ratio of the length to the width of the rectangular orifice.

The preceding results for elliptical and rectangular orifices provide a basis for estimating the end correction for orifices of other shapes.

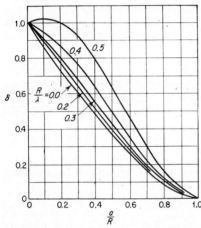

FIG. 21.15. Correction factor to account for the influence of the tube wall on the end correction for a circular orifice that is centered inside a circular tube.   (*Bolt, Labate, and Ingard.*[11])

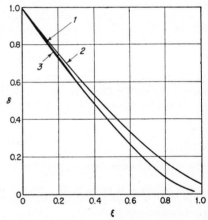

FIG. 21.16. Correction factor to account for the influence of the tube walls on the end correction for (1) a circular orifice centered in a circular tube; (2) a circular orifice centered in a square tube, and; (3) a square orifice centered in a square tube.   (*Ingard.*[12])

If, instead of being in an infinite baffle, the orifice is in a baffle that is inside of a tube, the presence of the tube wall restricts the flow and therefore affects the value of the end correction.   In the case of a circular orifice of radius a centered in a circular tube of radius R, the end correction at one end can be written:

$$\alpha = 0.82a\delta$$

where δ is a correction factor accounting for the presence of the tube.[11]   For a circular orifice centered in a circular tube, this correction factor is plotted in Fig. 21.15 as a function of a/R for several values of R/λ.

Similar correction factors have been calculated for a circular orifice in a square tube and for a square orifice in a square tube.[12]   These correction factors, for small values of R/λ, are given in Fig. 21.16, which also includes the case of a circular orifice in a circular tube for comparison.   The ordinate ξ is, for the circular orifice in a circular tube, the ratio of orifice diameter to tube diameter, for the circular orifice in a square tube, the ratio of orifice diameter to tube width, and, for the square orifice in a square tube, the ratio of orifice width to tube width. A rough approximation for δ (for $\xi < 0.4$) is:

$$\delta \approx 1 - 1.25\xi$$

The end correction for a rectangular orifice in a square or rectangular tube can be found in Ref. 12 together with corrections for eccentric circular orifices as well as the interaction between two circular orifices.

In the case of a slit in a baffle in a rectangular duct (see Fig. 21.17) the end correction on one side is:[3,13]

$$\alpha = \frac{d}{\pi} \log_e csc \left(\frac{\pi}{2} \frac{d}{b} \right)$$

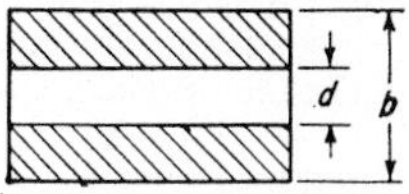

This result is an approximation valid when $\lambda \gg d$.

FIG. 21.17. Sketch of a rectangular baffle with an open slit.

If the slit is not on the centerline of the duct, the end correction increases until, when the slit is at the top or bottom of the duct, the correction is:

$$\alpha = \frac{2d}{\pi} \log_e csc \left(\frac{\pi}{2} \frac{b}{d} \right)$$

In the preceding discussion, the influence of viscosity on the reactance has not been considered. This is permissible in such fluids as air and engine exhaust gas except for extremely small orifices. For an orifice diameter of only 0.5 cm at a frequency of 250 cps in air at room temperature, the contribution of viscosity is only about 5 per cent. The effect of viscosity is considered in Refs. 14, 15, and 16. Included in these references are end corrections measured in water and silicone fluid.

Up to this point, the discussion of orifices has been confined to those cases where the particle-velocities, particle displacements, and sound pressures are sufficiently small so that the orifices behave in a linear manner; i.e., the orifice reactance is independent of the sound intensity.

If viscosity and second-order terms are taken into account in the solution of the wave equation, however, it is found that time-independent streams of flow necessarily follow under certain circumstances.[17] These circulation effects have been studied experimentally for the case of acoustical orifices.[18] They are important considerations in filter design because they cause nonlinearities in the acoustical impedance of orifices. Experimental measurements of reactance in the nonlinear range have been made in gases[12] and liquids.[15] It is shown that the nonlinear part of the reactance is nearly zero until s/t approaches 1, where s is the displacement amplitude and t is the orifice thickness.[12] For $s/t > 1$, the reactance first decreases rapidly with increasing particle-displacement and then appears to approach a limiting value. Consideration of this problem on an energy basis resulted in a prediction that when the particle-displacement in the orifice becomes appreciably greater than the orifice diameter, the reactance of a thin orifice will be reduced by about five-eighths of its linear value.[19] A nonlinearity of this magnitude is obviously too large to neglect.

Nonlinearity is found in the orifice resistance as well as in the reactance. Although the linear resistance is normally small enough to be negligible in the design of filters for noise control, nonlinearity can cause a large increase in the resistance. The resistance of thin orifices is approximately doubled when $s/t = 1$, and when $s/t = 10$, the resistance may be 20 times as high as in the linear range. For thick orifices, the nonlinear resistance is shown to be dependent on the particle velocity and nearly independent of the orifice diameter and thickness.[12] There are insufficient data, however, to show the dependence on frequency of the nonlinear resistance for thick orifices.

The decrease in reactance and the increase in resistance are due to turbulence which may also be caused by steady airflow through or past the orifice. Steady flow is known to affect the resonant frequency of orifices.[20] Also, the results of experiments with a filter that had orifices in series with the steady flow show a definite effect of the steady flow velocity on the transmission loss.[21]

Available information on nonlinear effects in thin orifices indicates that the maximum value of s/t should be 1 or less. Because the sound intensity and the frequencies in the filter are fixed by the particular application, particle velocities can be reduced only by increasing the orifice area. This, in turn, requires an increase in orifice thickness to hold the reactance constant. Thus, the orifice is replaced by a tube. This scheme of using a tube to replace an orifice in an acoustical circuit is often useful for avoiding or reducing nonlinearities in filters that must work under extremely high noise levels. Furthermore, any error due to uncertainty regarding the value of the end correction α will be reduced in importance if a tube is used.

Because of the many sources of uncertainty with regard to orifice reactance, it is desirable to check this part of a filter design experimentally under the actual operating conditions whenever this is economically feasible.

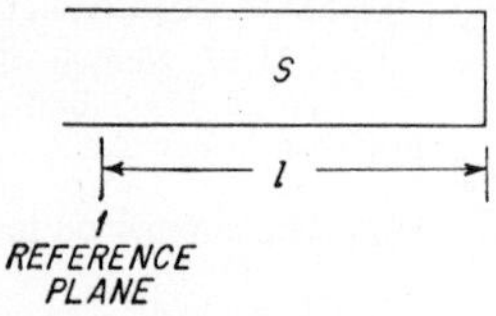

Closed Tube. Figure 21.18 shows a closed tube. For a plane wave incident on the reference plane at 1, the reflection factor is:

$$R = e^{-2ikl}$$

The impedance at 1, looking toward the closed end, is:

FIG. 21.18. Diagram of a tube closed at one end.

$$\frac{Z}{Z_0} = -i \cot kl \qquad (21.24)$$

If the tube is sufficiently short so that $\tan kl \approx kl$, this impedance can be written:

$$Z = -i\frac{\rho_0 c}{S} \cdot \frac{1}{kl} = -i\frac{\rho_0 c^2}{\omega V} \qquad (21.25)$$

where $V = lS$, the volume of the tube to the right of 1.

Volume Chamber. Where the dimensions of the chamber are all small enough in comparison to the sound wavelength so that the approximation given in the previous paragraph is valid, then the impedance of the chamber is given by Eq. (21.25):

$$Z = -i\frac{\rho_0 c^2}{\omega V}$$

TRANSMISSION LOSS OF FILTERS TERMINATED WITHOUT REFLECTION

Terminology. A *low-pass acoustical filter* is a filter that transmits sound below a certain frequency, called the *cutoff frequency*, and attenuates sound at higher frequencies.

A *high-pass filter* is a filter that transmits sound above the cutoff frequency and attenuates sound at lower frequencies.

A *bandpass filter* transmits sound in a band of frequencies between a lower limit, called the lower cutoff frequency, and an upper limit, called the upper cutoff frequency. Sound is attenuated at frequencies below the lower cutoff frequency and above the upper cutoff frequency.

The frequency bands within which sound is attenuated are often called *stop bands*.

It is important to recognize that these filter classifications are commonly used in a manner that lacks precision. For example, consider a low-pass filter designed for a cutoff frequency of 100 cps. To cover the entire audible range above 100 cps, the filter would have to provide transmission loss for acoustical waves having wavelengths from about 11 ft to 1 in. For tubes of the size encountered in engineering practice, attenuation of the longer waves often requires filter elements with dimensions of 1 ft or more. At certain discrete wavelengths between the limits of 11 ft and 1 in., various natural vibration modes of the filter elements will be excited. Thus the filter will not behave strictly as a low-pass filter but will have several upper passbands in the audible range. Similar considerations apply to the use of the terms high pass and bandpass with reference to acoustical filters.

Series Filters. *Single-expansion Chamber.* A schematic diagram of a single-expansion chamber is shown in Fig. 21.19. The equations for continuity of pressure and volume current at junctions I and II are:

$$A_1 + B_1 = A_2 + B_2$$

$$\frac{1}{Z_{01}}(A_1 - B_1) = \frac{1}{Z_{02}}(A_2 - B_2)$$

or

$$A_1 - B_1 = m(A_2 - B_2)$$

where $m = S_2/S_1$.

$$A_2 e^{-ikl_e} + B_2 e^{ikl_e} = A_3$$
$$m(A_2 e^{-ikl_e} - B_2 e^{ikl_e}) = A_3$$

If these four equations are solved simultaneously for the transmission and reflection factors based on the junctions I and II, the results are:

$$T = \frac{A_3}{A_1} = \left[\cos kl_e + i\frac{1}{2}\left(m + \frac{1}{m}\right)\sin kl_e \right]^{-1} \tag{21.26}$$

$$R_I = \frac{B_1}{A_1} = -\frac{i\frac{1}{2}\left(m - \frac{1}{m}\right)\sin kl_e}{\cos kl_e + i\frac{1}{2}\left(m + \frac{1}{m}\right)\sin kl_e} \tag{21.27}$$

The transmission loss, determined from Eq. (21.8), is:

$$10\log_{10}\left[1 + \frac{1}{4}\left(m - \frac{1}{m}\right)^2 \sin^2 kl_e\right] \quad \text{db} \tag{21.28}$$

These same results could have been obtained by starting with either the impedance at the contraction and expansion, given by Eq. (21.9), or the reflection and transmission factors at the contraction and expansion given by Eqs. (21.10) and (21.11).

The method of solution using reflection and transmission factors will be given for illustrative purposes. Let the reflection and transmission factors at junction II for the sound incident from the left be called R_{II01} and T_{II01}, the characteristic reflection and transmission factors. At junction I the characteristic factors for sound incident from the left will be termed R_{I01} and T_{I01}, and for sound incident from the right R_{I02} and T_{I02}. The true factors at junction I of the expansion chamber will be called R_I and T_I.

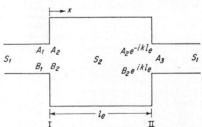

FIG. 21.19. Schematic diagram of a single-expansion chamber. (*Davis, Stokes, Moore, and Stevens.*[22])

Substituting these symbols in Eq. (21.3) gives:

$$R_I = R_{I01} + \frac{R_{II01}T_{I01}T_{I02}e^{-ik2l_e}}{1 - R_{II01}R_{I02}e^{-ik2l_e}}$$

From Eqs. (21.10) and (21.11), using m to symbolize S_2/S_1 for the expansion chamber (Fig. 21.19):

$$R_{I01} = -\frac{m-1}{m+1}$$

$$R_{II01} = -\frac{1/m - 1}{1/m + 1} = \frac{m-1}{m+1} = R_{I02}$$

$$T_{I01} = \frac{2}{m+1}$$

$$T_{I02} = \frac{2}{1/m + 1} = \frac{2m}{m+1} = T_{II01}$$

Thus
$$R_I = -\frac{m-1}{m+1} + \frac{\left(\frac{m-1}{m+1}\right)\left(\frac{2}{m+1}\right)\left(\frac{2m}{m+1}\right)e^{-ik2l_e}}{1 - \left(\frac{m-1}{m+1}\right)^2 e^{-ik2l_e}}$$

which, when simplified, yields Eq. (21.27).

Similarly, substitution in Eq. (21.5) gives:

$$T_I = \frac{T_{I01}}{1 - R_{II01}R_{I02}e^{-ik2l_e}} = \frac{\dfrac{2}{m+1}}{1 - \left(\dfrac{m-1}{m+1}\right)^2 e^{-ik2l_e}}$$

For the complete expansion-chamber filter, the transmission factor is

$$T = T_I e^{-ikl_e}T_{II01} = \frac{\left(\dfrac{2}{m+1}\right)e^{-ikl_e}\left(\dfrac{2m}{m+1}\right)}{1 - \left(\dfrac{m-1}{m+1}\right)^2 e^{-ik2l_e}}$$

which reduces to Eq. (21.26).

The transmission loss for a single-expansion chamber is plotted in Fig. 21.20 as a function of kl_e for several values of the expansion ratio m. These curves can be used in the design of expansion-chamber filters. The significant characteristics of this type of filter are that the transmission loss increases as the expansion ratio increases and that the transmission-loss curve is cyclic, repeating itself at frequency intervals determined by the length of the expansion chamber l_e and the velocity of sound c (since $k = 2\pi f/c$). Because these are low-pass filters, and broad stop bands can be obtained, expansion chambers are useful as noise-control filters.

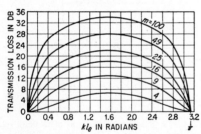

FIG. 21.20. Expansion-chamber design curves. (*Davis, Stokes, Moore, and Stevens.*[22])

The results of several actual measurements of transmission loss are presented to indicate the accuracy of the theory and to point out some of the limitations. Fig. 21.21 shows that the theory holds over a wide range of filter length. Fig. 21.22 shows that the ends need not be perpendicular to the center line. (An average length has been used in the calculations.) Although the filters are relatively insensitive to the steep tapers tested, it is probable that a long slender taper would act as a horn and reduce the filter effectiveness severely at high frequencies. This effect is shown in Fig. 21.23, which gives the transmission loss for conical connectors as a function of the ratio of taper length to wavelength for several values of the expansion ratio.[22,23]

When the largest cross-sectional dimension of the chamber is as great as one-half to one wavelength or more, the exact number depending on the shape of the cross section, the assumption of plane waves is no longer valid. Experiments show that in such cases the transmission loss can be quite different from the value given by Eq. (21.28). This is evident in the test results from the first filter in Fig. 21.24, where the plane-wave theory did not predict the large reduction of transmission loss at 700 cps.

The occurrence of higher-order modes has been mentioned earlier in connection with the transmission loss of a right-angled bend. In the case of a circular expansion chamber, with sound entering and leaving at the center of the ends, the first expected higher mode would be symmetrical. The lowest frequency at which this mode could be transmitted without loss is given by $f = 1.22c/d$, where d is the chamber diameter. This limiting frequency is 694 cps for the first filter in Fig. 21.24. Thus it is con-

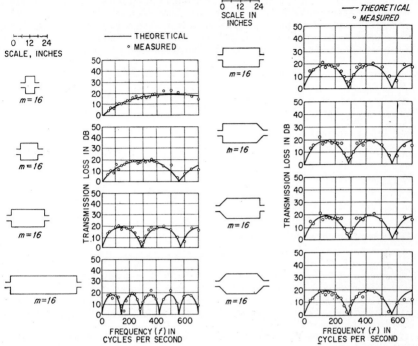

FIG. 21.21. Effect of length. (*Davis, Stokes, Moore, and Stevens.*[22])

FIG. 21.22. Effect of tapered ends. (*Davis, Stokes, Moore, and Stevens.*[22])

cluded that the reduction of transmission loss at 700 cps is due to the appearance of this mode.

The second filter in Fig. 21.24 has an approximately elliptical cross section. The plane-wave theory [Eq. (21.28)] gives good results through most of the frequency range, but a reduction of transmission loss is noted at 650 and 700 cps. At these frequencies, the wavelength is slightly shorter than the major axis of the ellipse, so the reduction of transmission loss is probably due to the appearance of a higher order vibrational mode.

Although this discussion has concerned

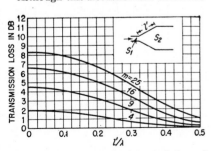

FIG. 21.23. Acoustical characteristics of truncated cones. (*Davis, Stokes, Moore, and Stevens.*[22])

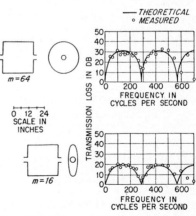

FIG. 21.24. Filters with large cross-sectional dimensions. (*Davis, Stokes, Moore, and Stevens.*[22])

expansion-chamber filters, note that a constriction in the duct will give the same transmission loss as an expansion chamber of the same length and area ratio [see Eq. (21.28)].

Orifice in Duct. A schematic diagram of an orifice in a duct is shown in Fig. 21.25. The impedance at 2 is $Z_0 = \rho_o c/S$, and the impedance of the orifice is $Z = i\omega\rho_o/c_o$, where c_o is the conductivity of the orifice. The impedance at 1 is:

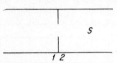

$$\frac{Z_1}{Z_0} = 1 + i\frac{\omega\rho_o}{c_o}\frac{S}{\rho_o c} = 1 + ik\frac{S}{c_o}$$

The reflection factor at 1 is [using Eq. (21.6)]:

FIG. 21.25. Schematic diagram of an orifice in a duct.

$$R = \frac{ik\dfrac{S}{c_o}}{2 + ik\dfrac{S}{c_o}}$$

The transmission factor is:

$$T = \frac{1}{1 + \dfrac{i}{2}k\dfrac{S}{c_o}}$$

The transmission loss [using Eq. (21.8)] is:

$$10\log_{10}\left[1 + \left(\frac{k}{2}\frac{S}{c_o}\right)^2\right] \qquad \text{db} \qquad (21.29)$$

The transmission loss is zero at zero frequency, and increases with increasing frequency. This arrangement is analogous to an inductance in series with an electrical transmission line. Equation (21.29) indicates that a single orifice, by itself, is a rather crude sort of low-pass filter.

Bend in Duct. The case of a right-angled bend in a duct has been discussed earlier. Within the frequency range where a bend provides transmission loss, it is a low-pass filter roughly similar in acoustical behavior to a series orifice.

Multiple-section Series Filters. The transmission loss of multiple-section filters can be determined from the characteristics of a single section by the method given under *Parameters Used to Describe Filter Characteristics* or by direct solution of the continuity equations at the junctions of the filter.

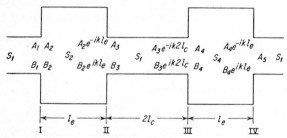

FIG. 21.26. Schematic diagram of a double-expansion-chamber filter with external connecting tube. (*Davis, Stokes, Moore, and Stevens.*[22])

Double-expansion Chamber with External Connecting Tube. A schematic diagram of a double-expansion-chamber filter with the connecting tube external to the chambers is shown in Fig. 21.26, with the symbols to be used also included. The effective length of the connecting tube $2l_c$ is equal to the physical length plus an end correction. Following the method used for the single-expansion chamber, the continuity equations at the four indicated junctures are

At junction I:

$$A_1 + B_1 = A_2 + B_2$$
$$A_1 - B_1 = m(A_2 - B_2)$$

At junction II:

$$A_2 e^{-ikl_e} + B_2 e^{ikl_e} = A_3 + B_3$$
$$m(A_2 e^{-ikl_e} - B_2 e^{ikl_e}) = A_3 - B_3$$

At junction III:

$$A_3 e^{-ik2l_c} + B_3 e^{ik2l_c} = A_4 + B_4$$
$$A_3 e^{-ik2l_c} - B_3 e^{ik2l_c} = m(A_4 - B_4)$$

At junction IV:

$$A_4 e^{-ikl_e} + B_4 e^{ikl_e} = A_5$$
$$m(A_4 e^{-ikl_e} - B_4 e^{ikl_e}) = A_5$$

The transmission loss is

$$10 \log_{10} \left\{ \left[R\left(\frac{A_1}{A_5}\right) \right]^2 + \left[I\left(\frac{A_1}{A_5}\right) \right]^2 \right\} \qquad db$$

where R and I signify the real and imaginary parts, respectively, of $\dfrac{A_1}{A_5}$.

Simultaneous solution of the equations at the junctions yields[22]

$$\frac{A_1}{A_5} = \frac{1}{16m^2} \{[4m(m+1)^2 \cos 2k(l_e + l_c) - 4m(m-1)^2 \cos 2k(l_e - l_c)]$$
$$+ i[2(m^2+1)(m+1)^2 \sin 2k(l_e + l_c)$$
$$- 2(m^2+1)(m-1)^2 \sin 2k(l_e - l_c) - 4(m^2-1)^2 \sin 2kl_c]\}$$

To work this problem by the method presented earlier, one would begin with the characteristic transmission factor for a single-expansion chamber, referred to junctions I and II [Eq. (21.26)]. Following the terminology of the section on *Parameters Used to Describe Filter Characteristics*, this transmission factor will be given the symbol T_0'. The next step is to refer the transmission factor to terminals at a distance l_c from the ends of the chambers, calling the new transmission factor T_0. Thus:

$$T_0 = T_0' e^{-ik2l_c}$$
$$= \frac{\cos 2kl_c - i \sin 2kl_c}{\cos kl_e + i\frac{1}{2}\left(m + \frac{1}{m}\right)\sin kl_e} \qquad (21.30)$$

The magnitude D and phase angle δ of T_0 are computed on the basis of Eq. (21.30). Once these are known, the attenuation of the double-chamber muffler can be computed from Eq. (21.7) or read from Fig. 21.3.

Because the reference terminals are not at the ends of the chambers, the transmission factor determined by this method will have a different phase than A_5/A_1, which

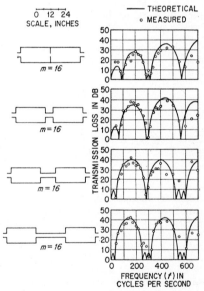

Fig. 21.27. Transmission loss for double-expansion chambers with external connecting tubes. (*Davis, Stokes, Moore, and Stevens.*[22])

is also a transmission factor. The magnitudes will be the same, however, as will the values of transmission loss computed from the two transmission factors.

The computed transmission loss curves for a few mufflers of this type are compared with measured values in Fig. 21.27. The transmission loss for these two-chamber mufflers is higher than for a single chamber. A low-frequency pass region is introduced as a result of resonance between the connecting tube and the chambers. When the connecting tube is lengthened, the lower cut-off frequency is reduced. An approximate equation for this cut-off frequency is[22]

$$f_c \approx \frac{c}{2\pi} \left[ml_e l_c + \frac{l_e}{3} (l_e - l_c) \right]^{-1} \quad \text{cps} \tag{21.31}$$

The maximum transmission loss in the first stop band above this cut-off frequency is shown to increase as the connecting-tube length is increased. On the other hand, however, regions of low transmission loss with a width of 50 cps or more occur between the stop bands when the connecting tubes are long. These passbands would be objectionable in a filter if a significant amount of noise were present in them.

Double-expansion Chamber with Internal Connecting Tube. A schematic diagram of a double-expansion-chamber filter with the connecting tube internal to the expansion

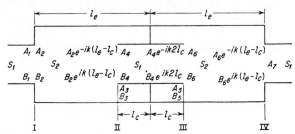

Fig. 21.28. Schematic diagram of a double-expansion-chamber filter with internal connecting tube. (*Davis, Stokes, Moore, and Stevens.*[22])

chamber is shown in Fig. 21.28, with the symbols used in the derivation of the transmission loss equation also indicated. (For a derivation see Ref. 22.) The transmission loss is:

$$10 \log_{10} \left\{ \left[R\left(\frac{A_1}{A_7}\right) \right]^2 + \left[I\left(\frac{A_1}{A_7}\right) \right]^2 \right\} \quad \text{db}$$

and

$$\frac{A_1}{A_7} = \{\cos 2kl_e - (m - 1) \sin 2kl_e \tan kl_c\} + \frac{i}{2} \left\{ \left(m + \frac{1}{m}\right) \sin 2kl_e \right.$$
$$\left. + (m - 1) \tan kl_c \left[\left(m + \frac{1}{m}\right) \cos 2kl_e - \left(m - \frac{1}{m}\right) \right] \right\}$$

The computed transmission loss for a few filters of this type is compared with experimental measurements in Fig. 21.29. The low-frequency pass region is again present, and the cut-off frequency is given approximately by Eq. (21.31). This type of filter is seen to be similar in many respects to the type with the external connecting tube. A significant difference is found, however, when the connecting tube length is equal to the chamber length (fourth filter, Fig. 21.29). Here the stop band is about twice as wide as for the other filters in Figs. 21.27 and 21.29. This is a valuable feature and it is directly due to the internal location of the connecting tube.[22]

Other Types. Many other types of multiple series filters are possible. Orifices or bends can be used in series, or elements of different types or sizes can be placed in series. Multiple-element filters formed by successive constrictions in a duct are discussed in Ref. 24. A wide variety of series filters can be analyzed using the basic methods that have been illustrated.

Side-branch (Parallel) Filters. Side-branch filters have elements connected in parallel with the main duct, in the form of branch acoustical circuits. (See Fig. 21.30.) The steady flow in the duct, if any, does not flow through these branches. At the juncture, the conditions of continuity of pressure and volume current are:

$$p_i + p_{re} = p_b = p_{tr} \tag{21.32}$$
$$U_i - U_{re} = U_b + U_{tr} \tag{21.33}$$

where subscripts i and re refer to the incident and reflected waves ahead of the branch, b refers to the branch, and tr refers to the transmitted wave beyond the branch. Waves i, re, and tr are assumed to be plane, and for plane waves $U = p/Z_0$. Making this substitution, and also $U_b = p_b/Z_b$, Eq. (21.33) becomes:

$$\frac{1}{Z_0}(p_i - p_{re}) = p_{tr}\left(\frac{1}{Z_b} + \frac{1}{Z_0}\right) \quad (21.34)$$

where Z_b is the branch impedance. Equations (21.32) and (21.34) can be combined to give:

$$\frac{p_i}{p_{tr}} = 1 + \frac{Z_0}{2Z_b} = 1 + \frac{Z_0}{2(R_b + iX_b)} \quad (21.35)$$

This is the reciprocal of the transmission factor. The transmission loss is:

$$10\log_{10}\left[\frac{\left(R_b + \frac{Z_0}{2}\right)^2 + X_b^2}{R_b^2 + X_b^2}\right] \quad \text{db}$$
$$(21.36)$$

This equation is perfectly general; all that is required to determine the transmission loss due to a particular type of side branch is to determine the impedance of the branch and substitute it in Eq. (21.36).

In a large number of practical cases, the resistance is sufficiently small so that it can be neglected in filter design. In such cases, the transmission loss is:

$$10\log_{10}\left[1 + \frac{Z_0^2}{4X_b^2}\right] \quad \text{db} \quad (21.37)$$

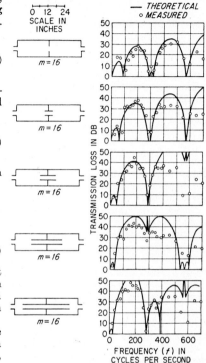

FIG. 21.29. Transmission loss for double-expansion chambers with internal connecting tubes. (*Davis, Stokes, Moore, and Stevens.*[22])

Orifice. A schematic diagram of a duct with an orifice as a side branch is shown in Fig. 21.31. The impedance of the orifice is, if the resistance is neglected,

$$Z_b = iX_b = \frac{i\rho_o\omega}{c_o}$$

where c_o is the conductivity of the orifice. If this is substituted in Eq. (21.37), the

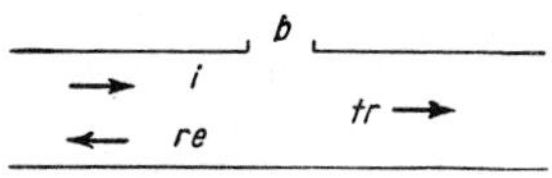

FIG. 21.30. Schematic diagram of a duct with a side branch.

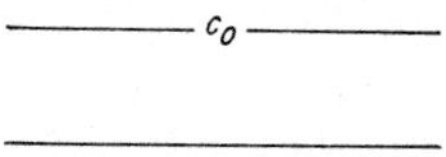

FIG. 21.31. Schematic diagram of a duct with an orifice as a side branch.

transmission loss is found to be

$$10\log_{10}[1 + (c_o/2kS)^2] \quad \text{db}$$

The transmission loss is high at low frequencies and is reduced as the frequency (hence, k) is increased. Thus, this would be classified as a simple high-pass filter.

Open Tube. A schematic diagram of a duct with an open tube as a side branch is shown in Fig. 21.32. The impedance of the branch is, from Eq. (21.17):

$$Z_b = iZ_0 \tan k(l + \alpha)$$

where in this case α must include an end correction at the open end and another at the end that joins the tube. The transmission loss is

$$10 \log_{10} [1 + \tfrac{1}{4} \cot^2 k(l + \alpha)] \qquad db$$

At low frequencies, the behavior is similar to that of the orifice. As the branch tube approaches antiresonance [$\cot k(l + \alpha) = 0$], however, the transmission loss decreases rapidly to zero. At higher frequencies, the transmission loss again increases. Stop bands occur at regular intervals, centered around those frequencies for which

$$\frac{l + \alpha}{\lambda} = \frac{n}{2},$$ where n is any integer. If the branch tube is of about the same size as the duct, or is smaller, these stop bands are found to be quite narrow.

Closed Tube. If the tube shown in Fig. 21.32 were closed at the end, the branch impedance would be [using Eq. (21.24)]:

$$Z_b = -iZ_0 \cot k(l + \alpha)$$

where α is the end correction to the branch tube at the juncture with the duct. The transmission loss is

$$10 \log_{10} [1 + \tfrac{1}{4} \tan^2 k(l + \alpha)] \qquad db$$

As the frequency approaches zero, the transmission loss approaches zero, so the closed-tube branch acts as a low-pass filter at low frequencies, whereas the open-tube branch acts as a high-pass filter at low frequencies. At higher frequencies the behavior of the closed-tube branch is sim-

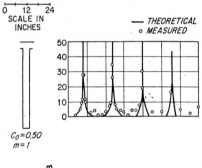

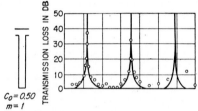

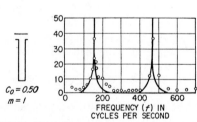

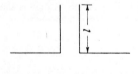

FIG. 21.32. Schematic diagram of a duct with an open tube as a side branch.

FIG. 21.33. Transmission loss due to a closed-tube side branch. (*Davis, Stokes, Moore, and Stevens.*[22])

ilar to that of the open-tube branch in that stop bands are encountered periodically. They are located at quite different frequencies, however, for they are centered around frequencies for which:

$$\frac{l + \alpha}{\lambda} = \frac{2n - 1}{4} \tag{21.38}$$

Experimental measurements of transmission loss for filters of this type are compared with calculated curves in Fig. 21.33. The area of the side branch is equal to the duct area in this example. Because the resistance has been omitted, the calculations predict infinite transmission loss at the frequencies given by Eq. (21.38). These infinities of course are not actually expected to occur. Very high peak transmission-loss values were measured, but the transmission loss reaches useful magnitudes only in very narrow frequency bands.

Resonators. A schematic diagram of a duct with a resonator as a side branch is shown in Fig. 21.34. The branch impedance is the sum of the impedances of the connector and the volume chamber. The connector impedance is given by Eq. (21.20), except that the end corrections at the two ends of the connector may differ due to differences in the boundaries surrounding these two ends:

$$\text{Connector impedance} = i\rho_o\omega(l + \alpha_1 + \alpha_2)/S = (i\rho_o\omega)/c_o \qquad (21.39)$$

Using the chamber impedance given by Eq. (21.25), the branch impedance is:

$$Z_b = i\left(\frac{\omega\rho_o}{c_o} - \frac{\rho_o c^2}{\omega V}\right) \qquad (21.40)$$

The transmission loss is:

$$10\log_{10}\left[1 + \frac{1}{4}\frac{\left(\dfrac{\rho_o c}{S}\right)^2}{\left(\dfrac{\omega\rho_o}{c_o} - \dfrac{\rho_o c^2}{\omega V}\right)^2}\right] \quad \text{db} \qquad (21.41)$$

Note that if the density is the same in the duct, connector, and chamber, it drops out of Eq. (21.41). When the denominator of the second term in this equation goes to zero, the transmission loss is infinite. The frequency at which this occurs is called the resonant frequency, f_r:

$$f_r = \frac{c}{2\pi}\sqrt{\frac{c_o}{V}} \quad \text{cps} \qquad (21.42)$$

From Eq. (21.41) the transmission loss then is:

$$10\log_{10}\left[1 + \left(\frac{\dfrac{\sqrt{c_o V}}{2S}}{\dfrac{f}{f_r} - \dfrac{f_r}{f}}\right)^2\right] \quad \text{db} \qquad (21.43)$$

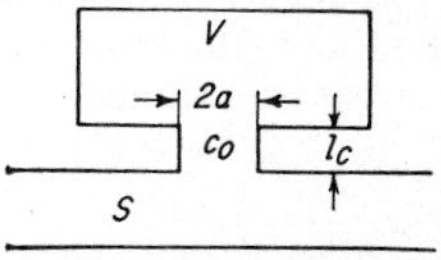

FIG. 21.34. Schematic diagram of a duct with a resonator as a side branch. (*Davis, Stokes, Moore, and Stevens.*[22])

The effect of the filter dimensions on the transmission loss characteristics is apparent from Eqs. (21.42) and (21.43). The resonant frequency is controlled by the ratio $\sqrt{c_o/V}$. The amount of transmission loss at a given frequency different from f_r is controlled by the parameter $(c_oV)^{1/2}/(2S)$. Equation (21.43) can be used to calculate transmission loss curves for use in the design of resonator filters. Curves of this type are presented in Fig. 21.35. As these curves show, the resonators act as low-pass filters, and by use of sufficiently large values of $(c_oV)^{1/2}/(2S)$ a broad stop band can be obtained. Thus, filters of this type have great practical usefulness in noise control work. The accuracy of the theory is indicated by the comparison with experimental measurements in Fig. 21.36.

The most serious limitation on the applicability of Eq. (21.41) is connected with the dimensions of the resonator elements. Both Eqs. (21.39) and (21.25) are approximations. If the connector and the chamber are longer than about one-eighth wavelength, the branch impedance should be determined from the more accurate Eqs. (21.22) and (21.24). Thus:

$$Z_b = i\rho_o c\left[\frac{1}{S_c}\tan k(l_c + \alpha_1 + \alpha_2) - \frac{1}{S_V}\cot(kl_V)\right] \qquad (21.44)$$

where the subscripts c and V refer to the connector and volume chamber, respectively.

Equation (21.44) can be substituted in Eq. (21.37) to calculate the transmission loss. This equation assumes plane-wave transmission in the chamber, so the theory is not applicable where the cross-sectional dimensions are such that higher modes of transmission are possible.

If the branch has resistance R_b, either in the connector or in the chamber, the transmission loss is:

$$10 \log_{10} \left[1 + \frac{1 + 4 \dfrac{R_b}{Z_0}}{4 \left(\dfrac{R_b}{Z_0} \right)^2 + \left(\dfrac{2S}{\sqrt{c_o V}} \right)^2 \left(\dfrac{f}{f_r} - \dfrac{f_r}{f} \right)^2} \right] \quad \text{db}$$

The effect of adding resistance is shown in Fig. 21.37, where X_{cr} signifies the connector reactance at resonance $\rho_o \omega_r / c_o$. The three upper curves are for $(c_o V)^{1/2}/(2S) = 10$. In this case the addition of resistance causes a large drop in the transmission loss near the resonant frequency, but has very little effect on the transmission loss at much lower or much higher frequencies. Adding resistance also causes a drop in the transmission loss near resonance for $(c_o V)^{1/2}/(2S) = 1$ (lower curves), but in this case the transmission loss at much lower or higher frequencies is increased significantly by the addition of resistance.

Curves such as those shown in Figs. 21.35 and 21.37 are useful in the design of resonator filters. By comparing the design requirements with these curves,

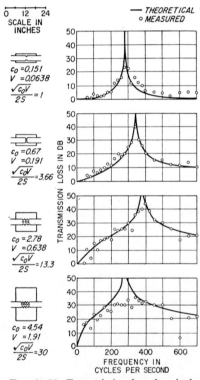

FIG. 21.36. Transmission loss for single-chamber resonators. (*Davis*, *Stokes*, *Moore*, *and Stevens*.[22])

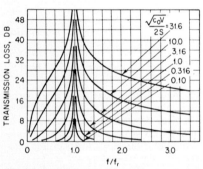

FIG. 21.35. Single-chamber-resonator design curves. (*Davis*, *Stokes*, *Moore*, *and Stevens*.[22])

suitable values of f_r and $(c_o V)^{1/2}/2S$ can be selected. The resonator dimensions are then found as follows:

$$\sqrt{\frac{c_o}{V}} = \frac{2\pi f_r}{c}$$

where c is the speed of sound in the gas in the duct *at the operating temperature.*

$$\sqrt{c_o V} = 2S \times \frac{\sqrt{c_o V}}{2S}$$

Resonator volume:
$$V = \frac{\sqrt{c_o V}}{\sqrt{\dfrac{c_o}{V}}}$$

The shape of the resonator is immaterial, except that Figs. 21.35 and 21.37 will apply only if no point in the resonator is farther than about $c/8f_r$ from the connector opening.

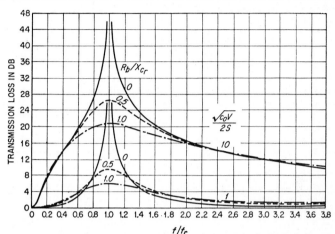

FIG. 21.37. Effect of branch resistance on the transmission loss due to a resonator in a duct.

This restriction in effect places an upper limit on the amount of volume that can be used.

Conductivity:
$$c_o = \sqrt{c_o V} \times \sqrt{\frac{c_o}{V}}$$

Any combination of length, diameter, and number of connectors that will give this conductivity is permissible so long as the acoustic particle displacement in the connector does not exceed the length of the connector. The determination of the conductivity of an orifice is discussed in detail under *Impedance of Filter Elements*. In preliminary design work the curve plotted in Fig. 21.38 is useful.[25] This curve is based on an approximate equation for the conductivity of a group of n orifices of length l and individual area S_c:

$$c_o = \frac{n S_c}{l + 0.8 \sqrt{S_c}}$$

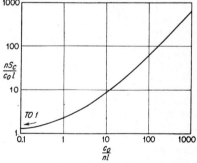

FIG. 21.38. Design chart for resonator apertures. (*Ingard.*[25])

If the total conductivity c_o is given and values are assumed for the number and length of the orifices, the orifice area can be determined rapidly with the assistance of this curve. The values can then be adjusted, if desired, with the aid of the more exact c_o equations presented earlier in this chapter.

Resonators in a Wall as a Sound Absorptive Construction. Although this chapter is concerned with the application of resonators to acoustic filters and mufflers, if properly designed they also may be used as a sound-absorptive construction in a room.

For example a resonator may be set in a plane wall with its opening flush with the wall surface.

For frequencies near the resonance, the effect of a resonator in a room is similar to that of a patch of highly efficient sound-absorbing material. Thus, the reduction of sound pressure which it provides in the room is dependent upon its location. Its absorption can be described by giving its sound absorption in sabins (sq-ft units).

A resonator is useful primarily when relatively large sound absorption is required in a narrow-frequency band, particularly below about 200 cps where it is often difficult to obtain large absorption by other methods. For example, resonators can be used effectively to reduce noise from a source having a large discrete frequency component such as the 120-cps "hum" in a transformer room. Where a wider absorption band is required, a group of resonators tuned to successively larger frequencies may be used. Resonators which are physically adjacent can be considered noninteracting when the difference in the resonance frequencies is greater than either of the bandwidths.

In a room intended for listening to music or speech, the reverberation time of the resonator used as an absorber should be less than that of the room at the frequency of resonance, in order to avoid a localized "holdover" following transient signals, a requirement which is ordinarily not difficult to satisfy.

The maximum absorption of a single resonator in a large wall, in sabins, is approximately $\lambda_r^2/2\pi$, where λ_r is the wavelength of sound in feet at the frequency of resonance, i.e., the frequency of maximum absorption. In all practical designs, the resonator dimensions are small compared with λ_r. The minimum Q (corresponding to maximum bandwidth) which can be obtained in a practical resonator having maximum absorption of the amount indicated above is about 13 for a resonator having its opening in a wall.

The width of the frequency band in which the absorption is not less than half the value found at resonance is equal to the frequency at resonance divided by Q. While the bandwidth of the absorption can be varied over wide limits by adjusting the size of the resonator and the resistance material placed in the aperture, the absorption for all frequencies decreases greatly as the bandwidth is increased. Thus it is usually not profitable to reduce the Q below the above values.

Tuning of Resonators. The approximations made in computing the frequency of resonance, or tolerances in construction, may result in serious miscalculation of the frequency of a high-Q resonator. Furthermore, as a result of construction inaccuracies or tolerances, the resulting resonant frequency may not be that which was intended. Thus, it is advisable to allow for tuning of the resonator to the proper frequency after installation. This adjustment may be accomplished by varying either the volume or the area of the opening, or both. An indication of proper adjustment may be obtained by use of a sound-level meter having its microphone located near the resonator opening. When the resonator is exposed to constant sound pressure of the frequency to be absorbed, tuning is accomplished by adjusting the resonator variable for a minimum sound level.

Another source of tuning error is the nonlinear contribution to the acoustic mass in the resonator, which becomes important at high sound levels. This nonlinear effect is generally less important than the nonlinear resistance. Provision for tuning adjustment is particularly desirable to compensate for this effect where high noise levels are expected. The effect of nonlinearity may become significant when the sound pressure level of the incident signal exceeds 80 to 90 db, but in large, low-frequency resonators this value may be much higher.[12] The effect of the nonlinear resistance is to decrease the resonance absorption and the Q of the system.

Design of Short-neck Resonators. Resonators intended for large bandwidths represent a special case in which the neck is very short. In the design formulas for short-neck wall resonators abstracted from Ref. 12 and given below, normal room air temperature and pressure are assumed. The numerical coefficients and the limiting values of the volume and the Q will be different if other values of the density and the viscosity of the gas are used; in this case the more exact analysis of reference should be used. The following simplified relations represent optimum-design combinations giving the maximum possible resonance absorption and maximum possible Q for a given resonator opening at a given frequency. In the case of a short-neck resonator the effective length of the resonator neck is small compared with the radius of the neck, i.e., $l_c/a \simeq 0$. Although it is assumed that the neck aperture is circular, having a radius a, the aperture can be square rather than circular, if the same area is maintained.

First select the desired resonant frequency f_r. Then, the optimum volume, in terms of the optimum Q and the frequency of resonance, is:

$$V = \frac{3.53 \times 10^7}{2Qf_r{}^3} \quad \text{cu ft}$$

The required aperture radius is:

$$r = 1.90 \times 10^{-4}f_r{}^2V$$
$$= 6.70 \times 10^3/(2f_rQ) \quad \text{in.}$$

The required flow resistance of the cloth screen in the aperture in rayls is $[(95/Q^2) - (3.26 \times 10^{-3})f^{1/2}]$. The minimum reverberation time in optimum designs is approximately $28/f_r$ sec.

Interactions may occur between adjacent resonators tuned to the same frequency, thus the above analysis applies only when the separation between individual resonators tuned to the same frequency is $\lambda_r/2$ or more.

When short-neck resonators are used in an optimum design, as is necessary to secure large bandwidth, the bandwidth is proportional to the resonator volume. Therefore, the volume occupied by a "stagger-tuned" array for a given frequency band is a constant for optimum design, no matter whether n resonators are used with one set of Q values, or $2n$ resonators are used with individual Q's twice as large.

The frequency of resonance f_r under ordinary conditions increases approximately 1 per cent for a temperature increase of 10°F. For a resonator having a Q of 50 or more, a 1 per cent frequency change reduces the absorption at constant frequency to one-half. Hence it is desirable to select the smallest optimum-design Q when a single resonator must absorb a constant frequency under conditions of fluctuating temperature. Temperature effects are not significant in the case of a stagger-tuned array of resonators, since all frequencies of resonance are affected by the same factor when the temperature changes.*

Multiple-section Side-branch Filters. A filter composed of several identical side branches, equally spaced along the duct, can be treated as follows.[26] The transmission loss of m identical chambers of an infinite filter of this type is given by:

$$8.69m \cosh^{-1} \left| \cos kl_1 + i\frac{Z_0}{2Z_b} \sin kl_1 \right| \quad \text{db} \qquad (21.45)$$

where l_1 is the distance between branches, and where the absolute value of the sum inside the bars is given a plus sign, as is the inverse hyperbolic cosine. Transmission loss is obtained when the sum is greater than 1. If the absolute value of the sum inside the bars is less than 1, it is not the hyperbolic cosine of a real number, and there is no transmission loss. This equation, like Eq. (21.36), is quite general and all that is required to calculate the transmission loss in a particular case is to insert the correct value for the branch impedance. Hence, only one of the previously discussed types of side branch is treated here in detail.

If there are only a few sections in the filter, the method of reflection factors described under *Parameters Used to Describe Filter Characteristics* may give more satisfactory results than Eq. (21.45). This equation, because it is based on an infinite filter, must be regarded as an approximation for finite filters.

For further information on multiple section side-branch filters see Refs. 23, 26, 27, and 28.

---

* For additional information concerning the use of wall-type resonators to provide sound absorption in a room see: V. L. Jordan, *J. Acoust. Soc. Am.*, **19**: 972 (1947); also papers by P. V. Brüel and A. J. King, *Acoust. Group Symposium* (1947), Physical Soc., London (1949).

Multiple-chamber Resonator. In the case of a filter composed of several identical resonator side branches without resistance,

$$\frac{Z_0}{2Z_b} = \frac{\rho_o c}{2S} \cdot \frac{1}{i\left(\dfrac{\omega \rho_o}{c_o} - \dfrac{\rho_o c^2}{\omega V}\right)} \tag{21.46}$$

making use of Eq. (21.40). The transmission loss can be computed by substituting Eq. (21.46) in Eq. (21.45), with the result:

$$8.69m \cosh^{-1} \left| \cos\left(k_r l_1 \frac{f}{f_r}\right) + \frac{\dfrac{\sqrt{c_o V}}{2S}}{\dfrac{f}{f_r} - \dfrac{f_r}{f}} \sin\left(k_r l_1 \frac{f}{f_r}\right) \right| \qquad \text{db} \tag{21.47}$$

This equation contains a new parameter $k_r l_1$, which is associated with the distance between branches.

In preliminary design work the following approximate equation[23] for the cut-off frequency of this type of low-pass filter is useful.

$$f_c = \frac{c}{\pi} \sqrt{\frac{S}{l_1 V}\left(\frac{1}{1 + \dfrac{4S}{l_1 c_o}}\right)} \qquad \text{cps}$$

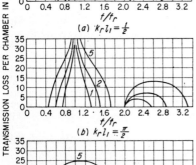

(a) $k_r l_1 = \frac{1}{2}$

(b) $k_r l_1 = \frac{\pi}{2}$

(c) $k_r l_1 = \pi$

TRANSMISSION LOSS PER CHAMBER IN DB

FIG. 21.39. Multiple-chamber-resonator design curves. (*Davis, Stokes, Moore, and Stevens.*[22])

The transmission-loss curves shown in Fig. 21.39 have been calculated from Eq. (21.47). The presence of the third parameter $k_r l_1$ makes it necessary to work with several sets of design curves in this case. For low values of $k_r l_1$, the resonant frequency is near the cut-off frequency and curves such as those in the top set result. When $k_r l_1 = \pi/2$, the resonant frequency is midway in the first stop band. When $k_r l_1 = \pi$, the resonant frequency is at what would otherwise be the first upper-pass frequency. Thus, the theoretical possibility of eliminating this pass frequency and thereby broadening the stop band is indicated. Actually the reactances of both the branches and the ducts between branches approach zero at the resonant frequency in this case, so the theory omitting resistance is inapplicable. Experimental data are presented later to show what actually happens in this case. When $k_r l_1$ is greater than π, but less than 2π, the resonant frequency is in the second stop band of the filter, instead of being in the first stop band.

Comparison of experimental results on two-chamber filters with calculations based on Eq. (21.47) are presented in Fig. 21.40. Although these calculations would be satisfactory in many cases of filter design, better accuracy would be obtained by the use of the reflection factor method described earlier for a two-section filter.

The results of an attempt to design a muffler with $k_r l_1 = \pi$ are shown in Fig. 21.41. Because of the length of the chamber, it was necessary in this case to use

$$-\frac{\rho_o c}{S_V} \cot(k l_V)$$ for the chamber reactance, as in Eq. (21.44). Because the connecting holes are in the middle of the chamber l_V was taken as half the actual chamber length,

and S_V as twice the chamber area. In this type of design (chamber length equal to branch spacing) $k_r l_1 = \pi$ only when the conductivity is infinite. The actual c_o is less than this, but it is interesting to note that, although the transmission loss decreased sharply in the critical range near the design resonant frequency, it did not drop to zero. Instead, the minimum transmission loss in this range was more than 20 db.

Bandpass Filter. A schematic diagram of one section of a multisection bandpass filter is shown in Fig. 21.42. The branch consists of a resonator, with impedance Z_{b1} (see Eq. (21.40)) in parallel with an open tube, with impedance Z_{b2} [see Eq. (21.39)]. Thus, the branch impedance is:

$$Z_b = \frac{Z_{b1} + Z_{b2}}{Z_{b1}Z_{b2}}$$

If this impedance is inserted in Eq. (21.45), and the transmission loss is cal-

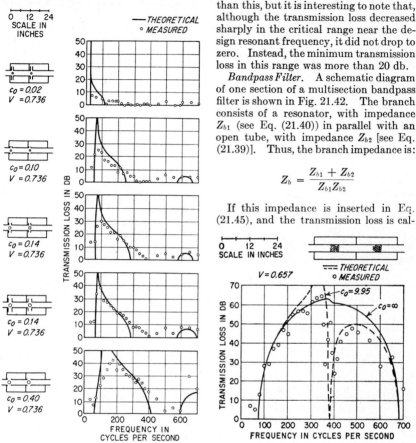

FIG. 21.40. Transmission loss for two-chamber resonator filters. (*Davis, Stokes, Moore, and Stevens.*[22])

FIG. 21.41. Transmission loss for a two-chamber resonator filter for which $k_r l_1$ is nearly equal to π.

culated, a stop band will be found in the frequency range between the frequencies given by the following equations:[23]

$$f_1 = \frac{c}{2\pi} \sqrt{\frac{c_o S_2}{V[(l_2 + \alpha_1 + \alpha_2)c_o + S_2]}} \qquad \text{cps}$$

$$f_2 = \frac{c}{2\pi} \sqrt{\frac{S_2}{V(l_2 + \alpha_1 + \alpha_2)} \left\{ \frac{1 + \dfrac{4S_1(l_2 + \alpha_1 + \alpha_2)}{S_2 l_1}}{1 + \dfrac{S_2}{c_o(l_2 + \alpha_1 + \alpha_2)} + \dfrac{4S_1}{l_1 c_o}} \right\}} \qquad \text{cps}$$

where S_1 is the area of the main duct.

This is only one of several types of bandpass filters that could be designed.

Combinations. When a filter is required to provide transmission loss over a very wide range of frequencies, several sections of different characteristics are normally used, with each section designed to provide attenuation in a particular part of the frequency range. Because of the infinite variety of possible combinations, transmission-loss equations cannot be given for all possibilities. Instead, general methods for computing the transmission loss are considered.

The procedure for handling such filters is to start with the impedance or reflection and transmission factors for the last section and work backward toward the first section. The reflection and transmission factors can be determined by repeated use of Eqs. (21.3) and (21.5).

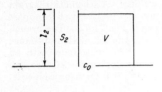

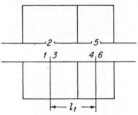

Fig. 21.42. Schematic diagram of one section of a bandpass filter.

Fig. 21.43. Schematic diagram of a filter composed of two resonators tuned to different frequencies. (*Davis, Stokes, Moore, and Stevens.*[22])

As an example of one method of treating such combinations, consider the resonator filter shown in Fig. 21.43. The transmission factor for the last section is given in terms of the branch impedance and the duct characteristic impedance by:

$$\frac{A_6}{A_4} = \frac{1}{1 + \dfrac{Z_0/Z_5}{1 + Z_0/Z_6}} \tag{21.48}$$

If the duct is terminated without reflection, $Z_6 = Z_0$ and

$$\frac{A_6}{A_4} = \frac{1}{1 + \dfrac{Z_0/Z_5}{2}} \tag{21.49}$$

The transmission factor for the first section, when in this combination, is given by an equation similar to Eq. (21.48), namely:

$$\frac{A_3}{A_1} = \frac{1}{1 + \dfrac{Z_0/Z_2}{1 + Z_0/Z_3}}$$

Because $A_4 = A_3 e^{-ikl_1}$

$$\frac{A_4}{A_1} = \frac{e^{-ikl_1}}{1 + \dfrac{Z_0/Z_2}{1 + Z_0/Z_3}} \tag{21.50}$$

For the complete two-section filter, the transmission factor is given by the product of Eqs. (21.49) and (21.50):

$$\frac{A_6}{A_1} = \left(\frac{1}{1 + \dfrac{Z_0/Z_5}{2}} \right) \left(\frac{e^{-ikl_1}}{1 + \dfrac{Z_0/Z_2}{1 + Z_0/Z_3}} \right) \tag{21.51}$$

The transmission loss is:

$$10 \log_{10} \left| \frac{A_1}{A_6} \right|^2 \quad \text{db}$$

where the bars signify that the absolute magnitude of the complex ratio inside is to be taken. This method may be extended to a three-section filter by multiplying Eq. (21.51) by an additional term of the same form as Eq. (21.50).

The branch impedances in Eq. (21.51) can be computed from Eq. (21.40) or (21.44). The impedance Z_3 is more difficult to obtain, but it is calculated by combining Z_5 and Z_6 in parallel to get

$$Z_4 = \frac{Z_5 Z_6}{Z_5 + Z_6}$$

and then transferring Z_4 forward through the tube to obtain

$$\frac{Z_3}{Z_0} = \frac{Z_4 \cos kl_1 + iZ_0 \sin kl_1}{Z_0 \cos kl_1 + iZ_4 \sin kl_1}$$

The transmission loss can also be obtained by use of the characteristic transmission and reflection factors of the two sections. Let these be signified by T_{I0}, R_{I0} for the first section and T_{II0}, R_{II0} for the second section, referred to terminals at the branch points. The second section is terminated in the characteristic impedance, so the transmission and reflection factors for this section are

$$T_{II} = T_{II0}$$
$$R_{II} = R_{II0}$$

From Eq. (21.5) the transmission factor for the first section, when in this combination, is

$$T_I = \frac{T_{I0}}{1 - R_{II}R_{I0}e^{-i2kl_1}} \qquad (21.52)$$

where, because the first chamber is symmetrical about the branch point,

$$R_{I01} = R_{I02} = R_{I0}$$

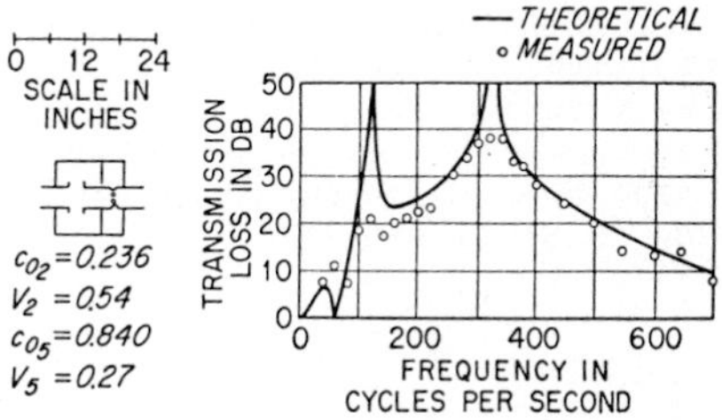

and $T_{I01} = T_{I02} = T_{I0}$. For the complete filter, the transmission factor is

$$T = T_I e^{-ikl_1} T_{II} \qquad (21.53)$$

Fig. 21.44. Transmission loss for a filter composed of two resonators tuned to different frequencies. (*Davis, Stokes, Moore, and Stevens.*[22])

This result is equivalent to Eq. (21.51). Although the algebra is somewhat tedious in any case, the procedure just described is straightforward and is general in application to multisection filters.

The calculated transmission loss of a filter of the type illustrated in Fig. 21.43 is compared with experimentally measured values in Fig. 21.44. Note that a transmission loss in excess of 10 db was obtained over an uninterrupted bandwidth equal to about six times the lowest frequency of the band. To obtain a comparable stop band with a single chamber would require a very high value of $(c_o V)^{1/2}/(2S)$, as can be seen by inspection of Fig. 21.35. For the filter shown, $(c_o V)^{1/2}/(2S) = 3.64$ for the first section and 4.86 for the second.

The transmission factor for filters composed of elements of different types, for example a resonator following an expansion chamber, can also be determined from the characteristic transmission factors for the individual elements by the use of Eqs. (21.52) and (21.53).

INFLUENCE OF FILTER TERMINATION

The transmission-loss equations presented in the preceding section are for filters terminated without reflection, a condition that does not usually exist. If the filter is terminated with a length of duct that is open at the end, the termination will have a very large effect on the transmission loss at certain frequencies. *The filter theory presented in this chapter applies only to cases where the duct cross-sectional dimensions are sufficiently small so that plane-wave propagation is assured.* But for ducts of these dimensions, large reflections occur at the open ends (see Fig. 21.11, for instance). Equation (21.17) gives the impedance of an open duct as $Z = iZ_0 \tan k(l + \alpha)$. At frequencies for which the tangent is zero, the open duct will short-circuit a single-side branch filter, and the effectiveness of the filter is destroyed. The lowest frequency, other than zero, at which this occurs is given by:

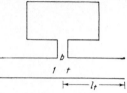

$$f = \frac{1}{2}\frac{c}{l + \alpha} \qquad \text{cps}$$

On the other hand, the effectiveness of the filter is increased at frequencies for which the duct impedance is much larger than Z_0, particularly in the vicinity of:

$$f = \frac{1}{4}\frac{c}{l + \alpha}, \quad \frac{3}{4}\frac{c}{l + \alpha}, \text{ etc.}$$

where the tangent becomes infinite.

If the reflection factor of the termination is known, the effect of the termination on the transmission factor of the filter can be accounted for by use of Eq. (21.5). Consider a single-resonator filter terminated by a duct of length l_t and area S, the duct being open to the atmosphere and unflanged at the end (see Fig. 21.45). The characteristic transmission factor of the filter is, from Eq. (21.35) with $R_b = 0$,

$$T_{01} = \left(1 + \frac{Z_0}{2iX_b}\right)^{-1}$$

The characteristic reflection factor is:

$$R_{01} = -\left(1 + \frac{2iX_b}{Z_0}\right)^{-1}$$

Because the filter is symmetrical when terminated without reflection:

$$R_{02} = R_{01}$$

The reflection factor at the open end is, from Eq. (21.14):

$$R_T = -e^{-2ik\alpha}$$

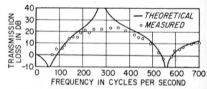

Fig. 21.46. Transmission loss for single-resonator muffler terminated with open tube. Experimental frequencies adjusted to $c = 2,000$ fps. (*Stokes and Davis.*[1])

Substituting these values in Eq. (21.5) gives the transmission factor for the filter with the open duct termination. It reduces to:

$$T = \left[1 + \frac{Z_0}{2iX_b}\left(1 - e^{-2ik(l_t + \alpha)}\right)\right]^{-1}$$

The transmission loss is:

$$10 \log_{10}\left[1 + \frac{Z_0}{X_b}\sin 2k(l_t + \alpha) + \left(\frac{Z_0}{X_b}\right)^2 \sin^2 k(l_t + \alpha)\right] \qquad \text{db} \qquad (21.54)$$

The calculated transmission loss of a filter of this type is compared with experimental measurements in Fig. 21.46. The tests were made at ambient outdoor temperature, but the frequencies of both calculation and experiment have been adjusted to $c = 2,000$ ft per sec.[1]

When the sum of the last two terms in Eq. (21.54) is equal to zero, there is no transmission loss, and when it is less than zero, the transmission of sound is actually *increased* rather than reduced by the presence of the filter-tube combination. The ower cut-off frequency is given approximately by:

$$f_c = \frac{f_r}{\sqrt{1 + \dfrac{c_0(l_t + \alpha)}{2S}}} \qquad \text{cps}$$

The upper passbands occur in the vicinity of the resonant frequencies of the terminating tube, i.e., near $\sin k(l_t + \alpha) = 0$. Thus, increasing the length of the terminating tube results in a decrease in both the upper and lower cut-off frequencies.

The same general procedure that was used in this example may be used to include the influence of the termination in the calculation of transmission loss of other types of filters. Note, however, that for unsymmetrical filters R_{02} is not equal to R_{01} and must therefore be separately calculated.

Because the terminating tube introduces passbands, it is often necessary to add one or more additional resonant chambers to provide transmission loss at frequencies that are included within these passbands.

INFLUENCE OF SOURCE IMPEDANCE

The transmission loss gives the relationship between the incident pressure ahead of the filter and the transmitted pressure. What is usually desired in noise control engineering is the insertion loss, which is a comparison of the sound pressure levels at a specified point, before and after the filter is inserted in the system. If the sound

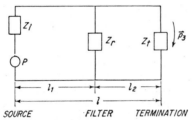

SOURCE   FILTER   TERMINATION

FIG. 21.47. Schematic diagram of a duct system including source, side-branch filter, and termination. (*Ingard.*[25])

pressure level of the incident wave is unchanged when the filter is inserted, the insertion loss is equal to the transmission loss. This is the case if the waves reflected by the filter are not re-reflected by the source; that is, if the effective source impedance is equal to the characteristic impedance of the duct. In all other cases, there will be a difference between the insertion loss and the transmission loss. The following discussion of this problem is based on an unpublished analysis from Ref. 25.

Insertion Loss of Side-branch Filter. A specific case of interest is the insertion loss of a side-branch filter in a duct. A schematic diagram of a duct system including such a filter is shown in Fig. 21.47. To find the insertion loss at the termination it is necessary to solve this network for the relationship between p_3, the pressure at the termination in the absence of the filter ($Z_r = \infty$), and $\overline{p}_3$, the pressure at the termination with the filter in place. The insertion loss J is:

$$J = 20 \log_{10} \left| \frac{p_3}{\overline{p}_3} \right|$$

$$= 20 \log_{10} \left| 1 + \frac{\dfrac{1}{\zeta_r}(\zeta_i \cos kl_1 + i \sin kl_1)\left(\cos kl_2 + \dfrac{i}{\zeta_t}\sin kl_2\right)}{\cos kl\left(1 + \dfrac{\zeta_i}{\zeta_t}\right) + i \sin kl\left(\dfrac{1}{\zeta_t} + \zeta_i\right)} \right| \qquad \text{db}$$

where $\qquad \zeta_r = Z_r/Z_0, \qquad \zeta_i = Z_i/Z_0, \qquad$ and $\qquad \zeta_t = Z_t/Z_0$

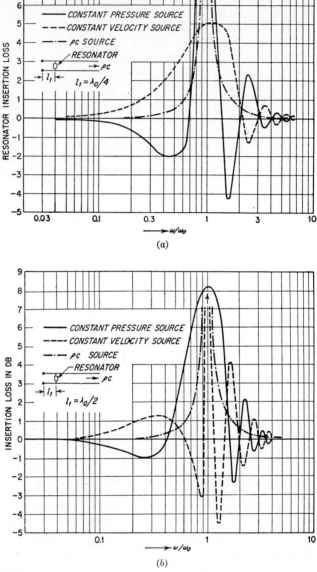

Fɪɢ. 21.48. Effect of source impedance on insertion loss for a resonator. $\zeta_t = 1$, $(c_o V)^{1/2}/(2S) = \frac{1}{2}$, $R_b = 0$. (a) $l_1 = \lambda_0/4$; (b) $l_1 = \lambda_0/2$. (Ingard.[25])

For a reflection-free termination ($\zeta_t = 1$)

$$J = 20 \log_{10} \left| 1 + \frac{\dfrac{\zeta_i}{\zeta_r}\left(\cos kl_1 + \dfrac{i}{\zeta_i}\sin kl_1\right)}{(1 + \zeta_i)(\cos kl_1 + i \sin kl_1)} \right| \quad \text{db}$$

nsertion-loss equations for various special cases can be derived from the preceding quations. Of particular interest are the following:

ource impedance $\zeta_i = 0$ *(constant-pressure source)*

$$J = 20 \log_{10} \left| 1 + i \frac{\frac{1}{\zeta_r}\left(\cos kl_2 + \frac{i}{\zeta_t}\sin kl_2\right)\sin kl_1}{\cos kl + \frac{i}{\zeta_t}\sin kl} \right| \qquad \text{db}$$

nd with $\zeta_t = 1$

$$J = 20 \log_{10} \left| \cos kl_1 + i\left(1 + \frac{1}{\zeta_r}\right)\sin kl_1 \right| \qquad \text{db}$$

ource impedance $\zeta_i = 1$ *(reflection-free source)*

$$J = 20 \log_{10} \left| 1 + \frac{\frac{1}{\zeta_r}\left(\cos kl_2 + \frac{i}{\zeta_t}\sin kl_2\right)}{\left(1 + \frac{1}{\zeta_t}\right)e^{ikl_2}} \right| \qquad \text{db}$$

nd with $\zeta_t = 1$

$$J = 20 \log_{10} \left| 1 + \frac{1}{2\zeta_r} \right| \qquad \text{db}$$

his equation is equivalent to Eq. (21.36).

ource impedance $\zeta_i = \infty$ *(constant-current source)*

$$J = 20 \log_{10} \left| 1 + \frac{\frac{1}{\zeta_r}\left(\cos kl_2 + \frac{i}{\zeta_2}\sin kl_2\right)\sin kl_1}{\cos kl - \frac{i}{\zeta_t}\sin kl} \right| \qquad \text{db}$$

nd with $\zeta_t = 1$

$$J = 20 \log_{10} \left| \left(1 + \frac{1}{\zeta_r}\right)\cos kl_1 + i\sin kl_1 \right| \qquad \text{db}$$

The effect of the source impedance on the insertion loss can be seen in Fig. 21.48. hese curves have been calculated for a resonator located at distances $\lambda_o/4$ and $\lambda_o/2$ om the source, where λ_o is the wavelength at resonance. The calculations are made r a reflection-free termination ($\zeta_t = 1$), with $(c_oV)^{1/2}/2S = \frac{1}{2}$ and with zero resist- ce in the resonator.

A comparison of parts *a* and *b* of Fig. 21.48 shows that the insertion loss is affected t only by the source impedance, but also by the distance from the source to the sonator. For a constant-pressure source the best location of the resonator for hieving a high insertion loss over a relatively wide frequency region is $l_1 = \lambda_o/2$. r a constant-current source the best location, for the same purpose, is $l_1 = \lambda_o/4$. ote that in both these cases the insertion loss remains finite at resonance even though ere is no resistance in the resonator.

When reflection occurs both at the source and at the termination, the frequency pendence of the insertion loss is rather complicated. Calculated results are shown Fig. 21.49 for a system composed of a constant-pressure source followed by a gth of duct, a filter, and then another length of duct that is open at the end. In is case the distance from the filter to the open end of the duct is also important. r a constant-pressure source, the best filter location would be $l_1 = \lambda_o/2$ and $= \lambda_o/4$.

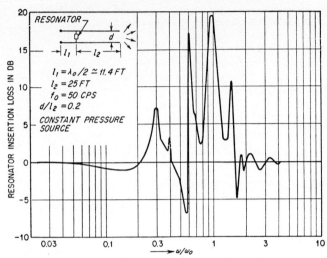

FIG. 21.49. Insertion loss for a resonator in an open duct. Constant-pressure source $l_1 = \lambda_0/2$, $l_2 = 1.1 \lambda_0$. (*Ingard.*[25])

Graphical Solution for Pressure Ratios in Ducts. In making calculations that require determination of the ratio between pressures at the two ends of a duct, graphical procedure has been found to be of great assistance.[25] The problem is to find

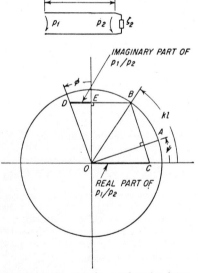

FIG. 21.50. Graphical procedure for determining pressure ratio between two ends of a duct. (*Ingard.*[25])

the pressure ratio between the ends of a duct of length l terminated by an admittance $\eta = \mu + i\epsilon$. Let the pressures at the end and the beginning of the duct be p_1 and p_2 respectively. The corresponding particle velocities are u_1 and u_2. Define the angles ϕ and ψ by the relations $\tan \phi = \mu$ and $\tan \psi = \epsilon$. The real and imaginary parts of the pressure ratio p_1/p_2 are then obtained graphically as illustrated in Fig. 21.50. The procedure is

1. Mark off the angles ψ and kl on the unit circle as shown (points A and B respectively), ($k = \omega/c$).
2. Draw a straight line from B normal to the line OA. The intersection C on the x axis gives the real part OC of the pressure ratio p_1/p_2.
3. Mark off the angle ϕ as shown and draw the line BD normal to the y axis. The imaginary part of the pressure ratio is then DE.

The validity of this construction is easily shown from the general equations. It should be noted that the current ratio can be obtained similarly if the admittance is replaced by the impedance and the angles corresponding to ϕ and ψ are defined by $\tan \phi_1 = \theta$ and $\tan \psi_1 = -\chi$. In the "slide-rule" version of this chart shown in Fig. 21.51, the admittances themselves rather than the angles are marked off on the circle. Correspondingly l/λ is also indicated rather than kl.

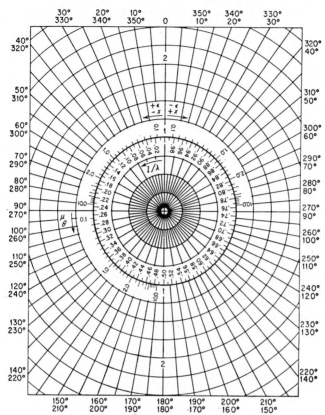

IG. 21.51. "Slide-rule" chart for determining pressure ratio between two ends of a duct. (ngard.[25])

The use of the "slide rule" is simplified if it is furnished by an arm OA which can be rotated around O. The arm should carry a sliding ruler at right angle to OA. In using the slide rule the bar is then set on the susceptance ϵ (corresponding to the angle ψ) and the sliding element is adjusted so that it passes through point B indicating l/λ. The intersection between the sliding ruler and the x axis then defines the real part of the pressure ratio. The imaginary part is obtained by setting the arm vertical and adjusting the sliding ruler to pass through B. The intersection with the radial line through the conductance μ (i.e., the angle ϕ) then gives the imaginary part DF of the pressure ratio.

The calculation of the insertion loss of a resonator in the case of a constant-pressure-or-current source can then be done in the following way: The duct is divided into two parts by the resonator. The terminating admittance is read from Fig. 21.52.

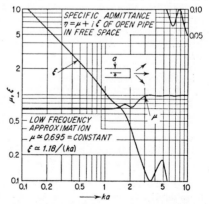

FIG. 21.52. Specific admittance of open pipe radiating into free space. (Ingard.[25])

The level difference between the ends of the last part of the duct, terminated in free space, is then determined by use of the "slide rule." The total admittance at the end of the first part of the duct is the sum of the resonator admittance and the terminating duct admittance. After finding this admittance, the level difference between the ends of the first part of the duct can be obtained from the slide rule. Finally, the total level difference is the sum of the level differences for the two parts of the duct. This total level difference is compared with the level difference calculated for the duct alone to obtain the insertion loss of the resonator.

DESIGNING FOR A PARTICULAR APPLICATION

Design Considerations and Methods. The first step in filter design is to determine the noise characteristics of the system *without a filter*. It is best to have actual measurements of the system noise, or noise spectrums of the components that generate noise. Discussions of noise from blowers, compressors, automobile engines, and aircraft engines are included in Chaps. 25, 28, 31, and 33. Further information on engine noise, and on the exhaust process that generates exhaust noise, can be found in Refs. 1, 29, 30, and 31.

Once the actual noise spectrum has been established, the next step is to decide upon the noise spectrum that is desired with the filter installed. This can be done by deciding what maximum noise levels will be regarded as acceptable in various frequency bands. The differences between the unfiltered and the acceptable noise spectra establishes the minimum insertion loss that the filter must provide as a function of the frequency. In the case of filter development, the process is somewhat different in that the noise with a given filter is measured and from these measurements additional attenuation is found to be required at certain frequencies. The filter is then modified to provide additional insertion loss where required.

The spectrum of required insertion loss can be compared with the known characteristics of various types of filters, as shown for example in Figs. 21.20, 21.35, 21.37, and 21.39. In some cases, it will be found that a simple single-element filter will be adequate, but if attenuation is required over a broad frequency range, it will be necessary to combine several elements, designed for different frequency ranges, in the filter design.

The simple curves of Figs. 21.20 and 21.35 can be used to arrive at a preliminary estimate of the number, type, and size of the elements that will be required. The attenuation curves of the various elements do not add directly, however, so the attenuation of the combination that has been selected preliminarily should be computed by the methods given in this chapter. Deficiencies that show up in the result of these calculations can be corrected by appropriate modification of the filter, and checked by a new computation. The termination is very important in many cases and it should be included in the calculations.

The dimensions of the proposed filter elements should be checked carefully against the limitations on element size that have been discussed. Some important limitations are:

1. For expansion chambers, the acoustic wavelength must be greater than about 0.82 times the chamber diameter.
2. For resonators, if the connector is longer than about one-fifth of the wavelength at the desired resonant frequency, the wave nature of the sound flow in the connector must be taken into account.
3. For resonators, if the acoustic path length from the connector to the closed end of the chamber is of the order of one-eighth wave length or more, the wave nature of the sound flow in the chamber must be accounted for.

It is very important that orifices or tubes connecting side-branch resonators to the main duct have adequate cross-sectional area. If the sound pressures in the system are high, as in engine exhaust, an accurate prediction of the insertion loss should not be expected. The theory is quite useful, nevertheless, in such cases.

The final stage in the design and development of a filter consists of experimental noise measurements with the filter in place. This is very important and modifications may be indicated as a result of these measurements. Where proper experimental equipment is available, some of the more tedious calculations in the design process can be eliminated if it is found more economical to build and test a sample filter than to make the calculations. This may be the case for a complex filter design.

Effect of Temperature. The primary effect of a change in duct temperature will be the corresponding change in the velocity of sound, which is proportional to the square root of the absolute temperature. It is necessary in the design of filters to use the actual sonic velocity of the gas in the duct. If the temperature and average density in the filter elements differ significantly from those in the duct, the difference can be accounted for by using the most accurate available values for ρ_o and c at each element in calculating the impedance of that element. In this connection, it is interesting to note that the impedance of a resonator chamber is proportional to $\rho_o c^2$ [Eq. (21.25)]. But because c^2 is proportional to T and ρ_o is proportional to T^{-1}, the chamber impedance is independent of the temperature. The connector impedance is a function of T, but in most cases the connector will be at the duct temperature. Thus, for resonator-type filters, a temperature difference between the duct and the chamber would be expected to have little effect on the performance of the filter.

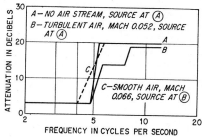

FIG. 21.53. Attenuation of 5- to 11-cps resonators with and without airflow. (*Beranek, Labate, and Ingard.*[32]),

Effect of Gas Flow in Duct. In the case of a filter in which the duct flow had to pass through orifices, the presence of duct flow was found to increase the transmission loss at low frequencies[21]. In the same experiments, duct flow was found to have little effect on the transmission loss due to a multiple resonator filter. In model tests of a group of resonators designed for reducing noise from a wind tunnel, smooth airflow had no appreciable effect on the insertion loss, while turbulent airflow reduced the insertion loss[22] (Fig. 21.53). The flow Mach numbers were considerably less than one in all of these experiments. Somewhat larger effects might be expected if the duct flow velocity approached the speed of sound.

Experimental Results. Noise measurements for automobile engines with various mufflers and intake silencers installed are presented in Chap. 31. These filters are quite effective, and from the figures included there it will be noted that the mufflers especially are rather complex devices. This complexity results from the fact that because of the wide range of engine speeds attenuation is required over a wide frequency range, and thus the mufflers consist of several elements tuned to different frequencies. Noise measurements on a helicopter with a pair of much simpler mufflers installed are presented in Fig. 21.54. A sketch of the muffler is shown in Fig. 21.55.

In cases where noise reduction is required over a very wide frequency range resonators can be combined with other acoustic devices. In one case, a reduction in the noise radiated from a wind tunnel was obtained by combining resonators, tuned ducts, parallel baffles, and lined bends.[32] This system (Fig. 21.56) provided a significant amount of noise reduction throughout the frequency range from 5 cps to more than 5,000 cps.

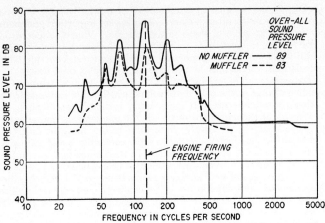

FIG. 21.54. Frequency analyses of helicopter noise with and without a muffler installed. (*Stokes and Davis.*[1])

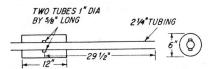

FIG. 21.55. Sketch of muffler used on helicopter. (*Stokes and Davis.*[1])

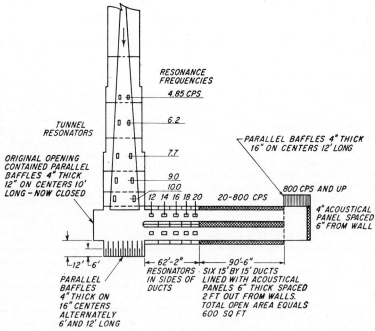

FIG. 21.56. Acoustical treatment for 8- by 6-ft supersonic tunnel. (*Beranek, Labate, and Ingard.*[32])

EXPERIMENTAL METHODS

A diagram of an experimental arrangement for measuring transmission and reflection factors in a particular case is shown in Fig. 21.57.[33] With sound at a single frequency propagated from the loudspeaker, the sound pressure level in the input tube is

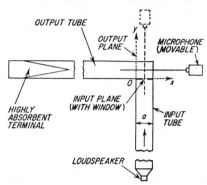

FIG. 21.57. Diagram of experimental arrangement for measuring transmission and reflection factors of a particular discontinuity (combination of a right-angled bend in a rectangular tube with window in the input plane). (*Lippert.*[33])

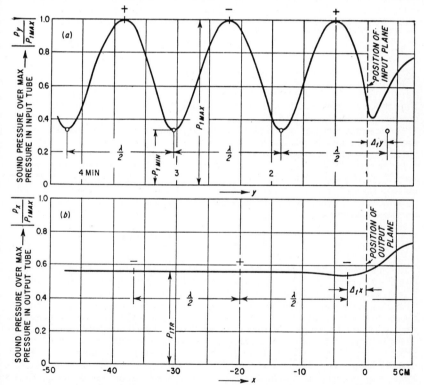

FIG. 21.58. A typical record of the sound pressure on both sides of a discontinuity showing the quantities to be derived from the measurements. (*Lippert.*[33])

measured as a function of the distance from the input plane by a small traveling microphone. Similar measurements, as a function of distance from the output plane, are made in the output tube, which is terminated without reflection. Plots such as those shown in Fig. 21.58 are then constructed. From the input tube measurements, the quantity $P_{1\,min}/P_{1\,max}$ and the distance $\Delta_1 y$ are determined. This distance is obtained by taking the difference between $\lambda/2$ and the distance between the input plane and the second minimum, because the position of the minimum labeled 1 is disturbed by the discontinuity. The reflection factor is then given by:

$$R = A e^{i\alpha}$$

where
$$A = \frac{1 - \dfrac{P_{1\,min}}{P_{1\,max}}}{1 + \dfrac{P_{1\,min}}{P_{1\,max}}}$$

and
$$\alpha = 4\pi \frac{\Delta_1 y}{\lambda} + \pi$$

From the output tube measurements, the quantity $P_{1\,tr}/P_{1\,max}$ and the distance $\Delta_1 x$ are determined. The determination of $\Delta_1 x$ requires a phase meter, because this is the distance from the output plane to the point in the output duct where the phase of the transmitted wave is π different from the phase of the maximum between the first and second minima in the input tube. The transmission factor is given by $T = D e^{i\delta}$, where

$$D = \frac{2 \dfrac{P_{1\,tr}}{P_{1\,max}}}{1 + \dfrac{P_{1\,min}}{P_{1\,max}}}$$

$$\delta = 2\pi \frac{\Delta_1 x + \Delta_1 y}{\lambda} - \frac{\pi}{2}$$

Note that if the phase angle of the transmission factor is not required, the phase-meter measurement can be omitted.

The transmission loss of a multisection filter, with reflectionless termination, can also be determined by this method. In this case, a measurement of the pressures is sufficient, for the transmission loss is $20 \log_{10} (1/D)$ in db.

In the case of a dissipationless filter, the experimental measurement can be further simplified. A fixed measuring station in the output tube will give $P_{1\,tr}$, if it is at a distance of say $\lambda/2$ or greater downstream of the output plane. The probe in the input plane need have only sufficient range of movement to measure $P_{1\,max}$. The transmission loss is given by:

$$20 \log_{10} \left[\frac{1}{2} \left(\frac{P_{1\,tr}}{P_{1\,max}} + \frac{P_{1\,max}}{P_{1\,tr}} \right) \right] \quad \text{db}$$

This simplification is made possible by the fact that $A^2 + D^2 = 1$ for dissipationless filters. A method similar to this was used in the experiments reported in Ref. 22. The experimental arrangement is shown in Fig. 21.59.

In such cases as air ducts that open into a room, or engine inlet-or-exhaust pipes, the sound measurements should be made outside the duct where the annoyance exists. An experimental arrangement that was used for this purpose is shown in Fig. 21.60. The quantity of interest in this investigation[22] was the insertion loss that resulted at a point outside the duct when a filter was added to the end of the original duct. A two-position value was used in order to facilitate rapid comparison of the sound pressure levels with and without the filter. Such a valve will be found useful in many cases where rapid comparisons between systems are desired. It is often desirable to get fairly close to the duct exit in order to reduce interference from extraneous noise.

It is necessary to have a sound-level meter and suitable electrical filters to obtain an adequate determination of the frequency spectrum of the noise.   For work with noise sources characterized by discrete frequencies, narrow bandpass filters are desirable for noise analysis.   For other types of spectra, octave bandpass filters are more convenient.

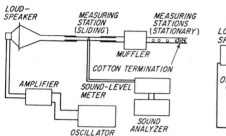

FIG. 21.59. Schematic diagram of experimental apparatus for transmission-loss measurements.   (*Davis, Stokes, Moore, and Stevens.*[22])

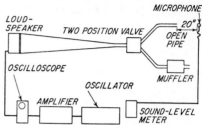

FIG. 21.60. Experimental arrangement for measuring insertion loss due to a muffler. (*Davis, Stokes, Moore, and Stevens.*[22])

High-quality magnetic tape recording equipment is very valuable for noise measurements because data can be obtained rapidly in the field and analyzed later in the laboratory.   It is particularly valuable when working with aircraft engines, where it is often impossible to obtain sufficient cooling to permit prolonged full-power operation on the ground.   See Chap. 17 for further information.

REFERENCES

1. Stokes, G. M., and D. D. Davis, Jr.: *NACA Tech. Note* 2943 (1953).
2. Lippert, W. K. R.: *Acustica*, **4**: 411 (1954).
3. Miles, J. W.: Part I and Part II, *J. Acoust. Soc. Am.*, **17**: 259, 272 (1946).
4. Miles, J. W.: *J. Acoust. Soc. Am.*, **19**: 572 (1947).
5. Lippert, W. K. R.: *Acustica*, **4**: 313 (1954).
6. Levine, H., and J. Schwinger: *Phys. Rev.*, **73**: 383 (1948).
7. Rayleigh, Lord, "Theory of Sound," II: Secs. 306 and 307, App. A.   2d ed., Macmillan & Co., Ltd., London, 1929.
8. Miles, J. W.: *J. Acoust. Soc. Am.*, **20**: 652 (1948).
9. Morse, P.: "Vibration and Sound," p. 324, McGraw-Hill Book Company, Inc., New York, 1948.
10. Sivian, L. J.: *J. Acoust. Soc. Am.*, **7**: 94 (1935).
11. Bolt, R. H., S. Labate, and U. Ingard: *J. Acoust. Soc. Am.*, **21**: 94 (1949).
12. Ingard, U.: *J. Acoust. Soc. Am.*, **25**: 1037 (1953).
13. Lamb, H.: "Hydrodynamics," Sec. 306, Dover Publications, New York, 1932.
14. Thurston, G. B.: *J. Acoust. Soc. Am.*, **24**: 653 (1952).
15. Thurston, G. B., and C. E. Martin, Jr.: *J. Acoust. Soc. Am.*, **25**: 26 (1953).
16. Thurston, G. B., and J. K. Wood: *J. Acoust. Soc. Am.*, **25**: 861 (1953).
17. Eckart, C.: *Phys. Rev.*, **73**: 68 (1948).
18. Ingard, U., and S. Labate: *J. Acoust. Soc. Am.*, **22**: 211 (1950).
19. Westervelt, P. J.: *J. Acoust. Soc. Am.*, **23**: 347 (1951).
20. Anderson, A. B. C.: *J. Acoust. Soc. Am.*, **24**: 675 (1952).
21. Davis, A. H. (with Appendix by N. Fleming): *ARC Rep. No.* 421 (February, 1935).
22. Davis, D. D., Jr., G. M. Stokes, D. Moore, and G. L. Stevens, Jr.: *NACA Rep.* 1192 (1954).
23. Stewart, G. W., and R. B. Lindsay: "Acoustics," D. Van Nostrand Company, Inc., Princeton, N.J., 1930.
24. Ingard, U., and D. Pridmore-Brown: *J. Acoust. Soc. Am.*, **23**: 689 (1951).
25. Ingard, U.: "Side-branch Resonators in Ducts," Unpublished information from files of Bolt, Beranek, and Newman, Inc.

26. Mason, W. P.: *Bell System Tech. Jour.*, **6**: 258 (1927).
27. Mason, W. P.: *J. Acoust. Soc. Am.*, **1**: 262 (1930).
28. Lindsay, R. B.: Part I, *J. Applied Physics*, **9**: 612 (1938).
29. Davis, D. D., Jr., and K. R. Czarnecki: *NACA Tech. Note* 1838 (1949).
30. Nielsen, M.: "Pressure Vibrations in Pipe Systems, With Reference to Engines," Nyt Nordisk Forlag Arnold Busck, Copenhagen, 1952.
31. Stanitz, J. D.: *Trans. ASME*, **73**: 319 (1951).
32. Beranek, L. L., S. Labate, and U. Ingard: *NACA Tech. Note* 3378 (1955).
33. Lippert, W. K. R.: *Acustica*, **4**: 307 (1954).

Chapter 22

SYSTEM CONSIDERATIONS IN NOISE-CONTROL PROBLEMS

RICHARD H. BOLT, PH.D., AND K. UNO INGARD, PH.D.

Massachusetts Institute of Technology

THE SYSTEM CONCEPT

The System Components: Source-Path-Receiver. Noise control is basically a *system* problem. In general there are many different *components* which may be manipulated to achieve a particular end result. The system, which is the combination of all the components, contains three major parts: the source, the path, and the receiver.

Each problem in noise control can be depicted (perhaps with the aid of a block diagram) as a particular system. The performance of this system—the desired end result—is described in terms of *system variables*. These, in turn, are derived from analyses of the several components as appropriate.

The *source* is that part of the system in which the vibratory mechanical (noise) energy originates. The source may be an unbalanced motor, or air rushing through a grille, or gear teeth striking gear teeth. There may be several such sources in a particular problem: different parts of the same machine, or entirely separate machines. The noise source that has given rise to a problem may have emitted just one instantaneous burst of energy, or it may have been putting noise into the "system" for weeks or years. Thus, the source must be viewed statistically as a family of noise generators that may have different physical characteristics, distributed in space and in time.

The sound energy from the source travels over the *path*. Again, this may be a multiplicity of paths, both in solid structures and in air. Different paths may have quite different properties of attenuation, radiation, and frequency dependence. The behavior may be nonlinear, or even vary with time. The total path, which may have to be described statistically, contains all possible avenues along which the noise in question may reach its destination.

The third major part of the system is the *receiver*. This may be a person disturbed in his sleep, a secretary trying to hear dictation, a lecture audience, or a factory worker at his machine. The receiver may be an instrument or a structure that is adversely affected by noise or vibration. The behavior of the receiver is inherently a statistical quantity. A given person may react quite differently at two different times. No two people are exactly alike in their response to noise, any more than they are identical in other human characteristics. Furthermore, there may be many people or many instruments exposed to the noise.

Noise control is not synonymous with noise reduction—any more than temperature control means turning the heat always down. It is true that many noise-control problems are best solved by effecting a reduction of some amount in the sound power or sound pressure. But there are situations in which the appropriate solution would be to modify the frequency spectrum without necessarily reducing the over-all sound level.   There are even cases in which an increase in sound level is the best noise control.   Noise from fans has been used in telephone booths to mask speech sounds from adjacent booths.   A nonobjectionable sound is sometimes introduced to mask an "unwanted" sound.   In fact, in the broadest meaning of the subject, noise control can be effected without any change whatever in the physical noise stimulus.   A noise that "disturbs" today may be turned into a thoroughly acceptable noise tomorrow by modifying the attitudes of those who hear it.

This chapter deals mainly with the *reduction* of physical noise stimuli and its specification.   In any actual problem, the possibilities of reduction should be viewed in proper perspective with noise control as a whole, analyzing the problem from the system point of view, including all relevant aspects, both physical and human.   All parts of the system should then be explored for possible solutions to achieve a functionally and economically acceptable solution.

Example of System Analysis.   The method of system analysis is illustrated by the following example.   Consider a noisy factory in which an operator works full time in the vicinity of a production machine.   Assume that a noise survey has been made, and that the results show that the operator runs a risk of permanent damage to his

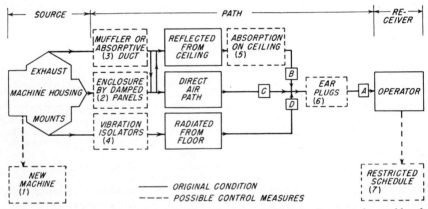

Fig. 22.1. Schematic diagram of noise-control system analysis for the example considered in the text.

hearing.   This conclusion is based on analysis of the sound pressure level of the noise at the operator's positions, the spectrum of the noise, the dynamic (impulsive) characteristics of the noise, and the time pattern of noise exposure of the operator.   With these data, one estimates the degree of risk by using the appropriate damage risk criterion (see Chap. 7).

The noise-control problem in this case is *to reduce the damage risk to a specified acceptable limit, at the lowest possible cost*.   The "total effective cost" may include operational restrictions, inefficiency, and adverse reactions of the operator.

A simplified schematic diagram for the system is shown by solid lines in Fig. 22.1.   The source is the machine as a whole.   Vibratory mechanical energy radiates from this machine as air-borne noise through the case and through the exhaust, and as structure-borne noise (vibration) through the mounting.   These three components of the source suffice for the present problem, but internal details of the machine (gears, unbalance, etc.) would be included if the immediate problem were to redesign the machine itself.

The path, as shown in Fig. 22.1, contains three components.   Some energy follows a direct air path from the source to the receiver, some reflects from the ceiling of the room, and some passes through the floor structure and is then radiated toward the receiver.   The receiver in this problem is the operator.

The next step is to make an analysis of the components which may involve measurements or theory or both. One of the results is a quantitative description of the noise spectrum at the position of the operator (point A in Fig. 22.1). This result is sketched in Fig. 22.2a as a plot of octave-band level vs. frequency. Also shown in this figure is a plot of the relevant criterion for damage risk. The difference between the two curves is the noise reduction required to meet the criterion.

The total noise at point A is the sum of contributions B, C, and D as shown in Fig. 22.1. The magnitudes of these contributions, also obtained from the above mentioned analysis, are sketched in Fig. 22.2b. Note that contribution C is greater than B or D or $B + D$. (See Fig. 2.17 for combining levels.) Continuing this method of analysis, one obtains the contributions in all lines of energy flow in the system diagram.

Now one is prepared to consider the effects of various "manipulations" of the system. Quantitative answers can be given to such questions as: What would be the sound level at point A if contribution B were reduced by 8 db in the 300- to 600-cps band? (All of the above discussed calculations are performed over a range of frequencies as required.) Or, noting that both the housing and the exhaust of the machine send energy to contribution C, one may ask how much C would be reduced if only the exhaust noise

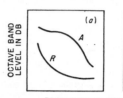

FREQUENCY IN CYCLES PER SECOND

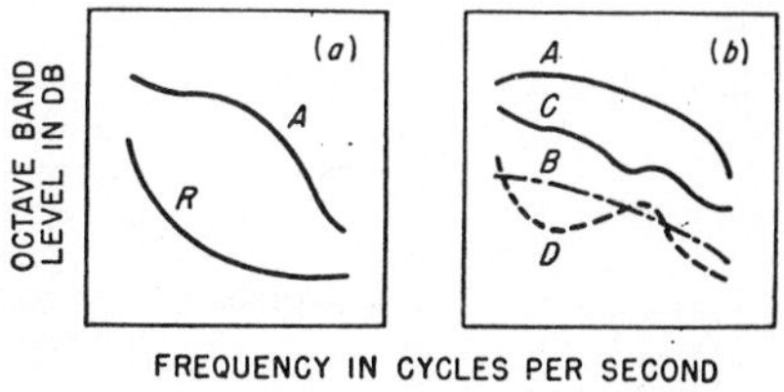

Fig. 22.2. Plots of octave-band level vs. frequency. R: Design requirement; A: Level at operator's position, point A in system diagram. B, C, D: Levels at points B, C, D in system diagram.

were reduced by a certain amount. Examining such questions is simply a systematic way of exploring the many possibilities of noise control.

Assume that these considerations have shown, in the present example, that some degree of noise control can be achieved by each of seven possible measures:

1. Replace the machine by a new type.
2. Enclose part of the machine with damped panels and rearrange the controls.
3. Attach a muffler or a specially designed absorptive duct to the exhaust of the machine.
4. Mount the machine on vibration isolators.
5. Apply sound-absorptive material to the factory ceiling.
6. Issue an ear-protective device to be worn by the operator continuously when he is at the machine.
7. Restrict the operator to a limited amount of time per day at this machine, transferring him to another operation for the remainder of his time.

These control measures are drawn in the system diagram, Fig. 22.1, with dashed lines.

The final results of the system analysis (omitting many intermediate steps) can be summarized as shown in Table 22.1. Five alternative solutions are proposed, using the seven possible control measures listed above. Each of these solutions has been "optimized," where possible, to achieve the design requirement as economically as possible. The direct cost of each solution has been estimated. Thought has also been given to operational restrictions and other consequences that might incur indirect costs, and these aspects have been summarized under "comments" in Table 22.1.

The type of information contained in Table 22.1, when worked out fully and accurately for an actual case, provides a rational basis for making a decision. It is unlikely that 2 + 3 would be chosen, because 2 + 3 + 4 + 5 costs less and has the same operational effects. Solution 1 might be selected if, for independent reasons, management was desirous of modernizing its equipment. Solution 6 might be chosen for a short term solution; but in another situation it might be rejected because it was found to be too costly over a period of years. Solution 7, likewise, might be either accepted or rejected, depending on policy considerations. The final result of this example, as summarized in Table 22.1, contains only one system variable: the *cost*. A

Table 22.1. Sample Results of a Noise-control System Analysis
(Hypothetical Example)

Control measures (see list of 7 measures in text)	Direct cost	Comments
1................	$15,000	New type machine also more efficient, but takes two years for delivery
2 + 3............	$ 6,000	Neither 2 nor 3 alone can achieve requirement; of several possible combinations of 2 and 3, only the least costly is listed
2 + 3 + 4 + 5.....	$ 4,000	Neither 4 nor 5 alone, nor 4 + 5 alone can achieve requirement
6................	small	Some cost in providing ear-protective devices, and in indoctrination, and in monitoring the consistency of their use
7................	negligible	Must restrict to 20 min exposure per day in this case; hidden costs in job scheduling and shifting*

* This proposed technique is included to indicate in principle that damage risk varies with exposure time (see Chap. 7).

second system variable, the *performance*, is hidden in the statement of the problem. It was assumed that no performance short of "negligible risk" would be acceptable, so all of the proposed solutions were designed to meet just this requirement.   In many problems both the cost variable and the performance variable are retained in the final results, perhaps as graphs of the type indicated in Fig. 22.3.

Summary of System Principles.   The principles that have been introduced in this section are summarized as follows:

1. Noise control is a system problem.
2. The goal is an acceptable noise environment at an acceptable cost.
3. The primary system variables are performance and cost.
4. System performance measures the noise environment in terms of the end effects, such as damage-risk probability, per cent articulation or probability of complaint.
5. System cost includes direct costs of noise-control measures and indirect costs of all operational consequences.

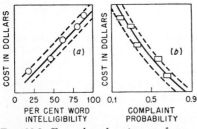

FIG. 22.3. Examples of system performance plotted vs. system cost.   Datum points calculated by analysis of several assumed solutions.   Dashed lines indicate design tolerances.

6. The system contains many possible components, grouped under source, path, and receiver.
7. Noise control may be effected on all parts of the system.
8. Design criteria give relations between physical noise characteristics and effects of noise on people or equipment.
9. The system design requirement for a particular problem is a policy compromise between performance and cost.

PROPERTIES OF NOISE-REDUCTION ELEMENTS

Mechanisms of Noise Reduction.   The remainder of this chapter deals mainly with the *path* portion of the noise-control system.   It should be noted, however, that the principles of sound transmission are applicable to the design of machines and noise generating devices in general.   Furthermore, the noise reducing effectiveness of control measures in the transmission path cannot be specified rigorously without imposing certain conditions on the behavior of the source.

The path has been defined broadly to include all possible channels of vibratory mechanical-energy transmission from the source to the receiver. The energy may flow along (1) air paths and (2) structure paths. Most practical problems involve both types, with some parts of the energy passing back and forth between air-borne and structure-borne sound. It is essential, therefore, to include both types in the analysis of noise control.

There are three distinct mechanisms by which noise is reduced along its transmission path: (1) energy spreading, (2) energy deflection, and (3) energy absorption. Examples of each mechanism, for both air and structure paths, are summarized in Table 22.2.

Table 22.2. Mechanisms of Noise Reduction in the Transmission Path

	Energy spreading	Energy deflection	Energy absorption
Air-borne Energy	Spherical divergence in space Area increase in duct Expansion from small opening into large room	Reflection at solid barrier Diffraction by partial partition or shield Refraction by wind and temperature gradients	Absorption in air owing to humidity, viscosity, etc. Absorption at surfaces of room Absorption by materials and resonators in a duct
Structure-borne Energy	Division of energy among structural elements at joints Decrease in vibration amplitude in sheet or wall as function of distance from localized source	Reflection at path discontinuities such as air, rubber gasket, mastic joint, vibration isolator Refraction in inhomogeneous walls and other structures	Vibration damping by viscous coatings on walls and frames Internal loss of energy in materials

Energy spreading of spherical waves in a free field produces a decrease in sound-pressure level of 6 db for each doubling of distance from the source (see Chap. 2). In a two-dimensional space, such as a flat region between two large parallel reflecting planes, the sound-pressure level decreases 3 db per double distance. Structure-borne sound, similarly, decreases in sound pressure level as it spreads out in a wall or divides itself among an increasing number of elements in a building.

Energy deflection occurs at a discontinuity or "acoustic boundary," such as a solid boundary in air or an air gap in a solid structure. Some of the incident sound is reflected back toward the source or in some other direction, and this property is useful for noise reduction. A shielding wall or partial enclosure can deflect some sound, but the amount of noise reduction that can be achieved is limited by diffraction at the free edges. Another example of deflection is the refraction of sound by temperature gradients and wind velocity gradients (see Chap. 3). Under certain conditions, this bending produces sound shadows that can provide a useful amount of noise reduction. All of these effects can occur in solid structures also. An air gap or soft gasket in a structural element reflects some of the energy, and energy is deflected by refraction in inhomogeneous solids.

Energy absorption occurs in porous acoustical materials and in many types of furnishings and finish materials used in buildings. In fact, there is some absorption in the boundary layer on any surface, no matter how hard and impervious. Some energy is also absorbed as sound travels freely through the air. A widespread use of energy absorption is found in mufflers and lined ducts. The absorption of structure-borne sound is rather small in most building materials, but can be greatly increased by the suitable incorporation of damping materials.

These three mechanisms are involved, either singly or in combination, in all possible components of noise reduction. Energy spreading is the major contributor to noise control by space arrangement of sites and buildings. Control by sound isolating structures and enclosures depends mainly on energy deflection. And the third general technique of noise reduction is control by sound-absorptive materials and devices.

Transmission and Absorption Coefficients. When a sound wave encounters an object, part of the energy is reflected, part is absorbed, and part is transmitted through the object. All of the energy can, in principle, be accounted for by evaluating these three parts—though the calculation becomes difficult if the wave is not plane and the object is irregular in shape and inhomogeneous in composition. If the fraction of incident energy that is absorbed and the fraction that is transmitted are given, then sufficient information is available to calculate the fraction that is reflected. The relevant equation for a plane wave striking an infinite-plane surface at normal incidence is:

$$\text{Reflected fraction} = 1 - \alpha - \tau$$

in which α is the *sound-absorption coefficient:* the fraction of incident sound energy absorbed by the surface or medium (see Chap. 18); and τ is the *sound-transmission coefficient:* the ratio of the transmitted to incident sound energy (see Chap. 20). These two types of quantities, α and τ, are the principal ones needed to specify the inherent characteristics of any noise-control component. The word *types* is used because there are many special forms of α and τ that are needed to cover all situations.

As indicated in Chaps. 18 and 20, both the absorption and the transmission characteristics of walls, materials, and special acoustic structures usually vary with frequency and angle of incidence of the sound; the α's and τ's for particular frequencies or angles, or for an average over frequency or angle may be required. The basic definitions of these quantities as given above can be extended to cover any situation with respect to frequency and angle.

The words *incident energy* used in the above definitions refer to the energy that flows toward the surface. Consider a plane-wave field intercepted by a large plane wall of finite thickness. Suppose a microphone is placed close to the wall on the side of the incident sound and another microphone just on the other side of the wall. Also assume that the experiment is done in an acoustic free field and that no sound passes around the edges of the wall. It might appear that the difference between the sound pressure levels on the two sides of the wall is a measure of the transmission coefficient. But on the input side some of the incident sound is reflected, and this reflected part is mixed with the incident part of the energy. The microphone measures a combined pressure that is not the same as the pressure in the incident wave alone. Therefore, care must be exercised to devise tests for α and τ in such a way as to measure exactly the quantity that is specified in the basic definitions.

The acoustical properties of sound-absorptive materials are usually designated by sound-absorption coefficients. In some applications, however, and particularly in the design of acoustic elements themselves (e.g., mufflers and resonators), the use of more fundamental quantities such as acoustic impedance, flow resistance, and porosity is required.

Many engineering calculations are simplified by using the logarithmic form of the transmission coefficient, the *transmission loss* $T.L. = 10 \log (1/\tau)$.

In the analysis of noise in enclosures a determination of the total amount of sound absorption within the enclosure usually is required. The unit for this quantity is either the *sabin*, i.e., the equivalent of 1 sq ft of a perfectly absorptive surface or the square meter in the metric system. The number of sabins of any particular treatment is obtained by multiplying its area in square feet by its absorption coefficient.

Sound-isolation Properties of Walls. The transmission loss of impervious panels, such as conventional wall and floor sections and special structures for noise-isolating enclosures, is discussed here in general terms. The common properties of all such elements are viewed in an ideal sense, in order to indicate certain relationships between the basic physical properties (e.g., mass, stiffness, internal damping) and the transmission coefficient τ or its logarithmic equivalent, transmission loss $T.L.$

Mass Effect.   For a single panel of uniformly distributed mass, with no air leaks through it, and with negligible stiffness, the transmission loss at a given frequency and angle of incidence is determined only by the mass.   This ideal case is represented by a heavy line marked "mass controlled" in Fig. 22.4 and is expressed by the theoretical *mass law*, which predicts an increase in transmission loss at a rate of 6 db for each doubling of frequency or mass per unit area.   In contrast, note that the experimentally determined values of *T.L.* shown in Fig. 20.4 show an increase of but 4.4 db per doubling of mass.

According to theory, transmission loss of a panel increases with mass in the same way that it increases with frequency.   One can, therefore, change the abscissa in Fig. 22.4 to measure frequency times mass (*f* in cps times *w*, the mass per unit area).   Then a single straight line can be used to find the theoretical mass law value at any frequency and for any weight of panel.

Such a theoretical curve is shown in Fig. 20.5.   The upper curve in that figure, marked "normal incidence mass law," predicts the behavior for a plane wave striking

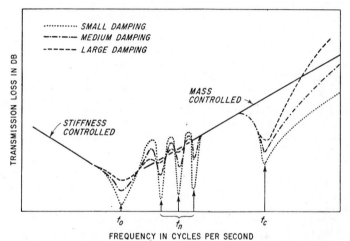

FIG. 22.4. Transmission loss vs. frequency for a single homogeneous panel having various amounts of damping.

the panel at normal incidence.   This curve follows the 6 db per *fw* doubling as discussed above, except for very low values of *fw* where the transmission loss levels off (this region is rarely met in practice).   The lower curve, marked "random incidence mass law," is derived by averaging the transmission loss over all angles of incidence. This curve, rather than the one for normal incidence, is the one that is most often used in practice because the sound usually comes from many directions.

Stiffness Effect.   The opposite extreme to a massive flexible panel is a very stiff panel of negligible weight.   If such a panel is mounted so that it behaves like a pure stiffness reactance, its transmission loss follows the line marked "stiffness controlled" in Fig. 22.4.   Here the transmission loss increases with *decreasing* frequency.   All real panels of walls and floors are stiffness controlled below a fundamental natural frequency f_o which is indicated schematically; but f_o is so low, in most constructions, of the order of 5 to 20 cps, that it is not of practical importance.   In general, stiffness control is a low-frequency characteristic, as distinct from mass control that predominates at high frequencies.

Stiffness behavior is important in certain special cases, such as in sound transmission through cylindrical pipes.   If the pipe is long, accurately circular, and of uniform thickness, and if the sound field is axially symmetrical, the "stiffness law" may be observed up to several hundred cps in metal pipes up to a few feet in diameter.   The stiffness control breaks down very easily, however, if the pipe has a seam or is irregular.

It is much more difficult to devise flat panels that are sufficiently stiff to yield a stiffness law transmission loss in the audible frequency range.

Resonance Effects. Consider now a single flat panel with all its edges clamped firmly into a very massive structure. If one strikes the panel, a ringing sound at a particular frequency can be heard. By using instruments one can measure this fundamental natural frequency of the panel. This fundamental frequency, corresponding to the point marked f_o in Fig. 22.4, is determined by both the mass and the effective bending stiffness of the mounted panel; it decreases as the weight is increased, and increases as the stiffness is increased. At the natural frequency f_o, the resonant panel is substantially transparent to sound; its transmission loss drops to approximately zero. It would be exactly zero if the sound wave had just the right shape and if there were no damping in the panel.

Actually, f_o is just the first of a series of natural frequencies. It is a general characteristic of panels, plates, and even clamped membranes, that they can "break up" into various forms of vibration called natural modes of vibration, each of which occurs at a particular natural frequency (some of these are indicated by f_n in Fig. 22.4). At each of these natural frequencies the transmission loss again approaches zero, just as it does at f_o. There are an infinite number of such resonances, dozens or even hundreds of which can be observed experimentally.

Damping Effects. In addition to mass and stiffness there is always a certain amount of internal damping in a panel. Steel has very little internal damping; wood and concrete have considerably more; and some kinds of rubber and fiberboard have large values of damping. A panel with small damping, when struck, vibrates at a natural frequency (f_o or f_n) for a relatively long time and gives a tone of musical character. A highly damped panel produces a full thud and stops vibrating very quickly.

Damping has a strong effect on transmission loss in the vicinity of the resonances, as is shown in Fig. 22.4. With small damping the dips in transmission loss are steep and approach a very low value of transmission loss. As the damping is increased the resonance ripples are smoothed out.

Resonances impose one of the practical limitations on the achievement of theoretical mass law values of transmission loss. Regardless of the weight or stiffness of an undamped panel, it will be rather transparent at many frequencies throughout the useful range.

Coincidence Effect. One further effect is sometimes confused with the above discussed resonance effects. If a large panel is vibrated at right angles to the plane of the panel, a flexural or bending wave is sent into the panel. A bending wave can also be set up by driving a panel with a sound wave, as shown in Fig. 22.5. The sound wave in air has a wavelength λ_a and that in the panel has a wavelength λ_p. The sound wave strikes the panel at an angle of incidence θ. In Fig. 22.5, θ, λ_a, and λ_p are selected in such a way that crests and troughs in the panel wave coincide exactly with crests and troughs (maxima and minima) of pressure in the sound wave. As the sound wave continues to move toward the panel, the flexural wave continues to move in such a way that the air waves and panel waves always keep in step. In this condition a pressure maximum in the sound wave is always pushing at just the right place to drive the panel.

The condition shown in Fig. 22.5 is called *wave coincidence*, which gives rise to the coincidence effect. At coincidence, the panel is substantially transparent to the sound wave. If either the frequency or the angle of incidence is changed, the coincidence condition for transparency no longer exists. But if sound with a band of frequencies strikes the panel at all angles of incidence, there will be many combinations of frequency and angle that are just right for coincidence transparency.

The speed of bending waves in a panel increases with frequency. This contrasts with sound waves in air, for their speed is substantially independent of frequency. At a particular value of frequency, therefore, the wavelength of the bending waves will be equal to the wavelength of the sound in air. Below this frequency it is impossible to get coincidence at any angle. This is called the *coincidence cut-off frequency* f_c, as marked in Fig. 22.4; in the region of f_c there are three curves, corresponding to three amounts of damping. These curves for coincidence effect are calculated for random incidence of the sound.   The curves break away from the mass law curve at a frequency somewhat below f_c, and drop to a minimum value near f_c.   At higher frequencies the transmission loss rises toward the mass law.   If the damping is very large, it is possible for the transmission loss to become even greater than mass law at frequencies well above f_c.   In practice, however, this condition is rarely reached.

Most walls and floors used in conventional building practice exhibit a pronounced coincident effect, dropping as much as 10 or 20 db below mass law near f_c and staying 5 or 10 db below mass law throughout the rest of the audio-frequency range.   The critical frequency for panels of homogeneous materials is inversely proportional to their thickness h.   The product $f_c h$ (cps × inches) is approximately 450 to 500 for aluminum, glass, steel, and timber; 600 to 650 for concrete; 750 to 800 for plywood; and 1,000 to 1,100 for brick and mortar.

Multiple Panels.   Many walls and enclosures are made of multiple panels, such as double stud construction, a cavity-brick wall, or a prefabricated panel of metal with an air space or absorptive material between two separate sheets.   In general, the sound transmission characteristics of multiple walls exhibit all of the features of single panels

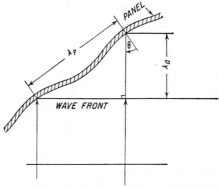

FIG. 22.5. Sound waves having a wavelength λ_a in air strike a panel in which the corresponding transmitted sound waves have a wavelength λ_p.   At a certain angle θ the crests and troughs in the panel wave coincide exactly with the crests and troughs in the sound wave; in this condition the panel is substantially transparent to the sound waves.

as discussed above.   As indicated in Chap. 20, there is usually some degree of coupling between the panels, and this introduces an additional characteristic.

For simplicity, consider a double wall made of two single panels, each of which alone would have the mass law transmission-loss characteristic.   Place these two panels parallel to each other at a distance d apart, with only air in the space between. Assume that the panels are very large and that they are clamped around the edges in such a way that there is no flanking.   The air space between the two panels behaves like a simple spring as long as the wavelength of the sound in air is very much larger than the spacing d.   The stiffness of this spring is inversely proportional to the spacing.   The two panels are simply two masses, one on each end of the spring.   This elementary discussion ignores wave propagation in the cavity and parallel to the plane of the walls.

At a particular frequency, f_d, the spring and mass will vibrate in resonance.   If there is only an air space between the panels (no bridging), and if both panels have a weight of 10 lb per sq ft, and if they are spaced 10 in. apart, the double-panel resonant frequency f_d will be about 24 cps.   If the weight of both walls is increased by a factor of 4, to 40 lb per sq ft, the resonant frequency drops to 12 cps.   If the walls remain at 10 lb per sq ft and the spacing is decreased to 2.5 in., the resonant frequency rises to 48 cps.

The behavior of a double wall is shown qualitatively in Fig. 22.6.   At the frequency f_d the transmission loss drops to a minimum, the value of which depends mainly on the amount of damping in the cavity or in the panels. The behavior in this region looks similar to that in the region of f_o. In this case, however, the damping could be introduced in the form of sound-absorptive material in the cavity instead of in the panel itself.

Above the double-panel natural frequency f_d, the transmission loss rises steeply and approaches a slope twice as great as that of the single mass-controlled panel. In this region, therefore, the (normal incidence) transmission loss increases 12 db for a doubling of either frequency or weight.

The behavior of double panels in practice can become quite complicated. If the two panels are of different materials or thickness they will have different values of f_n, and both may exhibit coincident effect in the range of interest. In triple constructions the complexities are even greater. For such reasons, engineering design is usually based on measured values of transmission loss such as are given in Chap. 20.

Sound-absorption Properties of Materials. (For a fuller discussion of sound-absorptive materials, see Chap. 18.)

Consider a very simple sound absorber consisting of a thin porous screen stretched in front of a hard wall as shown in Fig. 22.7. The screen will absorb most energy from the sound wave if it is located where the particle-velocity is largest. If the

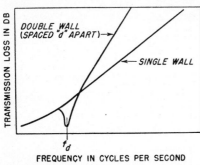

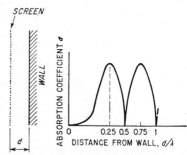

FIG. 22.6. Transmission loss for an "ideal" double-wall construction which assumes no flanking transmission.

FIG. 22.7. A thin porous screen is placed at a distance d from a wall. A graph is given showing the absorption coefficient of the screen as a function of distance from the wall in terms of the ratio d/λ.

incident sound has a wavelength λ the "best" location of the screen will be a distance $\lambda/4$ from the wall as shown in the figure. In fact, if the flow resistance of the screen is chosen properly, the absorption coefficient can be made 100 per cent at this wavelength for sound of normal incidence. For sound of normal incidence the flow resistance of the screen should be chosen equal to the characteristic impedance ρc in order to make the absorption maximum as high as possible. However, for diffuse sound the "best" flow resistance is higher, of the order of 2 or $3\rho c$. If the wavelength increases, the region of maximum particle-velocity moves outside the screen and the absorption coefficient approaches zero with decreasing frequency. If the wavelength decreases, on the other hand, the region of maximum particle-velocity will move inside the screen and the absorption coefficient will again decrease. It becomes zero when the wavelength is twice the thickness of the air space, in which case the screen is located in a region of zero velocity. In general, the absorption curve, as shown in Fig. 22.7, has maxima whenever d is an odd number of quarter-wavelengths and minima when d is an even number of quarter-wavelengths.

If the air space is now filled with additional screens, whenever the wavelength is less than $4d$ there will always be a screen in the region of high particle-velocity, and the resulting absorption curve will take the form shown in Fig. 22.8. The dashed curve is the absorption curve obtained for one screen as already shown in Fig. 22.7. It should be noticed that the low-frequency absorption is not appreciably affected by the introduction of the additional screens.

The multiple-screen absorber illustrates the behavior of the class of absorbers usually referred to as *porous absorptive materials*, the absorption curve shown in Fig. 22.8 being characteristic for such materials. The absorption is seen to be high at high frequencies, but it decreases rather rapidly below a certain frequency that is determined by the thickness of the layer. The thicker the layer the lower in frequency will the region of high absorption extend.

Although the general behavior of the absorption curve of a porous layer is given by Fig. 22.8, it is evident that, besides thickness, other physical properties of the material also play a role in the absorption characteristics. One of these factors is the flow resistance of the material, which largely determines the real part of the impedance of the boundary, and is in general chosen so that this real part is about two or three times the characteristic impedance of air.

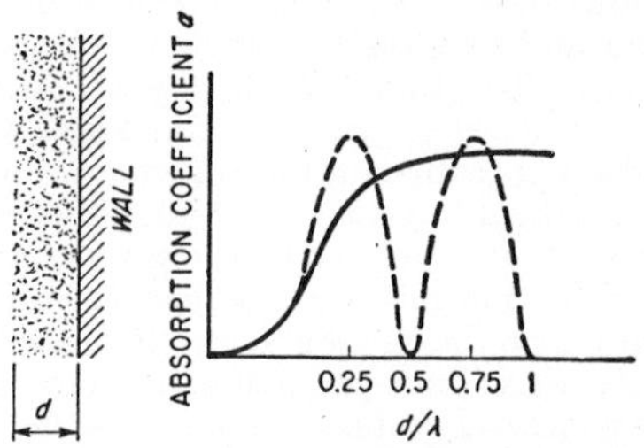

To illustrate in principle the second main class of absorptive materials, the *resonance absorbers*, one may add to the porous layer just described an impervious membrane representing a mass load in the acoustic system. This mass together with the air cushion behind it will form a resonator with an absorption curve of the general character shown in Fig. 22.9. It should be noted that the increase in the absorption at low frequencies is obtained

FIG. 22.8. Multiple-screen absorber which illustrates the acoustic behavior of porous absorptive materials. The over-all thickness of the screens which are placed in front of a hard wall is d. The heavy line in the graph shows the over-all absorption vs. the thickness of the structure; the dashed line gives the normal absorption coefficient for a single screen as a function of distance of the screen from the wall.

at the cost of a decrease in the high-frequency region. An added mass in the system can also be obtained by means of a rigid perforated panel (of which the cavity resonator is a special case) as shown in Fig. 22.10. All of these absorbers have similar absorption curves: increasing the mass in the system decreases the resonance frequency, and also the relative width of the resonance curve, if the air space and the absorption material are kept constant.

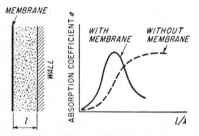

FIG. 22.9. Characteristics of a "resonance absorber" consisting of a porous blanket covered by an impervious membrane. The absorption coefficient of the blanket, with and without the membrane, is given as a function of frequency.

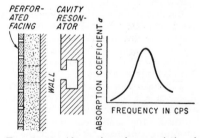

FIG. 22.10. Absorption characteristic of two "resonance" type absorbers: a porous material covered by a perforated facing, and a cavity resonator in a wall.

The third class of materials, usually referred to as *panel absorbers*, may be represented by the panel or membrane of Fig. 22.9, with all the other material removed. This panel must be flexible and have some internal damping. If this is the case the panel will behave as a resonance absorber with an absorption peak at its fundamental resonance. In addition, some absorption is also expected at frequencies in the range of the higher resonances of the panel. These resonances are, however, generally masked by the damping of the system. Also some effect should be expected at frequencies above the coincidence frequency. In fact, the complete absorption curve should have the same general form as the transmission-loss curve in Fig. 22.4, but inverted.

Sound-attenuation Properties of Ducts. Ducts, filters, and mufflers are noise-reducing elements designed to attenuate sound along passages through which air (or other gases) can flow. The attenuating property of such ducts is specified by the transmission loss, in complete analogy with the acoustic specification of a solid partition. The transmission loss is defined as the ratio between the incident and the transmitted energy, and is identical with the insertion loss if the source and termination impedances in the system are equal to ρc. Once the transmission loss is known, the actual insertion loss of the duct in any specific application can be determined as already illustrated by the examples in a previous section.

The transmission loss depends only upon the physical parameters of the duct and not upon the environment. Some of the basic relations between the transmission loss and these duct parameters are now discussed. A more detailed analysis, including engineering of ducts, is presented in Chap. 27.

An attenuating duct consists generally of one or several parallel channels, straight or with bends, which are provided with sound-absorptive material on the side walls or in the form of obstructions in the duct itself. The attenuating effect is basically caused by *absorption* or reflection or both. The relative importance of these factors may vary from one design to another, as illustrated in the examples below.

The attenuation of sound in a straight duct lined by absorptive material is directly proportional to the absorption coefficient of the material only at sufficiently low frequencies, where the pressure distribution of the duct is uniform. For example, if the boundary lining consists of a porous layer, the attenuation in this low-frequency region will increase with the *square of the frequency*. When the frequency increases, resulting in wavelengths smaller than the cross dimension of the duct, the pressure distribution across the duct starts to become nonuniform. The sound field recedes from the boundary with increasing frequency, and this concentration of the energy toward the center of the duct results in a decrease of the attenuation. The pressure decrease in the boundary can be thought of as a destructive interference between the direct and reflected sound from the duct wall at grazing incidence. For a rectangular duct lined with a porous layer the attenuation in this region varies approximately as the *inverse second power of frequency*.

Because of the above mentioned low- and high-frequency dependence of the attenuation, it is clear that a maximum will result in some intermediate-frequency region. This maximum usually occurs when the wavelength is approximately equal to the characteristic cross dimension of the duct. For example, in a square duct with side length of 2 ft, the maximum should occur at a frequency of about 1,000 cps, provided the absorption coefficient of the porous layer is not a limiting factor.

The maximum attenuation for a properly designed duct can be made about 5 db per distance a, where a is the cross dimension of the duct. Since ducts of this kind are selective with a fairly well defined attenuation peak, they are sometimes referred to as "tuned" ducts, although the tuning has nothing to do with any resonances of the absorptive surfaces. The lower the frequency to which the duct is tuned, the wider and longer must the duct be in order to yield a certain total attenuation. Because of this behavior, which is characteristic of many noise-reduction elements, the *cost per db of reduction increases with the wavelength*.

Because of the concentration of energy toward the center of the duct ("beaming") the attenuation at high frequencies cannot be increased significantly by a change of the absorptive properties of the side-wall material. Increased high-frequency attenuation can be obtained by the used of a bend in the duct, which becomes effective for wavelengths smaller than the cross dimension of the duct. The bend provides primarily reflection of sound, but if an absorptive surface is added the total effect is a combination of reflection and absorption.

Side-branch Resonators. (For a fuller discussion of resonators, see Chap. 21.)

The limitation in the attenuation in ducts at low frequencies is set mainly by the properties of the absorptive material on the side walls and cannot be improved much by introducing bends or curves in the ducts.   An efficient attenuation at those low frequencies requires specially designed low-frequency absorbers such as side-branch cavity resonators such as shown in Fig. 22.10.   Such designs are usually intended for frequencies between 20 and 100 cps.   In extreme cases, resonators for even lower frequencies, a few cycles per second, may be called for.

The side-branch resonator is described acoustically by the acoustic impedance of the aperture, which in turn depends on the geometry of the resonator and the damping material in the aperture as discussed in Chap. 21.   The effect of such a resonator is due to absorption and/or reflection of sound, but is dependent not only on the properties of the resonator per se, but also, often to a great extent, upon its environment.   Factors like the location of the resonator and the source and termination characteristics of the duct may affect the insertion loss as much as or more than the inherent properties of the resonator.

At the low frequencies of interest in this connection, there will often be considerable reflection of sound from the end of the duct.   The resulting sound field in the duct will then exhibit pressure maxima and minima, the last minimum being approximately at the end of the duct.   The influence of the location of the resonator on the insertion loss is then apparent.   A resonator inserted in a pressure maximum in the tube will be more efficient than in a minimum.   The best location of the resonator from this point of view is approximately an odd number of quarter wavelengths from the end of the duct.

The influence of the nature of the source is readily seen by considering a resonator located very close to the beginning of the duct.   If the source is such that it keeps constant pressure at the entrance of the duct (for example, a loudspeaker driven with a constant current) the sound field radiated from the duct will not be affected by the introduction of the resonator, i.e., its insertion loss will be zero.   On the other hand, if the sound source is such that the particle-velocity of the sound at the entrance of the duct is kept constant, the introduction of the resonator will change the field considerably.   The resonator will act as a short circuit so that no pressure can be built up at the resonator.   The insertion loss can thus be changed from zero (or even negative values) up to very large positive values by varying the source conditions or the location of the resonator.

In many cases of practical importance (for example, a constant power source located in a room from which a duct leads) the duct can be considered to be driven by a source with an internal impedance equal to ρc.   The insertion loss of a resonator in the duct will then be independent of the distance from the source to the resonator, but still dependent on the distance from the resonator to the end of the duct.

Isolators and Dampers for Structure-borne Sound.   As in the case of air-borne sound, the mechanisms of structure-borne noise reduction may be divided into spreading, deflection, and absorption (see Table 22.2).   Energy spreading is utilized by increasing the distance between source and receiver.   Energy is deflected or blocked by compliant vibration isolators and reactive filters.   Structure-borne noise is dissipated by viscous damping materials, in the form of sheets or coatings applied to vibrating surfaces, or as damping elements incorporated in isolators or mounts.

Unlike sound in air, however, there are many types of wave motion in solids: compressional, shear, bending, surface waves, etc.   Isolation and damping are, therefore, usually more complex processes in solids than in air.   A particular device may work quite well in reducing one type of wave, but not at all for another.   A mass appropriately attached to a long beam of steel, for example, will provide a relatively strong reflection of bending waves but will have practically no effect on compressional waves.   Isolators and dampers can also act as converters, transforming one wave type into another.

For these reasons, the acoustical description of structure-borne noise-reducing elements may require several reflection and absorption coefficients, as, for example, one reflection coefficient r_{ll} for the ratio between the reflected longitudinal and the incident longitudinal waves, and another reflection coefficient r_{lt} for the ratio between the reflected transverse and the incident longitudinal waves, etc.   Fortunately, however, in many engineering problems, one type of wave predominates, and the description can be simplified correspondingly. Thus it is often adequate to specify the acoustical properties of a coil spring simply in terms of its spring constant for compression—but one should not overlook the possibility that the transmission of longitudinal waves along the metal may "short circuit" the isolation at high frequencies.

Isolators. A vibration isolator is a device which functions primarily by reflecting or blocking structure-borne energy (see Chap. 13). In practice, isolators are designed in many forms and with many kinds of material, but all operate basically by providing a large change in the impedance of the vibration path.

The "noise reduction" which is obtained by inserting an isolator depends not only on the isolator itself but also on the associated mechanical system. In the isolation of a machine from its foundation, for example, the attenuation obtained by inserting a spring depends not only on the spring constant, but also on the mass load on the spring, on the mechanical properties of the foundation, and on the nature of the source—whether it drives the spring with constant force, or constant amplitude, etc. Thus, if the foundation has a high impedance at all frequencies, and if the machine vibrates with constant *amplitude*, the reduction in force on the foundation is independent of frequency; whereas a constant *force* applied to the spring yields a reduction in force that varies with frequency in accordance with a well known resonance curve (see Chap. 12). In the former case the force reduction depends only on the spring constant, and is always positive (unless the spring is "stiffer" than the foundation). In the latter case the force reduction is negative (force increases) at the resonance frequency, is zero at $\sqrt{2}$ times the resonance frequency, and increases at higher frequencies. In this high-frequency range the driving force is balanced by the inertial force of the mass of the machine, and relatively little force is transmitted through the spring.

At still higher frequencies, when the length of the compressional wave in the spring becomes comparable with the length of the spring, the mass of the spring in addition to its stiffness plays an important role. Standing waves occur in the spring, and the specification of the isolator must involve the characteristic impedance of the spring or similar quantities.

The simple vibration isolator, when used at sufficiently low frequencies, is analogous to an electrical LC circuit. Correspondingly, one may build up other filter networks with different characteristics, which all come under the class of isolators or mechanical filters.

In many problems the noise-reduction effectiveness of an isolator or filter is measured by the insertion loss as defined above—the reduction in sound pressure level at a specified point. In other problems it may be more useful, or even essential, to determine the reduction in magnitude of a particular quantity that is associated with the structural vibration such as the force, displacement, velocity, or acceleration. One may extend the concept of insertion loss to the measurement of these quantities also, but the quantity should then be specified explicitly (e.g., the insertion loss for force).

Dampers. Dampers are devices used to introduce dissipation into a vibrating system. Some dissipation is, of course, always present due to unavoidable air, fluid, or internal friction. However, this contribution is generally so small that a mechanical system, such as the vibration oscillator discussed in the previous section, will attain very large amplitudes at resonance. The major purpose of a damper is to prevent these large resonance oscillations, and their application is a necessity in systems where the frequency of excitation varies continuously, going through the resonances of the system, as in an automobile, for example.

Dampers may be designed as separate units, like dashpots utilizing air or fluid friction; or they may be applied as damping coatings on vibrating surfaces; or they may even be built directly into vibration isolators or vibrating systems as internal damping, using various kinds of viscoelastic and fibrous materials. (See Chap. 14.) The effect of a damper in a mechanical system is governed by the ratio between the viscous force provided by the damper and the inertial forces in the vibrating system. This is why a coating of damping material on a sheet of metal has to be roughly proportional to the thickness of the metal in order to obtain the same degree of damping in all cases.

Although the application of dampers to a vibrating system generally is motivated by the reduction of the mechanical vibrations themselves, it should be remembered that the sound radiated from the vibrating surfaces will be reduced correspondingly.   In fact, the application of damping materials on walls is often made for the sole purpose of improving the transmission loss for air-borne sound.   Furthermore, the application of dampers may *prevent* mechanical systems from starting to oscillate.   This applies to nonlinear phenomena such as the excitation of a plate by flow.

HOW TO SPECIFY NOISE REDUCTION IN A SYSTEM

Insertion Loss.   Up to this point the term *noise reduction* has been used loosely; now a precise definition must be given.   This term has acquired several different meanings.*   Using the standard definition of noise as any unwanted sound, one could say that noise reduction has been achieved whenever the sound has been rendered more acceptable.

The words *noise reduction* will be used here as a qualitative term only, meaning any decrease in the physical noise stimulus.

Noise reduction is achieved by inserting some element into the system.   The consequence of inserting this element is measured quantitatively by the *insertion loss J* in decibels, the amount by which the sound pressure level at a specified point is reduced by the insertion of the element, holding all other conditions constant.   This definition is extended to include the insertion loss that is produced by two or more elements— but the combined insertion loss may or may not be equal to the sum of their individual insertion losses if they were used one at a time.

The insertion loss is not a unique measure of the intrinsic performance of a noise-control element.†   Under certain conditions the insertion loss may turn out to be negative (the sound level increased!) even though the same element would produce a positive insertion loss when used in another system.   The magnitude of the insertion loss is governed by three types of factors:

1. The physical characteristics of the element itself; for an isolating wall these would include the mass, the stiffness, and the internal damping; for a muffler they would include the internal geometry and the absorptive properties of the materials.
2. The environment of the element; for a wall this includes the geometry and absorptive characteristics of the surrounding rooms; in general, it includes the terminating acoustic impedances that are seen by the component, or the location of the component in a wave field (e.g., the position of a resonator in a duct).
3. The behavior of the source that is used to measure the insertion loss or that is assumed in calculating it; the source may generate constant pressure or constant particle-velocity or constant power, etc.; the directivity of the source may also be relevant.

A fourth category, flanking paths, might be included.   (See Chaps. 19 and 20.) The effective isolation of a wall can be greatly reduced by sound leaks through cracks

* The terms *noise reduction* and *noise-reduction factor* have been used to specify the change in noise level caused by the application of a control measure.   In this context, noise level has been measured by sound pressure level and by various weighted sound pressure levels.   For example, if there are two adjacent rooms with a sound source in one, and the average sound-pressure levels in the two rooms are measured, the difference between these levels is often called the noise reduction in decibels.

As a matter of fact, the primary technique in the analysis of noise control is the calculation of sound-level differences.   Whether one is designing in advance of construction or improving an existing noise condition, he is constantly dealing with level differences: between the existing level and the criterion level, or, for example, between the level at the factory exhaust and the level at the window of a home.

† It has been well recognized in vibration engineering that insertion loss depends not only on the stiffness of an isolator, but also on the mass of the floated element and on the mechanical impedance of the structure to which the isolator is attached; equally important distinctions in air-borne noise control are apt to be overlooked.

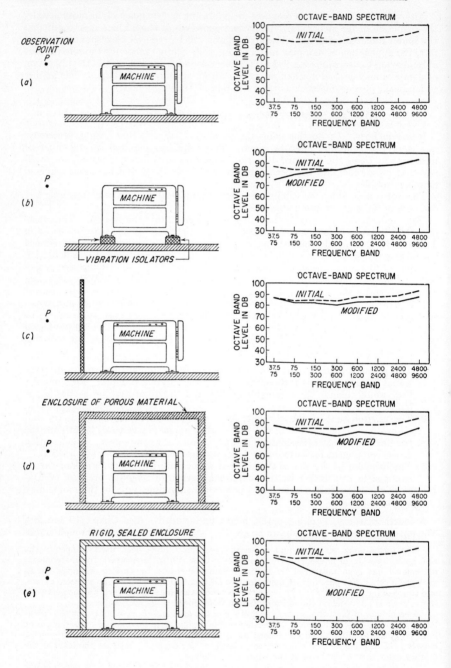

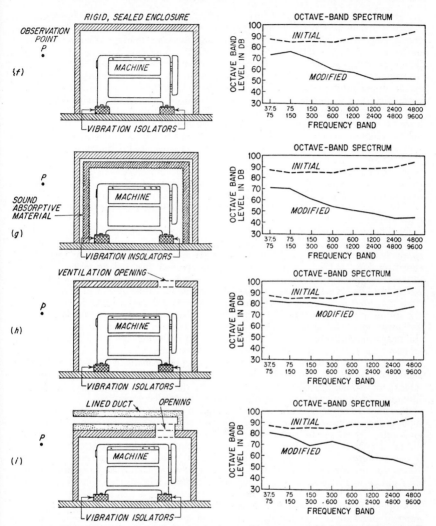

FIG. 22.11. The octave-band noise spectrum of a machine, measured initially at the point P, is shown in (a). Figures 22.11b through i show the effects on the octave-band spectra measured at P when various elements are inserted. The insertion loss in each case is the difference between the initial and modified spectrum.

or through the supporting structure. Mufflers sometimes yield much less than their designed attenuation because energy is flanked by contacting structures—or even by the wall of the muffler itself. Strictly speaking, however, flanking is not a basic factor in the sense of the three types listed above. Rather, one should consider each possible flanking path, whether air or structure, as a separate element and analyze its own insertion loss. In practice it sometimes turns out that the inherent flanking paths set an upper limit to the total noise reduction that can be achieved. Engineering economics then demands a balance in the design of the additional elements so that they are not "wasted." The properties of structural flanking paths only recently have been introduced quantitatively into noise-control engineering and there is not as yet an adequate compilation of flanking values for practical constructions.

Insertion loss as defined above is the most generally useful single measure of the effect of an element *as it is used in the system.* The element—a muffler, a machine enclosure, an absorptive lining in a duct, or a vibration isolator—is inserted to reduce the noise at a certain point in space, such as the position of a man. The insertion loss measures directly the change in level at that point. If the reduction at several points is of interest, an *average* insertion loss can be used, in which case the method of averaging should be stated.

Qualitative Example of Noise Reduction. The effects of some sound-attenuating elements in a system are illustrated qualitatively by the following example. The noise source is assumed to be a machine producing a noise with a spectrum at a point P as shown in Fig. 22.11*a*. A series of elements are now inserted as indicated in Fig. 22.11*b* through Fig. 22.11*i* and the corresponding change in the *octave-band* level is recorded at P. Qualitatively the modified noise spectrum at P will then have the form indicated in the figures. The insertion loss in each case is the difference between the initial and the modified noise spectrum. Note that the insertion losses of the various elements are generally not additive, the effect of one element may depend on the presence of others. A comparison of Fig. 22.11*d* and *e* shows the relatively small transmission loss provided by an enclosure of porous material as compared with one of a solid impervious material. If a ventilation opening is made in the solid enclosure as shown in Fig. 22.11*h*, a considerable increase in level at P will result. However, by adding an attenuating duct, as in Fig. 22.11*i*, the sound pressure level at P can be brought back almost to that corresponding to the sealed enclosure.

The duct design in this example is assumed to be such that the insertion loss of the duct is just about equal to that of the wall section which was removed from the enclosure. It should be realized that no appreciable gain in insertion loss would be obtained by making the duct longer or more complicated, because the sound level at P is determined by the sound coming through the rest of the enclosure. This illustrates the importance of *balanced* system design; a very bulky and expensive muffler may not always produce a larger insertion loss than a relatively small and inexpensive one.

A Sound-isolating Partition in a Room. Consider a room with a noise source near one end and a study near the other end. The study area is to be quieted by erection of a partition that will divide the room into two smaller rooms. The partition has a known value of *transmission loss* (see Chap. 20) and is ideally installed so that its value is fully realized over its whole area S. "Flanking" is neglected. The sound is assumed to be diffuse* throughout the space, both before and after the partition is added. No sound absorption is introduced.

Problem: Determine the insertion loss obtained by the installation of the partition.

First, compute the total number of absorptive units separately for the two parts of the divided room: a_1 in the source room, and a_2 in the receiver room; the total initial absorption is $a_1 + a_2$ because the dividing partition has not introduced any sound absorption.

---

* A diffuse sound field is one in which the average sound pressure is essentially uniform throughout the space and the sound energy flows with equal probability in all directions. Diffuse conditions are met within practical limits if the room is reasonably irregular in shape, and if $Vf^2/10^8 t_{60}$ is greater than unity (V is room volume in cu ft, f is frequency in cps, t_{60} is reverberation time in sec).

The characteristics of the inserted element are fully specified, in this case, by its transmission loss $T.L.$ The environment is described by the wall area S having a transmission coefficient τ, and by the absorptive values a_1 and a_2; if diffuse conditions had not been assumed further information would be required and the problem would be more complicated.* The source characteristics have not been specified, and indeed they are commonly ignored in the presentation of problems such as this. So an assumption must be made. Suppose the noise source generates a constant power W.

The mean square sound pressure before inserting the wall is:

$$p_0{}^2 = \frac{4\rho_0 c W}{a_1 + a_2} \tag{22.1}$$

where ρ_0 represents the density of air, and c is the velocity of sound.

After the wall is inserted, the power is dissipated in different amounts in the two rooms. Let $p_1{}^2$ and $p_2{}^2$ be the mean square pressures in the source and receiver rooms respectively. Then:

$$W = \frac{p_1{}^2 a_1 + p_2{}^2 a_2}{4\rho_0 c} \tag{22.2}$$

From diffuse room theory, the ratio of sound pressures in the two rooms is given by:

$$\frac{p_1{}^2}{p_2{}^2} = \frac{a_2}{\tau S} \tag{22.3}$$

Since W is the same in Eqs. (22.1) and (22.2) by the constant-power assumption, it can be eliminated by simultaneous solution of these equations. One then inserts $p_1{}^2$ in terms of $p_2{}^2$ from Eq. (22.3) and obtains:

$$\frac{p_0{}^2}{p_2{}^2} = \frac{a_2}{S}\left[\frac{\left(\frac{\tau S}{a_2}\right) + \left(\frac{a_1}{a_2}\right)}{1 + \left(\frac{a_1}{a_2}\right)}\right] \tag{22.4}$$

The insertion loss for constant power is then:

$$J_w = 10 \log \frac{p_0{}^2}{p_2{}^2} = 10 \log \frac{a_2}{\tau S} + K \tag{22.5}$$

in which K, 10 times the log of the bracketed factor, in Eq. (22.4), plays the role of a correction term for insertion loss at constant power. The reason for separating this term is brought out in the following discussion.

Suppose it had been assumed that the mean square sound pressure level on the source side of the partition had remained the same as the initial $p_0{}^2$. Setting $p_0{}^2$ equal to $p_1{}^2$, in Eq. (22.3) one obtains:

$$\frac{p_0{}^2}{p_2{}^2} = \frac{a_2}{\tau S} \tag{22.6}$$

Eq. (22.6) is used for determining τ (and $T.L.$) by the two-room method using diffuse room theory. Furthermore, $10 \log p_0{}^2/p_2{}^2$ is the quantity that is sometimes designated as the noise reduction between the two spaces; this quantity is actually the difference in level for constant (incident mean square) pressure:

$$L_{p_0} - L_{p_2} = 10 \log \frac{a_2}{\tau S} \quad \text{db} \tag{22.7}$$

Therefore, Eq. (22.5) can be written in the general form:

$$J_w = (L_{p_0} - L_{p_2}) + K \tag{22.8}$$

Values of K are plotted in Fig. 22.12.

* It is assumed that the direct sound can be neglected in comparison with the diffuse sound.

A Partial-height Partition in a Room.   Partial-height partitions are frequently used to subdivide large offices and factory spaces—and sometimes with the hope of obtaining noise isolation.   The amount of isolation that can be achieved is usually relatively small.   Consider the same room of the previous example.   However, now suppose the partition is erected to a height h that is less than the ceiling height of the room. Furthermore, assume that $T.L.$ is very large, say 40 db, so that the sound that is transmitted through it can be neglected, and consider only the sound that passes over the top of the partition.

Problem: determine the insertion loss of the partial-height partition.

Let S_o be the open area above the partition.   Assume that a_1 and a_2 are the respective absorptions in the two parts of the room as before, and assume that the source generates constant power.   The initial mean square sound pressure is again given by Eq. (22.1), and the total power dissipation is given by Eq. (22.2).   But Eq. (22.3) is replaced by:

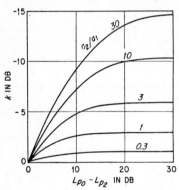

FIG. 22.12. The quantity K plotted as a function of the level difference $L_{p_0} - L_{p_2}$ for various absorption ratios (see text).

$$\frac{p_1{}^2}{p_2{}^2} = \frac{a_2}{S_o} \tag{22.9}$$

Energy is transmitted only through the open area S_o, and the transmission coefficient τ for this area is unity, i.e., $T.L. = 0$ (in diffuse room theory); diffraction and other effects that would be included in a detailed wave theory analysis are neglected.

The mean square pressure ratio is

$$\frac{p_0{}^2}{p_2{}^2} = \frac{a_2}{S} \left[\frac{\left(\dfrac{S_o}{a_2}\right) + \left(\dfrac{a_1}{a_2}\right)}{1 + \left(\dfrac{a_1}{a_2}\right)} \right] \tag{22.10}$$

which is the same as Eq. (22.4) with the substitutions: $\tau = 1$, $S = S_o$.   Using the same substitutions in K we get for the present problem:

$$J = 10 \log \left(\frac{a_2}{S}\right) + K$$

The curves in Fig. 22.12 can be used to compute K.

For example, assume that the room is 10 ft high, 20 ft wide and 30 ft long; the partition of height h is 20 ft long, centered along the 30-ft length of the room.   Also. assume that the ceiling is covered with material having $a = 0.5$, so that

$$a_1 = a_2 = 150 \text{ sabins (other absorption neglected)}$$

Some calculations are tabulated as follows:

h (ft)	S_o (sq ft)	$L_{p_0} - L_{p_2}$	K	J (db)
6.	80	2.7	−1.2	1.5
8.	40	5.7	−2.0	3.7
9.	20	8.8	−2.5	6.3
9.5.	10	11.8	−2.8	9.0

Chapter 23

GEAR NOISE

Kurt G. F. Moeller, Dr. Rer. Nat.

U.S. Naval Engineering Experiment Station

INTRODUCTION

Gears, i.e., assemblies of tooth wheels, are found in a variety of sizes, from the weight of a few fractions of an ounce up to thousands of pounds. In prime movers (sources of motive power), speed is a very important parameter in determining the efficiency of the machine. However, these speeds are rarely the same as the speed requirements of driven machinery so that gears may be required with various ratios to provide the necessary speed transformation. Gear assemblies may be used to distribute power to a number of devices or to collect power from various sources and feed it into one shaft, as torque converters, or to reverse the direction of rotation.[1,2] Although substitutes for gears can be helpful in reducing noise in special applications, their effectiveness is limited.

Usually the term "gear" is associated with the production of noise. This chapter considers sources of gear noise and means for their control.

TYPES AND ASSEMBLIES OF GEARS

In the field of gears a special terminology is used. The American Gear Manufacturers Association (AGMA) in connection with the American Society of Mechanical Engineers (ASME) has issued standards which list all necessary terms with definitions and explanations.[2]

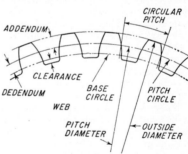

Fig. 23.1. Gear terms.

A gear wheel consists of a *hub*, which fits the gear to the shaft, a *web*, and a *rim*. The rim carries the teeth. The *pitch* surfaces are the imaginary planes, cylinders, or cones which roll together in slipfree motion while two gears are in contact (see Fig. 23.1). In friction drives, these surfaces are the actual means of contact, and the "tooth form" is generally involute. In simple gears without any appreciable power transmission, the older cycloidal form is still used to a limited extent.

Types. Gears can be divided into two types—those which connect parallel or "in-line" shafts, and those which connect shafts at an angle, usually under 90°.

Spur Gears. *Spur gears* are defined as gears having teeth which are placed radially about, and parallel to, the shaft (see Fig. 23.2). During the meshing process, every part of the tooth is in phase with every other part of the tooth face; therefore only extreme accuracy can guarantee uniform motion. Therefore, the application of these gears is limited to applications where power transmission is of secondary or no importance, where the speed is very low, or where gear-shifting is involved.

Helical Gears. *Helical gears* are defined as gears having teeth which are at a specified angle ("helix angle") with respect to the shaft (see Fig. 23.3). They have the advantage that, during the meshing process, the teeth come in contact gradually until the full tooth face is engaged; then they disengage gradually. This principle, which

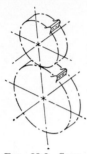

is widely used, is able to mask inaccuracies to some extent and to avoid sudden changes from one tooth to the next. Helical gears are generally used in power transmission, particularly where quiet operation is desired. Helix angles of 8 to 20° are common; although in special cases helix angles up to 45° have been used. There is, of course, an axial force W_t resulting from the helix angle ψ increasing with this angle which must be compensated by a suitable thrust bearing. It is

$$W_t = W \cdot \tan \psi \qquad (23.1)$$

where W is the tangential tooth load. For example, for a 300-kw gear having a tangential tooth load of 1,690 lbs and a helix angle of 9° 2', the axial thrust is 269 lb.

Fig. 23.2. Spur gears. (A.G. M.A.[2])

Double-helical Gears (Herringbone Gears). Double-helical gears are designed to compensate the above thrust force by combining two helical gears with opposite helix angles (see Fig. 23.3). This compensation, and therefore the omission of any thrust bearing, is advantageous. The requirements regarding accuracy for double-helical gears are very much higher than for the single-helical gears so they are much more expensive to fabricate.

Bevel Gears. Bevel gears are gears having conical pitch surfaces (see Fig. 23.4). They are suitable for connecting shafts which are nonparallel, for angles less than 90°, if the two shafts are in one plane. Bevel gears are made either with straight teeth corresponding to spur gears, or with curved teeth corresponding to helical gears.

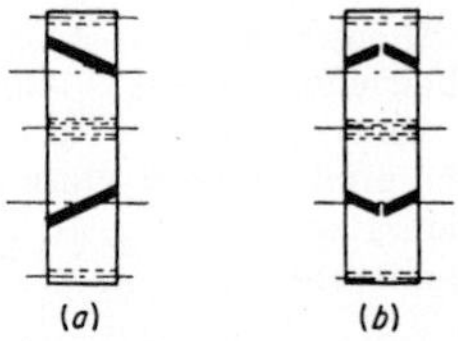

Hypoid Gears. Hyperboloidal gears, commonly called *hypoid gears*, are derived from the curve involved in their basic design. They are a special type of bevel gear having their shafts in two different planes (see Fig. 23.5). These gears are widely used in the rear transmission of automobiles because they allow for the location of the driving shaft above the rear axle. They are also in use where one shaft drives two or more parallel shafts at right angles to the driving shaft.

Worm Gears. Worm gears consist of a worm wheel together with an endless screw, forming a device by which rotary motion of one shaft can be transmitted to a shaft at right angles to it. The mating gear (worm wheel) has convex teeth to fit the worm (see Fig. 23.6). Since there are usually several teeth in contact, the change over from one tooth to the next is very smooth so that these gears are relatively quiet. Unfortunately, their load capacity is very limited.

Assemblies. For certain purposes two or more tooth wheels in mesh may be assembled in a common gear box. Such a gear box serves three purposes: (1) To give support to the bearings of the shafts; this support must be sufficiently stiff to maintain the bearings in proper alignment. (2) To enclose the space around the gear wheels in order to confine the lubricant to this space. (3) To provide a shield for air-borne noise. In most gear assemblies no particular care need be taken to provide this function. However, since the gear box usually has a heavy wall casing, it provides air-borne noise insulation.

Single Pinion and Bull Gear. The most common assembly for a reduction gear which serves the purpose of adapting a high-speed prime mover to a lower-speed machine is the combination of a single pinion with a gear, sometimes referred to as a

Fig. 23.3. (a) Single-helical gears, and (b) double-helical gears. (A.G.M.A.[2])

bull gear. Except for providing accurate geometry, nothing special can be done with respect to basic design for noise control.

Double Pinion and Bull Gear. Frequently two or three pinions are assembled with one bull gear in order to connect two high-speed prime movers to a common output shaft. It is recommended that the placement of the two pinions be such that they contact the bull gear with some phase difference. Then the switchover from one tooth to the next takes place at the pinions at different instances of time. This is helpful in reducing the initial contact pulse and therefore the noise output.

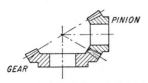

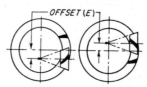

FIG. 23.4. Bevel gears. (A.G.M.A.[2])   FIG. 23.5. Hypoid gears. (A.G.M.A.[2])

Planetary Gears. Planetary or epicyclic gears show an entirely different arrangement (see Fig. 23.7). The driving shaft is, in a certain type, connected to a centrally located gear ("sun gear"), around which are arranged three or more "planet" gears held in the relative position by a "spider" which is connected to the outgoing shaft. The planets are also engaged with a ring gear which is concentric to the sun gear. The latter is fastened to the housing and is stationary. Other arrangements may be used where the spider is stationary and the ring gear is connected to the outgoing shaft. In any case, two of the three basic elements are connected to the ingoing and outgoing shaft, respectively, while the third one is stationary. These epicyclic gears have certain advantages which stem from their basic design: (1) The ingoing and the outgoing shaft rotate about the same axis in the same or opposite direction, depending upon the type. This principle requires that less restoring force be provided by the housing; therefore, the housing can be lighter than in other types of gears. (2) Since

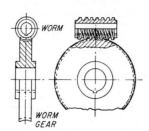

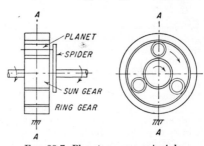

FIG. 23.6. Worm gears. (A.G.M.A.[2])   FIG. 23.7. Planetary-gear principle.

the transmission of torque is performed by three or more planets, the load capacity is equivalent to a gear with a face width equal to the face width of one planet multiplied by the number of planets. Thus the size of the gear is much smaller than in other types of gears. (3) The weight of epicyclic gears is lower than that of other gears. (4) With the smaller size of the single-tooth wheels, the accuracy of machining can be higher than in other types of gears.[4] The sun gear is forced in its position by the symmetrical radial forces of the planets; therefore, modern designs do not provide bearings for the sun gear in order to avoid possible misalignment of the axis defined by the planets and the axis of the bearings. In one type of gear the ring gear is mounted elastically in the housing.[5] This results in better load distribution and quieter operation.

Special Arrangements. There are many cases where a large number of gear wheels are assembled in one gear box to serve a specific purpose—as, for example, gears in automobiles to adapt various speed ranges to the speed of the engine; gears in internal-combustion engines to drive auxiliaries; gear boxes on machine tools for speed adaptation and other specific purposes.   These multiple gear assemblies may offer particular noise problems stemming from the variety of exciting frequencies as well as the effects of idling gears.   Each case must be treated individually.

NOISE SOURCES IN GEARS

The noise produced by the simplest combination of gears is quite complex.   The numerous sources which contribute to gear noise may be classified in two groups: (1) Those which are characteristic of a specific design and manufacturing method, and (2) those which are excited by operation of the gear.

Sources Resulting from Improper Design and Manufacturing Imperfections. Small gears are, except in special cases, low in price and mass-produced.   Therefore, any final design and manufacturing method is usually applied to one or more trial series until the final dimensions and tolerances are established.   Since large gears usually are custom-made and produced in small quantities, it takes longer to acquire the experience for optimum design.

Shape of Gear Bodies; Natural Frequencies.   Figure 23.8 shows on the left two bells in a back-to-back arrangement, and on the right a gear cross section of a fairly common shape.   The significant design parameters are easy to find in both cases. They are the "sound bow"; the "waist," which is much shortened in a gear; the "shoulder"; and the "crown," which is, in the gear, identical with the hub.   From this comparison, one may reason that such a gear will ring out loudly when hit at the sound bow.   Experience has shown that any gear which is an approximation to a bell shape is apt to be particularly noisy.

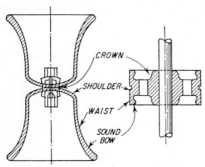

CROWN
SHOULDER
WAIST
SOUND BOW

FIG. 23.8.   Bell and gear, a correlation. (*K. G. F. Moeller, unpublished.*)

Every gear has a series of natural frequencies.   It is important that these natural frequencies do not interfere with the frequencies which are produced by the operation of the gear.   It is very difficult to calculate the natural frequency of a gear accurately unless it has a very simple form, e.g., a disc; but in many cases it is possible to make an approximation.[6]   Experimental methods using plastic models are sometimes helpful.[7]

Accuracy of Teeth and Tooth Ring.   Since a gear runs by having one pair of teeth after another in contact, it is evident that accuracy of tooth form and tooth spacing is a basic requirement for quiet operation.   A deviation in tooth form produces a sudden acceleration or deceleration of the gear in mesh.   These speed changes are converted into tangential as well as radial forces, causing torsional vibration and excitation of the tooth wheels and the structural elements which are connected with them through the bearings.   A deviation in tooth form can also cause a displacement of the next tooth which comes into contact, producing a slight impact at the beginning of the meshing.

TIP AND ROOT RELIEF.   Tip and root relief (cutting below the theoretical profile) are often applied to ensure that the beginning and end of the contact occur in a sliding fashion without knock.

TOOTH SPACING.   Another requirement of accuracy is the equal tooth spacing about the rim.   Any deviation in spacing causes a rough contact of the next tooth involved and may produce additional noise.

ECCENTRICITY.   Eccentricity has two consequences.   It causes a pronounced rotational frequency; and, by changing the line of contact throughout the circle, a periodic change in gear ratio takes place which accentuates the rotational frequency component.

LEAD ERROR.   Lead error, a problem particularly in larger gears having a fairly wide face, is the deviation from the theoretical curve of the tooth along the face.

Even the slightest deviation causes a nonuniform load distribution along the tooth, overloading certain parts and not utilizing other parts of the face width. Therefore a large lead error affects the load-carrying capacity of the gear. It also contributes to the noise by increasing the frictional forces beyond the design figures. It is becoming common practice to apply "end relief" to the teeth, i.e., the thinning of teeth toward both ends of the face. This helps to provide a smooth engagement and disengagement, and it prevents tooth ends from becoming overloaded; tooth ends are more liable to fracture than the inner portions. Rounding of the outer edges also helps in this respect.

Other Design Parameters. The shafts of gears must be sufficiently stiff to prevent the gear axis from becoming nonparallel due to bending of the shaft under load. The "center distance" (distance from center to center) of the gears is as important a dimension of the gears as the others mentioned above. A variable center distance as a result of excessive bearing clearance, for example, results in effects similar to those caused by eccentricity. In Fig. 23.9 C_G is the nominal center of the gear, C_P the nominal center of the pinion, and CD the center distance. Because of excessive bearing clearance assume that the gear moves to the location C_G' and the pinion to the location C_P'; the center distance becomes $C_G'C_P'$, which is different from C_GC_P in length and is also dislocated. The change in length causes a change of gear ratio resulting in acceleration or deceleration particularly in the large driven gear, as well as in the pinion. The dislocation of the center line could cause the same type of effect. These motions may occur at random or periodically particularly if oil-film whirl occurs in the bearings (see Chap. 24). In any event, the effect described will add either white noise to the lower frequency range of the gear spectrum or discrete frequency components.

If the gear is exposed to axial motions due to thrust, this produces adverse effects on the uniformity of the gear motion except in spur gears. In helical gears, an axial motion is equivalent to deceleration or acceleration, depending upon the direction.

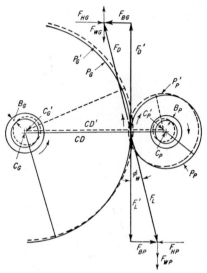

FIG. 23.9. Reduction gears, effect of bearing clearance.

Gear Noise Generated by Operation. The noise sources grouped under this heading are simply a result of operation of the gear; basic design of the gear has little influence on them.

Stress Waves. The contact of gears causes local compressive stresses at the points or lines of contact and bending stresses in other areas, particularly at the root of the teeth. Figure 23.10 shows two meshing-plastic gear models where the stresses are made visible by using the photoelastic method.[8] The right tooth of the upper gear touches the mating tooth with the tip while the second tooth of the upper gear has progressed in its meshing action beyond the pitch line. In both cases the compressive stresses are clearly indicated. After a tooth is disengaged, these compressive stresses are released, causing a stress wave to run through the gear. These local compressive stresses are similar to those which can be caused by a local impact; for example, a hammer blow which makes any vibratory element vibrate in its natural frequency. Such compressive stresses in the gear teeth do not have as high a gradient as an impact; therefore, it is very likely that only the fundamental frequency will be excited— not the harmonics as in the case of an impact. However, with higher tooth loads that are achieved in modern gears, these stresses are rapidly increasing; and they are an unavoidable source of gear noise. The picture shows a second phenomenon: While the upper gear has the roots of its teeth rounded, the lower gear has sharp edges. The rounded root does not show nearly as much stress concentration as that shown in the lower gear. Proper geometry helps to diminish these stress concentrations at the root of the teeth and therefore to decrease noise generated by stress waves.

Air Pocketing. Air pocketing, an effect not completely understood, is the expulsion of air from the space between two teeth of one gear by the meshing tooth of the corresponding gear, and the suction caused by the vacuum between two teeth when the meshing tooth goes out of mesh. This continuous pumping action occurs periodically at a rate equal to the number of meshing teeth per second, producing a siren effect. It is questionable whether this effect is of sufficient intensity to be of major concern. A noticeable effect could only be expected in high-speed gearing, but there the backlash is usually (for other reasons) such that sufficient space is provided for the air flow in and out of the space in between teeth.

Oil Pocketing. A similar effect as described above for air may occur with the lubricating oil if it is supplied in abundance. This problem is more serious because of

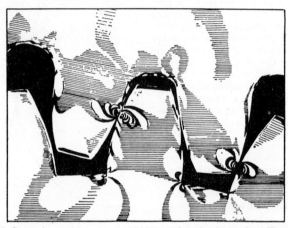

Fig. 23.10. Stress in meshing gears. (*After a photoelastic graph of The Texas Co.*)

the fact that oil is practically incompressible; so, if a meshing tooth hits a space between the meshing teeth filled with oil, a heavy shock is unavoidable. In high-speed gearing, most of the lubricating oil is supplied for cooling purposes so that much more volume per unit time flows than is needed for lubrication. If the lubricating oil is fed into the ingoing side of the gears so close to the meshing point that the centrifugal forces cannot be effective, such pocketing may occur.

To a first approximation, the minimum amount of lubricant in gallons per minute

$$V_{\min} = d_o \times U_n \times F_t \times \frac{1}{2}31 \qquad (23.2)$$

where d_o = minimum thickness of oil film in in., U_n = pitch line velocity in in. per min., F_t = total face width of the gear in in. There is always an additional amount of lubricant needed for cooling purposes which can be introduced as an additional layer of oil on top of the lubricating film of a thickness d_c. Then the practical volume of lubricant per minute

$$V = (d_o + d_c) \times U_n \times F_t \times \frac{1}{2}31 \qquad (23.3)$$

The order of magnitude of $(d_o + d_c)$ can be given as $d_o = 2 \times 10^{-4}$ in. and

$$d_c = 1 \times 10^{-3} \text{ in.}$$

Finally, the maximum volume of lubricant which may lead to oil pocketing and to serious noise troubles is:

$$V_{max} = C \times U_n \times F_t \times \tfrac{1}{2}31 \tag{23.4}$$

where C = gear "clearance" (see Fig. 23.1). Therefore, any rating of lubricant supply to a gear should be smaller than V_{max}.

Gears operated at lower speeds are frequently lubricated by filling the gear casing with oil to such an extent that the lower parts of the gears are running through the oil. If such an arrangement is used for higher speeds, oil-splash noise may be a noticeable source.

Friction. Friction is one of the major sources of gear noise, if not the major source of noise.[9-13] Extensive investigations of the origin of automobile gear noise have indicated a definite relation between friction and gear noise. A distinction has been made between "root friction" or "pushing action" and "head friction" or "pulling action." The change from one type to the other occurs suddenly at the pitch line, an effect called "pitch line shock." This change reverses the direction of forces acting radially on the gears which leads to a pronounced *tooth-contact frequency* (f_{tc}), i.e., number of teeth coming into contact per second. An important fact is that this type of frictional excitation is independent of the accuracy of the gear. Thus a perfect gear of absolute accuracy would be subject to noise excitation by friction. The major frequency components are the tooth contact frequency and its harmonics, the natural frequencies of one gear wheels and of the system's gear-wheels shafts. They may be modulated by any exciting frequency.

Impact. The impact of a gear tooth on the tooth of a meshing gear is an effect which produces a bell-like tone. In modern gears, particularly with helical teeth and increasing accuracy of our gear-manufacturing processes, this noise source is losing its predominant character. However, in cheaper gears, particularly in appliances, it is still a major noise source. There are two reasons for such impacts; first, inaccuracies in gear manufacturing, and second, deflection of the tooth under load which changes the relative position of the pinion with respect to the bull gear. Tip-root and end relief are remedies for both cases.

Variation of Radial Forces. As already explained, inaccuracies of gears can cause a variation in radial forces. In addition, insufficient lubrication of the gear-shaft bearings or variations in the lubricating-oil pressure may cause radial motions of the gears produced by unbalance of the radial gear forces and the forces stemming from the oil film in the bearings. This possibility requires that the operational conditions of bearings be maintained constant. The installation of the gears requires that they be kept free of any disturbing forces in transverse direction. The coupling of input and output shafts should be such that only torque is transmitted, not thrust nor transverse loads. Frequently, economical considerations require the incorporation of major thrust bearings of the driving shaft in the gear housing, but this arrangement may result in an increased gear noise level.

NOISE CONTROL

In noise control, economy dictates bringing all parameters in the design of a piece of machinery or apparatus to an adequate common level. The noise should be reduced to the economical minimum instead of to the lowest possible minimum.

Application of Gears. Gears by their nature are always used in connection with other pieces of machinery as a connecting link between a driving motor or engine and a power-consuming machine. Thus the noise level of the driving or driven system determines the goal for noise control in the connecting gear. Any costly efforts to reduce the noise of the gear beyond that goal cannot be justified.

Apparatus. In apparatus, gears are either used to reduce the speed of a driving motor to a suitable value or to connect different elements of the apparatus with a certain speed ratio. A typical example of such an application is a clock based on a synchronous motor running from the power line or some other suitable source. The gears are needed to link the three pointers for seconds, minutes, and hours. The transmission of power does not play any part in this kind of assembly since the bearings involved are usually of sufficient low losses. Emphasis must be placed here on operation as quiet as possible.

General Machinery. In heavy machinery, for example, in a large variety of machine tools, the gear situation is quite different from that described in *Apparatus.* Here the forces to be transmitted are sometimes very large. Although such machines usually generate a considerable amount of noise themselves, there are three considerations that require all effort to keep the noise of the gears as low as possible:

1. Noise is an indication of vibration. This vibration may disturb the smooth operation of the machine. For example, it may result in a waviness of lathe cut.
2. The operator of a machine usually uses his ear as a supplementary indicator of the correct operation of the machine. This is impossible if masked by gear noise.
3. The operator of the machine is exposed to the noise while the machine is operating. Gear noise should be sufficiently low so that he is not exposed to an equally high noise level when the machine is idling.

Automotive Gears. The subject of automotive gears is treated in Chap. 31.

Aircraft Gears. High quality of noise control is not usually required for aircraft gears. Weight limitations in aircraft power plants reduce the application of means for engine noise reduction to the necessary minimum.

Marine Gears. The modern trend in ships' propulsion units is toward high-speed prime movers. The most common source of motive power in ships is the steam turbine, supplemented by gas turbines. The speed of these turbines is about 3,000 rpm and higher. A suitable speed of a propeller shaft is less than 500 rpm. Therefore, the application of reduction gears is unavoidable unless hydraulic or electric transmissions are employed. In spite of large power ratings, the turbines are fairly quiet, making the reduction gear the most pronounced noise source in the propulsion plant. Since these gears are always custom-made, no method of selection from mass production can be utilized, as is done with automotive gears. The high power rating, together with increased difficulties with regard to mechanical accuracy and size, make the noise control of these gears a difficult problem.[14–19]

Design and Manufacturing Measures. Unfortunately, it is common practice in industry to design and manufacture all kinds of machines, including gears, with very little consideration for noise control. The end product frequently is classified as being excessively noisy.

Suitable Selection of Gear Parameters. In the design of a gear, the first decision to be made is the selection of a suitable gear type. Helical gears must be used in any load transmitting gear and they must be dimensioned such that overloading is avoided, particularly if a high degree of quietness is required. A large number of small teeth is preferable to a small number of large teeth, i.e., a larger "diametral pitch" is better than a small one from the standpoint of noise control for the rotation is more uniform with increasing diametral pitch. This results in an increased tooth contact frequency. However, higher frequencies are easier to damp and easier to isolate than low frequencies. Bearings should be oversized rather than undersized in order to maintain the center distances between gears. The gear clearances should be in proper proportion to the allowable tolerances of the center distance of mating gears.

Accuracy of Manufacturing. The accuracy of a gear represents a true picture of the accuracy of the machines on which it was fabricated. In particular, the tooth spacing is one of the parameters which is most affected by the gear-cutting machine.[16] It is often found that gears show a periodic error in tooth spacing due to the error in the gears of the fabricating machine. The wear of cutting tools used in the machines is also a very important parameter. To obtain high quality gears, it is necessary to divide the gear cutting process into various steps, not only in order to decrease the deviations gradually, but also to overlap periodic errors so that they will be reduced. Experience shows clearly that grinding yields the highest attainable accuracy. The relationship between manufacturing accuracy and gear noise output is quite complex. First, our measuring techniques and instruments are only of the same accuracy, at least for large gears, as the manufacturing processes. This makes a correlation of accuracy and noise output very difficult. Second, the possibility exists that there may be an optimum of accuracy regarding quietness as indicated qualitatively in Fig. 23.11;[9] it is assumed that, beyond the point A of optimum accuracy, more and more random deviations are eliminated and the rest approaches a pattern which lends to accumulative effects due to equal phasing and, therefore, to increasing noise. As yet it cannot be ascertained whether such an optimum exists and what accuracy is required.[20-32]

Materials. For gears with high load capacity, materials of high tensile strength are required. However, material and fabricating processes are closely connected. If the gears must be hobbed because of economic reasons, a material with a surface hardness much greater than 300 Brinell cannot be used. Therefore, gears made of high-alloy steel or of case hardened steel must be ground. Unfortunately, the requirements of noise control are basically opposed to those of a high load-carrying capacity since materials of high strength have less mechanical damping than softer materials. Cast iron, for example, has about 100 to 200 times higher damping capacity than cold rolled steel, and the tensile-strength values of these materials have a ratio of about 1:3. In gears having low load requirements but high speed requirements, the application of materials with high damping capacity is highly recommendable to achieve low noise levels. Gears in many applications, usually one of two mating gears, are now fabricated from rawhide, plastics laminated with textile layers for reinforcement, and nylon.[33-34] Gears made of such materials, by contact with the metal gear, provide vibration damping.[34-44] However, the favorable influence of internal damping cannot be effective if the gears are so thin compared to the face width that the disc has not sufficient stiffness. There are low-priced electric clocks that produce a whirring sound resulting from disc vibrations of a thin plastic gear.

Detuning. In cases where certain materials are required because of the load rating which have a low damping capacity, the natural frequency may appear with a high amplitude. One method of attacking this noise-control problem is to alter the natural frequency by

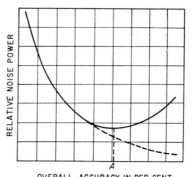

FIG. 23.11. Relation of noise output and mechanical accuracy in gears.

varying thickness or other geometric parameters so that the natural frequency is shifted outside the range of operational frequencies generated by the gear (detuning). That does not make the gear especially quiet, but it avoids high noise levels at particular speeds caused by "resonant magnification."

Damping. If the speed range is very wide and the geometric limitations do not allow detuning of the natural frequency of the gear, the only cure is the application of damping, which decreases the amplitude in cases of resonance. At resonance, the amplitude does not depend on the exciting forces but on the damping coefficient of the vibrating element. Materials of low damping capacity if needed for strength reasons require the application of damping devices externally. There is quite extensive patent literature on this subject.[45] Methods of damping may be divided into two groups. The first group describes methods of attaching damping rings or plates to the gears in order to provide energy dissipation by frictional contact, or by attaching materials of high damping capacity such as lead or Babbitt metal to the gears for energy dissipation in these materials.

Babbitt metal coatings have been applied throughout the web and the rim of an experimental gear. By cutting out the damping layer gradually, it was found that the excitation is in the rim and that the damping material applied there is most effective.

The second group of noise-reduction methods deals with isolation in gears by separating the tooth-carrying rim from the web and the hub. Although a wide variety of such design has been proposed, this group has very limited application because the isolation requires the introduction of a compliant material. Any compliance influences the basic accuracy of the gear, at least the meshing process, in the form of a pulsating radial distance. Investigations of such gears have shown that the over-all noise level did not decrease in comparison with identical solid gears; the energy is merely shifted from higher to lower frequencies. There may be cases where this shift is helpful since the ear is more sensitive at the higher frequencies.

Lubrication. Lubrication of gears, a problem which is far from solved, is completely different from the lubrication of bearings. High specific-load ratings make it nearly impossible to achieve hydrodynamic lubrication. Due to mechanical inaccuracies, the face is not equally loaded so that in most cases gear lubrication is of the boundary type.[46] Thus the metal surfaces of meshing gears are in contact by means of their microscopic "peaks" while the "valleys" are filled with lubricant. The "running in" of gears wears down the peaks, gradually increasing the load-carrying area. The oil film is probably reduced to a monomolecular layer. Under these circumstances the coefficient of friction in steel gears has been given as 0.03 to 0.04; in case of hydrodynamic lubrication its range has been given as 0.003 to 0.004.[47] This situation makes stick-slip motion or frictional excitation of noise very probable. Efforts toward noise control are directed here toward the application of all possible means for the reduction of friction.[48]

Common lubricants often are not satisfactory even for well-designed gears. For gears with high load ratings most oil companies have developed so-called *EP* (excessive pressure) lubricants which contain additives that cause the development of a chemical combination on the metal surfaces. This action improves the wettability and provides an emergency lubricant as well.[49-52] Dry lubricants, as powdered graphite and molybdenum disulfide,[53] may be useful as emergency lubricants and at higher temperatures up to 400°C.

Housing-gear Case. The housing of a gear assembly often is as important a component in noise control as the gears themselves. The three functions of the housing have been pointed out above. The first, that of providing rigid support for the shaft bearings, requires sufficient stiffness to keep the shafts in alignment. Since there is no absolutely rigid structure, the deflection under maximum load must be at least one order of magnitude smaller than the tolerances defining the prescribed gear mesh. In designing the housing and determining the required stiffness, not only the forces involved in the gearing must be considered, but also any distorting forces which may act from the outside on the gear casing. The support of the housing in the plane of the shafts saves weight and simplifies the conditions regarding distortion. A three-point support or suspension is more desirable than a four-point suspension because three points define a plane, whereas four points frequently lead to distortions of the gear case since the fourth point may be out of the supporting plane. In heavy machinery wide footings with four or more bolts may be used. Such footings cannot be regarded as "point supports" because each footing defines a plane in itself. In stationary installations where bedplates and concrete blocks are the most common supports, the basic conditions for good alignment are favorable. Gears for automobiles, railroads, airplanes, and ships must be supported by a structure which is somewhat less rigid than the gear housing. Here a three-point suspension is necessary to avoid misalignment stemming from distortions of the supporting structure. In considering the effect on load-carrying capacity, the effect on the noise output is appreciable. Any kind of gear, even the smallest instrument gear, requires a housing sufficiently stiff to conserve precise alignment of the gear shafts.[54]

The second function of the gear housing, to confine the lubricant to the gear space, has less relation to the noise output. The housing should provide sufficient space so that the free flow of lubricant is not interfered with. Furthermore, it should not have unnecessary protrusions on the inside that may cause splashing of the lubricant, thereby producing additional noise. Any materials used in making the casing oiltight should be carefully selected to avoid the contamination of the lubricant. These contaminants, in passing through gear mesh, could cause increased friction and therefore increased noise.

The third function of the housing is to act as an acoustic shield. This requires rigidity and a mass as large as feasible so that the natural frequencies of the housing will be above the rotational range.   Of course, higher harmonics may undergo "resonant magnification" by parts of the housing.   In any case, damping is helpful.   It may be achieved in light structures by proper coatings, or by a sandwiched construction (see Chap. 14).   In close relation with the housing, which determines the location of the shafting relative to the environmental structure, is the coupling of the driving and the driven shaft.   Whether the flexible coupling with or without quill action is required depends upon the particular conditions.   The guiding rule should always be that no forces other than the torque to be transmitted should affect the gear.

Installation.   In many cases, a fairly quiet gear may be ruined and become noisy as a result of improper installation.   Therefore, installation as such is part of noise control.

Mounting Base.   Before setting a gear on the prepared base, all structure dimensions should be checked, not only for distance of hold-down bolts, but also for proper leveling of the supporting points.   The substructure should be checked carefully to determine whether the rigidity of the substructure is within the limits of the allowable compliance.   Concrete sub-bases require at least several weeks to settle.   Therefore, if an early installation must be made, after one month and three months alignment checks should be made.

Shaft Couplings.   As has been mentioned, the protection of the gear may require the application of flexible shaft couplings.   A common misconception is that a flexible

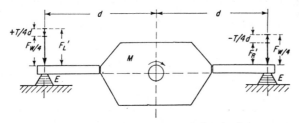

FIG. 23.12. Forces on mountings of an isolated prime mover.

coupling will take care of any inaccuracies in alignment.   Two shafts which are coupled by means of a "flexible coupling" must be aligned as accurately as they would be if a solid coupling were used, since most of the flexible couplings show increasing unbalance with increasing angular deviation of the two shafts.   Furthermore, flexible couplings run best at zero misalignment.   The flexibility is provided only to avoid mechanical damage in case of misalignment.

Isolation.   If all other efforts to reduce the noise output do not lead to a satisfactory low level, isolation of the noisy gear system is indicated.   This isolation must be two-fold considering both solid-borne vibration and air-borne sound.

STRUCTURE-BORNE NOISE ISOLATION.   (See Chap. 13 for a detailed discussion of the application of resilient mounts.)   First, find the lowest operational frequency of the gear system.   This frequency, together with the amount of isolation that is required, determines the frequency to which the vibratory system consisting of the machinery installed on its mounts must resonate.   If the mounted machinery is self-contained (as, for example, a motor-generator set having a reduction gear between the motor and the generator, or a compressor assembly consisting of a motor, a reduction gear, and a compressor), no problem is involved if pipe and electrical connections are made sufficiently flexible.   However, in cases where the prime mover and reduction gear are installed on resilient mountings and the mechanical torque must be transmitted from the mounted assembly to another machine connected to the surrounding solid structure, the torque reaction must be considered in the arrangement and rating of the resilient mountings.   For example, Fig. 23.12 shows a prime mover M mounted on four isolation mounts E, two of which are shown in the figure.   The weight of the machinery is W; each mount carries $W/4$ as a static load.   The torque is T. Due to the torque arm d, the force imposed on the mounts is T/d.   Because of the clockwise rotation of the shaft, the torque reaction is directed counterclockwise, i.e., down on the leftside mounts and up on the rightside mounts. Thus the total force on the left side is:

$$F_L = W/2 + T/2d \tag{23.5}$$

and on the right side

$$F_R = W/2 - T/2d \tag{23.6}$$

and for a single mount

$$F_L' = W/4 + T/4d \tag{23.7}$$
$$\text{and} \qquad F_R' = W/4 - T/4d \tag{23.8}$$

respectively. If the mount is selected for a load of $W/4$, then $\pm T/(4d)$ determines the load variation the mounting is exposed to. For commercial mounts, the variation $\pm T/(4d)$ should not exceed 15 per cent of $W/4$ in order not to alter the natural frequency of the system. There are mounts available which allow a larger variation of the load without changing the natural frequency of the system. In any case, the torque arm d should be as long as possible. The center of gravity should be as close as possible to the plane of support. If lack of space may prevent this, then it is recommended that the total available space be used for a mounting platform even though it is necessary to include on the platform items which do not need isolation. This may result in the application of larger size mounts; but it satisfies Eqs. (23.5) and (23.6) more closely and results in lower rocking frequencies.

AIR-BORNE NOISE ISOLATION. If the air-borne noise level is too high for the operational conditions, the use of an isolating enclosure is recommended. This enclosure may be a separate room or merely a hood built around the piece of machinery (see Chaps. 20 and 22 for further considerations). A particular problem is offered by the necessity to bring the shafts out through the wall of the enclosure. There are two possible ways of accomplishing this. An effective enclosure usually has two walls, each of which should be brought in close contact with the shaft by means of a seal. So-called *oil seals*, in which lubrication must be provided, can be used for this purpose. If space is available, the shaft can be brought out by using concentric enclosures of heavy material such as concrete or cast steel lined with sound-absorptive material. The attenuation which can be achieved per foot of length is in the order of 5 db, so that a total length of 5 to 6 ft is sufficient in most of the cases to reduce the noise at the end of the duct to the ambient level.

GEAR-NOISE INVESTIGATIONS

There are two objectives in gear-noise investigations: (1) the study of the origin of noise in gears, and (2) the testing of gears coming off a production line in order to determine whether or not they meet the specifications. The first is part of applied research and requires more elaborate facilities and professional personnel; while the second type is restricted to simpler facilities operated by specially trained technicians.

Test Site. The test site must be selected with two viewpoints in mind: (1) The ambient noise must be low enough so as not to interfere with the noise investigation or test, and (2) The noise generated by the test facility should not interfere with surrounding operations.[55]

Structure-borne Tests. The test stand requires isolation from the building foundation since such facilities in production plants are usually located in places having a high ambient structure-borne noise level. The type of isolation to be applied depends upon the problem. In many cases, a cork mat between a mounting block and the lower foundation may be satisfactory. For other test facilities this lower foundation must be separated from the building structure and imbedded in a layer of dry sand of sufficient thickness. Other facilities may require a mounting system which resonates at very low frequencies (see Chap. 13).

Air-borne Tests. The isolation of ambient air-borne noise which may interfere with gear noise measurements, or the protection of the environments from the gear test noise requires air-borne sound isolation of reasonably high quality (see Chap. 20).

Test Methods. Test methods may be divided into two general categories, those required for factory testing and those required for research. While factory testing follows more or less of a routine, methods used for research depend upon the objectives of the laboratory study.

Factory Testing. Factory testing is usually done by installing a complete gear assembly, or gear elements, in a special rig for test. It is most common practice to use a microphone as the sensing device since air-borne noise provides an estimate of the most offensive noise. Although vibration measurements give more complete information, microphone measurements are easier to perform. The technique employed in such microphone measurements depends upon the test site. If measurements are made in a free-field (anechoic) room, a number of different measurement positions should be used to take care of possible directionality at higher frequencies. From these data the sound power of the source may be calculated (see Chap. 17). In cases where a reverberent room is available for measurements, the directionality does not offer any problem; the measuring techniques follow the methods described in Chap. 17. A third test technique is more common than either of the above because it does not require any special type of room. This method consists of placing the microphone at a constant distance around the gear in many places, for example, at a distance of 1 in., 6 in.,[56] or 8 in.,[57] depending on the structure being measured. Although this method has definite shortcomings, it is preferred by many in view of its simplicity, and the results it provides answer most of the questions involved, particularly if only comparative data are required.

It is common practice to make magnetic-tape recordings on test stands. Although the initial cost is higher, in the long run this technique is more economical because the duration of operating the test object can be limited to the time required for a sufficient length of tape. Time-consuming analytical methods can be carried out easily on the basis of this tape without extending the running time of the test object. This is advantageous, particularly in cases of gears of high load rating which are quite expensive to operate on the test stand. An important question is, "What is a sufficient length of recording?" This decision should be made after an initial observation of the test object. As a rule, a recording should cover at least three periods of the slowest variation in the noise. The type of analysis of the recording depends on the problem. For instance, because of economic considerations automotive gears cannot be tested for long periods. Tests on such production gears are restricted to a measurement of over-all noise level. For custom-made gears, the situation is different. Here a detailed analysis, including a spectrum showing the single frequency components, may be required. (For details see Chap. 17.)

Research. Since general research procedures cannot be prescribed, the discussion here is restricted to a brief description of some research investigations concerning gear noise.

The first thorough investigation of gear noise[56] aimed at air-borne noise specifications for large reduction gears. Measurements were made on eight 4,000-kw units and two smaller units in operating power plants. Noise readings were made 6 in. from the gear casings in the frequency range of 50 to 5,000 cps at 10 microphone positions. Corrections were made for ambient and background levels. A narrow-band analysis disclosed the discrete frequencies. The application of two different speeds provided discrimination of frequency components which depend upon the speed of rotation and the natural frequencies which are independent of speed. The results show the surprising fact that at an average level of 96.2 db the difference between the quietest and noisiest gear was only 2.8 db. An accuracy of 1 db is stated for the analyzed frequency components. The important conclusion which can be drawn from the small spread of 2.8 db is that the noise from these gears of the same type depends upon specific dimensions which were held to close tolerance. Therefore, the noise outputs were closely alike.

The calculated tooth-contact frequencies did not predominate in the spectrum, probably due to the double-helical gearing. However, certain discrete frequencies could be correlated with errors in the gear-cutting machines. The smaller gears produced a higher frequency spectrum and a noise level 1 db higher than the larger units.

Increased load caused a very small increase in noise. This illustrates that the noise output of gears is dependent upon their design and does not necessarily depend on the size of the gears or their load rating.

It was recommended, as a result of this investigation, that the following items be given in gear-noise specifications: "Total noise," and "largest single note" (largest single-frequency component), the "combined musical notes" (summation of all discrete-frequency components), and the "unpitched sound" (white noise). The first two data were measured, the latter two computed.

The experimental setup for a study of friction as a noise source in gears is shown in Fig. 23.13.[9] A 16-hp motor drives a shaft with the experimental gear wheel A meshing with another experimental gear wheel B. The shaft of the latter is coupled through a torque meter to a loading generator. The bearings of the gears are mounted

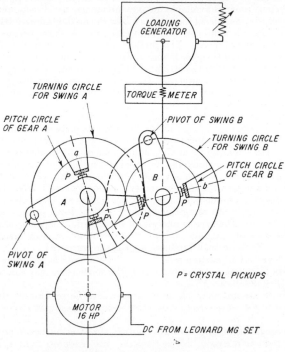

Fig. 23.13. Gear test setup. (*G. Dietrich.*[9])

in swings which are mounted with their pivoting points on rings. The latter can be turned concentric to the gear shafts. On each ring, perpendicular to the symmetry—axis of the swing two force—pickups are installed which provide force measurements in the direction of the A and the B axes. Since the rings with the pivoting points and the swings can be turned to any position, any directional force component can be selected. The bearings were made of a special cast iron and the journals were diamond-ground; the diameter clearance was 0.0003 in. The lubricant was an emulsion (90 per cent water, 10 per cent oil) under 40 lbs pressure. In order to have friction as the major source of noise high precision, gears of master gear quality were selected so that engagement impact was reduced to a minimum. Cathode-ray oscillographs showed that the frictional force at tooth engagement starts in a pushing direction and continues until the rolling contact area is reached; then the pulling motion starts in the opposite direction and continues to the point of disengagement.

An investigation has been conducted to determine which mechanical pulses cause the noise excitation in common automotive gears and what the radiation mechanism of this noise into the air is.[11] The experimental setup consisted of three major parts: The driving motor with a flywheel to maintain constant speed, the experimental gear flanged to a concrete block on rubber mountings, and a loading generator. The three items were acoustically separated by sound barriers; the metal shafting was accordingly interrupted by rubber isolated couplings. Above the gear was a platform with an opening adjacent to the gear and a funnel connecting the gear housing to the platform. Provisions were made to measure the noise transmitted through the funnel either in the open space (free field) above the platform or inside an enclosure around the gear. This enclosure was a reverberant chamber which could also be modified by the introduction of sound-absorptive material. A contact device on the shaft was applied to correlate the various phases of gear meshing with the various effects. This setup provided for the possibility of discriminating between the first engagement pulse and the pitchline pulse stemming from the change in sliding direction.

Presentation and Interpretation of Results. As with any other measurements the experimental error is determined by three groups of factors in addition to those introduced by the human element:

1. Instruments (precision, readability).
2. Test object (degree of constancy of operation, speed, temperature, etc.).
3. Environment (ambient noise, temperature, etc.).

In most cases instruments introduce less error than the two other factors; therefore, data presented to a fraction of 1 db very often are meaningless or misleading.

If the test object lacks the desirable constancy of operation or noise output and if an automatic narrow band analysis is used, the analyzing speed must be set sufficiently low in order to cover the maxima. Consider the following example.

A reduction gear with a bull gear of 300 teeth and a pinion of 51 teeth may have a periodic error in both tooth wheels, due to an error in the gear-cutting machine. Then both gears will have a "bad" tooth. The maximum noise will occur when the "bad" tooth of the pinion meets the "bad" tooth of the bull gear. This will repeat periodically and represents the "tooth repeat frequency." If the bull gear turns at 1,200 rpm, i.e., 20 rps, the tooth-repeat frequency is:

$$f_{TR} = \frac{20 \text{ (number of bull gear turns per second)}}{51 \text{ (number of teeth of pinion)}} = 0.39 \text{ cps}$$

or the time required, i.e., the period is $T_{TR} = 2.6$ sec. Because of this relatively slow repeat frequency, if the analyzer sweeps across the spectrum too rapidly, it may not show the relative magnitude of the components correctly or their correct maximum levels. Environmental conditions such as ambient noise level and room temperatures are the minimum to be put on record.

The presentation of the results depends of course upon the methods of test or investigation and the variety of detailed data. The general practice is treated in Chap. 2. For gears in particular the following recommendations are made. A simple broad-band noise test requires:

1. Speed in rpm.
2. Load in hp or watts.
3. Noise level in db or vibration velocity level in db per sec for structure-borne noise.
4. Test environment (whether reverberant or anechoic room with dimensions).
5. Location of microphones and/or velocity pickups.
6. Ambient noise level in db.
7. Lubrication (condition, type, and amount of lubricant, method of application).

Mechanical data such as gear parameters, alignment, etc., though very important, are disregarded here.

If the broad-band level data are supplemented by octave band, half- or third-octave band data, they may best be presented in the form of a graph as shown in Fig. 23.14. For a detailed analysis, correlation of noise components and noise sources, a presentation like Fig. 23.15 will be necessary.

Such spectra must be taken for a number of different speeds in order to discriminate operational, i.e., forced, frequency components from natural frequency components. For the correlation another plot is recommended as shown in Fig. 23.16. Here the forced components go up in frequency with speed while the natural frequencies as excited by friction remain constant.

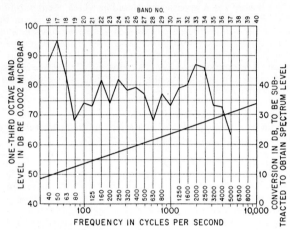

FIG. 23.14. Third-octave band spectrum of a reduction gear.

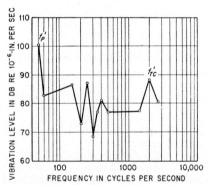

FIG. 23.15. Narrow-band spectrum of a reduction gear, level vs. frequency; f_p' = fundamental rotational frequency of pinion; f_{TC}' = tooth-contact frequency, first harmonic.

Note that at 2,000 cps the natural frequency $f_n{}^b$ (the natural frequency of a structural member b) is crossed by the first harmonic of the tooth contact frequency f_{TC}' at a speed of 510 rpm. This may be called a "noise critical" C, since the coinciding of the natural frequency and an exciting frequency results in "resonant magnification."

Finally, a variation in load is advisable because the influence of friction can be observed best this way by comparing the first and second harmonic of the tooth-contact frequency f_{TC}. As noted earlier, the pitchline pulse due to change in sliding direction emphasizes the second harmonic. An example is given in Table 23.1; it indicates that at higher loads the second harmonic becomes higher in level than the first harmonic.

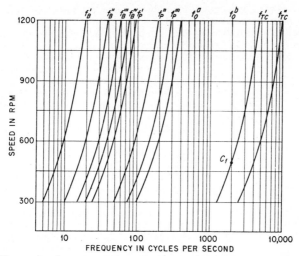

Fig. 23.16. Narrow-band spectrum of a reduction gear, frequency vs. speed of rotation

Table 23.1. Noise Levels of Tooth-contact Frequency Components (f_{TC}) of a Reduction Gear at Higher Loads

Speed of bull gear: 300 rpm.
Number of teeth: 247.
The vertical component of structure-borne noise is expressed in decibels.

Load in % of rating	f_{TC}': 1,235 cps	f_{TC}'': 2,470 cps
100	86 db	92 db
125	87 db	92 db

The interpretation of the results of measurements is completed when every component in the noise spectra of a gear is identified regarding frequency, type of excitation, and cause of relative magnitude.

SUBSTITUTES FOR GEARS

It has been shown above that gears have several inherent sources of noise which can be controlled to a certain extent. Even after these noise-control measures have been applied there may be cases where the remaining noise is still greater than that which is acceptable. Possible substitutes which may have a lower noise level are considered here.

Friction Drive. A friction drive usually consists of two discs of equal or different diameter which are in rolling contact at the periphery, their axes being parallel. In another type of friction drive the axes are perpendicular so that the cylindrical circumference of one disc (a) rides on the plane surface of the disc circle (b) (see Fig. 23.17). If the point of contact between discs can be shifted along a radius, then the ratio of speed can be changed continuously. This is one of the major advantages of this type of drive. But, as every friction drive, it is only applicable to cases where the power to be transmitted is low; that is, no higher than the possible frictional force permits. This sets a relatively low limit to the power rating even if the surfaces are especially treated to increase the coefficient of friction. A very common application of such frictional drives is in phonograph turntables, where low noise level and extreme uniformity of circular motion are required.

Belt Drive.   The belt-drive system has been extensively used not only for transmission of power between two shafts located at some distance but also to change the speed ratio of two such shafts.   The flat belt has been replaced in many applications

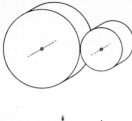

by the V belt because the latter allows higher power ratings and stays in place more easily.   However, if a definite phase relation between two shafts must be maintained, such belts are not applicable since all drive systems based on friction include some slippage.   The "timing" belt drive system overcomes this limitation by the use of rubber "teeth" as shown in Fig. 23.18.[58] Due to the compliance of the rubber, the torque rating is limited so that it cannot be used in place of gear drives of higher power ratings.

Chain Drive.   Properly designed chain drives, in their various forms, are neither quieter nor noisier than gear drives.   In comparison with belt drives, they have the advantage that the phase relation between the two wheels is fixed.   Certain types of chains have been produced in which single links of the chain are shaped like gear teeth.   Since they have no advantage regarding noise, their use is usually restricted to such cases where

Fig. 23.17. Friction-drive, principle.

a given distance between the two shafts can be satisfied more easily in this way than by using a series of gears.

Torque Converter.   In marine and automotive applications, hydraulic torque converters are used extensively.[59]   In the marine field, they were used particularly where gears of suitably large power ratings could not be manufactured satisfactorily.   Now,

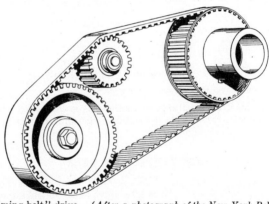

Fig. 23.18. "Timing-belt" drive.   (*After a photograph of the New York Belting and Packing Co.*)

however, higher power gears are available and are usually preferred because of their higher efficiency; although, in special applications, the use of torque converters is still advantageous.   In the automotive industry, the hydraulic torque converter has been introduced in spite of its lower efficiency because of the simplification of operation that it provides.

REFERENCES

1. Buckingham, Earle: "Analytical Mechanics of Gears," McGraw-Hill Book Company Inc., New York, 1949.
2. American Standards Association, Standard B6.10-1950. American Gear Manufacturers Association, Publication 112.02.

3. Merritt, Henry Edward: "Gears," Sir Isaac Pitman & Sons, Ltd., 3rd ed., London, 1953.
4. Allen, H. N. G., and T. P. Jones: *Trans. Inst. Marine Engrs.*, **LXIV**: 79 (1952).
5. Allen-Stoeckicht: *Engineering*, **171** (4436): 117 (February 1951).
6. Peterson, R. E.: *Trans. ASME*, **52**: APM–52–1 (1930).
7. *Westinghouse Corporation, Indust. Labs.*, p. 113 (April 1953).
8. Gear-Tooth Stresses, The Texas Company, *Lubrication* (June, 1948).
9. Dietrich, G.: *Dtsch. Kraftf.-Forsch.*, **25**: *VDI* Verlag (1939).
10. Dietrich, G.: VDI lecture, November 1943.
11. Glaubitz, H., and K. Goesele: *Dtsch. Kraftf.-Forsch.*, **64**: Berlin, *VDI* Verlag (1942).
12. Glaubitz, H., and K. Goesele: *Automobiltechn. Zschr.*, **45**: 175 (1942).
13. Glaubitz, H., and K. Goesele: *Deutsche Kraftfahrforschung*, **83**: Berlin (1944); *ACSIL Translation No. 457.*
14. Ball, H. T.: *Journal ASME*, **38**: 812 (1926).
15. Davis, A. W.: *Amer. Soc. Nav. Engrs.*, **62** (1): 165 (February 1950).
16. Dorey, S. F., and G. H. Forsyth: *Trans. Northeast Coast Inst. of Engrs. & Shipbldrs.*, **63** (6): 267 (8 pp. D183–208).
17. Dorey, S. F.: *Proc. Inst. Mech. Engr.*, **162** (3): 373 (London, 1950).
18. Joughin, J. H.: *Proc. Inst. Mech. Engr.*, **164** (2): 157 (London, 1951).
19. Joughin, J. H.: *Proc. Inst. Mech. Engr.*, **164** (2): 1951, announced in *Journ. Inst. Mech. Engrs.*, London (November 1950) *Engineering*, **171** (4432): 25 (January 5, 1951); **171** (4433): 55 (January 12, 1951).
20. Anstey, W. J.: *Inst. Prod. Engrs.*, **17**: 263 (1938).
21. Bürger, K.: Dissertation T. H. Dresden, 1935.
22. Cederleaf, F. W.: *Journ. SAE*, **33**: 353 (November 1933).
23. Grist, H. S.: *Automotive Industries* (May 15, 1951).
24. Hall, W.: *Engineering*, **137**: 138 (1934).
25. Harz, H.: *Dtsch. Kraftf. Forsch.*, Zwischenber. 110/1942.
26. Hofer, H.: *Z. VDI*, **70** (44): 1460 (October 30, 1926).
27. Lehnert, G.: *VDI Zschr.*, **96** (8): 213 (March 1954).
28. Meyers, W. E.: *Product Engineering*, **6**: 259 (July 1935).
29. Sykes, W. E.: *Mech. Engineering*, **58**: 423 (July 1936).
30. Timms, C., A. A. King, and L. E. Jeans: *Engineering*, **166** (4315): 337 (October 8, 1948).
31. Tuplin, W. A.: *Engineering*, **172** (4473): 484 (October 19, 1951).
32. Bjornberg, S. O.: *Steel*, 46 (February 7, 1938).
33. Martin, Louis D.: *Tool Engineer* (July 1954); *AGMA News Digest*, **13** (1) (July 1954).
34. Wrinke, W.: *Werkstatt und Betrieb*, **71**: 288 (November 1938).
35. Bennewitz, K., and H. Rotger: *Phys. Zschr.*, **39**: 835 (1938).
36. Cochardt, A. W.: *Journ. Appl. Mech.*, **21** (3): 257 (September 1954).
37. Lazan, B. J., and T. Wu: *Proc. Am. Soc. Test. Mat.*, **51**: 649 (1951).
38. Lazan, B. J.: *Trans. ASME*, **75**: 201 (1953).
39. Nowick, A. S.: *Journ. Appl. Physics*, **25** (9): 1129 (September 1954).
40. Pattison, John R.: *Rev. of Sci. Instr.*, **25** (5): 490 (May 1954).
41. Dean, R. S., E. V. Potter, R. W. Huber, and H. C. Lukens: *SAM, Trans.*, **40**: 355 (1948).
42. Potter, E. V.: *U.S. Dept. of the Interior, Bureau of Mines, R. I.* 4194, (March 1948).
43. Zener, C.: *Phys. Rev.*, **52**: 230 (1937).
44. Robertson, J. M., and A. J. Yorgiadis: *Journ. Appl. Mech., Trans. ASME*, **68**: A173 (1946).
45. Sawyer, John W.: *Journ. Am. Soc. of Naval Engineers*, **65** (4): 791 (1953).
46. Blok, H.: *SAE Trans.*, **46**: 54 (February 1940).
47. Kutzbach, K.: *Z. VDI*, **70** (30): 999 (July 24, 1926).
48. Wakefield, C. C. & Co. Ltd., London: "Gear Lubrication," C. C. Wakefield & Co. Ltd., Grosvenor Street, London.
49. Symposium on Lubrication of Gears, Inst. of Petroleum, London, 1952.
50. Linn, Frank C., and John T. Burwell: *Trans. Soc. Nav. Arch. and Mar. Engrs.*, **58**: 385 (1950).
51. Merritt, H. E.: **172** (4480): 734 (December 7, 1951); **172**: (4481) (763) (December 14, 1951).
52. Peppler, W.: *VDI Forsch. Heft* 391, VDI Verlag, (Berlin, 1938).
53. Spengler, G.: *VDI Zschr.*, **96**: 506 (June 11, 1954).
54. Hofer, H.: **14**: 433 (August 1935).
55. Lübcke, E.: Schallabwehr im Bau und Maschinen Wesen (Noise Reduction in Architecture and in Engineering), Julius Springer Verlag, Berlin, 1940.
56. Abbott, E. J.: *J. Acoust. Soc. Amer.*, **3**: 445 (1931).

57. Davidson, R. S., and L. J. Gollins: *Machine Design*, **10**: 31 (December 1938).
58. Case, Richard Y.: Timing Belt Drive, Engineering Handbook, McGraw-Hill Book Company, Inc., New York, 1954.
59. Brose, W.: *Jahrbuch Schiffbautechn. Ges.*, **46** (XIV): 154 (1952).
60. Clark, J. A.: *Machine Design* (April 1942).
61. Drummond, R. S.: *American Machinist*, **82**: 477 (June 1, 1938); 768 (August 24, 1938).
62. Firestone, F. A., and E. J. Abbott: *Iron Age*, **134**: 10 (1934).
63. Glaubitz, H.: *Arch. Tech. Messen*, **56–1** (158) (December 1948); *Appl. Mech. Rev.*, **4**: 457 (January 1951).
64. Graf V. Soden, A.: *VDI Zschr*, **77**: 221 (1933).
65. Hare, J., and R. B. Conn: *Trans. Inst. of Engrs. & Shipbldrs., Scotland*, Vol. **97** (6) (August 16, 1954) *Paper* (1180): 417.
66. Harz, H.: *VDI Zschr*, **87**: 571 (1943).
67. Harz, H.: *Dtsch. Kraftf. Forsch.*, **69**: Berlin VDI Verlag (1942).
68. Kuhns, A.: *Journ. Am. Soc. Nav. Engr.*, **49**: 375 (1937).
69. Kurdryavtzev, V. N.: *Engineer's Digest*, **14** (4): 135 (April 1953).
70. Meldahl, A.: *Brown Boveri Mitt.*, **29**: 284 (1942).
71. Merritt, H. E.: *Proc. Inst. Mech. Engrs, London*, **166** (2): 196 (1952).
72. Mills, K. N.: *Machine Design*, **21** (1): 88 (January 1949).
73. Moeller, Kurt G. F.: Noise Reduction in Gears, Paper presented at the November 28, 1951, Meeting of the Navy Gear Industry Committee's Testing Subcommittee.
74. Moeller, Kurt G. F.: Gear Noise Reduction, *Noise Control*, **1** (2) (March 1955).
75. Monk, Ivan: *Trans. ASME*, **71** No. (5): 487 (July 1949).
76. Schmitter, W. P.: *Iron Age*, **138**: 38 (October 8, 1936).
77. Schmitter, W. P.: *Machine Design*, **8**: 42 (October 1938).
78. Sekiguti, Y., *et al.; Trans. Soc. Mech. Engrs.*, Japan, **4**: 144 (May 1938).
79. Sykes, W. E.: *Steel*, **98**: 34 (May 18, 1936).
80. Timms, C.: *Proc. Inst. Mech. Engr.*, **157**: 418 (1947).
81. Waclawek, M. J.: Torque Converters for Industrial Applications (Borg and Beck Div., Borg Warner Corp.), *Product Engineering,* Annual Handbook, E2–E6 (1955).
82. Walker, H.: *Engineer*, **166**: 409 (1938).
83. Williams, A. E.: *SCL Lubrication*, **6** (1): 20 (January 1954).
84. Yates, H. G.: *Trans. Northeast Coast Inst. Engrs. & Shipbldrs.*, **65**, and *Journ. Am. Soc. Nav. Engineers*, **62** (2): 512 (May 1950).

Chapter 24

BEARING NOISE

KURT G. F. MOELLER, DR. RER. NAT.

U.S. Naval Engineering Experiment Station

INTRODUCTION

Bearings are elements of vital importance in all rotating machinery. However, since they are generally thought of as a kind of necessary evil or auxiliary, proper attention is not always paid to their design, installation, and maintenance. Thus, in noisy machinery, they may be a significant source of noise. This chapter discusses the role of bearings as a noise source and indicates means of noise control.

TYPES OF BEARINGS

A bearing may be defined as a support which is provided to hold a revolving shaft in its correct position. In its simplest form, a bearing is one of the oldest mechanical elements. Bearings may be classified in two types, *plain bearings* and *rolling-contact bearings.*

Plain Bearings. Plain bearings are of three types: journal bearings, thrust bearings, and guide bearings. For any of these types, the bearing surface usually consists of a material different from that of the shaft in order to provide adequate protection in case of emergency. Thus, if the lubricant supply fails before the equipment can be stopped, excessive surface wear will not result. A schematic diagram of a journal bearing is shown in Fig. 24.1: B is the inside diameter (ID) of the bearing shell; the dotted circle S_o about the center 0 represents the shaft cross section, assuming that the shaft and bearing are concentric and the gap between is filled with a lubricant. However, the shaft almost never takes this concentric position. At rest, it drops to the bottom of the bearing, as S_1 indicates with its center at point 1. When the shaft

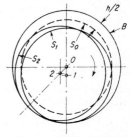

FIG. 24.1. Shaft location in journal bearing with hydrodynamic lubrication.

rotates in the direction of the arrow, it climbs to a position S_2 with its center at point 2, riding on an oil wedge. Therefore, a shaft which rotates in a journal bearing does not have its axis in common with the axis of the bearing. This is illustrated by the following figures: The usual clearance between bearing surface B and shaft S is about $C = D \times 0.001$ in., where D is the outside diameter (OD) of the shaft in inches and C the diametral clearance which makes the gap $C/2$. For example, for a 4-in. shaft, the gap is about 2 mil. According to Fig. 24.1, the actual gap could be, at the lower left side, 1 mil and, at the upper right side, 3 mil, resulting in a 1-mil misalignment of the shaft. A 1-mil misalignment may be regarded as a minimum value. Particularly at higher speeds, the clearance is usually larger in order to keep the frictional losses low. Some journal bearings are provided with three lubricant supply grooves 120° apart around the bearing circle. They provide a symmetrical pattern of three oil wedges, keeping the shaft fairly well centered. In another improved design, the surface of the bearing consists of several elements–cutouts of a cylinder with edges parallel to the axis of the bearing. These elements are pivoted so that the gap between the element surface and shaft can adjust itself to best fit the oil wedge.

Thrust Bearings. Thrust bearings of the plain type usually consist of a plain bearing surface of ring form whereupon a shoulder or a special collar of the shaft is riding. The lubricant is introduced by means of radial grooves of various shapes. In the case of large thrust loads, a multiple-collar arrangement is necessary. The Kingsbury thrust bearing with pivoted segments allows large loads at high speeds, with main application in marine installations and hydro-turbogenerators with vertical shafts. For further information concerning journal bearings, see Refs. 1 and 2.

Guide Bearings. These bearings are employed where the motion is linear and of an oscillating or randomly aperiodic character. Their main application is in machine tools and reciprocating engines. For example, the internal surface of a cylinder in a piston engine is such a guide bearing. Particular attention must be given to lubrication because the periodic reversing of direction of motion tends to scrape off the lubricant.

Rolling-contact Bearings. All rolling-contact bearings introduce rolling elements between the bearing shell and the shaft in order to replace sliding motion with rolling motion, thereby reducing the friction. For this reason, these bearings are frequently

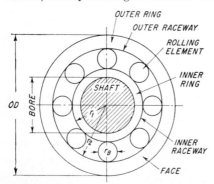

FIG. 24.2. Parts and major dimensions of rolling-contact bearings, schematic.

called "anti-friction bearings." Practically, there is still some friction involved so that lubrication is required. The rolling elements are either balls, rollers, or needles. Figure 24.2 shows the cross section of a rolling-contact bearing which illustrates its principle of operation. The outside diameter of the outer ring fits into a bearing housing or support; the height of the cylindrical ring is called the width of the bearing. Between the outer raceway of the outer ring and the inner raceway of the inner ring, the rolling elements (balls, rollers) are located. They are held in their relative position by a "cage" or "retainer" (not shown for reasons of simplicity). The inside diameter of the inner ring, called the bore, fits on the shaft. For the rolling mechanism, the radii of the inner raceway, r_1; of the outer raceway, r_2; and of rolling elements, r_B, are related by the following equation:

$$r_2 = r_1 + 2r_B + C/2 \qquad (24.1)$$

where C is the diametral clearance of the bearing. For detailed information, see Refs. 1, 2, 3, 4, and 5.

Ball Bearings. Ball bearings are rolling-contact bearings with balls as rolling elements. Theoretically, the balls have point contacts only; but, due to elastic deformation, the contact widens to a circle on a plane and to an oval on a curved surface. Nevertheless, the area acquired this way is very small and the load per unit area high, so that very hard materials are required for their fabrication. Such materials have low internal damping, a disadvantage noisewise. Due to the symmetrical arrangement of the balls, only about half of them carry the load at radial application; the others, which are unloaded, are carried by the cage around the upper half-circle with a play determined by the clearance C of the bearing. So-called *preloaded bearings* have no clearance and therefore have all balls in contact with the inner and outer raceway throughout the circle. These bearings are used in machine tools and in other applications where the slightest play would be intolerable. They have higher frictional losses. Because of the high specific load, any deterioration of the ball bearings usually shows up in the form of pitting or "spalling" as a result of fatigue. This subject is extensively treated in Refs. 6 and 8. Unfortunately, the wear and other damage are restricted to the loaded area, the lower half-circle causing an irregularity of the outer raceway or inner raceway, whichever is stationary. The present practice represented by manufacturers' tables and government standards calls for a close sliding fit which allows, in most cases, random creep of the outer raceway and, therefore, provides even raceway deterioration. A tight fit is advocated by some opponents of this method. This has definite shortcomings, not only regarding noise, but also because it requires a more difficult installation and increases the possibilities of damage through installation and thermal expansion.

Roller Bearings. In order to increase the load-carrying capacity of a rolling-contact bearing of a fixed diameter, a *roller bearing* may be used in which the rolling elements consist of cylinders. Here, the theoretical point contact is extended to a line contact. Elastic deformation takes place, causing a contact area having the shape of a strip whose length is equal to that of the roller. For less strict requirements of parallel axis, barrel-shaped rollers also are used. Spherical roller bearings are also available; they are of the self-aligning type. Tapered rollers may be employed, especially where thrust is involved. For detailed information, see Refs. 2 through 8.

Needle Bearings. Needle bearings are roller bearings in principle, but differ significantly in details of design. Here, the rolling element is called a *needle* because its length is much larger than its diameter, the ratio usually being between 6:1 and 10:1. In general, the diameter does not exceed $\frac{1}{4}$ in. Usually, the inner raceway is not a separate element, but is identical with the shaft surface. Some needle bearings are designed with an inner ring. The needles are not held by a cage. The outer raceway frequently is a thin shell with a retaining rim on either side. Thus, a needle bearing does not occupy more space than a journal bearing. The frictional losses are larger than in other rolling-contact bearings mainly because of the sliding contact between the needles themselves. For the proper selection of bearings, see the catalogues or handbooks issued by all rolling-contact bearing manufacturers. See also Refs. 9 and 10.

BEARING NOISE SOURCES

Any mechanism which causes the excitation of bearing vibration and noise may be regarded as a source of bearing noise.

Friction-Surface-Lubrication. In plain bearings, friction is the most important parameter with regard to noise production. A frictional force F_f is a resistive force opposing a force F_n which pulls one body along the surface of a second body in a sliding motion. These forces are related by the following equation

$$F_f = \mu \cdot F_n \tag{24.2}$$

where μ is called the coefficient of friction. The problem in bearing design is to reduce μ to a value as small as possible. As long as there is a metal-to-metal contact, μ is a function of the surface quality and the characteristics of the metals in contact. In order to prevent welding in the case of local heating, it is common practice to use dissimilar metals for journal and bearings. "Babbitt metals," i.e., tin and lead alloys of very low hardness, various copper-bronzes, cadmium and silver alloys, are among the metals which are used, depending upon the load and speed. In rolling-contact bearings, friction is of secondary influence in noise production. For normal bearing operation, lubrication is applied, i.e., a lubricant is introduced between the two metal surfaces. In this case, Eq. (24.2) loses its significance since μ is eliminated and replaced by the shear coefficient η of the lubricant. Then:

$$F_f \sim \eta \cdot F_n \tag{24.3}$$

a condition of full hydrodynamic lubrication. However, there are many intermediate states between dry metal-to-metal friction and full lubrication. These intermediate conditions may be caused by one of the following:

1. Insufficient supply of lubricating oil.
2. Overloading of the bearing, either totally or partially.
3. A reversing motion in which the speed passes through zero.

In these cases, the oil film becomes so thin that its thickness is the same order of the magnitude of the surface roughness. This state of lubrication is called *boundary lubrication.* If the dragging frictional force is greater than the restoring force holding the other surface and if the restoring force increases with increasing displacement, the process reaches the point where both forces are equal. Any further displacement will lead to a sliding back of the second surface, and the process is repeated. This is called a *stick-slip motion* or the "violin-bow effect." Thus, any mechanical system consisting of mass and elasticity can be excited in its natural frequency or harmonics thereof when exposed to a stick-slip motion. For further discussions of this phenomenon, see Refs. 11 and 12.

Journal bearings with forced lubrication seldom show any frictional excitation except where proper means of lubrication are neglected, as frequently occurs, in small machines. A special case of vibration excited by friction is the "squeal" of propeller shafts in stern tube bearings which are water lubricated. Here, the bearing surface consists of wood or synthetic nonmetallic material. Due to the relatively small load-carrying capacity of these materials, the bearing surface is large, i.e., the bearing is long. Misalignment leads to overload in certain regions, increasing the frictional force beyond the limit of excitation. The vibration is either of the lobar type in the skin of the shaft or of the compression-wave type which is transmitted radially or axially.

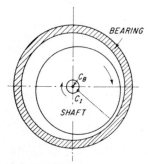

FIG. 24.3. Oil-film whirl, schematic.

Sufficient lubrication may prevent frictional excitation, but another source of vibration is *oil-film whirl.* Figure 24.3 illustrates this effect: The bearing center is C_B, the shaft is rotating about its center C_T. The phenomenon under discussion causes a rotation of the center of the journal C_T on a circle about the center of the bearing C_B. Figure 24.1 shows that the centers C_B and C_T are not identical, but slightly offset due to the action of the oil wedge which gives the starting position for the oil whirl. The speed of whirl is always smaller than the speed of the shaft—usually less than half of it.[1] Clearance, pressure and viscosity of the oil, and load are the most significant parameters for an oil-film whirl condition.

Rolling-contact bearings minimize friction in the load-carrying contact area. However, due to elastic deformation, the contact is extended in area; then there is a mixed rolling and sliding action which requires lubrication. In ball and roller bearings, the rolling elements are held in cages where sliding motion occurs. The excitation of vibration of these cages by friction in their natural frequency is an often-observed but not very offending phenomenon. In connection with dirt particles, this noise source can become offending.

Mechanical Inaccuracies and Failures. Eccentricity is a possible source of noise in plain bearings as well as rolling-contact bearings. It may lead to overloading on one side. Deviation from the true circular form may also lead to overload of parts of the bearing surface with increasing friction values and possible excitation of vibration. In rolling-contact bearings, for quiet operation it is of utmost importance to keep the raceways and the rolling elements in close tolerances at high speeds (above about 2,000 rpm). For example, assume that one rolling element is larger than the others: Riding through the upper half-circle unloaded, no effect will be noticed; but, as soon as this element enters the lower half-circle, the shaft will be lifted through a distance about equal to the difference in diameter of the rolling elements, causing a pulse every revolution of the ball train or roller train. Even if the over-all dimensions are in close tolerance, there are certain distinct frequencies determined in rolling-contact bearings. They do not necessarily appear, but they will do so if certain inaccuracies or irregularities are in the bearing elements. For a detailed explanation, the following list of terms is defined:

r_1 = radius of inner raceway in mm.
r_2 = radius of outer raceway in mm.
r_B = radius of rolling elements in mm.
r_T = radius of train of rolling elements in mm.
m = number of rolling elements (scalar).
n_R = speed of inner raceway or shaft in rpm.
n_T = speed of train of rolling elements in rpm.
n_B = spin (rotational speed) or rolling elements in rpm.
f_R = fundamental rotational frequency of shaft in cps.
f_T = fundamental rotational frequency of train in cps.
f_B = fundamental rotational frequency of rolling elements in cps.
f_1 = frequency due to inner raceway in cps.
f_2 = frequency due to outer raceway in cps.

According to the geometry of the bearings, the major parameters are interrelated as follows:

$$r_T = r_1 + r_B \tag{24.4}$$

Clearance is neglected here because the nominal dimensions provide sufficient accurate data for the calculation of frequencies:

$$n_T = n_R \frac{r_1}{r_1 + r_2} \tag{24.5}$$

$$n_B = \frac{r_2}{r_B} \cdot n_T \tag{24.6}$$

Then, the five most prominent discrete frequencies are:

$$f_R = n_R \cdot \tfrac{1}{60} \text{ cps} \tag{24.7}$$

This is the fundamental rotational frequency which appears at the slightest unbalance or eccentricity:

$$f_T = n_T \cdot \tfrac{1}{60} \text{ cps} \tag{24.8}$$

This frequency, due to the rotation of the train of the rolling elements, indicates any irregularity of a rolling element or the cage:

$$f_B = n_B \cdot \tfrac{1}{60} \text{ cps} \tag{24.9}$$

This is the spin frequency of a rolling element; any rough spot or indentation of an element causes a frequency component $f_B' = 2 \cdot f_B$ because the spot hits the inner and outer race alternately:

$$f_1 = (n_R - n_T) \cdot \tfrac{1}{60} \cdot m \quad \text{cps} \tag{24.10}$$

This frequency occurs if there is an irregularity (high spot or indentation) on the inner raceway. In the case of many spots, the harmonics of f_1 will be more pronounced:

$$f_2 = n_T \cdot \tfrac{1}{60} \cdot m \quad \text{cps} \tag{24.11}$$

This frequency component depends upon the existence of irregularities on the outer raceway.

For example, consider the following numerical illustration:

$r_1 = 11$ mm. $f_R = 30$ cps.
$r_2 = 19$ mm. $f_T = 11$ cps.
$r_B = 4$ mm. $f_B = 82.5$ cps, $f_B' = 165$ cps
$n_R = 1{,}800$ rpm. $f_1 = 190$ cps.
$m = 10$ $f_2 = 110$ cps.

If the second harmonics are included, we will have the following row of frequency components:

11, 22, 30, 60, 82.5, 104, 110, 165, 190, 220, 330, 380 cps

i.e., in a total range of 10 to 400 cps, there are at least 12 possible frequencies of noise excitation not including the third and higher harmonics. The amplitudes of these frequency components are very small, if excited at all; but any vibrating system in mechanical contact and with a corresponding natural frequency will resonate with magnified amplitude.

"Classification and causes of damage in ball and roller bearings" can be divided into the following main headings:[6]

1. Flaking, a form of pitting resulting from fatigue.
2. Electric pitting, caused by the passage of electrical current across the surface.[7]
3. Fluting, a form of pitting in a regular pattern so as to form grooves or flutes.
4. Corrosion, the wearing away of a substance by chemical action.
5. Cracks, narrow openings usually without the removal of material.
6. Smearing, removal of material from one area and redeposition on another area.
7. Indentation, depression by deformation without removal of material.
8. Wearing, rubbing away of a surface by mechanical action.
9. Miscellaneous causes, such as cracking or breaking of cage, broken flange on raceway.

Any one of these failures is sufficient to favor the excitation of discrete frequency components listed above.

Materials. Here we consider the role of materials in the excitation and/or conduction and radiation of noise in bearings. For plain bearings, the excitation is of the frictional type; materials suitable for low friction and good emergency properties have been given above. For rolling-contact bearings, materials for high specific loading are needed—in other words, hard materials; friction is of secondary importance. Major excitation is of pulse type due to small displacements of bearing parts caused by deviation from circularity. The problem of noise conductivity and resonant magnification involves different parameters. Conductivity is usually negligible because of the small thickness of the material concerned. Resonant magnification, however, plays a much greater part in possible noise excitation in bearings. Stick-slip motion will excite the natural frequency of the bearing shell and so will any hitting by the rolling elements of rolling-contact bearings. Therefore, it is important that the bearing shells or outer rings have a high internal damping capacity. If a babbitted bearing shell is struck with a test hammer, a dull sound is produced that decays very rapidly, indicating high damping capacity. Although the shell may be made of steel or bronze, materials of low damping capacity, the thin layer of babbitt metal causes high damping of the unit. If the same experiment is performed with an outer ring of a rolling-contact bearing, one finds a low damping which is indicated by a loud ringing and a long decay time. When the bearing is placed in a housing with a good sliding fit, the decay time becomes shorter because the frictional contact between ring and housing provides damping. The fit is important; there is an optimum—damping is not provided if the fit is too loose or too tight. The latter condition may force the bearing into a position slightly off alignment.

Nonmetallic materials are used in bearings with small specific load where heavy corrosion problems exist—for example, in the chemical industry and also where lubricants are not feasible because of possible contamination as in the food industry. Reference 13 describes the application of nylon in ball bearings for the outer raceway, retainers and seals with inner raceway, and balls made of steel. For nylon type FM10001 with a Rockwell hardness of R118, the load rating is given as 15 per cent of an all-steel bearing for temperatures, maximum 200 to 250°F and speeds, maximum 2,000 rpm.[14]

NOISE CONTROL

Bearing noise is caused not only by improper design, but also by improper installation and improper operation.

Design. Design as a parameter in the control of bearing noise covers two subjects: the design of bearings and the proper incorporation of the bearings into a piece of machinery. Unfortunately, the situation often arises where a machine or apparatus is completely built which turns out to be too noisy for a particular application. While certain corrective measures can be applied to a completed machine, it is more effective to consider noise-control measures in the design stage.

Design of Bearings. The design and manufacture of bearings have become more and more a special field of engineering. Even the selection of a proper bearing for each application requires an adequate knowledge of bearings and their lubrication. In plain bearings, the load rating and the type of loading are the first items to be considered. For quiet operation, it is essential not to overload a bearing—oversize, rather than undersize, bearings. This is particularly important in the case of rapid load changes as in internal-combustion engines and in case of oscillating motion, in contrast to rotation. Particularly in oscillating bearings at low speed, the coefficient of friction is sometimes about 10 times higher than at higher speeds. Vegetable oils or compounded lubricants seem to be most appropriate.[15] Rotating machinery at higher speed ratings should be free of oil-film whirl. Five remedies have been recommended,[16,17] variation of:

1. Shaft speed.
2. Bearing pressure.
3. Oil viscosity.
4. Clearance.
5. Diameter of bearing.

The first remedy, a change in shaft speed, generally is not practical since the shaft speed is usually determined by other parameters and can hardly be changed to reduce noise from a bearing. Diminishing bearing clearance to 1 mil per in. diameter and using tilting-pad bearings of Michel design which are free of whirl have been recommended. For rolling-contact bearings, a few recommendations have been given:

1. Eccentricity should be less than 0.0001-in.[18]
2. All tolerances should be kept to a practical minimum. AFBMA Standards[5] presents the permissible values. For axial play, 0.001 to 0.0025 in. has been recommended instead of the usual 0.0025 to 0.0045 in. for small units.[19] Manufacturers claim that low waviness and a suitable surface finish like lapping contribute more to quietness than the close tolerances specified by high-precision bearings.
3. Retainers should be made of materials of high damping capacity or made as a sandwich structure.
4. A slight thrust is helpful in maintaining quiet bearings.
5. There is an optimum fit of the inner ring on the shaft and the outer ring in the housing causing frictional damping. Too tight a fit increases the possibility of noise excitation and transmission. Too loose a fit increases noise by rattling.
6. Balancing of a rotor should be performed on its own bearings.

It is uneconomical to quiet the bearings of a machine when other sources of noise have a much higher level. For example, a test was conducted at the U.S. Naval Engineering Experiment Station with a motor-generator set alternately equipped with journal bearings and with good ball bearings. No difference in the over-all noise level could be found due to the different bearings. (Also see Ref. 34.)

Design of Bearing Supports. Noise-control measures can be particularly effective in the design of bearing supports. It was indicated earlier that, particularly in rolling-contact bearings, the rolling elements perform random irregular motions causing impacts on the raceways and on the retainers which act as exciting forces on vibratory systems. Alignment requires stiff bearing supports which results in rather high natural frequencies of the structural elements. Cast iron, because of its reasonably good damping qualities, is a very suitable material for such structures provided structural considerations permit its use. Modern copper-manganese alloys with a manganese content of about 80 per cent provide even higher internal damping[20,21,22] and a structural strength comparable with mild steel. However, because of its relatively high price, its application is restricted to special problems. In many cases, the use of damping plates, rings, or other shapes is advisable. These damping devices should be bolted or riveted to areas which are liable to vibrate and radiate sound; a layer of asbestos paper or any kind of gasket material should be inserted. The thickness of the gasket is not critical; a maximum of $\frac{1}{16}$ in. is sufficient. (See Chap. 14 for further information.) There are also commercially available roller-contact bearings with a rubber insert around the outer ring which breaks the metal path. This method is quite effective for higher frequencies, depending upon the thickness and compliance of the rubber layer. The term "rubber" is used here to include all rubber-like materials such as neoprene and buna.[23] A special case of bearing support is the so-called *end bell* used in electrical machines. The name *end bell* indicates a tendency to vibrate. The increase of damping by selection of proper materials and/or application of damping devices is useful if a high degree of quietness is essential. In industrial plants as well as aboard ship, long shafts are used which require bearings at certain intervals. The supports for these bearings are more frequently noise sources than the bearing themselves. A common mistake is shown in Fig. 24.4a. A bearing installed on a single, though sturdy, I-beam, with its flexibility in the plane of the paper in combination with higher friction at one end of the bearing due to misalignment, may cause vibration as indicated by the arrows. These vibrations cause irregular wear and *hour glassing* which leads to larger vibrations. Figure 24.4b is an

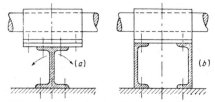

FIG. 24.4. Bearing supports; (a) Wrong; (b) correct.

example for a more stable arrangement which is less susceptible to vibration. One concludes that noise control in bearing supports encompasses isolation, damping, detuning, and limiting the degrees of freedom in the system.

Installation. At least half of the problems of bearing noise can be traced to incorrect installation, particularly of rolling-contact bearings. These bearings have smaller tolerances than plain bearings and do not provide the possibility of being "run in." Alignment is therefore of paramount importance in order to avoid asymmetrical loading which leads to local overloading, greater friction, and noise excitation. If outer or inner ring or both are to be installed with close tolerances, the necessary force for placing should be of the pressing type, not the impact (hammer) type. If no other means are available and a hammer must be used, a bridging device must be applied for symmetrical application of the force; one should use either a nonmetallic mallet or nonmetallic damping piece for transforming the sharp impact into a more driving force. Force should never be applied to the outer ring in order to drive the inner ring and vice versa. This leads to "brinelling" of the raceways and to a noisy bearing. A ball bearing which has been removed should not be used again until a careful test has been made to show that it is in perfect condition. Roller bearings are more rugged, but the same precautions should be taken. Maintenance instructions given by the manufacturers should be followed minutely.

BEARING NOISE MEASUREMENTS

Both manufacturers and consumers are interested in methods of specifying and classifying bearing noise. For this purpose, special equipment and techniques have been developed. The discussion here is restricted to noise investigations on bearings which have passed the functional test, so that methods of checking tolerances, clearances, internal alignment, etc., have not been included. Noise evaluation tests must deal with two effects:

1. The solid-borne vibration of the bearing which sets the shaft, housing, or support into vibration.

2. The air-borne sound which is radiated by the bearing elements and the surrounding structural elements that have been set into to vibratory motion.

Since bearing noise arises principally from vibration which is transmitted to an efficient acoustic radiating surface, it depends more upon the surroundings than upon the bearing itself. Thus the test method for an individual bearing should be based on vibration of the bearing itself. The measurement of radiated air-borne noise may be used as a supplement.

Test Facilities. The test site and equipment are selected according to the purpose of the investigation. A facility for the study of bearing noise sources need be no more elaborate than a test stand for rank ordering the noise from bearings in a production plant. Test facilities include three major components:

1. Test site including the room.
2. Bearing-operating equipment.
3. Measuring apparatus.

Test Site. The space used for bearing investigations must be enclosed, at constant temperature, at low humidity, and dust free to maintain uniform conditions in the mechanical system. A low ambient air-borne noise level is required. "Suitability" depends upon the methods applied and the objective of the test. The means necessary to achieve the suitable ambient levels in a particular case depend upon the surrounding disturbances. For example, in order to stop solid-borne vibration from

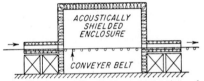

Fig. 24.5. Conveyor—Service to an acoustic enclosure.

affecting the test setup in a factory, one may employ a platform resting on rubber inner tubes or on other types of vibration isolators (see Chap. 13). Air-borne noise measurements may be made in either a reverberant room or a free-field (anechoic) room. The former is satisfactory for measurements of total acoustic output power and is less expensive; the latter type of environment is required for frequency analyses and investigations of the directional patterns of the radiated sound.[23] In order to transfer test bearings continuously in and out of an acoustically shielded test enclosure, a quiet conveyor belt may be used which runs through the enclosure. In order to prevent factory noise from entering the openings around the belt and disturbing the acoustic measurements within the enclosure, tunnels in the form of lined ducts are required surrounding the belt entrance and exit. Attenuation values of 5 db per ft can be achieved in the duct without difficulty.[24] Figure 24.5 shows the principle of such an arrangement. Noise must be prevented from entering the duct through its walls for it would reduce appreciably the over-all attenuation of the duct. A concrete channel with a heavy, sandwiched, steel cover resting on foam-rubber gaskets is one practical construction which has a high value of transmission loss and provides access to the conveyor for servicing.

Bearing-operating Equipment. The bearing under test must operate free of interference by other sources at a suitable speed, which is usually in the range between 1,500 and 3,000 rpm, if no special applications are under consideration. Vibration in the spindle which actuates the bearing must be as low as possible. Therefore, it is not advisable to use a motor spindle as such, but to employ a separate spindle having high-precision plain bearings and driven by means of flexible couplings. A better alternative is to use a belt (V belt) because a belt usually provides better isolation of vibration. In research devices, air-lubricated bearings have been used because of their very low friction. However, their use may be accompanied by an undesirable amount of air-borne noise due to the flow and exhaust of compressed air. Another actuating method[25] omits all auxiliary bearings and is based on an assembly of the test bearing placed in a Cardan suspension (gimbals) with a vertical shaft hanging down and a flywheel at the lower end. Figures 24.6 and 24.7 show the details. The driving motor is coupled temporarily to the upper or the lower end of the shaft until the flywheel is brought up to speed. The motor is then decoupled, but the test shaft continues to

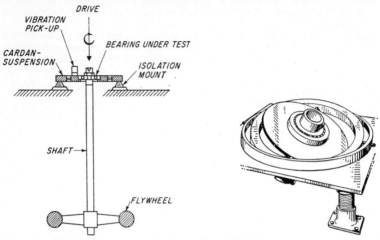

FIG. 24.6. Principle of a new setup for rolling-contact bearing investigations. (*H. Baugh and K. G. F. Moeller.*)

FIG. 24.7. Cardan suspension for test bearing.

run due to the inertia of the flywheel. The rate of decrease of speed of the shaft is a measure of the frictional losses. In any case, the operating device must be isolated from the socket to avoid disturbance from ambient vibration and resonant magnification by structural elements of the setup.

In case of a horizontal spindle in most devices, one end carries an adapter with a slightly tapered stub in order to hold the inner ring of the test bearing. Others use a

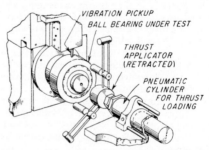

FIG. 24.8. Pneumatic-thrust applicator for anderometer. (*R. R. Audette, U.S. Naval Engineering Experiment Station.*)

straight arbor with square shoulders. The outer ring is frequently held with the hand by the operator to prevent the outer ring from turning and to give the bearing a somewhat defined position by applying a slight thrust. The vertical shaft utilizes the weight of the flywheel as thrust to establish the position of outer ring and inner ring relative to each other. The results obtained by the first method are very dependent upon the skill of the operator and may not be reproducible. If a bracket is used to hold the outer ring either by a wire under tension or by a spring or if a pneumatic device such as that shown in Fig. 24.8 is employed, reproducible conditions are assured.[26]

Noise-measuring Equipment.   In many cases, a noise test is performed on a bearing simply by listening to it while it is running.   The equipment may consist of a conical box similar to a loudspeaker horn, with the test bearing running at the mouth of the horn (see Fig. 24.9).   Such tests usually do not provide significant results.   The

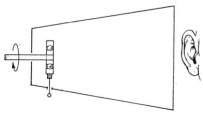

Fɪɢ. 24.9. Bearing test stand for listening method, schematic.

simplest setup of a physical measuring system consists of a vibration pickup which is connected to an amplifier and indicating instrument; the pickup is placed on the outer ring.

A more satisfactory measuring instrument is the "anderometer"[27] shown in Fig. 24.10.   It consists of the bearing rotating device on a base and a noise-measuring set. The latter includes a moving-coil pickup mounted on a sliding block with spindle

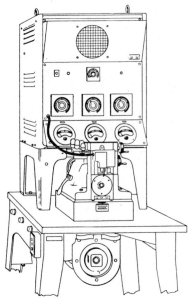

Fɪɢ. 24.10. Anderometer of Micrometrical Manufacturing Company, Ann Arbor, Michigan. (*Chaney, Bragg, Trytten, and Abbott.*[27])

adjustment.   The pickup point is connected to the moving coil and is spring-loaded so that the outer race receives a radial thrust of about 1.5 lb.   This system has the advantage of indicating only relative motions of the outer race with reference to the base of the instrument and therefore is fairly independent of ambient noise.   The output of the pickup is connected to the input of four amplifiers in parallel, three of which include the following bandpass filters: 50 to 300 cps, 300 to 1,800 cps, and 1,800 to

10,000 cps; the output of each filter is connected to an attenuator and meter. The fourth amplifier is connected to a loudspeaker for aural observation. The name *anderometer* is derived from the unit chosen—the anderon = micro-in. per radian per sec, a unit chosen to have numbers of convenient size for typical present-day production bearings. This instrument is useful and reproducible results can be obtained if the bearing is held by a mechanical device.[26]

Another type of instrument utilizes a torque meter and vibration indicator which operates from the output of a crystal pickup.[28] This device may be considered as a consumer's instrument, since it combines a functional test by measuring frictional torque and a vibrational test by picking up the motion of the outer ring relative to the inner ring.

Noise Measurements. Proper preparation of the bearings is very important if reliable, i.e., reproducible, measurements of bearing noise are to be obtained. It is necessary to clean the bearings thoroughly and to wash away all rust-preventing grease

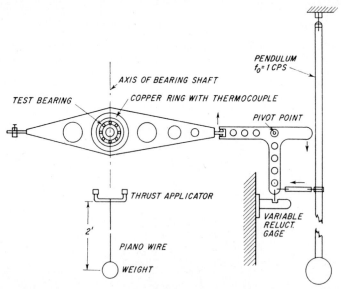

Fig. 24-11. Measuring device for frictional torque and temperature used on anderometer. (*K. G. F. Moeller.*)

or lubricant. A very thin film produced by a few drops of light oil is the best lubrication for the test. This is particularly important if the investigation includes a torque test as another indication of the mechanical condition of the bearing such as surface roughness of the races and rolling elements. With a greater amount of lubricant, the torque caused by the lubricant is usually greater than the torque caused by surface friction. For possible correlation of frictional torque and noise, an accessory has been built to the anderometer for torque and temperature measurements as shown in Fig. 24.11. The bearing holder incorporates a copper ring around the outer ring of the bearing with built-in thermocouples. A connecting link in T-form couples the bearing holder to the pendulum which provides the restoring counterforce. The variable-reluctance gauge indicates the pendulum displacement in inch-pounds.

Measurements have been made of torque and temperature versus time for three bearings which indicate that bearing noise is caused primarily by the impact of rolling elements. These bearings were new; after about 20 min, the curves approached a constant value, but with considerable spreading. Initially, the temperature increased due to the heat capacity of the bearing and its holder. After 50 min, the temperatures become constant; bearing 1 shows decreasing temperature with decreasing torque.

After 40 min, the temperature curves were in the same relative sequence as the torque curves, indicating correlation. A correlation between torque and/or temperature and noise output could not be observed supporting the contention that the excitation is primarily caused by impact of the rolling elements and only secondarily, if at all, caused by friction. However, the data show that a running-in period of several minutes is advisable prior to any noise test. In case of large series of noise tests to be made in the course of production, this preparatory run can be made on a simple multiple setup.

The noise test itself depends upon its purpose, i.e. investigation, quality control, or classification. The noise of a rolling-contact bearing (plain bearings are usually not tested for noise). "This noise although steady is a combination of several fairly narrow frequency bands which could be traced back to natural frequencies of the outer ring of the bearing. However, it is characteristic of the noise that the frequencies do not add up to a uniform band, as for instance in the sound of a bell, but that they are excited irregularly and decay rapidly due to the damping by the rotating bearing."[30]

Details of the correlation between frequencies and failures have been given above under *Bearing Noise Sources*. The frequencies given as an example would all produce an indication on the "low" range of the anderometer. Multiple failures would shift the maximum output to "medium" or "high" range. One very pronounced failure would keep the reading in "low," but would affect the readings in "medium" and/or "high" because a hard blow excites many harmonics in addition to the fundamental natural frequency.

The loudspeaker provides an audible impression which supplements the anderometer method. An experienced operator can recognize the type of failure involved from aural observations.

The simple method of measurement which uses a vibration pickup, instrument, and loudspeaker allows numerical classification, but the results obtained depend on the experience of the operator regarding discrimination of failures. Although it is possible for an operator to achieve great skill in the use of this equipment, this skill is nontransferable.

REFERENCES

1. Shaw, M. C., and E. F. Macks: "Analysis and Lubrication of Bearings," McGraw-Hill Book Company, Inc., New York, 1949.
2. Juergensmeyer, W.: "Die Waelzlager" (Rolling-Contact Bearings), Springer-Verlag OHG, Berlin, 1937.
3. Michell, A. G. M.: "Lubrication," Blackie & Son, Ltd., London, 1950.
4. Allen, R. K.: "Rolling Bearings," Sir Isaac Pitman & Sons, Ltd., London, 1946.
5. *Standards, AFBMA* (Anti-Friction Bearing Manufacturers Association, Inc.), New York 17.
6. Kaufmann, H. N.: *Am. Soc. Lubr. Engrs.*, Chicago, 1953.
7. Schenk, O.: *Maschinenschaden*, **26** (1953); *Engineers Digest*, **15**: 108 (1954).
8. Walp, H. O.: *Am. Soc. Lubr. Engrs.*, Chicago, 1953.
9. Marks, L. S.: "Mechanical Engineers Handbook," pp. 948, 967, 1016, McGraw-Hill Book Company, Inc., New York, 1941.
10. Oberg, E., and F. D. Jones: "Machinery's Handbook," pp. 518, 653, Industrial Press, New York, 1954.
11. Bowden, F. P., and L. Leben: *Proc. Royal Soc.*, **169**: 371 (1939).
12. Blok, H.: *SAE Trans.*, **46**: 54 (1940).
13. Recknagel, F. W.: *Product Engineering*, **23**: 119 (February 1952).
14. Akin, R. B.: *Modern Plastics*, **27**: 114 (1949).
15. Fogg, A., and C. Jakeman: "The Friction of An Oscillating Bearing," His Majesty's Stationery Office, London, 1938.
16. Sherwood, R. S.: *Engineers Digest*, **15** (1954); *Machine Design*, **25**: 163 (1953).
17. Hagg, A. C.: *Journ. Applied Mechanics*, **13**: A-211 (1946).
18. Morrison, T. W.: *Electrical Manufacturing*, 104 (1947).
19. Kendall, G. H.: *Product Engineering*, **22**, 150 (December 1951).
20. Dean, R. S., E. V. Potter, R. W. Huber, and H. C. Lukens: *Trans. SAM*. **40**: 355 (1948).
21. Potter, E. V.: *U.S. Dept. of the Interior, Bureau of Mines, R. I.* 4194, 1948.

22. *Engineers Digest*, **15**: 413 (1954).
23. Stark, J. M.: *Product Engineering*, **22**: 188 (September 1951).
24. Geiger, P. H.: "Noise Reduction Manual," p. 54, Engineering Research Institute, University of Michigan, 1953.
25. Baugh, H., and K. G. F. Moeller, Patent Application, Navy Case No. 14,462, Ball-Bearing Test Machine.
26. Prestipino, V. J.: *USNEES Report No.* 090004B, Annapolis, 1953.
27. Chaney, L., E. Bragg, J. Trytten, and E. Abbott: *Mechanical Engineering* (1944).
28. Baker, A. K.: *Shell Aviation News*, **26** (1955).
29. Styri, H.: *Mechanical Engineering*, **62**: 886 (1940).
30. Kallenbach, W.: *Akustische Beihefts*, **4**: 403 (1954).
31. Mundt, R.: *Werkstatt Technik*, **27**: 41 (1933).
32. Nemeth, Z. N., and W. J. Anderson: *Soc. Auto. Eng. Trans.*, **63**: 556 (1955).
33. Palmer, V. M., and C. L. Pope: *Mechanical Engineering*, **62**: 891 (1940).
34. Unterberger, M.: *VDI Zschr.*, **98**: 209 (1956).

Chapter 25

FAN NOISE

R. J. WELLS

General Electric Company

R. D. MADISON

Buffalo Forge Company

INTRODUCTION

Aerodynamic noise from all types of fans may be broadly divided into a rotational component and a vortex component. The rotational component is associated with the impulse given to the air each time a blade passes a given point and is hence a series of discrete tones at the fundamental blade-passing frequency and harmonics thereof. The vortex component of noise is largely due to the shedding of vortices from the fan blades. It is random in character and has a continuous spectrum over a wide range of frequencies determined by the fan geometry and operation. Since the laws of generation of these two types of noise are different, they will vary in importance for different types of fans and operating conditions.

In addition to aerodynamic noise, there are usually several nonaerodynamic sources of noise in equipment involving fans. Such sources include noise resulting from unbalance, bearing noise, brush noise, magnetic noise, and gear noise.

This chapter discusses these various classes of fan noise and their control, and outlines several procedures that may be followed in the measurement of fan noise.

TYPES OF FANS

In the broad sense, fans are generally understood to be air-moving devices using a centrifugal or axial-flow type of air propulsion. Wing or lobe types of displacement blowers usually are excluded from the fan category.

Fans may be divided into two general classifications, centrifugal and axial (see Fig. 25.1). In centrifugal fans the flow through the impeller is essentially radially outward from an axis of rotation; centrifugal force causes a flow and compression of the mass of air enclosed in the rotor. In axial-flow fans the flow is essentially in an axial direction. Occasionally a combination of axial and centrifugal actions is used, which is referred to as a *mixed-flow* fan.

Axial-flow fans that operate against little or no static pressure require simpler housings and are generally referred to as *propeller* fans. They may have widely different blade shapes and are chiefly used for exhaust and circulating purposes. Although propeller fans are referred to as a different type, they are essentially low-pressure axial-flow fans.

Centrifugal Multiblade Fans.　There are three general types of centrifugal multiblade fans, a division that depends upon whether the tip of the fan blade curves into or away from wheel rotation or whether it is radial:

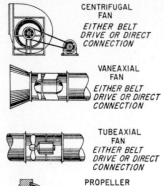

CENTRIFUGAL
FAN
*EITHER BELT
DRIVE OR DIRECT
CONNECTION*

VANEAXIAL
FAN
*EITHER BELT
DRIVE OR DIRECT
CONNECTION*

TUBEAXIAL
FAN
*EITHER BELT
DRIVE OR DIRECT
CONNECTION*

PROPELLER
FAN
*EITHER BELT DRIVE
OR DIRECT
CONNECTION*

FIG. 25.1. Classifications of fans. (*Reproduced with the permission of the Natl. Assoc. of Fan Manufacturers, Inc.*[12])

(1) Forward-curved fans direct the air into the fan scroll with a velocity greater than tip speed; (2) Backward-curved fans discharge the air backward so that its absolute velocity is less than tip speed; and, (3) Radial-blade fans discharge the air into the scroll with a velocity substantially equal to tip speed. All of these fans have the inner edges of the blades bent forward to meet the air with minimum shock loss. Each has different pressure and horsepower characteristics, making it particularly suited for a given application.

Forward-curved-blade Fans. The blade shape and velocity diagrams of a forward blade fan are shown in Fig. 25.2. Note that as flow through the wheel is increased, the absolute velocity leaving the blade is increased so that the pressure increases with capacity as indicated in Fig. 25.3. Thus, for a given capacity and pressure, such a fan operates at relatively lower speeds and occupies smaller space than fans of other-blade type. Low speed results in low bearing noise, but not necessarily low fan noise. Generally the air velocity and turbulence are higher in a forward-curved-blade fan and the noise from this source is greater.

Since the depth of blade is relatively shallow in this type of fan, there must be more blades to give the proper guiding influence through the channel between adjacent blades. Thus, most forward-curved-blade fans have from 36 to 64 blades per wheel, depending on the depth of blades. In addition, the tip angle influences the number of blades required, lower tip angles requiring more blades and greater curvature. The

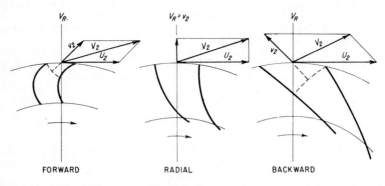

TYPES OF FAN BLADES

U_2 = VELOCITY OF WHEEL TIP　　　　V_R = RADIAL VELOCITY
v_2 = VELOCITY RELATIVE TO BLADE　　V_2 = ABSOLUTE VELOCITY

FIG. 25.2. Blade shapes and velocity diagrams of different types of fan blades.

number is generally fixed by good design and seldom varies more than 20 per cent from optimum. In centrifugal fans, a number greater than optimum tends to produce slightly more pressure, slightly less capacity and noise. However, the increase in weight and cost generally offset any value of noise reduction by this means. Because of the greater number of blades, the fundamental blade frequency of forward-curved-blade fans is somewhat higher than that of other types and therefore may be more easy to control.

The horsepower characteristic of the forward-curved-blade fan rises rapidly with increase of capacity. Where the load is uncertain or variable, some margin should be given in the selection of the driving motor. Smaller fans of this type generally are belt-driven in order to make possible the selection of a higher motor speed.

Backward-curved-blade Fans. The blade shape and velocity diagrams of a backward-curved-blade fan are shown in Fig. 25.2. As the flow through the wheel is increased the absolute velocity of the air leaving the blade is decreased; thus the pressure decreases rapidly with capacity. This means a steep pressure curve for such fans as indicated in Fig. 25.4. For a given rate of airflow and pressure, the speed is nearly twice that of a forward-curved fan. This increases bearing noise and may require careful selection of bearings. The aerodynamic

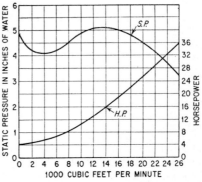

Fig. 25.3. Performance characteristics of centrifugal fan with forward curved blades.

noise is of lower frequency and lower intensity than for the forward-curved-blade type because the relative air velocity between the blade and fan housing is reduced.

The number of blades on backward-curved-blade fans is usually from 10 to 16 to give good channel effect, although in the smaller sizes it may be as few as eight and in the larger sizes as many as 24. More than the optimum number tends to produce slightly higher pressure and slightly lower capacity and noise.

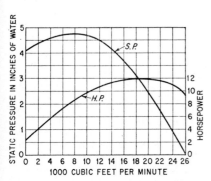

FIG. 25.4. Performance characteristics of centrifugal fan with backward curved blades.

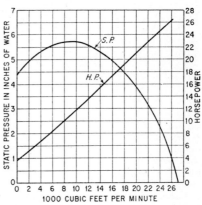

FIG. 25.5. Performance characteristics of centrifugal fan with radial blades.

The horsepower characteristic of the usual backward-curved-blade fan tends to be self-limiting as the capacity is increased. Since peak horsepower is near peak efficiency, the motor can be selected for peak horsepower without danger of overload due to change in capacity.

Several variations of this type of fan are to be found, depending on the shape of the blades which are all backwardly inclined: flat blades, curved blades with the use of inlet guide vanes, and airfoil-shape blades. The airfoil-shape blade has an inherently lower tip angle, slightly higher efficiency, reduced capacity, and lower noise.

Radial-blade Fans. Fans for blowing light dust and other material are usually radial throughout the blade length. The blades are usually six to eight in number and of heavy construction to withstand considerable wear. In ventilating-type fans only the tip is radial, the leading or inner edge being curved well forward to meet the air with minimum shock loss. The number of blades is usually from 12 to 24. Figure 25.5 shows characteristic curves of this type of fan. The pressure and horsepower curves lie between the forward- and backward-curved types.

From Fig. 25.2 it will be seen that the tangential component of the air flow leaving the tip of the fan blade is constant and substantially equal to tip speed. The pressure in this type of fan holds up well with varying amounts of air flow.

The noise from a well-designed fan of this type lies somewhere between that of the forward- and backward-curved types. The "material-type wheel," however, with few blades and with higher shock loss at entrance, is much noisier and should not be used for the higher pressures where noise consideration is of prime importance.

Deep-radial-blade Fans. Deep-radial-blade fans, frequently termed *compressors*, have blades which are usually radial throughout their length in order to better withstand the stresses occasioned by high speed. On supercharger fans the inlet is further modified to provide an axial-flow component which lessens noise and gives added pressure. Much of the static pressure is developed within the impeller proper. To insure good regain of velocity from the air leaving the impeller tips, considerable care is given to the fan scroll and diffuser outlet. While these fans are quite noisy, they may be considered relatively quiet for high-pressure applications. The pressure and horsepower characteristics are quite similar to the radial-blade fan of the multiblade type.

Axial-flow Fans. Axial-flow fans are divided into two classes, one type with inlet or discharge vanes called *vaneaxial* fans and one without such vanes called *tubeaxial* fans. All axial-flow impellers impart some spin to the air which passes through them, the amount of spin depending largely upon the pressure for which they are designed.

Since their blade structure is essentially radial they are well equipped to withstand the stresses occasioned by high speed. Even so, static pressure equal to those of the deep-blade centrifugal fan is not to be expected of single units.

For equal pressures, axial-flow fans operate at higher peripheral speeds than do other types. In spite of this, when carefully designed, their noise characteristics are comparable to the best of other types.

The axial impeller may have blades of a uniform thickness, a hollow airfoil shape, or a solid-cast airfoil shape. The airfoil shape, while more expensive, can be somewhat more efficient and quieter, and will provide higher pressure for equivalent diameters and speeds. For many applications the uniform thickness of blade is satisfactory. Almost all axial fans have nonuniform pitch; the pitch at the hub is greater than that at the tip in order to more fully utilize the peripheral speeds at these points. If these fans are operated at pressure conditions above those for which they have been designed, ideal airflow breaks down near the hub, generating considerable noise. For that reason axial fans should be carefully selected for their duty. Furthermore, some axial fans require careful motor selection if the power tends to climb near shutoff conditions.

Vaneaxial Fans. The chief characteristics of the vaneaxial fan are the ratio of hub to tip diameter, the pitch of the blades, and the number of blades. High-pressure types are generally characterized by large ratio of hub to tip diameter and larger number of blades. Hub ratios of 0.60 to 0.80 and from eight to 26 blades are typical. The larger this ratio, the shorter the blade length, and the greater may be the number of blades. Low-pressure types usually have hub to tip ratio of 0.40 to 0.60 and from two to seven blades. The pitch of the blade is largely a function of air capacity while the number of blades is a function of pressure.

Some efficient vaneaxial fans have a dip in the pressure curve as indicated in Fig. 25.6. Fan operation is quietest near the peak of static efficiency. If used just below peak pressure, that is, in the dip, the airflow separates from the blade and considerable turbulence and noise are generated. Therefore, care should be used in the selection of all axial-flow fans. Many vaneaxial fans have a rising horsepower curve near shutoff pressure, so that if there is any danger of the fan ever operating in this region, the motive power should be selected accordingly. However, such operation should be avoided if possible.

The purpose of discharge vanes is to remove the whirl component inherent in all axial-flow fans. Entrance vanes commonly are made adjustable for throttling purposes. Throttling by this means reduces the fan horsepower below that obtained by straight dampering. Less commonly, the entrance vanes direct the flow into the fan against wheel rotation.

Tubeaxial Fans. Where low pressures are desired in an axial type of fan there is only a small whirl component and little need for guide vanes. Consequently, tubeaxial fans are simple in construction with no vanes other than those required to support the bearings or motor. Tube-axial fans generally are designed for low pressure, and as such have smaller number of blades with greater angle of pitch than vaneaxial fans.

Propeller Fans. Propeller fans are used principally for air-circulation or exhaust purposes. The hub is small and the blades are wide, with little curvature.

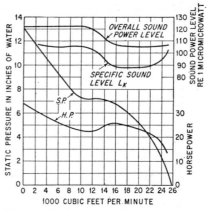

FIG. 25.6. Performance and sound characteristics of vaneaxial fan.

Some form of inlet shroud may be used particularly when the fan is wall-mounted for exhaust purposes. For quietest operation the fan diameter is large and operates at low speed. Consequently they are often belt-driven from small high-speed motors. The familiar attic fan is of this type.

Propeller fans may have little or no dip in their pressure curves. Since they may be designed for low pressure and horsepower near the shutoff region, they are less likely to overload. Most propeller fans operate at or near free-delivery conditions.

AERODYNAMIC SOURCES OF FAN NOISE

Rotational Noise. *Noise Generation by Blades.* Rotational noise, commonly called blade noise, is basic to all types of fans. Every time a blade passes a given point, the air at that point receives an impulse. The repetition rate of this impulse—the blade-passing frequency—determines the fundamental tone of this type of noise.

The intensity of the blade noise and the relative strength of the various harmonics are determined by the shape of the air impulse.[1] For an axial fan, increased blade width will, in general, reduce the intensity of the harmonics relative to the fundamental. The thickness of the blade appears to have only slight effect on rotational noise.

Doubling the number of blades of a fan doubles the frequency of the fundamental. However, its effect is somewhat more important than that. Consider an element of area in the disk of a propeller fan. Each time a blade passes this area, the air will receive an impulse as indicated in Fig. 25.7. This impulse may be resolved by Fourier analysis into a steady component which gives rise to the desired air flow, and a series of oscillating components whose frequencies are integral multiples of the impulse frequency. These oscillating components are the sources of blade noise and consist not only of the fundamental frequency but a large number of harmonics. If another blade is added to the one-blade fan, all of the odd harmonics of the one-blade fan will be canceled, and the strength of the even harmonics will be doubled.

However, the capacity of the fan has also been increased. For the same capacity and rpm a somewhat smaller size fan may be substituted. The net result is that all of the odd harmonics of the single blade are eliminated and the amplitude and frequency of the even harmonics are essentially unchanged, as indicated in Fig. 25.8. In general, for symmetrically spaced blades, the fundamental frequency is determined by the product of the number of blades and the rpm. Only multiples of this frequency will be present. Increasing the number of blades will reduce the number of audible harmonics; but, assuming constant capacity and rpm, the strength of the remaining tones will be essentially unchanged. Hence, there will be a decrease in the total rotational noise—the sum of the sound powers being radiated at each of the discrete frequencies. How much the noise will be reduced depends upon the relative strength of the various harmonics for a single blade. Assuming subsonic tip speed, if the blade is very narrow, all such harmonics will be of about the same intensity; then, doubling the number of blades decreases the total rotational noise about 3 db. However, if the blades are wide, the higher harmonics are, in general, progressively weaker. If this be

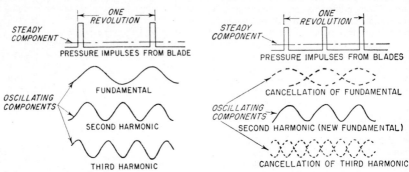

FIG. 25.7. Schematic diagram of the steady and oscillating components of the impulses to the air by a one-blade propeller fan. (*After Regier and Hubbard.*[1])

FIG. 25.8. Schematic diagram of the steady and oscillating components of the impulses to the air by a two-blade propeller fan. (*After Regier and Hubbard.*[1])

the case, doubling the number of blades results in somewhat more than a 3-db decrease in rotational noise.[1-3]

The above observations also apply to centrifugal fans having few blades. However, the number of blades of a centrifugal fan generally is governed by optimum airflow design, and the noise generation decreases but slightly for more than the optimum number of blades.

A shroud around a propeller fan may serve to reduce noise considerably if it is working properly. Such reduction is generally most effective at the higher harmonics. However, if the flow breaks down over part of the shroud, the noise may become considerably worse than for an unshrouded case.[4]

As pressure against which axial fans operate is increased, the maximum sound intensity is shifted from the fundamental to higher harmonics. This effect is not observed for centrifugal fans.

Effect of Guide Vanes of an Axial Fan. If a vaneaxial fan has the same number of guide vanes as blades, the passage of air over the guide vanes will accentuate noise at the blade frequency and its harmonics—especially if the vanes are close to the blades. For minimum noise, the number of the vanes should not equal the number of blades, and the vanes should be spaced as far as practical from the blades.

Unequal numbers of blades and vanes will give rise to product frequencies, but such tones are generally low in intensity.

Effect of Scroll and Cutoff of Centrifugal Fans. The scroll of a centrifugal fan may take the form of an involute where the axial clearance increases directly in proportion to the angle traversed. This is required for a constant mean velocity of flow around the scroll, under the assumption of a uniformly distributed air supply from the blade-discharge area. Such a scroll is desirable for minimum noise. If the scroll clearance increases more rapidly, the velocity at the exit is reduced and the pressure is increased. While increased pressure may be desirable for certain applications, it causes an abrupt pressure change at the cutoff and thus serves to increase the noise at the blade-passing frequency.

The cutoff clearance is also critical. In general, the smaller the clearance, the more the rotational noise that will be generated at the cutoff. A clearance of 5 per cent of the wheel diameter is generally considered as about a minimum, and this should be increased somewhat for low-noise applications.[5]

Vortex Noise. *Generation by Blades.* The fan blades are a major source of vortex noise. When a blade moves through the air a pressure gradient is built up across the blade in the direction of its thickness. If the airflow next to the blade is steady, or laminar, this pressure gradient is essentially constant and little noise results. However, with an incorrectly designed blade profile, the flow may separate from the convex side of the blade, thus giving rise to rather large eddies. Moreover, this point of separation is variable. Hence, the pressure pattern and eddy formation fluctuate rapidly and cause considerable noise. Also, Von Karman vortices will be shed from the trailing edge of the blade since this edge must have a finite thickness. These vortices are shed alternately from opposite sides of the blade. Since they are random in size and point of release from the blade, a broad-band noise spectrum results. For axial fans the noise due to such vortices increases with the thickness of the trailing edge. For centrifugal fans, this is true only if the air completely fills the space between the blades. Also for axial fans, vortex noise increases sharply when the air flow is such that the eddies peeling from one blade are struck by the following blades. This effect may be minimized by the use of curved trailing edges so designed that most of the vortices are shed at the tips of the blades.

In centrifugal fans not having airfoil-shaped blades, vortices can be created at the inlet edge of the blade. Care should be exercised to insure proper entrance angles to minimize this effect.

The hot-wire anemometer furnishes a valuable tool for use in studying vortex formation.[6] Another study technique commonly used is the taking of high-speed motion pictures of smoke injected into the fan.

Air-stream Turbulence. Noise may also be generated in an air stream itself, for example, in a mixing zone where the air stream enters relatively still air. Since velocity gradients must exist in the mixing region, vortices will arise. The strength, size, and motion of these vortices are a function of the velocity field in the mixing zone. In general, the vortices grow, decay, and move in a random fashion, thus giving rise to a broad-band noise spectrum. An obvious way of reducing this noise is to avoid high relative velocities, when possible, in such mixing zones.

Perhaps a more controllable source of turbulent noise is that due to obstructions in the air stream, either at the inlet or outlet. The presence of any sharp edges or bends will cause increased turbulence and noise. Also, the placement of heat exchangers too near either the fan intake or exhaust will result in increased noise. The generation of noise at an outlet grille itself is sometimes a problem, especially in quiet living areas. The most objectionable type of grille, from the standpoint of noise, is one designed to create a widespread airflow.[5] (For further details on *Grille Noise*, see Chap. 27.)

Effect of Ducts. Theoretically, the rotational noise of an axial fan has zero amplitude on the fan axis.[8] This is because any point on the axis is, at all times, a fixed distance from the steady-rotating pressure pattern associated with any one of the blades, and, hence, experiences no time-varying pressure or sound. For this reason, if a duct system is designed so that all rotors, stators, and the duct have perfect circular symmetry there should be no propagation of rotational noise down the duct axis. The axial-flow compressor, discussed below, furnishes an important example of such equipment. In many duct systems such symmetry is not present and the rotational noise is propagated down the duct as air-borne sound. Because of its random nature, no phase cancellation is possible for vortex noise. Hence, this type of noise is always radiated down a duct.

Noise also may be radiated effectively as a result of resonance of fan housings and ducts. Since the aerodynamic noise from a fan contains all possible frequencies in the audible range, any mechanically resonant system will be excited at its natural frequency of vibration. Such resonances may usually be controlled with outside lagging.

However, where possible, the use of an inside duct liner is often preferable since it will serve to reduce air-stream noise as well as duct vibration.

A flaring-fan outlet or inlet bell may serve to amplify internal fan noise. The action corresponds to that of a horn-type loudspeaker. The flare acts as an impedance-matching transformer and serves to deliver more sound power to the room. However, for a high-velocity blower, a properly designed bell may reduce the generation of aerodynamic noise at the inlet or outlet.

Axial-flow Compressors. An axial-flow compressor consists of a sequence of multiple-blade propellers (rotors), with stators placed between them and possibly at the ends of the array. The entire assembly is usually contained in a circular duct. Assuming the symmetry to be complete, no rotational noise can be propagated down the duct as plane waves, though higher-order modes which die out in about one duct diameter do exist.

The vibration of the case in the immediate vicinity of the rotors is responsible for most of the external noise of a compressor, and vibration breaks should be placed near the compressor to prevent the transfer of this energy into air-borne noise within the duct.

The sound pressure of the rotational noise within the compressor, opposite the rotor tips, may be estimated from the relation:[8]

$$p = 213 \, \Delta P \left(\frac{\delta + 1}{\delta - 1} \log_{10} \delta \right)^{1/2} \quad \text{microbar} \qquad (25.1)$$

where

ΔP = pressure rise across the plane of rotation, inches of water,

δ = ratio of inside compressor radius to hub radius.

The fundamental frequency is the blade-passing frequency of the rotor, or:

$$f = \frac{N(\text{rpm})}{60} \quad \text{cps} \qquad (25.2)$$

where N is the number of rotor blades. The sound pressure level within the case is given by:

$$L_p = 20 \log_{10} \frac{p}{0.0002} \quad \text{db} \qquad (25.3)$$

The level immediately outside of the case may be computed by subtracting the sound-transmission loss of the case from the result of Eq. (25.3). Additional data on axial-flow compressors are contained in Ref. 7.

NONAERODYNAMIC SOURCES OF FAN NOISE

There are several sources of noise that are not strictly due to the aerodynamics of the fan itself. As far as possible the fan builder incorporates the best over-all design to keep these noises to the minimum. Some of these may be in the driving equipment which may or may not be furnished with the fan proper.

Fan Unbalance. Fan unbalance may be a serious source of noise. Unbalance results in a complete vibration once per revolution. Thus speeds of 900 to 3,600 rpm result in vibrations of 15 to 60 cps which are either inaudible or in the low-frequency range of hearing. If the fan is rigidly mounted on supports that are good sound radiators, low-frequency tones may be radiated efficiently and be difficult to suppress. If the housing construction is very light, higher-frequency tones may be generated by such vibrations.

For quietest operation, vibration-isolation mounts should be used (see Chap. 13) as well as flexible connections to duct work. For very flexible mounting a high degree of isolation is likely to be obtained, in which case a fair amount of vibration of the fan unit, itself, may not be objectionable. The more perfect the fan balance, the less the likelihood of noise generation from this source.

Bearing Noise. Good bearings are not generally a source of objectionable noise.

Well-lubricated sleeve bearings are somewhat quieter than ball or roller bearings. Precision antifriction bearings can be obtained and in the larger units where the fan noise is higher, antifriction bearings are quite satisfactory. Where the ball or roller bearings are damaged or the raceways pitted, a high-frequency noise is usually present and may be detected by a stethoscope or sensitive vibration indicator. Where it is advisable to use silicone grease in antifriction bearings some increase in noise is to be expected. This is of a recurrent nature and not a steady noise (see Chap. 24).

Structural Resonance. A wide range of frequencies is present in most fan noise. If the energy in a given band is high and corresponds to the natural frequency of some part of the fan (generally flat panels) the resulting noise may be radiated efficiently. Added bracing can be used to raise the natural frequency of the part to some higher value or damping material may be applied to it in order to reduce the noise radiation.

Motor Noise. Noise of magnetic origin may be radiated by the fan if the impeller is mounted directly on the motor shaft. In some low-speed, very quiet installations, the fan is isolated from the fan shaft to reduce this possibility. The usual precautions for isolating the motor feet should be observed. For higher-speed, higher-pressure fans, su h a mount is less practical and less important, since the sound emitted is of lower intensity than the fan noise. A frequent source of noise that may give trouble is that of the built-in motor cooling fan. These fans usually have radial blades, open on one side, and may deliver air close to obstructions. The aerodynamic noise from this source increases with speed much the same as fan noise, so that increased speed will not mask this source of noise. Where the motor must be especially quiet, consideration should be given to the design of the motor cooling fan. Longer blades of the backward-curved-blade type will help in this respect if the direction of the motor is not to be reversed. For ducted fans the motor fan blades do not contribute substantially to the noise going down the duct (also see Chap. 30).

Couplings. Good fan couplings do not contribute much to fan noise. Squeaks usually can be eliminated by better alignment. Dry couplings are corrected only temporarily by lubrication. Encased, oil-lubricated couplings generally give little trouble. Hydraulic couplings, if out of balance, usually show a beat frequency that varies with the slip. Objectionable noise results from such unbalance if the floor on which the coupling is mounted is a good noise radiator.

Belts. Flat and V belts seldom are a source of objectionable noise. If designed with too low a safety factor, there may be some noise on acceleration. Flexible-chain and skewed-gear drives are usually encased for oil lubrication. Ordinary chain and straight-spur-gear drives may be quite noisy and should be avoided if quietness is to be expected. Pulleys for the various types of drives should run true and be well balanced.

EFFECT OF FAN PARAMETERS ON NOISE VS. PERFORMANCE

Fan Laws. The laws governing fan performance, whether centrifugals or axials, are fairly well established. Aside from the small influence of fluid friction and the fact that not all sizes are absolutely proportional, these relationships are quite useful. In the smaller sizes of fans the construction may be simplified by using fewer blades, relatively thicker gauges of materials, and relatively rougher surfaces due to rivets and welding. These features tend to make the smaller size units somewhat less efficient than the larger units that have less surface per unit of volume and relatively less roughness of these boundaries. The law of speed variation is adhered to very much more closely than that of size* and the slight variation of surface friction (which is only a part of the total loss) is indeed a very small part of the whole.

The principal "fan laws" are as follows:

$$\text{Capacity varies as:} \quad (\text{size}_2/\text{size}_1)^3 \times (\text{speed}_2/\text{speed}_1)$$
$$\text{Static pressure varies as:} \quad (\text{size}_2/\text{size}_1)^2 \times (\text{speed}_2/\text{speed}_1)^2 \qquad (25.4)$$
$$\text{Power varies as:} \quad (\text{size}_2/\text{size}_1)^5 \times (\text{speed}_2/\text{speed}_1)^3$$

* Fan size refers to wheel diameter, housing height, or some dimension that is directly proportional to linear units.

$$\text{Capacity varies as:} \quad (size_2/size_1)^2 \times (pressure_2/pressure_1)^{1/2}$$
$$\text{Speed varies as:} \quad (size_1/size_2) \times (pressure_2/pressure_1)^{1/2} \quad (25.5)$$
$$\text{Power varies as:} \quad (size_2/size_1)^2 \times (pressure_2/pressure_1)^{3/2}$$

From these equations, 10 fan laws may be deduced which apply to any fixed point of rating of a fan.[5] If a point of rating of a given size fan at a given speed is such that the pressure is 50 per cent of the static-no-delivery pressure and the capacity is 75 per cent of the free-delivery capacity, these same relative values will hold for any other size fan and speed of a symmetrical series of fans. This fixed point of rating will also have a fixed efficiency within the limitations previously stated. If one of the variables remains constant, its ratio is unity and the remaining variable applies as indicated.

Example 1: Consider a fan having a wheel diameter of 36.5 in. and a capacity of 10,000 cfm when operated at a static pressure of 2 in. and 700 rpm; 4 hp are required. What will be the capacity and static pressure for a wheel diameter of 49 in. operating at a speed of 1,000 rpm? From Eq. (25.4):

$$\text{Capacity} = 10,000 \times \left(\frac{49}{36.5}\right)^3 \times \frac{1,000}{700} = 34,500 \text{ cfm}$$

$$\text{Static pressure} = 2 \times \left(\frac{49}{36.5}\right)^2 \times \left(\frac{1,000}{700}\right)^2 = 7.4 \text{ in.}$$

$$\text{Power} = 4 \times \left(\frac{49}{36.5}\right)^5 \times \left(\frac{1,000}{700}\right)^3 = 51 \text{ hp}$$

The power may be computed from an alternate expression. Since the efficiency remains constant, the power will vary as: (capacity) $\times$ (pressure). Therefore:

$$\text{Power} = 4 \times \frac{34,500}{10,000} \times \frac{7.4}{2} = 51 \text{ hp}$$

Example 2: Using the data of Example (1) for the 36.5-in.-diameter fan, what will be the capacity and speed of a 49-in.-diameter fan to give the same pressure, i.e., 2 in.? From Eq. (25.5) (pressure constant):

$$\text{Capacity} = 10,000 \times \left(\frac{49}{36.5}\right)^2 = 18,000 \text{ cfm}$$

$$\text{Speed} = 700 \times \frac{36.5}{49} = 521 \text{ rpm}$$

$$\text{Power} = 4 \times \left(\frac{49}{36.5}\right)^2 = 7.2 \text{ hp}$$

Correlation of Fan Noise with Size, Static Pressure, Speed, and Capacity. The empirical relationships between the noise generated by a fan and its size, static pressure, speed, and capacity are as follows:

Change in over-all sound power level varies as:

$$70 \log_{10} (size_2/size_1) + 50 \log_{10} (speed_2/speed_1) \quad (25.6)$$
$$20 \log_{10} (size_2/size_1) + 25 \log_{10} (pressure_2/pressure_1) \quad (25.7)$$
$$10 \log_{10} (capacity_2/capacity_1) + 20 \log_{10} (pressure_2/pressure_1) \quad (25.8)$$

These relationships also apply only for a fixed point of rating. If one of the variables remains constant, $\log_{10} (1) = 0$ and the other applies as written. Thus, in Eq. (25.7) where tip speed for a given series of fans remains constant, the static pressure will be constant and the sound power level will vary as $20 \log_{10} (size_2/size_1)$.

A double-width fan is essentially two fans of the same size, speed, and sound power level; therefore, its sound power level will be $10 \log_{10} (2)$ or 3 db greater than the smaller one. Likewise, the sound power of a multistage fan is less than that of a single-stage fan of the same capacity and pressure. Thus, if a single-stage fan is

90 db, the sound power level of a six-stage fan to give the same air and pressure is $10 \log_{10} (6) + 20 \log_{10} (\frac{1}{6}) = 7.8 - 15.6 = -7.8$ or 7.8 db less.

Example 3: Consider the 36.5-in.-diameter fan of Example (1). If it produces a noise level of 70 db, what will be the change in level if a 49-in.-diameter fan operating at 1,000 rpm is substituted for it?

Change in level $= 70 \log_{10} \dfrac{49}{36.5} + 50 \log_{10} \dfrac{1,000}{700} = 16.8$ db

Noise level of second fan $= 70 + 16.8 = 86.8$ db

Example 4: Check Example (3) by use of Eq. (25.8). From Example (1) the capacity ratio, $34,500/10,000 = 3.45$. The pressure ratio $= 7.4/2 = 3.7$. Therefore,

change in level $= 10 \log_{10} (3.45) + 20 \log_{10} (3.7) = 16.8$ db

Example 5: Consider the 36.5-in.-diameter fan of Examples (1) and (2). Assume that it has a capacity of 10,000 cfm and that it produces a noise level of 70 db at a specified location. What will be the change in level if the 49-in. fan which handles 18,000 cfm, at the same pressure, is substituted for this fan? From Eq. (25.7), since the pressure is constant:

Change in level $= 20 \log_{10} (49/36.5) = 2.6$ db

or from Eq. (25.8):

Change in level $= 10 \log_{10} (18,000/10,000) = 2.6$ db

Fans do not follow exactly Eqs. (25.6), (25.7), and (25.8). The radiated sound power of a centrifugal fan, for example, is not all concentrated on the blade frequency as the spectrum of Fig. 25.16 shows. While the over-all sound power level follows these equations closely, the various components in the different frequency bands may show greater deviation. In the case of axial-flow fans there is a wider range in characteristics of the vortex noise, so it would be expected that a slightly greater deviation from these equations exists than for centrifugal fans. This is particularly true as speed is increased. The fundamental or blade frequency exists over a wider range of pressure in the case of the centrifugal fan. In the axial fan, the harmonics are more easily excited and often the second and third harmonics exceed the level of the fundamental.

Specific-sound Level. It is desirable in many cases to represent a whole series of fans with a "specific-sound characteristic" in much the same way as specific speed characterizes fans. Specific speed is defined[5] as (speed) $\times$ (capacity)$^{1/2}$/(static pressure)$^{3/4}$ and is a fixed quantity for a given point of rating of a like series of fans, regardless of size or speed. It is the speed at which a theoretically similar small fan would run to give 1 cfm at 1-in. static pressure. Similarly, an arbitrary term *specific sound level* L_K may be defined to designate the sound power level a similar fan would make when operating at 10,000 cfm and 1-in. static pressure.

Suppose three types of fans are selected for 20,000 cfm at 3-in. static pressure and their values of L_K are 80, 85, and 87 db respectively. From Eq. (25.8) the sound level will be higher than these respective values by $10 \log_{10} \left[\dfrac{20,000}{10,000} \times \left(\dfrac{3}{1}\right)^2 \right] = 12.6$ db.

Thus the difference in the respective values of L_K will also be the difference in the actual sound power levels. Hence, fan #3 will be 7 db noisier than fan #1 for the same air and pressure and the same point of rating. Figure 25.6 shows an axial-flow fan with both the measured sound and the calculated value of L_K. Note that the value of L_K is a minimum near the point of maximum efficiency while the sound levels off toward free delivery. The mistake is often made in selecting a fan for quiet operation well out toward free delivery. The specific-sound level curve shows that if a larger fan at lower speed were used the actual sound level should be as much lower as the value of L_K is lower.

Noise Study of Small Centrifugal Fans. An interesting approach to the fan noise problem has been suggested.[9] Based upon a study of a number of small centrifugal fans of a single design, ranging in diameter from 3 to 6 in., it has been concluded that fan noise is separable into two parts: one associated with the developed head, and the other associated with the flow. The total radiated sound power is expressed as:

$$W = \frac{C_1 H^3}{\alpha} + \frac{C_2 Q^5}{D^{12}\alpha^4} \tag{25.9}$$

where W = over-all sound power, watts
H = static head, inches of water
Q = capacity, cu ft per min
α = aspect ratio (width/diameter)
and C_1 and C_2 are empirical constants for which the particular fans tested yield the values $C_1 = 0.90 \times 10^{-4}$, $C_2 = 5.2 \times 10^{-10}$ with the above units. The constants were chosen for best fit at shutoff and free delivery. While the extreme conditions of shutoff and free delivery are not considered as highly desirable for noise measurements, as under neither of these conditions is the air flow through the blades good, the measured sound power for other points of the pressure characteristic agrees with Eq. (25.9) to within $+2$ to -3 db.

For minimum noise Eq. (25.9) indicates a large aspect ratio to be desirable. Also, the noise power decreases with an increase in fan diameter, until the head noise predominates. The optimum fan diameter is thus that which causes the head noise to just dominate the total noise. In general it has been found that such a fan operates near its maximum efficiency when delivering the required flow against the specified head.

This study was confined to small fans of the forward-curved-blade type. It would be risky to extrapolate the results to large fans. The constants are appropriate only to a single forward-curved-blade design. They would be subject to change if the shape of the blade or the design of the housing were changed. The constants would no doubt be considerably different for backward curved blades.

Assuming the aspect ratio to be constant so that the fan laws, Eq. (25.4), may be applied, it may be shown that Eq. (25.9) predicts the shutoff noise to vary as the rpm to the sixth power and the size ratio to the sixth power. Also, the free-delivery noise is found to vary as the rpm to the fifth power and the size ratio to the third power. Except for the low exponent for the size ratio under free delivery, this is in general agreement with previous investigations [see Eq. (25.6)]. The noise spectra observed were characteristic of centrifugal fans (see Fig. 25.16).

TEST PROCEDURES FOR MEASURING FAN NOISE

There are a number of methods by which fan noise may be measured. Some of these methods are outlined in the following section. Noise analyses are usually obtained as sound pressure levels (for a given frequency band) at specified locations. However, the total radiated sound power for each band is a more fundamental quantity and data should be converted to that form, if possible. Formulas are given for this conversion. Which method is superior depends to some degree on the circumstances of the test. While other measurement procedures are possible, any scheme should be discouraged which permits only "relative" data to be obtained. Such measurements are usually of limited value and often minor changes in the equipment completely invalidate their worth. In general, a method is good acoustically only if its use allows one to make a reasonably accurate determination of the total sound power.

Duct Tests. The measurement of sound within a duct usually requires the placement of a microphone directly in a moving air stream. Such a procedure has usually been avoided since aerodynamic noise will be generated by the flow of the air over the microphone housing, and this noise will tend to mask the sound being measured. However, although they have not been used extensively, techniques are available for measuring sound in a moving air stream of appreciable velocity.

Windscreen. The use of a windscreen over a microphone improves the signal-to-noise ratio by keeping the turbulent eddies away from the microphone sensing element itself.   Most crystal and dynamic microphones have a form of built-in windscreen and may not need additional screening for low air velocities.   However, most condenser microphones are not so equipped and may require screening in relatively light air currents.

In general, microphone wind noise is predominantly at the lower frequencies— especially with a built-in screen.   Thus, while it may not be possible to measure the over-all sound pressure in a moving airstream with the ordinary crystal microphone without additional shielding, it may be quite feasible to obtain data in the higher octave bands which are often the cause of noise complaints.   The need of a windscreen, for a particular series of tests, may be established by taking a few measurements both with and without such a screen.   Correction must be made for the sound attenuation offered by the windscreen.   This may be determined by octave-band analyses of a steady noise in still air, both with and without the screen.   For further information on the design and use of windscreens, see Chap. 27.

Correlation Technique.   An alternative scheme for making measurements in an air stream involves correlation techniques.[10]   Two microphones are placed side by side in the air stream and their electrical outputs are correlated by suitable electronic equipment.   Since no time delay is required, this equipment need not be complex.   This correlation procedure tends to discriminate against microphone wind noises—which are random and different at each microphone—and thus provides an improved signal-to-noise ratio.   The basic limitation involves the propagation of wind-generated sound from one microphone to the other.   If the pressure attenuation for this propagation is D db, then the signal-to-noise ratio is improved by $(D/2 - 3)$ db.   Since this microphone cross-talk decreases as frequency increases, filters are usually employed to eliminate the very low frequencies.   Signal-to-noise ratio improvements of 20 to 30 db have been obtained by such methods.

Acoustic Termination.   Care must be exercised to prevent sound waves from being reflected back from an open end of a duct.   If such reflection occurs, longitudinal standing waves will exist within the duct, thus interfering with an accurate measurement of the sound.   This problem may be solved by providing the duct with an acoustic termination as indicated in Fig. 25.9.[11]   The sound-absorptive wedges are required to minimize reflections at low frequencies.   This wedge treatment should cover an area equal to that of the duct cross section, and identical in shape.   In addition, all walls of the termination should be lined with a glass-wool blanket.   The flare is chosen to provide a minimum of airflow restriction, the area around the wedges equaling the area of the duct.   However, guide vanes should not be employed in the flare section, as they will reflect sound.

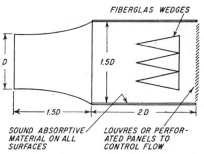

Fig. 25.9. Acoustic termination for duct sound tests.   (*After Beranek, Reynolds, and Wilson.*[11])

Airflow is controlled by means of movable, perforated panels or louvers at the exit of the acoustic termination.   Some noise will, of course, be generated at these openings—especially when high-pressure fans are being tested under reduced flow.   However, for most cases the termination will serve as an acoustic plenum chamber and thus minimize the transmission of such noise to the microphone.

Vibration Transmission.   It is essential that vibration be prevented from being transmitted along the duct to the microphone location.   Such vibration often excites panel resonances which serve to increase the noise being measured.   A recommended procedure is to insert a short section of canvas coupling at about 3 duct diameters from the fan; and to support the remainder of the duct (away from the fan) on inflated rubber pads, which will provide good vibration isolation, particularly at the low frequencies.   The walls of a duct to be used for sound testing should be smooth, heavy, and as nonresonant as possible.   Cement asbestos board, 1 in. thick, is very satisfactory for rectangular ducts.

Test Specifications.   Figures 25.10 through 25.12 show the recommended specifications for measuring the noise of ducted fans, both exhaust and intake.   In general the

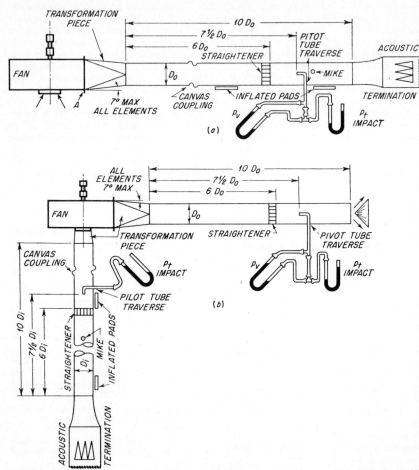

Fig. 25.10. Sound-test specifications for centrifugal fans—single or double inlet with discharge duct, and single inlet with inlet duct.   (*Modified NAFM procedure.   Reproduced with the permission of the Natl. Assoc. of Fan Manufacturers, Inc.*[12])

specifications follow the accepted NAFM procedure for air-flow tests as closely as possible.[12]   The modifications necessary for sound measurement are noted below:

Exhaust Fans

1. Canvas coupling at $3D_0$.
2. Exhaust end of duct mounted on inflated rubber pads.
3. Reflection-free termination at duct outlet.
4. Microphone at about $8D_0$, along center line of duct.
5. Windscreen over microphone, or twin-microphone and correlator, if required.

Intake Fans

1. Canvas coupling at $8D_0$.
2. Intake end of duct mounted on inflated rubber pads.
3. Reflection-free termination at duct inlet.
4. Microphone at about $3D_0$, along center line of duct.
5. Windscreen over microphone, or twin-microphone and correlator, if required.

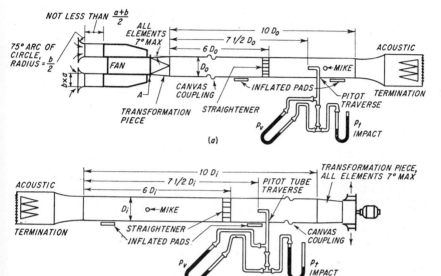

Fig. 25.11. Sound-test specifications for centrifugal fans—single or double inlet with inlet boxes, and radial delivery. (*Modified NAFM procedure. Reproduced with the permission of the Natl. Assoc. of Fan Manufacturers, Inc.*[12])

For any given test condition, sound pressure level measurements should be made for each of the various octave bands. The sound power level for each octave band may now be determined from the equation:

$$L_w = L_p + 10 \log_{10} S - 10.6 \quad \text{dbp} \tag{25.10}$$

where L_w = sound power level, re 1 picowatt (i.e., 1 $\mu\mu$watt).
L_p = sound pressure level within the duct, re 0.0002 microbar.
S = cross sectional area of the duct in square feet.
In the metric system, Eq. (25.10) becomes:

$$L_w = L_p + 10 \log_{10} S - 0.3 \quad \text{dbp} \tag{25.11}$$

where the definitions are as above except that S is measured in square meters. See Chaps. 2 and 17 for further details regarding the concept of sound power level. If desired, W, the total sound power in watts, may be computed from:

$$W = 10^{-12} \operatorname{antilog}_{10} \frac{L_w}{10} \tag{25.12}$$

At high frequencies, this same sound power will be radiated from the end of an open duct. At low frequencies, such radiated sound power will be less than that measured within the duct (see Fig. 27.14). The actual sound power radiated into a room may be determined either by a free-field survey at the duct end, or by a reverberant-field measurement within the room in question.

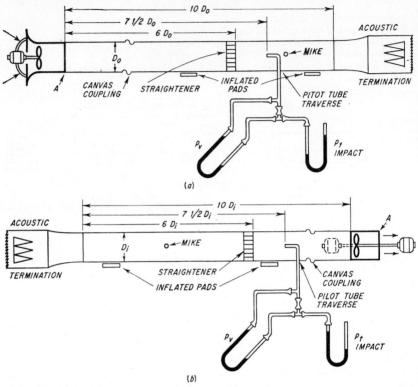

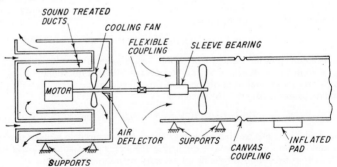

FIG. 25.12. Sound-test specifications for axial fans with discharge and inlet ducts. (*Modified NAFM procedure. Reproduced with the permission of the Natl. Assoc. of Fan Manufacturers, Inc.*[12])

FIG. 25.13. Sound-isolated drive motor for axial-fan duct tests.

Only exhaust- or intake-sound power is measured in the above tests. If the total power is required it may be found by determining the sound power of the fan for both directions of airflow and adding values thus obtained.

This method of measurement gives the total ducted noise of the fan system, including motor noise. If only aerodynamic noise is desired, it may be necessary to sound-isolate the motor. Figure 25.13 shows such an isolated drive applied to an axial fan. A similar scheme can also be adapted to centrifugal fans.

A possible source of error in the above method is the lack of a perfectly plane sound-wave front across the duct, especially at the higher frequencies. In general, however, a centrally located microphone appears to give reasonably accurate data.[11]

An alternative duct test system has recently been suggested which keeps the microphone out of the moving airstream.[9] The main duct, containing the microphone, is terminated in an airtight acoustic treatment, and an auxiliary fan is employed to draw the air out of the system through a side tube and plenum chamber. This plenum chamber is acoustically treated to avoid the introduction of noise from the auxiliary fan. The presence of the side tube does, of course, affect the noise reaching the microphone to a certain extent. However, it was concluded that reliable measurements could be made for the octave bands from 75 to 2,400 cps.

Free-field Tests. In certain cases it is desirable to make free-field sound measurements. One such test is the measurement of the sound at the exit of a duct where it enters a room or free space. Also, certain equipment is not intended for use with ducts, e.g., room fans, unit heaters, and room air conditioners. For such devices, it is generally more desirable to make measurements under normal conditions of operation.

Since sound radiation is usually directive, especially at the higher frequencies, accurate measurements require data to be taken at a number of locations. An axis of symmetry, if present, may be utilized to minimize the number of measurement points.

Spherical Measurements. For greatest accuracy, the measuring point should be distributed as uniformly as possible over the surface of a sphere. The number of points chosen depends upon the directivity of the source. For the higher octave bands it is advisable to use the 20-point array if high accuracy is desired. Coordinate positions for 20-, 12-, and 8-point spherical arrays are given in Tables 17.1, 17.2, and 17.3, respectively.

Hemispherical Measurements. When the equipment to be tested is normally mounted in a wall, or on the floor or ceiling, it is usually desirable to test it in such a position. In this event, one hemisphere of the point-array sets mentioned above may be used. However, for the 12-point hemisphere, where points are required in the base plane, it is advisable to place the microphone several inches from the room surface in order to minimize pressure doubling effects. See Tables 17.4, 17.5, and 17.6 for coordinate positions of 12-, 6-, and 4-point hemispherical arrays.

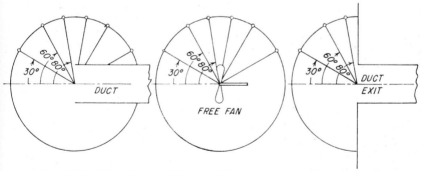

Fig. 25.14. Microphone positions suitable for cases of circular symmetry.

Axis of Symmetry. In many spherical or hemispherical tests, a certain degree of symmetry may be present due to the shape of the noise source. If desired, such symmetry may be utilized to minimize the number of measurement positions required. Thus, for the exit of a rectangular duct, one might choose a single point in each of the planes parallel to the base and hence reduce the 12-point array to four points.

The case of circular symmetry is also of interest. This may apply to the exit of a circular duct or to a free-field test of a room fan. Here a number of points may be chosen in a single plane as indicated in Fig. 25.14. The angles specified were computed by dividing a hemisphere into three equal zones and placing the microphone in the middle of each zone. More accurately, these angles are 33°, 60°, and 80°. If the source is highly directive, a five-zone hemisphere might be chosen using angles of 25°, 45°, 60°, 73°, and 84°. It should be noted that this procedure does not require the placement of a microphone at angles near 0°. Hence, the use of windscreens is seldom necessary.

Calculation of Sound Power Level. In each of the above schemes the microphone positions are chosen so as to represent equal areas of the hypothetical sphere or hemisphere. Hence, the average sound pressure level over the surface is simply the average of the several readings on a power basis. If the total range is less than 6 db, a simple arithmetical average is usually sufficient. For further details, see Chap. 17. If certain measurement points have been eliminated by symmetry, correction should be made for this fact before averaging. This may be done by assigning to each missing position the reading obtained at the symmetrical location. Thus, in the case of the rectangular duct exit, it is necessary to add 6 db to the reading obtained in the base plane, 3 db to the reading in the second plane, etc.

Once the average sound pressure level, $\bar{L}_p$, has been obtained, the sound power level re 1 picowatt in the particular frequency band may be obtained from either Eq. (17.1) or (17.6). Thus, in the English system we have:

for a sphere: $\qquad L_w = \bar{L}_p + 20 \log_{10} r + 0.6 \qquad$ dbp $\qquad$ (25.13)
for a hemisphere: $\qquad L_w = \bar{L}_p + 20 \log_{10} r - 2.4 \qquad$ dbp $\qquad$ (25.14)

where r is the radius of the measuring sphere in feet. From Eqs. (17.5) and (17.7) in the metric system, the above equations become:

for a sphere: $\qquad L_w = \bar{L}_p + 20 \log_{10} r + 10.9 \qquad$ dbp $\qquad$ (25.15)
for a hemisphere: $\qquad L_w = \bar{L}_p + 20 \log_{10} r + 7.9 \qquad$ dbp $\qquad$ (25.16)

where r is the radius in meters.

Reverberant-field Tests. In some cases it is desirable to measure the sound in a reverberant space. In fact, a very satisfactory combined airflow and sound test

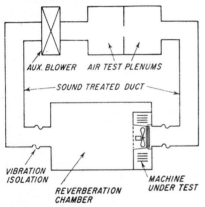

FIG. 25.15. Schematic diagram of a combined reverberation and airflow test.

involves the use of reverberant-plenum chambers. It is necessary, of course, to provide sound isolation for flow-control orifices and auxiliary-blower systems (see Fig. 25.15). This method of measurement is fully described in Chap. 17.

In a large reverberant enclosure, the sound pressure level due to a given sound source is essentially independent of position. Thus, for any particular reverberant room, the sound level is determined solely by the power of the sound source. Hence, assuming that the room is properly calibrated, the sound power developed by an apparatus theoretically may be obtained from a single sound-level measurement. In practice, the sound is never perfectly diffused, so the use of average sound level for several locations is preferable. See *Reverberant-field Method*, Chap. 17. According to Eq. (17.8), the sound power level re 1 picowatt of a source may be determined from the average sound pressure level by means of the relation:

$$L_w = \bar{L}_p + 10 \log_{10} a - 16.4 \qquad \text{dbp} \qquad (25.17)$$

where a = total absorption in the room in sabins
In the metric system, Eq. (25.17) becomes:

$$L_w = \bar{L}_p + 10 \log_{10} a - 6.1 \qquad \text{dbp} \qquad (25.18)$$

where a is the absorption in square meters. The use of this equation requires that the measurement point, or points, be located in the reverberant field. This may be ascertained by noting that the sound pressure level does not increase and decrease systematically with motions of a foot or two toward and away from the sound source.

The accuracy of sound-power measurements in a reverberation room is, in general, limited by the degree of sound diffusion within the room and by the constancy of its calibration. [See Eq. (17.10).] The constancy of the room calibration is dependent upon the constancy of the contents of the room. An additional source of error at the higher frequencies may result from absorption of sound by the air itself. Since such absorption varies with atmospheric conditions, care should be taken to maintain the temperature and humidity constant if high accuracy is required above about 2,000 cps, otherwise the effects of air absorption should be taken into account, as in Eq. (17.9).

FAN SELECTION

Sound-control criteria are usually specified in terms of the sound pressure level at the location of interest. However, if the total radiated sound power is known, it is possible to compute the sound pressure level at any point, within engineering accuracy, for a given enclosure and system configuration. The basic advantage of the sound power approach is its relative independence of installation conditions. Most sound pressure level data not only vary somewhat with installation but also are seldom recorded at locations which people are expected to frequent.

Average Sound-power Spectra. Most accurate sound analyses are based upon measured sound-power spectra. However, if such data, or facilities for measurement are not available, it is possible to obtain a reasonable estimate of the sound power from the rated horsepower of the fan. Measurements[11,13,14] have indicated that the over-all acoustic power, W_A, is related to the nameplate power, W_E, by the equation:

$$W_A = \eta W_E \qquad (25.19)$$

assuming the fan to be operated at rated output. However, the acoustic power is not simply proportional to shaft horsepower, or air horsepower, if the operating conditions are varied [see Eqs. (25.6) to (25.8)].

The efficiency, η, of conversion to sound is not constant but, rather, varies somewhat from one fan to another. However, the use of an average value:

$$\eta \approx 1.3 \times 10^{-6} \qquad (25.20)$$

will, in general, give the sound power level within about plus or minus 5 db for fans in current use. This value yields the equation*

$$L_w = 90 + 10 \log_{10} (\text{hp}) \qquad \text{dbp} \qquad (25.21)$$

for the over-all sound power level, re 1 picowatt (i.e., 1 $\mu\mu$watt) where hp is the rated shaft horsepower.†

The sound-spectrum shape depends upon the type of fan. Figure 25.16 gives typical spectra, and probable variations, for both centrifugal and vaneaxial fans. These spectra are referred to the over-all level, so the estimated octave-band power spectra may be obtained by adding the ordinates of this chart to the value for L_w obtained from Eq. (25.21). For the design of acoustic treatments, the use of the upper curves will provide a reasonable factor of safety.

The study upon which this work was based was confined to large fans ranging between 1.6 and 40 hp. However, other measurements indicate that this approach may be extrapolated to quite small fans.[16] The over-all sound power levels of two kitchen exhaust fans: (1) a $\frac{1}{30}$-hp centrifugal fan, and (2) a $\frac{1}{70}$-hp axial fan were measured and found to agree with Eq. (25.19) within a few db. Also, the spectrum shapes agree well with those of Fig. 25.16.

---

* If the static pressure P, in inches of water, exceeds unity, the term $10 \log_{10} P$ should be added to Eq. (25.21).[9,15]

† 1 horsepower = 745.2 watts.

Sound-level Criteria. Once the sound power delivered to a room is known, the average sound pressure level within the room may be computed from the acoustical properties of the room (see Chap. 18). If the fan is coupled to the room by means of ducts, correction must be made for the effect of various branches in the ductwork (in general the power divides roughly in proportion to area), for the sound absorption of

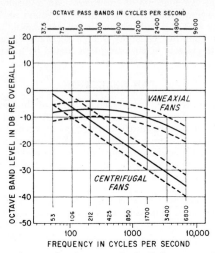

Fig. 25.16. Average sound-power level spectra, in decibels re over-all level, for centrifugal and vaneaxial fans. (*After Beranek, Kamperman, and Allen.*[14])

sound treated duct sections, for the effect of turns, for losses due to sound radiation through duct walls, and for noise generated at outlet grilles.

The acceptability of the fan system may now be evaluated by a consideration of tolerance criteria. See Chap. 27, *Acceptable Noise Levels in Rooms; A Noise Criterion.*

REFERENCES

1. Regier, A. A., and H. H. Hubbard: *J. Acoust. Soc. Amer.*, **25**: 395 (1953).
2. Gutin, L.: *NACA TM* 1195 (1948).
3. Hubbard, H. H.: *NACA TN* 2968 (1953).
4. Hubbard, H. H.: *NACA TN* 2024 (1950).
5. Madison, R. D., ed.: "Fan Engineering," Buffalo Forge Co., Buffalo, N.Y., 5th ed., 1949.
6. Gas Turbine Laboratory, Mass. Institute of Tech., "Aerodynamic Measurements," 111–138 (1953).
7. Staff of Bolt, Beranek, and Newman, Inc.: *WADC Technical Report* 52-204, **1** (1952).
8. Staff of Bolt, Beranek, and Newman, Inc.: *WADC Technical Report* 52-204, **1**: Supplement 1 (1955).
9. Goldman, R. B., and G. C. Maling, *Noise Control*, **1**: 26 (November, 1955).
10. Goff, K. W.: *J. Acoust. Soc. Amer.*, **27**: 236 (1955).
11. Beranek, L. L., J. L. Reynolds, and K. E. Wilson: *J. Acoust. Soc. Amer.*, **25**: 313 (1953).
12. Natl. Assoc. of Fan Manufacturers, Inc., *Bulletin No.* 110 (1952).
13. Peistrup, C. E., and J. E. Wesler: *J. Acoust. Soc. Am.*, **25**: 322 (1953).
14. Beranek, L. L., G. W. Kamperman, and C. H. Allen: *J. Acoust. Soc. Amer.*, **27**: 217 (1955).
15. Allen, C. H., *Noise Control*, **3**: 28 (January, 1957).
16. Young, R. W.: unpublished data.

Chapter 26

NOISE IN WATER AND STEAM SYSTEMS

D. B. Callaway

Koppers Company, Inc.

INTRODUCTION

In residential and public buildings and in many industrial machinery installations noise is often generated in piping systems, which serve as transmission lines to telegraph the noise throughout the structure. Solutions to this problem are usually not simple because of the many sources at which the noise may originate and because of the complex mechanism by which noise travels through the system and is eventually radiated to the air. In this chapter we will discuss piping-system noise in terms of (1) its causes and sources, (2) its transmission and radiation, and (3) general principles and specific methods of noise control.

Although noise in steam and other gas pipes is a problem of practical concern in both residential and industrial installations, most of the experimental work reported in the literature is concerned with liquid-piping systems. However, although most of the discussion in this chapter is based on data obtained in liquid-filled systems, most of the principles for noise reduction are also applicable to steam and gas lines.

It will be necessary at points in the discussion to differentiate between domestic or commercial plumbing systems and industrial piping, because different factors are likely to be more important in one case than in the other. Methods discussed for reducing piping noise may, in many cases, be practical in principle but not consistent with generally established plumbing practices, because such practices are usually governed by established codes which were prepared with primary consideration for other factors. As in so many other cases of noise in mechanical devices or systems, technical knowledge of noise-control principles is translated into quiet design only when reaction by the user eventually becomes sufficiently strong.

SOURCES OF NOISE IN PIPING SYSTEMS

Basic Principles of Liquid Flow. It is well known that there are two entirely different types of flow of liquids in pipes. These are generally referred to as "viscous" (or "laminar") flow and "turbulent" flow. In viscous flow the liquid moves in such a way that individual small particles suspended in the liquid would move along paths parallel to one another and to the general direction of motion. In turbulent flow there is an irregular, random motion of the fluid particles in directions transverse to the direction of the main flow. See Fig. 26.1. The major factors which determine whether flow will be viscous or turbulent are (1) the pipe diameter, D, (2) the density of the fluid, ρ, (3) the absolute viscosity, μ, and (4) the flow velocity, v. These variables are related by a dimensionless quantity known as the Reynolds number, which is defined as

$$R = \frac{Dv\rho}{\mu}$$

For Reynolds numbers less than about 1,200, flow is viscous, while for Reynolds numbers greater than about 2,200, flow is turbulent. Between these two values lies a transition region in which the flow may be either viscous or turbulent.

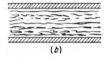

Generally, noise generated by viscous flow is so low in intensity as to be of no concern, even under the most critical design conditions. In most practical systems, however, velocities are high enough to result in turbulent flow. For example, in domestic plumbing systems, typical velocities are of the order of 8 ft per sec. For a pipe of 1-in. inside diameter carrying water at 60°F, the flow would have a Reynolds number of

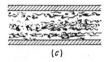

$$\frac{0.083 \times 8 \times 62.5}{0.000766} = 54,000$$

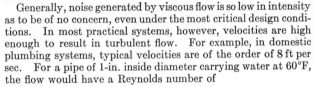

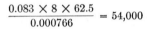

Fig. 26.1. The nature of viscous and turbulent flow, demonstrated by injecting small streams of a colored fluid into a transparent fluid flowing in a glass pipe. (a) Viscous flow in which colored filaments are carried along undisturbed by the fluid. (b) Transition region in which the filaments begin to break up, showing that the flow is becoming turbulent. (c) Turbulent flow which completely disperses the colored filaments a short distance downstream from the point at which they were injected. (*From Crane Co. Tech. Paper 409, May,* 1942.)

and would be turbulent in nature.

Noise Due to Turbulent Flow. The best quantitative data on the magnitude and spectra of noise generated by turbulent flow in pipes, orifices, fittings, and valves are given in Ref. 1. Sound pressure levels as a function of flow velocity at a water pressure of about 25 lb per sq in. and temperatures of the order of 50°F were measured for 1-in. pipe by inserting a microphone through a hole in the pipe wall, thus determining sound pressure levels *in the water.* No investigation of resulting noise radiation has been reported to date. The relationships between sound pressure level and velocity for a section of test pipe 7.3 ft long are shown in Fig. 26.2. It is immediately evident from the curves that sound levels due to turbulent flow are appreciable, even for a straight length of pipe. Sound pressure levels radiated to the air will, of course, be considerably lower and will depend on the radiation characteristics of the piping and support system.

The most significant information presented in these curves lies in comparison of the relative sound pressure levels due to various piping components. For a straight pipe, an open gate valve, four 90° elbows, and an open globe valve, the increase in over-all noise level with velocity of water flow follows a smooth curve. The relative levels for these components increase in the order in which they are listed above, and open globe valves (which are the type commonly used in domestic and commercial plumbing) are significantly noisier than the other components at all velocities.

In Ref. 1 a study was made of the noise generated by orifices in 1-in. pipe. Results for one orifice having an open area one-fourth that of the pipe are plotted in Fig. 26.2. Noise levels are considerably higher than those for the components mentioned above, and furthermore exhibit a sharp discontinuity at a particular velocity. It has been shown that this critical velocity decreases with decreasing area of the orifice, and it is believed that the break in the curve is associated with the onset of cavitation, a phenomenon which will be discussed later;[1] the break in the curve was always associated with a sudden increase in level of noise radiated to the air by the test pipe.

Figure 26.2 also shows over-all sound levels in the pipe as a function of flow velocity for two different globe valves when partially open. This is, of course, a condition commonly encountered in practice. While there was some difference for the two

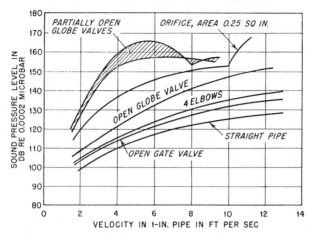

FIG. 26.2. Sound pressure levels, in decibels, as a function of linear velocity for water flowing in a 1-in. pipe. Sound pressure levels were measured in the water by means of a microphone inserted through the pipe wall. (*After Rogers.*[1])

valves, the most striking fact is that both were by far the noisiest of the components tested. At 5 ft per sec, for example, the sound level for the partially open globe valves was 40 to 50 db higher than for the straight pipe. These data confirm that in typical plumbing installations valves usually are the most significant noise sources.

The effect of flow velocity on the frequency spectrum of the noise of various plumbing components has been investigated.[1] Some such data are summarized in Fig. 26.3. Octave-band level curves for straight pipe and for standard elbows are quite similar in shape, with most of the sound energy in the octave bands below 600 cps. On the other hand, the octave-band level curves for orifices and partially opened valves are generally similar and contain relatively little low-frequency energy. The greater energy content at high frequencies for valves and orifices, combined with the fact that high-frequency sounds (1) are more readily radiated and (2) sound louder to the ear, emphasizes the importance of such fittings in noise-reduction studies.

Noise Due to Cavitation. Although most of the noise in plumbing systems is probably due to turbulent flow, conditions sometimes exist, particularly in nearly closed valves, which give rise to the phenomenon of *cavitation*, which results in greatly increased noise levels.

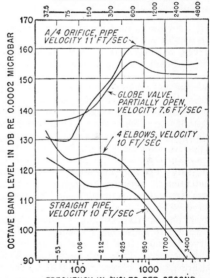

FIG. 26.3. Octave-band spectra for various piping components. Sound pressure levels were measured in the water in a 1-in. pipe by means of a microphone inserted through the pipe wall. (*After Rogers.*[1])

Cavitation occurs at flow velocities which are quite critical for a particular system but which are difficult to predict because the onset of cavitation is also a function of static pressure, temperature, and the geometric configuration of the system. In order for cavitation to occur, a local restriction in the flow path must exist which results in localized high velocities and low pressures.

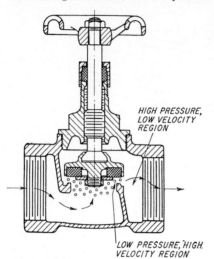

HIGH PRESSURE,
LOW VELOCITY
REGION

LOW PRESSURE, HIGH
VELOCITY REGION

FIG. 26.4. Schematic view of a globe valve showing regions of high-velocity flow with partial valve opening, which results in cavitation noise.

At a particular velocity, pressure falls low enough so that vapor bubbles are formed. As these bubbles move past the restriction, velocity decreases and pressure increases, resulting in the sudden collapse of the bubbles, with extreme local-pressure fluctuations. The cutaway section of a typical globe valve in Fig. 26.4 shows how cavitation can occur in a practical plumbing-system component.

Very little quantitative data on noise levels due to cavitation in piping-system components can be found in the literature. Measurements on air-borne noise produced by a domestic type of valve for two slightly different rates of flow suggest that the difference in noise at the two flow rates is due to cavitation.[2] These data are reproduced in Fig. 26.5. In the test system used, a ½-in. pipe was rigidly attached to a wall panel installed in an opening between two reverberant rooms. Air-borne noise levels in frequency bands ⅓ octave wide were measured in the reverberant room opposite the side of the panel to which the piping system was attached. The measurements reported are, therefore, a function of radiation characteristics of the test panel supporting the pipe. The relative levels between the two curves, however, are an indication of the effect of cavitation on noise radiated to the air. Curve A presents the measurements with the valve delivering 4.7 gallons per min, while curve B represents the noise when the valve was delivering 4.8 gallons per min. A relatively large decrease in noise level with a small increase in rate of flow due to increasing the valve opening suggests that cavitation was occurring inside the valve. Increasing the valve opening apparently resulted in decreasing the pressure drop across the valve, thus eliminating cavitation and decreasing the noise level. It should be noted that the curve representing cavitation noise slopes upward with increasing frequency, while the curve for flow rate below that producing cavitation varies little with frequency. This confirms typical observations that a nearly closed faucet often produces a hissing or singing noise, which disappears when the faucet is opened further. For frequencies above 1,000 cps, the increase in noise level due to cavitation is large—actually more than 20 db at some frequencies. Considerable attention has been given in Europe to design of plumbing fittings which will not produce cavitation at normal flow velocities. Some results of these studies will be discussed in a later section.

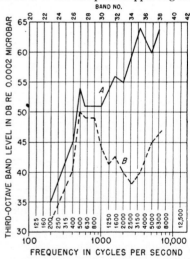

FIG. 26.5. Frequency spectrum in third-octave bands for a globe-type valve at two rates of flow. Air-borne noise levels radiated by the supporting panel were measured. Curve A is for a flow rate of 4.7 gallons per min. Curve B for a flow rate of 4.8 gallons per min. (*After Ingerslev.*[2])

Water Hammer. The sharp, intense noise known as *water hammer* occurs when steady flow in a liquid distribution system is suddenly interrupted, for example, by closing a quick-action valve. With the fluid in motion throughout the whole piping system, the momentum, even at relatively low flow velocities, can be great. Since most liquids are essentially incompressible, the sudden interruption of flow results in extremely sharp pressure rise at the point of interruption, and the entire distribution system is shock-excited into vibration. The steep wave front of the shock excitation can be reflected numerous times back and forth through various parts of the system until the energy finally is dissipated. Methods for dealing with this type of noise are simple and relatively effective, as will be pointed out later.

Mechanical Noises Excited by Fluid Flow. Noise in piping installations at relatively low flow velocities is frequently due to mechanical resonances in parts such as valves and pumps. Smooth flow of fluid past part of a fitting such as a valve seat or its stem extending into the liquid stream can excite the part into vibration, resulting in a steady noise of a nearly pure tone. Proper attention to stiffness and support for movable parts should eliminate such problems. In steam and gas systems, valves and other fittings can behave as Helmholtz resonators, resulting in very intense noise.

Mechanical Noises Due to Pumps. Noise in piping systems is often generated by the operation of rotating equipment such as pumps. Such devices have vibrating components in close mechanical contact with the fluid or the pipe wall, with resulting high energy transfer to the piping system. Often noise due to such sources consists mostly of pure tones associated with the rotation speed of the pump or motor. While some manufacturers of such devices have given attention to methods of designing quiet equipment, most of the work has been on an empirical basis, and few quantitative performance data are available.

TRANSMISSION OF NOISE THROUGH PIPING SYSTEMS AND RADIATION OF NOISE TO THE AIR

The most common sources of mechanical energy responsible for generation of noise in piping systems have been discussed. Very seldom, however, is the noise radiated to the air directly from its source. It is usually the case that the piping system transmits noise readily and that this mechanical noise energy follows complicated flow paths through the pipe and its support system to surfaces which eventually radiate the noise. Information on the nature of noise transmission in piping and support systems is essential in attempting to reduce radiated noise using currently available piping components.

A piping system containing a localized source of noise was studied to determine its natural modes of vibration and its noise-transmission characteristics.[3] In a series of experiments with a 53-ft length of 2-in. pipe, water-filled and supported by a soft-rubber suspension system, single-tone sound energy was introduced at one end of the pipe both into the water and into the pipe wall. It was found that the damping in the system was so low as to be almost negligible, both for vibrations in the water column and in the pipe wall. Noise attenuation in the range of 0.001 to 0.1 db per ft was observed for different types of vibrations at different frequencies.

It was also found that longitudinal vibrations in the water column were closely coupled to the pipe wall and excited both longitudinal and flexural vibrations in the pipe. It was concluded that for frequencies below 1,000 cps flexural vibration modes are most important in transmission of noise through a piping system, regardless of the source and type of exciting energy. From this study it is apparent that any noise-reducing device installed in a piping system, such as a flexible coupling, must absorb or attenuate noise energy transmitted not only through the pipe wall but through the water as well. If only one of these paths is interrupted, the other will remain as an effective short circuit, and noise energy will be fed into the system beyond the noise-reducing device.

In domestic and commercial piping systems where pipe sizes smaller than a few inches in diameter are usually encountered, noise radiated to the air by the pipe itself is nearly always negligible compared with that transmitted to and radiated by the supporting structure. In such systems, therefore, noise reduction can best be achieved either by interrupting the flow of noise energy from its source into the piping system or by isolating the pipe system from the structure supporting it. In industrial piping systems, however, where the pipe diameter may be several feet and where noise levels in the fluid may be very intense, appreciable noise can be radiated by the pipe walls. Usually in such systems the support structure will be extremely massive in comparison to the pipe and will radiate proportionally little noise. In such systems more noise reduction can be expected from properly designed lagging or pipe covering than from isolating hangers which decouple the pipe from its supports. Some data on the effectiveness of various noise-reducing devices will be presented below.

METHODS FOR NOISE REDUCTION

Damping Devices. Since typical piping systems possess little inherent damping, it might be expected that transmission of noise through such systems can be appreciably decreased by introduction of damping treatment or devices. Consideration of the amount of damping required to produce appreciable noise attenuation, however, reveals that this is not a particularly hopeful method for attacking the problem.

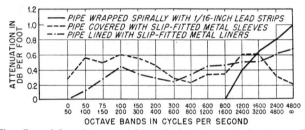

FIG. 26.6. The effect of damping material in reducing pipe-wall vibrations. The damping treatment was applied to the entire test pipe and measurements of pipe-wall vibrations made at points 18 feet apart. The difference in vibration levels at these two points is expressed in terms of decibels reduction per foot. (*After Callaway, Hardy, and Tyzzer.*[4])

Experiments have been made to determine the damping obtained by wrapping a 2-in. pipe with $\frac{1}{16}$-in.-thick lead strips and by covering and lining the pipe with slip-fitted metal sleeves.[4] The attenuation achieved by these treatments for various octave bands, in decibels per foot, is shown in Fig. 26.6. Most of the values are below 0.6 db per ft, so that great lengths of pipe would require treatment in order to achieve appreciable noise reduction. One type of plastic pipe was also tested and was found to give negligible noise reduction. Since the experiments were performed on a system having very little damping before treatment, reductions which might be expected in a practical system with higher original damping may be even smaller than those which the test results reported.

Flexible Connections. Many types of flexible connectors for use in piping systems are available commercially. Noise reduction is claimed as a feature for several, but quantitative data on their noise-reducing performance are usually not available from the manufacturer. Most commercial types of flexible coupling are designed to permit relative motion between two sections of pipe or to allow for misalignment between two pipe sections, and not primarily for noise reduction. Five types of commercial couplings were evaluated with the performance characteristics shown in Fig. 26.7.[4] For these tests, noise energy was introduced into the pipe wall on one side of the test coupling and noise measurements made on opposite sides of the coupling to determine the noise reduction in decibels. Comparable results were obtained when noise was introduced into the water column.

The results reported were for the system under atmospheric pressure. It is pointed out by the authors that many types of commercial devices which are effective at low pressures may become stiff and ineffective at high operating pressures. This was found to be particularly true for couplings of the type designated "number 3" in Fig. 26.7, which became quite ineffective in the range of pressures normally encountered in commercial systems. One type of coupling, however, which was designed for shipboard use was found to give essentially the same results for a wide range of operating pressures.[5]

Actually, none of the commercial couplings tested was as effective for noise reduction as a section of rubber-and-fabric hose a few feet long. Noise attenuation of

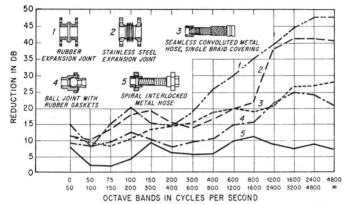

FIG. 26.7. Reduction in pipe-wall vibration levels by various types of commercial flexible couplings. Pipe-wall excitation was used with the system at atmospheric pressure. (*After Callaway, Hardy, and Tyzzer.*[4])

17 db per ft at 200 cps and of 30 db per ft at 1,000 cps has been obtained with canvas-reinforced rubber tubes 1 to 1½ in. in diameter.[6] Measured attenuations of 2.3 db per ft at 200 cps and of 5.5 db per ft at 1,000 cps for similar tubes about 2 in. in diameter are reported by another investigator.[7] The difference in reported results is probably due to differences in measurement methods; both reports, however, indicate sizable noise reduction for this type of flexible connector. The obvious objection to such a noise-reducing device is that its physical condition may deteriorate with time, resulting in leaks which will cause structural damage.

Extensive experimental work on the effectiveness of various types and configurations of flexible couplings has been conducted.[8] As a result of these studies, some manufacturers of commercial flexible connectors are adding data on noise reduction to their sales literature.

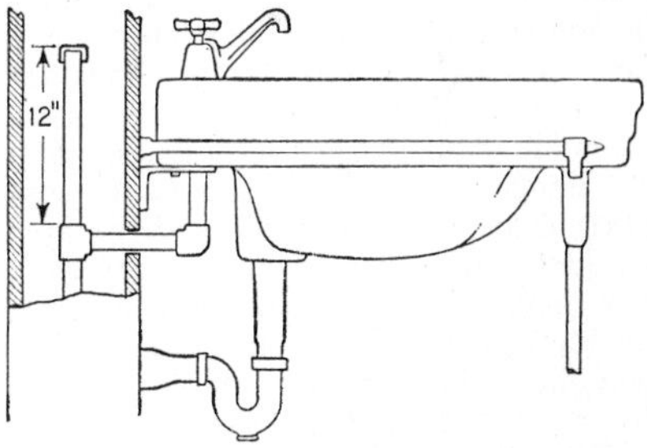

Shock-absorbing Devices. One type of noise in plumbing systems, mentioned earlier, was water hammer due to sudden interruption of fluid flow. Much could be done in design of valves and other flow-control devices to assure that flow is terminated slowly even though the valve is closed rapidly. In this regard, globe valves are generally superior to gate valves, although the former tend to generate more noise due to turbulence and cavitation.

FIG. 26.8. Installation of pressure-relief stubs near a faucet to eliminate water hammer noise.

An effective way to eliminate noise due to water hammer, regardless of the type of valves used, is the installation of shock-absorbing chambers near control valves. In many areas it is common practice to install a vertical pipe stub in the system near faucets in a manner similar to that shown in Fig. 26.8. The air entrapped in the stub

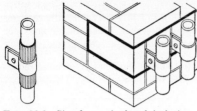

Fig. 26.9. Simple methods of isolating a pipe system from its supports. (*After Wagner.*[15])

provides a cushion to absorb shock due to sudden valve closure. Reports that such devices are ineffective appear to be due to the fact that in time the stub becomes filled with water and no longer functions as designed. This condition can be corrected simply by draining the entire system periodically. Flexible connections installed to prevent transmission of noise through a piping system can also serve as shock-absorbing devices if they are of such a design as to provide pressure relief and if they are installed at a location close to the valve at which the shock originates.

Isolating Supports. In piping systems utilizing pipe sizes a few inches in diameter or smaller, such as those customarily found in residential and commercial installations,

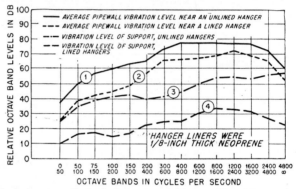

Fig. 26.10. Typical test results for isolating hanger liners. The difference between curves 1 and 2 shows the damping effect due to the liners tested. The difference between curves 3 and 4 shows the total damping and isolating effect for this particular liner. (*After Callaway, Hardy, and Tyzzer.*[4])

isolation of the pipe system from its supporting structure by means of resilient mountings provides one of the most effective methods for reduction of noise radiated to the air. One of the simplest methods for achieving such isolation is the use of resilient liners between the pipe itself and the hanger which connects it to the support structure. Examples of isolated hangers of this simple type are shown in Fig. 26.9. Some data have been obtained on the effectiveness of such liners in decoupling vibrations of a piping system from the support structure.[4]

Figure 26.10 shows relative vibration levels with and without hanger liners of ⅛-in. thick neoprene. Curve 1 shows vibration levels in the pipe wall near an unlined hanger. Curve 2 shows vibration levels at the same point after lining the hanger with neoprene. There were five such hangers in the test pipe, and this reduction indicates that they added some damping in the mechanical system.

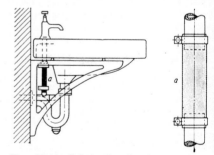

Fig. 26.11. Schematics showing construction and installation detail for a flexible connector near a faucet. Such a device can prevent noise from the piping system from being radiated by the sink and also prevents noise generated at the faucet from being transmitted back into the piping system. (*After Wagner.*[15])

Curve 3 shows vibration levels in the massive steel supports to which the hangers were attached before insertion of the hanger liners. Curve 4 shows vibration levels in the support after addition of the liners. Comparison of curves 3 and 4 indicates the extent of noise reduction which can be expected by use of hanger liners of this type.

These measurements were made with a support system for the pipe which was much more massive than customarily found in residential installations. As in the case of vibration isolators, noise reduction calculated from theory which assumes that the mounts are attached to a structure possessing infinite mass will not be achieved in practice if the isolator is connected to a flexible support structure. As a general rule, in plumbing installations the number of hangers used to support a system should be kept at a minimum consistent with structural requirements, and hangers should be attached to massive building members rather than to lightweight panels.

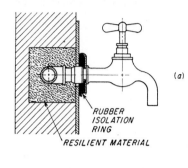

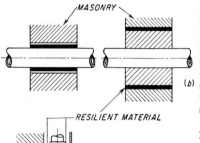

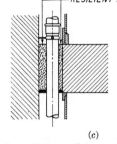

(a)

(b)

(c)

RUBBER ISOLATION RING

RESILIENT MATERIAL

MASONRY

RESILIENT MATERIAL

The same principles and theory which apply to vibration isolators are applicable to hangers for piping systems. In addition, attention must be given to decoupling fittings such as faucets from their support structures or to insertion of noise-attenuating devices close to fittings. Examples of methods for decoupling pipes and faucets from structures which could act as radiating surfaces are shown in Figs. 26.11 and 26.12.

Pipe-wall Lagging and Covering. Since pipes of the sizes used in residential installa-

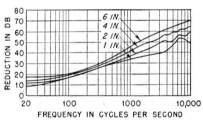

FIG. 26.12. *a.* Schematic showing isolation of a faucet from its supporting structure. *b.* and *c.* Methods of isolating pipes from walls through which they pass. (*After Wagner.*[15])

FIG. 26.13. Calculated noise reduction due to covering a pipe with various thicknesses of 6 lb per cu ft glass fiber and an impervious skin weighing 1 lb per sq ft. (*WADC Rept. 52-204.*[9])

tions themselves radiate little noise, not much noise reduction can be expected from lagging or other external treatments applied to the pipe. In industrial systems, however, where noise levels inside pipes may be extremely high and where pipe diameters of several feet are frequently encountered, pipe coverings can be quite effective, especially at high frequencies. Such lagging ideally consists of a wrapping of porous, resilient material in contact with the pipe, covered with an outer layer of impervious material such as light-gauge sheet metal or asbestos cement. Such coverings may be effective for two reasons: first, the material in contact with the pipe can add some damping, thereby reducing pipe-wall vibration levels; and second, because of the inertia of the outer covering, the energy of the vibrating pipe wall is dissipated in the porous structure, so that the outer-shell vibration level is appreciably reduced. The theory for performance of pipe lagging and calculations of noise reduction which can be expected are given in Ref. 9.   Figure 26.13 shows the reduction in noise radiation as a function of frequency which the theory predicts for wrapping a pipe with various thicknesses of 6 lb per cu ft density glass-fiber material when an outer skin weighing 1 lb per sq ft is installed.   While this theory undoubtedly predicts the shape of the noise-reduction curve which can be expected from such treatment, it is doubtful whether reductions as great as those calculated will be achieved, except in special cases. According to the same reference, some reduction can be expected simply by wrapping the pipe with porous material, without the addition of an impervious outer layer. Calculated noise reductions for various thicknesses of 6 lb per cu ft glass-fiber material are shown in Fig. 26.14.

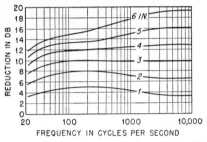

FIG. 26.14. Calculated noise reduction due to covering a pipe with various thicknesses of 6 lb per cu ft glass fiber. (*WADC Rept.* 52-204.[9])

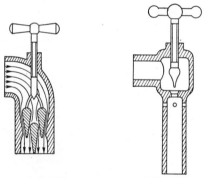

FIG. 26.15. Two types of silent water taps. (*After Mengeringhausen.*[19])

Design of Piping Components.   The main sources of noise in most piping systems are valves or flow-control devices of some type.   There is little in the literature on work in this field.   Two designs for proposed or experimental silent water valves are shown in Fig. 26.15.   Noise measurements made on two valves, one rated "very noisy" and one "very quiet," are shown in Fig. 26.16.[2]   Plotted also in Fig. 26.16 are ambient-noise levels which might exist in a quiet home.   Comparison of these levels with those for the two water valves indicates that even the quieter one would be audible, although much less offensive in such a noise environment.

An interesting study has been carried out in the redesign of a large pressure-reducing valve in a high-velocity steam system.[10]   Octave-band measurements of noise radiated by this valve before redesign were made.   The results showed noise levels a few feet from the valve as high as 115 db, with most of the noise energy in the high-frequency bands.   The sound spectrum was also analyzed with a narrow-band analyzer, with the finding that very strong pure-tone components existed at high frequencies.   A study of the valve construction revealed that these frequencies were due to resonances in the air cavity inside the valve, which were excited by high flow velocities.   The valve housing was later redesigned to provide streamlined flow conditions, with a resulting significant decrease in noise radiation. Figure 26.17 shows over-all sound levels near the valve before and after redesign for various quantities of steam flow.

A study of ball-cock mechanisms for control of water flow in flush-type toilets indicates that most manufacturers use valve designs essentially similar to that shown in Fig. 26.18. This is an inherently noisy device, typically producing a higher pitch and more intense noise as the flow rate is steadily decreased by the rise of the float.

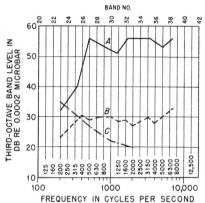

FIG. 26.16. Frequency analysis in third-octave bands of noise of two faucets, one very quiet and one very noisy. (*After Ingerslev.*[2])

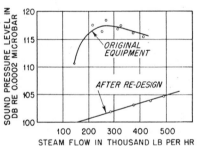

FIG. 26.17. Air-borne noise levels radiated by a 10-in. steam pressure-reducing valve before and after redesign. (*After Harris.*[10])

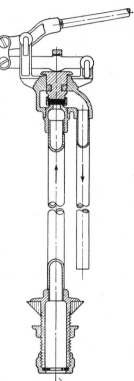

FIG. 26.18. Schematic view showing the construction of a typical ball-cock valve for a gravity-flush toilet.

REFERENCES

1. Rogers, W. L.: *Trans. ASHVE*, **60**: 411 (1954).
2. Ingerslev, F.: "Acoustics in Modern Building Practice," p. 268, The Architectural Press, London, 1952.
3. Callaway, D. B., F. G. Tyzzer, and H. C. Hardy: *J. Acoust. Soc. Amer.*, **23**: 550 (1951).
4. ———: *J. Acoust. Soc. Amer.*, **24**: 725 (1952).
5. Armour Research Foundation, Summary Technical Report No. 8, Project 90-768A, BuShips Contract Nobs 50016.
6. Constable, J. E. R.: *Proc. Phys. Soc.* (*London*), 360 (1938).
7. Ganitta, E.: *Akust. Z.*, **5**: 87 (1940).
8. U.S. Naval Experiment Station Engineering Reports 050078, C-3590-2, 050078C, 5A(6)066735, 5A(4)066735, 5A(5)066735, C-3590-1.

9. Bolt, Beranek, and Newman: *WADC Rept.* 52-204, **1**: 249 (1952).
10. Harris, C. M.: unpublished consulting reports, "Noise Tests on 10 Inch and 4 Inch Pressure Reducing Valves," Dec. 5, 1944, and March 30, 1946.
11. McGhan, F. W.: *Housing and Home Finance Agency Tech. Bull.* 15, September, 1950.
12. Chapman, D.: A Survey of Noise in British Homes, *Natl. Bldg. Studies Tech. Paper 2,* H.M. Stationery Office, London, 1948.
13. Geiger, P. H.: "Noise Reduction Manual," p. 130, Engineering Research Institute, University of Michigan, Ann Arbor, 1953.
14. Flow of Fluids Through Valves, Fittings, and Pipe, *Tech. Paper* 409, Crane Co.. Chicago, 1942.
15. Wagner, K. W.: *Z. Ver. deut. Ing.*, **77** (1) (January, 1933).
16. Wintergest, E.: *Gesundh. Ing.*, **28**: 129 (Feb. 28, 1931).
17. Kiel Naval Arsenal: Sound Measurements on Pumps, *BuShips Tech. Library Translation PG* 52175, *PG* 52176, *PG* 52183, *PG* 52184.
18. Kiel Naval Arsenal: The Damping of Pipe Vibration of Shock Absorbing Connections, *BuShips Tech. Library Translation PG* 52188.
19. Mengeringhausen, M.: *Gesundh. Ing.*, **56**: 217 (January, 1933).
20. Hirshorn, M. (T. R. Finn and Co.): *Navy Contract* 53569, Bureau of Ships.

Chapter 27

HEATING AND VENTILATING SYSTEM NOISE

ROBERT W. LEONARD, PH.D.

University of California at Los Angeles

INTRODUCTION

The term "heating and ventilating system noise" covers any sounds produced in the operation of a heating and ventilating system regardless of how the sounds are conducted to the room being serviced. The emphasis in this chapter is on the problems of large systems which involve an extended distribution system.

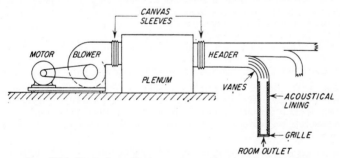

FIG. 27.1. Typical ventilation system reduced to its essentials.

Figure 27.1 shows a typical ventilating system reduced to its essentials. Return-air ducting is not shown, and the details of heat exchangers and air washers have been omitted, as these vary considerably from installation to installation. The system shown presents nearly all the troublesome noise sources, with the exception of the circulating pumps, boilers, and refrigeration machinery.* The return-air ducting and exhaust grilles may or may not constitute a serious noise source, depending on airflow velocities and duct attenuation. This part of the system cannot be overlooked in any systematic study of the problem.

GENERATION OF NOISE

Generation of Discrete Frequencies.

a. The generation of discrete frequencies, which appear as lines in the noise spectrum, may occur in a number of ways. The blower-blade frequency (number of blades passing a fixed point per second) and its harmonics will be present. Each

---

* Refer to Chap. 28 for a discussion of noise from air-conditioning systems.

blade, in giving its impulse to the air, produces a compression which propagates as a sound wave. The superposition of the compressions results in a noise consisting of a fundamental and a series of harmonic components. The noise spectrum of a system such as shown in Fig. 27.1 depends largely on the type of fan used. Details concerning fan and blower noise are presented in Chap. 25.

   b. Discrete frequencies are caused by mechanical unbalance in the rotating machinery, which results in vibration transmitted to the building structure or to the ducting and, finally, to the room being ventilated. In electric motors, magnetic as well as mechanical balance is important (see Chap. 30).

   c. Discrete frequencies sometimes result from an interaction between the flame and an acoustic resonance in the combustion system. If the flame is placed at a pressure antinode in a high-Q resonant acoustic system, the natural frequency of the system (at the operating temperature) will be excited. The combustion rate is increased by the compression associated with the sound wave, and thermal energy is given to the wave in just the proper phase to increase its amplitude. The amplitude builds up until nonlinear effects limit it.

   d. In high-velocity systems, discrete frequencies may be generated by the shedding of vortices by an obstruction in the flow. These frequencies, usually in the upper audible ranges and known as *Strouhal frequencies*, may be calculated approximately from the relation

$$f = 0.18 \frac{v}{d} \quad \text{cps} \tag{27.1}$$

where v = airflow velocity
      d = smaller dimension of obstacle perpendicular to flow
This effect is much reduced by streamlining the obstacle.

   e. It is possible to obtain discrete frequencies in a noise spectrum due to the excitation of a section of ducting in a manner similar to that of an organ pipe, but the probability of this occurring is small because of the critical angle of airflow required to couple the vortex separation with the resonant duct section.

   f. A very common cause of discrete frequencies is the interaction of turbulence in the flow with the undamped resonances of the side walls of an untreated duct. Since there are many such resonances, it is difficult to observe their frequencies as distinct; but the characteristic rumbling sound is usually clearly evident.

Generation of Continuous-noise Spectra. The continuous-noise spectrum is almost entirely due to airflow. Its intensity depends on the generation of turbulence in the airflow. Since in all practical duct systems the critical Reynolds number is exceeded, turbulent flow is to be expected. Turbulence is not in itself noise, but it can give rise to noise in a number of ways:

   a. A turbulent region may radiate sound. This process is very inefficient because of the "quadrupole" nature of the source.

   b. When turbulent flow interacts with a rigid wall, the momentum change at the wall results in a compression of the air, and the resultant density change is radiated as sound. The sound has all the randomness of the turbulent flow, and thus a broad-band noise is produced. This radiation is much stronger than that from the turbulence itself, since it results from random dipole sound sources at the surface of the wall.

   c. The forced oscillation of the walls at frequencies other than the resonant frequencies of the wall structure may produce noise. This is even more efficient, since reasonably large areas of the wall may move in phase and radiate coherently both into the duct and into the surrounding space.

   d. A noise source occurs at the grille where the flow enters the room being ventilated. This is an important source because it is located beyond the point where duct treatment can have any effect. Grille noise is strongly velocity-dependent. It will be considered in detail later in the chapter.

   e. Combustion processes produce continuous-noise spectra because of fluctuations in the rate of combustion. There are little or no quantitative data available, except through the manufacturer of a specific type of combustion heater.

THE TREATMENT OF SYSTEM NOISE

Installation of Ventilation Equipment.

Location of Equipment. The location of the blower and heating equipment should be given careful consideration. From the point of view of the reduction of mechanical vibration transmitted to the building structure, the machinery should be on a separate, ground-floor slab resting on earth. This gives a maximum impedance mismatch between the vibration isolators and the building structure, and therefore the least transfer of energy. This is particularly important in light-frame structures such as steel-frame factory buildings. The vibration problems encountered in locating machinery on one of the upper floors of a light structure can be overcome, but only with the additional expense of multiple isolation (see Chap. 13). Cast floor-ceiling slabs in modern buildings make remarkably good transmission paths for solid-borne vibration.

Vibration Isolation of Equipment. The blower and its driving motor should be mounted on a base weighing about three times the combined weight of the motor and blower. The base should then be isolated from the floor slab with vibration isolators. The electrical power must be delivered to the motor through flexible conduit. Any rigid connection between the floor slab and the mounting base will bypass the isolators and nullify their value. The outlet of the blower must be connected to the plenum chamber by means of a flexible canvas collar to prevent vibration from being transmitted from the blower housing to the plenum chamber and ducting.

If refrigeration equipment is used, the compressor and its motor should be mounted on a base supported on isolators similar to that used for the blower and its motor. The pipes connecting the compressor and heat-exchanging coils require flexible connectors as vibration isolators. The construction of these flexible connectors makes them compliant for lateral motion and not for axial or longitudinal motion. Hence two flexible connectors with a 90° bend between them must be used in each pipeline to take care of all three components of vibration. It is sometimes necessary to load the piping at the heat-exchanger end of the second flexible coupling in order to prevent resonance, which may result in actual mechanical failure in the piping. This merely emphasizes the rule that all flexible isolators must be followed by a high mechanical impedance.

An additional canvas collar between the heat-exchanger section and the header delivering air to the ducting may be necessary to prevent the vibration due to circulating pumps from being transmitted to the header.

Acoustic Isolation of the Equipment Room. The noise levels in the blower room may be near 90 db. Thus proper isolation must be provided between this room and the space being ventilated. Double walls are essential in most cases, so that the separation of the blower room by a passageway or storage space on the sides and an attic or access space above and/or below greatly simplifies the problem. The problem is further simplified by locating the machinery as far as possible from areas where low noise levels are required.

Acoustic Treatment in the Machinery Room. Unless some sound absorption is added to the walls of the equipment room, the effect of reverberant build-up will materially increase the noise level in the machinery room. Since the noise in the room may have strong low-frequency components, for which the walls will have a minimal transmission loss, the use of a thick layer of inexpensive sound-absorptive material is indicated. Two inches of mineral wool blanket on the ceiling and halfway down two adjacent side walls will usually produce a marked reduction in room-noise level. This may be very important where wall isolation is marginal. The effectiveness of the treatment depends on the change in the total absorption in the room: each time the total number of units is doubled, a reduction of 3 db is achieved. A fourfold increase in absorption reduces the noise level 6 db. [See Eq. (18.4).]

Reduction of Machinery Noise in Ducting.

Vibration Isolation of Ducts from Machinery. The plenum chamber must be isolated by a canvas collar from the blower. If a heat exchanger is an integral part of the plenum structure, then the vibration due to circulating pumps must be prevented from reaching the header leading to the supply ducting by means of another canvas collar.

Treatment of the Plenum Volume. A considerable reduction in blower noise may be obtained by covering the walls of the plenum chamber with a sound-absorptive material. The reduction may be computed from the expression

$$\text{Reduction} = 10 \log \frac{a}{S_\alpha} \quad \text{db} \tag{27.2}$$

where a = total absorption of plenum walls ($a = \bar{\alpha} S$)

S_α = discharge area of blower at plenum wall

As an example, suppose the plenum has an area of 200 sq ft and is covered with a material having an absorption coefficient of 0.5 in a $\frac{1}{2}$-octave frequency band. If the blower discharge area is 5 sq ft, then the reduction will be 13 db in the $\frac{1}{2}$-octave band.

Reduction of Aerodynamic Noise.

Velocity Dependence. The noise resulting from turbulence is strongly dependent on the flow velocity in the duct. The intensity of aerodynamic noise may depend on the fifth power of the velocity, and in extreme cases on as high as the eighth power of the velocity. Thus, doubling the flow velocity may increase the aerodynamic noise as much as 15 to 24 db. Conversely, doubling the area of the duct and maintaining constant volume flow will reduce the aerodynamic noise by 15 to 24 db.

Reduction of Duct Radiation. One result of turbulent flow in ducts is the setting of the walls into vibration. As a result of the vibratory motion of the walls, sound is radiated both in and outside the duct. This source of sound may be reduced by loading the duct walls with vibration-damping material. In many installations, the layer of heat insulation covering the duct serves this purpose. Vibration-damping materials are listed in Chap. 14.

Treatment of Bends. It is well known that the pressure drop associated with bends in air ducting is less for bends with a radius of curvature which is large compared to the duct width. The same separation of flow in short bends that increases the pressure drop results in additional turbulence in the flow and, hence, additional aerodynamic noise. If abrupt bends are necessary, both the pressure drop and the noise may be reduced by the use of turning vanes. The turning vanes are constructed of sheet metal and usually require the addition of a vibration-damping material. Further information on the attenuation at right-angled bends is given in Chaps. 21 and 34.

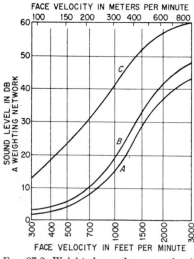

Fig. 27.2. Weighted sound pressure level (*A* network) as a function of face velocity in three grilles. Curve *A* is for a grille providing almost no spread. Curve *B* is for a honeycomb type giving a small spread. Curve *C* is for a grille producing wide spread. (*P. H. Geiger.*[1])

Grille Noise.

Velocity Dependence. The noise generated at outlet grilles is strongly velocity-dependent. Figure 27.2 shows the sound levels near the grille face for three types of grilles vs. grille-face velocity. The wide-angle grille C which gives a large spread (vertical vanes) generates the most noise. Grille B (a honeycomb type), with a smaller spread, is less noisy. And grille A (perforated metal), with little spread, is still quieter. These curves were taken 6 ft from grilles having a face area of 0.5 sq ft.[1] The sound levels were determined using the A weighting network.

Figure 27.3 shows sound level vs. airflow for an Anemostat Air Diffuser, type CM-1, 25-in. size, neck diameter 10 in. The sound level was measured with the A weighting network in a room having a total absorption of 100 sabins, with the microphone 3 ft out and 3 ft down from the diffuser. It is worth noting that the slope of this curve indicates approximately a dependence on the seventh power of the airflow velocity. Thus, cutting the velocity in half reduces the noise level by 20 db.

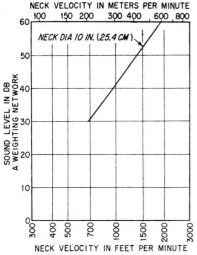

FIG. 27.3. Weighted sound pressure level (A weighting network) vs. neck velocity for an Anemostat Air Diffuser, type CM-1, 25-in. size, neck diameter 10 in. The average level is given for a room containing 100 sabins. (*Courtesy Anemostat Corp. of Am.*)

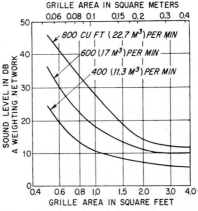

FIG. 27.4. Sound level (A weighting network) at a grille vs. grille area for a constant volume flow. The volume flow in cubic feet per minute and in cubic meters per minute is given for each curve. (*P. H. Geiger.*[1])

This is typical of the velocity dependence to be expected for noise of aerodynamic origin.

Area Effects. If the face velocity of a grille is held constant, the total sound power radiated increases in proportion to the area of the grille. Each time the grille area is doubled, the sound level in the room increases 3 db. This behavior is the result of the incoherent nature of the multiplicity of turbulent sources. If the volume of air supplied by a grille is held constant and the area of the grille changed, the sound level changes markedly. Figure 27.4 shows the sound level versus grille area for three different volume flows.

The power spectrum of grille noise has not been determined quantitatively for a wide variety of diffusers, but in general the level of the low-frequency end of the spectrum depends on the volume of airflow through the grille and on its size and opening shape; the level of the high-frequency end of the spectrum depends on the grille area and the pressure drop across it, and on the actual velocity of the air at the face of the grille. (In the case of a grille providing a wide spread, the actual velocity at the face of the grille will be considerably higher than the average velocity through the duct.) If the power spectrum of noise from a grille is known, the noise level in the room resulting from this source can be determined from Eq. (27.6). Then its acceptability can be determined by the use of Table 27.1 and Fig. 27.7.   See *Acceptable Noise Levels in Rooms; A Noise Criterion,* below.

Location of Grilles.   Some reduction in sound level is possible by proper location of grilles in a room.   Locations near the center of the ceiling are to be preferred from the standpoint of noise suppression.   The next most favorable position is near the center of the edge where the wall and ceiling join, and as much below the ceiling level as is practicable.   The worst position (that is, the position most strongly coupled to the normal modes of the room, so that it will be the noisiest) is in a corner at ceiling level.   The difference between the best and worst positions may be as much as 6 db.

Multiplicity of Grilles.   If more than one grille supplies or exhausts the air in a room, the sound level in the room will be proportional to the total power radiated by all the grilles in operation.   The calculation of the resulting noise level when the noise level of each of the grilles is known requires a special type of addition.   (See

FIG. 27.5. Chart for computing the sound level, in decibels, resulting from the addition of two random noises.   If D is the difference in the individual levels in decibels, N is the number of decibels to be added to the higher level to get the total level.

Fig. 2.17.)   First consider the case of n equally noisy grilles.   The increase in level over a single grille will be

$$\text{Increase} = 10 \log_{10} n \qquad \text{db} \tag{27.3}$$

Thus two equal grilles will be 3 db noisier than one; four will be 6 db noisier; and ten will be 10 db noisier.   The case of several grilles having different noise levels requires the use of the chart in Fig. 27.5.   This chart gives N the number of decibels to be added to the higher level when D the difference in levels is known.   Suppose we have three grilles with noise levels of 45, 42, and 38 db, respectively.   Taking the first two, we note that D is 3 db, giving $N = 1.75$ and a resultant level for the pair of 46.75 db.   The difference D between this sum and the third level is 8.75 db, giving a value of $N = 0.55$ and a total level for all three of 47.3 db.   This sample calculation illustrates the importance of reducing the major sources of noise before attention is given to the minor ones.

Effects of Room Absorption on Room Sound Level.   The total number of absorption units in the room being ventilated affects the sound level in the room due to sound radiated by a grille or conducted through it from an upstream source.   According to Eq. (18.3) the average sound pressure level in a room having a total absorption of a sabins, produced by a noise source of W watts, is

$$\bar{L}_p = 10 \log (W/a) + 136.4 \qquad \text{db} \tag{27.4}$$

According to Eq. (2.17), the acoustic power output of source may be expressed in terms of its power level in decibels re 1 picowatt (i.e., 1 $\mu\mu$ watt) by the equation

$$L_w = 10 \log (W/10^{-12}) \qquad \text{dbp} \tag{27.5}$$

where the p affixed to the abbreviation db indicates the 1 picowatt reference.   Thus if the power of a noise source W is expressed in terms of its corresponding power level L_w, from Eq. (27.5), Eq. (27.4) becomes*

$$\bar{L}_p = L_w - 10 \log a + 16.4 \qquad \text{db} \tag{27.6}$$

---

* For the corresponding formulas in the metric system of units see Eq. (18.3a).

Thus when the output of the noise source is constant, the steady-state sound level varies inversely with the total absorption in the room. Figure 27.6 shows the effect of varying the total room absorption on the noise level in the room; the total absorption is varied about a value of 100 sabins (sq ft units).

Acceptable Noise Levels in Rooms; A Noise Criterion. It is important to have a noise criterion of acceptability on which engineering requirements for attenuation in a ventilating system may be based. Table 27.1 gives recommended acceptable average over-all noise levels in unoccupied rooms with ventilation system in operation; here the weighted, A network, sound pressure levels are given. Table 27.1 is based on a typical room noise‡ having a spectrum level which has a negative slope of about 5 db per octave, i.e., decreases with increasing frequency. This is a flatter spectrum than that of a typical centrifugal fan, with a spectrum level having a negative slope of 8 db per octave. Since fans may differ widely in the shape of their noise spectra, a criterion is given below which enables one to calculate the maximum permissible noise level in any octave band. Such a computational procedure is useful since it is economical not to reduce the low-frequency end of the ventilating system noise spectrum more than is really required.

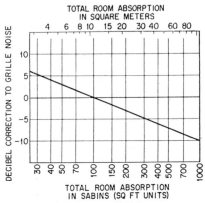

Fig. 27.6. The effect of varying the total absorption in a room on the noise level in the room; the total absorption is varied about a value of 100 sabins.

Table 27.1. Recommended Acceptable Weighted Sound Pressure Levels
in Unoccupied Rooms*

Location	db†
Radio, recording, and television studios	25–30
Music rooms	30–35
Legitimate theaters	30–35
Hospitals	35–40
Motion-picture theaters, auditoriums	35–40
Churches	35–40
Apartments, hotels, homes	35–40
Classrooms, lecture rooms	35–40
Conference rooms, small offices	40–45
Courtrooms	40–45
Private offices	40–45
Libraries	40–45
Large public offices, banks, stores, etc	45–55
Restaurants	50–55

* Source: V. O. Knudsen and C. M. Harris[2]
† The levels in this table are to be measured using the "A" (40-db) weighting network of a standard sound-level meter.

In order to determine the maximum permissible room noise level in any octave band, first determine the recommended acceptable weighted over-all level from Table 27.1. Then in Fig. 27.7 use the over-all level curve corresponding to this recommended value to determine the corresponding maximum permissible levels in each of the octave bands. For example if the weighted over-all acceptable noise level is 40 db, the maximum permissible noise level in the 300- to 600-cps band would be 36 db, and in the 600- to 1,200-cps band it would be 30 db. The contours in Fig. 27.7 are based on spectral shapes resulting in equal masking, following the work of Ref. 3. The num-

‡ See Fig. 18.32.

bers on the curves represent the weighted pressure levels measured with the standard *A* weighting network. This type of spectral distribution will produce less masking

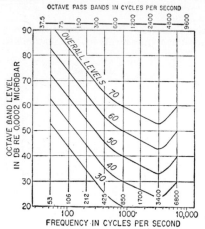

FIG. 27.7. Noise criterion curves for determining the maximum permissible sound level in any octave band if the weighted sound pressure level on the *A* scale of a standard sound-level meter is not to exceed the over-all levels shown on the curves. The permissible weighted over-all values may be obtained from Table 27.1. (*R. W. Leonard, modified from Ref. 3.*)

in the bands important for speech communication for a given level on the *A* network than the typical room noise. The values in Table 27.1 can be increased by about 5 db if the spectral shape is optimized. This correction may be applied for all room types, with the exception of certain radio, recording, and television studios.

Room-to-room Transmission in Ducts. The importance of the problem of room-to-room transmission through ducting depends on the use of the rooms connected by the ducting.

Noise Transmission from Machinery Room. The simplest case might be exemplified by the prevention of noise from a room containing machines from being transmitted to office space through ducting.

In this situation, the power transmitted through lined ducts from room to room should be no greater than about 25 per cent of the power transmitted through the separating partition. (See Chap. 20 for a discussion of the transmission of sound through walls.) The minimum required liner attenuation is

$$\frac{1}{2}\left[\text{T.L.} - 10\log_{10}\left(\frac{S_w}{S_d}\right)\right] + 3 \qquad \text{db} \qquad (27.7)$$

where S_d = duct area
  S_w = wall area
  T.L. = transmission loss of wall

As an example, if the transmission loss of the wall is 40 db, if the duct area is 2 sq ft, and if the wall has an area of 200 sq ft, then the loss required of each liner will be at least 13 db.

Interroom Speech Transmission. In this case, we are interested in preventing intelligible speech from being transmitted from one room to another in order to maintain privacy between rooms. Here, it is necessary to have the transmission loss in the lined sections at least equal to that of the dividing wall. Provision for adequate lengths of lined sections for each room feeder must be made in the original design. This larger attenuation is necessary because audition close to the surface of a grille is not affected by total room absorption. It should be pointed out that audition is a function of the noise level in the receiving room because of the phenomenon of masking, and that a large difference in noise level in the two rooms may result in a more or less unilateral transmission of speech from the noisy room to the quiet one if the total duct attenuation is insufficient. This effect is enhanced by the fact that a speaker tends to raise his voice in a noisy environment.

Multiple Feeder Outlets. Sometimes a high acoustic insulation is required between a number of closely spaced small rooms which are fed from a common supply duct. In such a case the ventilation system is apt to reduce the effectiveness of a construction that is otherwise well designed from the standpoint of acoustic insulation. For example, consider a group of small music-practice rooms which are fed from a single lined duct as shown in Fig. 27.8*a*. Even though 1-in. lining may be used, sufficient attenuation along the ducting that separates the rooms probably will not be obtained. In this case it is desirable to split the main supply duct at an appropriate distance from the first practice room and to feed adjacent rooms in pairs or groups of three, as indicated schematically in Fig. 27.8b.

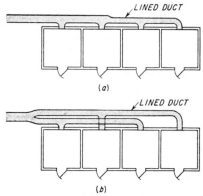

ATTENUATION OF SOUND IN LINED DUCTS*

The Attenuation Process. Sound waves in ducts are attenuated by the dissipation of energy at the walls of the duct. Even in the case of a rigid, impervious wall, a small loss results from the scrubbing of the wall by the tangential particle-velocity in the viscous boundary layer at the wall. This type of loss varies as the square root of the frequency. In this case, the losses are quite small, yielding attenuations of the order of 0.01 db per ft in a 12-in. square duct at 500 cps—a loss usually too small to be of practical importance.

If the walls are covered with a sound-absorptive material, an additional loss will

FIG. 27.8. (a) Multiple-feeder outlet installation, which may result in poor sound insulation because of transmission between rooms through ducts. (b) A good example of multiple-feeder outlet installation in which the attenuation through the ducts between rooms has been increased.

occur because of the viscous motion of the air in and out of the pores. The magnitude of this loss depends on the acoustic properties of the material. Attenuations of several decibels per foot may be obtained with highly absorptive walls. In both of the above cases, the losses are proportional to the perimeter of the linings, and the total energy flux in the wave is proportional to the cross-sectional area of the duct; hence, the attenuation is proportional to the perimeter divided by the cross-sectional area.

Computation of Duct Attenuation.

The Use of Absorption Coefficients. The attenuation of sound in a lined duct may be computed from the following empirical formula:[4]

$$\text{Attenuation} = 12.6\,\frac{P}{A}\,\alpha^{1.4} \quad \text{db/ft} \qquad (27.8a)$$

where P = perimeter, in.
A = cross-sectional area, sq in.
α = absorption coefficient for liner material

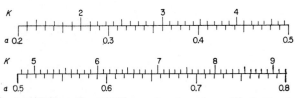

FIG. 27.9. Chart of K [from Eq. (27.5)] as a function of α. (*V. O. Knudsen and C. M. Harris.*[2])

* Other information on the propagation of sound in ducts and the use of acoustical filters that may be applied to ventilation systems is given in Chap. 21.

In alternate form,

$$\text{Attenuation} = K \frac{P}{A} \quad \text{db/ft} \quad (27.8b)$$

where K is obtained from the chart in Fig. 27.9.

The absorption coefficient appropriate in this calculation must be obtained from reverberation measurements where the absorptive material is backed with sheet metal

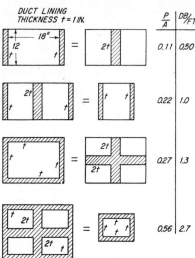

DUCT LINING
THICKNESS $t = 1$ IN.

	$\frac{P}{A}$	DB/FT
18″ 12	0.11	0.50
	0.22	1.0
	0.27	1.3
	0.56	2.7

FIG. 27.10. Duct-liner configurations having equal attenuations. P/A and the attenuation in decibels per foot appear at the right of each equivalent pair. All ducts in the left-hand column have equal open area. The absorption coefficient α is assumed to be 0.5. The attenuation is computed from Eq. (27.8).

and supported on 1- by 3-in. furring strips, 24-in. o.c. ["No. 6 mounting" (see Chap. 18).] The above formula, within limits, is independent of duct proportions. Clearly, if the area A and absorption α are held constant, the total attenuation will be proportional to the product of the perimeter and the length of lining. Thus, the total area of lining material used to give a prescribed attenuation is independent of the duct proportions. This formula has been found to be accurate, within 10 per cent, for ducts having cross-sectional dimensions in the ratio of 1:1 to 2:1, for absorption coefficients between 0.20 and 0.40, and frequencies between 250 and 2,000 cps.

The use of splitters, or "egg-crate" type separators, to increase the perimeter-to-area ratio results in a more compact attenuator. In computing the attenuation from a splitter-type liner, use the absorption coefficient for a thickness of material equal to one-half the thickness of the splitter. For example, with 1-in. thick splitters, the absorption for ½-in. material should be used. This results from the fact that, for sound waves moving parallel to the splitter, the sound pressure is equal on either side of the splitter and there is no particle motion perpendicular to and at the median plane of the splitter. As far as this type of wave is concerned, there may as well be a

Table 27.2. Absorption Coefficients of Various Materials Used for Ventilation-duct Lining

Manufacturer	Material	Thickness	Coefficients					
			125 cps	250 cps	500 cps	1,000 cps	2,000 cps	4,000 cps
Celotex	QT Ductliner	½″	.04	.36	.38	.76	.80	.85
Celotex	QT Ductliner	1″	.37	.47	.74	.88	.86	.82
Owens-Corning Fiberglas	Coated duct insulation	⅝″ 1″	.11 .13	.46 .46	.50 .70	.68 .85	.77 .85	.87 .80
Johns-Manville Sales Corp.	Airacoustic	½″	.11	.42	.43	.77	.84	.82
Johns-Manville Sales Corp.	Airacoustic	1″	.17	.49	.76	.89	.94	.85
Gustin-Bacon Mfg. Co.	Ultralite	½″	.11	.46	.42	.67	.80	.80
Gustin-Bacon Mfg. Co.	Ultralite	1″	.15	.53	.65	.90	.90	.87

rigid metal sheet dividing the splitter in half longitudinally. This consideration is most important at the low frequencies, where the absorption is strongly dependent on the thickness of the absorber and where all the energy is carried by waves moving parallel to the duct walls. To be equally effective, splitters should be twice as thick as the material used in the lining proper. This same principle applies to an egg-crate structure, i.e., two sets of splitters perpendicular to each other. See Fig. 27.10 for various configurations and equivalences. See Table 27.2 for the absorption coefficients of some available liners.

Calculation of Duct Attenuation from Acoustic Impedance. A rigorous treatment of the propagation of sound waves in ducts lined with a wall material characterized by a normal acoustic impedance which is independent of angle of incidence has been developed. The calculations outlined here are based entirely on the theory of Ref. 5, with only slight changes in notation. The advantage of the impedance theory is that it takes into account the nonuniform transverse-pressure distribution resulting from low-impedance liners. It also permits the computation of the attenuation of higher-order waves (multiple reflecting) as well as that of the "plane-wave" mode of energy propagation. Since the higher-order modes (multiple reflecting waves) are in most practical cases attenuated more rapidly than the principal mode ("plane wave"), we will confine our attention to the calculation of the attenuation of the principal mode only.

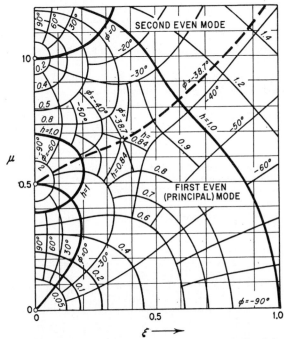

FIG. 27.11. Distribution parameters ξ and μ for pressure wave in lined duct as a function of h and ϕ. The section of the chart below the dashed line is to be used for principal mode ("plane wave"). (*P. M. Morse.*[5])

The parameters required for the computation of duct attenuation are

$Z = R + jX$ = specific normal acoustic impedance of material, rayls

ϕ = phase angle of acoustic impedance

$\lambda = \dfrac{1,130}{\text{frequency}}$ = wavelength of sound in air, ft

l_1, l_2 = transverse inside dimensions of lined duct

$$h = \frac{42}{\sqrt{R^2 + X^2}} \frac{l}{\lambda} = \text{wavelength parameter}$$

ξ, μ = distribution parameters given by Figs. 27.11 and 27.12 in terms of h and ϕ

$$U = \xi\lambda/l, \text{ and } V = \mu\lambda/l$$

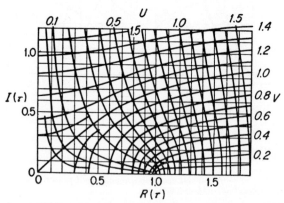

Fig. 27.12. Expanded section (lower left-hand corner) of Fig. 27.11. ξ and μ for small values of h. (*After P. M. Morse.*[5])

Case 1. One Wall Absorbing. For this case only the duct width is labeled "l"/2 in order to use a single expression for the wavelength parameter.

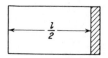

1. Compute h and ϕ, and enter Fig. 27.11 or 27.12, obtaining ξ and μ.
2. Compute U and V, and enter Fig. 27.13, obtaining $I(\tau)$.
3. Compute attenuation in decibels per foot from

$$\text{Attenuation} = \frac{54.6}{\lambda} I(\tau) \quad \text{db/ft} \tag{27.9}$$

Fig. 27.13. Real part [$R(\tau)$] and imaginary part [$I(\tau)$] of complex transmission coefficient τ as a function of U and V. This chart is to be used for Cases 1, 2, and 3 only. (*R. W. Leonard.*)

Case 2. *Two Walls Absorbing.* Impedance is identical for both walls.

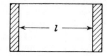

1. Compute h and φ, and enter Fig. 27.11 or 27.12, obtaining ξ and μ.
2. Compute U and V, and enter Fig. 27.13, obtaining $I(\tau)$.
3. Compute attenuation as in Case 1.

Case 3. *Uniformly Lined Square Duct.*

1. Compute k and ϕ and obtain ξ and μ as in Case 2.
2. Compute U and V from

$$U = \sqrt{2}\,\xi\,\frac{\lambda}{l} \qquad \text{and} \qquad V = \sqrt{2}\,\mu\,\frac{\lambda}{l}$$

and obtain $I(\tau)$ as in Case 2.
3. Compute attenuation as in Case 1.

Case 4. *General Case of Rectangular Duct.* In this case the impedance of each member of a pair of parallel walls is the same, but the impedance of the two pairs may differ.

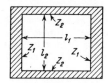

1. Compute h_1 and ϕ_1 from

$$h_1 = \frac{42}{\sqrt{R_1{}^2 + X_1{}^2}}\,\frac{\lambda}{l_1} \qquad \text{and} \qquad \phi_1 = \tan^{-1}\left(\frac{X_1}{R_1}\right)$$

and enter Fig. 27.11 or 27.12, obtaining ξ_1 and μ_1.
2. Compute h_2 and ϕ_2 from above equations (substitute the subscript *2* for *1*). Now enter Fig. 27.11 or 27.12, obtaining ξ_2 and μ_2.
3. Substitute ξ_1, ξ_2, μ_1, and μ_2 in

$$\tau^2 = 1 - \lambda^2\left[\frac{\mu_1{}^2 - \xi_1{}^2}{l_1{}^2} + \frac{\mu_2{}^2 - \xi_2{}^2}{l_2{}^2} + 2j\left(\frac{\mu_1\xi_1}{l_1{}^2} + \frac{\mu_2\xi_2}{l_2{}^2}\right)\right]$$

and solve for $I(\tau)$, the imaginary part of τ. This may be done by putting τ^2 in polar form after substitution of the numerical values for ξ_1, ξ_2, μ_1, and μ_2 and then extracting the root. The attenuation is given by Eq. (27.9).

End Reflection Losses. The various sources of noise in a ventilating system have been described above. Not all of the noise from these sources that travels to the end of the duct, which terminates in the room, is radiated. Some of it is reflected back toward the supply fan. Figure 27.14 indicates the theoretical values of attenuation to be expected as a result of end reflection.[6]

Distribution of System Attenuation. There are two places in the ventilating system where sound-absorptive linings may be used effectively.* The first is in the

* Effective use may also be made of acoustics filters in ventilation systems (see Chap. 21), especially where a single frequency—the blade frequency—of the blower or exhaust fan is to be suppressed.

header which feeds the branches which terminate in the individual rooms. This location is most effective in attenuating the blower and machinery noise in the airstream as it leaves the machinery room. Here, a single lined section will attenuate noise for the whole duct system where a multiplicity of liners is required for the same purpose farther downstream. However, it is not wise to place all the attenuation in the system in the header preceding the branches. Attenuating liners are useful just preceding the grilles or in the feeder duct supplying the grilles if more than one is used for a single room. Attenuation here reduces not only the residual machinery noise but any aerodynamic noise generated in the supply ducting. Attenuation in the duct supplying the air for a single room reduces sound transmission from room to room.

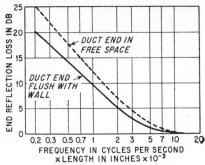

FIG. 27.14. The attenuation in decibels at the open end of a square duct of area L^2 as a result of end reflection losses. The abscissa equals $fL/1,000$ where f is the geometric mean frequency of an octave band in cps and L is the duct dimension in inches. If the duct is not square, assume $L = (L_x L_y)^{1/2}$. The computed losses for two cases are shown: (1) duct end flush in the wall, and (2) duct end projecting into the room. (*I. Dyer.*[6])

Computation of the Amount of Attenuation Required in a Ventilating System. The attenuation, expressed in decibels, in each octave band that is required in a ventilating system between a fan and the room it supplies with air in order to reduce the fan noise to an acceptable level can be determined by the following procedure:

1. *Determine the sound power level of the fan in each octave band.* This information may be supplied by the manufacturer. If not, it may be measured according to the methods indicated in Chap. 25, or it may be estimated as follows: According to Eq. (25.21), the total sound power level L_w produced by a fan is approximately

$$L_w = 90 + 10 \log_{10} (\text{hp}) \qquad \text{dbp} \qquad (27.10)$$

in decibels re 1 picowatt (i.e., 1 $\mu\mu$ watt), where hp is the rated shaft horsepower. The sound power level in each octave band can then be obtained by subtracting the values obtained in Fig. 25.16 from the over-all sound power level from Step (1).

2. *Now determine how much noise will be produced by the fan in the room in each octave band, assuming that there is no attenuation in the system.* These octave-band levels may be computed from Eq. (27.6) using the value of the power levels in each octave band, determined in Step (1). It will be necessary to compute the total absorption in the room at the center frequency of each of the octave bands.

3. *Determine the octave-band levels in the room that will be permissible; these values may be obtained from Table 27.1 and Fig. 27.7.*

4. *The attenuation which is required in the system in each octave band in order to reduce the fan noise to an acceptable level will be given by subtracting the values obtained in Step (3) from those determined in Step (2).*

Example. Suppose a room having a volume of 6,000 cu ft is supplied with air by a fan having a rating of ½ hp. According to Table 27.1, in this room a level of 50 db measured on the *A* network of a standard sound-level meter is acceptable.

According to Eq. (27.10) the total sound power level produced by the fan is 87 dbp (i.e., 87 db re 1 picowatt). Then from Fig. 25.16, the values of acoustic power in each octave band are given relative to this total power. These are listed in the following table. The values of room absorption which are tabulated are typical of those which might be found in a room of this size. From these values of absorption and power levels in each of the octave bands, the sound pressure level in each of the octave bands is computed from Eq. (27.6). These are listed below, together with the values of required attenuation, computed by the above procedure. Having determined the amount of attenuation that is

Octave-band center frequencies, cps	53	106	212	425	850	1,700	3,400
Octave-band power level, db re total sound power level	−1	−6	−11	−16	−21	−26	−31
Octave-band power level, db re 1 picowatt	86	81	76	71	66	61	56
Room absorption, sabins	60	100	190	475	555	545	500
Octave-band level in room, db re 0.0002 microbar	85	77	69	60	55	50	45
Maximum permissible octave-band level, db re 0.0002 microbar	73	64	55	50	40	37	33
Required system attenuation, db	12	13	14	10	15	13	11

required in each octave band, it is of interest to calculate the amount of attenuation that can be provided by lining the duct which supplies the room with air. Suppose this duct is 1 ft by 1 ft, so that the perimeter-to-duct area ratio $P/A = 0.33$. Following the useful rule of thumb that the duct should be lined for a distance equal to at least 10 diameters, suppose the lining is assumed to be 10 ft and that it has the values of absorption coefficients listed below.

Octave-band center frequencies, cps	53	106	212	425	850	1,700	3,400
α for 1-in. duct liner	0.10	0.37	0.47	0.74	0.88	0.86	0.82
K [from Eq. (27.8b)]	0.5	3.1	4.4	8.3	9	9	9
$K(P/A)$, db/ft	0.165	1.0	1.5	2.7	3	3	3
Attenuation on 10-ft room feeders, db	1.7	10	15	27	30	30	30

It will be noted that the attenuation by the feeder ducts provides all the attenuation required except in the lowest two bands. In the 37.5- to 75-cps band, centered at 53 cps, the required system attenuation, determined above, is 12 db; whereas the duct lining provides only 1.7 db attenuation. Therefore an additional 10.3 db attenuation is required. Similarly, an additional 3 db is required in the 75- to 150-cps band, centered at 106 cps. This may be achieved by the addition of sound-absorptive treatment to the plenum chamber. For example, the 10.3 db necessary to meet the design criterion requires a total of 13 sabins in the plenum chamber. This may be obtained with 26 sq ft of Fiberglas 1 in. thick having a density of 10½ lb per cu ft and spaced 8 in. from the plenum shell.

Note that no attenuation has been assumed for the unlined ducts, end reflection at the grille, bends, etc.; although these elements in the system do contribute some attenuation, the amount usually cannot be predicted reliably. Since the attenuation from the latter is frequently small, it may be entirely neglected to allow for some additional factor of safety.

MEASUREMENT OF VENTILATION NOISE

Measurement Objectives. Measurements of ventilating-system noise are made with two objectives in mind: evaluating "weighted" sound pressure levels in the ventilated space, and finding means of reducing an overly noisy system. In the first case, a weighted sound pressure level using the A weighting network usually satisfies the requirement.

The second, diagnostic-type measurement usually requires some estimate of the spectral distribution of the sound energy. For the wideband noise, of aerodynamic origin, an octave- or fractional-octave band filter set is most convenient for a rapid, on-the-spot analysis. In some cases, careful listening will identify a single component such as the fan-blade frequency. Where reasonably precise frequency measurement is needed, a narrow-band analyzer may be required.

Measurements in Rooms. Measurement of noise level in the room being ventilated provides the most direct evaluation of the acoustical treatment of the over-all ventilation system, including the effects of grille noise and room absorption. Measurements in the room present a minimal number of technical problems.

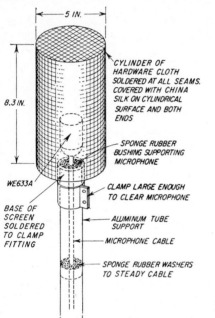

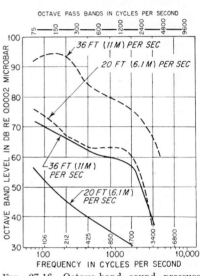

FIG. 27.16. Octave-band sound pressure levels vs. wind velocity for 5-in. diameter windscreen shown in Fig. 27.14. The dashed curves are for the unscreened microphone, the solid curves for the screened microphone. The wind velocity is given for each curve. (*R. W. Leonard.*)

FIG. 27.15. Cylindrical windscreen for use with the Western Electric Type 633A microphone. See Fig. 27.16 for performance data.

Microphone Placement. The proper position for the microphone in a room depends on the measurement objectives. For noise measurements in a room, several microphone positions, located with due consideration to the personnel using the space, provide a practical average sound pressure level. For the techniques required for a more accurate average sound level in the room, see Chap. 17.

In determining the relative noise output of intake and exhaust grilles, it is convenient to place the microphone about 1 ft from the grille being measured. Care should be taken to keep the microphone out of the moving airstream, unless precautions are taken as covered in the next section.

Measurement in Moving Airstreams. (Also see *Test Procedure*, Chap. 25.) This type of measurement requires special equipment. The microphone must be shielded from the steady airflow, or aerodynamically induced self-noise will be produced by turbulence at the microphone grille. Windscreens can reduce this self-noise by as much as 30 db. Figure 27.15 shows the constructional details of a 5-in. diameter windscreen. Figure 27.16 shows the octave-band sound pressure levels as a function of airflow velocity for the windscreen in Fig. 27.15 and for an unscreened

W.E. 633A microphone. These curves show the strong velocity dependence characteristic of aerodynamic noise. A 3-in. diameter windscreen exhibits a similar spectrum but is 6 to 10 db noisier than the 5-in. screen. The size of windscreen should be as large as possible without increasing the local duct velocity more than 10 per cent due to the presence of the screen. This increase in velocity at the surface of the windscreen will raise its self-noise by about 2 db.

A sound pressure level measurement inside the ducting is sometimes useful for diagnostic purposes, but it does not necessarily indicate a high transmission of noise energy through the duct. At low frequencies most of the noise energy may be stored in a standing wave system because of the small radiation resistance of the grille. Further, it is only possible to estimate the standing wave ratio in the duct by measuring the pressure at various points along the duct, using a narrow-band filter.

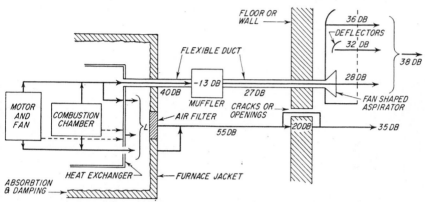

FIG. 27.17. Noise transmission paths in a hot-air furnace. (*D. B. Callaway.*[7])

Hot-air Furnace. One method of portraying an analysis of the transmission of noise from its various sources by different paths to the point of observation is by means of a "sound-flow diagram" which (1) identifies the sources, (2) traces the paths of the noise transmission, and (3) indicates the relative contributions from the various sources. An example of a sound-flow diagram for a forced-hot-air furnace is given in Fig. 27.17.[7] The sources responsible for the noise generation are shown within the furnace jacket. The insertion of a muffler in the flexible duct reduces the noise level in this path from 40 to 27 db. As a result of secondary sources such as grille noise and deflector noise, the sound level contributed by this path is 38 db. Note that the noise in the furnace room, 55 db, is reduced 20 db in transmission through the wall.

REFERENCES

1. Geiger, P. H.: Heating, Piping, and Air Conditioning, **8:** 601 (1936).
2. Knudsen, V. O., and C. M. Harris: "Acoustical Designing in Architecture," John Wiley & Sons, Inc., New York, 1950.
3. Fletcher, H., and W. A. Munson: *J. Acoust. Soc. Amer.*, **9:** 1 (1937).
4. Sabine, H. J.: *J. Acoust. Soc. Amer.*, **12:** 53 (1940).
5. Morse, P. M.: "Vibration and Sound," 2d ed., p. 368, McGraw-Hill Book Co., Inc., New York, 1948.
6. Dyer, I.: Courtesy of Bolt, Beranek, and Newman, Inc.
7. Callaway, D. B.: Machine Design, **23:** 1 (December, 1951).

Chapter 28

COMPRESSOR, HOUSEHOLD-REFRIGERATOR, AND ROOM AIR-CONDITIONER NOISE

H. E. WEBB

Product Evaluation Laboratory, General Electric Company

INTRODUCTION

The prime factor which directs our efforts in accomplishing a satisfactory solution of noise problems in mass produced hermetic refrigeration appliances is that of customer satisfaction, tempered by the economics associated with mass production.

Desirable Noise Spectrum. Customers of refrigeration equipment seem to have the least objection to a noise spectrum consisting of low-level "white noise" having a minimum of the higher frequencies. Pure tones, pulsating noises, intermittent clicks, and rattles or buzzes are all objectionable. In the laboratory the problem is to locate the noise and determine measures for controlling it. There are four general rules which should be followed in reducing objectionable refrigeration-appliance noise: (1) Reduce the acoustic or vibrational energy at its source. (2) Isolate the vibrating source from the acoustic radiator. (3) Absorb the vibratory energy in its transmission path between source and radiator. (4) Damp objectionable resonances.

Identification of Noisy Compressor Parts. There is no simple way of identifying compressor parts which emit noise. If the problem is complex, as most are, it requires skillful utilization of noise-measuring instruments and ingenuity in interpreting the data which are obtained. Having once identified the source, the vibrator, the radiator, and the transmission path, one can then apply the four steps listed above.

NOISE-MEASURING EQUIPMENT

Laboratory Facilities. In order to obtain significant data, measurements should be made in a fairly quiet room. For example, a room having a background ambient-noise level approximating that shown in Fig. 28.1 will be satisfactory. It is not absolutely necessary that it be a "free-field" room. An acoustic treat-

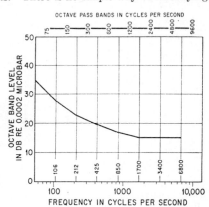

FIG. 28.1. Background-noise level considered to be satisfactory for testing refrigerators and room air conditioners.

ment on the walls and ceiling consisting of mineral-wool blanket furred out from the wall should suffice for most refrigeration-noise investigations.   Equipment which is essential for proper noise-analysis investigations includes a sound-level meter, octave-band analyzer, frequency analyzer, and source of variable frequency power.   An audio oscillator, oscilloscope, vacuum-tube voltmeter, contact microphone or stethoscope, and tape recorder can also be of considerable help in these analytical investigations.

Factory Noise Room.   A subjective noise test of the operating refrigeration units as they pass along a moving conveyor prior to assembly in cabinets is desirable.   A trained operator is capable of rejecting obviously noisy units by this listening test.   A typical factory sound room with proper acoustic approach and exit is shown schematically in plan in Fig. 28.2.

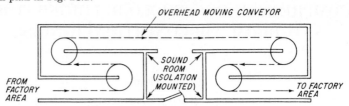

FIG. 28.2. Schematic diagram of a typical factory acoustical test setup for the subjective testing of operating refrigerator units.

SOURCES OF COMPRESSOR NOISE

Complex Relationship between Refrigeration-compressor Noise and Operating Conditions.   Figure 28.3 shows a schematic diagram of a typical refrigeration compressor.   Such factors as room temperature, change in load or in thermostat-control

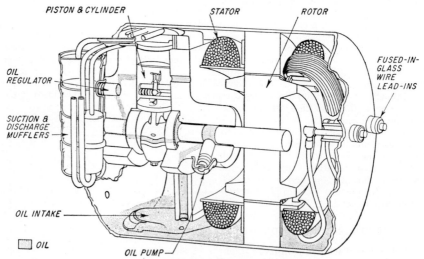

FIG. 28.3. Schematic diagram of a typical refrigeration compressor.

position, force on the bearings, pressure drop through the valves, valve lift, oil viscosity, compressor speed, and refrigerant-gas evolution from the lubricating oil all affect the noise produced by the compressor; and they are variable.   To make the problem more difficult, a particular noise can be very irregular and may never reach steady-state condition.

Compressor noises generally can be classed under (1) bearing noise, (2) motor noise, (3) valve noise, (4) gas noise, and (5) lubrication-system noise.

Bearing Noise. (See Chap. 24 for further details.) The more common bearing noises are generally caused by excessive bearing to journal clearance, poor surface finishes, nicks, scratches, burrs or other foreign material, and improper lubrication. Noises from these sources usually can be identified quite rapidly by an experienced listener, and sometimes can be confirmed by disassembling the compressor and inspecting each part. Most of these noise sources can be controlled by a rigid factory quality-control program.

Example. Consider a compressor bearing-noise case history. The customer complained that the refrigerator sounded like a V-8 automobile running on five cylinders. The noise lasted for about ten seconds and gave the impression that a breakdown was ready to occur. After the noise was listened to, it was agreed that the customer had a legitimate complaint, and the refrigerator was returned to the laboratory for analysis. After careful listening on several occasions, it was observed that the most favorable condition for the noise to occur was when the compressor was cool—about one minute after the start of the normal "on" cycle. It was not possible to produce the noise by adding sufficient heat to the evaporator to cause continuous operation or by pumping air instead of refrigerant gas. It was concluded that an investigation should be made to determine how critical main-bearing clearances were and whether or not refrigerant gas was evolving from the lubricating oil in the bearing. As a result of these investigations, it was shown that the noise was due to improper crankshaft lubrication. Refrigerant gas is very soluble in the lubricating oil, and the oil was not being flushed through the bearing at a sufficient rate to prevent a moderate temperature rise of this oil-refrigerant solution; thus the noise was occurring because small bubbles of gas were forming in the bearing and actually sweeping areas of the bearing free of lubricant. In other words, as the bearing temperature increased, refrigerant gas came out of solution in the bearing.

This accounts for the erratic nature, the time of occurrence in the cycle, and also the duration of the noise. As the normal "on" cycle progressed, the compressor-case pressure was lowered and the crankcase-oil temperature was raised. This resulted in lubricating oil with a relatively low concentration of refrigerant available for bearing lubrication, and the noise ceased to occur. The faulty lubrication was corrected by the strategic location of an oil groove on the crankshaft. This groove was designed to give a positive type of lubrication to the crankshaft bearing, so that sufficient oil was flushed through to minimize evolution of the refrigerant gas from the oil in the bearing.

Induction-motor Noise. (Also see Chap. 30.) Motor noise is a significant factor in the over-all noise quality of hermetically sealed compressors used in household refrigerators and room air conditioners. Motor noise is more pronounced in externally spring-mounted compressors than in those which are internally suspended.

TYPES OF ROTORS. At least two types of rotors are used for hermetic motors. Each has a substantially different type of noise characteristic. Motors having an enclosed bar rotor may produce a significant amount of lower-frequency noise, which is characterized by a definite "pulsating" or "hunting" sound, occurring at harmonics of electric line frequency and covering the range from the fundamental line frequency through about four or five hundred cycles per second. The vibratory energy from this source is sufficiently great to have a definite effect on noise from bearings, mounting springs, compressor cases, and suction and discharge tubing. The level of this noise at motor slip frequency is affected by the eccentricity of the air gap between the rotor and stator. Variable air gaps may cause extremely noticeable pulsating noises.

Hermetic motors using the open, or exposed, bar rotor may produce a minimum of the low-frequency noise. Instead, their noise is characterized by a steady "sing" or "squeal" at a discrete frequency, usually in the medium-high portion of the audible spectrum. The driving energy from this source is usually not great enough to cause an appreciable amount of noise to be transmitted to other parts of the system. Hermetic motors with open-bar-type rotors are more acceptable than motors with closed-bar-type rotors for use in refrigerators or room air conditioners because they radiate less total acoustic power and because the high-frequency sound which is radiated is easy to absorb with acoustical material; in many instances this noise is masked effectively by other compressor noises.

Valve Noise. There is no simple answer to the question, "How is the valve noise made, and how can it be reduced?" Special equipment to study valve noise as a function of crank position is sometimes helpful. More often, however, the application of such instrumentation is difficult to interpret, so that one relies on detailed frequency analyses and aural observations.

DISCHARGE VALVES. Discharge valves usually contribute more acoustic energy to the noise spectrum than suction valves. Sudden openings and closings of the valve against dense gas at high velocity tend to produce impact noises and associated resonant amplitudes.

Example. Consider a ¼-hp reciprocating-type compressor. The discharge valve is of the circular-disk type. Valve lift is limited by means of a curved backstop. The compressed gas is forced through equally spaced holes around the circumference of a hardened valve plate. The crimped edge of this valve seats on the outer edge of the hardened plate. The compressed gas forces the valve open and is then directed through an annular groove in the head, through the discharge muffler, to the condenser. The noise from this type of machine sounds somewhat like an active cricket on a hot summer's night and is almost steady-state in nature.

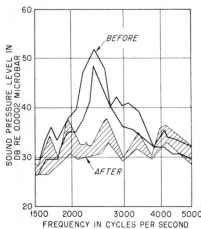

FIG. 28.4. Valve-noise analysis—before and after change (see text).

The envelope bounded by the solid lines in Fig. 28.4 shows a composite spectral analysis of a group of six machines. Note that the frequency of the noise is approximately 2,500 cps. Careful listening to a normal refrigeration cycle revealed that the noise is hardly audible at the beginning of the cycle. As the refrigerator progresses through its cycle, the noise gradually becomes higher in level, reaching a maximum approximately one minute before the end of the cycle, and thereafter remaining constant.

After the evaporator had been stabilized at the temperature at which maximum compressor noise was produced, frequency analyses were made. From these observations it was concluded that a valve was the cause of the noise. Confirmation was obtained by the following tests: (1) a variation in the speed of the refrigerator unit produced no change in the peak frequency or level of this noise, and (2) with the refrigerator unit running, the noise gradually disappeared when refrigerant gas was slowly bled off and air introduced in the system. It was concluded that, since the noise did not change in peak frequency or sound pressure level as compressor speed was varied, it was not caused by one compressor part hitting another. Furthermore, since the noise varied in level as gas density changed and since the noise was completely absent when the compressor was pumping air, it was concluded that this noise must be caused by a resonant valve.

Another significant test confirmed this conclusion. By using a dummy cylinder head with no discharge valve, the resonant frequency of the suction valve was checked. A similar test setup which used the complete head minus the suction valve made it possible to check the resonant frequency of the discharge valve. By varying the refrigerant-gas flow through these two systems, it was possible to make the valves resonate in much the same manner as a saxophone reed. A determination of the resonant frequencies indicated that the discharge valve was the probable noise source.

Although several modifications were evaluated, the one adopted was unique. The valve plate, with holes equally spaced around the circumference, was removed for one with the same number of holes equally spaced around half the circumference. This caused the compressed gas to be concentrated on one side of the valve and produced a nonuniform valve lift. The envelope enclosing the crosshatched area in Fig. 28.4 shows a composite spectral analysis of a group of six machines after the valve plate was changed. A comparison of the two composite spectra illustrates the effectiveness of the final solution.

SUCTION VALVES. Suction-valve noises can be identified in a manner similar to that described for discharge valves. A steady-state noise source, such as for the valve noise just discussed, usually is more easily identified than is that of an intermittent noise.

Gas Noise—Discharge and Suction Mufflers. (Also see Chap. 21.) The refrigerant-gas stream is a prolific source of noise. In the reciprocating-type compressor, where both the suction and discharge gases are evidently disturbed by the rapid opening and closing of valves, this is especially true. Suction and discharge mufflers are used to lessen the force of such impacts in the gas and to reduce the amount of emitted acoustic power.

DISCHARGE MUFFLERS. The primary function of the discharge muffler is to convert the pulsating gas flow to a continuous stream. Any appreciable pulsation in the discharge gas stream will excite the refrigerant condenser and may result in a serious noise problem, since the gas condenser acts as an acoustic radiator of appreciable area. There are many possible discharge-muffler designs. One, for example,

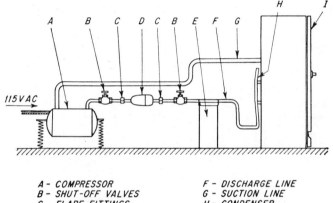

A – COMPRESSOR   F – DISCHARGE LINE
B – SHUT-OFF VALVES   G – SUCTION LINE
C – FLARE FITTINGS   H – CONDENSER
D – TEST MUFFLER   I – REFRIGERATOR CABINET
E – STEEL MASS WITH 4-6"
      DISCHARGE TUBING SOFT
      SOLDERED ALONG TOP

FIG. 28.5. Test setup for the evaluation of discharge mufflers.

employs a series of volumes separated by restrictions. This can be an effective design for a particular range of frequencies. There are others, such as a volume filled with small-diameter shot and a resonant-cavity-type silencer. Compromises are necessary when a muffler is selected for application to refrigeration compressors. These are generally caused by the limitations of space, effect on efficiency, and cost.

EVALUATION OF DISCHARGE MUFFLERS. Several proposed muffler designs may be evaluated from the noise standpoint by the successive-difference type of test. In this test setup a complete refrigerator is used. The test compressor, minus discharge muffler, is vibration-isolated from the cabinet. See Fig. 28.5. Note that two shutoff valves and two flare connections are employed. By using these fittings one can easily and rapidly change the test muffler. The large steel mass reduces the mechanical-vibrations setup in the tubing by the gas impacts in the muffler and by the motion of the compressor. Any significant disturbance in the condenser, therefore, must be caused by refrigerant-gas excitation only. In order to determine the effectiveness of a muffler in reducing condenser excitation, the vibrational energy in the condenser may be measured. One method of measurement requires the use of a vibration pickup in conjunction with a sound-level (or vibration) meter and octave-band analyzer. There is some advantage in obtaining the readings from several fixed vibration pickups, since experience has shown that measurements taken at a single position may not be representative. A more simple and direct approach is to use the human senses of touch and hearing. Although human calibration varies over a period of time, the setup has been designed for test in rapid succession from one muffler to another, which gives an adequate preliminary answer. Another method for obtaining muffler-design information employs the use of pressure-indicating pickups in the gas stream. One pickup should be located in the discharge tubing immediately prior to the muffler undergoing test, and the other immediately downstream from the muffler. The mufflers selected by any of the above methods then undergo further test. Final selection and approval of a muffler design, should be, from the noise standpoint, a subjective evaluation made on the completed product.

SUCTION MUFFLERS. Suction-muffler design is influenced not only by noise considerations but by space limitations, effect on efficiency, and cost. It is usually a compromise among these factors. The evaluation of suction-muffler designs, as with discharge mufflers, usually is made by a simple test of the successive-difference type.

EVALUATION OF SUCTION MUFFLERS. An experimental setup is shown in Fig. 28.6 consisting of a compressor, less suction muffler, enclosed in an acoustically treated box; a controllable restriction in the discharge line; a short, flexible hose from the com-

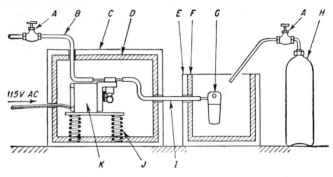

A - VALVE
B - DISCHARGE LINE
C - COMPRESSOR ENCLOSURE
D - ACOUSTIC TREATMENT
E - MUFFLER ENCLOSURE
F - ACOUSTIC TREATMENT

G - TEST MUFFLER
H - REFRIGERANT SUPPLY
J - FLEXIBLE TUBE
J - COMPRESSOR ISOLATION
K - COMPRESSOR

FIG. 28.6. Test setup for the evaluation of suction mufflers.

pressor gas intake, through the acoustically treated box, terminating in another acoustically treated open container; a source of refrigerant gas;* and a supply of mufflers which can be quickly connected to and disconnected from the flexible hose. The test procedure is as follows: First "flood" the open container with refrigerant gas. Then start the compressor. Adjust the discharge-line restriction to hold the desired pressure. Connect a muffler to the flexible hose and listen carefully for sharp impact noises and resonant "howls." If the ear is used as a detector, the subjective impression is obtained; then one can quickly change to another muffler and make similar observations. If the final choice between two mufflers is difficult to make, alter the flexible intake tube to form a "Y." Connect a muffler to each end of the "Y." With this setup, it is possible to check rapidly either muffler by closing the other. A minimum delay between "readings" and careful attention to the noise quality and loudness characteristics of each muffler will aid in selection of the best of the proposed designs. Octave-band analyses of the noise from each of the proposed mufflers usually will help confirm this preliminary sorting. This is followed by final subjective-proof testing in the completed refrigerator.

Lubrication-system Noise. Noises in a refrigeration compressor caused by or associated with the lubrication system frequently are very troublesome. Some of the common noises associated with a compressor lubrication system are as follows: If the compressor is splash-lubricated, then churning, gurgling, and splashing noises of the oil

* In this particular test setup, nontoxic, heavier-than-air refrigerant gas was used.

will be produced. Sometimes the elimination of these noises can be accomplished by strategic location of oil deflectors or baffles, or by a design change in the oil slinger. If the compressor has a pressurized oil system, assuming proper mechanical construction of the parts to the specified design, noise problems will most likely be associated with the hydraulic behavior of the system. The multiplicity of dilution ratios of refrigerant gas to lubricating oil contributes to difficulties in lubrication. Restrictions, hot spots, trapped volumes of liquid, and centrifugal forces are factors in the design which must be thoroughly analyzed.

Example. Inadequate lubrication may cause noise in other parts of the compressor not normally associated with the oil system. For example, consider the effect of passing oil through the cylinder head for valve damping. The noise is a metallic-sounding click or tick and is never present at the start of the refrigeration cycle. It appears suddenly at approximately mid-cycle and often disappears just as suddenly. Frequently the noise seems to wander aimlessly in and out of audibility until the normal "on" cycle of the refrigerator is completed. This noise may appear in only a small percentage of the total compressor production. Because it is not a steady-state noise, mechanical defects such as nicked or scratched parts can be eliminated as a probable source. Since it is a light "click" instead of a heavy "clunk," in all probability the bearings need not be considered. The valves remain as the probable noise source.

One method of evaluating the effect of passing oil through the head for valve damping is by the use of a capillary tube introduced into the gas-intake system between suction muffler and suction valve. The capillary extends from this location through a needle valve to the compressor oil sump, which controls the amount of oil pumped through the capillary. The compressor may be completely enclosed in a case with the valve mounted on the exterior of the case and may be either used in a complete refrigeration system or set up separately to pump against a definite restriction. In either setup, the oil rate through the cylinder head may be measured accurately after compression. As the oil flow is varied from minimum to maximum rate, the audible noise varies from a definite tick, through a quiet zone, to a hydraulic pounding. Assuming the valves to be the offenders, the oil-flow rate for quiet operation should be measured. The final design should provide this rate of oil flow through the head to ensure quiet operation. The above example illustrates a problem not normally associated with the lubrication system which was solved by a change in design of a part of that system. It also illustrates the kind of problem which one can encounter after a design has been in production. If this occurs, a meticulous review of all changes and past test records may help to indicate the deviation in design which caused the noise.

VIBRATORY EXCITATION FROM MOTOR AND COMPRESSOR

The problem of reducing vibratory excitation from the motor and compressor may be approached in two ways. One is to spring-mount the compressor internally; the other is to suspend it externally. These methods are illustrated in Fig. 28.7.

Relative Merits of Internal and External Suspension. From the standpoint of noise, the compressor designer should consider several basic features of the internally or externally mounted compressor. When more primary cooling surface is added to the externally spring-mounted compressor, the noise problem becomes increasingly difficult, because this added surface, which forms a good acoustical radiator, is in direct contact with the source of vibration. The externally spring-mounted compressor requires two flexible gas passageways between the compressor and the rest of the system, but the flexible gas-return tube may be eliminated on the internally spring-mounted design. Intermittent noises occurring during starting and stopping of the unit are a cause of the return of internally spring-mounted equipment to the factory, because such noises cannot be eliminated by a serviceman.

Effect of Internal Spring Mounting on Noise Attenuation. The following example should be used only as a guide. The data presented are not to be used as absolute quantities applicable to all internally spring-mounted compressors; they apply to one particular spring suspension, case configuration, and refrigerant gas. The equipment used to obtain the following measurement consisted of a sound source, a sound-level meter, an octave-band analyzer, an enclosing case to house the sound source, a supply of refrigerant gas, and a quiet room. One must select a source that will remain rela-

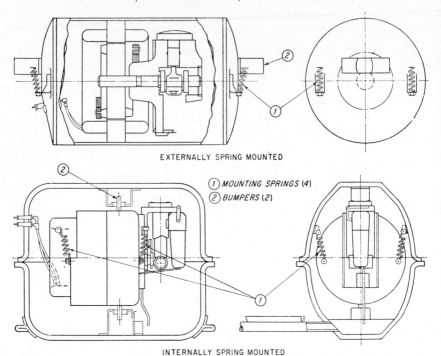

EXTERNALLY SPRING MOUNTED

① MOUNTING SPRINGS (4)
② BUMPERS (2)

INTERNALLY SPRING MOUNTED

FIG. 28.7. Schematic diagram showing external and internal spring mounting for compressors.

tively constant in output regardless

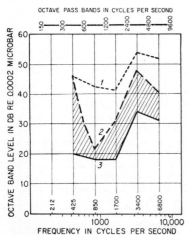

FIG. 28.8. Comparison of octave-band analyses for three conditions of measurement. Curve 1, sound source, not enclosed; curve 2, simulated rotary compressor; curve 3, simulated reciprocating compressor. (See text.)

of the varying conditions of refrigerant-gas density inside the enclosure. (A loudspeaker should not be used as a sound source, since the refrigerant-gas pressure inside the enclosing case will be varied to simulate actual operating pressures. Thus the loudspeaker-diaphragm amplitude of motion will be constantly changing because of changes in refrigerant-gas pressures.)

Example. A small motor completely enclosed in its own case, with a defective shaft and bearing assembly to intensify the noise, was used as a noise source for the experiment. The noise source was vibration-isolated from its supporting member by two springs. A thin layer of rubber was wrapped around the active turns of each spring to minimize transmission of energy in the audible range. The microphone was located 6 in. from the source, and readings were taken in six positions around the circumference. An octave-band analysis of the source chosen for this experiment is shown by the dotted line in Fig. 28.8. The first two octave bands (20 to 75 and 75 to 150 cps) were no higher than the room ambient-noise level; therefore, they are not included in this test. After the noise source had been analyzed, it was enclosed in a ⅛-in.-thick steel case. Leads for the motor were flexibly connected. The sound source was suspended from the original two damped springs. A connection was provided on the container to allow for evacuation, refrigerant-gas charging, and pressure checking. Damping of the container was accomplished by strategic placement of small amounts of mastic.

A cross section of the test setup is shown in Fig. 28.9. Pressures were varied from 200 lb per sq in. down to 75 microns, in increments of 10 lb per sq in. Bandpass analyses were taken again as previously outlined. The results, which have been corrected for background noise, are shown in Fig. 28.10. (The key in the upper left corner shows the octave-band levels of the unenclosed source.) From these data, it was determined that (1) noise in the two high octave bands (2,400 through 9,600 cps) is composed of approximately 30 db direct transmission through the mounting springs plus variable sound transmission through the gas, and (2) the attenuation of sound energy through the gas becomes quite significant at gauge pressures of less than 25 lb per sq in. Not included are the effects of cavity resonances which occurred under certain refrigerant-gas pressures.

Internal Spring Mounting—Reciprocating vs. Rotary Compressor. Consider the operating conditions of reciprocating- and rotary-type compressors. Assume a 10-psig case pressure for the reciprocating type and a 180-psig case pressure for the rotary type. Assume noise characteristics of both types of compressor to be similar. The crosshatched portion of Fig. 28.8 illustrates the anticipated attenuations of these compressors internally spring-mounted.

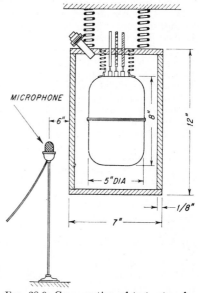

MICROPHONE

Fig. 28.9. Cross section of test setup for evaluating sound attenuation through refrigerant gas.

A test setup of this kind can be used to good advantage to study the attenuation properties of different kinds of refrigerants at varying pressures, the effect of compressor-case thickness on sound attenuation, and cavity-resonance effects at various refrigerant-gas pressures and case configurations.

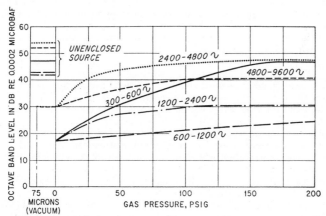

Fig. 28.10. Attenuation of sound through refrigerant gas at various pressures.

Mounting Springs, Spring Damping, and Rubber Isolation Mounting. (Also see Chaps. 12 and 13.) The design of the compressor vibration-isolation system for refrigerators or room air conditioners is compromised by the requirements of mechanical strength to resist fatigue and impact-load failure.

Rubber Isolation Mounting vs. Steel Springs.   Bonded-rubber shear mountings are probably as desirable a noise or vibration isolator as is possible to achieve for this purpose.   They provide adequate damping to limit stopping transients.   Bonded-rubber mounts made of butyl or neoprene are capable of long life with no appreciable change in their physical characteristics; however, manufacturers of mass-produced refrigeration appliances prefer steel springs for vibration isolation, mainly for economic reasons.   In either the compression- or tension-type spring mounting, some manufacturers use springs alone; others use springs in conjunction with a rubber seat.   Internally mounted compressors use only springs, since the life of rubber in contact with oil and refrigerants at elevated temperatures is somewhat difficult to predict.

Mounting Springs and Spring Damping.   Mounting springs for compressor vibration isolation have resonances in the audible range.   With no spring damping, it is quite possible that the springs may resonate during some period of the normal operating cycle.   There are several ways of overcoming this resonant condition.   One way is to damp the springs; another is to redesign the springs to shift the resonance frequencies.   Damping may be accomplished by a thin metal sleeve in contact with the inner or outer surface of the spring or by a thin coating of a resilient plastic or rubber over the active turns of the spring.   Caution must be exercised to avoid shorting out some, or all, of the active turns of a spring.   The resonant frequencies can be shifted by changing the physical dimensions of the spring.   For instance, changing the wire diameter 5 per cent and reducing the number of active turns was very successful in eliminating spring resonance in one compressor-mounting problem.   The result was a spring having the same linear and transverse constants.   The resonance was shifted to a frequency not encountered during normal operation.

Determination of Noise Transmission through Isolation Mounting.   The experimental evaluation of the vibration isolators must include methods for determining the amount of noise transmission from the compressor to the supporting framework.   A quick indication of the transmitted noise may be obtained by disconnecting the compressor from its supporting framework and observing the effect.

Suction- and Discharge-tube Noise.   The audible and mechanical resonances of a suction or discharge tube during normal operation, the maximum stresses which may be imposed during shipment or operation, and the actual noise transmission between compressor and refrigeration unit can best be determined by test.   A change in wall thickness, length, or configuration, and the addition of damping or mass loading will change the characteristics of a suction or discharge tube.   In considering these variables, compromises are made on the basis of economic and space limitations.   To begin with, tubing-wall thickness should be kept to a minimum.   An undamped section of tubing long enough to accomplish minimum energy transmission and to produce very little audible and no mechanical resonances during normal operation will probably require a prohibitive amount of space and may result in metal-fatigue problems.   Therefore, damping and the shifting of resonant frequencies by mass loading have been found to be most effective.   A good tubing design should be free of audible or mechanical resonances when the compressor is running normally.   Freedom from undesirable tube resonances within a reasonable range of the normal input frequency will assure a uniformly satisfactory tubing arrangement, even though there are slight variations in manufacturing processes and material.   Sharp bends in the tubing should be avoided, since they are points of potential stress concentrations.   A fatigue test of the tubing configuration will show any mechanical weakness in the tubing.

Test Method for Evaluation of Tubing Configuration.   To illustrate a method of testing a tubing configuration, the following equipment was used to obtain the data shown in Fig. 28.11: a household refrigerator, a sound-level meter, an octave-band analyzer, a sound room, a calibrated microscope, and a source of variable frequency power.   The refrigerator was operated over the input frequency range of 45 to 65 cps.   The microphone was located 3 ft from the floor and 6 in. from the front of the refrigerator cabinet.   Figure 28.11a represents the subjective response to the noise; (*b*) is the sound pressure level in the 75- to 150-cps octave band, and (*c*) is the total motion of the discharge tubing, in mils, as observed through a calibrated microscope. The plotted curves show the tube with and without mass added to the tube. The actual amplitude of visible motion of the tube is at a minimum for both these conditions in the input frequency range between 55 and 65 cps. The audible noise is quite variable for the tube in the free condition, reaching its maximum sound pressure level between 58 and 61 cps. Note that by adding mass to the tube the audible hum was substantially reduced. The mechanical resonance was lowered, resulting in a greater factor of safety from metal fatigue. Experience has shown that the noise and vibrational characteristics of production tubing configurations are not always representative of handmade samples. A careful test evaluation of the first samples from the production line should be made to make certain that the final product is acceptable.

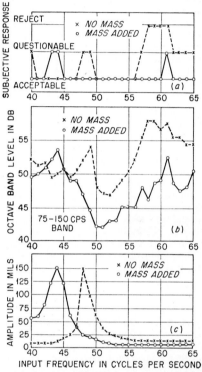

REFRIGERANT-CONDENSER NOISE

Since the condenser is a heat exchanger, adequate circulation must be provided and maximum surface exposed to the air for high efficiency. Therefore, mastic damping of the condenser is usually avoided. Isolation of the free-convection-type condenser from its mounting will probably not provide a satisfactory solution, because the condenser is only the noise radiator. Although forced-convection condensers have the same inherent mechanical and gas forces driving them, the noises resulting from these sources are usually reduced in level because of the smaller acoustic radiating area of the forced-convection type. If the condenser noise is audible, the mechanical energy may be great enough to vibrate the mounting surfaces. Isolation of the condenser from the mounting may help reduce the total noise in this instance. A noisy condenser is usually caused by mechanical vibrations from the compressor or by unabsorbed gas pulsations in the discharge tubing. The control of these types of energy has been discussed in earlier sections.

Fig. 28.11. Analysis of household refrigerator noise. (*a*) Subjective responses to the noise; (*b*) octave-band analyses; (*c*) vibration analysis of discharge tube. Note that by adding mass to the discharge tube the noise was substantially reduced.

REFRIGERANT-EVAPORATOR NOISE

Evaporators are excellent acoustic radiators. The most probable source of the energy exciting the evaporator is the refrigerant liquid-gas mixture leaving the capillary. A description of the noises radiated from the evaporator surfaces includes intermittent hissing, squealing or whistling, and rumbling. In household refrigerators the insulated cabinet is a very effective sound barrier, and evaporator noise is usually not a problem. In room air conditioners fan noise usually predominates, but capillary noises can be a very irritating part of the total noise output.

Capillary Noise. Two of the methods used to minimize these refrigerant-impact noises are mass loading of the capillary tube and liquid line in the immediate area of the capillary exit, and muffling of the liquid-gas mixture as it leaves the capillary. A length of heavy wall tubing with a smaller inside diameter than the evaporator tubing between the capillary exit and evaporator entrance was effective in reducing the noise energy in a particular instance.   An alternate method of reducing the radiated acoustic power is to use a sintered, porous plug at the capillary exit.   Changing the angle at which the capillary meets the evaporator tube or bending the liquid line before it reaches the main portion of the evaporator may also help reduce the noise level.   If the capillary entrance is flooded constantly with refrigerant liquid, the noise generated at the capillary exit should be less intermittent.

Evaporator Valves.   Some household-refrigerator designs incorporate modulating valves to combine freezer and fresh-food evaporators in single-system refrigerating units.   Other designs employ solenoid valves to perform such functions as automatic ice cube making, automatic defrost, etc.   These valves are usually located on or near the evaporator.   Vibration isolation is helpful in minimizing the noise from these sources.

MOTOR-RELAY NOISE

Types Used.   Two types of relay used for starting and for overload protection of refrigeration compressors are (1) the electromagnetic type, with a plunger armature or a spring-supported armature in a magnetic field; and (2) the thermal type, with a hot wire or a bimetal strip.   All are apt to produce impact noise as they operate.   Since the thermal-type relay keeps the starting winding activated for a longer period of time than does the electromagnetic type, the customer will probably notice the change in compressor noise but not the relay noise.

Plunger-type-relay Noise and Its Suppression.   The electromagnetic-plunger type is probably the noisiest of the two relay types.   The plunger causes an impact noise and also can cause a momentary buzzing sound inside the coil.   To reduce this relay noise, a simple isolation of the relay utilizing rubber grommets has been found satisfactory.   Impact noise can be minimized by damping of the contact arms or by providing semiresilient pads or seats for these arms to strike as they open and close.   The reduction of such noise is limited by relay-design characteristics and also by cost.

THERMOSTAT NOISE

Thermostat controls are generally spring-activated; therefore, when the contacts close or open, an impact noise will occur.   Strategic location of the control is probably the most economical method of minimizing this noise source.   In household refrigerators, thermostat-control noise is not a problem, since the control usually is mounted so that it is at least partially surrounded by insulation.   The location of the thermostat in room air conditioners is governed by such factors as appearance and accessibility; therefore, this problem should be given careful attention while the air conditioner is still in the design stage.

ROOM AIR-CONDITIONER NOISE

Figure 28.12 shows typical data for the sound-power level of a 1-ton room air conditioner mounted in an ordinary double-hung window set in a frame wall.   These data are considered to be representative for the noise output in a typical house room.   Since other components, such as the compressor and evaporator, have already been discussed, this section deals primarily with airflow noise.

Design Considerations.   The acoustic design of self-contained room air conditioners cannot be separated from such other considerations as appearance, size, cooling capacity, and cost.   Therefore, the design might logically progress through the following steps:

1. Refrigeration-component selection.
2. Component arrangement and layout of airflow circuits.
3. Airflow and pressure-drop determinations.
4. Fan selections.
5. Design integration.
6. Experimental development.

In each of these phases of the development, decisions will be made which will affect the final noise performance of the machine. For instance, the evaporator (face area, depth, number of fins per inch) may be designed purely from the standpoint of heat transfer. This, then, will largely determine airflow and airflow-pressure drop; and, consequently, major aspects of the noise problem are involved. In other words, no decision should be made in any stage of the design without considering the effect on noise.

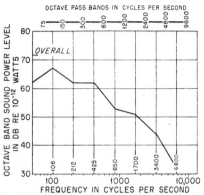

Fig. 28.12. Octave-band sound-power levels of a 1-ton room air conditioner mounted in a double-hung window set in a frame wall.

Component Arrangement and Layout of Airflow Circuits. Appearance and installation considerations will probably determine the size and shape of the enclosure. These considerations may require an arrangement of components which do not produce best airflow-circuit characteristics. Minimum pressure drop is conducive to low noise level; and therefore it would be wise, when laying out the airflow circuits, to keep

1. Air velocities low.
2. A minimum number of flow-area contractions and expansions.
3. A minimum number of bends.

Fan Selections. (Also see Chap. 25.) After a trial refrigerant-component arrangement and airflow-circuit layout have been determined, airflow and pressure drop become known quantities, and the fans can be selected by extrapolation from known test data by using the "fan laws." This data can be obtained by running tests on representative-type fans from manufacturers' catalogues or from other sources. To make the best theoretical fan selection, one must determine the proper fan type, size, and speed for lowest noise level. In general, the procedure used follows the method established in Chap. 25.

Design Integration and Experimental Development. With the tentative selection of the fans, further details of the components' arrangement and design can be studied. More compromises will probably be made. For instance, fan housings and scrolls must frequently be altered from the ideal shape to fit space requirements. After the component parts have been integrated into a theoretically workable system, the design is ready for construction and test. A prototype of the design is built, and design details such as appearance possibilities, performance, efficiency, cost, and noise are evaluated.

From the standpoint of noise, one must evaluate fan motors and motor-isolation mountings, hub and fan-blade isolation, blade resonances and blade materials, water noise, acoustic material in airflow passageways, resonant panels, obstructions in the air stream, and vibration transmission to walls and floors. In this experimental development work, where original samples are fabricated and changed to improve the design, sound pressure level measurements and octave-band analyses can be quite helpful.   Once the sample is changed, these data can be used to determine if there has been an actual improvement.   Then comparison noise tests, by subjective reaction of the final proposed design with previous designs—known standard or competitive units—will very quickly show whether the new design represents a significant improvement from a noise standpoint.

GENERAL PRODUCT NOISE

Any noise occurring in a new refrigerating machine or room air conditioner which is objectionable to the customer will inevitably require a service call.

Cabinet Noises.   Cabinet noises are usually resonances, intermittent buzzes, or rattles.   Methods for minimizing resonances are changing the stiffness of the part (1) by adding or removing ribs, and (2) by mass loading.   Generally mass loading is more satisfactory than a change in stiffness, since the latter may only change the frequency.   The intermittent buzzes and rattles are usually caused by poorly fitted cabinet or hood members, and by loose name plates, grilles, and air deflectors.   Noises emanating from these surfaces are most often caused by poor isolation of the compressor assembly or fan motor.   Sometimes refrigerant-gas pulsations in the condenser result in noise being radiated from the housings enclosing the mechanism.

Transient Stopping Noises.   Noises occurring when the compressor stops can be caused by improper termination of mounting-spring ends, inadequate clearances around flexible gas passageways, combinations of framework spot welding and paint between spot-welded members, poor contact of the compressor mounting frame with the cabinet or housing, or insufficient tension on the various bolts which hold compressor mounting structure and cabinet or housing together.

Chapter 29

REDUCTION OF THE NOISE OF IRON-CORE TRANSFORMERS AND CHOKES

Arthur J. King, D.Sc.

Metropolitan-Vickers Electrical Company, Ltd., Manchester, England

INTRODUCTION

It is a matter of common knowledge that iron-core transformers and chokes connected to a-c lines produce a humming noise. This noise may or may not be a nuisance to a person hearing it, depending on its loudness and on that of the background noise, and also, to a considerable extent, on the desires of the person at the particular time in question. For example, the noise of a large transformer may be hardly noticed in a large generating station owing to the noise of the turbines and generators; but the noise from a very small choke for a fluorescent lamp may be a nuisance to a person wishing to sleep in an adjoining room in the middle of the night, when other noises are subdued. In the medium-size range, transformers installed in the basements of flats and large office blocks and also those installed in suburban residential districts, either in the open air or in substation housings, frequently give rise to noise complaints of a more or less serious nature, depending on the local conditions.

In nearly all cases the reduction of noise involves additional expense, so it is difficult to prevent nuisance from noise by laying down hard and fast rules governing the maximum noise emission of transformers and chokes without imposing extensive restrictions in many cases where they are quite unnecessary.

When it is apparent that the noise of a transformer is, or will be, greater than is tolerable, it becomes necessary to consider the available ways of reducing it. These ways can be roughly grouped under the three headings *reduction at the source, reduction in transmission,* and *enclosure.* It is necessary to consider them all in respect to performance and to cost in order to obtain an economic, and in some cases esthetic, solution. These questions are considered in the following sections.

CAUSES OF NOISE OF IRON-CORE TRANSFORMERS AND CHOKES

It is a straightforward matter to show, with the aid of sound-analyzing equipment' that the hum emitted by iron-core transformers and chokes connected to a-c supply lines consists of a harmonic range of component tones based on a fundamental of twice the supply frequency. On 60-cps lines the fundamental is therefore of 120 cps, and harmonics up to 1,200 cps can often be detected. The smaller the transformer, the higher the frequency of the loudest harmonic; conversely, larger transformers tend to have louder low-frequency components. For example, for 100 kva the loudest component may be 480 cps; for 1,000 kva, 360 cps; for 10,000 kva, 240 cps; and for 100,000 kva, 120 cps. This effect is largely due to the size of the transformers relative to the wavelengths of the harmonics, as it is not until the linear dimensions of the tank approach a wavelength that good conditions for radiation of sound waves, as opposed to mere circulation of air, are reached.

Noise analyses of typical sizes of transformer are given in Table 29.1a and b.

Table 29.1a. Frequency Spectrum of Transformers
The weighted* sound pressure levels are given for transformers having different ratings.

Trans-former ratings, kva	Over-all	Weighted* sound pressure levels, db									
		Frequency components									
		120 cps	240 cps	360 cps	480 cps	600 cps	720 cps	840 cps	960 cps	1,080 cps	1,200 cps
500	54	47	51.4	45.1	43.2	37.5	30.5	35.1	36	39.2	31.8
5,000	68	65.6	59.9	60.8	48.4	52.0	54.7	53.4	47.1	46.5	44.7
5,000	66	63.7	56.0	59.0	51.2	53.6	54.6	58	51.3	51.7	54.1
60/75,000	76	74	70	67	55	50	40				
60/75,000	84	75.3	70.0	81.7	72.3	73.0	67.4				
25,000	77	76.2	57.1	62.2		65.9	55.7		61.1	62.7	

* These sound levels were obtained using the A.weighting network, and they are expressed in decibels re 0.0002 microbar.

Table 29.1b. Typical Analyses of Transformer Noise
Microphone 1 ft from tank. Line frequency 50 cps.

L_p = Sound pressure level, db re 0.0002 microbar.

L_a = Weighted sound level, expressed in decibels re 0.0002 microbar, employing the A weighting network.

L_N = Loudness level, phons.

Component frequency, cps	150 kva, B = 13 kilogauss						15,000 kva, B = 11 kilogauss			36,000 kva, B = 13.5 kilogauss		
	Hot-rolled			Cold-rolled			Hot-rolled			Cold-rolled		
	L_p, db	L_a, dba	L_N, phons	L_p, db	L_a, dba	L_N, phons	L_p, db	L_a, dba	L_N, phons	L_p, db	L_a, dba	L_N, phons
100	53	32	30	58	37	37	66	45	49	84	63	73
200	37	24	23	46	33	35	66	53	59	63	50	55
300	53	46	48	46	39	40	65	58	56	76	69	73
400	31	27	27	34	30	30	49	45	46	60	56	58
500	35	33	33	29	27	27	43	41	41	56	54	55
600	27	26	26	23	22	22	48	47	47	56	55	55
Over-all loudness level, phons	57			56			72			84		
Over-all weighted sound pressure level, dba	47			42			60			70		

It has been shown by tests on open circuit, short circuit, and up to full load that the vibration and noise of a transformer originate in the core and not to any appreciable extent in the current-carrying coils.[3] The noise increases steadily with the flux density in the core; typical curves showing the relation are given in Fig. 29.1. The absence of any appreciable change in noise with load is in agreement with the dependence of noise on flux density, since the latter varies very little with load.

It has been established that one of the main causes of the noise of transformers is the magnetostrictive effect in the cores.[3,4] This change in length when magnetized is experienced to a greater or lesser extent by all ferromagnetic materials, although some extend, some contract, and others change over from extension to contraction at particular magnetizations. The effect is very small, amounting usually to only a few parts in a million. Figure 29.2 shows typical curves for hot- and cold-rolled silicon steel as used in many transformers. Since the extension is independent of the direction of magnetization, there are two extensions per cycle of magnetization, which accounts for the double-frequency fundamental of the resultant vibration and radiated sound. It is interesting to speculate that, if only it were possible to develop a material with a parabolic magnetostriction curve, i.e., with the extension proportional to the square of the flux density,

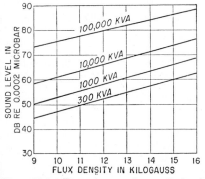

FIG. 29.1. Dependence of sound level (*A* weighting network) of transformers on flux density in the core.

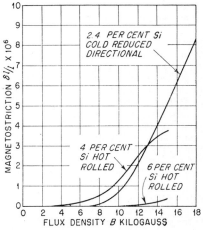

FIG. 29.2. Magnetostriction of 0.014-in. silicon steel, 4 and 6 per cent hot-rolled and 2.4 per cent silicon cold-reduced directional.

the resultant vibration and sound would, for a sine wave of flux, be of one frequency only—namely, twice the line frequency.[4]

While explorations of the vibration of transformer cores by means of vibration pickups and analyzers have confirmed the presence and magnitude of the magnetostrictive extensions, they have also revealed the presence of other modes of vibration. Some of these other modes, especially the transverse ones of low frequency, have been assisted by insufficient or too widely spaced clamping. The origin of these transverse modes is not fully understood. Whatever the causes, transverse vibrations are present in the cores of transformers and in many cases are responsible for as much radiation of sound energy as the magnetostrictive longitudinal mode. In the case of large iron-core shunt reactors for power-factor correction on high-capacitance lines, noise is generated by core vibration in a manner similar to that of a transformer. The main difference lies in the way in which sinusoidal flux is obtained in the cores. In transformers, the magnetizing current automatically follows the varying core reluctance throughout each cycle to produce a sinusoidal flux and back emf to match the sinusoidal line voltage. In shunt reactors, on the other hand, the core reluctance is linearized by air gaps so as to give a sensibly constant reactance and impedance throughout each cycle. Since the impedance increases with frequency, the core flux is at least as sinusoidal as the line voltage.

The possibility that some of the vibration and noise may be associated with imperfect joints in the magnetic circuit has been investigated by building a transformer with normal interleaved joints and then rebuilding with a new joint involving square and mitred ends to the laminations. The new joint made possible three alternative ways of assembling the strips, which provided at least 66 per cent effective section of the core throughout the joints. The standard joint presents two alternatives, and the section falls to 50 per cent. It was felt that this improvement in effective section at the joints would reduce stray flux there and might well also reduce the noise, especially at high flux densities. However, tests showed that, although the new joint was effective in reducing the reluctance and magnetizing current by some 10 per cent, it had no appreciable effect on the core loss or the noise. If the laminations are so loose at the joints as to be able to "buzz," the noise will be increased; but very little clamping is sufficient to prevent this. It appears, therefore, that the normal interleaved core joint with moderate clamping does not contribute appreciably to the noise emitted.

The vibrations of the core give rise to sound waves of corresponding frequencies in the surrounding air, either by direct radiation from the core, in the case of air-cooled units, or by transmission through the oil to the tank side with subsequent radiation from there, in the case of oil-immersed units. If the dimensions of the core are small compared with a wavelength of a particular component in the surrounding medium, parts of the core vibrating out of phase will lead to circulation of the medium rather than to acoustic radiation. The velocity of sound in air is approximately 1,100 ft per sec so the wavelengths of sounds of 120 and 600 cps are, respectively, 9 ft and 1 ft 10 in. This is one of the reasons why small transformers and chokes have a higher-pitched hum than the large ones, which are able to radiate the fundamental and lower harmonics effectively. The velocity of sound in oil is approximately 4,000 ft per sec, but the distances between core and tank sides in oil-immersed transformers are usually smaller than the distances to parts moving out of phase; thus the vibration of the tank side tends to follow that of the nearest surface of the core. In addition to the radiation to the air from the transformer core or tank, there is in many cases appreciable radiation from surfaces which are in solid contact with the transformer, and so are caused to vibrate. Such surfaces, whether they be the floor of a building or the reflector of a fluorescent lamp, can greatly increase the noise from a transformer or choke, or even render audible what would otherwise be inaudible. They may be classed as secondary sources of the noise. Methods of suppressing these structure-borne effects are discussed later in this chapter and in Chaps. 12 and 13.

TRANSFORMER-NOISE MEASUREMENTS AND STANDARDS

In the interests of standardization, maximum values of noise emission have been laid down by NEMA for the range of sizes and classes of power transformers encountered in practice.[1] Values for class OA, OW, FOW, FA, and FOA transformers are given in Table 29.2. These values are given as sound levels measured at 1 ft from the tank side by a sound-level meter conforming to ASA Standard and operating on the A network. Further particulars are given in the AIEE committee report together with a brief discussion of the differences encountered with transformer and other complex noises between the sound level as read on the meter and the loudness level as given by the sound pressure level of the tone of 1,000 cps, which sounds equally loud.[2] With certain complex noises having many components, the loudness level in phons may be, numerically, up to 30 higher than the sound level in decibels; but with transformer noises the difference is usually of the order of 5 to 10, rising to 15 at low levels. Therefore, whenever it is necessary to consider the relative loudness of sounds of very different composition, reliance should not be placed entirely on readings in decibels of sound-level meters but rather on the corresponding loudness levels in phons, or loudness in sones. The point is important, for example, when considering the amount of hum from a transformer that can be tolerated by a person lying in bed at night compared with an indefinite background noise of distant traffic. Experience suggests that, apart from individual idiosyncrasies, a person in a good-class residential district can tolerate a noise having a loudness level of 40 phons at his bedroom window.

Table 29.2. Audible Sound Levels for Class OA, OW, FOW, FA, and FOA Transformers

Column A—OA,* OW,* and FOW ratings.
Column B—FA* ratings which do not exceed $1\frac{1}{8}$ times the self-cooled rating with fans in operation.
Column C—FOA* ratings and FA* ratings which exceed $1\frac{1}{8}$ but do not exceed $1\frac{2}{3}$ times the self-cooled rating with fans in operation.

| Equivalent 2-winding, 55°C kva ratings† | | | | | | | | | Avg sound level,‡ db |
| 350 kv BIL and below | | | 450, 550, & 650 kv BIL | | | 750 kv BIL and below | | | |
A	B	C	A	B	C	A	B	C	
300									56
500									58
700									60
1000									62
1500									63
2000									64
3000									65
4000									66
5000			1000						67
6000			1500						68
7500			2000						69
10000	2667		3000						70
12500	5333		4000						71
15000	6667		6000	1333		3000			72
	10000		10000	2667		4000			73
20000	13333		12500	4000		6000			74
25000	16667	12500	15000	5333		10000			75
30000	20000	16667	20000	13333		12500	5300		76
40000	26667	20800	25000	16667	6667	15000	8000		77
50000	33333	25000	30000	20000	16667	20000	13333	6667	78
60000	40000	41667	40000	26667	25000	25000	16667	16667	79
80000	53333	50000	50000	33333	33333	30000	20000	20800	80
100000	66667	66667	60000	40000	41667	40000	26667	25000	81
	80000	83333	80000	53333	50000	50000	33333	33333	82
	106667	100000	100000	66667	66667	60000	40000	41667	83
				80000	83333	80000	53333	50000	84
				106667	100000	100000	66667	66667	85
							80000	83333	86
							106667	100000	87

* See TRI-2.001 for classes of transformers.
† The equivalent 2-winding, 55°C rated kva is defined as one-half the sum of the kva ratings of all windings.
‡ db re 0.0002 microbar A weighting network.
NOTE: For intermediate kva ratings, use the next-higher kilovolt rating.

Even if the window is open, the level at the bed will be somewhat less because of the absorption usually present in a bedroom; and if the window is closed, there will be a further reduction of about 10 phons. A transformer noise having a loudness level of 40 phons usually corresponds to a reading of a sound-level meter of about 25 db on the A weighting network, so it is often necessary to attain low levels such as these in order to avoid complaints.

In spite of the shortcomings of the sound-level meter, its simplicity and portability

Table 29.3.* Correction of Sound-level Readings for Background Noise†

Difference between combined sound level and background, db	10	7	5	3
Correction to be subtracted from combined sound level, db	0	1	2	3

* See Fig. 17.4 for a graphical method of obtaining the correction.

† Corrections of less than 1 db for differences between 10 and 7 db are given in NEMA TRI-54, part 2, p. 23, TRI-2.068.

make it so attractive compared with other, more comprehensive noise-measuring apparatus that it is used almost exclusively for routine noise checking of power transformers and reactors. The special arrangements which are necessary for testing the small chokes used with fluorescent lamps are discussed later. For power transformers and reactors, the testing procedure laid down by NEMA, involving the measurement of the average weighted sound pressure level at 1 ft from the tank, was designed to permit tests in the confined conditions usually encountered in factory test areas. It also helps to cut down the effect of background noise, which should, if possible, be 10 db or more below the sound level of the transformer under test. If the sound level of the background noise alone is less than 10 db below that of the combined noise and background, then the correction to be subtracted from the combined level to give that of the transformer alone is given in Table 29.3 (also see Fig. 17.4). Tests with a difference of less than 5 db are deprecated. The NEMA standard also specifies that readings shall be taken with the sound-level meter on the *A* weighting network, even though the transformer-noise level may be much higher than this. As indicated in the AIEE committee report, it is usually at distances where the transformer noise is reduced to around the 40-db level that arguments as to nuisance arise.

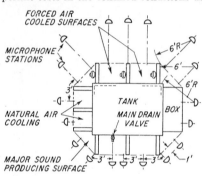

FIG. 29.3. Determination of microphone locations for measurement of audible sound. (*NEMA.*)

For convenience, the NEMA directions for carrying out the noise measurements are appended. Figure 29.3 shows the standard positions for the measuring microphone.

Extract from NEMA Standard TRI-2.068—Audible Sound Level Tests.*

Measurements.

1. Sound levels shall be measured with an instrument which is in accordance with the American Standard for Sound Level Meters. Weighting network *A*, specified in Z24.3, shall be used.
2. The average sound level is defined as the arithmetic mean of the sound level readings taken in accordance with par. 4 and 5.
3. The major sound producing surface of a transformer is a vertical surface which follows the contour traced by a string stretched around the horizontal projection of the transformer outline. This outline is to be determined by including radiators, coolers, tubes, switch compartments, terminal chambers, etc., but excluding bushings and minor extensions such as valves, oil gauges, thermometers and conduit terminal boxes and projections at or above cover height.
4. For transformers having an over-all tank height of less than 8 ft, measurements shall be made at approximately half height. For transformers having an over-all tank height of 8 ft and above, measurements shall be made at approximately $\frac{1}{3}$ and $\frac{2}{3}$ height.
5. Microphone locations shall be determined as follows [(see Fig. 29.3)]. Starting at a point opposite the main drain valve and proceeding clockwise around the transformer as viewed from above, mark off reference points at 3 ft intervals measured in a horizontal direction along the major sound producing surface defined in par. 3. There should be no fewer than four reference points, which may result in intervals of less than 3 ft for small transformers. One sound measurement shall be taken opposite

* Recommended Standard 1-26-1948, NEMA Standard 7-23-1953.

each reference point The microphone shall be located on a straight line which is perpendicular to the major sound producing surface at the reference point. The microphone shall be 1 ft from the major sound producing surface except that, where fans are in operation, the microphone shall be 6 ft from any portion of the transformer radiators, coolers or cooling tubes cooled by forced air at the time that sound measurements are being made.

Audibility Method. As an alternative to the sound-level method of measuring the noise of a transformer, the AIEE committee has suggested a method depending on the audibility of the noise in the presence of background noise.[2] To avoid "beating" or coincidence effects at certain frequencies, the background noise should contain all audio-frequencies—a so-called "white" noise. Tests in the Chicago and Evendale residential areas have shown that the background noise there very roughly approximates a white noise, the spectrum level being as shown by curve A of Fig. 29.4.

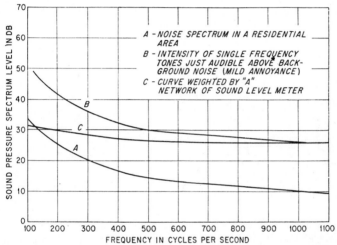

FIG. 29.4. Spectrum level for noise in residential areas and sound pressure level of single-frequency tones just audible above background noise. (*AIEE committee report.*[2])

Curve B gives the sound pressure level of single-frequency tones just audible above the background noise, causing mild annoyance, while curve C is curve B weighted by the A network of a sound-level meter. If the levels of the harmonic tones of a transformer noise are determined by a narrow-band analyzer, it will be possible to tell whether any of the components will be audible above the background noise shown in curve A. The background noise gives a reading of 54.5 db on the C (flat) network and of 41.5 db on the A network of a sound-level meter.

REDUCTION OF NOISE AND VIBRATION AT THE SOURCE

Core Material. It was thought in the late 1930s that magnetostrictive extension of the core is the main, if not the only primary, cause of transformer noise.[3,4,5] In particular, an exhaustive investigation was carried out on the determination of magnetostriction in transformer steels and the prediction of the resultant noise of complete transformers.[4] Neglecting magnetostrictive hysteresis, which was also investigated, substantial agreement was obtained between the sound levels of the harmonics as calculated from magnetostriction data on the core material and as measured with a sound analyzer on the built-up cores.[4,6] One of the relations that were obtained between magnetostrictive extension and flux density in the form of a hysteresis loop is shown as Fig. 29.5. The effect of hysteresis on displacement waveform is shown as Fig. 29.6.

Subsequent experimental explorations of core vibration have shown the presence of other modes than the simple ones in the plane of the laminations which are directly attributable to magnetostriction. But since it is known that magnetostriction of the core is responsible for much of the vibration and resultant noise of transformers and chokes, it would appear at first sight to be a logical step in the reduction of noise to choose or develop a core material having zero magnetostriction. However, there are two reasons why this course does not warrant a concerted attack.

First, it is usually found in practice that the energy contributed by the transverse modes of vibration is about equal to that due to the simple magnetostrictive extension. From a consideration of a well-clamped core having many laminations, it appears statistically very improbable that any large fraction of the transverse vibrations can be due to difference in magnetostrictive extension between adjacent laminae, causing bending. Any such differences, whether due to dissimilarities in permeability or in magnetostriction coefficient, will be of random distribution at any core section and so will not produce any general tendency to bend one way rather than the other. In the absence of magnetostriction, therefore, the power of the noise source would probably be halved—a drop of only 3 db in sound pressure level.

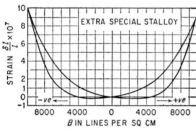

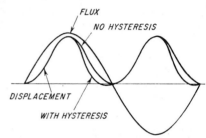

FIG. 29.5. Variation of magnetostriction hysteresis with flux density. (*After Swaffield.*[4])

FIG. 29.6. Effect of magnetostriction hysteresis on displacement waveform. (*After Swaffield.*[4])

Second, there are already so many requirements for core materials—e.g., low hysteresis, high resistivity, ductility when rolled into thin sheets, high permeability up to high densities, and low price—that to add another, namely, low or zero magnetostriction, is regarded as making the search quite hopeless. Six per cent silicon sheet steel has less than one-tenth the magnetostriction of 4 per cent, as can be seen in Fig. 29.2; but it is very brittle and difficult to punch or shear. In addition, when made up into a transformer core, it was certainly no quieter than 4 per cent steel and at high densities was noisier, thus bearing out the general reasoning given above. The new cold-reduced oriented sheet steel also has less magnetostriction than hot-rolled sheets at flux densities below 13,000 gauss, but at higher densities, Fig. 29.2 shows that the increase with density is much greater than with the hot-rolled sheet. Tests on medium-sized similar cores in the two materials have shown no significant difference in noise level at flux densities up to 13,500 gauss, but when advantage is taken of the ability of cold-rolled steel to operate at 16,500 gauss, there is an increase in sound level of 8 db. In addition, noise analyses on small transformers have shown (see Table 29.1*b*) that the fundamental is louder compared with the harmonics with the cold-rolled steel than with the hot-rolled cores; so larger transformers, where the fundamental is more important, may be still louder with cold-rolled steel cores. It appears, therefore, that it would be unwise to rely on achieving a reduction in noise with new materials of lower magnetostriction.

Reduction in Flux Density. The variation in sound level with flux density shown in Fig. 29.1 suggests one certain way of reducing the inherent noise of transformers and chokes. At a reduced density there is a corresponding reduction in rating; so to maintain a given rating, it is necessary to increase the size of the core and coils. A little of the improvement is, therefore, lost; but it is nevertheless possible to secure appreciable noise reductions in this way. However, the increase in cost is also appreciable, and, in considering the economics of the matter, it is necessary to compare this increase with the cost of other possible ways of effecting an equal reduction in noise.[7,15] Costs naturally vary with particular manufacturers; but it has been estimated that for a medium-sized transformer using hot-rolled steel a reduction in sound level of 10 db could be achieved by using a flux density of 9,500 instead of 13,500 gauss, with an extra cost perhaps of the order of 20 per cent. Reductions of more than 20 db would necessitate the use of such a low flux density as to be either impracticable or obviously uneconomic. It is apparent that the method of operating at a reduced flux density does not provide a complete answer to the problem but is rather a method to be compared with others—particularly the use of an enclosure, discussed later.

Effect of Core Clamping and Cementing. It might appear possible to reduce the vibration of the core and the consequent noise by more effective clamping of the laminations. Considering first the longitudinal vibration due to simple magnetostriction and assuming that the core is stiffness-controlled at this frequency, clamping the core on its ends with a clamp as stiff as the core itself would reduce vibration to one-half—a drop of 6 db in sound pressure level. A clamp as stiff as this is obviously impracticable; but any practical clamp with a stiffness less than one-tenth of this will reduce the vibration and the associated noise by a negligible amount.

The possibility of noise reduction by reducing transverse vibration of the core is not so remote. Owing to the fact that the laminations are not perfectly flat and that they are separated by paper or varnish to reduce eddy currents, the core is much less stiff transversely than longitudinally and can be compressed appreciably with quite practical clamps. By fitting clamps at points where the transverse vibrations are greatest, it is possible to effect reductions of a few decibels in the magnitude of the fundamental component; but the harmonics are often accentuated by the resultant stiffening of the laminations, leaving the

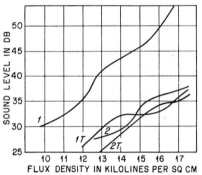

FIG. 29.7. Variation of sound level with treatment of core. (*After Mason.*[8])

total sound level almost unaltered in magnitude. Confirmation of this is provided in several papers: (1) Small differences covering a spread of only 2 phons in the noise of a 100-kva, 3-phase core were found with the core bolts "thumb tight," "well clamped," and "very tightly clamped."[3] (2) The magnitude of the harmonics in the noise of a core of "extra special" stalloy with "very slight" clamp pressure and with pressures of 100 and 200 lb per sq in.[4] varied considerably—up to 15 db—but as some were increased and others decreased, the rms sum varied very little. (3) In another study no difference was found in the noise of a number of cores when the core bolts were adjusted from a very slack condition to one as tight as possible consistent with the tensile strength of the bolts.[8] Only when the bolts were so slack as to permit rattling of the laminations of cores in air was there any appreciable increase in noise, and even this increase disappeared when the cores were immersed in oil. The damping effect of the oil was due to the stiffness of the oil films between laminations, the oil itself being virtually incompressible and there being insufficient time for it to flow laterally during each cycle of vibration. A reduction from 48 to 37 phons upon immersion of a core in oil was also noted in (1).

An alternative method of clamping by varnishing the laminations and baking them under pressure has also been investigated. For a core in air, a reduction of 10 to 20 db was obtained, increasing with flux density, when treated in this way.[8] However, when the core was immersed in oil, the bonding of the laminations had only a small effect of a few decibels, as seen in Fig. 29.7. Similar findings are reported in Ref. 3 and are summarized in Table 29.4.

With a ring core having no joints, cementing the laminations together effected a

Table 29.4. Effect of Cementing Cores

(4 per cent Silicon Steel. B_{max} = 13,000 gauss. Frequency = 50 cps.)

Core	Condition	Loudness level, phons
Ring core, 15-in. OD, 9-in. ID, 1-in. axial length..	Tightly bound with tape	43
	Cemented	<10
10-kva, single-phase core......................	Before oil immersion	48
	After oil immersion	37
	Cemented	26
10-kva, 3-phase core..........................	After oil immersion	65
	Cemented	64

Source: After Churcher and King.[3]

marked reduction in noise; but with larger built-up cores, the effect became less and less with increasing size, especially after immersion in oil, until for the 10-kva core it had practically disappeared.

Core Vibrations and Resonance. A thorough investigation of the modes of vibration of transformer cores and of the effect on them of clamping has been carried out.[9] In one case a resonance was found at 136 cps corresponding to a line frequency of 68 cps,

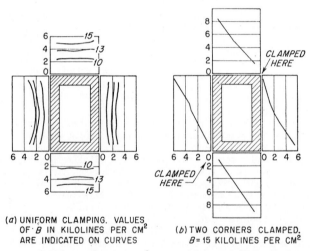

(a) UNIFORM CLAMPING. VALUES OF B IN KILOLINES PER CM^2 ARE INDICATED ON CURVES

(b) TWO CORNERS CLAMPED. B = 15 KILOLINES PER CM^2

DEFLECTION IN INCHES X 10^5 VS. POSITION AROUND CORE

FIG. 29.8. 120-cps core deflections parallel with plane of laminations at 60-cps excitation. (*After Fahnoe.*[9])

and the amplitudes of vibration of the legs in the plane of the laminations at resonance were up to 16 times those to be expected from simple magnetostrictive extension. These results are illustrated in Figs. 29.8 to 29.11, all of which refer to vibrations in the plane of the laminations. In addition, the phase of vibrations perpendicular to the plane of the laminations of a 3-phase core was explored. It appears from this study that a clamped corner is very stiff, making the gravest (lowest) mode of vibration of a core like that of a box, as illustrated in Fig. 29.10. Perhaps a more common mode of core vibration is that which results from the elongation of the ends of the legs; meas-

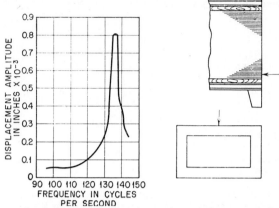

FIG. 29.9. Curve showing mechanical resonance in a shell-type transformer having an unclamped core. (*After Fahnoe.*[9])

ured on the top of the yoke, this elongation is approximately what would be expected from magnetostriction in the legs.

If a very simple case of resonance of a single-phase rectangular core is considered, it will indicate the order of magnitude of the factors concerned. Assume that the vibrating core can be broken down to a mass corresponding to half that of the yoke and to a stiffness corresponding to that of half a leg. If the mean length of the yoke,

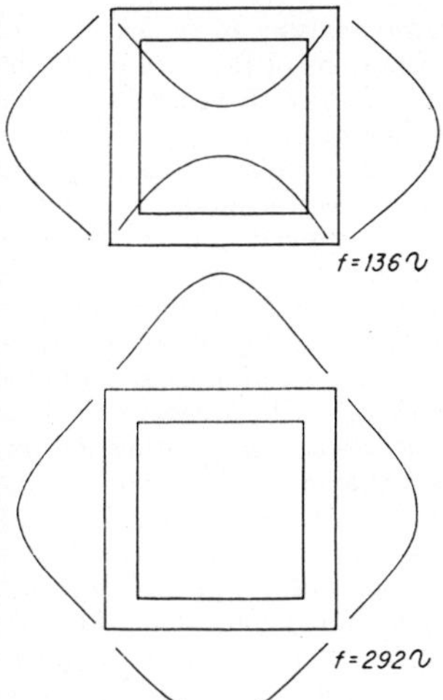

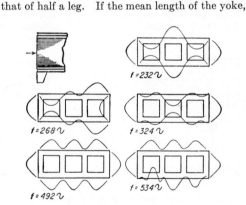

FIG. 29.10. Two modes of vibration of a rectangular core. (*After Fahnoe.*[9])

FIG. 29.11. Modes of vibration of a three-phase shell-type transformer. (*After Fahnoe.*[9])

top or bottom, is l_1 inches, cross section a_1 square inches, and density d, the half mass is

$$M = \frac{l_1}{2} a_1 d \qquad \text{lb}$$

If the mean length of a leg is l_2 inches, section a_2 square inches, and Young's modulus E, the stiffness s of half a leg is

$$s = \frac{2Ea_2}{l_2} \qquad \text{lb/in.}$$

The resonant frequency f_0 is given by

$$f_0 = \frac{1}{2\pi} \sqrt{\frac{sg}{M}} \quad \text{cps}$$

where g = acceleration due to gravity, in./sec²

$$\therefore f_0 = \frac{1}{\pi} \sqrt{\frac{Ega_2}{l_1 l_2 \, da_1}} \quad \text{cps}$$

If $a_1 = a_2$,
   $E = 3 \times 10^7$ lb per sq in.
   $l_1 = l_2 = 100$ in.
   $d = 0.28$ lb per cu in.
   $g = 386$ in./sec²
   $f_0 = 645$ cps

If due allowance were made for the distributed mass of the leg, the resonant frequency would be somewhat lower. However, the order of the first resonant frequency confirms the work of Ref. 9 (although the experimental values given in this study seem rather low, probably because of the reduced stiffness of a built-up, jointed leg as compared with that of a continuous, solid one). Furthermore, the presence of joints and differences, both magnetic and mechanical, between adjacent laminations inevitably increases the damping of the resonance and reduces the sharpness of the resonances in most practical transformers.

Harmonic Suppression. It can be seen from the noise analyses of typical sizes of transformer given in Table 29.1 that without the contributions of the harmonics, the total sound level would be reduced considerably—approximately 15 db for small sizes with hot-rolled cores. This reduction would be most helpful in dealing with many complaints of transformer noise; so an attempt was made to suppress the harmonics in the noise of a small transformer by injecting suitably phased harmonic voltages in series with the applied primary voltage. The method proved to be successful, a reduction of 15 db in the second harmonic of the noise being readily obtained by the addition of a few per cent second harmonic of the line voltage. The necessary range of harmonic voltages for suppressing the important components of the noise can be produced by a series of small alternators driven by a synchronous motor, the stators of the alternators being adjustable to obtain the correct phase for suppression. Alternatively, static frequency changers and phase regulators can be used. Even if the harmonics are not completely suppressed, substantial reductions in total noise can be achieved. The method is not as promising in the case of cold-rolled steel cores or in larger sizes, owing to the greater importance of the fundamental in these cases.

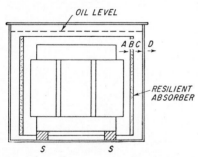

FIG. 29.12. Diagrammatic illustration of an oil-immersed three-phase transformer with resilient absorbers and supports. (*After Churcher and King.*[3])

Resilient Barriers in Oil-immersed Transformers. In the case of oil-immersed transformers and chokes, it has been demonstrated that the transmission of vibration from a core through the surrounding oil to the sides of the enclosing tank can be greatly reduced by interposing resilient barriers in the oil as shown diagrammatically in Fig. 29.12.[3] Rigid barriers such as bakelite or sheet steel do not give appreciable reductions, because their radiation properties do not differ sufficiently from those of oil. The reduction in transmission that can be achieved with resilient barriers is dependent on making the stiffness reactance of the barriers at the fundamental frequency of the pulsations in the oil (120 cps for a 60-cps supply) small compared with the mass reactance of the oil and tank outside the barriers, the theory being similar to that for reducing the transmission of vibration from machines by resilient mountings. The stiffness of the barriers can be reduced by making them in the form of thin film envelopes filled with a gas, keeping to a minimum any solid connection between the inner and outer films.

If the space between these two films is d inches and the pressure of the gas inside P lb per sq in., the stiffness of the barrier to waves radiating from the transformer is given by

$$s = \frac{rP}{d} \qquad \text{psi/in.}$$

where r = ratio of specific heats of gas
The reactance of this at a frequency of f cycles per second is

$$X_s = \frac{-s}{2\pi f} = \frac{-rP}{2\pi fd}$$

If M is the mass in pounds per square inch of the oil and tank outside the barriers, the mass reactance of this at a frequency of f cycles per second is

$$X_m = \frac{2\pi fM}{g}$$

If $X_m/X_s = N$ where $N \gg 1$, then the attenuation provided by the resilient barrier is roughly $20 \log (N - 1)$ db. By this means attenuations of 25 db have been achieved.[3] Although tests were carried out to show that such resilient barriers did not interfere appreciably with natural thermal circulation of the oil and that their life under repeated warmings and coolings was satisfactory, it was felt that their use would add yet another hazard to those already besetting transformers; consequently, they have not been supplied commercially.

Spray Cooling. Another way of reducing the vibration reaching a transformer tank is to avoid transmission via the oil by keeping the tank almost empty and cooling the transformer by spraying a suitable insulating liquid over the windings and core. At the same time it is necessary to reduce transmission via the transformer feet by interposing resilient mountings between the feet and the bottom of the tank. Several ways of carrying out this method have been tried. In one* a pump is used to drain the tank and force the oil through a cooler to sprays above the windings and core. In another the transformer is enclosed in an inner tank filled with oil, the outer surface of this tank being sprayed with water, which is drawn off by a pump so as not to couple the inner and outer tanks. Resilient mountings are again necessary between the two tanks.

Evaporation and Gas Cooling. Instead of relying on normal liquid methods of cooling, advantage can be taken of the abundant latent heat of vaporization of suitable liquids. An indirect method,† which does not call for insulating properties in the coolant, makes use of a double tank, a tray on top of the inner tank containing the liquid to be evaporated and a cooler supported above to condense the vapor. Alternatively, there are now organic liquids available which have vapors with good electrical insulating properties and so permit direct cooling of the core and coils while still preserving only gaseous, as opposed to liquid, coupling between the transformer and tank. In both cases it is essential to attenuate the vibration reaching the outer tank by interposing resilient mountings; otherwise most of the possible improvement will be lost.

REDUCTION OF SOLID-BORNE NOISE

If the vibration of a transformer or choke is communicated to the surface on which it is mounted or to any other neighboring surface, the vibration of the surface will

---

* British Patent No. 718,129.
† British Patent No. 714,524.

radiate a sound of similar composition to that radiated directly to the air by the source.   The principal way in which this conduction of vibration takes place is through the supports of the transformer or choke to the mounting surface, and then by solid connections to other surfaces, such as those of an enclosure or even of a distant room in a building.   A common example is provided by an electric clock resting on a wooden cabinet beside a bed.   At night, when other noises are reduced, the hum of the clock may be objectionable; but if it is lifted off the top of the cabinet, the noise usually disappears or is very much reduced.   This accentuation of the noise by a "sounding-board" action is avoided by interposing a resilient mounting under the vibrating source (a soft-rubber or felt pad being usually sufficient in the case of the clock).   The same principle of resilient mounting is applied throughout the whole range of electrical apparatus—from the clock, weighing a few ounces, to a 100,000-kva transformer weighing 100 tons or more.

In many cases special resilient mountings have been developed for particular types of apparatus.   These range from shaped bushes or grommets for small transformers and chokes mounted in such places as on shelves, wall brackets, or inside boxes to large proprietary mountings rated at several tons each.   Between these limits there are many intermediate sizes of mounting, mostly using rubber but in some cases incorporating springs.   Where rubber is used, it is sometimes necessary to protect it from oil, especially with oil-filled transformers, or to use synthetic rubber.   For medium and large transformers, pads or strips of sheet rubber, of Shore hardness 50 to 60, usually 1 to 3 in. thick, and operating at 100 lb per sq in. are very convenient for putting under tanks and can be protected from dripping oil by sheet-metal trays, the inverted one above the rubber overlapping the lower one without touching it or preventing the rubber from spreading laterally.   Some of the available types of mounting are illustrated in Chap. 13, which also goes thoroughly into the problem of their design. It is usually sufficient to ensure that the natural frequency of the transformer or choke on its resilient mountings in the vertical direction is low compared with the fundamental vibration frequency, i.e., twice the line frequency.   The natural frequency depends on the supported mass and the dynamic stiffness of the mountings, and so on the linear compression of the mountings.

If W pound is the weight of the transformer or choke, h inch the compression of the mountings, and k the ratio of dynamic to static stiffness of the mountings, the vertical natural frequency f_0 is given approximately by

$$f_0 = \sqrt{\frac{10k}{h}} \quad \text{cps}$$

For rubber, $k = 1.2$ to 2 (average value 1.6).

If f_1 is the fundamental vibration frequency (120 cps for a 60-cps line frequency), the attenuation of this vibration by mountings of low damping, such as rubber, when $f_1/f_0 > 3$ is given approximately by $(f_1/f_0)^2$.   For the vibration isolation of large transformers it may be necessary to provide the requisite area of rubber in the form of strips spaced at intervals under the tank.   If these strips pass under the tank from one side to the other, they will leave air channels in between of a length equal to the width of the tank and a rectangular cross section corresponding to the space between strips and the thickness of the strips.   These channels are liable to be excited in the manner of open-ended organ pipes by the vibrating bottom of the tank, especially if their length corresponds to a half wavelength or a number of half wavelengths of a note radiated by the tank.   In one case, of a large shunt reactor, where this effect was observed, the tank was 5.5 ft wide, and the channels consequently of this length and roughly 6 in. by 1½ in. in cross section.   The line frequency, of 50 cps, gave a fundamental vibration and noise frequency of 100 cps and, with a velocity of 1,100 ft per sec, a half wavelength in air of 5.5 ft.   The channels therefore greatly emphasized the fundamental tone, the excessive noise being obviously determined as coming from the bottom of the tank.   When the open ends of the channels were filled with resilient material, the accentuation of the fundamental ceased and noise became normal for the size of reactor.

At frequencies greater than 1,000 cps and for thicknesses of rubber greater than 1 in., the attenuation is liable to be reduced by as much as 17 db as a result of standing waves in the rubber. Fortunately, for transformers operating on power systems, the vibration components of 1,000 cps and above are usually very small; and for transformers operating at these high frequencies, thicknesses of rubber much less than 1 in. are usually adequate to give the required attenuation.

Rubber can also be used in shear. This method is often useful for supporting small loads for which pieces in compression would be mechanically unstable. The vertical displacement under load to give the required attenuation is determined in the same way as for direct compression. The shear modulus G of soft rubber is of the order of 300 lb per sq in., so the vertical displacement h inch for a shear load of W pound per square inch on rubber of thickness T inch is

$$h = \frac{WT}{G} = \frac{WT}{300} \text{ in. (approx)} \qquad \text{for} \qquad \frac{h}{T} \not> 0.2$$

As in the case of direct compression, it is necessary to increase the displacement by some 60 per cent on account of the factor k.

Coil springs are not often used, as they are more expensive than rubber for transformer isolation. Leaf springs have been used when large attenuations at low frequencies call for deflections under load of up to 8 in. In one such case, a static deflection of 8 in. was found to correspond to a natural frequency of 6 cps instead of 1.1 cps, showing that static friction, or "striction," between leaves was increasing the dynamic stiffness to small-amplitude vibrations to 30 times the static value. As a result, the vibration was accentuated instead of attenuated. The insertion of pieces of thin sheet rubber between the leaves near their tips completely removed this "striction" and brought the natural frequency down to the calculated value of 1.1 cps. The vibration was then attenuated satisfactorily.

A similar case which was dealt with satisfactorily concerned a synchrotron weighing 140 tons which is pulsed five times a second with damped wave trains of 150 cps. The apparatus is installed in a university laboratory near to the professor's sleeping quarters, and the leaf-spring suspension has attenuated the harmonic range of components, of from 5 to at least 100 cps, sufficiently to avoid causing any annoyance.

When mounting a transformer or choke resiliently, it is important to ensure that all other connections to the ground and building are at least equally, and preferably more, resilient. Such flexibility requirements for cables and grounding straps are sometimes forgotten. The former require a long, free length to the first rubber-bushed cleat, and the latter call for a flexible cable rather than a strap. Pipe connections to external radiators must also be flexible.

REDUCTION OF NOISE FROM FLUORESCENT-LAMP BALLASTS (CHOKES)

Ballasts (i.e., chokes) for connecting in series with fluorescent lamps to stabilize them (they are otherwise unstable) are rather different from transformers in their noise-generating properties. In the first place, their current and flux waveforms are far from sinusoidal, the nonlinearity of the lamp discharge causing many harmonics—up to the 50th order or even higher. The effect of these harmonics on the sound spectrum can be seen in Fig. 29.13, which shows the greatly increased number of harmonics present in the sound of a ballast feeding a fluorescent lamp compared with the sound of the same ballast fed with sine-wave current of 50 cps.[12] The concentration of harmonics in the region of 2,000 cps is particularly unfortunate, as this is the region of maximum sensitivity of the human ear.

In the second place, these chokes are provided with air gaps in order to maintain their impedance over a wide range of current. The air gaps inevitably give rise to pulsating forces tending to pull the opposite faces together and so causing additional vibrations to those encountered in transformers with interleaved core joints.

It has been suggested that vibration from these two sources be reduced by an arrangement such that they tend to neutralize each other.   The tendency of normal cores is to extend because of magnetostriction but to contract because of tension

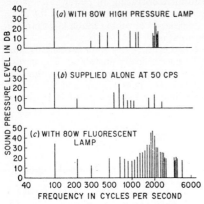

Fig. 29.13. Analysis of noise from 80-watt fluorescent-lamp ballast.   (*After Mason.*[12])

across the air gaps.   Both forces have fundamental frequencies equal to twice the line frequency, so it is only necessary to choose a nonmagnetic material of suitable stiffness with which to fill the gap in order to effect cancellation of the two fundamentals.   Fig. 29.14 illustrates the simple symmetrical case of a three-limbed core with a gap in the center limb carrying the coil.   The case of a two-limbed, unsymmetrical core with a gap in one limb is illustrated in Fig. 29.15; in (*b*) the ingenious device of concentrating the gap-filling material to the side of the gap remote from the other limb is adopted in order to counteract the tendency of the core to bend.   It is not to be expected that all the harmonics would also neutralize each other, neither would all transverse vibrations of the core be eliminated.

Another effect of the air gaps is to increase the magnetic-leakage flux around the ballast so that any sheet-metal enclosure provided to reduce the radiated noise may

be vibrated by the leakage flux and actually increase the noise.   This effect was investigated, and it was shown that by locating the air gap in the magnetic circuit of a choke solely within the coil (as opposed to the early designs, which had gaps in the yoke as well as the core) the leakage field was very much reduced.[12]   These results are summarized in Fig. 29.16.   Quite apart from the question of noise generation, the reduction of this stray field is very important in many cases where such chokes are mounted near to electronic or other apparatus sensitive to or affected by stray magnetic fields.

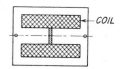

Fig.   29.14.   Sectional view of symmetric core construction.   (*Van Heuven.*[10])

A fluorescent-lamp ballast is usually mounted in the lamp housing or lantern, which, being made of sheet metal and being of large area, makes an excellent sounding

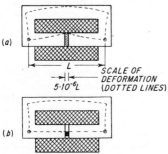

Fig. 29.15. (*a*) Deformation pattern of nonsymmetrical core with symmetrical gap filling; (*b*) same, with nonsymmetrical gap filling. (*Van Heuven.*[10])

board for radiating as noise any vibration transmitted to it from the choke.   The paths for noise transmission are shown in Fig. 29.17.

In the measurement of noise from a fluorescent-lamp fixture, variables other than the mount of the ballast must be controlled:[13] (1) the fluorescent lamps, and (2) the ballast temperature.   Lamps that are near the end of their life generally produce about 2 db higher noise level than new ones.   Also, as a fluorescent lamp warms up to its operating temperature, the noise level increases by as much as 4 db.   Therefore, in any noise-test procedure, a 30-min minimum warm-up period is required for conditions to become stabilized.   The temperature of the ballast itself also affects the output by as much as 4 db, increasing with temperature for some ballast installations and decreasing with others.

A type of measuring system is described in Ref. 13 which makes it possible to measure conveniently the noise output of a fluorescent-lamp fixture in a standard mounting by fitting a hornlike structure over the fixture, a sound-level meter being placed at the mouth of the horn.

As with larger apparatus, it is necessary to reduce the transmitted vibration and noise by interposing a resilient mounting between the choke and lamp housing. On 50- and 60-cps lines, the fundamental vibration frequencies of 100 and 120 cps, respectively, call for a very flexible mounting with a natural frequency of the order of 20 cps. In certain applications, higher line frequencies such as 400 cps are used, so a correspondingly higher natural frequency of mounting is permissible. The design of these mountings is dealt with in Chap. 13; but there is a special requirement which must be taken into account. Some lamps attain a temperature greater than 60°C, which is the upper limit for satisfactory operation of rubber, since at higher tem-

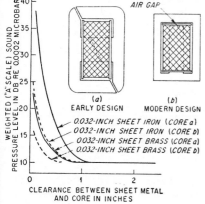

FIG. 29.16. Noise level from 400-cps choke with 12-sq-in. sheet metal near the core. (*After Mason.*[12])

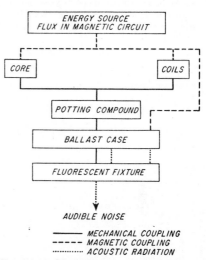

FIG. 29.17. Block diagram of the paths for transmission of ballast noise to the fluorescent-lamp fixture. (*After Hayes and Gould.*[13])

peratures it deteriorates much faster than at lower temperatures. In such cases metal spring supports should be used; for example, Fig. 29.18 shows two types.

Owing to the large size of lamp housings, the noise falls off slowly with distance up to distances corresponding to the height of a room. In addition, reflection of sound from the floor and walls conserves the sound energy and tends to make the sound pressure level more uniform over a room than it would be in free space. For the latter reason, too, doubling the number of lamps in a room usually increases the sound level by 3 db, except when the room dimensions are large compared with those of the lamp—in which case the increase is less and the noise from each lamp tends more to be as if it were confined to the region which the lamp serves with light. For production testing of small chokes to ensure that they are sufficiently quiet in operation, it is usually inconvenient or impossible to keep the noise in a test room low enough to permit

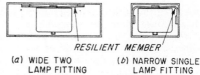

(*a*) WIDE TWO LAMP FITTING   (*b*) NARROW SINGLE LAMP FITTING

FIG. 29.18. Examples of metallic resilient mounts for fluorescent-lamp chokes. (*After Mason.*[12])

measurement of the choke noise by sound-level meters. A test cabinet may, therefore, be used, the choke under test being flexibly supported in a stout wood or transite box about 18 in. cube lined with sound-absorptive material 1 or 2 in. thick and provided with a removable lid. This box is in turn flexibly mounted in a similar box about 2 ft cube. If the boxes are well fitted and the walls 1 to 2 in. thick, moderate room noise can be attenuated sufficiently to permit measurement of the choke noise by means of a microphone suspended in the inner box and connected by flexible leads to an external amplifier and indicating instrument. A test box of this type is described in Ref. 11; it was reported to be very effective for use under the noisy conditions found in a factory, measurements being possible down to 20 or even 10 phons.   If it is desired to test a complete lamp housing with choke fitted, the boxes must be made correspondingly larger.   In this way, it is possible to keep a check on production by testing a suitable fraction of the output without involving undesirable delays or necessitating extreme quiet in the test room.

Another system that is suitable for production testing is the measurement of ballast vibration.   Correlation has been obtained between ballast noise and case vibration, provided the measurement of vibration is made over a relatively large area and not at a single point.   By isolating the vibration pickups from external vibration, low ambients are possible, making this method suitable for production testing.

REDUCTION OF NOISE BY DISTANCE

One way of solving the problem of installing a large power transformer in a quiet residential district is to acquire such a large plot of land that, with the transformer at

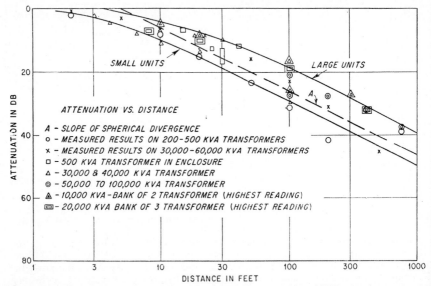

FIG. 29.19. Transformer-noise attenuation with distance.   (*After AIEE committee report.*[2])

the center, the noise is reduced purely by the distance to a tolerable level at the nearest house.   Once more the economic aspect becomes important, the question being whether the cost of the requisite plot of land and the additional cable that is required is greater or less than the cost of other ways of attaining the same noise level at the nearest houses.   To decide this question in any given case, it is necessary to consider the rate of attenuation of noise with distance from a source.   For a point source of sound on the ground radiating into semi-infinite space, the sound energy is spread uniformly over expanding hemispheres; so the sound pressure at a distance r is inversely proportional to r.   Each doubling of the distance r therefore corresponds to a reduction in sound pressure level of 6 db.   This is true for each component of the radiated sound and for the total value as read in a sound-level meter, provided the same frequency weighting network is used throughout.   The latter requirement is met if all readings of sound level are taken on the A weighting network, as recommended by NEMA.   The first requirement, that the source of sound behave as a point source radiating uniformly in all directions, cannot be expected to apply in the immediate vicinity of large transformers and chokes.   As a result of the large, flat surfaces on enclosing tanks, the sound level falls slowly with increasing distance at first; it is not until a distance corresponding roughly to the sum of the three linear dimensions—length, width, and height—of the source is reached that the sound field begins to decrease 6 db per doubling of distance. At this distance the sound level has usually fallen approximately 12 db compared with the average value at 1 ft from the tank surfaces, and thereafter falls a further 6 db for each doubling of the distance. Curves showing the attenuation of noise with distance for large and small transformers are given in Fig. 29.19.[2] At distances greater than 1,000 ft the attenuation of any components with frequencies greater than 1,000 cps is increased by atmospheric absorption, and uncertainties associated with meteorological conditions may be considerable. See Chap. 3.

REDUCTION OF NOISE BY EXTERNAL BARRIERS

The suggestion is sometimes made that the noise from an outdoor power transformer be prevented from reaching a nearby house by the placement of a wall between. This suggestion is based on the incorrect assumption that the sound shadow cast by a wall is sharply defined in the same way as is a light shadow. However, owing to the enormous difference in wavelength between light waves and sound waves, diffraction results in a bending of the sound waves, with a consequent reduction in the barrier's effectiveness. A mathematical investigation of the problem has shown that the attenuation to be expected from a barrier is dependent on the effective height of the barrier and upon the angle into the sound shadow. These parameters are illustrated in Fig. 3.3. The attenuation that can be achieved in this way is given as a function of effective barrier height expressed in wavelengths. The poor attenuation achieved by barriers in many practical cases is due to the low effective height brought about by tall sources and high listening points and, in the case of power transformers, the long wavelengths of the sound, for example, 9.3 ft for a tone of 120 cps. It is clear from Fig. 3.3 that it is difficult in practice to get an attenuation of 10 db for the fundamental of a transformer noise. Although the higher harmonics are more highly attenuated because of their smaller wavelengths, the over-all reduction is seldom much more than 10 db. While such an attenuation is useful in some cases, it is usually insufficient to give complete satisfaction and, in view of the cost involved, often gives an unsatisfactory return for the capital outlay. In one case a satisfactory reduction of noise was achieved; no figures were given for the height of the transformers and barrier, but an attenuation of 13 to 14 db was obtained, roughly confirming the above theoretical estimate.

SOUND CANCELLATION

One possible method of reducing transformer noise is by adding an equal one so phased as to cancel out the transformer noise.[14] A loudspeaker placed as close as possible to a transformer in the open air is made to emit a harmonic range of tones, each one of which is adjusted in magnitude and phase so as to cancel, at the location where quiet is desired—the corresponding tone of the same frequency in the noise from the transformer. A power amplifier supplying the loudspeaker is fed from a suitable source of harmonics, with amplitude and phase adjustment for each. The harmonics can be obtained from the line voltage through a rectifier or from a vibration pickup attached to the transformer tank, suitable filters being included to pick out each harmonic for individual control. At a point, say 100 ft away from a transformer, it is possible to effect complete cancellation of any one harmonic for a short time; but attenuations of 20 db are more representative. Over an angle of 35° the average attenuation of the noise is somewhat less, and may be only 6 db. Increases in noise are inevitable in other directions unless directional loudspeakers are used. The method does not appear to be suitable for cases where a reduction of noise is desired in all directions or, indeed, in anything more than a very restricted cone.

REDUCTION OF NOISE BY ENCLOSURE

It is often better from both manufacturing and economic viewpoints to take a standard distribution transformer and normal size of plot and reduce the radiated noise by enclosing the transformer in a suitably designed building or other enclosure, instead of trying to manufacture a special transformer which would be inherently quiet or buying a very large plot of land so that it may be placed at a large distance from those it may disturb.   The attenuation to be expected from various types of wall structure is discussed in Chap. 20.   It is shown there that for solid walls, the sound attenuation at frequency f cycles per second is dependent on the surface density of the wall.   If they are quite separate, two walls should give twice the attenuation in decibels of one, whereas doubling the weight of one wall gives an increase of only 4 to 6 db.   However, in practice, it is never possible to avoid some degree of coupling of double walls, either at the foundations or in the air between them; so the attenuation of two walls is always somewhat less than the sum of the individual attenuations.   A double enclosure, referred to in Ref. 15, gave an additional attenuation of only about 6 db.   This was a double-tank transformer of 20,000 kva, the spacing between the two tanks being about 6 in., and precautions were taken to minimize the transmission of noise from the inner to the outer walls.   The precautions were not described, but the poor result indicates that some factor, possibly the small spacing or the resilient mounting, was limiting the attenuation.

An area of an enclosure which has a reduced surface density will transmit sound energy at a greater rate per square foot than the remainder.   For this reason it is important to make the doors and windows as heavy as possible and to keep them small, well fitting, and, if necessary, double.   Approximate values of the magnitudes involved can be obtained by assuming that the acoustic power transmitted through each wall of an enclosure is proportional to its area and inversely to the square of the surface density.   If the area of a door or window is $1/N$ the total area and its surface density $1/M$ that of the enclosure, M must be not more than $N^{1/2}/2$ if the attenuation is not to be reduced by more than 1 db.   For example, if the total area is 1,000 sq ft and a door 10 sq ft, $N = 100$; and if the enclosure is 90 lb per sq ft, the door should be not less than 18 lb per sq ft.   This corresponds to a ½-in. steel plate, so the door would have a total weight of 180 lb, which might be inconveniently heavy.   In this case, two lighter doors in well-spaced, separate frames, having the same transmission loss could be used instead.   Windows should be avoided entirely and artificial light used if maximum acoustic insulation is to be obtained.

It is apparent from the example given that, where it is necessary to make provision for getting a large transformer in and out of a building, doors become impracticably heavy.   One solution is to build one wall of the enclosure so that it can be removed.

The use of a layer of porous material such as mineral wool a few inches thick is sometimes proposed for enclosing machines to reduce the emitted noise.   As indicated in Chap. 20, such layers are poor sound insulators, even though they are good absorbers.   Thus, while it is possible to obtain useful attenuations of transformer noise by porous materials, the thickness involved—1 to 2 ft—and the difficulties of support and protection are such as to make the method unattractive in most cases as compared with solid enclosures.

When considering the enclosure of a source of sound, there are three points to which careful attention must be given: (1) the effect of the enclosure on the sound inside; (2) the reduction of the attenuation by vibration conducted by solid contact between the source and the enclosure; (3) the thermal consequences of enclosure.   Of these, (2) has already been dealt with; so the remaining two points will now be considered.

Effect of Enclosure on the Noise of a Source.   When a source of sound such as a transformer is totally enclosed by a reflective enclosure, the sound pressure near the source is increased from its level before enclosure, the amount of increase depending on several factors.   If the distances between the source and walls are smaller than a half wavelength (4.6 ft at 120 cps) of a component of the noise, there will not be normal radiation of that component from the vibrating surface of the source but rather adiabatic compression and expansion of the volume of air between the source and enclosure.   As this volume is made smaller, the sound pressure will increase, until it may react on the source and also cause appreciable vibration of the enclosure walls.   In practice, the sound pressure level may rise 6 to 10 db from the unenclosed value.

If the distances from the source to the reflecting surfaces of the enclosure are larger than a wavelength, the radiated sound energy is conserved, and builds up the sound pressure until the rate of dissipation of energy by reflections at the inner surfaces and transmission through the enclosure to the outside just balances the rate of emission of sound energy by the source. The increase in sound pressure level due to "build-up effect" is therefore dependent on the total sound absorption inside the enclosure, the energy absorbed in this way being usually much greater than that transmitted through the enclosure. In practice the build-up may be of the order of 5 to 10 db.[3,8,16]

Some idea as to the reduction provided by an increase in the absorption within an enclosure designed for a power substation may be obtained from a consideration of the following example.

If the absorption coefficient of the interior surface is 0.01, the area of the inner surfaces in square feet multiplied by .01 gives the total absorption of the surfaces in sabins. If this absorption is doubled by adding sound-absorptive material having an absorption coefficient of about 0.05, the "build-up effect" will be reduced by 3 db. Since each doubling reduces the sound pressure level only 3 db, the law of diminishing returns soon makes this an uneconomic way of reducing the noise inside, and correspondingly outside, the enclosure. A special case of build-up occurs when the internal dimensions of the enclosure are such as to cause resonance with one of the components of the noise. In one actual case, a room 20 ft by 13 ft 10 in. by 15 ft high had a marked resonance at 50 cps (the line frequency); changing the length from 20 ft to 15 ft reduced the noise level by 25 phons, probably corresponding to about 20 db.[16] The expression for the natural frequencies of a room of dimensions L, W, and H is[17]

$$f = \frac{c}{2} \sqrt{\frac{A^2}{L^2} + \frac{B^2}{W^2} + \frac{C^2}{H^2}} \qquad \text{cps}$$

where A, B, and C = integers

c = velocity of sound

However, this formula does not apply when a large fraction of a room is taken up by a transformer.

Noise Problems Associated with Ventilation of Transformer Enclosures. When air-cooled transformers larger than 100 kva are enclosed, it is usually necessary to make special provision for ventilation. Up to 500 kva, a few louvers at top and bottom of the enclosure, preferably at opposite sides, often provide sufficient ventilation either naturally or with the help of a small fan and do not allow too much noise to escape. For larger air-cooled units ventilation can be provided by ducts fitted with sound-absorptive linings, which attenuate sound while allowing free passage of air. The attenuation in decibels per foot of length that can be obtained varies with the frequency, the width of air passage, and the thickness and acoustic properties of the porous-material lining, as indicated in Chap. 27. It is important that calculations be carried out at frequencies that are apt to be most disturbing. On 60-cps supply lines, noise components of 240, 360, and 480 cps are usually the largest present in transformers of small and medium sizes; but as the size increases, the fundamental of 120 cps becomes more important. The magnitudes of the harmonics can be determined in any given case by noise analysis, and the attenuation required for each computed. If a fan is necessary to ensure adequate ventilation, its noise will be added to that of the transformer and may affect the design. A frequency analysis will show whether it has any components which will not be adequately attenuated by the noise-control measures chosen for the transformer. In estimating the amount of attenuation that the duct must provide, it must be remembered that low-frequency sound begins to spread out and die away at shorter distances from a small-duct orifice than from a large transformer. At a distance equal to the sum of the two linear dimensions of the orifice, transformer noise usually is attenuated roughly 6 to 10 db; thereafter, each doubling of the distance reduces the noise by about 6 db.

An alternative method can be used for transformers with separate radiators. Most of the noise comes from the tank; thus the radiators can be mounted outside the enclosure and so leave only the comparatively small heat dissipation from the tank inside the enclosure. It is essential to have flexible couplings in the oil pipes between the tank and the walls of the enclosure so as to prevent too much vibration from being transmitted via this path, thus nullifying the attenuation of the enclosure. Further flexible couplings are advisable for mechanical reasons—although their necessity for acoustical reasons is debatable—in the pipes between enclosure and radiators and flexible bushes where the pipes pass through the enclosure walls. The layout for a transformer fed by underground cables is illustrated diagrammatically in Fig. 29.20.

Where a transformer is connected to an overhead network, complete enclosure involves another set of bushings to bring the leads through the roof. This involves considerable extra cost, which is difficult to justify in cases where a moderate attenuation of 20 db would be sufficient. For such cases, partial enclosure in a building looking like a small house with a truncated sloping roof has been suggested.[18] If, in an attempt to make the enclosure more complete, the roof is brought over the transformer and around, but not quite touching, the bushing turrets, there is a danger of

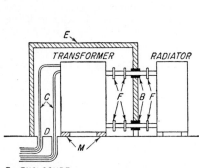

E = ENCLOSURE
F = FLEXIBLE COUPLINGS
B = RESILIENT BUSHES
C = CABLES, LONG FREE LENGTH BEFORE
    FIRST RESILIENT CLEAT
M = RESILIENT MOUNTINGS
D = CABLE DUCTS

FIG. 29.20. Diagrammatic illustration of a cable-fed transformer in an enclosure. External radiator.

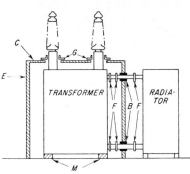

E = BRICK OR CONCRETE ENCLOSURE, ONE SIDE REMOVABLE
C = OVERLAPPING CONCRETE SLABS ON REINFORCED JOISTS. REMOVABLE
B = RESILIENT BUSHES   G = FLANGES WITH RESILIENT SEALS
F = FLEXIBLE COUPLINGS
M = RESILIENT MOUNTINGS

FIG. 29.21. Diagrammatic illustration of an H-V overhead line-fed transformer in an enclosure. External radiator.

creating a Helmholtz resonator from the volume of air in the enclosure and the mass of air in the gap opening around the turrets, and so accentuating one component of the noise. This can be avoided by filling the gap with resilient material, such as felt, which, if loosely packed, will not transmit too much vibration to the enclosure but will have enough acoustical absorption to prevent resonance. An overhanging cover is required to provide protection of the gap from rain, and the support of the roof presents some difficulties. A layout which is being tried on a 45,000-kva transformer is shown diagrammatically in Fig. 29.21. It is difficult to devise a construction which is sufficiently massive to give the desired attenuation and also readily demountable to permit removal of the transformer for transport to another site or for repair. One solution is to make one wall of panels slid into grooves in removable concrete pillars, spaced a few feet apart. Alternatively, the panels could be bolted to the pillars with resilient gaskets between.

REFERENCES

1. Standards for Transformers, *NEMA Publ.* 48-132, New York, rev. May, 1954.
2. Transformer Noise Measurement Methods, *AIEE committee rept.*, **73**: III 683 (1954).
3. Churcher, B. G., and A. J. King: *J. Inst. Elec. Engrs. (London)*, **87**: 539 (1940).
4. Swaffield, J.: *J. Inst. Elec. Engrs. (London)*, **89** (pt. I): 212 (1942).

5. Fahnoe, H.: *Elec. Eng.*, **60**: 277 (1941).
6. Brailsford, F., and R. G. Martindale: *J. Inst. Elec. Engrs. (London)*, **89** (pt. I): 225 (1942).
7. Specht, T. R.: Discussion, *AIEE Trans.*, **69** (pt. II): 1416 (1950).
8. Mason, C. A.: *BTH Activities*, **14**: 129 (1938).
9. Fahnoe, H.: *Elec. Eng.*, **60**: 277 (1941).
10. Van Heuven, E. W.: *Acustica*, **5** (2): 101 (1955).
11. Mason, C. A., and D. A. Nutt: *Elec. Rev. London*, **148**: 489 (1951).
12. Mason, C. A.: (symposium), *Phys. Soc. of London*, Acoustics Group, p. 174 (1949).
13. Hayes, C. P., and H. R. Gould: *Trans. AIEE*, **70**: 573 (1951).
14. Conover, W. B., and R. J. Ringlee: *Trans. AIEE*, **74**: III, 77 (1955).
15. Forrest, J. S.: *CIGRE Paper* 129, 1946.
16. Mason, C. A.: *Engineering*, **167**: 459 (May, 1949).
17. Morse, P. M.: "Vibration and Sound," p. 390, McGraw-Hill Book Company, Inc New York, 1948.
18. McLean, Corbett: *Proc. AIEE*, **69**, 1409 (1950).
19. Gordy, T. D., and W. S. Hill: *Elec. World*, **138**: 94 (December, 1952).

Chapter 30

ELECTRIC-MOTOR AND GENERATOR NOISE

R. O. Fehr, Sc.D., and D. F. Muster, Ph.D.
General Electric Company

INTRODUCTION

Electric motors and generators are used more widely today than ever before, many of them in locations such as homes, hospitals, industrial plants, and offices, where their noise may constitute a serious problem. They are used in air conditioners, electric typewriters, machine tools, pumps, and forced-draft blowers, with power ratings from as little as a fraction of a horsepower to as large as 5,000 hp.

Motors in air-conditioning equipment may be an important source of noise, which may be conducted efficiently by ventilating ducts. Series-wound or induction motors are the source of power in many household appliances, such as refrigerators, mixers, and vacuum cleaners. Any of these may present a serious noise problem; for example, although the so-called "120-cps hum" of a refrigerator motor is usually not objectionable, slip noise or starting noise of the same motor may be the cause of complaints.* Mechanical and electrical unbalance or bearing misalignment in motors used, for example, in food mixers may cause a noise which makes the appliance unacceptable.

Some elevator motors in residential or office buildings have a disturbing high-frequency whine which is heard each time the motor is started. Air-borne noise from the motor itself is often not of sufficient magnitude to be objectionable, but vibration of the motor may be transmitted through the foundation into the building proper. Partitions or wall panels located some distance from the motor may then be excited into resonance.

Power plant equipment is now frequently installed outdoors, very often adjacent to a residential area. For example, the noise from boiler feed-water pumps in such a plant may be objectionable in a quiet neighborhood, although its level may be rather low.

Sound pressure levels in the vicinity of large electric motors may, if proper precautions are not taken, be of such magnitude as to constitute a health hazard. The sound spectrum of these motors, when objectionable, usually has large single-frequency components superimposed on a broad-band noise. The single-frequency components are due either to magnetic forces which excite natural frequencies of the structure or to the rotor bars which periodically interrupt the flow of cooling air.

The reaction of people to noise determines the need for control. If a need for control exists, motor noise is reduced either at the source or attenuated by sound barriers before it reaches a noise-sensitive area. It can be reduced at the source by decreasing the magnitude of the magnetic forces, by preventing the excitation of natural frequencies, or by acoustically treating the motor air ducts. Sound attenuation by

* *Slip noise* is a low-frequency beating of higher-frequency components; because of its intermittence, this noise may be objectionable even though its level is relatively low.

Table 30.1. Electric-motor and Generator Noise Sources and Controls

Noise source	Cause	Component causing noise	Noise-control remedy
Mechanical	Impact	Sleeve bearings	Tighten oil ring, reduce end play of shaft
		Ball bearings	Reduce radial play, tighten separator, reduce shaft or housing tolerances; natural frequency of end shield should not equal characteristic ball-bearing frequency
		Brush holders and brushes	Tighten brush holder, change natural frequency, bias brush, and polish commutator
		Loose laminations	Improve clamping of laminations
	Friction	Ball bearings	Clearance too tight, lubricant too viscous or lacking; rectify
	Unbalance	Rotor	Mechanical balance required
	Instability	Bearings	Change oil grooves in bearings
Airflow	Modulation	Rotor bars chopping flow	Add acoustic filters or acoustically treated ducts
		Rotor vibration changing air gap and hence flow	Balance rotor or remove magnetic forces, change their frequency if equal to rotor natural frequency
	Turbulence	Fan	Redesign fan and scroll or add acoustic filters or acoustically treated ducts
Magnetic	Eccentricity	Air gap	Correct eccentricity of rotor or stator by machining and adjustment
	Variable field in circumferential direction	Synchronous machines having pronounced poles	Use resilient fastenings to mount machine or pole cores
		Slot-tooth variation of rotor and stator punchings	Avoid resonance of any motor components for this frequency, skew rotor slots
		Dissymmetry harmonics due to higher harmonics in stator current	Reduce dissymmetry by improved magnetic-circuit design; avoid resonance of rotor frame, particularly at lower modes, which are more effective sound radiators

barriers is discussed in Chap. 3.   Different types of machines require different methods of noise reduction, since noise may be caused by any one or all of several sources, including periodically varying magnetic forces, modulated or turbulent airflow, mechanical-unbalance forces, friction, and impact forces.   In Table 30.1 various noise sources in electric motors and generators and possible controls are tabulated. The noise sources are usually identified originally by a frequency analysis.

INDUCTION MOTORS

The noise from an induction motor can be attributed to the periodic motion of its parts under the action of periodic or impactual forces. This qualitative statement is an oversimplification that does not indicate the relative importance of the various sources of vibration within the motor, nor does it discriminate between those forces which perform useful work and produce noise as a by-product and those which do not contribute useful work but produce noise.

An induction motor produces two types of vibration: structure-borne vibrations, which are transmitted through the motor mounting system directly to the substructure upon which the motor rests; and air-borne vibrations or noise, which are radiated to the surrounding air at the surfaces of the motor parts. Although the structure-borne vibrations may excite severe resonances elsewhere via the substructure, their effects are not considered here, since they are dependent upon such factors as founda-

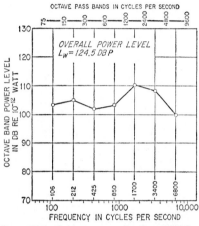

Fig. 30.1. Octave power levels—4,000-hp, 4-pole, 3-phase, 2,300-volt, open dripproof construction.

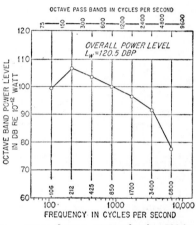

Fig. 30.2. Octave power levels—600-hp, 2-pole, 3-phase, 440-volt, open dripproof construction.

tion resilience and wall-panel resonances, which are outside the control of an electric-motor designer. They are discussed here only in so far as the mounting system directly affects the noise from certain motor parts.

Typical octave power-level spectra for various-size induction motors are shown in Figs. 30.1 to 30.3.

Noise Sources. Figure 30.4 shows the noise-transmission paths of a typical induction motor, indicating the normal sources of the noise and the paths which they may follow. Air-borne induction-motor noise can be categorized loosely, according to its source, as magnetic noise, ventilation noise, and mechanical or bearing noise.

Ventilation noise is usually a broad-band component of the over-all noise, but single-frequency components associated with resonant volumes within the shell of the motor, the radial flow of the cooling air through the motor, or the number of fan blades may appear superimposed on it.

Most mechanical noises are associated with the bearing assembly and can be appreciable if, for example, the bearing parts are deformed in some manner, or if excessive clearances permit axial travel of the shaft. Usually, mechanical noise is excited by impactual forces associated with the mechanical unbalance of the rotor-shaft assembly.

No general rule can be given for induction motors as to the relative importance of these three types of noise or of the two types of force which excite them. Individual design characteristics set the pattern which makes one or the other a major noise source.

Magnetic Noise.   Magnetic noise is caused by periodic forces which are almost exclusively in the air gap between the stator and rotor.[1,2,3,4]   At every point on the air-gap surfaces there is a varying force proportional to the square of the flux density. The sum of the tangential components of this force is proportional to the total torque which produces the useful work of the motor.   Pulsations of the tangential force produce a torsional vibration of the stator which, in turn, can cause the stator frame to rock in its mountings.   This torsional vibration is a major source of structure-borne vibrations.   The radial components of the magnetic force do not contribute useful work but serve only to produce noise. These *parasitic forces* appear at harmonics of the line frequency and at frequencies related to the slip and line frequency.

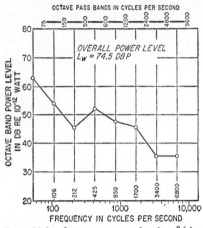

Fig. 30.3. Octave power levels—¾-hp, 4-pole, single-phase, 110/220-volt, open dripproof construction.

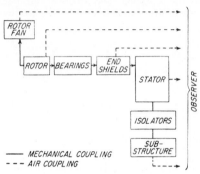

Fig. 30.4. Noise-transmission paths of a typical induction motor.

The *magnetic forces* are due to many mechanical and electromagnetic properties of the stator-rotor assembly.   They include (without regard to relative importance):

1. The number of rotor and stator slots and the difference between these two numbers.[2]
2. The characteristics of the fundamental flux field for which the motor is designed.[3]
3. Permeance variations in the air gap caused by stator slots, rotor slots, the slot pattern, saturation, and air-gap eccentricities.[2]
4. The manner in which coils of the pole windings are formed, i.e., the number of turns per tooth group for approximating a desired sinusoidal magnetomotive force in the fundamental field.[5]
5. The radial length of the air gap.[2]

In addition, although many characteristics are described as "uniform," "sinusoidal," or "concentric," current manufacturing practice inevitably introduces dissymmetries, nonuniformities, eccentricities, and nonlinearities, which, in some motors, account for a large part of the noise produced.   These *dissymmetry harmonic forces* are responsible for the dominant components in the over-all noise of some motors.

Force Waves.   The worst noise-producing forces are those which distort the rotor or stator in one of two ways: (1) a two-node bending motion of the rotor (such as occurs when the motor is unbalanced), and (2) a rotating, four-node elliptical distortion of the stator[1] (Fig. 30.5).   The two-node rotor motion can be caused by running the rotor at its *critical speed** or by exciting this bending mode with a two-pole force wave of the proper frequency.   Such a force wave can be produced in the fundamental field of the motor or by combining two force fields which differ by two poles. Elliptical stator deformation is caused by four-pole force waves which either occur in the fundamental field of the motor or are produced by combining two waves which differ by four poles.

* *Critical speed* is the rotating speed at which a bending mode of the rotor is excited.

These are not the only possible modes of distortion of the stator and rotor. The combination of two force fields with p and q poles, respectively, tends to distort the stator in a rotating polygon of $(p \pm q)/2$ sides. However, the stator and rotor offer greater resistance to distortion in higher-mode shapes, so that they are usually not important to noise production in induction motors. Furthermore, the corresponding energy radiated from these higher modes is less than from the lower modes.

The radial force waves which cause these distortions of rotor and stator occur at both twice the line frequency and at multiples of the synchronous speed and the actual speed. Although it can be shown that these harmonics occur at every multiple of the rotational speed of the motor, the relative contribution of most of them to the over-all noise of the motor is either small or can be made so. As the electrical characteristics of the motor and the mechanical response of the motor parts to various frequencies are changed, there are corresponding changes in the relative contribution of these harmonic waves. For example, if the frequency of the two-node bending mode of a rotor-bearing assembly coincides roughly with that of a two-pole radial force wave, then

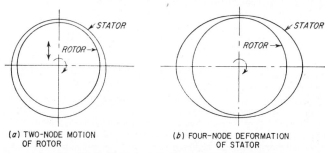

(a) TWO-NODE MOTION
OF ROTOR

(b) FOUR-NODE DEFORMATION
OF STATOR

Fig. 30.5. Rotor and stator modes of vibration.

there will be a strong component of noise at about this frequency. If the same force wave exists in another motor but the stiffness characteristics of the rotor-bearing assembly are such that the resonance is well above the frequency of the force, then there may not be a corresponding component in the over-all noise output of the motor—or it will be less than that of the first case.

Calculation of Force Waves and Their Frequencies. For the case of a polyphase induction motor, let us assume that there is no saturation in the iron of the motor and that the air-gap length is uniform around the periphery of the motor. Let us choose a polar coordinate system (r, α) oriented such that the axis $\alpha = 0$ passes through a stator pole center and $r = 0$ coincides with the center of the stator-pole assembly. Any point x on the periphery of the air gap is measured from the axis $\alpha = 0$, that is, $x = \alpha r_g$, where r_g is the radial distance to the air gap.

Let $\mathcal{P}_0$ denote the average permeance intensity between the surfaces of the stator or rotor and a cylindrical surface midway between them. With reference to the stator, the permeance intensity $\mathcal{P}_R$ between the rotor and mid-surfaces is given by

$$\mathcal{P}_R = \mathcal{P}_0 + \sum_{k=1}^{\infty} \mathcal{P}_r{}^k \cos kR(\alpha - 2\pi nt) \tag{30.1}$$

where $\mathcal{P}_r{}^k$ = amplitude of kth harmonic of rotor-slot intensity
  R = number of rotor slots
  n = actual speed of rotor,* rps
  t = time

Similarly, the permeance intensity $\mathcal{P}_S$ between the stator and mid-surfaces is given by

$$\mathcal{P}_S = \mathcal{P}_0 + \sum_{l=1}^{\infty} \mathcal{P}_s{}^l \cos lS\alpha \tag{30.2}$$

* $n = (1 - s)f/P$, where s = slip, f = line frequency, P = pairs of stator poles.

where $\mathcal{O}_s{}^l$ = amplitude of lth harmonic of stator-slot permeance intensity
$\quad\quad S$ = number of stator slots

We recall that permeance is the reciprocal of magnetic reluctance $\mathcal{R}$ and that

$$\mathcal{R}_T = \mathcal{R}_S + \mathcal{R}_R \tag{30.3}$$

where $\mathcal{R}_T$ = total reluctance
$\mathcal{R}_S$ and $\mathcal{R}_R$ = reluctances between the stator and mid-surface, and the rotor and mid-surface, respectively

Equation (30.3) yields

$$\mathcal{O}_T = \frac{\mathcal{O}_S \mathcal{O}_R}{\mathcal{O}_S + \mathcal{O}_R} \tag{30.4}$$

where $\mathcal{O}_T$ = air-gap permeance intensity
From Eqs. (30.1) and (30.2) in (30.4), we obtain[2,3]

$$\mathcal{O}_T = \mathcal{O}_a \left(\mathcal{O}_0 + \sum_k \mathcal{O}_r{}^k \cos kR(\alpha - 2\pi nt) + \sum_l \mathcal{O}_s{}^l \cos lS\alpha \right.$$

$$+ \sum_k \sum_l \frac{\mathcal{O}_r{}^k \mathcal{O}_s{}^l}{2\mathcal{O}_0} \{\cos [(kR + lS)\alpha - 2\pi kRnt]$$

$$\left. + \cos [(kR - lS)\alpha - 2\pi kRnt]\} \right) \tag{30.5}$$

where $\mathcal{O}_a = \mathcal{O}_0/(\mathcal{O}_s + \mathcal{O}_R)$

The principal harmonics in the magnetomotive force of a symmetrical stator winding with q phase belts per pole, P pairs of poles, and S slots are the two phase-belt harmonics of order $(2q \pm 1)$ and the two slot harmonic waves of order $(S/P) \pm 1$. The rotor winding produces additional magnetomotive force waves of order $(R/P) \pm 1$. If we neglect all harmonics of higher order, the total air-gap magnetomotive force wave $\mathfrak{F}$ is[3]

$$\mathfrak{F} = A \cos (P\alpha - 2\pi ft) + B \cos [(2q - 1)P\alpha + 2\pi ft] + C \cos [(2q - 1)P\alpha - 2\pi ft]$$
$$+ D \cos [(S - P)\alpha + 2\pi ft] + E \cos [(S + P)\alpha - 2\pi ft]$$
$$+ F \cos [(R - P)(\alpha - 2\pi nt) + 2\pi fst] + G \cos [(R + P)(\alpha - 2\pi nt) - 2\pi fst] \tag{30.6}$$

where A, B, C, etc. = numerical coefficients that depend on such factors as currents, winding pitch, slots per pole, slot openings, etc.
$\quad\quad P$ = the pairs of stator poles
$\quad\quad f$ = line frequency

Coefficient A is proportional to the vector sum of stator and rotor fundamental currents; B, C, D, and E are proportional to the stator current only. Coefficients F and G are proportional to the rotor current only (neglecting the induced opposing harmonic currents).

The total air-gap flux wave in the motor is found by multiplying the expressions given in Eqs. (30.5) and (30.6). The air-gap forces are proportional to the square of the expression for the flux wave.

Harmonic Fields. In the flux wave there are six groups of harmonic fields:

1. The fundamental field.
2. The basic permeance harmonic field.
3. The phase-belt harmonic fields (not present in single-phase motors).
4. The stator-slot harmonic fields.
5. The rotor-slot harmonic fields.
6. Higher-order fields, which may be neglected.

The groups of important force waves (from the noise viewpoint) which are obtained by squaring the flux density obtained from Eqs. (30.5) and (30.6) are tabulated in Table 30.2, group A. In general, the only force waves which are likely to be potential noise sources in induction motors are those with 2, 4, 6, or 8 force poles or those which in combination can produce force fields with this number of poles. In small polyphase motors, the optimum number of rotor slots is usually equal to $S \pm 4P$. The exceptions to this general rule are 2-pole motors and wound-rotor motors, for which the numbers of rotor slots are normally $S - 8$ and $S - 6$, respectively.[3]

In most well-designed induction motors having a minimum amount of dissymmetries, eccentricities, etc., the main sources of magnetic noise (other than the so-called "induction-motor" hum at twice the line frequency) are the basic-slot-harmonic force fields at $Rn - 2f$, Rn, and $Rn + 2f$, with corresponding pole pairs of $R - S - 2P$, $R - S$, and $R - S + 2P$, respectively (Table 30.2, group A).

The assumptions upon which many designs are based are frequently violated in practice. Rotor castings are sometimes porous, the rotor periphery may be noncircular or eccentric with respect to the journals, the stator bore may be noncircular or offset with respect to the motor bearings, etc. The presence of any or all of these dissymmetries is reflected in the noise spectrum of the motor.

Table 30.2. Summary of Force Waves[6]

Source	P',* poles	f',* cps
A. Basic rotor- and stator-slot harmonics	$2(kR - lS) \underset{\circ}{\pm} 4aP$† $4(kR - lS) \underset{\circ}{\pm} 4aP$	$kRn \underset{\circ}{\pm} 2bf$ $2kRn \underset{\circ}{\pm} 2bf$
B. Intermodulation—Basic slot and rotor dissymmetry harmonics...	$2(kR - lS)(\pm)2p \underset{\circ}{\pm} 4aP$†	$[kR(\pm)p]n \underset{\circ}{\pm} 2bf$
C. Intermodulation—Basic slot and stator dissymmetry harmonics..	$2(kR - lS) \pm 2q \underset{\circ}{\pm} 4aP$	$kRn \underset{\circ}{\pm} 2bf$
D. Intermodulation—Basic slot, rotor, and stator dissymmetry harmonics..................	$2(kR - lS) \pm 2q(\pm)2p \underset{\circ}{\pm} 4aP$	$[kR(\pm)p]n \underset{\circ}{\pm} 2bf$
E. Rotor dissymmetry harmonics....	$2p \underset{\circ}{\pm} 4aP$	$pn \underset{\circ}{\pm} 2bf$
F. Stator dissymmetry harmonics....	$2q \underset{\circ}{\pm} 4aP$	$\underset{\circ}{\pm} 2bf$
G. Intermodulation—Rotor and stator dissymmetry harmonics....	$2p \pm 2q \underset{\circ}{\pm} 4aP$	$pn \underset{\circ}{\pm} 2bf$

* $(a,b) = (1,2,3, \ldots)$. a and b assume positive integral values determined by the respective harmonic contents of the expressions for the space distribution ν of the pole winding and the time-dependent function of the stator current i. For example, if $i = I_1 \cos(\omega t) + I_3 \cos(3\omega t) + I_5 \cos(5\omega t)$, then $b = 1, 2, 3, 4, 5$.

† The symbol $\underset{\circ}{\pm}$ indicates that the term which follows should be added, omitted, and subtracted to obtain all possible combinations. The symbol ($\pm$) indicates that the term which follows must be used with the same sign in the pole-structure and frequency expressions; that is, $+2p$ in P' is associated only with $+pn$ in f'. The expressions for P' and f' in this table characterize (for fixed values of k, l, . . .) radial force waves with 81 pole structures at 27 frequency values. It is possible that several waves of the same pole structure and frequency will result, which reduces the total number of different force waves.

Effect of Dissymmetry Harmonics. The presence of components in the over-all noise of single-phase induction motors which are due to electromagnetic and mechanical dissymmetries in the rotor-stator combination is accounted for by existing theory.[6] The extension to polyphase motors has not been made.

In order to reduce the forces caused by dissymmetries (mechanical and electromagnetic) which exist in the rotor-stator combination, we must first understand their effect upon magnetic noise. If we denote the order of the rotor and stator dissymmetries by p and q, respectively, and the order of pole changing caused by a nonsinusoidal pole winding by a, then the pole structures (i.e., number of poles in a force wave) of all important harmonic forces and their frequencies are given in Table 30.2, where k and l denote the order of the stator- and rotor-slot harmonics, respectively, and b is the order of harmonics in the stator current.

An examination of the waves given in Table 30.2 discloses an important difference in the effect of rotor and stator dissymmetries. A dissymmetry of the rotor produces force waves at frequencies *and* with pole structures determined in part by the order of the dissymmetry. In contrast, stator dissymmetries affect only the pole structure of force waves at the same frequencies.

Narrow-band analyses of noise spectra have shown components at closer intervals than Kron's theory (and its modifications) predicts. If we return to the waves characterized in Table 30.2, which extends Kron's theory, we see that rotor- and stator-slot permeance harmonics cause force waves at frequencies no closer than 120 cps apart but that rotor dissymmetry harmonics add new force waves which (at synchronous speed) are 60 cps apart for a 2-pole motor, 30 cps for a 4-pole motor, etc.

Example of Effect of Dissymmetry Harmonics. As an example, let us consider an induction motor with the following general characteristics: $\frac{1}{2}$ hp, 1,725 rpm, 115/230 volts, 60 cps, single phase, capacitor start, 4 poles, 36–44 slot combination, and sleeve bearings. In terms of the parameters of Table 30.2, the motor is characterized by $R = 44$, $S = 36$, $p = 0$ or 1,* $q = 0$ or 1,* $P = 2$, $f = 60$, and $s = 0$ (for no load) or 0.042 (for full load). We will consider only the basic slot permeance harmonics; thus, $k = l = 1$.

In addition, let the two-node bending mode of the rotor occur at 515 cps when the machine is operating, and let the four-node circumferential mode of the stator be at 1,180 cps. Suppose the stator bore and rotor periphery to be concentric and perfectly circular; then there is no rotor or stator dissymmetry, and $p = q = 0$. It follows from the theory that there will be radial force waves with 8, 16, and 24 poles at frequencies of 1,200, 1,320, and 1,440 cps (at synchronous speed).† Even if current harmonics and poor winding distribution were introduced, no pole structure smaller than 8 poles would exist.

There must be a 2-pole force wave of the proper frequency to excite the rotor resonance. Similarly, there must be a 4-pole force wave at another frequency in order to excite the resonance of the stator shell. Since these requirements are not met by the magnetic force waves predicted by the usual theory (Table 30.2, group A), it would be expected that the motor considered in this example would operate quietly. However, a spectrum analysis of the over-all noise of the motor indicates strong peaks in the vicinity of both the two-node and four-node resonances of the rotor and stator, respectively. Therefore, forces of appropriate pole structure and frequency must exist in the magnetic field of the motor to excite these resonances.

If in this motor first-order stator and rotor dissymmetries exist concurrently (that is, $p = q = 1$), then their presence produces from the values in Table 30.2, group D, force waves with 4 poles at frequencies of 1,170, 1,290, and 1,410 cps (at synchronous speed), which can excite the four-node stator resonance.

In this same motor, let the winding distribution introduce some low harmonics ($a = 1$) and let a third and fifth harmonic of the stator current be present ($b = 1, 2, 3, 4, 5$). By using this additional information, from Table 30.2, group E, it can be shown that a 2-pole force wave at ($8f + n$) cycles per second exists in the motor, which coincides almost exactly with the two-node bending mode of the rotor at 515 cps.

Choosing a Slot Combination. Since dissymmetries can cause radial force waves by intermodulation with existing waves due to other sources, it is necessary to choose a rotor-stator slot combination with associated rotor-tooth permeance harmonics of high-order pole structures, which cannot be reduced to 2 or 4 poles in the presence of low-order stator and rotor dissymmetries. For example, the combination of 36 stator slots and 56 rotor slots will produce rotor-tooth permeance-harmonic waves of 32, 40, and 48 poles at frequencies of 1,560, 1,480, and 1,800 cps. The presence of a first-order rotor and stator dissymmetry will produce, at the worst, only a 28-pole force at frequencies of 1,530, 1,650, and 1,770 cps.

Open- vs. Closed-rotor and -stator Slots. Open-rotor or -stator slots cause abrupt changes in air-gap permeance. The high harmonic fields associated with these changes produce, in turn, corresponding high-frequency components in the over-all noise of the motor. The noise level of such components can be reduced by closing the slots in the rotor and stator. The periphery of such a rotor or stator is a smooth arc, and only lower-order harmonics appear in the air-gap permeance.

It is impractical to use closed-stator slots in an induction motor, irrespective of size, because of the costly pole windings that are necessitated. Closed-rotor slots are used commonly in smaller sizes—particularly in single-phase, fractional-horsepower motors where the bars and end rings for squirrel-cage rotors can be die-cast from aluminum at relatively low cost. Reductions in over-all noise level of approximately 5 db are possible by the use of closed-slot rotors.

---

* This motor can be adjusted to control low-order rotor and stator dissymmetries.
† Table 30.2, group A.

Means of Reducing Forces in Air Gap.   The forces in the air gap can be reduced effectively by altering either the electromagnetic or mechanical characteristics of the rotor-stator assembly.   It is not always practical to make these changes, since they also affect the torque characteristics, core losses, and other electrical characteristics.

An ideal induction motor from the viewpoint of low noise production and small air-gap forces would have the following characteristics: (1) A perfectly circular and con-centric rotor-stator combination would eliminate dissymmetry-harmonic forces, (2) A skewed (spiraled) rotor would be an effective means for suppressing noise due to high-order fields.   If the slots of either the rotor or stator are skewed, the variations in flux density, torque, and the radial magnetic forces due to slot openings will be displaced in time phase along the axial length of the rotor.   This results in more uniform torque, less noise, and better voltage waveform.[3]   (3) The slots on the rotor and stator would be closed.   (4) The rotor-stator slot combination would be chosen so that the number of magnetic fields of appreciable magnitude which differed by 2 or 4 poles would be minimized.   (5) A large air gap would be allowed to decrease the permeance varia-tions.   However, this would also decrease the power factor.   (6) The rotor of the motor would be of a squirrel-cage type rather than phase-wound.

Unfortunately, a motor with the above characteristics would also probably have poor torque characteristics and high core losses and would probably be very expensive to fabricate.   An optimum design from the noise viewpoint includes as many of these features as can be tolerated by the required electrical design characteristics.

Response of Rotor to Force Waves.   Although the rotor and stator can vibrate in several modes of vibration, only a few of these are important from the noise viewpoint. The two-node bending mode of the rotor is prob-ably the only rotor resonance which will be ex-cited.   In large induction motors, it is possible that this mode of vibration will be low enough to be excited by the fundamental field of the motor or at harmonics of the rotational speed. This is a condition which is easy to check early in the design process and which can generally be avoided.   In small motors, the rotor resonance is usually sufficiently high that only higher har-monics of the fundamental field can excite it.

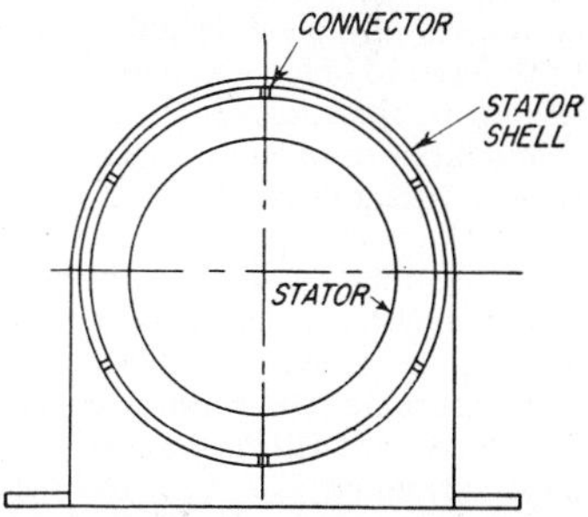

The frequency of the rotor resonance is also dependent upon end-shield and bearing charac-teristics.   The clearance of the bearings, the lubricant used, the length of the bearing, the stiffness characteristics of the bearing mounting

Fig. 30.6.   Stator–stator-shell con-nections.

(that is, the stiffness characteristics of the end shield, in which the bearings are mounted) all affect the resonant frequency of the rotor.   In general, the rotor-bear-ing assembly should be made as stiff as possible in order to raise the lowest natural frequency of the rotor to a value well above that where 2-pole magnetic force fields are likely to occur.[7]

Response of Stator to Force Waves.   In large induction motors, it is possible to excite as many as three or four modes of vibration of the stator—usually with those having four, six, and eight nodes.   It has been shown that in most cases the stator shell behaves sensibly as a ring rather than a hollow cylinder; i.e., there are usually no nodes along the axial length of the motor shell.   This can be corroborated by measur-ing the phase shift along axial lines drawn on the stator shell.[5]

In the computation of the natural frequencies of a large induction-motor stator shell, a further complication is introduced by the fact that it is common practice to have direct connection between the stator proper and the stator shell at four to eight points around their peripheries, as indicated in Fig. 30.6.   This type of construction has the effect of suppressing modes of vibration having nodes at points other than at these points of direct contact between the stator and the stator shell.   In small induc-tion motors, where the stator is press-fitted into a stator shell, the combination of the two parts behaves essentially as a thin shell with a strongly reinforced central portion.

In such motors, the stiffness of this combination and the friction damping which occurs in the press fit usually suppress all but the circumferential mode of vibration having four nodes.

Modern engineering practice requires the use of light materials for stator-shell and end-shield assemblies. This has the effect of reducing the frequencies of the various modes of vibration of these parts. Quite often it is necessary to reinforce them with stiffeners or ribs in order to raise their natural frequencies to values above those at which they are likely to be excited. If possible, it is best to avoid the use of end shields which are essentially unstiffened plates. Impact forces at the bearings and the bending of the rotor can cause severe vibration of the end shields in several modes of bending vibration if they are not properly stiffened.

Calculation of Natural Frequencies. Although it is not always possible to compute the frequency of the first bending mode of the rotor, it is possible to calculate the two frequency values between which it is likely to occur. Consider the rotor as a massless shaft which supports a large rotor weight at some point between two simple supports; this will provide a lower limit to the first bending mode of the rotor.[9] Now consider the points of support as behaving like rigid bearings which do not permit rotation about an axis transverse to the axis of the rotor; then the first bending mode of this configuration will yield an upper limit to the probable first bending mode of the rotor that it represents.

The actual bearings in the motor can be considered to behave as a combination of a linear, vertical spring support and a moment spring which resists rotation about an axis transverse to the axis of the rotor. If the stiffnesses of these two springs are known for each bearing (which is usually not the case), then it is possible to predict accurately the bending modes of vibration on the rotor shaft. Usually, the rotor is considered to behave as a shaft with partially elastic supports at the bearings, and it is left up to the individual designer's experience with bearing and end-shield stiffness characteristics to compute the proper frequency.[10] Some designers prefer to consider the shaft weight evenly distributed, the rotor weight concentrated, and the bearings as simple supports.

Satisfactory results have been obtained in computing the natural frequencies of the stator shell by considering it to behave as an elastic ring. Observations have been made by various investigators which substantially corroborate this assumption.[8]

Measurement of Natural-frequency and Nodal Patterns. It is important to know the modes in which the various components will vibrate and their corresponding natural frequencies. Any component can be caused to vibrate in resonance by means of an electromagnetic driving coil which is supplied by a variable frequency source, such as an oscillator followed by a power amplifier. Its vibration can be detected with a pickup, the output of which is applied to one axis of a cathode-ray oscilloscope while the oscillator voltage is applied to the other.[11] As the frequency of the oscillator is changed, Lissajous patterns appear on the cathode-ray oscilloscope. As a resonant frequency is approached and passed through, the signal from the pickup increases rapidly and the Lissajous pattern on the oscilloscope indicates a 180° phase shift. At the lowest natural frequency, the Lissajous pattern is U-shaped or a modified figure eight, since the actual vibration is at twice the oscillator frequency (Fig. 30.7). Although the flux in the coil varies directly with the oscillator frequency, the forces produced by the coil are proportional to the square of the flux, resulting in a constant force and a harmonic force at double the flux frequency.

The nodal lines of the mode of vibration can be found by moving the vibration pickup across the surface of the part and locating the lines along which the signal from the pickup is zero. Along such lines the Lissajous pattern will be a straight line. The nodal lines can be marked on the surface of the part or recorded on an appropriate drawing.

Means of Reducing Response. Any part of a motor may act as a noise source if it is excited with sufficient amplitude. At resonance, two remedies can be effected: damping can be introduced into the system, or the stiffness characteristics of the system can be changed so that the resonance will occur at another frequency. Methods of introducing damping vary according to the size and shape of the part. For example, resonant panels can be damped effectively with mastic-type compounds which are applied directly to the surfaces of the panel (see Chap. 14). Friction damping can be introduced at all mechanical joints; however, the actual amount introduced in this manner will vary widely with time and slight changes in surface conditions.

It is more convenient in some cases to change the natural frequency by changing the stiffness characteristics. For example, in a fractional-horsepower motor where the dominant noise was caused by a resonant-rotor vibration, the over-all noise of the motor was reduced 15 db by merely changing the resonant frequency of the shaft from 510 to 350 cps.

The response of end shields can be reduced by both these methods. Ribs or other stiffeners can raise the lowest natural frequency to a less objectionable range.

If the vibrating part is forced to vibrate off resonance, then the only effective method is to increase the resistance of the part to the exciting forces. In most cases there is little value in introducing damping alone. Panels, plates, or disk-type parts can be reinforced by ribs; rods and shafts can be made larger and more rigid.

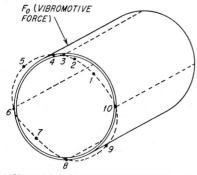

F_0 (VIBROMOTIVE FORCE)

LISSAJOUS FIGURES OBTAINED AT POINTS 1–10

FIG. 30.7. A method of locating nodal lines.[11]

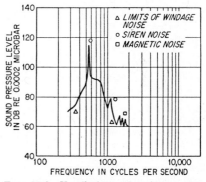

FIG. 30.8. Ventilation noise with superimposed siren effect (36-56 Stator-rotor slot combination, 1,800 rpm).

Ventilating Noise. The noise caused by the flow of air through and out of an induction motor can be a serious problem in motors of all sizes—from fractional to several thousand horsepower. In most cases it is broad-band noise with essentially no significant discrete components (Fig. 30.8). However, in large motors which use radial air ducts, the air noise is due primarily to a siren effect, which manifests itself as a series of strong peaks superimposed on the broad-band noise.[12] Most motors above 125 hp include a ducting system for the cooling air as an integral part of the motor frame. Occasionally, for very large motors, a system of external ducts is provided. Since the general topic of noise in ventilating systems is treated in Chap. 27, the discussion here is confined to direct ventilation noise due to the flow of cooling air in the motor and to the siren effect caused by radial airflow from the rotor to the stator.

In induction-motor design procedure, it is normal to allow 100 to 150 cu ft per min cooling air per kilowatt of loss. The loss varies from about 10 per cent in small sizes (5 to 10 hp) to 6 per cent in the large size (1,000 hp and larger), or about 40 to 80 cu ft per min for the small sizes to over 6,000 cu ft per min for large sizes. A typical general-purpose fractional-horsepower motor (½ hp) has about 12 cu ft per min air flowing through it. The castings and built-up frames of large induction motors and the punched and die-cast parts of fractional-horsepower motors have many sharp edges and orifices, past which the cooling air must flow. In many motors, a marked improvement in ventilation noise is possible if care is taken to minimize the number of these edges. For example, in a ½-hp motor, a 5-db reduction in over-all noise level was accomplished by applying a puttylike compound to all exhaust ports and to the sharp edges in the interior of the motor. Inevitably, the applicability of such improvements in the flow path of the cooling air is governed by the cost per unit. Consequently, these methods of reducing the ventilation noise are applied more readily to large motors where the unit cost permits greater flexibility. In all sizes, preventative measures can be taken to include rounded corners before the patterns are made, and the finished castings and punchings can be chipped or tumbled to remove flashing or other sharp edges.

Siren Effect. The siren effect in open motors with radial air ducts through the rotor and stator may produce discrete components of air-borne noise having a sound pressure level in excess of 100 db. In these motors the air is admitted near one end of the rotor shaft (Fig. 30.9). It flows axially through a spoked rotor (spider) to radial air ducts between the rotor slots, and then through the air gap into another set of openings between the stator slots. A duct system integral with the motor frame accumulates and discharges the air. The noise is produced by the sudden interruption of the radial flow of air as the stator and rotor slots change their relative peripheral positions. The frequencies usually observed are

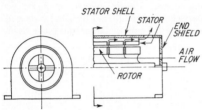

$$f = \frac{Rn}{60} \text{ cps} \quad \text{and} \quad f = \frac{2Rn}{60} \text{ cps}$$

where R = number of rotor slots
$\quad\quad n$ = speed of motor, in rpm (see Fig. 30.8)

FIG. 30.9. Rotor and stator radial cooling slots (siren effect).

This noise is usually above 1,000 cps, and harmonics of it higher than the second are usually not troublesome. Other frequencies may be generated by modulation of the air by fan blades, spider arms, etc.

The siren effect can be reduced by setting the rotor and stator conductors back from the air-gap surfaces. However, this has the disadvantage of interfering with the effective placement of rotor and stator conductors. In one 300-hp motor the noise level was reduced 10 db by tapering the spacing blocks (which are the rotor parts that form the radial air ducts) at the air-gap end so as to diffuse the air exhausting into the air gap. In machines with form-wound rotor coils, similar results can be obtained by notching the actual wedges between coils at the exit ends of the rotor air ducts.

Sound-attenuating Ducts. Noise may be radiated through the openings in the stator shell for the ventilating air or it may be radiated from the motor frame. Two cases are here considered. It is assumed that the noise is radiated almost entirely from either one of these. In the first case, noise is transmitted almost entirely through these openings, to which sound-attenuating ducts are then attached. In the second case, noise is radiated from the motor frame; here it is desirable to enclose the machine in a sound-isolating enclosure. The cooling air from the motor then enters and leaves this enclosure through sound-attenuating ducts. The isolation provided by the enclosure and the ducts may be short-circuited by structure-borne sound conduction through the base. To prevent this short circuit, the motor must be mounted on vibration isolators, preferably located inside the enclosure.

The ducts are lined with sound-absorptive material. In addition, those with large cross sections contain splitters made from or lined with sound-absorptive materials (see Chap. 27). Introduction of 90° or 180° bends into the ducts is very advantageous, particularly for the control of low frequencies (up to 400 cps), where the absorption coefficients of commercially available sound-absorptive materials are low. The design of these ducts depends, to a great extent, on the frequency components of the noise to be attenuated, the amount of attenuation desired, and the space available.

Attenuating ducts may be made ineffective because of short-circuiting of the duct by transmission through the duct walls to the outside. Thus a 40-db-attenuation duct is only effective if the attenuation through the wall is made at least that high. Air leaks also may reduce the wall attenuation. When parallel baffles are used, the space near the wall must also be treated on all four sides. Vibration breaks should be provided to prevent transmission of vibration to the duct exit.

Where space is limited, effective reduction can be obtained by constructing baffles of absorptive material in a zigzag arrangement so as to offer an obstacle path to sound waves with a comparatively small resistance to airflow. (See Chap. 27.) Noise may also be reduced by the introduction of bends into the duct system. A folded path may be easily incorporated into a cover for an electrical machine by simply inserting a few partitions and so making a labyrinth of the intake and exhaust opening.

Noise containing strong single-frequency components may be effectively controlled by the use of resonators attached to openings in the machine, particularly to the exhaust ports, or incorporated in the ducts. Attenuation so obtained is generally higher than with ducts requiring equal space; however, the frequency range over which resonators are effective is limited.[13]

BEARING NOISE

(For a complete discussion of bearing noise, see Chap. 24)

In general, induction motors should be equipped with sleeve bearings when extreme quietness is required and when the bearing noise is not masked by noise from other sources.

Antifriction Bearings. Excessive noise in antifriction bearings is often caused by nonuniform balls, poor surface finish, separator rattle, and eccentricity, which results in shock or resonance excitation of the end shields, air deflectors, and other parts that are efficient noise radiators. A study of this problem is difficult, since the results are not always repeatable; the noise spectrum often changes after a motor has been taken apart and reassembled. A change in spectrum has even been observed during one continuous run. It is possible to reduce the high-frequency components of bearing noise by inserting a section of resilient material between the bearings and the end shields. Usually, rigid end shields produce less vibration and noise than those which are more flexible.

Precision bearings are usually quieter than the more common industrial grade because of their closer tolerances and better surface finish.

Noise Sources. The most common noises in antifriction bearings of electrical machines are listed below, along with their remedies. Where the remedy for a noisy condition is obvious, it is not mentioned.[14]

1. NOISE DUE TO INHERENT BEARING CHARACTERISTICS.
   a. Mounted-bearing radial clearance too tight or too loose.
   b. Separator too tight and rubbing or too loose and rattling.
   c. Poor race finish, as from chatter.
   d. Excessive eccentricity and runout.
   e. Shield or separator resonance.
   f. Shield interference with separator or cone.
2. NOISE DUE TO LUBRICANT.
   a. Grease tacky (remedy: use softer grease).
   b. Ball skidding in race (remedy: add lubricant).
   c. Excessive oil present (remedy: clean bearings).
   d. Shellac present on races because of long storage.
3. NOISE DUE TO MACHINING.
   a. Housing or shaft fit too tight or too loose.
   b. Out-of-round housing.
   c. Poor shaft or housing finish (shaft finish should be 20 to 30 μin.).
   d. Bent shaft.
   e. Misalignment (shoulder against which bearing rests is not perpendicular to axis).
   f. Interference from adjacent parts.
4. NOISE DUE TO ABUSE OR NEGLECT.
   a. Brinelled races and nicked balls.

    b. Dirt and dust indentations.

    c. Rust.

    d. Damage to shield.

    e. Ball-skidding damage.

The noise due to some of these sources is distinct enough to be identified easily. For example, brinelling can be recognized by a low-pitched noise; the presence of dirt in the bearings causes a shrill noise; and skidding at low temperatures with insufficient lubrication results in destruction of the surface, causing a high-frequency noise. An intermittent crackle is often due to the grease. A noise in the frequency range of 100 to 300 cps is caused by the passage of the balls or rollers and is apparently characteristic of antifriction bearings. This noise is generally of low level and not disturbing unless it excites motor parts to vibrate at their natural frequencies. Therefore, care should be taken to avoid natural frequencies of end shields and other parts in this frequency range.

Effect of Size on Noise. The influence of the type and size of bearing on the noise is apparently considerable. A series of measurements shows that the sound pressure level increases almost linearly with the diameter of the bore and decreases with the ball diameter for a constant bore diameter. It was also found that a more massive bearing is quieter than a lighter one.[7]

Sleeve Bearings. Sleeve bearings do not generally cause objectionable motor noise unless they are unstable. If there is sizable radial clearance, the oil film in the bearing may lift the shaft center above the bearing center. This unloads the oil film and reduces the pressure, and consequently the shaft drops, knocking against the bearing walls and causing noise. This instability may be accentuated when the shaft is so located that the motor air gap is smaller at the top than at the bottom. Such a design is sometimes made to compensate for the gravitational force. This instability may be rectified by decreasing clearances in the bearings, by changing the shape and location of the oil grooves, or, sometimes, by changing the viscosity of the oil.

For very quiet operation, bearings made from Teflon, Textolite, nylon, or similar materials are used.

Axial bumping may be another noise source. Closer tolerances and better workmanship generally overcome this problem. However, in some cases axial bumping is due to bending or torsional resonances of the shaft; then, changing the natural frequency of the shaft assembly suppresses this noise.

D-C MACHINES

The noise from d-c motors, like that from induction motors, can be classified, according to its source, as magnetic, ventilation, or mechanical. There is a large area of overlap common to the noise problems of both types of motor, particularly in magnetic and ventilation noise. In addition, d-c motors use commutators and brushes, which are a noise source peculiar to this type of machine.

The sound-pressure spectrum levels of d-c and induction motors of the same rating are similar at various loads, but the design problems encountered differ significantly. Whereas the speed of an induction motor varies only slightly from a synchronous speed when it is loaded, d-c motors can be run normally at full load–full speed, half load–full speed, and other combinations, which give a new dimension to their magnetic noise and also make it impossible to avoid resonances in the design of their major motor parts. For example, in a d-c machine, if the lowest natural frequency of the rotor is changed, only at certain speeds will the noise be reduced—at other speeds it may be increased. Brush noise, although it is of a mechanical nature, is usually considered separately and not lumped with other mechanical noises, such as bearing noise.

In general, most d-c motors are used in industrial applications: in electric trucks and cars, elevators, submarine propulsion units. They may be used anywhere that a variable-speed source of power is required, such as in a rolling-mill drive. In most applications, the power source is less noisy than the environment in which it is placed.

For low-speed d-c machines, the noise sources, in probable order of their importance,

are magnetic, mechanical, brush, and ventilation.   In high-speed machines the order
will be brush, ventilation, mechanical, and magnetic noise.

Magnetic Noise.   In d-c machines, magnetic noise can be reduced effectively by
enlarging the air gap or by skewing at least one slot in the rotor bars.   Both methods
are effective in reducing no-load and full-load noise; but the skew may result in excitation of vibration modes of relatively high frequency (about 2,000 cps) in which poles
move axially.   The noise of bearings introduces no different problems in d-c machines
other than those described earlier.

Brush Noise.   The rasping screech due to brush friction is sometimes hard to suppress.   The emitted noise usually consists of a series of discrete frequency components
in the band from 2,500 to 6,500 cps (Fig. 30.10), which gives an objectionable quality
to the over-all noise of the motor although it contributes only a small amount to the
total acoustic power.   It is produced by rubbing and sliding between carbon and
metal surfaces and depends upon the nature of these surfaces.   The noise due to
rubbing can be reduced by sloping the brushes in the direction of the motion, by
adjusting the normal pressure between the two rubbing surfaces, and by changing the
composition and hardness of the brushes.
In general, softer brushes generate less
noise, but they are subject to more rapid
wear.

Brush vibration caused by individual
contacts with the commutator segments
can cause sufficiently large vibratory
forces to excite the brush holder or its
parts.   This may produce noise at a frequency of cn cycles per second, where c
is the number of commutator bars and n
the rps, and at the natural frequency of
the excited part of the brush holder.   By
regrinding and polishing the commutator
surfaces, the cn components can be reduced, but the noise emitted from the
brush holder may still be present.   The
parts likely to be excited are usually small

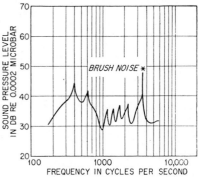

Fig. 30.10. Brush noise in over-all noise of a
d-c motor.

and will radiate only high-frequency noise.   For example, an objectionable 3,000-cps
noise from a desk calculating machine was found to be caused by the resonance of
brush-holder parts.   The successful remedy was to raise the resonant frequency to
approximately 6,600 cps by making the brush holder of a stiffer material.   This did
not eliminate the resonance excited by the rubbing of brush and commutator, but
it raised its frequency to a range where the ear is less sensitive.[15]

In d-c machines where the commutator assembly is enclosed, it is important to use
access covers with high attenuation characteristics for the 2,500- to 6,500-cps range.
Ribs or bends to increase stiffness, vibration isolation, or the addition of damping all
provide possible improvements.

INDUCTION REGULATORS

In its elementary form an induction regulator consists of a stator and a rotor that is
rotated relative to the stator by means of a worm drive.   The stator, as well as the
rotor, is generally composed of slender, cylindrical stacks of punchings.   The assembly
is placed in a tank filled with oil.

The magnetic force across the air gap may cause vibration of the rotor or of the
stator.   In the case of complete symmetry, the cross section of the stator is deformed
into an elliptical shape, as shown in Fig. 30.5.   The frequencies of vibration are
double the power-supply frequencies and harmonics thereof.   Generally the third,
and sometimes the fifth, harmonic are the disturbing ones.   In case of a single-phase
regulator, the plane of vibration remains constant.   In the case of a polyphase regulator, the field rotates and the deformation of the stator follows the rotating force field.[16]

If the air gap is not uniform, vibration of the rotor results. The greater the eccentricity, the worse the vibration. For very slender regulators, the eccentricity may become so large that the rotor is pulled over far enough to touch the stator, resulting in a sudden and very large increase in noise. Torsional vibration of the rotor has been observed in some cases. This causes impact between gear teeth, resulting in an objectionable rattle.

Vibration of the stator and rotor is transmitted through the oil and the base to the tank walls, where it is radiated as sound. Vibration can be reduced by a more rigid construction of stator and rotor. Vibration isolators can be used to reduce the transmission of vibration. Sound baffles may be installed to attenuate sound transmission through the oil. Natural frequencies of parts of the assembly equal to multiples of double power line frequency must be avoided. The deflections to be expected due to the magnetic forces may be calculated for the stator by using equations for bending of rings and for the rotor by applying beam formulas. It is very difficult to predict, by calculations, the natural frequencies of the tank walls. It is almost impossible to avoid resonance of individual panels. Cooling tubes are apt to resonate, and thus they may become important sound radiators.

Panel vibration at higher frequencies does not cause as much noise radiation as vibration at the lower frequencies. The panels break up into many smaller areas which vibrate in opposite phase. This results in cancellation of the radiated sound energy. Hence, only seldom are noise complaints due to frequencies above 600 cps.

SYNCHRONOUS GENERATORS

Noise is an important consideration in the design of larger-size synchronous generators. The greatest number of these are turbine generators of 1,000- to 50,000-kva rating, having 2 poles, and running at 3,600 rpm. Although the following discussion is primarily concerned with these machines, it is applicable also to generators of lower output rating and lower rpm.

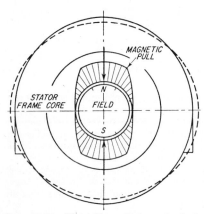

FIG. 30.11. Magnetic pull in a typical 2-pole a-c generator.[18]

Noise Sources. The predominant noise in generators is caused by magnetic forces in the air gap. The generator rotors have two or more salient magnetic poles. The pull of these magnetic forces deforms the stator laminations and also the stator shell, if it is not vibration-isolated. This deformation rotates with the salient magnetic poles and causes vibration (see Fig. 30.11). Noise of aerodynamic origin is less pronounced in large machines but may become important in smaller machines. The aerodynamic noise sources may be attributed to gas discharge from fans, gas discharge through the vent tunnels in the rotor, and gas turbulence caused by the surfaces moving at high speed—for example, the outer rotor surface, which may move as fast as 500 to 700 ft per sec. Other causes of vibration are mechanical unbalance and a difference in stiffness of the rotor in two planes perpendicular to each other.

Large machines (above about 15,000 kva) are, in general, quieter than small ones. They are hydrogen-cooled and hence hermetically sealed. Their shell is rather heavy and, therefore, provides good sound insulation. Noise is due to vibrational excitation of generator parts and adjacent structures, despite the fact that vibration isolation is provided. Medium-size machines of 10,000 to 15,000 kva are generally air-cooled, their shells are thinner, and the air seal is not complete. Noise from the inside is transmitted through the shell and also through the incomplete seal. As in the case of larger machines, generator parts and adjacent structures are vibration-excited, some vibration being conducted through the vibration isolators. Smaller machines (below 7,500 kva) are not provided with vibration isolators.

Smaller machines, having salient poles and small air gaps, may have the additional noise-producing magnetic forces of tooth frequency [17] due to the flux variation under the moving salient pole. This flux variation results from the periodic variation of the ratio of slot area to tooth area under the pole. It produces force waves with 2, 4, or more poles along the circumference of the stator. A machine will be noisy even without any load when the frequency and the pole structure of these force waves coincide with a natural frequency of the rotor or stator. Under load condition, additional force waves may be due to the armature currents. These force waves are superimposed on the previously mentioned waves. Proper coil grouping may eliminate some of them. Other factors which influence noise and which often can be changed without interfering with the performance of the machine are the width of the pole face and the number of stator slots.

Noise Control. *Aerodynamic Noise.* Aerodynamic-noise sources may be held to a minimum by the following considerations: (1) the adoption of rotor-slot wedges which are flush with the rotor surface; (2) the moving of the stator windings into the slot, away from the air gap; (3) the proper design of the fan and the associated scroll to prevent excessive noise generation (see Chap. 25); (4) the avoidance of ribs and other obstacles near the rotating fan blades; (5) the streamlining of air ducts; (6) the provision for adequate seals to reduce aerodynamic noise in a closed machine. (An opening of only 1 per cent in an enclosure with walls having an attenuation of 30 db results in an increase in noise transmission of about 10 db.)

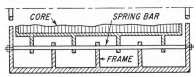

Fig. 30.12. Diagram showing application of spring bar to a vibration-mounted stator core.

Magnetic Noise. Noise generation due to magnetic forces (as high as 40,000 to 100,000 lb in large machines) can be best controlled by a flexibly mounted stator-core construction. This flexible mounting isolates the magnetic forces in the radial direction from the shell, which otherwise would radiate noise. The core is mounted on spring members, which must be flexible in the radial as well as in tangential direction and also sufficiently strong to support transient torques due to possible short circuits. The forces on the frame may then be reduced by a factor of as much as 30 to 1. If only radial flexibility is provided, a reduction of only about 5 to 1 can be obtained. Further improvement may be achieved by stiffening the core—for example, making it deeper.

One large manufacturer uses spring bars as a vibration mount. The ends of these bars, which have a rectangular cross section, are attached to the frame, while the center is bolted to the cage carrying the stator stack. The bars are flexible in the radial as well as in the tangential direction. For long machines, the alternate points on the spring bar are attached alternately to the stack assembly and to the frame (see Fig. 30.12). The stiffness of the bars is chosen so that the system has a natural frequency of 15 to 30 cps.

The core itself is a relatively rigid structure, and its four-node natural frequency is usually above the 120-cps forcing frequency. This is not necessarily true of the frame, to which especial consideration should be given so that its individual parts will have natural frequencies well away from 60 or 120 cps. Particular attention also should be given to the end shield. Natural frequencies of flat shields are usually too low; shallow, spherical shields are somewhat better in this respect. [19]

Natural frequencies of the core may be calculated or determined from measurements on one-quarter-scale models. For the model test an electromagnet, energized by a power amplifier and an audio oscillator, is applied to the model surfaces. The oscillator frequency is varied until resonance of the various parts is detected either by listening or by the use of a vibration detector. Similar tests are made later on the full-scale generator as a production check.

Installation. Synchronous-generator foundations are seldom rigid, especially for large machines. There is a great deal of flexibility, generally in the horizontal plane, which must be taken into account when designing the vibration mounting of the generator core.

The vibrating system, then, is quite complex, comprising the rotor, core, spring mounting of the core, frame, and foundation. The mechanical impedance of the generator components may be obtained from model tests or calculations. The mechanical impedance of the foundation is best measured by vibrating the foundation with a vibration exciter and measuring the vibratory force, the resulting vibration velocity, and the phase angle between the force and the velocity.[20] (See Chap. 15.)

Synchronous generators are often installed in buildings having tiled walls and tiled floors. Considerable reduction of the noise can be obtained in the reverberant field by applying sound-absorptive materials to the walls. This reduction may be of the order of 10 db.

TESTING FOR DESIGN PURPOSES

Rotating electrical equipment is tested for design purposes in acoustic laboratories and for quality control on the production line. Although the instrumentation for either purpose is similar, the acoustic environment in which tests are conducted introduces special problems.

It would be useful to the designer of rotating electrical machinery if he could compute the probable spectrum levels and important frequency components of a proposed design. It is not possible to do this, although some designers have sufficient experience to predict the probable levels. Consequently, most acoustic design in this field depends upon educated guesswork, which is checked by laboratory tests on a few model shop samples of the future equipment. From the results of these tests, modifications are suggested for the final design.

In some cases, acoustic laboratories conduct tests to try out various slot combinations, rotor configurations, amount of skew, herringbone skew, tapered surfaces of the rotor, open slots, closed slots, pole winding distributions, and other characteristics of the motors which affect their noise. It is largely from such empirical studies that our current acoustic-design information has been gathered.

Equipment. A basic tool used in these studies is a free-field room or a chamber with highly absorptive walls. Obviously, the chamber in which information is obtained for the design of the large induction motors need not have the same acoustic properties as that where design information for clock motors is sought.

Since the motor or generator itself acts as a noise source, the necessary equipment for most tests consists of a sound-level meter and a suitable analyzer in order to identify accurately the components of the over-all noise (see Chaps. 16 and 17). Although the constant-percentage bandwidth analyzer can be used to identify most frequencies, a constant bandwidth analyzer having a fixed bandwidth of, say, 2 cps is better for this purpose. For example, the radial dissymmetry-harmonic forces in a 4-pole induction motor occur at successive multiples of 30 and $30(1 - s)$ cycles per second, where s is the slip. At 1,400 cps, a constant-percentage bandwidth analyzer cannot detect two such peaks which differ in magnitude by more than 3 db.

The air-gap flux of a motor can be studied by means of search coils. Normally, these are custom-made to suit the particular configuration of the test motor. An analysis of the flux is made on a suitable wave analyzer. If it is desired, a permanent record can be made with a level recorder.

It is difficult to vary one parameter of a production-line motor without, at the same time, causing several others to vary as well. In order to obtain fundamental information which will be useful to an engineer, it is almost necessary to construct special devices and fixtures. For example, the effect of eccentricity in the rotor-stator assembly of a motor cannot be studied by using the motors themselves, except statistically on a large sample basis. The normal manufacturing tolerances and clearances built into each motor preclude using it to control the eccentricity or out-of-roundness with any precision.   For such a study it is necessary to fabricate a special motor with a rigid pedestal bearing base having an adjustment which permits movement of the stator relative to the rotor (Fig. 30.13).   With such a device it is possible to show conclusively that eccentricity affects motor noise significantly.

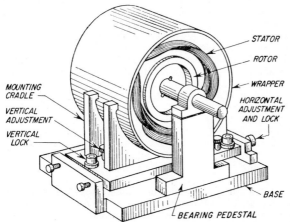

Fig. 30.13. Special motor for studying effect of rotor eccentricity on magnetic noise.

The converse is also partially true: if the test devices depart too greatly from the configuration of the motor, then the results are difficult to apply.   This can best be illustrated by considering the design of a motor fan.   Test information on fan types is useful to an electric-motor designer only when it is considered together with other factors such as winding configuration, stator-shell orifices, rotor contours, end-shield profile, and all motor characteristics which affect the flow path of the cooling air and, in turn, affect fan noise appreciably.   These factors must be accounted for in a test device, if only qualitatively.

QUALITY-CONTROL NOISE TESTS ON A PRODUCTION LINE

Production-line testing of a motor for noise serves one purpose—to determine whether or not its noise characteristics fall within the limits of a previously established criterion of acceptability.

Current methods of production-line testing vary widely—from a skilled worker placing his ear on the surface of the motor to elaborate setups for measuring near- and far-field levels of noise after installation in the customer's site.   In general, size governs the amount of effort devoted to production testing: the larger the motor, the more elaborate and complete the test.

High ambient-noise level at the sites where production-line testing must be done presents a serious acoustic problem.   In order to obtain reliable acoustic measurements, the factory ambient-noise level should be at least 10 db below the motor noise at the point of measurement.   The following methods are used to obtain satisfactory test conditions.

An obvious way of reducing the effects of the local ambient noise is to enclose the test motor in a separate room.   Usually, this is not possible; so a small box or hood may be used as a compromise solution.   Unfortunately, the economic advantages of such a space saver are often offset by complexities resulting from new problems introduced by the small size of the test cell.

A system of baffles which attenuates the factory noise in the immediate vicinity of the test motor may be suitable.   However, they are not effective at low frequencies, and adjacent reflecting surfaces can reduce the beneficial effect of the baffle.

When it is impractical to reduce the local level of ambient noise in a factory, its effect can be reduced for motor testing by using a highly directional microphone.   A large, parabolic reflector, say 8 ft in diameter, with a microphone at its focus makes a practical device for factory installation, often making useful measurements possible when the ambient- and motor-noise level are almost the same.   It must be emphasized that it is only directive when the diameter of the reflector is at least equal to the wavelength of the noise being measured.   Sensitivity and directivity of such a reflector increase with frequency.   (See Chap. 16.)

The instrumentation required for production-line testing depends to a large extent upon the criterion of acceptability which is established.   The sound-level meter is the instrument most widely used because of its simplicity.   It is recommended that this instrument be equipped with a dynamic microphone for environments where conditions of high temperature and humidity exist.   The ideal device for production testing should be stable and should maintain its calibration for long periods in a variable environment.

When a sound level alone is not sufficient to differentiate between what is acceptable and what is not, some form of frequency selection—an analyzer—is required.   To be effective, the bandwidth of the analyzer must be narrow enough to provide the required frequency selectivity but not so narrow that the analysis will take unduly long.   A $\frac{1}{3}$-octave analyzer is suitable for many types of motor-noise tests in this category.

Probably the most widely used system of production testing in current use involves nothing more than a skilled operator, who listens to the motors as they pass his station at the end of the production line.   Despite the many disadvantages of using memory and personal bias, skilled operators with normal hearing can provide a good basis of comparison if they have some means of recalibrating themselves occasionally by listening to a standard.

MECHANICAL BALANCE OF MACHINERY

It is possible to balance any rigid rotor completely by use of only two additional weights, irrespective of its unbalance or its shape; the problem is to determine the position and the size of these two weights.   Balancing machines make this determination; trial-and-error methods generally waste money.   Balancing of nonrigid rotors is a fine art and requires experienced operators.   The latter applies, for example, to rotors running close to or above their critical speed.   Most electrical machines operate below the first shaft critical, and hence the rotor may be considered as being rigid.   Exceptions are turbogenerators.

Static and Dynamic Balance.   Mechanical unbalance in a rigid rotor always can be completely represented schematically as shown in Fig. 30.14.[21]   The weight A takes account of the displacement of the center of gravity of the rotor from its true axis; weights B and B' represent a couple, depending on how much the rotor is twisted sideways from its true axis.   The three weights can be replaced by two by splitting A into two parts, placing one in the plane of B and the other in the plane of B'.   The two weights in each of these planes can then be replaced by a single one in each plane by applying the parallelogram of forces (centrifugal in this case).   That part of unbalance represented by A is static unbalance which can be detected by a static or gravity test by placing the rotor on the ways and noting its heavy spot.   The component represented by weights B and B' is dynamic unbalance; it can be detected only by a rotational or dynamic test which develops a centrifugal couple.   A rotational test, however, does not separate dynamic from static unbalance but combines the effect of both; otherwise, mechanical balance would be comparatively simple.   For this reason, specially designed machines and special methods, described below, must be used to determine the amount and position of balance weights.

Unbalance is corrected by attaching or removing weight in two balancing planes.   Provisions for easy application of these corrections should be made when designing the rotor.   Weights are generally attached to larger rotors, but on small rotors it is more advantageous to remove weight.   For large synchronous generators, the weights consist, in general, of steel blocks 2 to 3 in. long, 2 in. wide, and about 1 in. thick. These blocks are fastened by means of bolts, or they are welded, or both. Space is generally provided at both ends of the rotor for the balance weights. In some cases, the unbalance may be so great that several weights have to be attached. Then these weights are placed along the radius. Their center of gravity coincides with the angular position which has been indicated by the balancing machine.

Weight is removed by drilling in a radial direction into the laminations or by machining or grinding. The center of gravity of the material removed coincides with the indicated angular position.

All balancing machines of the present day work on the assumption that the rotor is rigid and that the bearings follow the vibration of the shaft. A linear relation between the unbalance force and the vibration amplitude is also assumed.

When the rotor runs above the first shaft critical, the assumption of a rigid rotor is not valid. The rotor must then be balanced in three planes instead of only two.

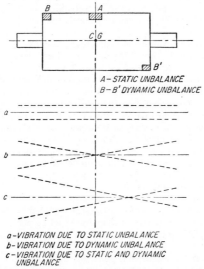

A – STATIC UNBALANCE
B – B' DYNAMIC UNBALANCE

a – VIBRATION DUE TO STATIC UNBALANCE
b – VIBRATION DUE TO DYNAMIC UNBALANCE
c – VIBRATION DUE TO STATIC AND DYNAMIC UNBALANCE

Fig. 30.14. Static and dynamic unbalance.

Machines for three-plane balancing are not available. In practice, these rotors are balanced using one of the available machines, and balance weights are distributed along the total length of the rotor in the indicated radial plane. The best distribution is based on experience.

Balancing Machines. Balancing machines are generally built for any one of the following purposes:

1. Balancing of rotors in the factory at a high production rate.
2. Balancing of rotors of individual design, as in service shops and in the factory for low production rate.
3. Balancing of the rotor while running in its own bearings. This is desirable for very large rotors or for balancing operations in the field.

High-production-rate Balancing. The rotors of most small and medium-size motors are balanced in the factory with balancing machines which must be calibrated for each individual design. The calibration requires about 15 to 30 min. A rotor is then balanced in about ½ to 1 min. This time includes the determination of the angular position and the amount of weight to be added or removed, and also the addition or removal of such weights. Highly skilled personnel are not necessary for this operation.

The rotor is run in the balancing machine, usually at less than 1,000 rpm, although its operating speed may be higher. The amount and location of unbalance in each of the balancing planes are read on the dials of the machine. The rotor is then taken out of the machine and drilled, or weights are added. Some machines have provisions for performing this correction automatically.

Many machines work on the principle of the "nodal bar." This bar connects the two bearings. It is always parallel to the rotor axis and vibrates with the rotor. There is one point along the nodal bar where all vibration is caused by unbalance in the left plane, and another point where all vibration is caused by unbalance in the right plane. Vibration pickups are located at these points.* Another type of balancing machine provides means for compensating the unbalance force. Here the readings of unbalance are taken after all vibration has ceased.

Balancing of Rotors of Individual Design. These balancing machines consist of a spring-suspended cradle for the rotor. The cradle can be clamped in pivots provided in two planes which are identical with the balancing planes of the rotor. When the rotor is run, there is no moment because of unbalance in the plane where the pivot is located. Hence, all vibration must be caused by unbalance in the nonclamped balancing plane. Corrections are made in this plane until vibration ceases. The process is then repeated with the other balancing plane clamped to its pivots. Good balance is generally obtained after three or four runs in each plane. Balancing of a rotor in this type of machine usually requires 1 to 2 hr operation by fairly skilled personnel. No calibration is required. For further information on the building and use of a "breadboard"-type balancing machine for small rotors, see Ref. 21.

Balancing of Rotors in Their Own Bearings. Rotors too large for available balancing equipment are balanced in their own bearings with portable equipment. Such equipment is also used where the rotor cannot be taken out of the machine. If a machine vibrates because of unbalance after installation (it may have been previously balanced in the factory), corrections may be made with portable dynamic balancing equipment.

This portable equipment consists of vibration detectors and a small alternator which is attached to the end of the rotor shaft serving as a phase reference. The associated electrical circuits are contained in a small box. A minimum of three runs is required—one with the rotor in the original unbalance, and two with trial weights attached to each of the balancing planes. Vector diagrams are plotted for proper interpretation of the readings, or computers are used. Balancing must be performed by highly trained personnel and may require from 1 hr's to several days' work, depending on the size of the rotor.

Specifying Unbalance. Unbalance is generally specified in terms of vibration readings. These may be given for the rotor running in its own bearings or in the balancing machine. Vibration readings taken directly on the shaft are more reliable than those taken on the bearing caps. Various maximum-vibration criteria for individual motors are used by individual manufacturers, with a few exceptions where other standards[22] exist. A chart proposed as a trend for judging vibration of turbine generators is shown in Fig. 30.15.[23] These values refer to vibration of running-speed frequency. Vibration of other frequencies must be filtered out. For example, in single-phase motors, there may be a vibration of considerable intensity caused by a torque pulsation of twice the a-c frequency, i.e., 120 cps for a 60-cps line frequency. Mechanical balance will not, of course, cure this vibration due to magnetic forces. The same holds true for vibration caused by ball bearings.

Vibrations as small as 0.000025 in. (25 μin.) may be detected when rotors are running in balancing machines. To measure this small a quantity requires special precautions in installing the balancing machine. The area must be free from floor vibrations (located away from punch presses or railroad tracks). The finite thickness of the oil film may limit the minimum vibration which can be reliably measured. Only for very special applications is it necessary to balance to this small an amount. A vibration of 0.0001 in. measured in the balancing machine is generally considered sufficient.

* A description of this principle may be found in the catalogue of the Gisholt Machine Co. of Madison, Wis.

Unbalance is also specified in terms of ounce-inches, or gram-inches. The vibration resulting from this unbalance may be calculated or determined by attaching trial weights to the rotor and plotting the vibration as a function of unbalance in ounce-inches or gram-inches. This calibration has to be done for each type of rotor and for each balancing plane. Ounce-inch or gram-inch specifications can be used without any calibration only in a force-compensating balancing machine. However, specifying unbalance in terms of vibration appears to be preferable, since vibration can more readily be measured than ounce-inches or gram-inches.

Good workmanship may reduce the amount of unbalance in rotors and may eliminate the need for balancing. However, rotors manufactured according to the best workmanship and manufacturing methods require balancing if noise is to be kept to a minimum. For example, for a ½-hp, 1,800-rpm motor, an unbalance weight of only 0.05 oz will produce appreciable vibration (about 0.002 in. amplitude).

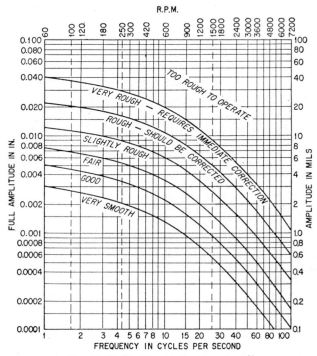

FIG. 30.15. Machinery-vibration chart.[23]

Specifying Sensitivity of Balancing Machines. The sensitivity of balancing machines may be expressed in terms of "residual unbalance."[24] It has been observed that rotors which have been balanced to 0.5 to 1 gram-in. in balancing machines (not in their own bearings) have exhibited considerably greater unbalance after assembly. These values were obtained from limited tests on hull ventilation exhaust fans, gyro-motor generator and a-c motor generator sets where the weights of the rotors varied from 40 to 1,200 lbs. For example, residual unbalances of 3 to 8 gram-in. have been measured indicating that the first order vibration induced by various assembly factors was far greater than by the unbalance of the rotor itself. Hence, it appears that a point of diminishing returns exists, below which no improvement is obtained by further balancing the rotor outside of its own bearings. Only by improving assembly tolerance, etc., would it be possible to decrease the vibration displacement further. These assembly deficiencies may be eccentricities of bearing journals or inaccuracies in ball bearing races. The effect of these eccentricities may be compensated by rebalancing of the assembled rotors in some machines. However, this is not always possible as in the case of gears, impeller rotors, and in electric motors where eccentricities of the outer rotor diameter cause once per revolution force variations.

Residual unbalance is measured by adding unbalance weights to the assembled rotor in various angular positions. The vibration displacement of the machine is plotted as a function of the angular position of the added unbalance. This plot consists of a group of sine waves. The residual unbalance is then that added unbalance for which the sine wave just touches the zero vibration displacement line.

REFERENCES

1. Hildebrand, L. E.: *Trans. AIEE*, **49**: 848 (1930).
2. Kron, G.: *Trans. AIEE*, **50**: 757 (1931).
3. Alger, P. L.: "The Nature of Polyphase Induction Machines," John Wiley & Sons, Inc., New York, 1951.
4. Jordan, H.: *Der Geräuscharme Elektromotor*, Girardet, Essen, 1950.
5. Appleman, W. R.: *Trans. AIEE*, **56**: 1359 (1937).
6. Muster, D., and G. L. Wolfert: *Trans. AIEE*, **74**: III, 1365 (1956).
7. Ordinanz, W. O.: *Product Eng.*, **18**: 110 (December, 1947).
8. Erdelyi, E.: "Predetermination of the Sound Pressure Levels of Magnetic Noise in Medium Induction Motors," unpublished doctoral dissertation, University of Michigan, Ann Arbor, 1955.
9. Den Hartog, J. P.: "Mechanical Vibrations," 4th ed., McGraw-Hill Book Company, Inc., New York, 1956.
10. Miller, D. F.: *J. Appl. Mechanics*, **20**: 167 (1953).
11. Shafer, S. N., and R. Plunkett: A Miniature Oscilloscope and Vibration Pickup for Nodal Pattern Tracing, *Proc. SESA*, **13**, No. 1, 123 (1955).
12. Lubcke, P. E., and H. Plattner: *Siemens Rev.*, **13**: 24 (1937).
13. Davis, D. D., *et al.*: *NACA Tech. Note* 2893, 1953.
14. Monich, M. T.: unpublished information made available, General Motors Corp., New Departure Div., Bristol, Conn.
15. Geiger, P. H.: *Elec. Mfg.*, **44**: 116 (1949).
16. Foltz, T. P., and W. F. Shirk: *Trans. AIEE*, **50**: 1052 (1931).
17. Graham, Q., S. Beckwith, and F. H. Milliken: *Trans. AIEE*, **50**: 1056 (September, 1931).
18. Penniman, A. L., and H. D. Taylor: *Trans. AIEE*, **60**: 283 (1941).
19. Shildneck, L. P., and A. J. Wood: *Trans. AIEE*, **72**: 36 (1953).
20. Plunkett, R.: *J. Appl. Mechanics*, **21**: 250 (1954).
21. Vibration and Noise Control, chap. 9 in "Kent's Mechanical Engineers' Handbook," 12th ed., John Wiley & Sons, Inc., New York, 1950.
22. Motors and Generators, *NEMA Standard* MG1-1955, pt. 4, p. 12 (MG1-4.22, 4.23).
23. Rathbone, T. C.: *Power Plant Eng.*, **43**: 721 (November, 1939).
24. Feldman, S.: Department of the Navy, Bureau of Ships Code 371, Report No. 371-V-24.

Chapter 31

AUTOMOBILE NOISE

DAVID C. APPS

Noise and Vibration Laboratory, General Motors Proving Ground

AUTOMOTIVE TEST FACILITIES

Engine Dynamometer. The engine dynamometer, by means of which the correct load and speed may be imposed for the study of a specific noise or vibration problem, is used for testing the engine alone, i.e., separated from the chassis. The electrical dynamometer and the engine, supported on jacks, are both mounted on a heavy cast-iron bedplate usually weighing several tons. The auxiliaries include an engine-water heat exchanger, an oil heat exchanger, an oil pump, oil and water temperature controllers, and the controls required for the electrical machine. The engine dynamometer should be placed in a dead room to avoid errors in measurement caused by standing wave patterns.

Chassis Dynamometer. The chassis dynamometer, or *chassis rolls*, is a facility for testing the complete automobile. The typical installation consists of a pair of rolls upon which the drive wheels rest; the shaft is coupled directly to the electrical dynamometer, which can be used either as a motor or as a loading generator. The electrical dynamometer is a low-speed, high-torque machine, usually cradled so that reaction torques can be measured for those cases which are torque-sensitive. The rolls, usually about 4 ft in diameter and having a 2-ft face width, have surfaces of steel, wood, or paper under axial compression.

The chassis dynamometer is used for the study of all engine and drive-line disturbances such as listed under *Noise Sources*. In the study of chassis-noise problems, the chassis dynamometer must be installed in a dead room or in an acoustical free field.

A portable control box offers complete control of load and speed to the observer inside the car. Modern controls provide for automatically holding a given speed while varying the load, and vice versa.

Electrodynamic Shakers.[1,2] Electrodynamic shakers or exciters are an indispensable test facility, to be used for confirmation of conclusions regarding vibration modes and natural frequencies reached during exploration under natural or normal exciting forces.

For example, a noise period is found to be due to starting-motor vibration. Probing with a vibration pickup indicates that it is apparently moving as a mass on the stiffness of the clutch housing casting. This may be confirmed by attaching an electrodynamic shaker. The resonant frequency can be determined and more exact information obtained on the vibration mode when excited at a single frequency. Such an attack also leads to extended information, inasmuch as the value of the force, the point of application, and the frequency can be varied independently. A wide range of force ratings are commercially available; 10-lb and 50-lb shakers will be found useful in automotive problems.

Road-noise Rolls. Because the control of road noise, or *road rumble*, is a perennial problem with current American cars, a set of road-noise rolls to permit laboratory study of this condition is a most convenient laboratory adjunct. These rolls have been made in the form of segmented cast-aluminum cylindrical shells, arranged to bolt over the peripheral surfaces of the chassis rolls.[3] The castings may be of the order of ½ in. thick and may have a surface which is a true replica of a short section of an actual rough asphalt road. Particular attention must be given to obtain the correct peripheral length and a true and correct radius to avoid slapping or pounding.

Another form of simulated noise road takes the form of a pair of rolls of unequal diameter to which short studs, or rods, have been welded in a perfectly random pattern.[4] The tire and wheel rest between these two rolls, one of which is driven by an electric motor. The unequal drum diameters constitute an effort to minimize the pattern and drum repetition effect, which is quite noticeable on the aluminum plates, discussed immediately above.

Both of these simulations suffer from various defects, and it appears that it would be better to use (1) a continuous rubber belt having a molded "road surface" and stretched snugly over the chassis roll, or (2) a one-piece cylindrical casting bolted to the roll.

Test Roads.

Engine and Drive-line Noise. To supplement the laboratory tests discussed above, measurements are also made on smooth-concrete or asphaltic-concrete road surfaces for the determination of full-throttle- and cruising-noise levels and spectra. The object is to minimize the excitation of road noise so that the engine and power-train noise can be evaluated.

Road-surface and Tire Noise. In addition to concrete surfaces, measurements are made on sections of road with surfaces of brick, cobblestone, rough asphalt, patched concrete, and sheet asphalt. Of these, the brick and cobblestone are probably the least important, since these surfaces are fast disappearing from American roadways. Rough asphalt, patched concrete, and spalled concrete excite the characteristic road noise, also called *body rumble*. Asphaltic concrete is usually too smooth in texture to produce representative levels of road noise yet somewhat too coarse-textured for tire thump. Tire thump is most easily produced on smooth sheet-asphalt roads, which are found in increasing mileage on boulevard-type streets in cities.

INSTRUMENTATION FOR AUTOMOTIVE-NOISE TESTING

In order to effectively handle the wide variety of noise and vibration problems encountered in the modern automobile, a complete line of instrumentation is required for identification of the source of noise, for the determination of the mechanism producing the noise, and for evaluation of remedial steps intended to control the noise. These are classified below as "conventional" and "special" instruments.

Conventional Instruments (see Chap. 16).

Noise Instruments. The sound-level meter is not particularly useful by itself in the automotive-noise field. This lack of utility arises from the fact that its readings do not correlate with personal judgments when used to indicate any of the several categories of automotive noise, such as road rumble, engine noise, etc. The sound-level meter cannot be used to rank-order properly several cars, nor can it be used in a before-and-after type of measurement with any degree of success. The sound-level meter, when used with a continuous-type wave analyzer or with octave-band filters, becomes an indispensable combination for automotive-noise problems. A sharp-tuning heterodyne wave analyzer having, say, 2- or 5-cps bandwidth enables the precise identification of frequency components in automotive-noise studies. However, when measuring bands of noise, the octave-band analyzer is somewhat more satisfactory.

The magnetic tape recorder can be used as a means for record-playback comparison tests (before-and-after tests) and as a means for storing data to be analyzed with the wave analyzer-recorder. The magnetic tape recorder, especially the binaural version, is so very useful in automotive-noise work because it is, by far, the most sensitive method now known for evaluating in a realistic manner experimental changes controlling unwanted noise.[5] As has been pointed out, it is extremely important that operating conditions be maintained identical from test to test. Over-all calibration of the tape recorder, including microphones, is required. The operational speed of the car must be closely held, and, in road-noise tests, a given track for the wheels must be maintained from test to test over the same section of road and while traveling in the same direction. If these precautions are not taken, experimental errors may easily swamp out or magnify small gains made in individual steps.

The polar-coordinate oscilloscope is an instrument which finds application in problems in which it is necessary to locate the time of occurrence of a noise within a regularly repeating cycle of mechanical events; for example, when a knock occurs in an engine. It is also useful in determining the exact number of events per revolution and their approximate location. In using this instrument, a small 2-phase generator is mechanically coupled to a shaft of the mechanism under study. The voltage output of this generator forms a circular sweep on the oscilloscope tube which is exactly synchronized with the shaft speed. A sensing device such as a microphone or vibration pickup is then coupled to the radial-deflection amplifier so that the disturbances so sensed appear as radial variations in the otherwise smooth circular trace. A stationary pattern indicates that the disturbance sensed occurs an integral number of times per revolution of the shaft. A pattern, revolving however slowly, indicates a lack of precise integral relationship. In another usage, the output of the generator can be recorded magnetically on a dual-channel sound track for positive determination of the ratio of the frequency of disturbance to the engine speed.

For an analysis of transient-type sounds or of those having a fluctuating spectrum, a visible-speech analyzer is used. This recording type of transient analyzer yields a three-dimensional plot on which the abscissa is time, the ordinate is frequency, and the amplitude, or sound pressure level, is proportional to the blackness of the graph. With this equipment, short-duration transients such as a door slam, the thud produced when a car rolls over a pavement joint, etc., may be analyzed. Such a device is also useful where there is a time variation in the strength of the various signal frequencies. This instrument also can provide a two-dimensional plot of amplitude versus frequency at any instant during the recording period, as selected by the operator.

Vibration Instruments. Since vibration-measuring equipment is discussed fully in Chap. 15, only the requirements for automotive-noise studies are reviewed here. A self-generating seismic velocity pickup of the moving-coil type having allowable free travel of the moving element of 1 to 2 in. is required, as well as a lighter and smaller type with an allowable travel of perhaps $\frac{1}{10}$ in. Low-frequency or static displacements are measured by a ground-connection-type displacement gauge, which requires the attachment to the two surfaces between which the relative motion is to be sensed. Ground-connection displacement gauge types include the differential-transformer type, the precision linear potentiometer, and the unbonded resistance strain gauge type. In working with systems where more than a few grams of weight will modify the vibration pattern, use is made of self-generating, small, light, seismic accelerometers.

The output of any of these pickups can be observed on a cathode-ray oscilloscope, on an indicating meter, and on the sound-level meter, either directly or through an analyzer. More frequently, in determining the mode of the complex vibrations found in the automobile—its body, frame, and components—multichannel recordings of several vibration transducers are made on a magnetic oscillograph to observe waveform, relative phase, relative amplitude, etc. Furthermore, the flexibility of modern multichannel amplifiers and recording oscillographs permits the simultaneous recording of other, related dynamic variables, such as hydraulic pressures, strains, and vibrations, the result of which is to greatly expedite determination of cause and effect.[6]

Special Instruments. In spite of the array of vibration- and noise-measuring equipment which is commercially available today, in automotive-noise analysis the need is frequently felt for rather special instruments, which in many cases have to be designed and developed by the individual laboratory.

Tire-thump Meter. (See *Noise Sources.*) Tire thump is a disturbance commonly found in present-day automobiles. It is due to discontinuities in any of several tire parameters as the tire rolls, including effective stiffness, crown thickness, radial runout, etc. Audible thump occurs at the same rate as tire rotational speeds and therefore sounds like a boot in the tire. The disturbance is due to the simultaneous excitation of at least two low-frequency components by adjacent harmonics of wheel rotational rate. These components interfere and produce a beat note, the frequency of which is equal to the wheel rotational rate.

An instrument is now commercially available for measuring audible tire thump to the exclusion of other disturbances[7] (see Fig. 31.1). This device measures the envelope amplitude (in the range of 3 to 10 cps) resulting from the interfering, or beating, of audio components in the range of 20 to 70 cps.

The block diagram of the instrument is shown in Fig. 31.1. Since there are many other sounds which are picked up by the microphone and which are totally unrelated to tire thump, these must be rejected by a 20- to 70-cps bandpass filter. After filtering, the familiar beat pattern is demodulated by passing it through a second filter to remove the carrier frequency. This leaves the envelope, the amplitude of which is taken as a measure of the severity of thump.

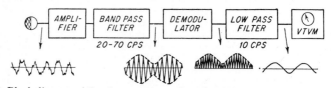

Fig. 31.1. Block diagram of tire-thump meter. Sound picked up by microphone is amplified and passed through bandpass filter to reject extraneous components. The resulting beat waveform is demodulated and filtered, leaving original envelope amplitude which is measured on voltmeter. (*After Apps and Vanator.*[7])

The automobile and tire industries judge tire thump on an arbitrary scale of 1 to 10, a practice followed in the thump meter. As a result of a series of listening tests, certain weighting networks for the 20- to 70-cps frequency range have been incorporated in the meter, as well as weighting for the thump frequencies after demodulation, i.e., in the range of 3 to 10 cps. In addition, certain ratio networks are incorporated because it was found that, while the ear responds to components of equal amplitude in proportion to the amplitude of the envelope, it does not respond in this way to components of unequal amplitude.[7] A standard response for the instrument has been fixed, and a calibration level has been set: two equal components having frequencies of 45 and 50 cps and sound pressure levels of 95 db yield a thump-meter rating of 10. Equal amplitude components of 89-db level yield a reading of 5, etc.

NOISE SOURCES

Engine, Drive Line, and Brakes.

Reciprocating Unbalance. Reciprocating unbalance forces are those counterforces due to the acceleration of the reciprocating parts of the engine—the pistons and upper parts of the connecting rods. These reciprocating forces follow from Newton's laws, which state that in a mechanical system the rate of change of momentum of the entire system along a given axis is equal to the resultant of all similarly directed external forces. In an engine there are no such external forces; therefore, when a piston is accelerated downward, the engine frame (or another piston) must be accelerated upward, so that the center of gravity of the entire assembly remains fixed. Vertical components due to unbalanced rotating masses are generally lumped in with the vertical reciprocating forces, and the sum is called "vertical inertia forces." The horizontal components due to the rotating masses are similarly called "horizontal inertia forces."

Because of the angularity of the connecting rod, the piston motion is not sinusoidal but contains fundamental- and higher- (mostly second-) harmonic components. The piston displacement, x_p, measured downward* from top center is, to a very close approximation,[8]

$$x_p = r + \frac{r^2}{4l} - r\left[\cos(\omega t) + \frac{r}{4l}\cos(2\omega t)\right] \tag{31.1}$$

where r = crank radius
  l = length of connecting rod
  ωt = crank angle measured from top dead center
The value of the second-harmonic component is seen to depend upon the ratio r/l. A double differentiation of Eq. (31.1) and substitution in Newton's second law yields an expression for the total vertical inertia forces for all moving parts:

$$F_v = (m_{rec} + m_{rot})r\omega^2 \cos(\omega t) + m_{rec}\frac{r^2}{l}\omega^2 \cos 2\omega t \tag{31.2}$$

The total horizontal inertia force is

$$F_H = m_{rot}r\omega^2 \sin \omega t \tag{31.3}$$

where m_{rec} = sum of mass of piston, m_p, and about one-third mass of connecting rod
  m_{rot} = sum of equivalent mass, m_c, of crank and balance of mass of connecting rod
The equivalent mass m_c is that mass obtained by concentrating the crank mass at its center of gravity and then shifting this mass from its center of gravity to the crankpin radius, with proper mass adjustment so that the radial force remains constant. Note that the second-harmonic inertia force appears only in a vertical direction, being absent in the horizontal-transverse direction.

If the gas pressures in the cylinder are now considered to the exclusion of the inertia forces (see Fig. 31.2), it is found that (1) there is an upward force, F, on the cylinder head, balanced by an equal force, F, pressing down on the piston through the connecting rod, crankshaft, and main bearing; and (2) there is a gas-pressure torque, $FY/\cos \phi$, on the shaft. This is balanced by a countercouple on the engine frame,

$$Fx \tan \phi = FY/\cos \phi$$

side force $F \tan \phi$ to the right on the piston wall and to the left at the main bearing, acting through a distance $x = Y/\sin \phi$.

Thus, the upward gas force on the cylinder head and the downward gas force on the main bearing balance each other, tending only to lengthen the structure in a vertical direction. There is a net-output torque about the crankshaft axis

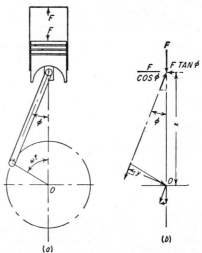

Fig. 31.2. Gas forces. Schematic of engine, piston, rod, and crank. The force F is balanced by the compression on the rod equal to $F/\cos \phi$ and the side thrust from cylinder wall equal to $F \tan \phi$. Output torque about 0 equals $FY/\cos \phi$ equivalent to countermoment on the engine block equal to $Fx \tan \phi = FY/\cos \phi$. (*After Den Hartog.*[8])

and an equal countertorque tending to turn the engine frame in the opposite direction. If the output torque is an intermittent or fluctuating torque, the reaction torques on

* The expressions "downward" and "horizontal" in the following discussion are used for brevity to indicate motion along the cylinder axis and transverse to cylinder axis, even though the cylinder may not be vertical.

the engine are also intermittent. Even if the output torque of the engine is smoothed by the installation of a flywheel, the reaction torque of the gas forces still maintains the full value of its cyclic variation. If the engine is connected to a load and delivering, in addition, some value of average torque, there results a steady deflection of the engine on its mounts, with alternating rolling deflections superimposed.

The horizontal and vertical inertia forces expressed in Eqs. (31.2) and (31.3) are capable of creating rocking couples about vertical and horizontal axes, respectively. Certain combinations of cylinder arrangements (discussed later) in multicylinder engines effectively balance out these forces and couples. Consider a 2-cylinder vertical engine with crankpins 180° apart. One piston, just past top center and accelerating toward the bottom, results in a vertical force on the engine frame directed upward. At the same time, the other piston, accelerating toward the top, results in a downward force on that end of the engine. Thus, a rocking couple is present, tending to rock the engine about a transverse-horizontal axis. In a similar fashion, the horizontal component of the unbalanced rotating forces [Eq. (31.3)] will lead to a couple which tends to yaw the engine about a vertical axis.

Summarizing the effect of inertia, rotating, and gas forces:

1. The net resultant force on the engine frame due to gas forces is zero.
2. There are no forces along the crankshaft axis because of either gas pressures or inertia elements, since there is no component motion along this axis.
3. There are inertia forces in a vertical direction, which may lead to a rocking about a transverse-horizontal axis.
4. There are inertia forces in a transverse direction, which may lead to a couple yawing the engine about a vertical axis.
5. There are both inertia and cylinder-pressure torques about the crankshaft axis.

Primary forces and couples and secondary forces and couples may be balanced out, depending upon the number of cylinders and the arrangement of the crank throws.

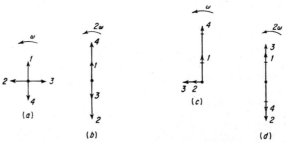

Fig. 31.3. Vector diagrams of inertia forces for four-cylinder engine with two-plane, four-throw crank. (a) primary vertical- and horizontal-inertia-force vectors rotating at engine speed ω; (b) secondary vertical-inertia-force vectors rotating at speed 2ω. Both of these are balanced; (c) primary-inertia couples about transverse-horizontal (and vertical) axis, unbalanced; (d) secondary inertia couples about transverse-horizontal axis, balanced. Moments are taken with respect to center of engine. Quantities in parentheses have magnitudes and phase different from unbracketed ones but identical diagrams. (After Den Hartog.[8])

The balance conditions in various engine types can be examined by the following method:[8] Consider the crank throw diagram as a vector diagram in which the horizontal projections of the rotating vectors represent the primary inertia forces, as shown in Fig. 31.3a for a 4-throw, 2-plane crankshaft. This diagram might represent the vertical inertia forces and a similar diagram the horizontal inertia forces, since there is a 90° difference in phase. The resultant of this vector diagram is zero; i.e., the (vertical and horizontal) primary inertia forces are balanced. The (vertical) secondary forces are considered in Fig. 31.3b. Whereas the vector representing the forces for throw 2 is 90° ahead of that for throw 1 in Fig. 31.3a, it is twice that, or 180°, in

Table 31.1. Inertia Balance of Piston Engines

No. cylinders	Crank arrangement	Inertia forces		Couples	
		Primary	Secondary	Primary	Secondary
4		Bal	Unbal	Bal	Unbal
4*		Bal	Bal	Unbal	Bal
6		Bal	Bal	Bal	Bal
8		Bal	Bal	Bal	Bal
90° V8†		Bal	Bal	Unbal	Bal

* This engine has unequal firing intervals.

† The unbalanced primary couple may be balanced (see text). Even-numbered cylinders in one bank, odd-numbered in the other bank.

Fig. 31.3*b*. Completing the diagram as shown indicates that the secondary forces for this crank arrangement are also balanced.

The primary and secondary couples are handled in a similar way, except that the moment arm lengths and their signs with respect to, say, the center main bearing must be taken into account.

In Fig. 31.3*c*, showing the (rocking and yawing) primary couples, vector 1 is drawn in the same direction as in Fig. 31.3*a* and of length 1½; vector 4 would be drawn 1½ units down, but the sign of the moment is oppositely directed with respect to the center of the engine; vector 2 is drawn as in Fig. 31.3*a* and of length ½; and vector 3 is drawn with reversed sign, since this throw is at the rear of the engine and has an oppositely directed moment. The primary couples are obviously unbalanced.

In Fig. 31.3*d* are shown the secondary couples, with vector directions based upon Fig. 31.3*b*, as modified by the sign of the moment arms. The secondary couples are obviously balanced.

Table 31.1 indicates the balance of these forces and couples in common American engine types.

The balance conditions in other engine types can be examined by the method described.[8] In Table 31.1, the smallest inherently balanced automotive-type engine is a 6-cylinder in-line. The unbalanced primary inertia couple shown for the 4-cylinder, 2-plane crank is inherent and cannot be balanced. When the same crank is used for a 90° V8 engine, advantage may be taken of the fact that a rotating force may be synthesized from two reciprocating forces directed along axes at 90° and phased 90° in time. This is the situation in a 90° V engine with both rods in the same row connected to a single crank. Thus, the unbalanced primary inertia couple shown in Table 31.1 for the 90° V8 engine may be eliminated by providing "local" balance at each crank throw. This can be done by counterbalancing each throw with a mass equivalent to $2m_{\text{rot}} + m_{\text{rec}}$ at crankpin radius, where these terms are as defined earlier, except that m_{rot} here implies *one-half* m_c for a crank throw, plus the rotating weight of one connecting rod. In practice, however, each individual throw in the 90° V8 is not completely balanced by itself because of the difficulty of forging such a crankshaft and also because the increased moment of inertia would adversely affect acceleration performance. Instead, throws 1 and 4, which have longer moment arms, are designed to carry more counterbalance weight than throws 2 and 3. Usually, throws 1 and 4 have counterweights opposite both cheeks, and throws 2 and 3 opposite the outside cheeks only, making a total of 6 counterweights for the engine.

Fig. 31.4. Vector diagram of rotating primary couple vectors for 90° V8 engine with two-plane, four-throw crank rotating at speed ω. The resultant rotating couple is *R*, which can be balanced by a vector, R_{cw}, or combination of vectors having the same direction and magnitude.

The important fact is that the reciprocating masses at each throw of a 90° V engine can be treated as an unbalanced rotating mass, which can then be counterbalanced (1) by another rotating mass directly opposite (actually divided on each side of the throw to allow the rod to pass by), or (2) by a rotating mass disposed elsewhere along the crank, with adjustment in value to account for the different length of moment arm. The latter method makes the most effective use of weights used to correct the primary unbalanced couple.

Referring to Fig. 31.4, it is clear that the unbalanced primary rotating couple produced by throws 2 and 3 of the 4-throw crankshaft used on V8 engines cannot be balanced by the couple produced by counterweights exactly opposite throws 1 and 4 only, because these would not be correctly located angularly. Since the resultant counterweight vectors must coincide with R_{cw}, the front and rear counterweights must be offset toward counterweights 2 and 3, respectively.

The balancing theory and procedure of internal-combustion engines is itself a rather involved subject. However, a few of the significant features of current practice are of interest here. Some V8 engines are electrically driven after assembly of the rotating and reciprocating parts, consisting of harmonic balancer, crank, rods, pistons, and flywheel, and are balanced as a unit. A common tolerance is ½ in.-oz. This follows a preliminary balance of the balancer, crank, and flywheel. During the preliminary operation, the equivalent weights $2m_{rot} + m_{rec}$ must be attached to the crankpins to simulate the actual rods and pistons; and a minimum of, say, 5 or 6 in.-oz unbalance is left in the No. 1 and No. 4 counterweights so that the final balancing of the engine assembly may be done by a drilling operation in those locations. In this connection, it is interesting that at least one manufacturer provides similar initial unbalance in the balancer and the flywheel, so that on final assembly the drilling is done on these units.

In other plants making in-line or V8 engines, the practice is to balance only the rotating parts as an assembly, i.e., the crank, the flywheel, and the harmonic balancer, to within about ½ in.-oz. For V8 crankshafts, the quantity $2m_{rot} + m_{rec}$ must be attached at the crankpins to simulate the actual rods and pistons.

In modern motor cars, residual inertia unbalance is not troublesome because the weights of the pistons and rods are held to within about $\pm\frac{1}{16}$ oz for essential elimination of inertia forces and rocking couples. There are exceptions to this close matching

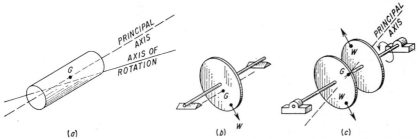

(a)   (b)   (c)

FIG. 31.5. Rotating unbalance. (a) the general case of rotating unbalance. Axis of rotation neither passes through G nor coincides with the principal axis; (b) pure static unbalance: axis of rotation parallel to principal axis but offset; (c) static balance, dynamic unbalance: axis of rotation passes through G but does not coincide with principal axis.

of piston and rod weights, and in some engines it is possible to get a "stack-up." The understanding of the principles of the generation of these forces and couples is, of course, an aid in identifying them in problems or cases where they do occur.

The effect of these residual forces and couples is usually minor but may become troublesome if they excite structural or acoustical resonance.

Rotating Unbalance. Rotating forces, as distinct from reciprocating forces, arise from the rotation of systems which are unbalanced. In the most general case, as shown in Fig. 31.5a, the rotational axis does not pass through the center of gravity and, further, does not coincide with a principal axis (here, an axis of symmetry). These two conditions lead to static and dynamic unbalance, respectively.

The case of static unbalance is exemplified in the initially perfectly balanced rotor, shown in Fig. 31.5b. A small weight, w, is then placed on the periphery opposite the center of gravity, thus causing the center of gravity to be displaced from the axis of rotation. When this rotor, thus unbalanced, is rotated, a centrifugal force of value $Wr\omega^2/g$ results. Its instantaneous direction is radially outward; the force rotates with the same speed as the rotor and causes bearing reaction forces which may lead to vibration problems. This type of unbalance is called "static," since it can be determined by static means, i.e., by placing the rotor on a pair of horizontal ways, where the heavy side will then seek the lowest position.

A dynamic unbalance may be produced on the initially perfectly balanced rotor of Fig. 31.5c by introducing two equal weights, w, symmetrically disposed from the plane of the center of gravity and on opposite sides of the periphery, as shown. These weights individually produce centrifugal forces which, acting together, produce a rotating couple, with resulting rotating reaction forces at the bearing supports. This type of unbalance is called "dynamic," since it can be sensed only when the system is rotating; i.e., a static test will not reveal its presence. This is true in the case assumed in Fig. 31.5c because the axis of rotation still passes through the center of gravity—the criterion for static balance.

Thus, a rotor may have static unbalance alone or dynamic unbalance alone; it may have both static and dynamic unbalance—the general case; or it may be balanced in both respects. After a rotor has been balanced by any of the dynamic-balancing machines used, both static and dynamic balance will have been corrected. It is easily shown that in the general case of static and dynamic unbalance, complete balance of a rigid rotor can be achieved by placing a single balance weight in each of two parallel radial planes. The procedure for determining the correction weights is extremely simple, provided the magnitude and location of the original unbalance are known. The balance machines used in production plants essentially determine these factors and even automatically remove weight in the proper places.

It is clear from the above that in a rotor with short axial dimensions, such as a disk, only a static unbalance can exist for all practical purposes.

In the case of wheels and tires, the axial dimension is definitely large enough to require some control and occasional correction of dynamic unbalance as a service procedure. This is especially true of the front wheels, where the resulting rotating couple will cause the wheels to wobble about the kingpin axis. The fixed axle construction at the rear is naturally less sensitive to dynamic unbalance.

At the factory, a representative close control is a static balance of the front brake drum and hub assembly to within 6 in.-oz, and of the rear drum to the same figure. In other cases, these figures become 8 and 12 in.-oz, respectively; or a sampling procedure may be employed on the machined drums, with a tolerance set on the rough castings.

A limit of 20 in.-oz static unbalance on the cured tire is the prevailing practice. Most car manufacturers then static-balance the wheel and tire assembly, the industry range being about 6 to 25 in.-oz.

In the automotive chassis, the crankshaft is potentially a source of rotating unbalance because of its high speed and large mass. Even so, because of the degree of corrective balance practiced in current production, rotating unbalance is not a serious problem in most engines. Some engines are balanced on the assembly line, with harmonic balancer (see *Noise Sources, Engine, Drive Line and Brakes, Torsional Vibration*), crankshaft, rods, pistons, and flywheel assembled. In other engines, the crankshaft, flywheel, and balancer are balanced as an assembly, using ring weights or bob weights on the crankpins to simulate properly the rods and pistons. Both are dynamic-balance procedures; typical unbalance limits are $\frac{1}{2}$ in.-oz.

Since the forces generated because of rotating unbalance are proportional to the square of the rotational speed, they may cause trouble only at higher speeds, say, above 2,000 rpm. Such exciting forces will be exaggerated when the exciting frequency coincides with the natural frequency of some other parts of the engine or vehicle, although properly designed engine-mount systems minimize the latter effect.

The generator is another potential source of rotating forces, because it is belted to run about twice as fast as the engine and because, in some cases, the mounting arrangement may exaggerate the effect. Generators are usually balanced to within about 0.1 to 0.3 in.-oz. In one case cited, the rotational unbalance forces of the generator were found to be very close in frequency to twice engine speed; the result was a very disturbing audible beat, which could be cleared up by making the generator inoperative.

Torsional Vibrations. Rotating shaft systems may execute torsional vibrations which are characterized by the superposition of a small alternating rotational velocity upon the average shaft velocity. Of the many shaft systems present in the automobile, (1) the crankshaft by itself or (2) the entire power-transmission system—consisting of the crankshaft, clutch, flywheel, propeller shaft, axle gear, rear axle shafts, and wheels—most frequently cause problems. The exciting moments are those due to the harmonics of the gas-pressure torque and those due to inertia forces resulting from the acceleration and deceleration of the reciprocating parts; the former is the more important by far.

The first mode of this entire system, characterized by the presence of a node at the rear wheels, may have a natural frequency as low as 5 to 10 cps. The crankshaft torsional amplitude is essentially constant over its length; i.e., it moves as a unit. Other, higher modes are present, characterized by successively higher natural frequencies and by the presence of additional nodes. Some of these low-frequency modes can cause problems such as transmission-gear rattle or rough clutch engagement. The effect of the clutch damper springs and the clutch friction lag are important in determining the natural frequencies and severity of some of these lower modes.

In considering the torsional vibration of the engine itself, we are actually examining only a portion of the complete power-transmission system; the crankshaft torsional amplitude varies throughout its length. The first mode has a node in the crankshaft near the flywheel; the second mode has an additional node nearer the center of the engine. It is possible to dismiss the shaft system behind the flywheel with a good approximation in dealing with crankshaft torsional vibration because of the low torsional rigidity of these rearward shafts. It is for the frequency of the lower mode that the harmonic balancer is tuned.

In general, the potential severity of gas-pressure-excited torsional vibrations depends upon the mode of the crankshaft vibration being considered, the order (or harmonic) of the gas-pressure torque, and the firing order. Most present-day American engines incorporate a damped, tuned torsional-vibration absorber, called a "harmonic balancer." These devices reduce the displacement amplitude of crankshaft torsional vibrations in modern V8 engines to less than 0.2°, measured at the front end on the crankshaft. The corresponding amplitude without balancer is typically 0.3 or 0.4° for the same engine type.

Just as the reciprocating weights of the pistons and connecting rods cause fundamental and second-order vertical reciprocating unbalance forces (because of the fact that the piston does not execute true harmonic motion), so the reciprocating weights are responsible for producing alternating torques about the crankshaft axis, consisting of a fundamental and higher harmonics. Only the first three terms are found to be of significance in a typical construction. The following expression gives the value of these inertia torques to a very good approximation:[8]

$$M = \frac{1}{2} m_{rec} \omega^2 r \left[\frac{r}{2l} \sin(\omega t) - \sin(2\omega t) - \frac{3r}{2l} \sin(3\omega t) \right] \qquad (31.4)$$

These inertia torques operate to excite the crankshaft in torsional vibration, quite independent of the gas torques, the expression having been derived using a uniform angular engine speed, ω.

Gas-pressure torques are the more important of the two torsional exciting forces. In the 4-stroke-cycle engine (usually called "4-cycle engine"), one complete cycle occurs for each two revolutions of the engine; and therefore a Fourier analysis of the resulting pressure card yields a series of harmonic terms—$\omega/2$, ω, $3\omega/2$, etc.—the fundamental of which is one-half engine speed. In automotive work, the various harmonics are called "orders" and are always understood to refer to engine rotational speed as the base speed. Thus, order 1 is the second-harmonic component of the gas torque function, but it occurs at one times engine rotational speed.

Fourier analyses have been made of the pressure cards of various engine types, including 4-cycle spark-ignition engines, and the coefficients have been tabulated for all orders and half orders through order 18 over a range of mean indicated pressures of 10 through 437.5 lb per sq in.[9] To obtain the total exciting torques for orders 1, 2, and 3, the inertia torques given in Eq. (31.4) must be added to the gas-pressure torques found in the reference.

The natural frequency of torsional vibration of the crankshaft system can be calculated with a fair degree of accuracy by one of several methods,[8,10] which need not be reviewed here. Typical first-mode natural frequencies of current V8 engines, with their short, rigid shafts, range from about 300 to 350 cps. The corresponding frequencies for typical 6-cylinder in-line engines range from 220 to 315 cps, and those for 8-cylinder engines are about 220 cps. At speeds such that the frequency of a given order coincides with the natural frequency of the shaft, resonance occurs, and that speed is called a "critical" speed. In an engine with even firing intervals, certain orders, called "major" orders, are distinguished by the fact that the vectors for all cylinders are in phase. This occurs in 4-cycle engines for orders n, so that $n/m = .5, 1, 1.5$, etc., where m is the number of cylinders. Speeds at which the frequencies of these major orders coincide with the natural frequency of the shaft are called "major critical" speeds. For example, in an 8-cylinder, 4-cycle engine with equal firing intervals (the usual case), these critical orders are 4, 8, 12, etc. If the crankshaft natural frequency is 320 cps, the major critical speeds become

$$N = \frac{320 \times 60}{n} \quad \text{rpm}$$

where $n = 4, 8, 12$, etc.

$N = 4{,}800, 2{,}400$, and $1{,}600$ rpm, as excited by orders 4, 8, and 12, respectively. The next-higher mode of crank vibration with two nodes in the crankshaft is, of course, of higher frequency. In the example cited, the order 4 critical would be above the operating-speed range for the second mode and, in many cases, for the first mode. In other cases, order 4 (or even nearby minor orders) may excite the lower critical of the pair formed by the attachment of the balancer. In general, orders 4 and 8 critical speeds are usually the most important ones in V8 engines, while orders 6 and 4 are usually the most important in in-line 6- and 8-cylinder engines, respectively.

Critical speeds other than major criticals discussed above are called "minor critical" speeds. The relative severity of torsional amplitude in various critical speeds is determined by the work done on the vibrating shaft by the various torque harmonics. This work is equal to the vector summation for all cylinders of the product $\pi M\beta$, where M is the harmonic torque amplitude and β the relative torsional-vibration amplitude, obtained from the normal elastic curve for the mode under consideration.[8]

This summation for various half-order vibrations depends upon the firing order of the engine, but that for integral orders can be shown to be independent of firing order. This is to say, the relative severity of certain minor critical speeds can be changed; but the severity of all integral-order critical speeds, which include the major critical speeds, cannot be changed by a change of firing order.

The torsional vibration of crankshafts is important not only as a noise source but also because excessive amplitudes of vibration may result in shaft failure caused by the high stresses induced. For this reason, torsional vibration is controlled in practically all present-day engines by the use of dampers or absorbers. Torsional vibration makes itself felt because of the bending of the crank webs, leading to sidewise displacement of the shaft center line, the restraint of which causes radial forces at the main bearings.

Resonant Flexure of Rotating Shafts. Rotating shafts may exhibit resonant flexural vibrations, the exciting forces for which are the unbalanced rotating forces of the shaft. Critical speeds thus occur when the rotational speed is equal to the natural frequency of flexural vibration of the shaft. The propeller shaft of the automobile provides the most frequently occurring example of these vibrations.

The mechanism of these vibrations is as follows: Consider the flexural vibration of the propeller shaft as a uniform beam with simple supports having the (lowest) natural frequency equal to

$$f_n = \frac{1.60 \times 10^5}{l^2} \sqrt{r_2^2 + r_1^2} \quad \text{cps} \tag{31.5}$$

for an annular steel shaft of length l inches having inside and outside radii of r_1 and r_2 inches, respectively.

With this shaft rotating with some unbalance, a centrifugal force is created which has both vertical and horizontal components. Under these forces, the shaft executes simultaneous vertical and horizontal vibrations; that is, it executes a circular vibration in step with the shaft rotation, which is to say that the shaft whirls. The whirl may become excessive or dangerous at the critical speed, i.e., when the shaft speed equals the resonant frequency. Automobile propeller shafts are designed for critical speeds considerably above the maximum operating speed, typical critical speeds being in the range of 4,500 to 5,300 rpm.   Because of the flexibility of the propeller-shaft supports, the actual critical speed as installed will be considerably lower than that calculated for the shaft on rigid supports.

At low speeds, the heavy side of the shaft flies out.   At the critical speed, the whirl amplitude is extremely large and the heavy side moves inward toward the center of the shaft.   At very high speeds, several times the critical, the whirl amplitude decreases, approaching the negative of the original eccentricity; i.e., the heavy side moves in, and the shaft rotates about its center of gravity.[8,11]

In automotive problems, propeller-shaft unbalance produces a rough feeling and sound observed at high speed and caused by the reaction forces occurring at the bearings at the shaft ends.   The transmission, which supports one end of the shaft, is rigidly attached to the engine and resiliently supported on the frame and frame cross member.   The flexibility of the (rear) mount is not likely to be the same for the vertical and horizontal directions; accordingly, the motions observed here will frequently be found to be elliptical rather than circular in pattern.

Another type of flexure of shafts occurs in the case of the crankshaft.   In this instance, the exciting forces are produced by the impact of the gas forces upon the piston and rod as the explosion occurs, and the rear cylinder or cylinders seem to be especially capable of producing this vibration.   The result is a damped flexural oscillation of the crankshaft and tilting of the flywheel, which is heard as an unpleasant, unmechanical sound at one time called combustion roughness.[*,12,13]   This resulting disturbance has been successfully controlled in one V8 engine by the use of the so-called "flexible" flywheel, in which the flywheel mass is coupled resiliently to the end of the crankshaft for the tilting mode.   This correction does not seem to be required with automatic transmissions, presumably because of the lighter flywheels and increased damping.

Engine Structural Distortion: Impact and Explosion Noise.   One of the most important types of noise in an automobile is so-called "engine noise"—that which is radiated because of the distortion of the engine structure by the explosive nature of the cylinder gas pressures.   Each time a charge explodes, the cylinder distorts in a sort of breathing fashion; and this distortion, transmitted to the exterior surfaces, radiates noise not only locally but throughout the entire exterior surfaces of the engine as these distortions are propagated along the engine structure.   This situation is exaggerated in modern engines, in which the trend is toward higher compression ratios and higher peak combustion pressures.   In engines where combustion-chamber design produces high burn rates intended to control detonation, a disturbance now generally known as "roughness" is produced which differs from a smooth combustion process in that there is excessive energy radiated from the engine in the range of 400 to 1,500 cps.[14] (Compare with description in previous section.)   Radiation from the engine block is further exaggerated by the attempt to reduce engine weight by heavily stressing the engine metal.   Structure-borne sound and vibration are held under control by the use of rubber engine mounts.

The air-borne engine noise as heard in the car is held under control by the use of

1. Acoustical-absorption blankets under the hood.
2. Adequate fire-wall attenuation (dash mats).
3. Toe- and floor-board mats with adequate attenuation and vibration-damping properties.
4. Acoustical material in the car interior.

The evaluation of the effects of the above control materials can best be made by the use of binaural record-playback procedures, as discussed earlier, possibly guided or supplemented by appropriate laboratory testing of the materials.

Typical absorption blankets used under the hood have thicknesses of $\frac{3}{4}$ to $1\frac{1}{2}$ in. and densities of 1 lb per cu. ft.   Curves a and b of Fig. 31.6 show the sound-absorptive properties of typical under-hood blankets.   In Fig. 31.7 are octave-band analyses of

* See next section.

the engine noise heard inside the car at various engine speeds, showing the effect of the under-hood blanket. The difference in these spectra represents a large change in noise as automotive-noise testing goes—one that is discerned unanimously by the

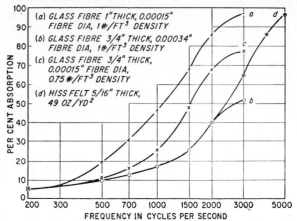

FIG. 31.6. Sound-absorption coefficients of various automotive acoustical materials, by standing-wave-tube method. (*a*) and (*b*) glass fibers used for underhood absorption; (*c*) glass fiber used as headlining backing. (*d*) carburetor-hiss felt. (*Apps, unpublished.*)

sound jury listening to binaural playback. Much smaller differences must consistently be discerned.

Although laboratory testing for the attenuation properties of dash mats has been devised, the effectiveness of a given material as installed must be evaluated in the car under actual operating conditions, for the following reasons:

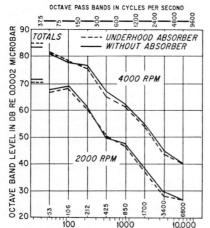

FIG. 31.7. Octave-band analysis of engine noise of 1955 sedan. Car standing, microphone in center front seat; with and without underhood absorption blanket. (*Apps, unpublished.*)

1. The flanking effect, i.e., sound entering the body cavity through other areas and surfaces.
2. The effect of leak holes around cables and controls leading into the engine compartment.
3. The effect of mounting conditions in which a fastener (for the dash mat) or a stud or support (for installed accessories such as heaters and defrosters) may couple the front face of the dash mat to a different degree than on a laboratory fixture.

Although the thermal- and acoustical-insulation properties of a dash mat are both of great importance, both requirements are usually best met by a dash mat having a soft blanket next to the fire wall with an impervious facing such as pressed board (K-B board). An additional impervious septum such as a heavy paper or asphalted felt placed within the blanket material is also helpful. Thus, the soft blanket, combined with the rather heavy facing, forms a low-pass mechanical filter, which is helpful in reducing the mechanical motion of the facing, whether the fire wall is acoustically or mechanically driven. The fibrous material is also helpful in providing transmission loss and helps, in addition, to seal the holes for cables and controls through the dash mat and fire wall. Typical dash-mat constructions on current cars are tabulated in Table 31.2.

Table 31.2. Typical Dash-mat Constructions

1 in. mixed-fiber blanket + K-B board facing
1 in. (1 lb per cu ft) glass-fiber blanket + K-B board facing
$\frac{5}{8}$ in. jute + K-B board facing
$1\frac{1}{2}$ in. ($\frac{3}{4}$ lb per cu ft) glass-fiber blanket + $\frac{3}{16}$ in., $1\frac{1}{4}$ lb per sq ft asphalted felt cemented to K-B board facing .

In Fig. 31.8 are shown octave-band analyses of engine noise as heard inside the car indicating the effect of dash-mat changes. The difference between the lower pair of curves is unusually large and is not often encountered. The upper pair of curves represents a similar analysis which is quite representative of the difference which must be consistently discerned in automotive work. While no sensible difference is indicated in the latter figure, the jury selected the experimental mat by a moderate margin: four choices for it and two standoff judgments. The standard mat received no preference.

The floor- and toeboard mats, like the dash mat, perform the multiple functions of thermal insulation, sound attenuation, and vibration damping. The most commonly used floor- and toeboard mats consist of jute $\frac{1}{2}$ to 1 in. thick cemented to a rubber facing. It is known from thick-plate damping tests (see Chap. 14) that jute laid on, but not cemented to, a metal surface constitutes an extremely good deadener, having thick-plate ratings of the order of 150 db per sec. This figure is about 200 db per sec when a rubber facing is added. Thus, most floor mats are laid directly on top of the metal floor pan—although some installations are found with saturated asphaltic felt cemented to the floor pans, over which the usual jute-and-rubber mat is placed. It is believed that the extra transmission loss provided by the deadener felt may be almost completely offset by the loss of damping due to the jute's not being directly in contact with the metal surface.

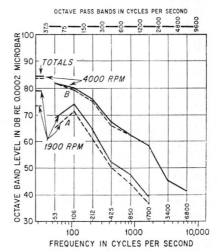

STANDARD DASH MATS: 1 1/2", 1 #/FT³ FIBERGLAS + KB BOARD

EXPERIMENTAL DASH MATS:
A $\begin{cases} 1\,1/2", 1\#/FT^3 \text{ FIBERGLAS} + 1\,1/4\,\#/FT^2 \\ \text{ASPHALT} + \text{KB BOARD} \end{cases}$
B $\begin{cases} 1\,1/2", 3/4\#/FT^3 \text{ FIBERGLAS} + 1\,1/4\,\#/FT^2 \\ \text{ASPHALT} + \text{KB BOARD} \end{cases}$

FIG. 31.8. Octave-band analyses of engine noise, car standing, measured in center front seat; one car (1952 sedan) with standard and experimental dash mat A and another car (1955 sedan) with (same) standard and experimental dash mat B. (Apps, unpublished.)

The sound-absorptive treatment found in the car interior is composed of the floor mat, the door and side trim, the headlining, the seat cushions, and the seat back. In some cars, additional control of engine noise is obtained by the use of an absorption blanket placed back of the headlining. Typical installations consist of $\frac{3}{4}$-in. thickness of glass-fiber blanket having a density of $\frac{3}{4}$ lb per cu ft. Various paper-base products are also used. Deadener felts should be retained on the metal roof surface, regardless of the use of lightweight absorbers, in order to provide the surface density required for adequate damping of impact excitations (see Chap. 14). The "headlining backing," as the absorbers are called, while offering some additional control for engine noise, also contributes a sense of quietness and luxury suggestive of thick rugs and heavy drapes in a room. The sound-absorptive characteristics of a glass-fiber backing are shown in curve c of Fig. 31.6.

The direct intercomparison of several under-hood isolators by the record-playback procedure, along with several dash mats and floor treatments, leads to an unmanageably large number of comparisons, if all possible combinations are directly intercompared. This unwieldy procedure can be avoided by a step-by-step method in which, for example, the under-hood isolator tests are run and the one desired (on a performance or cost basis) selected and left in position to form a new bogey, or standard. Thereupon, the tests involving several dash mats will be made, intercomparing them directly, and the one desired left in place for another new bogey, etc. It is clear that if materials are being selected which control the noise through parallel paths, some retesting may be required. For example, differences in floor mats may not show up when an ineffective dash mat is in place.

Engine-noise tests can probably best be made with the car standing and engine running at several fixed speeds, including one at least as high as approximately 3,000 rpm. In this way, extraneous noises such as wind noise, road noise, etc., are eliminated from consideration. It has been found that speeds must be duplicated with great precision—within about 10 to 20 rpm; otherwise the jury during playback unconsciously tends to judge speed rather than loudness.

Resonant Structural Flexure. Although the engine structure would appear to be an extremely stiff beam because its vertical and lateral dimensions are quite large, it is known that some engines show a pronounced tendency to vibrate as a free-free beam in the vertical and transverse directions. These vertical and transverse flexural frequencies can be determined by suspending the engine and transmission from above and exciting it vertically and laterally with an electrodynamic shaker, a small contrarotating exciter, or simply a small unbalanced motor. The mode exhibits two nodes, which are conveniently spotted by a survey with hand-held vibration pickups. While these frequencies vary from engine to engine and are different for a given engine with different transmission types, the frequency range of about 80 to 150 cps embraces most resonances in both the vertical and transverse planes. The mode of vibration of V8 engines probably involves bending in the plane of cylinders in one block with simultaneous bending in a plane perpendicular to the cylinder axes in the other block. The nodes seem to be less well defined than for the in-line engines.

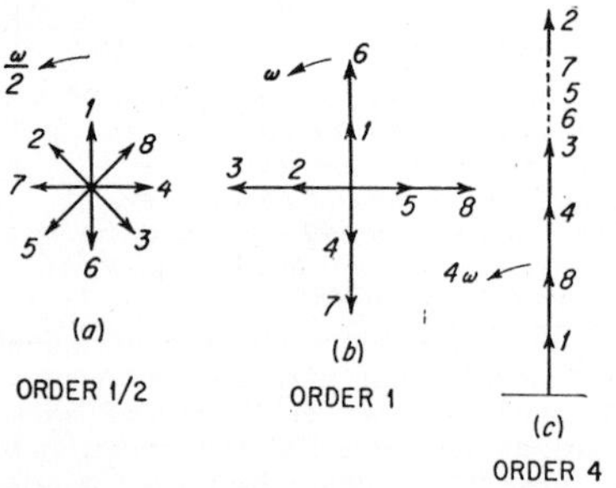

Resonant flexural vibrations occur when the firing frequency coincides with the natural frequencies and can result in loud periods inside the car. These troublesome vibrations are usually avoided by designing adequate transverse stiffness in the crankcase structure[15] and by strengthening the normally weak construction at the juncture of the engine and bell housing.

It is sometimes possible to avoid trouble, where such vibrations are serious, by locating the engine mounts as close to the nodes as possible, provided that other effects resulting from such engine-mount positions do not conflict.

In one case, the resonant flexure of the entire rear-axle housing in a vertical mode was found to be associated with a loud, low-frequency booming within the car at about

FIG. 31.9. Idealized exhaust noise vector diagrams for 8-cylinder engine. (*a*) fundamental half-order vectors, balanced; (*b*) Order 1 vectors, balanced; (*c*) Order 4 vectors (firing frequency), unbalanced, i.e., showing a net acoustical output. (*After method of Den Hartog.*[8])

65 cps. This flexure was excited by road irregularities. The effect was reinforced to some extent by a longitudinal-cavity resonance of the interior of the car which lies in the same frequency range.

Exhaust Noise. Exhaust noise is potentially the greatest noise source of the automobile. Figure 31.9a is a vector diagram of the gas explosion forces for an 8-cylinder engine. The order in which they occur is the firing order of the engine, and the vectors rotate at half engine speed, $\omega/2$. Figure 31.9b is a vector diagram of the second harmonic of the same vectors rotating at engine speed, ω. Here cylinder 2, for example, 45° ahead of cylinder 1 in Fig. 31.9a, is now 90° ahead. These two-star diagrams for exhaust noise are balanced, indicating that there should be no net acoustical resultant for these orders. This assumes, of course, that all the vectors are

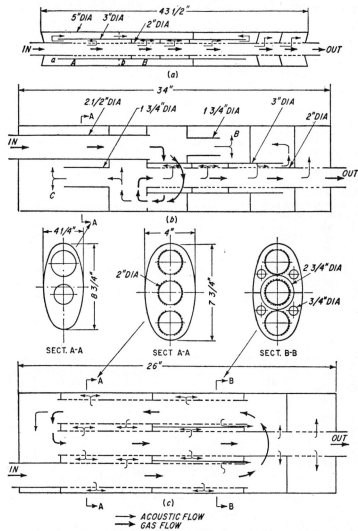

Fig. 31.10. Cross sections of typical muffler types. (a) straight-through; (b) two-tube, three-pass; (c) three-tube, three-pass.

of equal strength, have identical time-pressure curves, and are evenly spaced, as indicated in Fig. 31.9a. These assumptions are not entirely realized, as will become apparent later. It is also assumed that the difference in path lengths through the manifolds and exhaust system is insignificant.

If similar vector diagrams are drawn for successive half orders, it will be found that all of them are balanced in one configuration or another until order 4 is reached, as shown in Fig. 31.9c. Here, all the vectors line up in one direction, indicating a net acoustical output from the exhaust system. This unbalanced diagram is for harmonic 8 (that is, eight times half rotational speed), commonly called order 4, or firing frequency in the 8-cylinder, 4-cycle engine assumed, since it is equal to the number of cylinders firing per second. That is, firing frequency $F = \text{rps} \times m/2$, where m is the number of cylinders. By an extension of these vector diagrams, it is easily shown that the next unbalanced diagrams are those of orders 8 and 12, or twice firing and three times firing, respectively. The fundamental and harmonics of firing frequency are the principal components which have to be dealt with in the exhaust-and-muffler system (see Chap. 21).

Figure 31.10 shows cross sections of typical current muffler types: straight-through; 2-tube, 3-pass; and 3-tube, 3-pass. In the straight-through type, the control is obtained entirely by resonators arranged as side chambers. Near the inlet end are two large chambers in tandem, the first having a neck a and volume A. The neck is provided by an overlap and is entered through perforations in the center tube. The connecting resonator has a neck b, consisting of several holes in the annular flange and opening from volume A into volume B. The small arrows show the acoustic flow paths. The other chambers are variously tuned and proportioned in size to provide a satisfactory-sounding exhaust.

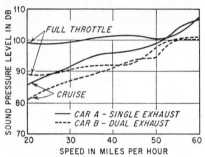

Fig. 31.11. Sound pressure level of exhaust noise vs. speed. Microphone, center of bumper, and 1 ft to the rear. (Flat weighting network.) Car *A*, average exhaust level. Car *B*, very quiet dual exhaust. Both 1955 sedans. (*Apps, unpublished.*)

In Fig. 31.10*b* the resonator marked *B* is tuned to 178 cps while the engine is hot, The resonator marked *C* is tuned to 126 cps while the engine is hot. The gases.

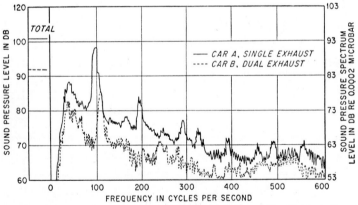

Fig. 31.12. Frequency analyses of exhaust noise for the cars of Fig. 31.11 at 40 mph, full throttle; 5-cps passband. (*Apps, unpublished.*)

following the heavy arrows, must turn forward and reverse again to enter the discharge tube, along which are located small, concentric chambers, entered through perforations in the center tube.

Figure 31.10*c* is a 3-tube, 3-pass muffler, in which the gases enter from the left, reverse through the upper tube, and turn again at the left end to enter the discharge tube. As shown, all the gas does not take this long route: small quantities can travel several bypass routes. This arrangement is called "bleeding" and helps reduce the back pressure without seriously impairing the muffler effectiveness.

An analysis of the ratio of net muffler volume to engine displacement volume of a group of typical 1954 passenger cars indicated values between 1.5 and 4.2; one of the two dual-exhaust installations doubled this ratio.[19]   The maximum back pressures of current passenger-car mufflers range from about 6 to 15 in. mercury when measured just below the manifold flange.

Figure 31.11 shows the relationship between sound pressure level measured close to the tail pipe versus speed for two 1955 V8 passenger cars.   Car B, with a dual exhaust, is an exceptionally quiet car; car A, with a single exhaust outlet, has a more or less typical exhaust-noise level.   These data were obtained for full-throttle as well as cruising load.   It is clear that over most of the speed range shown the full-throttle exhaust noise of car B is lower than the cruise exhaust noise of car A.

In Fig. 31.12 are shown the frequency analyses of the exhaust noise of these same cars at 40 mph.   The large peaks just below and above 100 cps are the firing frequencies; several harmonics of firing are also apparent.   A similar frequency analysis for car A at 55 mph indicated that at the higher speeds the individual frequency components are masked by a more continuous spectrum, probably

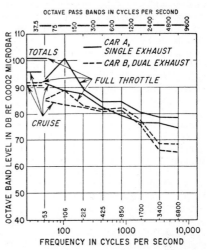

Fig. 31.13. Octave-band analyses of exhaust noise of the two cars of Fig. 31.11 at 40 mph. (*Apps, unpublished.*)

because of the turbulence noise associated with the high velocity of the exhaust gases.

In Fig. 31.13 octave-band data are shown for cars A and B at full throttle, 40 mph.

To show a different type of spectrum, Fig. 31.14 is included.   Here again, the speed was 40 mph, the load was about three-quarter-throttle, and the engine speed

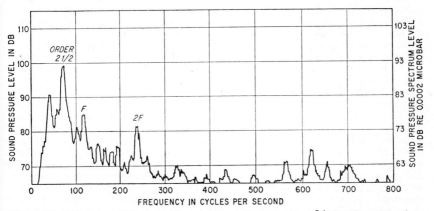

Fig. 31.14. Frequency analysis of exhaust noise at 40 mph, about ¾-throttle, 1954 sedan. Microphone 1 ft behind and 1 ft to the left of tail pipe.   Notice the half-orders present, not accounted for in the simple vector diagram of Fig. 31.9; 5-cps passband. (*Apps, unpublished.*)

was 1,800 rpm, or 30 rps.   Firing and twice firing frequencies are 120 and 240 cps, respectively, and their levels protrude above the adjacent levels distinctly.   Note that, contrary to the simplified analysis of Fig. 31.9, orders other than F, 2F, etc., are present presumably because the idealized assumptions are not realized.   All orders and half orders from 1½ through 9 are clearly evident. The system has an over-all resonance of 75 cps, which at this speed is excited by order 2½.

Exhaust-system mechanical hanger resonance is another problem which might be mentioned here. The period is characterized by extreme sharpness and comes through usually as a firing-frequency boom inside the car. Investigation will indicate mechanical resonance of the exhaust system on one of its flexible supports. The problem can usually be taken care of by using a softer mount or a less sensitive location on the exhaust or tail pipe or on the part of the car from which it is suspended.

Induction Noise. The generation of the firing-frequency acoustic signal in the induction or air-inlet system may be explained by the same vector diagrams discussed above. The chief difference, of course, is that the magnitude of the pressure change is not as great for the induction system, because we are dealing with considerably more gradual (usually negative-going) change in pressure as the intake valve opens and the piston descends.

Induction noise is characterized by the existence of periods at certain speeds with an induction sound consisting largely of firing frequency and one or two harmonics. Induction noise may be checked on the road by turning off the key at the speed where the period occurs and opening and closing the throttle, meanwhile matching the sound which comes in with that which is heard with the ignition on. This procedure, however, does not reveal one type of noise emitted through the induction system which is actually due to exhaust noise feeding back through the induction system as a result of the valve overlap between the exhaust and induction strokes. This exhaust noise escaping through the induction system will, of course, not be heard on the check described above, with ignition off. Perhaps the best way to check for the existence of this type of disturbance is, with the car standing, to remove completely the induction noise by attaching a long, flexible hose to the carburetor, with the far end placed in another room or outdoors and terminated with a silencer. The conclusions regarding the presence of exhaust feedback noise are then based upon comparison of the noise levels of the normal versus the remote induction systems.

A useful technique in determining the speeds at which induction noise periods occur is to sweep slowly through the speed range of interest while motoring (not firing) on the chassis dynamometer with the ignition off, fan blades removed, and gasoline line disconnected. The total sound pressure is recorded on a level recorder during a speed sweep while the accelerator is alternately opened and closed about once per second. In such a record, made with the microphone under the hood, the vertical distance on the recording at a given speed is a measure of the increase in level due to the opening of the throttle. By placing the microphone inside the car, this technique can be used to show that, owing to the effects of body-cavity resonance, a noise source with a reasonably flat output will appear to have one or more periods or peaks as observed inside the car body.

Having identified the periods which occur as heard in the car, frequency analyses can now be made at these speeds to determine what components are causing these "lifts." In one case, for example, frequency analyses made at three speeds showed a large response at frequencies of 60 to 70 cps, 125 cps, and 160 cps, singly or in combination. These were readily excited by the firing and twice-firing components of induction noise: At 30 mph, 60 and 125 cps were excited by F and 2F; at 36 mph, 70 and 160 cps were excited by F and 2F; at 57 mph, 125 cps was excited by F. Thus, a period or lift occurs whenever F or 2F coincides in frequency with one of the body-resonance modes and, in the parlance of torsional vibration, they are "critical" speeds. The three frequencies 60 to 70, 125, and 160 cps are the half-wave closed-tube resonances of the body interior in the longitudinal, transverse, and vertical directions, respectively.

Figure 31.15 shows the sound pressure level versus speed as measured under the hood on a typical 1954 V8 car. Here, the operation is motoring with the ignition off, and curves are shown for both silencer on and silencer off. The difference is a measure of the effectiveness of the silencer. In silencer design or in a program to improve present silencers, frequency analyses can be made at the peak speeds or periods. Frequency analyses of the 45-mph period of Fig. 31.15 are shown in Fig. 31.16. The analyses show strong F and 2F components without silencer, and the silencer reduces these 13 and 10 db, respectively. Note the cluster of half-order components above 400 cps, which, according to simple vector treatment with idealized conditions, should not be present. In other cases, a series of strong integral-order components appear throughout the range, with half orders for the most part absent.

Essentially all intake silencers are of the straight-through design, that is, using side chambers to control both low-frequency and high-frequency noise. This applies to both viscous-impingement and oil-bath-cleaner types. Figure 31.17 shows cross sections of typical silencers; Fig. 31.17a is a concentric oil-bath type. Induction air follows the path shown by the heavy arrows. The induction noise enters the silencer from the carburetor and is controlled by several resonators arranged as concentric side chambers. The first chamber is tuned to 430 cps; the neck consists of several large perforations opening into the wedge-shaped volume behind them. The next chamber is tuned to 140 cps; its neck is formed by an overlap and perforations.

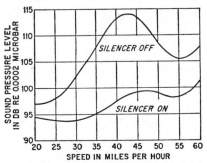

Fig. 31.15. Sound pressure level measured under hood vs. speed, with and without silencer, 1954 sedan with V8 engine, wide-open throttle, motoring. Flat weighting network. (*Apps, unpublished.*)

Figure 31.17b is a concentric dry type, having two side chambers tuned to 130 and 550 cps. The top chamber is called a "hiss gap"; it eliminates frequencies in the neighborhood of 1,500 cps.

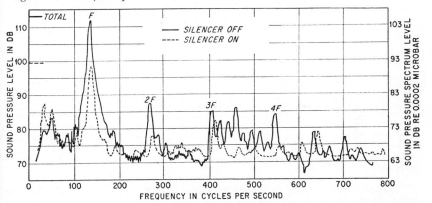

Fig. 31.16. Frequency analyses of induction noise of Fig. 31.15. V8 engine, microphone under hood, wide-open throttle, motoring, 2,050 rpm. Note firing frequency, *F*, and its harmonics; also the cluster of half-orders present above 400 cps, not explained by simple vectors of Fig. 31.9. 5-cps passband. (*Apps, unpublished.*)

In Fig. 31.17c, the control of the low-frequency component, 110 cps, dictated that the large chamber required be provided as a branch from a horizontal tube. The volume above the cleaner element in the concentric part of the unit acts as an untuned expansion chamber. The chamber at the front is tuned to 270 cps.

Induction-silencer design, as muffler design, is a combination of art and science. The large, flat areas of some silencers may radiate noise due either to the large dynamic pressures in the chambers or to vibration "telegraphed" through the connection to the carburetor. These areas may be stiffened and damped by a double thickness, spot-welded together. In some instances, a rubber gland is used.

Worthy of mention is the pad of jute, called a "hiss felt," which is located directly opposite the carburetor air horn to absorb the hiss produced by the induction air passing through the carburetor passages and ports.   The hiss spectrum lies above 2,000 cps.   These pads are usually about ¼ in. thick and are sized on one side to make them flame-resistant.   A typical absorption-versus-frequency characteristic is shown in curve d of Fig. 31.6.

Cooling-fan Noise.   (Also see Chap. 25.)   At high engine speeds, cooling-fan noise is frequently annoyingly loud.   The level of a fan noise depends upon a combination of many factors, including tip speed, blade shape, blade spacing, and spacing between fan and radiator or between other obstructions.   Body-cavity resonance will affect the

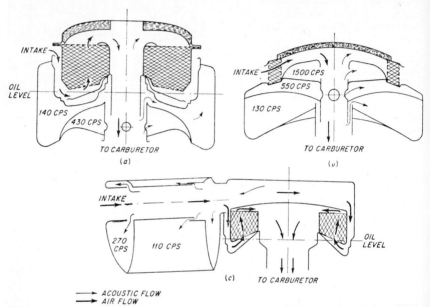

Fig. 31.17. Cross sections of typical induction silencers.   (*a*) Two-chamber oil bath, concentric type, tuned as indicated.   Note hiss felt; (*b*) dry-type concentric silencer with two main chambers tuned as indicated.   The top chamber, called a hiss gap, is effective on hiss frequencies around 1,500 cps.   Note hiss felt; (*c*) concentric oil-bath cleaner with horizontal silencer extension.   Chambers tuned as indicated.   Large chamber over concentric part acts as untuned expansion chamber.   (*Courtesy of AC Spark Plug Division, General Motors Corporation.*)

level heard inside the car.   In general, the direct approach to reducing fan noise is to lower the tip speed by reducing the rotary speed.   This reduction in rotary speed must be reconciled with reduced water-pump speed and pumping capacity, since the pump is frequently integral with the fan blades.   Since the airflow is decreased by reducing the fan-to-engine speed ratio, the total airflow may be maintained by increasing the number of blades, by increasing the pitch, or by providing a shroud to channel the airflow through the radiator and prevent recirculation or bending of the blade tip toward the radiator.

An approximate method for predicting the relative strength of the various harmonic components of sound produced by various blade arrangements (not blade shapes) is found in the vector representation method discussed under *Exhaust Noise.*   Thus, a 4-blade fan with 90° spacing yields only orders 4, 8, 12, etc.   As shown in Fig. 31.18, the 60-to-120° X blade arrangement yields all even orders.   The even orders 2, 4, and 6, by this analysis, yield relative pressures of 2, 2, and 4; the series then repeats so that 8, 10, and 12 yield outputs of 2, 2, and 4, respectively.

A similar analysis was carried out for the first six orders of a 4-blade fan with blade spacing of 113, 129, 42, and 76°. These irregular spacings are frequently used to "spread" the acoustic output over several orders, instead of concentrating it in a few orders. An empirical weighting factor for each order was developed by comparing the results obtained by these star diagrams for the 60-to-120° X fan and for the above irregularly spaced fan with the experimental results obtained for the same fans.[16]

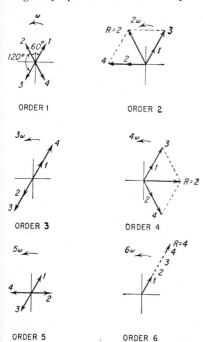

ORDER 1

ORDER 2

ORDER 3

ORDER 4

ORDER 5 · ORDER 6

FIG. 31.18. Vector diagrams for sound components of 60° X fan. All odd orders balanced, even orders with relative outputs as shown. Correction factors of Fig. 31.19 must be applied. (*After method of Den Hartog.*[8])

The weighting factors are plotted in Fig. 31.19. Thus, the relative strength of various orders obtained for various blade spacings may be roughly predicted by determining the vector result of the star diagrams for each order and multiplying them by the empirically determined weighting factor.

Figure 31.20 shows the relative strength of the various (even) orders as a function of blade spacing for 4-blade X fans as determined experimentally.[16] Note how order 4 decreases and order 2 increases as the acute angle is made smaller, i.e., as the fan

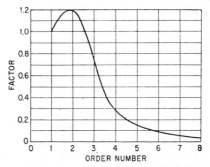

FIG. 31.19. Empirical correction factors to be applied to resultants of various fan-blade orders determined from Fig. 31.18 or equivalent vector diagrams. (*Apps, unpublished.*)

approaches a 2-blade configuration. Note also that order 6 peaks at 60°, because 6 is the factor by which 60° must be multiplied for blade 2 vector to come around and lie on top of blade 1 vector. At the same time, vector 3 travels three complete revolutions and also coincides with vector 1, etc. An X fan with 76° spacing is frequently used. According to Fig. 31.20, this is the angle at which orders 2 and 4, the larger components present, are approximately equal.

The adoption of air conditioning has heightened the cooling-fan-noise problem. The condenser for such a system is mounted directly forward of the radiator, thus reducing the airflow to the radiator and, in addition, warming the air which reaches it. To balance this effect, thicker radiators and higher-capacity fans must be used. Radiator shrouds are frequently used on the air-conditioned installations, or, alternately, more blades or ring shrouds on the fan itself. Radiator shrouds sometimes vibrate violently at definite speeds, excited in natural resonances by alternating aerodynamic forces. Fan blades commonly vibrate as cantilever beams—in a bending-torsion mode—causing noise of a definite frequency, as well as possible blade fatigue and failure. This is especially true where an obstruction such as a water hose lies close to the plane of the blades, thereby increasing the amplitude of the aerodynamic forces. Ring shrouds are useful in raising the natural vibration frequency of the blade.

Torque Reaction. The torque developed by an internal-combustion engine is delivered in relatively large packets, one packet each time a cylinder fires. As a result, there is a relatively large alternating component of torque superimposed upon the average, or steady, value, and these produce alternating components of angular acceleration of the crankshaft system. The forces which produce these alternating angular accelerations, of course, have their reaction on the engine block, tending to move it in the opposite rotational direction.

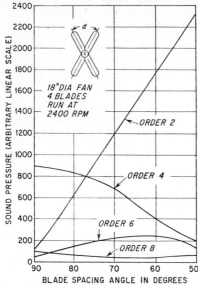

Fig. 31.20. Fan noise. Measured sound pressures of various components measured on X-type fan as blade spacing angle is varied. Note absence of odd orders. (*After Cary.*[16])

All automotive engines incorporate some form of resilient mounting to isolate engine vibrations, and the engine mass on these mounts forms a system capable of executing several resonant modes of vibration. At low speeds, usually just above idle, when the firing frequency (rps times number of cylinders divided by 2) is equal to one of the natural frequencies of the engine on its mounts, the engine executes a rather violent motion, which is still more severe with increased torque. With automatic transmissions, this torque reaction is greatly reduced in severity. Because of the relatively high stall speed of the fluid coupling, the engine cannot be loaded heavily at speeds just over idle. Torque reaction usually excites all three antisymmetric modes of the engine on its mounts and possibly a structural frame and body resonance in the same range of frequencies. To avoid a violent torque reaction resonance, all three or four modes must be held to frequencies below operating range. Attempts to arrange mounting geometry so that only one mode will be excited, while the others are uncoupled, have not been fully successful.

Gear Noise. (Also see Chap. 23.) In the automobile, the cam gears, transmission, and rear-axle gears appear to be the most frequently encountered sources of gear noise.

Gear noise is characterized by a whine of gear-tooth-contact frequency (and/or its second or third harmonics) and, in its simplest terms, is apparently due to the variation in loading of the teeth as they pass through the contact area with the mating teeth.

Camshaft-drive noise is usually held under control by using a linen phenolic gear. Camshaft drives of the chain type are also recognized as silent drives.

Some manual-shaft transmissions exhibit gear noise frequently with a very broad peak, if any. This suggests a forced vibration of gear shafts, the gear case itself, or other parts, caused by the torque variation associated with the transfer of load from tooth to tooth.

Some planetary transmissions, such as those used in the current automatic-transmission types, exhibit gear-noise periods, frequently rather sharply resonant in response. It is difficult or impossible to state in general terms what the resonance element or system may be in a given transmission design.

Rear-axle-gear noise is frequently encountered in current automobiles. This noise may occur on drive, float (with essentially zero load transferred in either direction), or overrun. The most difficult rear-axle noise to control is that produced under light contact pressure, as on float or overrun. Under these conditions, a very small oscillation of gear or pinion is enough to separate the two and to let them re-engage with a shock. Rear-axle noise is usually, but not always, characterized by a rather sharp period where the tooth frequency is in the neighborhood of 400 to 500 cps. This same period can be excited at one-half the road speed by the second harmonic of tooth-contact frequency.

It is probable that if an ideal tooth shape could be designed and parameters such as tooth shape and helix angle maintained in manufacture within a narrow limit, gear noise would be essentially nonexistent.

Some control of axle noise may be obtained by isolating the rear-axle springs by means of rubber-spring seat pads, and also by use of softer rubber in the front-spring eyes in the case of leaf springs. However, only limited improvement may be obtained in practice because of the undesirable effects on handling resulting from the excessive use of rubber.

Fluid-coupling and Converter Noise.[35] Blade-frequency noise may become a problem when the number of blades in adjacent rotating units such as pump, turbine, and stator is such that several pairs of blades pass each other simultaneously. The usual procedure is to design according to the hydraulic requirements and to check the noise on the prototype units. At that time, if blade noise is objectionable, a frequency analysis will reveal which units are causing the trouble. In fluid couplings, the practice is to provide uneven blade-spacing intervals to scramble the noise. In hydraulic converters, this approach cannot be used without a loss in efficiency. The approach here is one of changing blade shape or spacing. Blade-frequency noise may make itself apparent either by the resonance of one of the bladed members or by its forced vibration. Important resonance effects are shifted, if at all possible, to speeds above the stall speed of the unit. This speed represents the maximum relative velocity and hence highest exciting blade frequency produced by a given pair of units.

Cavitation is a potential source of noise in fluid couplings and converters if the angle of attack or the blade design is improper. Cavitation noise can be reduced or eliminated by increased static operating pressure. In current designs, fluid couplings are supercharged to about 20 lb per sq in., and fluid converters to about 60 to 80 lb per sq in.

High-turbulence phenomena are responsible for another noise source in couplings and converters. This noise cannot be reduced by increased supercharging as can cavitation noise but must be controlled by a change in blade shape. As a result, the design of fluid couplings and converters is a compromise among efficiency, converter ratio, noise, and cost.

Universal Joints. There are two methods used in current American automotive practice for transmitting the power from the transmission to the rear axle.

The first is the so-called "torque tube," in which the rear-axle reaction torque is resisted by a hollow structural tube enclosing the rotating drive shaft. The longitudinal thrust propelling the car is transmitted (1) via the torque tube through a ball joint to the engine, and finally through the engine mounts to the frame; or (2) via the front eyes of the rear springs. In the torque-tube drive there is only one universal joint, and one slip joint in the propeller shaft.

The other and more commonly used method of power transmission is the "Hotchkiss drive," consisting of a rotating drive shaft with a universal joint on each end and a slip joint usually on the front end. The reaction torque of the rear axle is resisted by the rear springs, and the thrust which drives the car is applied to the frame at the front eyes of the rear spring.

The Cardon or Hooke universal joints used on automobiles are characterized by the fact that they do not transmit motion smoothly (except under particular, angular configurations). For a pair of shafts connected by one universal joint, the following expression has been derived for the ratio of the instantaneous velocities of driven and drive shafts as a function of the misalignment angle ϕ:[17]

$$\frac{\omega_b}{\omega_a} = \frac{2 \cos \phi}{\cos 2a(1 - \cos^2 \phi) + 1 + \cos^2 \phi} \qquad (31.6)$$

where ω_b and ω_a = instantaneous velocities of driven and drive shafts, respectively
ϕ = angle of misalignment (see Fig. 31.21)
a = drive-shaft angle, referred to position shown for joint at left (i.e.,
$a = 0$ when axis of drive-shaft trunnions is perpendicular to plane
of paper)

Thus, for a uniform velocity of the drive shaft, the driven shaft experiences a variation in velocity of a frequency twice the mean shaft velocity.

When *two* universal joints are used, there are two possible shaft arrangements which will provide for uniform rotation of output shaft c. The requirements are that the yokes on shaft b be aligned in the same plane and that the input and output shafts make the same angle, ϕ, with the intermediate shaft and (1) lie on opposite sides (see Fig. 31.21a), or (2) lie on the same side of the intermediate shaft (Fig. 31.21b). The three connected shafts of Fig. 31.21 lie in the same plane, but if all shafts do not lie in the same plane, the configuration for uniform velocity can be achieved by an adjustment of the relative position of the two yokes on the intermediate shaft b.

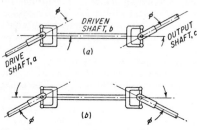

FIG. 31.21. Universal joints. Drive Shaft a misaligned at angle ϕ with Driven Shaft b. Angle a (not shown) for drive shaft is zero in position shown for the left universal joints. a and b illustrate the angular arrangement which must be met to provide uniform velocity of Output Shaft c in a two-joint system and when all three shafts are in one plane. (*After Heldt.*[17])

Various universal joints have been designed to provide constant velocity of the driven shaft. These include the Bendix-Weiss joint and the Rzeppa joint. Both these universal joints meet the requirement that the plane where the transfer of motion occurs bisect the angle between the connected shafts, as exemplified by the use of a pair of bevel gears.

The significance of the velocity variation in the ordinary Hooke joint in the automobile is that the large inertias connected at the drive and loaded ends of the drive shaft resist rapid velocity change. Accordingly, the shaft is stressed with an alternating stress at twice its rotational speed, and the resultant reaction forces on the end of the transmission and the rear axle can lead to troublesome resonances.

This universal-joint force of twice rotational frequency can excite a bending vibration, for example, of the so-called "transmission extension" as a cantilever beam, producing an annoying period. In overdrive transmissions where the drive shaft normally turns 1.43 times faster than the engine, the 2-cps-per-rps excitation becomes 2.86 cps per rps of the engine, which has been known to produce an audible beat in conjunction with the firing frequency (3 cps per rpm) of a 6-cylinder engine. At 2,400 rpm of the engine, the beat frequency would be

$$(3.00 - 2.86) \, 2,400/60 = 5.6 \text{ cps}$$

Brake Squeal.[24] Brake-squeal frequencies cover a range from 2,000 to 50,000 cps, with frequencies between 10,000 and 15,000 cps constituting the significant range of annoyance. There is some evidence that resonance of some part of the brake in the inaudible portion of this range may be a contributory factor in the production of audible brake squeal due to vibration.

By relating the measured frequencies of sound radiated from a squealing brake with experimentally determined natural frequencies of these parts in their many vibrational modes, it has been determined that the brake drum and brake shoe vibrate at some of their natural frequencies during the production of brake squeal. It has been observed that brake squeal sometimes occurs when the natural frequency of a brake shoe is near one of the natural frequencies of the brake drum. In other types of squeal, this coincidence of frequencies does not seem to be required.

Very little seems to be known about the fundamental mechanism of brake squeal. Outside of some cut-and-try cures applying only to a single design, the only general remedy for brake squeal is internal hysteresis or applied damping on the brake drum. Changes of geometry and of stiffness are not generally effective; they only shift the squeal from one group of frequencies to another. It appears that at many modes brake drum and shoe do not remain in continuous contact but only touch at some limited areas and for a fraction of each cycle. At the higher frequencies observed it is then almost certain that pressure is not in phase with displacement, and frictional force not in phase with pressure. It is therefore too much to expect a basic understanding of the vibration cycle until something is known of the properties of the friction lining at these frequencies.

Road and Tire Noise.

Road Noise. Road noise (also called "road rumble" and "body rumble") started to become a serious problem in cars of the late 1930s. With postwar production, increased control measures have been required. Changes in suspension, frame, or body construction frequently cause considerable difficulties in this regard, signifying that very little is probably known about the actual mechanism producing the noise.

Road noise is associated with the vibration of the tire casing, which is excited by roughened road surfaces such as concrete spalled by road salt and high-coefficient asphalt. The frequency range which characterizes road noise is limited to a band of about 100 to 200 cps, and the composition is independent of road speed. In fact, in some models which are particularly susceptible to road noise, it is observed that the characteristic road noise persists as long as the wheels are turning, however slowly. The noise appears to be of the same general character over a wide variety of car and body-structure types, except that it appears to be higher-pitched in the body-frame integral or unitized construction.

The disturbance, the frequency-determining element of which seems to be the tire casing, is transmitted from the tire through wheel, spindle, suspension, and frame to the body. Most of the disturbance is generated by the front wheels. Road noise is controlled in most cars by the use of rubber body mounts, frequently in combination with rubber isolation in the front-suspension members. Such rubber suspension isolation cannot approach ideal isolation conditions, for to do so would impair the handling and stability characteristics of the car. Extensive use is made of vibration-damping materials applied to the body and certain other sheet-metal areas.

The vibrational modes (i.e., longitudinal, flexure, torsional, etc.) by which the disturbing energy is principally transmitted from tires to body is probably not known. However, the isolation of vibration at various points along the path of transmission is very helpful. These points might include rubber-isolated wheels, rubber bushings in the front-suspension inner pivot points, rubber isolation between the suspension cross member and frame, and rubber body mounts inserted between the body and frame. All these means of isolation have been

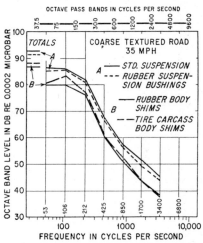

FIG. 31.22. Road noise; effect of rubber suspension bushings (1952 sedan) and rubber body shims (1953 sedan). Flat weighting network; microphone in right front seat. Independent sets of data from two different cars. (*Apps, unpublished.*)

tried many times, singly or in combination, and most of them are helpful in varying degrees. Figure 31.22 shows some typical results of various isolation tests.

Many times it has been suggested that perhaps the level of road noise has not really increased over the years but merely appears louder because of the suppression of other noises in the automobile. To check on this possibility, a 1935 car in good condition was procured. This car, tested on a road under typical test conditions, was found to be remarkably free from road noise. It used a coil-spring type of independent front suspension not unlike current designs, from which we may conclude that the current suspension design is not in itself responsible for the problem. Other features of this car which were quite different from our current constructions are

1. Large tires, 7 by 17 in., mounted on wire wheels carrying 32 lb per sq in. pressure, in contrast with current 15-in. wheels carrying 24 lb per sq in. pressure.
2. A heavy frame and suspension members of generous proportions.
3. A body of composite wood-and-steel construction, with a wood body sill, wood inserts in the center and forward door pillars, and wooden floor boards.
4. A fabric top.

It is interesting to note that some present-day pickup trucks are extremely free from road noise; these have a solid front axle and leaf springs. Further, they have all-steel bodies, which would seem to eliminate the importance of this factor in current cars. In addition, they have very little sound-absorptive material inside the cab.

Figure 31.23 is a plot of road noise versus speed, as measured in the front seat at ear level using a B weighting network. Car A represents a 1955 model of average level, while Car B represents the best in the industry. Data were obtained for each car on two different textures or degrees of coarseness of asphalt pavement. The B weighting was used to minimize the contribution of boom frequencies to the reading (see analysis, Fig. 31.24), since they are not heard as characteristic road noise. The spreads due to the road surfaces are about 5 and 7 db for the two cars, while the differences between cars on a given road surface range from 3 to 7 db.

Unitized construction is not inherently noisier than that used in body-and-frame-type cars, even though the body-frame isolation obviously cannot be employed. It has been found important, in unitized cars with Hotchkiss drive, to mount the spring hangers directly under the body sills rather than cantilevering them from the sides of the sills. The former method introduces less excitation to the floor panels, which are, in this construction, attached directly to the top flanges of the body sills.[18] Further, road noise (as well as axle-gear noise) is alleviated by the use of tension-type rear shackles. Road noise in unitized cars can be controlled by isolation of the suspension system from the body, by application of damping materials to the body, and by recognizing the importance of body structural resonances and localized deflections.

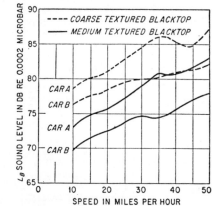

FIG. 31.23. Road noise; sound level vs. speed (B weighting network) for Cars A and B on two test roads having different coarseness of texture; 35 mph, 1955 sedans. Microphone in right front seat. (*Apps, unpublished.*)

As with most noise problems, an extremely small amount of power appears to be involved in the road-noise problem. For example, at 35 mph on a coarse-textured road, typical strain measurements on frame and suspension structural members summed for frequencies in the band of 100 to 300 cps yielded results of 0.3 μin. per in., or 9 psi.[19]

Vibration-damping materials are a necessary factor in controlling road noise in modern cars. Most attempts to weaken or stiffen the body or frame structures have failed to produce significant changes in noise level inside the car. It is common experience that changing structure stiffnesses merely "chases" the energy and the activity from one part of the structure to another. It is especially important to use vibration-damping materials on the entire floor area and under-seat area, recognizing that the usual floor mats can provide not only trim but the required damping as well on the areas that they cover. Door outer panels are treated with spray-on-type deadeners or asphaltic felts to control the impact type of noise (such as door slam and knuckling); this damping is useful in controlling road noise as well. In Fig. 31.24 are sound analyses of road noise to show the reduction obtained by the use of additional damping treatment on the front-end under-car sheet metal (except front fenders) and rear-end underbody and fenders.

In the 100- to 200-cps range, the only marked difference is a 2½-db reduction in the peak at about 165 cps. These analyses demonstrate the difficulty of detecting small differences in over-all noise levels and point up the value of a record-playback listening technique.[5] This set of experimental changes was evaluated with relative confidence by a jury: 8 preferred the damped condition, 2 were undecided, and none preferred the standard condition. The high peak at 37 cps is scarcely noticed by the ordinary observer. Thus, in making sound-level measurements of road noise, these boom frequencies are attenuated by using the A or B weighting network.

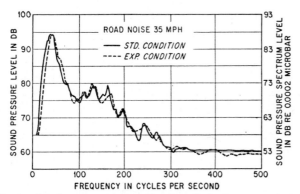

Fig. 31.24. Road noise; frequency analyses showing effect of spray-on damping material applied to certain sheet metal areas of 1954 sedan (see text). Flat weighting network. Microphone in right front seat. Speed 35 mph on coarse-textured road; 5-cps passband. (*Apps, unpublished.*)

In addition to providing vibration damping on the body surfaces enumerated above, materials applied elsewhere on the car are of some value. For example, an efficient deadener was applied to an X-type frame of a 1952 car. The deadener treatment consisted of ¾ in. wood conversion material to the outer surface of which was cemented 18-gauge sheet metal; this sandwich was in turn cemented to all accessible parts of the frame and X member. This material has a thick-plate rating (see Chap. 14) of 360 db per sec—very high compared with asphaltic felt and spray-on materials commonly used, which have a rating of from 5 to 15 db per sec. The reduction in road-noise sound pressure level was about 1½ db.[19] It has been determined that the damping of the sheet-metal surfaces (for example, the car underbody rearward of the rear floor, gas tank, wheel housings, bumper splash shields, and radiator splash shields) is more effective in controlling road noise than the damping of the frame, for at least two reasons: (1) the vibration amplitudes of the sheet-metal areas are larger, and therefore more energy can be dissipated per unit of area; and (2) a large area is available for such treatment.

It has been found that applying a 1-in. layer of glass fiber to the entire car underbody, fender walls, and engine compartment results in a noise reduction of 3 db and contributes materially to the feeling of quality within the car.[20] The approach here was to reduce the general level of the noise underneath the car with absorptive material.

Another approach to the road-noise-reduction problem is that of isolating the roof and floor surfaces from the air in the body cavity by a low-pass mechanical filter. A separate roof stamping was trimmed at the edges to fit inside the car top. It was cemented to 1½-in. foam rubber, which was in turn cemented to the underside of the roof. The purpose here was to prevent the vibratory motions of the roof from being transmitted to the false roof panel by use of the soft intermediate suspension. A 0.6-db reduction in the band 100 to 300 cps for the front seat and somewhat less for the rear seat were observed. The floor, which was found to have a higher vibration amplitude than the roof, was then isolated in the same manner. A further reduction was obtained of approximately 1 and 2 db for the front and rear seats, respectively. These reductions were not considered significant or practical enough to pursue this approach further.

The reduction of road-noise levels inside a car by increasing the total interior sound absorption has been studied. Some years ago, a study was made of the absorption

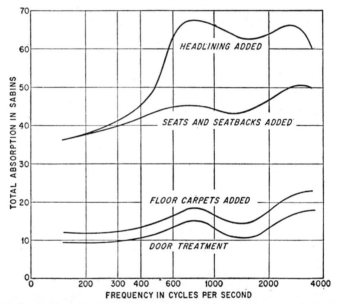

Fig. 31.25. Sound absorption in the automobile. Each curve represents the accumulative absorption in sabins for all curves beneath it, *circa* 1940. (*Apps, unpublished.*)

present in a typical 1940-production sedan; these results are shown in Fig. 31.25. Thus, approximately 36 sabins absorption are present in the road-noise frequency range. Even if it is assumed that the headlining material could be made 100 per cent absorptive, the absorption would become 65 sabins; thus, according to Eq. (18.4), the reduction in sound level would be about $10 \log_{10} (65/36) = 2.6$ db. Therefore, this method of approach will not provide a satisfactory solution to the problem. There is not much choice, except to do as effective a job as possible with vibration-damping materials. The evaluation of experimental changes made to control road noise is best done by using the binaural record-playback technique.

The front wheels provide more road-noise excitation in current suspension designs than the rear wheels. This situation, however, can possibly change as a result of some structural peculiarity. In any case, the relative importance of the two may be determined by making and comparing tape recordings with only one pair of wheels on the road, the other end of the car being lifted and pulled by a tow truck.

Brick-road Noise. In Fig. 31.26 is shown the *B* weighted sound level versus speed measured in a car traversing a brick road. The microphone was in the right front seat. With bricks laid three to the foot, the resulting joint frequency is equal to 4.4 times the mph. The four obvious peaks in Fig. 31.26 are marked with the calculated frequencies, showing lifts at 107, 127, 155, and 180 cps. Another peak can occur below 15 mph. The point of interest here is the reason for the peaks. Apparently some of them can be accounted for on the basis of body-cavity resonance, while others may be due to tire resonance or structural resonance.

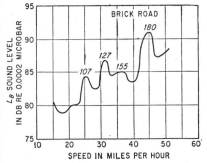

FIG. 31.26. Brick-road noise, 1955 sedan; sound level vs. speed (*B* weighting network). Microphone in right front seat. The small figures on the peaks are the brick frequencies calculated according to $f = 4.4 \times$ mph. (*Apps, unpublished.*)

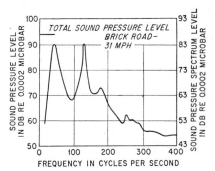

FIG. 31.27. Frequency analysis of brick-road noise. Flat weighting. Microphone in right front seat. Speed 31 mph. The 37-cps peak is hardly heard. The peak at 127 cps is the brick-joint frequency; 5-cps passband. Note higher total-noise level (cf. Fig. 31.26) due to flat weighting. (*Apps, unpublished.*)

In Fig. 31.27 is shown a frequency analysis obtained from a tape recording of the period at 31 mph. The 37-cps peak noted in road-noise recordings is again present, while the 127-cps peak is the brick-joint frequency. The study of brick-road noise and its frequency analysis is probably more important from the standpoint of contributing to the understanding of road noise than for the brick noise itself.

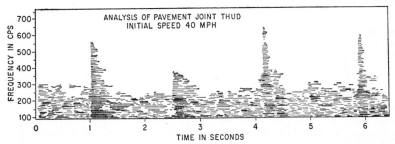

FIG. 31.28. Vibragram of pavement joint thud, 1955 sedan. Microphone in right front seat. The front wheels, striking first, produce a louder sound than the rear. (*Apps, unpublished.*)

Pavement-joint Noise. Pavement-joint noise is the dull thud produced when a car strikes the joints usually found in concrete pavements. The thud is produced whether the joint contour has a slight hump above or a depression below the level of the pavement.

One of the factors which may contribute to the sensitivity to this road disturbance is the lack of fore-and-aft flexibility in the front suspension. Whatever its cause, a considerable variation is found in the sensitivity of various cars.

The resulting thud from striking such a joint gives the definite impression that the noise is largely concentrated in the low-frequency range. Transient analyses have been made of the resulting sound using a visible-speech type of analyzer. Figure 31.28 shows that the frequency spectrum of the sound is essentially continuous up to 600 to

700 cps. The higher frequencies are damped out sooner. It also shows that there is a significant increase in level in the range of 100 and 250 cps as the wheels strike the joint.

It is clear that the front wheels are responsible for considerably more disturbance than the rear wheels. This agrees with common experience.

Tire Thump.[7] A study of the problem of tire thump has been made on a chassis dynamometer with only the one, thumping tire rolling. Recordings of the audible thump, made using a microphone pickup inside the car, were correlated with vertical vibrations of the wheel spindle. Simultaneous oscillograms were made of these two disturbances which showed a waveform of approximately 33 cps, having one complete

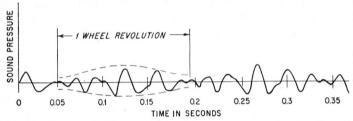

FIG. 31.29. Tire thump. Oscillogram of sound pressure in a car due to a thumping tire. The scalloped envelope is the result of the interference of two harmonics of wheel speed; envelope frequency is precisely equal to the wheel rotational rate in rps. (*After Apps and Vanator.*[7])

modulation cycle for every revolution of the tire. A reproduction of the sound trace is shown in Fig. 31.29 which is explained by the following hypothesis:

Discontinuities in the tire in the form of radial runout, crown thickness, lateral runout, effective stiffness, etc., result in spindle excitation as the tire turns. These exciting forces may consist of either one principal bump per wheel revolution (as in the case of a poor tread splice), or a considerably randomized function. In any case, the fundamental repetition frequency is the wheel rate in rps, and in general several higher harmonics of significant amplitude are present.

These harmonic forces excite resonant members, or systems, and it is evident that if two members or systems are excited simultaneously, the difference in their frequencies is some integral number times wheel rps. In tire thump, this integer is usually 1, i.e., there are present frequency components which differ in frequency by wheel speed. These components interfere and produce a beat frequency which is heard as tire thump.

A numerical example will help to illustrate the principle. Suppose tire thump is heard in a car traveling at 30 mph; the (typical) tire size is such that wheel speed is approximately 6 rps. The nonuniformities in the tire produce a series of harmonics differing in amplitude, and in general the relative magnitudes change as a function of speed. Let us say that the sixth and seventh harmonics of this 6-cps exciting force excite strong 36- and 42-cps responses, respectively. These 36- and 42-cps tones in the car interfere and produce a beat equal to their difference—6 cps. This 6 cps is, of course, precisely equal to the wheel rotational speed, and so it is mentally visualized as a bump, or boot, in the casing.

The severity of tire thump will vary as the car speed changes, frequently but not always building up to one or more maxima, or periods. When such periods occur, they frequently, but not always, occur in the 30- to 40-mph range. Periods occur at those speeds where relatively strong exciting harmonic components coincide in frequency with responsive acoustic or mechanical systems, i.e., at conditions of resonance or near resonance. At other speeds where the exciting forces of the tire harmonics are low or where the acoustic or structural responses are low, tire thump will be relatively suppressed. It can be easily demonstrated by the use of an electrodynamic shaker that the interference, or beating, of two low-frequency tones of approximately equal amplitude lying in the 30- to 40-cps range does indeed sound like tire thump. The speed range in which thump is heard is between 20 and 50 mph. At speeds lower than

20 mph, the exciting forces are generally too low to give much trouble; while the higher limit of 50 mph, or 10 rps of the wheel, is imposed by the fact that beat frequencies above approximately 10 cps take on the character of roughness and thereby lose their thump characteristic.

It is common experience that when a moving car exhibits thump, the thump is frequently not constant but rather continuously changing in severity and character. This is called "phasing," or "cycling." When only one thumping tire is rolling, the thump observed at a given speed is, of necessity, constant in character and severity, since each wheel revolution produces the same events. However, when two thumping tires are rolling, two sets of exciting forces are present. In the most general case, the tires are not exactly synchronized in rotational speed; rather there is a gradual gain by the faster tire on the slower one. Since each of the harmonic forces generated by a tire has a definite phase angle associated with it relative to some radial reference plane of the tire, it is clear that as the reference planes of the two tires progress or regress with respect to each other, the phase angles of the forces do likewise. This phasing process is shown by vectors in Fig. 31.30, where the sixth-order forces for the left and right wheels are shown in (a) as F_{L6} and F_{R6}. The left and right wheels have angular velocities of ω and $\omega + \Delta\omega$, respectively. Since $\Delta\omega$ is extremely small compared with ω, the resultant, R_6 rotates practically at speed 6ω, producing an audible beat with

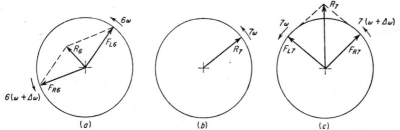

FIG. 31.30. Vectors showing phasing of tire thump. (a) Sixth-order vectors from the left and right wheels with resultant R6; (b) seventh-order vector coming largely from one wheel; (c) seventh-order vectors from left and right wheels with resultant R7. In (a) and (c), the right wheel is rotating $\Delta\omega$ faster than left. (Apps, unpublished.)

R_7 of Fig. 31.30b, here shown to be of constant amplitude, as when generated predominantly by one tire. Gradually, however, F_{R6} moves ahead and lies directly opposed to F_{L6}, so that if it is of the same amplitude as F_{L6}, as shown, the resultant R_6 eventually becomes zero and the thump temporarily vanishes. The envelope-amplitude vector of R_6 moves at velocity $6 \Delta\omega$, so that if the right wheel turns one complete additional revolution more than the left in a period of 12 min, the phasing cycle will recur six times as fast, or every 2 min.

Of course, phasing cycles of this kind can take place very much faster or slower than one every 2 min; furthermore, the phasing period will be changed while negotiating a turn, however slight. At 30 mph, $6\omega = 226$ radians per sec, while the $\Delta\omega$ assumed $= 0.0087$ radian per sec. Now, if R_7 is not constant but has significant components from each of two tires as shown in Fig. 31.30c, its phasing cycle is $1\frac{3}{4} = 1.71$ min. Then R_6 and R_7 move at relative rates of $6\Delta\omega$ and $7\Delta\omega$, producing a phasing frequency equal to their difference, $\Delta\omega$, and a complete phasing cycle every 12 min.

Other pairs of orders are simultaneously experiencing similar variations. When one of the beating components, such as R_6, is temporarily reduced in magnitude, then the other component, R_7, may beat with, say, R_8 to produce a thump, possibly of different strength and character than the R_6–R_7 combination. Alternately, when R_7 is temporarily reduced, a tire roughness (see *Tire Roughness*) may appear which is due to R_8 beating with R_7. Since the above sequence of events relates to only two thumping tires, it is not difficult to see how a set of four thumping tires can create an almost endless variety of combinations of tire thump and roughness.

Thus, thump does not usually progress evenly from minimum to maximum and back to minimum, etc. A roughness characteristic (see *Tire Roughness*) breaks up this orderly progression of thump, resulting in a complex yet definitely and accurately repeating sequence—for example, pure thump, to various degrees of thump combined with various kinds of roughness, to no thump, to another combination of thump and roughness, back to predominant thump, etc. As stated above, the time of a complete period is inversely related to the difference in wheel speeds.

The understanding of the simple principle that low-frequency interfering tones are the phenomenon which our ears identify as tire thump suggests a method for measuring it. A fairly good approximation to human judgment of the severity of thump is obtained by measuring the amplitude of the envelope, which is, of course, a measure of the variation of the level of the higher, or "carrier," frequency. (See *Tire-thump Meter* under *Instrumentation for Automotive-noise Testing.*)

In working with tire-thump problems on a given car, the best procedure is to work with one wheel on a chassis dynamometer where the important, or principal, response frequencies of the car are determined as a function of wheel speed. Once these frequencies are determined, the next step is to determine the mode of vibration of the structural members of the car, such as suspension, frame, etc., which are responsible for these principal frequencies. Electrodynamic shakers are extremely useful in the later stages of such a program in determining modes and their frequencies. Improvement in the thump response of the car should follow from steps taken to reduce the sensitivity of the structure at these principal frequencies. No specific recommendations can be made for a given car, inasmuch as each system possesses unique response characteristics.

Tire Roughness. Tire roughness is a disturbance which is currently of as much concern as tire thump. It sounds much like a defective wheel bearing or unbalanced propeller shaft and, like tire thump, is due to discontinuities in such tire variables as crown thickness, radial runout, lateral runout, effective stiffness, etc. Unlike tire thump, however, there is no obvious association with wheel turning speed. It is heard and felt in the speed range above 30 or 40 mph. The road surface need not be as smooth as for tire thump.

Tire roughness first began to assume importance in some cars about 1950. One of the earliest cases caused some difficulty in identifying its source. The rough feeling and sound were ascribed to such things as wheel bearings and an unbalanced propeller shaft and correct diagnosis was not made until the tires had been changed, all other conditions remaining the same. It is indeed uncertain what changes in car structures or in tires have taken place in the last several years to introduce and emphasize the problems of tire roughness.

Tire thump is due to the simultaneous excitation of two audio-frequency tones differing in frequency by the wheel rotational rate, which might be called a response at difference order 1 caused by the interference of adjacent orders. Tire roughness, on the other hand, may be caused by difference orders 1 or 2, the latter exemplified by orders 5 and 7. There is a characteristic rough sound of beat frequencies which are higher than about 10 cps. Thus, roughness under about 50 mph is probably due to difference order 2 (since difference order 1 would sound like thump) and above this speed to difference orders 1 or 2.

Tire roughness exhibits phasing, or cycling, and for the same reasons as tire thump (see Fig. 31.30). If only one tire is rolling, the roughness characteristic at a fixed speed is constant, i.e., unchanging in severity and character.

In working on the car structure to reduce roughness sensitivity, the same approach outlined for attacking the problem of tire thump is productive. This involves placing one wheel with a rough tire on a chassis dynamometer and measuring the principal frequency components present when roughness is heard. A survey using hand-held vibration pickups can then be made of the structural parts of the car, including the suspension, frame, and body, to determine the mode of vibration associated with the principal frequencies earlier determined. In checking to determine whether one of the modes associated with one of the principal frequencies has been eliminated, it should be borne in mind that two modes having closely spaced frequencies may have been present, elimination of one leaving the other largely undisturbed.

Tire Squeal. Tire squeal is a high-pitched, irritating noise produced by the vibration of the tire-tread elements when cornering. The problem was aggravated with the introduction of extra-low-pressure tires. The vibrations of the tread elements are transmitted throughout the tire and radiate noise from the side wall.[21] The intensity of the squeal is proportional to the product of the slip angle and the forward velocity. It is extremely sensitive to the coefficient of friction of the pavement, being lower, the lower the coefficient.

Squeal is developed at different points across the face of the tire, depending upon the tread design. Therefore, the method of minimizing it varies according to the design. Softer tread stocks tend toward lower squeal, although the extent to which this approach can be used in practice is limited by other considerations, such as tire wear, high-speed performance, and stability. Tremendous improvements have been made in the reduction of tire squeal by the tire industry, so that the present designs do not constitute a serious problem.

Tire-tread Noise. Directional tread noise is the noise which the tire produces when operated on a smooth road with no change in direction. This noise is generated when the tread-design elements leave contact with the road.[21] During road contact, the tread experiences both circumferential and lateral compression, while immediately behind the contact area the tread is in slight extension. This sudden transition from a compressed to an extended condition causes vibration of the tread elements and radiation of noise directly from the tire side walls. The method of achieving an acceptable tread design is to avoid tread elements of the same length, which would result in a steady tone. The tread elements are made of different lengths so that the sound radiated is more or less scrambled in such a fashion as to be easily obscured by noise already present in the car. The variation in element length is known to tire engineers as "pitch sequence" and is considered an important and involved subject.

Wind Noise.

Wind Flutter. Wind flutter is a low-frequency disturbance which is heard inside a car when one of the front windows is partially or totally open and the air stream is free to impinge upon the rear edge of the window frame without deflection by no-draft devices or their equivalent. Figure 31.31 is an oscillogram of the pressure inside a car traveling at 50 mph under the conditions specified above, indicating a frequency for the more regular cycles of the pressure trace of about 14 cps. The portion of the oscillogram shown is more or less typical in that both regular and nonregular waveforms are present. This frequency is generated by a Helmholtz-resonator action in which the area

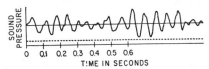

FIG. 31.31. Oscillogram of sound pressure occurring with wind flutter. The regular waveform shown at the center right has a frequency of 14 cps and an rms amplitude of 120 db. The observed frequency checks that calculated by a simple Helmholtz-resonator formula. (*Apps, unpublished.*)

of the neck is the open window, the length of the neck is the thickness of the door and window frame, and the volume is that of the entire car, including the trunk. The frequency may be calculated from the approximate expression for a Helmholtz resonator:

$$f_n = 178\,[A/(l_c V)]^{\frac{1}{2}} \qquad \text{cps} \qquad\qquad (31.7)$$

where A = neck area, sq ft

V = volume, cu ft

l_c = corrected neck length = $l + 0.8\,\sqrt{A}$, ft

Applying this expression to the above example, the frequency so calculated is 14 cps, which checks with the 14 cps observed. The sound level of the regular cycles shown is 120 db.

Other Sources. Other sources of wind noise include[22] (1) aerodynamic noise, (2) edge tones, and (3) the shedding of vortices. Noise generated in the boundary layer as air flows over a surface is referred to as "aerodynamic noise." This noise has a random-type spectrum including frequency components throughout the audible range and into the ultrasonic range. The sound pressures are roughly proportional to the square of the velocity. It is known that aerodynamic noise is less for a good aerodynamic shape than for a poor one. Edge tones are discrete frequencies which arise from the unsteady flow in the region of a sharp edge. They are believed to involve a feedback mechanism, although a detailed knowledge of the phenomenon is still lacking. Another source of discrete frequency noise is the shedding of vortices from blunt bodies such as a door post. The frequency in cycles per second can be expressed approximately as $0.2V/d$, where V is the air velocity in feet per second and d is the thickness of the body in feet. In general, the sound pressures are proportional to the cube of the velocity.

Miscellaneous Noise Sources and Effects.

Body-cavity Resonance. Body-cavity resonance is here understood to be the reinforcement of certain automobile noises because of excitation of normal modes of vibration of the interior body space. Some of these modes are damped very little. For example, some of the vertical and transverse standing-wave resonances play an important part in the emphasis of certain road-noise frequencies, thereby exaggerating the problem. In other cases, the fundamental longitudinal resonance which falls in the range of 70 to 80 cps for present body designs has been known to reinforce induction noise.

Body Impact Noise. Body impact noise is here meant to include local impact excitation, such as hail, rain, and knuckling. The inclusion of knuckling is in deference to the time-honored custom of the potential buyer who raps the door, fender, or top of the car in a showroom with his knuckles as a measure of the quality of construction of the car. In order to control these local impact excitations, vibration-damping material is applied to the top, door, and quarter panels of modern cars. The desirable quality-sounding thud excited by knuckling light sheet-metal panels is dependent upon the surface density (weight per unit of area) rather than upon the damping properties of the material applied. (See Chap. 14.) These same materials, of course, provide damping for all kinds of vibration excitation, including road noise. The impact noise of gravel stones striking the underside of the floor is best controlled by the application of some mastic spray-on material to the underside, because this actually reduces the value of the impact energy delivered to the panel.

Power-steering Noise. The wide acceptance of power steering on modern automobiles has created another potential noise source, producing a disturbance which may be classified as

1. A gearlike noise heard when the steering gear is in the straight-ahead position or at some moderate turning angle.
2. A "squishy," fluid type of noise heard when the steering is against the stops.

The latter is of less importance because of its infrequent occurrence during normal operation.

Hydraulic-power-steering-noise problems are handled as any hydraulic-pump noise. The frequency of the noise heard is equal to the number of vanes or teeth in the pump unit passing a given point per second. Any means of reducing the magnitude of these individual vane impulses are helpful. With a given pump design, a hydraulic accumulator may be used to reduce effectively the value of the alternating-pressure component in the discharge line. As an example, a pressure-release type of material[23] consisting of nonintercommunicating cells in a foam rubber, perhaps $\frac{1}{2}$ in. thick and 1 in. long, has been found effective.

With a given pump design and a given installation, the usual problem of the paths of the disturbance to the interior of the car is to be solved. Such paths will be

1. Air-borne.
2. Structure-borne through the engine block.
3. Structure-borne through the hose connections.
4. Fluid-borne through the hose connections.

With ingenuity, the importance of these various paths can be determined. For example, placing a restriction valve in a short "U" tube connecting the pump discharge with the inlet and adjusting for proper pump discharge pressure eliminates the coupling of the pump through the lines to the rest of the car yet maintains normal pump conditions. If the disturbance in the car has disappeared under these conditions, it is known that the sound did not travel through either of the first two paths; this leaves the last two for further consideration.

To determine whether the disturbance is caused by hydraulic-pressure variations, the dynamic pressure can be reduced by a hydraulic acoustic filter of large capacitance inserted in the discharge line near the pump. An evaluation of its effectiveness for reducing hydraulic-pressure variations can be made by measuring the dynamic hydraulic pressure before and after insertion of the filter. If the disturbance in the car is absent with the filter in place, it can be concluded that the pressure fluctuations (however transmitted), and not the mechanical vibration of the pump, are the source of the trouble.

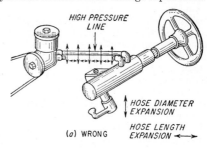

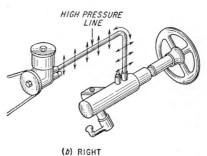

(b) RIGHT

To reduce these pressure fluctuations permanently, an external filter may be used in the line, or, as is quite commonly done, a discharge hose of the type with resilient walls may be used. In this connection, it is important to realize that the radial vibration of the hose, which is relieving the hydraulic pressure, will in turn cause an alternate lengthening and shortening of the hose, thus transforming a hydraulic-pressure variation into a mechanical forcing function. (See Fig. 31.32.) To obviate this trouble, it is important to avoid direct, slackless connections to the hydraulic power unit in the steering system and to provide a bend, so that the shortening and lengthening can be harmlessly dissipated in the motion of the flexible bend. The method is illustrated in Fig. 31.32. It is also important that the connecting hoses do not touch the sheet metal of the car.

The squishing sound mentioned above, heard when the wheel is against the stops, is due to the heavy, unrestricted flow of fluid through the steering unit over the various

FIG. 31.32. Power-steering noise. (a) the hydraulic-pressure fluctuation occurring at vane frequency of the pump causes a radial expansion of the rubber hose, especially if of the soft-walled type. Straight hose line causes the resulting longitudinal length changes to transmit considerable forces to the steering unit; (b) a bend in the hose causes the longitudinal dimensional change to be harmlessly dissipated. (*Apps, unpublished.*)

sharp edges of the valve spools or other parts. In some cases this can be reduced by the use of a restrictor in the line which limits the volume of flow. Such an approach must be reconciled with the maximum fluid-flow requirements at other operating conditions or positions.

Air-conditioning Systems. The air-conditioning installation on an automobile does not, in general, require the same degree of quieting as domestic refrigerators or window-type air conditioners, because of the obvious differences in the noise environments. Partially offsetting this advantage is the fact that the compressor in the automobile must run reasonably quietly over a wide speed range (about 10 to 1), in contrast to the constant speed of the units just mentioned.

The compressors used in automotive air conditioning include the axial compressor with a wobble plate, the piston type, and the rotary type. Each of these compressor types possesses its own noise characteristics. For a discussion of compressor noise, see Chap. 28. With such a wide range of speeds and the resulting wide range of operating conditions such as head pressure and suction pressure, many different kinds of noises are produced.

The successful handling of air-conditioning noise in the automobile depends largely on the identification of the source of noise (such as valve noise or piston or vane frequency), followed by a determination of the means by which that disturbance is transmitted to the body. Provided that the various noises radiated directly from the compressor are not so loud as to require correction, the approach or procedure from that point is to try to isolate the disturbances from the body of the car. It has been found generally necessary to use rubber hoses for the connection of the compressor to the condenser and to other parts rigidly fastened to the car. Care must be exercised in the use of rubber hoses, because in some cases they have been found to emit noise caused by gas pulsations emanating from the compressor. It may also be necessary that the condenser be mounted on rubber to further isolate those vibrations which are transmitted through the rubber hose and those which are propagated by the fluid. Suppression of disturbances propagated by the fluid may call for the use of mufflers in either the suction or the discharge line. In some instances, it seems necessary to isolate the compressor itself from the engine block.

In some installations, the noise caused by the air-circulating system is more objectionable than the noise associated with the compression and expansion of the refrigerant. Such noise usually is due to the high velocity of the air in the system or to fan or blower noise or vibration.

Horn Noise and Horn Testing. The physical factors which govern whether a horn can be heard inside the signaled car are the acoustical power of the horn signal, its frequency spectrum, the length of the sound path, and the noise-reduction factor of the car body receiving the horn signal. There are obviously other, subjective factors, such as the masking-noise levels inside the car, distractions, acuity of hearing, etc.

Because of the multiplicity of the physical factors present, it is believed that the best way to test the effectiveness of a horn is under actual operating conditions, using two cars. In this test, observers are located in the front seat of the lead car, where they are signaled by the horns located in the rear car. The lead car maintains a steady speed—say, 50 mph—and the horn on the signaling car is sounded at intervals at a known distance between the cars which can be measured by any convenient method. In operation, the horn is given a 1-sec blast; a signal indicating how many of the three observers in the lead car received it is then transmitted back to the trailing car. The distance between the cars is then changed and this procedure repeated, until enough data are obtained to draw a plot as shown in Fig. 31.33.

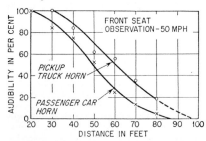

FIG. 31.33. Horn audibility vs. bumper-to-bumper distance for two types of horns. (*Apps, unpublished.*)

This is a plot of per cent audibility versus bumper-to-bumper distance at 50 mph, where per cent audibility is defined as the ratio of the number of positive observations divided by the total observations. This sort of data plots into a fairly smooth S curve, and a figure of merit for a given horn then can be expressed in terms of the distance at which it is heard 50 per cent of the time, i.e., 50 per cent audibility. For the two horns shown, this figure is approximately 50 and 60 ft, respectively, showing that the pickup-truck-type horn can penetrate the car spectrum more effectively. It is true, of course, that the variation of the spectrum of the receiving car will affect the figure of merit for a given horn, but this must be recognized as a variable in any horn-rating system. An indication of this variation between two extremes in current passenger cars is shown in Figs. 31.35 and 31.36.

The spectra for the two horns under discussion are shown in Fig. 31.34. The pickup horn is known as a "disk" type, in which a centrally supported free-edge disk, tuned to about 2,500 cps, is impact-excited by a vibrating-contactor arrangement. A clamped-edge diaphragm tuned to about 310 cps moves with the rod to which the disk is fastened. This horn has a very raucous, unpleasant sound, and its spectrum reveals a series of integrally related harmonic frequencies, with a pronounced cluster in the region from 2,000 to 3,000 cps which are not integrally related.

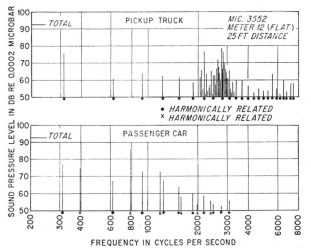

FIG. 31.34. Horn spectra for the horns shown in Fig. 31.33. The upper spectrum, disk-type horn used in a pickup truck; lower spectrum, a pair of passenger-car horns, all components of which are harmonically related in each of the two series. (*Apps, unpublished.*)

The passenger-car "horn" is actually a pair of horns having a fundamental musical interval of $\frac{5}{4}$—a major third. A typical frequency combination is 310 and 390 cps. The clamped diaphragm is driven by a vibrating-contactor arrangement, and the trumpet is of such length as to reinforce the diaphragm frequency. The spectra for these horns have integrally related components, and these two series are indicated on the plot by dots and X's. As a result, this horn has a pleasingly melodious sound.

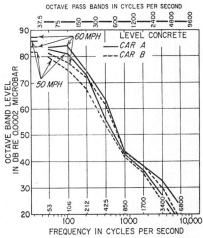

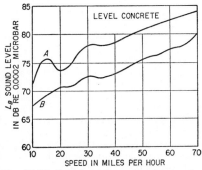

FIG. 31.35. Cruising noise on level concrete, 1955 sedans. Weighted (*B*) sound level vs. speed for two cars. Microphone in right front seat. Car *B* one of the best; Car *A* one of the poorest. (*Apps, unpublished.*)

FIG. 31.36. Cruising noise on level concrete. Octave-band analyses for the cars of Fig. 31.35 at two speeds. Microphone in right front seat. (*Apps, unpublished.*)

Apparently a raucous-sounding horn has a better penetration than the melodious-sounding horn, according to the audibility curves. Since the spectra of the two horns have about the same density and arrangement below 2,000 cps, it appears that the better penetration may be attributed to the dense grouping of frequencies in the 2,000-to-3,000-cps range.

Spectra inside Car. In other sections of this chapter, the levels and spectra of various noises have been considered by themselves. These include road noise, induction noise, exhaust noise, etc. In Fig. 31.35 are shown the B weighted sound pressure levels versus speed for two different cars traveling on level concrete; they represent a very quiet and a rather noisy car. The peaks shown at approximately 15 and 30 mph are engine or drive-line periods. Present in these data is the sum total of all of the various noise sources, such as engine noise, road noise, fan noise, induction noise, exhaust noise, wind noise, etc. In Fig. 31.36 are shown the octave-band data for the same cars at speeds of 50 and 60 mph.

The differences in the levels and spectra shown in these two figures are due primarily to the differences in engine noise and road noise.

Engine Mounts. The theory of the isolation of machinery to prevent the transmission of disturbing vibration into the support or foundation is covered in Chap.12. The vibration-isolation problem as applied to the automotive engine is different from many machinery problems in at least two important respects:

1. The support is relatively flexible: it is not infinitely rigid or massive.
2. The support itself, excited by road surfaces, in turn excites the resiliently mounted engine, thereby introducing another set of requirements.

In the automotive application, only a very complex theory can take into account the differences in mechanical impedances of the supporting structure from point to point, and considerable experimental work is required to determine these impedances. As a result, empirical methods are employed to design an automobile-engine-mount installation. In some cases, the motion of the frame side of the mount is found to be greater than the motion on the engine side, thus providing a "negative" isolation. Figure 31.37 is an example of this.

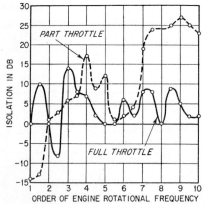

Fig. 31.37. Vibration isolation. Engine speed, 2,375 rpm. Note that the isolation is zero or negative for some orders and that it changes as torque is changed from part throttle to full throttle. (*After Larsen.*[6])

Regarding item 2 above, the excitation by road irregularities of the large mass of the suspended engine can produce unpleasant motions or vibration, which are fed back into the frame. As a result of these and other considerations, the usual procedure is to choose mount stiffnesses in keeping with the natural vertical frequency desired and locate them where practicable. Final adjustment of the stiffnesses in all three directions, together with some adjustment of location on the engine and experimental changes of the supporting structure, must be guided by frequent evaluations by road testing.

This procedure can be materially aided by the use of a bump-and-shake rig,[25] which artificially shakes the engine by application of in-phase or out-of-phase displacements to the two front wheels or to the suspension. Personal observations are made inside the car, and disagreeable effects can be correlated with engine motions and structural distortions using stroboscopic light. These unpleasant vibrations fed back into the frame from the engine are a part of a more extensive problem or disturbance known as "shake." Shake on an automobile is a secondary vibration due to the so-called "unsprung" mass of the suspension acting on the tires as a spring. In most automotive designs, this frequency is about 10 to 12 cps. These disturbances are held under control by design factors forged largely from long experience. However, the severity of the disturbance is affected by the engine-mount design, and the behavior in this respect is one of the criteria of satisfactoriness of an installation.[25,26]

The engine on its mounts has six modes of vibration, all corresponding natural frequencies of which should be spaced away from 10 cps to avoid energy pickup from shake. Insulation of noise and high-frequency harshness requires mountings with resonance below 15 cps. If resonances are below 5 cps, static deflections under torque become large; forced displacements due to ride motions are also large and give the feeling of a flexible frame with the engine bouncing on every road wave. Hence, all six modes are usually designed fairly close to 10 to 12 cps, and some are often coincident with suspension shake. Such cars can still feel good to drivers and passengers if large amplitudes occur only where driver and passengers cannot feel and see them. The front mounts of some engines are located in the vertical plane containing the center of percussion of the engine-transmission unit. This location is said to minimize the reaction of the engine, excited by road irregularities, upon the supporting frame and body structure.

A good engine-mount installation provides vibration isolations of many kinds. It provides a very smooth idle and a smooth take-off in the higher gears, and it minimizes clutch chatter under severe operating conditions. It should minimize the inherent presence of shake in the automobile.

An automotive engine mount installation should not be designed so that the elastic axis coincides with the principal inertia axis of the engine transmission, since the engine does not roll about its principal axis when excited by torque impulses. The axis about which the engine should be suspended is the axis of rotation belonging to the torque axis,[27] which is not the principal axis in automotive engines. However, this design is not without defects, because additional constraints are imposed at the point where the drive shaft is connected to the engine, since the drive-shaft connection is not in general on the axis of rotation. With such a point of attachment, the drive line resists the roll motion, resulting in the undesirable transfer of roll-motion forces through the drive line to the axle and frame.

TRUCK NOISE

The truck-noise problem is largely one of exhaust noise. In some instances, the exhaust noise of new trucks has been found to be excessive, indicating that the problem includes, besides the aspect of good maintenance by the operator, the specifying of proper original equipment. Assuming the adequacy of the original muffler on a given truck, the new-condition performance must be retained by maintenance of the exhaust system and muffler and by avoidance of modification, of inferior replacement, and of deliberate destruction of the interior flanges or baffles of the mufflers.

Such modification of exhaust systems or gutting of the muffler has been done under the assumption that significant increases in power, engine life, or fuel economy follow from the reduced back pressures. While these effects are present, it is believed that the error lies in the misconception of the degree to which they obtain. Another important effect of back pressure is its result on valve life, engine operating temperatures, etc. In this connection, it appears that there are considerable differences in the sensitivities of various engines to back pressure and that naturally aspirated engines are more sensitive than supercharged engines.[28] The effect of increased back pressure on power output, fuel economy, and engine life is a problem which requires intimate knowledge of each individual design and so is best known to each of the several engine manufacturers.

Whatever the various reasons for the existence of the exhaust-noise problem on the larger trucks (and many of the smaller ones), it has been recognized for some time that the state of the art of muffler design was not and is not the limiting factor.[29] The recent improvement in truck mufflers has been due more to the acceptance of a larger muffler volume and increased muffler cost than to any sudden increase in the advance of the muffler-design art.

Truck-noise Rating. Considerable attention has been focused upon the problem of rating truck noise. The use for truck-noise rating of the standard ASA sound-level meter has been explored by several investigators[30,31,32] using (1) the A weighting network, (2) the B weighting network, (3) the flat weighting network, and (4) a 600-cps high-pass filter in the line. The choice between the A- and C-scale readings lies with the A scale for the better correlation when judgments are made on the basis of loudness[30] or objectionableness.[31] In judging both loudness and harshness of passing trucks, it was found that the B-scale readings and filtered-noise-meter readings, respectively, provided correlation.[32] However, these measurements did not provide adequate correlation; so an instrument was developed having three filter bands driven by a single pickup microphone and reading simultaneously on three indicating meters. The results indicated that maximum levels could be set for each of the three bands so that if a passing truck exceeded the level on one or more of the three meters, it could be considered in need of improvement.

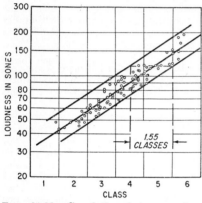

FIG. 31.38. Correlation between calculated loudness and average-class judgments for 15 observers, using Equivalent-Tone Method. Correlation coefficient, 0.94. Regression line in center, outside lines drawn parallel indicating a "scatter" of 1.55 classes. (*After Callaway.*[30])

A.M.A. Design Standard. The Equivalent Tone Method (see Chap. 5) has been applied to the truck-noise-measurement problem. For example, see Fig. 31.38, in which a correlation coefficient of 0.94 was obtained using a playback jury who divided their loudness judgments into six classes.[30] In 1954, the A.M.A. adopted the use of this method for rating the loudness of new vehicles and set a maximum limit of 125 sones at a distance of 50 ft from the center line of the lane in which the vehicle is traveling.* Since the Equivalent Tone Method requires that the band-pressure level be measured in eight different octave bands, magnetic tape recordings are made as the truck passes and these recordings later played back through an octave filter. The band-pressure level in each band is converted to a loudness in sones, and the sones of the eight bands are then added to obtain a single loudness reading for the truck.

In adopting this method, the A.M.A recognizes its inherent shortcomings for this purpose, and its adoption does not necessarily exclude improved methods from future consideration. Since this procedure is not an instantaneous-reading method, it is obviously unsuited to enforcement purposes.

At present, there is no instrument known to the writer which adequately indicates the objectionableness of truck noise in terms of a single meter reading.

Progress in Truck-noise Reduction. At present, with the adoption by the A.M.A. of a new-vehicle design standard of a 125-sone loudness measured at 50 ft, there is a definite trend toward improvement in the situation. Starting with the 1954 models, one large truck manufacturer has completely equipped his entire line of trucks with mufflers which are better than this design standard. Figure 31.39 is a bar graph comparing the ratio of net muffler volume to engine displacement of the old mufflers with that of the new, improved mufflers. Maximum back pressures measured 2 in. below the manifold-flange range from 2 to 4 in. Hg. Each of the bars does not necessarily represent the same level of quieting. No data are presented for 4-cycle diesels. The relatively large volume ratios shown in Fig. 31.39 indicate that past standards must be cast aside and a new concept of muffler size accepted to obtain adequate silencing with low back pressures.

At the present time, truck manufacturers representing about 99 per cent of truck sales are reviewing their muffler-noise problems in order to introduce new mufflers

* The rating procedure is described in a brochure available from the Automobile Manufacturers Association.[33]

which meet the standard as early as possible.   Replacement-type mufflers are now being made available for an increasingly larger portion of the various older truck types now on the road.   Further, the very existence of some large trucks on the road which

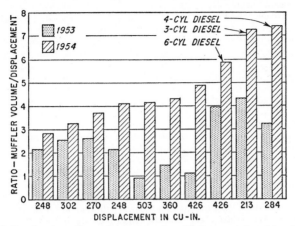

FIG. 31.39. Ratio of net muffler volume to engine displacement for old and new muffler designs on one line of trucks.   Net muffler volume is gross volume enclosed by muffler shell less the volume of the exhaust pipe whether or not it actually exists as such.   Note large volume required for the three- and four-cylinder, two-cycle diesels.   Other engines are four-cycle gasoline engines.   (*After Apps.*[19])

operate quietly should be a powerful inducement to the trucking industry toward improvement of the offensive ones.   While exhaust noise is, without question, the worst single source of noise on the road today, it should be expected that as this problem is brought under control, other noise sources will then stand out.   These include tire noise, fan noise, and backfiring. As in the case of muffler noise, none of these noises presents insurmountable technical problems.   Again as in the case of mufflers, a recognition of the need for adequate devices or designs and the willingness on the part of the manufacturers and operators to bear whatever equipment costs are incurred in bettering the situation are required.

Figure 31.40 is a plot of the cumulative-noise-level distribution measured on the *B* scale at a 50-ft distance for three geographical locations.   The extremely interesting feature of this chart is that a maximum level of 100 db was found to obtain for all locations.   Further, the distribution plots for the Virginia and Michigan trucks are essentially the same. The California data, taken from the SAE report,[32] lie to the right of the other two

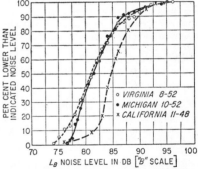

FIG. 31.40.   Truck noise.   Cumulative-noise-level distribution for three geographical United States locations.   All levels measured at 50 ft from lane, maximum reading, *B* weighting network sound level. Note that the maximum level is the same for all locations.   (*Apps, unpublished;* California data *after Huber.*[32])

curves.   This is as it should be, because measurements in the California plot were restricted to the so-called "Pacific-type" trucks—those of gross combined weight over about 65,000 lb, with correspondingly larger engines.

Other Aspects.   Other aspects of the control of truck noise have to do with such things as the rerouting of truck traffic through less sensitive areas, the elimination of stop signs and through streets where possible, a change during the night hours from full-cycling stop signals to blinker lights, and the improvement of truck-driving techniques and procedures. In some cases, these aspects have been exploited successfully in handling specific problems.

Another approach which has met with considerable success in Virginia has been at the state-police level. Trucking operators were invited to a meeting, at which the seriousness of the truck-noise situation was explained and their cooperation in using improved muffling and drivers' techniques solicited. Here, this approach was quite successful, probably largely because the state's traffic consisted principally of operators with large fleets. Small truckers with one, or at the most a few, trucks comprise the large bulk of truck traffic on the roads. They are not represented by any association and for the most part are probably unaware of the great efforts that are being made to improve the public relations of the trucking industry as a whole.

The passing of legislation based upon an instrument reading to regulate truck noise is obviously dependent upon the development of a simple and adequate means for its rating. It is now generally recognized that a sound-level meter which meets ASA standards does not adequately rate truck noise. The strong agitation in many areas to pass legislation based upon the reading of a sound-level meter has fortunately been held in check, since it is doubtful if the law could be successfully defended if vigorously attacked in court. In the few instances where noise statutes have been written around the use of the sound-level meter for this purpose, such as in Columbus, Ohio, results have not been entirely satisfactory, and the meter has largely been relegated to disuse.

At present, the best method of control appears to be one of self-policing—the approach being taken by the trucking and the truck-manufacturing industries. The cost of such control will certainly be more than offset by the value of improved public relations.

BUS NOISE

The decade from 1920 to 1930 saw the displacement of the familiar interurban car lines by personal transportation and the newcomer, the bus, or coach. In a similar fashion, the decade starting with 1950 has witnessed the discontinuation of city street-car lines in favor of transit-type automotive buses (or coaches) and trolley coaches. From the point of view of noise abatement, this situation is somewhat ironical, inasmuch as the newer and quieter PCC streetcars were in process of replacing the noisier Peter Witt streetcars.

This transition to transit-type coaches for urban public transportation has focused attention upon exterior bus noise. The problem is aggravated by two factors:

1. Most present-day city-service coaches are equipped with a hydraulic torque converter which causes the coach to pull away from a standing start under full throttle and at a relatively high engine speed, i.e., the stall speed of the hydraulic converter, leading to increased engine and exhaust noise.
2. Practically all buses are now equipped with the somewhat noisier diesel engine.

Additional information on the control of interior bus noise is contained in Chap. 32. **Noise Sources.** The important noise sources in present-day transit buses include

1. Exhaust noise.
2. Engine noise and noise radiated from the engine block.
3. Fan noise.
4. Gear noise and blower noise (if engine is supercharged).

The above noise sources are not necessarily listed in their order of importance, since in general this will vary from type to type.

Test Procedures. It is recommended that a moving microphone be used, i.e., one attached to a boom 10 or 12 ft behind the coach. This is a more realistic approach than using a stationary microphone, because the peak value of the disturbance will be sensed regardless of whether or not it occurs at initial take-off; this, of course, is not true with a stationary microphone. The microphone should be resiliently supported and a windscreen provided.

In order to identify the loudest noise source(s), one or more of the following experimental test procedures can be used.

To check on the contribution of exhaust noise, a Y-and-valve box can be installed aft of the muffler in the usual tail-pipe line to divert the exhaust noise through a long tail pipe and additional muffler, terminating at the forward end of the coach. With the valve in one position, the normal exhaust system, including muffler, is in use; if thrown in the other position, exhaust noise is essentially eliminated from consideration.

To determine the importance of engine noise, the engine compartment can be sealed off and the interior lined with 20 to 30 sq ft of 2-in. acoustical-absorption blanket. Overheating can be prevented in warm weather by conducting the tests during short intervals with cool-down periods between. Alternately, the contribution by engine noise can be deduced from the test described above. The effect of the fan can be determined by replacing it with one known to be quiet, or by removal entirely.

This procedure is materially aided by the use of a recording technique which requires only a minute or two of operation to obtain a record which can be analyzed later in the laboratory. It also affords a means for evaluation of the effects by playback to a jury.

Once the most important noise source is determined, attention can be directed toward its reduction. For example, if exhaust noise is shown to be louder than engine noise on the basis of the above tests, improved muffling is indicated. As shown in the section on *Truck Noise*, there is no insurmountable technical problem in obtaining adequate exhaust silencing. Rather, it requires a recognition of the fact that large mufflers must be used to obtain adequate silencing with low back pressures. In some coaches, the available space in the engine compartment is such that two mufflers are used in series. For example, the total enclosed volume for a 426 cu-in., 2-cycle diesel engine is 3,426 cu in. The net muffler volume of the pair for this engine, that is, gross volume minus the volume of the exhaust pipe, is 3,016 cu in.

If engine combustion noise is next to be reduced, then (1) the engine compartment must be provided with an essentially complete closure, (2) the equivalent of an acoustic duct must be provided for the exit of cooling air, and (3) additional quieting can be obtained by lining as much of the area of the engine compartment as possible with a 1- or 2-in. acoustical blanket, retained with a perforated covering. It is important that the engine compartment be closed as a first step; i.e., the acoustical blanket is practically worthless if the engine-compartment closure is not essentially complete. A relatively complete closure is one with snug-fitting engine pans, oil sump hole closed, absence of louvers in doors or elsewhere, drive-line hole tightly closed, etc. The thickness of the sheet metal of the entire closure is usually adequate to provide a satisfactory transmission loss if sealing is good.

When these three steps have been taken, the engine noise can still get out through the radiator, placing a practical limit on the reduction that can be obtained in this way. In this connection, the placement of the engine-cooling fan and the radiator in a compartment separate from the engine would provide for a complete enclosure and containment of engine noise yet permit a satisfactory cooling arrangement.

Some of the factors which lead to quiet fan design are covered in *Noise Sources, Cooling-fan Noise*.

In coaches or buses with torque converters, it is especially important that fan periods and exhaust periods be avoided in the engine speed range corresponding to converter stall. If such is not the case, the rapid acceleration of the engine to the stall speed at which the period manifests itself results in a high time rate of change of noise, calling attention to the noise period. In coaches having engines which are supercharged, two additional noise sources are present. These are the blower drive gears and the blower itself. The blower noise is produced by the passage of the blower lobes or blades past the air inlet, resulting in a medium-frequency moan. Blower silencers, similar to the induction silencers discussed for gasoline passenger-car engines, can be used to reduce this noise source. The blower drive gears, especially when badly worn, emit a penetrating screech of high frequency.

Example of a Bus-noise-reduction Program. A noise-reduction program was carried out on a diesel bus after it had been determined that the loudest noise sources fell into the following order:

1. Engine noise.
2. Exhaust noise.
3. Fan noise.

The program consisted of the evaluation of four cumulative improvements:

1. The standard-production coach.
2. Closed and acoustically lined engine compartment.
3. Improved mufflers.
4. Fan removed (experimental substitute for a very quiet fan).

The program was carried out by recording the curb, or pull-away, noise on a disk recorder with the microphone stationary. These recordings were later played back through a

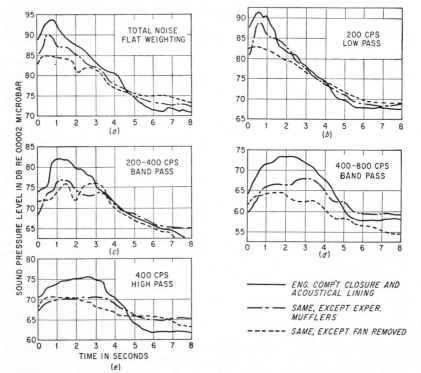

Fig. 31.41. External bus noise for full-throttle pullaway on six-cylinder, two-cycle diesel bus (*circa* 1947) with hydraulic torque converter. Microphone stationary, 4 ft above ground, 12 ft to rear of coach (at start) on center line. Plots show accumulative effect of experimental changes listed. (*Apps, unpublished.*)

bandpass filter and graphic-level recorder, with the results shown in Fig. 31.41. Inasmuch as the standard-coach data (item 1 above) appeared to be unreliable, the effect of the first step, that of sealing and treating the interior of the engine compartment, is not shown for this coach (see below).

In Fig. 31.41a it is shown that there is a fast build-up and a peak in the total noise at 0.75 sec after the start of acceleration. This hump is reduced with the improved mufflers and eliminated with the removal of the fan. Inspection of the 200-cps low-pass curves (Fig. 31.41b) shows similar behavior regarding these experimental changes, indicating the fundamentals of fan-blade frequency and of engine firing frequency (both of which fall below 200 cps) to be responsible for this initial hump showing up in the total noise curve. Inspection of the 200- to 400-, 400- to 800-, and 400-cps high-pass curves indicates that the improved mufflers reduced the noise in all these bands; the removal of the fan, however, appears to have helped only in the 400- to 800-cps band (in addition to the 200-cps low-pass noted above).

In order to show the effect of sealing the engine compartment reasonably well, as discussed earlier, and then lining the interior with 25 sq ft 1-in. glass-fiber blanket spaced out 2 in., the data from another noise-reduction program are shown in Fig. 31.42. In this example, too, the loudest noise source was the engine. These tests were carried out in identical fashion with those shown in Fig. 31.41, except that in this instance the microphone was carried at the end of a 10-ft boom attached to the bus—the preferred method. Here, the general level of the noise as a function of time tends to stay essentially constant, as might be expected.

This set of data showed essentially no reduction due to the closure and lining for the total noise and the next two bands, and these three plots are not reproduced here. The lowest frequency band showing any sensible difference is 400 to 800 cps, reproduced in Fig. 31.42a. The closing of the engine compartment produces a sound level at the end of the boom intermediate between that for the standard coach and that for the condition with combined closing and acoustical treatment. The cumulative effect of both steps is a generous 5 db. Figure 31.42b shows similar data for the 400-cps high-pass, indicating a somewhat larger reduction—approximately 6 or 7 db.

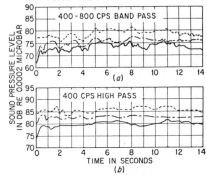

----- *WITHOUT ENG. COMP'T CLOSURE OR ACOUSTICAL LINING*

— — — *WITH ENG. COMP'T CLOSURE ONLY*

——— *WITH ENG. COMP'T CLOSURE AND ACOUSTICAL LINING*

FIG. 31.42. External bus noise for full-throttle pullaway on four-cylinder, two-cycle diesel bus (*circa* 1947) with hydraulic torque converter. Microphone on boom 18 in. above ground and 10 ft to rear of coach on center line. Plots show accumulative effect of experimental changes listed. (*Apps, unpublished.*)

The disk recordings were also used for playback through a speaker for subjective evaluation of the various steps in the reduction program. The results obtained, as evaluated by listening to the playbacks, were deemed to be greater on both programs than might be implied by the decibel reduction. In the case of the curve of Fig. 31.41a, the initial blast, due to both the unfortunate peaking of the fan noise and exhaust noise, was removed and the "bite" of the combustion noise tempered over the entire pull-away operation. The net result was a rather pleasant, velvety sound on pull-away.

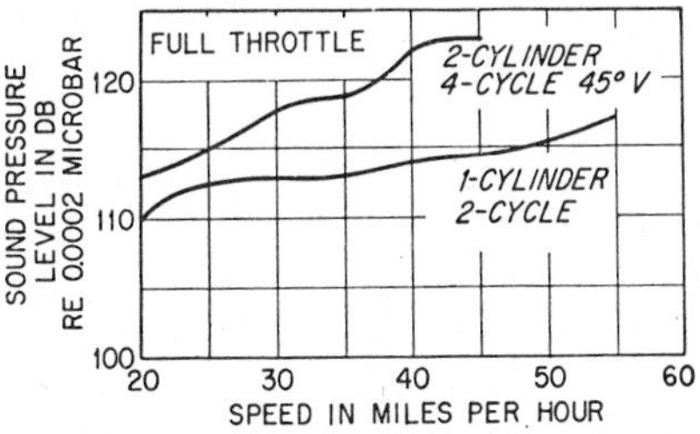

FIG. 31.43. Motorcycle noise. Sound pressure level vs. speed for two motorcycles having engine types indicated. Flat weighting. No mufflers used. For two cylinder, microphone 18 in. above and flush with end of tail pipe; for one cylinder, 18 in. above and 24 in. to rear of tail pipe. (*Apps, unpublished.*)

MOTORCYCLE NOISE

Motorcycle noise has long been considered in the nuisance class.

In Fig. 31.43 is shown the sound pressure level versus speed for a 2-cylinder, 4-cycle, 45° V motorcycle and for an imported motorcycle having a 1-cylinder, 2-cycle engine.

The 2-cylinder motorcycle is without muffler and equipped with an exhaust pipe with increasing diameter, the outlet diameter of which is about 3 in. The engine displacement is 74 cu in.

The 1-cylinder motorcycle has a displacement of 250 cu cm (15.2 cu in.). This unit is also without muffler. The microphone positions are as indicated in the caption.

In Fig. 31.44 is shown the frequency analyses of these exhaust noises at 40 mph. The motorcycle having the 1-cylinder, 2-cycle engine has one firing impulse per revolution. At 40 mph, calculated engine speed and firing frequency are 74 cps, which is about twice the lowest frequency shown in the analysis. Order 1/2 should not be present in a 2-cycle exhaust system. Its presence may be due to poor scavenging, an

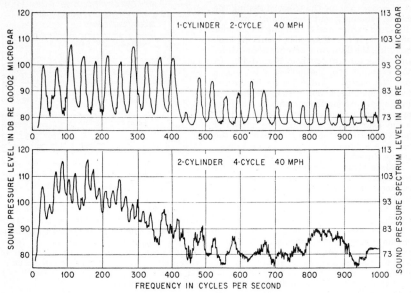

Fɪɢ. 31.44. Frequency analyses of motorcycle noise shown in Fig. 31.43; full throttle; 5-cps passband. (*Apps, unpublished.*)

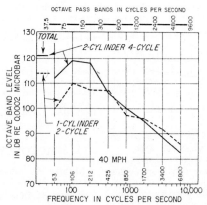

Fɪɢ. 31.45. Motorcycle octave-band analyses for the motorcycles of Fig. 31.44. Flat weighting network; 40 mph, full throttle. (*Apps, unpublished.*)

extreme example of which is the "4-cycling" of such engines when idling. The resulting spectrum is seen to consist of a long series of strong harmonics; the significance of the existence of these strong, higher harmonics is that they are required to account for the square-wave-like nature of the unmuffled pulses of gas as they escape.

The corresponding frequency analysis for the 2-cylinder motorcycle is considerably different in appearance, although it, too, has a long, strong series of harmonics of firing frequency. The 2-cylinder, 4-cycle engine also has one firing impulse per revolution; and, since the firing interval is not even, the lowest component should be order 1/2, which was calculated to be 21 cps. This finding checks the analysis. In this analysis, the sharpness of the individual components starts to disappear at about 600 cps; at higher frequencies, it has a trend toward a gray- or white-noise spectrum

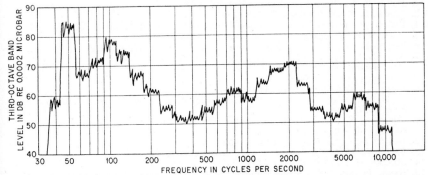

Fig. 31.46. Third-octave band analysis of the noise from a Vespa motor scooter of the "closed" type, in stationary position, running at 3,100 rpm at 30 per cent load. (*Brüel, unpublished.*)

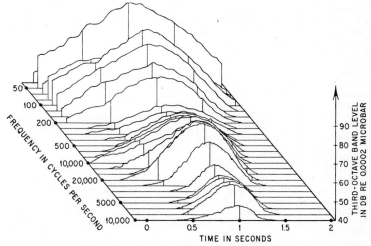

Fig. 31.47. Noise output from a Vespa motor scooter, same model as that analyzed in Fig. 31.46, as a function of time of passage past nearest point to the microphone. The various curves indicate the sound pressure level in third-octave bands as a function of time. (*Brüel, unpublished.*)

not apparent in the other motorcycle. Figure 31.45 represents an octave-band analysis of the same two motorcycles. These octave data are presented for comparison with similar data of automotive noise. Other analyses are given in Ref. 34.

Noise analyses are given in Figs. 31.46 and 31.47 for a Vespa motor scooter of the "closed" type running at 3,100 rpm. In Fig. 31.46 the data were obtained with the scooter standing still, operating under a 30 per cent load. The data given in Fig. 31.47 are for a passing scooter traveling up a slight grade at 3,100 rpm and were obtained from the analysis of a magnetic tape recording. The analysis was made from a closed magnetic tape loop taken from that part of the tape corresponding to the position of the scooter nearest the microphone. In both analyses the microphone was located 1 meter above the ground and 2 meters to the side.

REFERENCES

1. Lewis, R. C.: *Analysis, Product Eng.*, **21**: 150 (November, 1950).
2. Dickie, J. A.: *Product Eng.*, **18**: 115 (July, 1947).
3. Muller, L. E.: *Mech. Eng.*, **67**: 723 (1945).
4. Ball, L. M.: private communication, Chrysler Engineering Labs.
5. Apps, D. C.: *J. Acoust. Soc. Amer.*, **24**: 660 (1952).
6. Larsen, H. W.: *Proc. Soc. Exptl. Stress Anal.*, **12**: No. 1, 125 (1954).
7. Apps, D. C., and G. M. Vanator: *SAE Trans.* **63**: 787 (1955).
8. Den Hartog, J. P.: "Mechanical Vibration," 3d ed., chap. 5, McGraw-Hill Book Company, Inc., New York, 1947.
9. Porter, F. P.: *Trans. ASME*, **65**: A33 (1943).
10. Myklestad, N. O.: "Vibration Analysis," chap. 6, McGraw-Hill Book Company, Inc., New York, 1944.
11. Thomson, W. T.: "Mechanical Vibrations," 2d ed., chap. 4, Prentice-Hall, Inc., Englewood Cliffs, N.J., 1953.
12. Ball, L. M.: *SAE Journal*, **60**: 61 (1952).
13. Fry, A. S., *et al.*: *SAE Quart. Trans.*, **1**: 164 (1947).
14. Mantey, H. L.: *General Motors Eng. Journal*, **1**: 4 (1954).
15. Heldt, P. M.: "High Speed Combustion Engines," 12th ed., chap. 6, Chilton Co., Philadelphia, 1944.
16. Cary, B. B.: *J. Acoust. Soc. Amer.*, **10**: 63 (1938).
17. Heldt, P. M.: "The Automotive Chassis," 2d ed., chap. 6, Chilton Co., Philadelphia, 1948.
18. Kishline, F. R.: Factors Influencing Road Noise As Applied to Unit Construction, *SAE Journal*, **62**: 103 (September, 1954) (summary from SAE panel on "Noise Suppression in Passenger Cars," June, 1954).
19. Apps, D. C.: *Noise Control*, **1**: 41 (1955).
20. Olson, H. F.: unpublished work.
21. Wallace, E. H.: *SAE Journal*, **62**: 103 (September, 1954).
22. Hubbard, H. H.: private communication, NACA, Langley Aero. Lab.
23. Hoover, R. M., D. T. Laird, and L. N. Miller: *J. Acoust. Soc. Amer.*, **22**: 38 (1950).
24. General Motors Corp., General Motors Research Laboratories Div.: unpublished information.
25. Ruegg, M.: SAE Preprint No. 275; also see *SAE Journal*, **62**: 56 (October, 1954).
26. Frailing, L. H.: SAE Preprint No. 272; also see *SAE Journal*, **62**: 56 (October, 1954).
27. Den Hartog, J. P.: "Mechanical Vibration," 3d ed., pp. 97–98, McGraw-Hill Book Company, Inc., New York, 1947.
28. Fast, M. L.: Engine Operation, SAE Preprint No. 175; also see *SAE Journal*, **62**: 17 (April, 1954).
29. Nelson, C. E.: SAE Preprint No. 177; also see *SAE Journal*, **62**: 17 (April, 1954).
30. Callaway, D. B., and H. H. Hall: *J. Acoust. Soc. Amer.*, **26**: 216 (1954).
31. Andrews, B., and D. M. Finch: Truck Noise Measurement, *Reprint* 17, University of California, Institute of Transportation and Traffic Engineering, Berkeley.
32. Huber, P.: Report of Automotive Traffic Noise Subcommittee, *SAE Quart. Trans.*, **5**: 533 (1951).
33. Automobile Manufacturers Association, Detroit.
34. Furrer, W.: *Noise Control*, **1**: 39 (May, 1955).
35. General Motors Corp., Engineering Staff: unpublished information.

Chapter 32

NOISE IN RAIL TRANSPORTATION

WILLIAM A. JACK

Johns-Manville Research Center, Manville, N.J.

A railroad passenger car must be safe and of a design which provides passenger comfort and fits into the operating routine of the railroad. Thus, a large, relatively heavy enclosure is required together with considerable auxiliary equipment to serve the passengers' needs and the railroad's requirements.

INTRODUCTION

A large tractive force is required to pull these relatively heavy cars on steel wheels over steel rails. As a result of this tractive force on the train-track system considerable noise is produced—a noise level which is increased by the auxiliary equipment. A passenger within the car will feel the vibration of the seat, floor, and portion of the wall he may lean against. He will hear noise inside the car. This chapter examines the nature of the noise sources in a train and discusses the application of noise-control techniques. Noise-control measures must be adapted to the requirements of railroad construction and safety. Various techniques are required to deal with the different aspects of the acoustical problem, depending on the noise source.

SOURCES OF NOISE HEARD INSIDE A RAIL PASSENGER CAR

A person inside a passenger car may hear an external source of noise because of sound waves which strike the walls of the car and set them into vibration. These vibrating walls then become secondary sources and generate noise inside. Furthermore, alternating mechanical forces acting directly on the car structure also set the walls into vibration. The noise level within the car depends on the magnitude of these external disturbances, on the surface area over which their resulting forces act, the transmission loss of the car walls and floor, on the location and size of holes and openings which permit air-borne noise to leak inside directly, and on the amount of sound absorption inside the car.

Noise from Solid-borne Transmission. Many forces, fluctuating with time, act on a railroad-car structure and produce audible noise. This section discusses those sources which transmit their energy into the structure, vibrate the walls of the enclosure, and result in passenger annoyance. Large impacts occur when a heavy car rolls over a rail joint at high speed; lesser impacts occur when rolling on the rail between joints because of nonuniformities in the wheels and rails. These impacts set rails and wheels into vibration and result in forces which are transmitted relatively undiminished into the axles, bearings, and lower part of the spring system. At the springs a portion of the transmitted energy is reflected. The remaining portion passes through the spring system, through the bolster connection between truck and car, and into the structural framework of the car. Another source of impact noise occurs at the stops which limit permissible motion in various parts of the truck-spring system. Bumping against these rigid stops produces vibratory energy which travels into the car structure. Relative motion between centerpost and its mounting on the car structure, play in the coupling connection between cars, and rubbing together of car-vestibule end frames, are all potential sources of solid-borne vibration. Other sources include auxiliary equipment units, typified by the air compressor.

Noise from Air-borne Transmission. The following are the principal sources of air-borne noises:

1. The solid-borne vibration, discussed above, generates noise in the air under, and at the ends of, the car. This air-borne noise strikes the underside of the floor, a portion of which is transmitted through the floor and, thus, increases the noise level inside the car. To a lesser extent, the windows and side panels are subjected to air-borne noise generated underneath the car. When two trains pass, the side panels of one are subjected to intense air-borne noise generated by the other. In a tunnel, along a wall, or along another train, the side panels of a car are subjected to substantially more air-borne noise emanating from under the car than when the car is rolling along in open country.
2. An important noise source is direct air-borne transmission. The floor contains spots where sound may be transmitted readily, for example, panels pierced by holes for piping, or wiring, drains, and toilet hoppers. Cabinets for electrical equipment which are set into the interior paneling and inadequate or poorly sealed doors may be weak spots in the over-all sound insulation.
3. Noise may enter the car through the air-conditioning system; it may be generated in the ducts or at the distributing outlets by the airflow.
4. Some air-borne noise is generated within the car itself, for example, fan noise.

NOISE LEVELS UNDERNEATH AND INSIDE A RAIL PASSENGER CAR

Measurement of Noise and Vibration. A sound-level meter, in conjunction with an octave or half-octave analyzer, is usually employed in measuring air-borne train noise. In railroad transportation work, it is usually not necessary to employ a narrow-band analyzer in acoustical analyses. However, cases may occur where it is useful to measure frequency exactly for the identification of specific noise sources. For example, with a narrow-band analyzer, an offending noise may be traced to gears having the same number of tooth contacts per second as the measured frequency. More elaborate measuring systems which may be employed are described in Chaps. 16 and 17. Vibration measuring equipment and techniques described in Chap. 17 may be employed to evaluate the behavior of various vibrating panels of interest. Noises associated with sources of solid-borne vibration cover a wide frequency range so it is extremely important to measure vibration as well as noise over the range covered.

The investigator of train noise must know the calibration of the over-all system employed in the acoustical analysis. For example, if his measurement technique employs microphones beneath the car, boxed for protection during the tests, calibration curves of the microphones in the boxes must be known.

Typical Noise Levels. Figures 32.1 through 32.4 present measurements of the noise of a railroad coach car which is in good condition. A knowledge of sound pressure level is necessary for making an estimate of the effectiveness of noise-control techniques that may be used. The noise levels inside the car are shown in Fig. 32.1. The octave-band levels decrease with frequency and increase with speed. The over-all noise levels are in the 70- to 85-db range for the equipment here reported. Other investigators have found higher levels,[1] possibly due to operating with open windows. The noise from equipment varies, depending on the type and condition. For example, differences in noise level of as much as 12 db have been measured in opposite vestibules of the same car. An auditor hears the noise of Fig. 32.1 as one having a wide frequency distribution. In this sound pressure level range, the conversion to phons

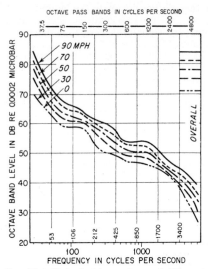

FIG. 32.1. Noise inside coach car at different speeds.[16] Typical passenger location near center of car.

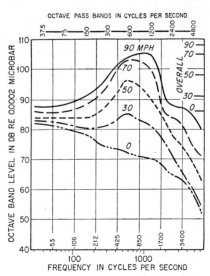

FIG. 32.2. Noise underneath coach car at different speeds. Microphone located 6 ft aft of rear axle, front truck, facing the rear truck.

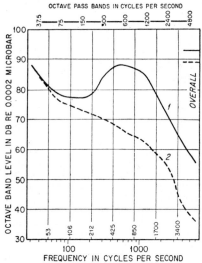

FIG. 32.3. Coach-car-vestibule noise at 70 mph. Curve 1—in vestibule; Curve 2—inside car near vestibule door.

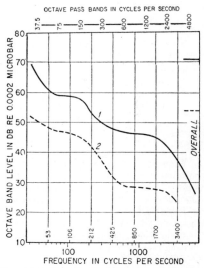

FIG. 32.4. Noise inside coach car caused by equipment, train stationary. Typical passenger location near center of car. Curve 1—air conditioner and gasoline engine generator running; Curve 2—gasoline-engine generator running.

reduces the lower-frequency bands so that they do not dominate the loudness-level spectra, which are in the 50- to 60-phon range.   For the case of the car stationary in a quiet place, in the event that all car auxiliary equipment were shut down, the octave-band loudness levels would be quite low, of the order of 30 phons or less.

The noise levels under the car are shown in Fig. 32.2.   The middle-frequency components are dominant, with the over-all levels in the 85- to 110-db range.

The noise levels in the vestibule and inside the car near the vestibule door, at 70 mph, are shown in Fig. 32.3.   In the middle- and high-frequency bands, there is a decrease in octave-band level in going from the vestibule into the car of the order of 15 to 25 db, which is a measure of the effectiveness of the door and its seals.   Comparison of Figs. 32.1 and 32.3 shows a decrease of the order of 10 db in the middle-frequency bands in going from the location near the vestibule door to the center of the car.

Table 32.1.[16] Wideband Weighted Sound Pressure Levels in db re 0.0002 Microbar, at 70 Mph—Six Types of Passenger Equipment

Equipment	Above 100 cps	100–800 cps	Above 800 cps
Club lounge:			
In car.............	71 db	70 db	57 db
In vestibule.........	93	92	89
Club car:			
In car.............	80	78	62
In vestibule.........	98	98	89
Dining car:			
In car.............	80	78	63
In vestibule.........	104	103	96
Heavy dining car:			
In car.............	88	86	66
In vestibule.........	98	97	94
Pullman:			
In car.............	67	66	58
In vestibule.........	98	98	89
Chair car:			
In car.............	69	67	52
In vestibule.........	90	89	93

The noise levels inside the car when stationary, caused by the operation of auxiliary equipment, are shown in Fig. 32.4.   Since the air conditioner plus generator produce a noise level 10 db higher than the generator alone, when the air conditioner is running the noise contribution of the generator is negligible.

Table 32.1 shows the results of a survey on six types of railroad passenger cars on one railroad.   A microphone was moved along the car aisle and noise levels recorded at various locations.   The results tabulated for "in car" were at the quietest location in each car, usually near the middle of the car.

Table 32.2 shows the results of a survey for special conditions occurring in operation.   Octave-band levels were obtained for the condition of "overtaking a freight." The large increase in over-all sound pressure level when passing over a bridge was due to additional noise being generated by mechanical excitation of the bridge structure. In passing through a tunnel the over-all level outside the window was increased substantially.   The over-all level at the passenger location was not increased by a measurable amount, although it is common observation that the noise increases in loudness in passing through a tunnel.   This is explained by a rise in the level of the higher-octave bands, which do not contribute significantly to the over-all level but do contribute significantly to the total loudness. This was shown to be the case by the measurements made in "overtaking the freight"; at the passenger location there was an increase in the bands above 512 cps of the order of 2 to 5 db, but there was no measurable increase in over-all level.

Table 32.2. Increase in Over-all Pressure Level in db re 0.0002 Microbar for Special Conditions—Coach-car Comparison Made to Level When Running Normally, at the Speed Designated

Condition and speed	Microphone location		
	Truck	Outside a window	Passenger seat
Passing through tunnel, 35 mph.......	0 db	5–10 db	0 db
Passing over bridge, 35 mph...........	9	Not taken	11
Overtaking a freight, 50 mph*.........	Not taken	Not taken	0
Upgrade, 50 mph....................	0	0	0
Brakes applied, 40 mph..............	5	Not taken	2

* An octave-band analysis was also made. In each octave band above 512 cps the increase was 2 to 5 db.

NOISE-REDUCTION TECHNIQUES

Experience has shown that railroad-car passengers prefer an environment free from rattles, squeaks, hisses, and sudden noise, and a noise level which is low enough to not interfere with speech and sleep. In order to achieve this, all contributing noise sources must be reduced to an acceptable level. Certain practical aspects of noise reduction are of importance. In general it is almost useless to adopt noise-reduction means for a weaker source, of two sources, if at the same time nothing is done to reduce the stronger source. For example, consider two pieces of mechanical equipment producing similar noise spectra in the car, when run individually. According to Fig. 2.17, which shows the effect of combining two sources, if both sources are initially equal in noise output the maximum reduction that can be obtained is only 3 db. If the weaker source is 6 db below the stronger, for example, the maximum reduction possible when applying noise-control means to the weaker source is only 1 db. The governing factor is not the noise level, but the decibel difference between the sources. If their noise spectra are similar, the stronger source should be sought out and reduced, if possible.

For dissimilar sources, producing widely differing noise spectra, a further consideration is necessary—the characteristics of the ear. Consider a car in which Source A creates an octave-band level of 70 db in the 100- to 200-cps band and 50 db in the 1,000- to 2,000-cps band. Also suppose that Source B creates levels of 45 db and 60 db, respectively, in these two bands. Although over-all level readings would show Source A to be higher in level an octave-band analysis would show Source B to be predominant in the 1,000- to 2,000-cps band, which is more important since the ear is more sensitive in this band. It is indicated, therefore, that Source B should receive the greater attention and that Source A possibly may be unimportant as far as passenger comfort is concerned. Thus, it is obvious that a frequency analysis should be made so as to assess the true importance of each source.

Noise levels in railroad cars considered acceptable by current standards lie in the range of 60 to 75 db as measured on a sound-level meter using the A weighting network. What is acceptable today may be considered too loud in the future when more effective noise-control means are adopted. In considering a railroad-car noise that it is desirable to lessen, the following subjective observations are of interest. The reduction of weighted sound pressure level is given in terms of subjective evaluation of noise reduction below 90 db:

1 db	Barely detectable
5 db	Definite improvement, worth some expenditure
10 db	Striking improvement, worth considerable cost
20 db	Outstanding improvement
25 db	Almost like "off and on"

At moderate levels, the reduction of an offending noise sufficiently to merge into the background noise is often all that is required. A frequent criterion for acceptable noise level, ease of speech communication, is discussed in Chap. 9.

In order to achieve the above acceptable noise levels, various noise-control methods are applied in railroad cars. For example, vibration-damping materials, described in Chap. 14, are applied to panels. Other noise-control measures are discussed below.

Vibration Isolation. Where it is practicable to do so, substantial reductions in noise level within a railroad car can be obtained by making use of vibration-isolation

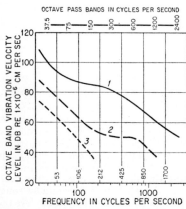

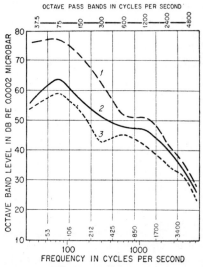

FIG. 32.5. Effect of using vibration isolators under equipment, shown by laboratory test on electric motor mounted on concrete slab. Motor run at 1,800 rpm, vibration of slab measured. Curve 1—motor bolted directly to slab; Curve 2—motor mounted on conventional rubber in shear isolators; Curve 3—motor mounted on compound rubber in shear isolators.

FIG. 32.6. Effect of eliminating direct structural connections, shown by laboratory test on interurban bus. Engine idled at 2,000 rpm, octave-band levels of noise measured in bus at typical passenger location near center. Curve 1—power plant on conventional mounting; Curve 2—power plant partially disconnected; Curve 3—power plant entirely disconnected.

techniques discussed in Chaps. 12 and 13. Consider the case of an air compressor mounted rigidly to the car underframe. The compressor radiates air-borne noise which strikes the underside of the car floor and at the same time vibrates the underframe via the rigid mounting. Even though the floor may be adequate to prevent the transmission of air-borne noise through it, the compressor may be heard inside the car because of the transmission of solid-borne vibration by the path available via the car structure. The interior-trim panels, typically carried directly on the structure, are set in motion by the frame vibration and radiate air-borne noise to the passenger. The compressor can be mounted on vibration isolators, effectively reducing the vibratory energy transmitted to the underframe.

Figure 32.5 shows the results of a laboratory test on the effectiveness of vibration isolators. Compared to direct bolting, reductions of 20 to 30 db were obtained by the use of conventional isolators. With special isolators providing a shear compliance in two directions even greater reductions were obtained. Figure 32.6 shows the results of a laboratory test demonstrating the importance of eliminating direct structural connections. The tests were conducted on an interurban bus but the principles involved are applicable here. The engine, a horizontal type, was mounted beneath the floor. Curve 1 shows the noise spectrum with the conventional arrangement, the engine being on its usual rubber mounts, with the usual connections, such as control rods and radiator hoses, between engine and body. Curve 2 shows the noise spectrum with the engine supported on blocks from the floor, but up in its conventional position. The fan was disconnected and the exhaust system hung from the body on fabric straps. Curve 3 shows the noise spectrum with complete disconnection, including generator, air lines, hose attachments to the radiator, control rods and silencer, and the exhaust system blocked up from the floor. The progressive improvement demonstrates the importance of examining critically all connections between a noise source and the passenger enclosure. For the conditions of Curve 3 the interior-noise level was produced predominantly by the transmission of air-borne sound through the floor. This was shown by an experiment with a separate source of air-borne noise consisting of a motor-driven clapper. The difference between underneath- and inside-noise level, for the case of the engine noise, averaged 32 db over the frequency range, rising gradually from 20 db in the 0- to 50-cps band to 42 db in the 4,800- to 9,600-cps band; with the clapper as a noise source the difference averaged 35 db, rising from 25 db to 45 db over this frequency range. An analysis of this type enables the experimenter to assess the contribution of air-borne and structure-borne noise energy and to decide whether it is worthwhile to improve the floor in the event that a portion of the structure-borne energy cannot be reduced.

Partitions. The contribution to the noise level inside a car which is caused by airborne noise striking the outside of the car can be reduced by providing a more effective enclosure. For purposes of illustration consider the floor of the car, exposed on its underside to a high air-borne noise level. The sound striking the underside sets it in vibration at a velocity inversely proportional to (1) the frequency and (2) the weight of the floor. This action generates sound which radiates into the car.

The "transmission loss" of a partition at a given frequency is equal to the number of decibels by which the sound pressure level is reduced in being transmitted through the partition (see Chap. 20). When the transmission loss is averaged over frequency this single figure of transmission loss (abbreviated $T.L.$) is related to the partition weight as follows [See Eq. (20.5)]:

$$T.L. = 23 + 14.5 \log_{10} m \qquad \text{db} \qquad (32.1)$$

where m is the weight in lb per sq ft. This equation indicates that the average transmission loss of a homogeneous partition increases 4.4 db each time its weight is doubled. Studies have shown that in general, for a given weight partition, transmission loss increases sharply with frequency.

Equation (32.1) relates the transmission loss to weight. Its use shows that a floor weighing 10 lb per ft, for example, has a predicted average transmission loss of 37.5 db. If the weight were increased by adding 2 lb per sq ft in a rigid manner by increasing the thickness of the steel, the new average transmission loss would be only 38.6 db. Improvements substantially beyond those predicted by Eq. (32.1) can be obtained, however, through the use of compound partitions. Thus, if a finish floor is "floated" on the car floor by the use of suitable compliant mountings and a mineral-fiber absorption blanket is placed between them, worthwhile improvements above 400 cps can be realized. For example, Fig. 32.7 shows the substantial improvement obtained by attaching a reinforced 16-gauge subpanel with shear rubber isolators to the underside of a floor panel weighing 11 lb per sq ft with a sound-absorptive blanket between the floor and the subpanel. This addition weighed 6 lb per sq ft. Figure 32.8 shows the improvement obtained by inserting a sound-absorptive blanket in a wall panel, between the main structure and the interior trim. The panel was of the order of 5 lb per sq ft, the blanket about 1 lb per sq ft.

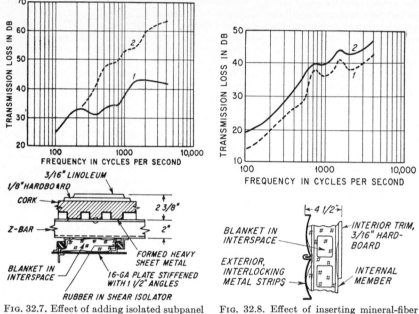

FIG. 32.7. Effect of adding isolated subpanel to floor test panel, shown by laboratory measurement of transmission loss on car section. Curve 1—floor panel; Curve 2—floor panel with isolated addition of 16-gauge plate and mineral-fiber blanket.

FIG. 32.8. Effect of inserting mineral-fiber blanket in wall test panel, shown by laboratory measurement of transmission loss on car section. Curve 1—wall panel; Curve 2—wall panel with blanket inserted.

Figure 32.9 shows the difference in level in decibels between noise underneath and noise inside a coach car for two cases:

1. The train traveling at 60 mph.
2. The train stationary—the air-borne sound produced by a loudspeaker underneath the car.

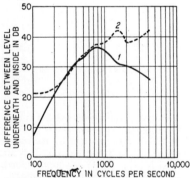

FIG. 32.9. Study of sources of coach-car noise. Difference between underneath and inside pressure levels. Curve 1—train at 60 mph; Curve 2—train stationary; air-borne noise generated under coach car from loudspeaker.

Between 225 and 1,000 cps the curves are close, indicating that the noise level inside this car when operated at 60 mph is due primarily to the underneath air-borne noise reaching the interior by passing through the floor. Below and above this frequency band there is indication that the vibration in the structure is responsible for the interior-noise level. Another car, having a different mileage since shop overhaul, or having a different design, may show a different relationship between the two methods of observation. This approach illustrates a useful technique for studying the two paths of energy transfer.

Figure 32.10 shows the improvement obtained by mounting a typical floor section on various shear-rubber isolators instead of directly to the frame. The lengths of isolators used were such that the static deflections were of the order of 0.2, 0.4, and 0.3 in., respectively, for the three cases shown. Here the frame was vibrated electronically, but the shape of the vibration velocity-level curve is similar to actual railroad-car conditions. These data represent the average of measurements taken at five positions on the test-floor section. Reductions of 7 to 22 db were obtained through the use of the above floating-floor construction.

Figure 32.11 shows the improvement in air-borne noise obtained during an experiment on a city-type bus, having a horizontal engine underneath the floor—results which are applicable to the train problem. An isolated floor was installed in the bus, consisting of ¼-in. millboard floated from the floor by a layer of 1½-in. thick mineral-fiber blanket. The marked improvement of up to 13 db in noise reduction was quite apparent to the ear. This demonstrated that originally the noise transmitted through the floor was the dominant source. Vibration measurements on the isolated floor showed even larger reductions than the improvement in air-borne sound.

Figure 32.12 shows the improvement in panel vibration obtained in an experiment on an interurban-type bus, having an engine in the rear. Again the results are applicable to the railroad-car problem. The most intensely vibrating panel was the rear

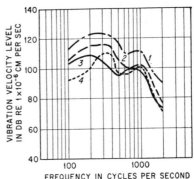

FIG. 32.10. Effect of using vibration isolators under car floor, shown by laboratory test on floor section mounted on angle-iron frame, with frame vibrated electronically. Vibration of floor measured. Curve 1—floor directly on frame; Curve 2—floor mounted on durometer 60 isolators, ⅜ in. thick; Curve 3—floor mounted on durometer 40 isolators, ⅜ in. thick; Curve 4—floor mounted on durometer 40 isolators, ¾ in. thick.

bulkhead between the engine and the bus interior. This panel had a shape providing support for the horizontal and vertical cushions of the rear seat. Simulated, isolated-interior-trim panels in the two planes were constructed by cementing 1-in. thick min-

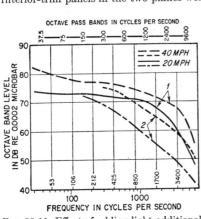

FIG. 32.11. Effect of adding light additional floor isolated by mineral-fiber blanket, shown by road test on city bus. Run at 20 and 40 mph, octave-band levels of noise measured in bus at typical passenger location near center. Curve 1—conventional floor; Curve 2—light isolated floor added.

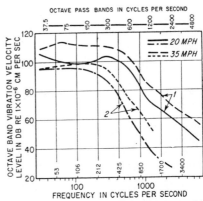

FIG. 32.12. Effect of isolating interior trim panel by mineral-fiber blanket, shown by road test on interurban bus. Run at 20 and 35 mph, vibration of panels measured. Curve 1—pickup on structural sheet panel; Curve 2—pickup on isolated trim panel carried on structural sheet.

eral-fiber blankets to the bulkhead, with ¹⁄₁₀-in. hardboard cemented to the blanket. The hardboard was cut to clear all metal portions of the bus. The bulkhead vibrated as much as before, but the hardboard was effectively isolated. Its vibration was of the order of 30 db less at 600 cps and above.

Ventilating-duct Treatment. The designer must ascertain whether air-conditioning noise is not to be heard (1) when the train is operating, or (2) when it is stopped in a quiet location, and he applies noise-control measures accordingly. The latter requirement is a severe one and some compromise is usually made. Design information for ventilating-duct quieting is given in Chap. 27. To be suitable for use in a railroad car a duct lining must be fire-safe and not dust or disintegrate from erosion caused by high-velocity airflow or train vibration.

Sound-absorptive Materials. According to Eq. (18.4), if a_1 units of absorption are initially present in an enclosure, and the amount is increased to a_2 by adding sound-absorptive material, the reduction in noise level is, approximately,

$$10 \log \frac{a_2}{a_1} \quad \text{db} \tag{32.2}$$

Only if a space is very reverberant originally can much reduction of the average sound pressure level be obtained by adding sound-absorptive material. Experience has shown, however, that ceiling treatment in dining and club cars gives a worthwhile improvement. It is possible that the explanation lies in the reduction of direct reflection from nearby hard surfaces, the greater ease of listening to conversation, and the reduction in peak levels to which impulsive sounds build up.

The selection of acoustical materials suitable for passenger train service depends on the decor and the space and weight restrictions imposed on transportation equipment. In general, an incombustible treatment which is easily maintained in its original condition is required. The perforated metal-facing type, with a mineral-fiber blanket acting as the sound absorber, has been used effectively. Good absorption in the middle- and high-frequency ranges is obtainable with blanket thicknesses of the order of 1 in. Moderately good absorption can be obtained in the low-frequency range by constructions employing a somewhat thicker blanket or a blanket with an air spacing.

SELECTED EXAMPLES OF CONTROL MEANS ADOPTED

Toronto Subway.[2] Several interesting noise-control measures are used in the Yonge Street Subway, Toronto, Canada. The two reinforced concrete walls of the tunnel are separated by a center wall which has two openings 5 ft × 7 ft in each 40-ft length. Both sides of the center wall are treated with 2-in. glass wool to a height of 4 ft. Expanded aluminum mesh covers the absorptive material. A train in one tunnel travels in an acoustical environment provided with absorption by the glass wool in this tunnel plus additional absorption from the openings to the other treated tunnel. No center wall is used at the stations, where acoustical treatment is provided by 2-in. glass wool on the underside of each platform. The track is supported on rubber pads ½ in. thick under steel plates, bolted directly to the concrete floor of the structure. This design was adopted for economy in construction and maintenance and not primarily as a noise-control measure. Welded rail joints contribute to quiet operation. The management considers that the following car-design features contribute to noise reduction: traction power applied to the axles through a system of hypoid gears; heavy burlap cemented to the inside of the outer steel sheet with a bituminous adhesive; floor covered with ¾-in. cork plus a wear surface of ¼-in. rubber; underbody protected by a heavy coat of anticorrosive paint.

London Subway.[3] In 1937, 1-in. drilled-asbestos felt-absorptive tile were installed in a test section of the London subway system as a horizontal projection and along the tunnel walls to a height of 20 in. above the rails. With windows open, the improvement was of the order of 5 phons. Other arrangements, utilizing different materials and in greater amounts, gave improvements up to 8 phons. The drilled-asbestos tile was considered a satisfactory answer to the many demands on such an installation and this treatment has been installed on all extensions since 1939. The treatment is fireproof, will withstand brushing with a hard broom, is not affected by other maintenance activities or the scouring action of drafts accompanying train movement, has a nonmetal surface and contains no metal strips. The absorption coefficient is 0.6 at 250 cps and 0.7 at 2,000 cps.

Table 32.3 gives the levels in London subway cars under various conditions. Sound-absorptive treatment P is the asbestos felt described above; treatment H utilized foamed slag retained between a vertical perforated asbestos board facing and the curved wall of the tunnel. It extended from approximately 8 in. above the rail to 36 in. above it. With this arrangement for each foot of running length, 2.3 sq ft of absorbent surface was presented to the noise energy. The maximum thickness of material at the top was 13 in. This thickness decreased to 4 in. at the bottom of the treatment. The top of the treatment was 12 in. higher than the car step. Treatment P was along the tunnel wall and on a horizontal projection. The portion on the wall

Table 32.3.[3] **Over-all Weighted Sound Pressure Levels in db re 0.0002 Microbar, Inside London Subway Car—Windows Open**

Position	1924 stock	1938 stock
On track in open air..................	86–88 db	91–92 db
In tunnel, untreated location..........	89–90	101–102
In tunnel, Treatment H...............	84–85	94–95
In tunnel, Treatment P..............	87–89	96–98

was 16 in. high, measured along the slant, approximately 30° from the vertical. The horizontal portion was 13 in. wide and was covered by concrete to save it from damage. With this arrangement for each foot of running length approximately 2.4 sq ft of absorptive surface is presented to the noise energy.

PCC Street Cars.[1,4,5,6] PCC street cars are constructed with several features which contribute to quiet operation, including: motors which are spring-borne on the frame, rather than being carried on the axle, resulting in a smaller unsprung weight on the wheels; resilient wheels with rubber sandwiches between hub and tread; rubber springs; bogie joined to car body through steel tube fitting into cylindrical bearing in bogie bolster with small clearances eliminating noise from older designs having loose play; smaller brake rigging, mounted to be rattle-free; welded body; and skewed armature slots.

European Cars.[7,8,9,10] Experimental work, covering all phases of the noise-control problem, is under way in Europe. There is considerable emphasis on the use of rubber with the observation that much work is still to be done on determining the service life of highly stressed rubber parts. Experiments are being carried out to evaluate more thoroughly the noise reduction and apparent maintenance-cost reduction offered by rubber-tired rail vehicles. Noise-control features in current use include: welded rails; rubber-mounted rails; rubber springs; rubber bumpers in the truck assembly; vibration isolation of driving motors; double windows; and vibration damping of wheels and rails.

American Railroads.[11,12] Noise-control measures which have been adopted in America include: isolation pads in the truck assembly and between bolster and car; sprayed-on vibration-damping materials; mineral-fiber blankets under the floor and against wall and ceiling panels; the reduction of openings to the outside; the use of tight couplers; and the use of effective door seals. Isolated floor and interior-panel structures are being studied as a means of obtaining significant noise reduction.

MISCELLANEOUS NOISES ASSOCIATED WITH RAIL TRANSPORTATION

Rail Transportation Noise at a Distance from Tracks. As noted above, noise generated by railroad-car wheels is intense. It radiates outward and may be heard at considerable distances. The sound absorption and vibration damping of the rail by a blanket of fresh snow contributes to quiet operation from the viewpoint of both the passenger and the resident at some distance from the tracks. The decrease in sound pressure level as a function of distance from the source may not be the same for each frequency band. This is due to the different ways that obstacles, diffraction, ground absorption and air attenuation act upon the sounds of different frequency (see Chap. 3).

Train noise at a distance can be decreased by reducing the noise generated

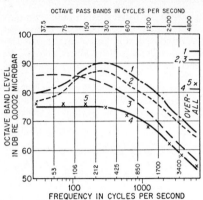

Fig. 32.13. Noise heard near tracks for different rail vehicles. Curve 1—subway train at 20 ft; Curve 2—old style street car at 20 ft; Curve 3—railroad train at 100 ft (diesel, steam, and cars); Curve 4—new PCC street car at 20 ft; Points 5—electric railroad train at 20 ft. (*After Bonvallet.*[1])

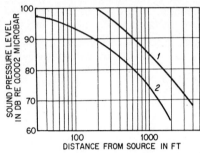

Fig. 32.14. Noise from trains at different distances. Curve 1—locomotive whistle; Curve 2—train noise. (*After Field et al.*[13])

underneath the railroad car. This can be accomplished by reducing the unsprung weight, using well-maintained or welded rail, and providing resilient bumpers in the truck system. A skirt enclosure can reduce the air-borne sound radiated outward, thus lessening the noise heard at some distance from the tracks. Trains on elevated steel

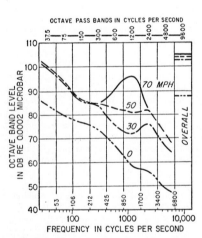

Fig. 32.15. Noise inside cab of diesel passenger locomotive at different speeds.

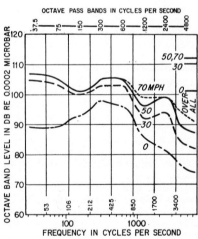

Fig. 32.16. Noise near supercharger of diesel passenger locomotive at different speeds.

structures set the steel work into vibration, this becoming a large secondary source radiating into the air. Adequate control of this problem requires vibration isolation between roadbed and steel structure, or use of noise-control techniques on the structure, or both.

Figure 32.13 shows sound pressure levels at a distance for various forms of rail transportation.[1]   These data are given for a distance of 20 ft from the street cars, subway trains, and electric-railroad trains, and 100 ft from the diesel and steam trains. Sound pressure levels are averaged from observations of several vehicles in each class.

Figure 32.14 shows train noise and train whistles at various distances, from studies made for comparison with aircraft noise.[13]   The data are averages from several observations in each class.

Studies were conducted on elevated train noise in connection with the building of the Royal Festival Hall in London.[14]   At a microphone location about 75 ft from the track, with old type rail of hard steel that had developed corrugations on the running surface, an over-all sound pressure level of 104 db was obtained.   When a new rail of carbon steel, which does not develop corrugations, was installed the over-all dropped to 87 db.   In each case the highest octave-band level was in the 200- to 400-cps range, being 102 db for the old rail and 85 db for the new.   For positions further away from the track, but on the building site, levels were 10 to 15 db lower.

Escalator Noise.   Escalator noise studies in a Moscow subway station showed that impact of chain rollers on curved guides was a major source of noise.[15]   The 85 db measured compared to the 50-db weighted sound pressure level desired for quiet operation.   The supporting framework is an effective emitter of sound energy generated by the impacts.   The necessity is stressed of evaluating all the possible noise sources and controlling the most intense.

Noise inside Diesel Locomotive.   Figures 32.15 and 32.16 show sound pressure levels at two locations: operator's cab position and near supercharger.   Levels as high as 112 db were found.

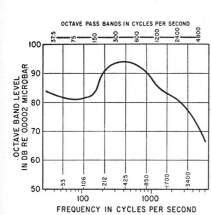

Fig. 32.17. Noise inside subway car in 30-mph range.   Typical passenger location near center of car.

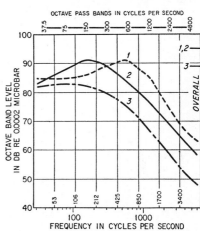

Fig. 32.18. Noise inside subway cars and street cars.   Curve 1—subways; Curve 2—street cars 20 years old; Curve 3—1947 PCC street cars.   (*After Bonvallet.*[1])

Noise inside Subway and Street Cars.   Figure 32.17 shows sound pressure levels in a subway car at a typical passenger location at the usual operating speeds in the 30-mph range.   Table 32.4 shows the dependence of over-all sound pressure level on

Table **32.4.** Over-all Sound Pressure Level re 0.0002 Microbar inside Subway Car for Various Speeds

Speed	Sound pressure level
15 mph	89 db
25	95
35	99
45	100

speed for this group of tests. Figure 32.18 shows results by another investigator[1] covering subway and street cars, including the PCC design noted above.

REFERENCES

 1. Bonvallet, G. L.: *J. Acoust. Soc. Am.*, **22**: 201 (1950).
 2. Private communication from Toronto Transit Commission, Toronto, Canada.
 3. Private communication from London Transport Executive, London, England.
 4. Private communication from Transit Research Corporation, New York, N.Y.
 5. Hirshfeld, C. F., and E. H. Piron, *Trans. ASME*, **59**: 471 (1937).
 6. Howard, R.: *Engineer*, **188**: 450 (1949).
 7. *Eisenbahn Technische Rundschau* (in German with English summaries), Supplement 3 (March, 1954).
 8. Taschinger, O.: (in German), *Glasers Annalen*, **75**: 242 and 269 (1951).
 9. Stappenbeck, H.: (in German), *Zeit. Ver. Deut. Ing.*, **96**: 171 (1954).
10. Heumann, G.: (in German), *Glasers Annalen*, **75**: 211 (1951).
11. Jack, W. A.: *Trans. AIEE*, **61**: 382 (1942).
12. Jack, W. A.: *Trans. ASME*, **71**: 197 (1949).
13. Field, R. L., T. M. Edwards, P. Kangas, and G. L. Pigman: *Technical Development Report No.* 68, U.S. Dept. of Commerce, Civil Aeronautics Administration, Washington, D.C. (July, 1947).
14. Private communication from P. H. Parkin, Building Research Station, England.
15. Kazanskii, V. S.: (in Russian), *J. Tech. Phys.* (U.S.S.R.), **10**: 1251 (1940).
16. Data not credited otherwise are from published and unpublished studies by the author and his associates in Johns-Manville Research Center.

Chapter 33

AIRCRAFT NOISE SOURCES

HENNING E. VON GIERKE, DR. ENG.

Aero Medical Laboratory, Wright Air Development Center

INTRODUCTION

The Aircraft Noise Problem.[1,2] Aircraft noise, its generation and propagation, has been of interest for many years. In the early days of aviation, noise studies were directed toward improving the comfort of crew and passengers and the detection and localization of enemy aircraft. Later, the development of radio techniques and the construction of multi-engine airplanes with greater numbers of passengers and crew members made speech communication in the airplane an increasing requirement for successful progress of aviation. Hence by the end of World War II, sound levels and sound control in aircraft had been thoroughly studied and there resulted a deeper understanding of the basic principles of noise generation and engineering techniques for controlling noise. Since that time, aircraft noise has become a problem which has increased tremendously in scope. No longer does it affect only the comfort and efficiency of the relatively small number of people inside the airplane, but it has become an increasing nuisance to the large number of people who live in communities near airports[3] (see Chaps. 35 and 36).

The development of more and more powerful aircraft, the increasing importance of air traffic and the increasing number of aircraft operating make it imperative that all efforts be expanded to prevent further increase in aircraft noise around airports and, where possible, to control current noise levels. Jet aircraft, predominating in military aviation, create one of the most powerful sources of man-made sound, which by far exceeds the noise power of conventional propeller engines. The sound levels around jet engines, where personnel must work efficiently, have risen to a point where they are an immediate hazard to man's health and safety and are now at the limit of human tolerance. Further increase of sound levels should not be made without adequate protection and control; technical and operational solutions must be found to the noise problem if it is not to be a serious impediment to further progress in aviation.

A realistic approach to the solution of the aircraft noise problem must answer three questions:

1. What are the characteristics of the noise sources and of the noise fields of aircraft?
2. What are man's bio-acoustic responses to such noise stimuli; what allowable noise levels should be specified for the different groups of people involved?
3. What can be done to reduce the noise levels around aircraft to the allowable levels for the different groups?

This chapter deals principally with the answer to the *first question*, describing the sound sources and their noise fields. It indicates the sound levels, i.e., the acoustical

33–1

stimuli, to which men around aircraft are exposed. This information, combined with man's bio-acoustic responses to noise, provides the basis for establishing the requirements for noise reduction. In addition, an accurate description of the sound source leads us to a physical understanding of the basic mechanisms of aircraft noise production, thereby helping to answer the vital question: Is it possible to design aircraft that produce less noise without reducing their performance? For engineering purposes the noise fields around present-day aircraft can be specified accurately. Estimates can be made of the noise power output of future engine designs based on present-day propulsion principles. But, with respect to the mechanism of noise generation, basic questions are still unanswered.

Although a consideration of the *second question* as to the bio-acoustic responses and allowable noise levels is not the purpose of this chapter, some discussion of this question is helpful here. Although there may be some difference of opinion concerning their accuracy, approximate criteria for engineering purposes exist which specify allowable noise levels (1) for extremely short exposure to noise, (2) for "everyday" exposure to noise up to a lifetime's duration, (3) for different amounts of interference with speech, and (4) for undisturbed sleep and rest in various types of residential districts. Methods for calculating the loudness of noise exist (Chap. 5) and attempts have been made to predict complex reaction of communities to a given airport noise. Since men's physiological and psychological reaction to noise depend not only on the physical stimulus, but on the requirements for man's activity at given locations, even when applying existing criteria, the following factors must be considered with respect to an exposed individual:

1. The physical stimulus and its temporal pattern (frequency, duration, time of day).
2. The required working efficiency.
3. The required amount of communication.
4. The necessity for rest and sleep during noise exposure.
5. The general motivation toward the aircraft noise.

On the basis of these factors a given aircraft noise field may be evaluated with respect to its effects on four major groups:

1. Air crew and passengers.
2. Ground crew and mechanics.
3. People working at, or in the vicinity of, the airport.
4. People dwelling in the vicinity of the airport (where this vicinity may extend for many miles).

Each group performs different functions and, therefore, has different requirements with respect to maximum allowable noise levels. Needs for noise reduction can be postulated on the basis of protection for these groups. Evaluation of a given noise source, therefore, must consider all—not just one group of individuals. Finally, the amount of noise reduction that must be achieved at a given point is equal to the amount by which the original sound level exceeds the maximum allowable sound level at this location.

Occasionally, the response to noise of a "receiver" other than man is so sensitive as to require noise reduction. For example, structural solidity or stability of an aircraft can be affected by its own noise field; such interactions usually arise only in the developmental stages of an aircraft and have been eliminated by the time it assumes normal flight operation. When exposed to noise fields, mechanical and electronic equipment can exhibit undesired responses, and thereby require relocation, sound and vibration insulation, or redesign of the equipment. Finally, buildings and structures on the ground can vibrate under the impact of noise in varying degrees—from annoying rattles of windowpanes, when an airplane flies over the house, to broken windows and structural damage resulting from "sonic boom." Noise control efforts must take into consideration responses of all possible "receivers": men, domestic animals raised for profit, equipment, structures, etc.   The most sensitive receiver determines the amount of desired noise reduction required.

The *third question,* as to how the required noise reduction can be achieved, is discussed in Chap. 34 and partly in this chapter.   Basically, noise reduction can be achieved by one or more of the following methods:

1. Noise reduction at the source, i.e., reduction of the sound power originally generated, discussed in this chapter in connection with noise generation.
2. Reduction of the noise at a given point by attenuation or deflection of the sound while on its way from the source to this point.   This attenuation or deflection can be accomplished either near the sound source (i.e., with mufflers, test cells, screening walls) or near the receiver (e.g., by means of soundproof buildings, protective walls, personnel protective devices).
3. If, because of physical, technical, or economical reasons neither approach—(1) or (2)—is able to provide the required noise reduction, there must be changes in aircraft design or operation.   Changes of run-up areas and flight patterns, reorientation of runways, shorter exposure times of ground crews, consideration of all noise aspects in the early design stages of an aircraft, and planning of airports and communities with respect to aircraft noise, all these measures fall under this category.

Possibilities (2) and (3) are discussed in Chap. 34 as far as they are typical or unique for aircraft noise control.   The basis for all these noise-control possibilities is the exact knowledge of the sound source and its sound field.

Aircraft Noise Sources and Their Acoustical Description.[4-7]   Aircraft noise sources considered here are the reciprocating engine, the propeller, the turbojet (with and without afterburner), the turboprop, the ramjet, the rocket, and the helicopter.   In addition, noises generated by the motion of airplanes through the air (the boundary-layer noise observed in the cabins of airplanes in flight) and noises observed on the ground from flying aircraft (static-pressure fields moving with low-flying aircraft and noise from supersonic flight) are included under this heading.   Noise from ventilation systems, industrial support equipment (starter compressor, motor generator, hydraulic systems, etc.) often may be the predominating noise at certain points in and around airplanes and might require noise reduction.   Treatment of these noise sources is discussed in other chapters; their noise power is usually very small compared to the aircraft power-plant noise, so that in spite of the existence of points of very high pressure the area involved is rather small and unimportant for the over-all aircraft noise problem.

The description of an aircraft noise source should be as complete as possible, and requires sound pressure measurements at many points.   This complete characterization requires a knowledge of:

1. The total acoustic power radiated into the air by the source and how this total power is related to the mechanical and operational characteristics of the engine.
2. The distribution of the total acoustic power over the frequency spectrum.
3. The spatial distribution of the acoustic power in the different spectral bands.

The methods used for obtaining such complete data on a noise source are discussed in sections which follow.

Aircraft noise is an unwanted, but apparently an almost unavoidable, by-product of propulsion.   For its technical evaluation and physical understanding, one must relate the noise of an aircraft noise source to its aerodynamic properties.   One expression of this relation is the acoustic-mechanical efficiency, i.e., the ratio of the total acoustic power output to the mechanical (kinetic) power output of the propulsive unit.   Higher flight velocities require higher velocities in the wake of the propulsive system.   Figure 33.1 indicates how much the kinetic power in the wake increases with the wake velocity of different systems, for constant static thrust.   Figure 33.2 gives an approximate picture of how, for constant thrust and at constant distance, the maximum sound levels increase with the wake velocity.   The relation

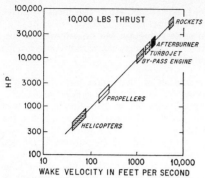

FIG. 33.1. Kinetic energy in wake or slipstream necessary to produce 10,000 lb of static thrust with different propulsive units. (*From Regier.*[5])

between wake velocity and acoustic sound output depends on the fundamental noise-generating mechanisms. For each propulsive unit a theoretical investigation of these mechanisms leads to an acoustical system combined of elements from one or more types of elementary sources, such as monopoles (simple source, representing a periodically changing volume), dipoles (representing a periodic external force in a free fluid) and quadrupoles (representing a shear moment). The relative acoustical efficiency of these sources can be seen by assuming a sphere radiating in such modes as to represent the above sources at a frequency having a wavelength of twice the sphere's circumference. The dipole's efficiency is $\frac{1}{3}$, and the quadrupole's is 1/1,000, that of the monopole.

If these sources are formed by streaming gas masses of the velocity V, making certain approximations, one can derive expressions which indicate that the acoustic power of the monopole increases as V^4, the dipole as V^6, and the quadrupole as V^8. For comparing experimental results with theory, a determination of the total acoustic power is, therefore, helpful.

Acoustic Sources in Motion. For measurements on fast aircraft in flight and evaluation of these measurements, an understanding of the effect of motion on

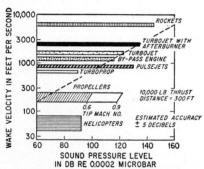

FIG. 33.2. Approximate sound pressure level at 300-ft distance at the angle of maximum sound radiation as a function of the wake or slipstream velocity for various aircraft noise sources of equal thrust (10,000 lb). The slope of the dotted line indicates an increase of the radiated sound power with the eighth power of the jet velocity, i.e., for constant thrust as assumed in this graph with the sixth power of the wake velocity. (*From Regier.*[5])

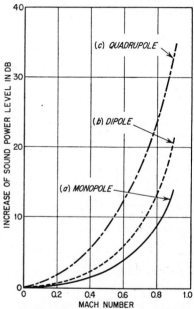

FIG. 33.3. Increase in total acoustic power radiated by uniformly moving sound sources as a function of the Mach number. (*a*) Monopole, (*b*) dipole with dipole axis perpendicular to direction of translation, (*c*) lateral quadrupole with one axis in direction of translation. (*Data from Oestreicher*[8] *and Lighthill.*[9])

the different sound sources is necessary. First, the sound generator itself might change its characteristics, its source strength, and its frequency spectrum. These effects are difficult to predict theoretically. However, there is a known effect, as a result of motion, on the sound radiated from a source which vibrates with the same velocity amplitude as it would in rest. This effect is two-fold: The radiated power increases with the velocity, and the directivity pattern turns toward the direction of motion, i.e., increases toward the front of the source and decreases behind it. In addition, for an observer at rest, the frequency is increased for the sound emitted forward and is decreased for the sound emitted backward, by the Doppler effect. These effects have been calculated for the basic sources[8,9] and are illustrated in Fig. 33.3.

Measurement of Aircraft Noise. Aircraft noise measurements may be divided into five classes: (1) measurement on isolated propulsion units on test stands; (2) measurements on airplanes stationary on the ground; (3) measurements on the ground of noise from aircraft in flight; (4) measurements in the aircraft in flight; and (5) model experiments under controlled conditions.

The following points require special attention for all types of aircraft noise measurements:

1. The dimensions of the noise source are relatively large, and the source power is great. Thus, considerable distance from the source is required before "far-field" conditions are reached, i.e., that for all types of sound sources the radial variation in sound pressure is in accordance with the "inverse square law." The usual rule that the near field ends at a distance which is at least several times the largest dimension of the source must be used with caution, since the source dimension is not always known exactly. In the case of a jet engine, for example, the turbulent gas jet stream is the noise source and not the tail pipe. Therefore, even 20 tail-pipe diameters distance is within the near field; some measurements indicate that the far field is not reached for low frequencies at distances less than 500 nozzle diameters. Deviations from inverse square law might seem quite negligible, but changes of the directivity pattern with distance indicate that one is still in the near field. In addition, close to the source where the sound pressure levels exceed 140 db, nonlinear properties of the air add additional absorption and the pressure drops more than that given by the inverse square law and normal atmospheric attenuation. Therefore, the inverse square law must be applied with caution and, in dubious cases, its validity should be verified.

2. Most aircraft noise measurements are outdoor measurements. This requires a certain stability and sturdiness of all equipment used. A windscreen around the microphone is necessary when it is used in wind or gas streams. In high winds, a second windscreen enclosing the first one might be necessary. Noise caused by turbulence around microphones can be reduced up to 30 db with such a screen. Care must be taken so that at all frequencies the turbulence noise is lower than the aircraft noise signal. Measurements at larger distances are subject to atmospheric influences.

3. At high intensities, microphonics of the amplifier tubes or vibrations of the microphone housing can result in distorted sound-level readings. This can occur even at relatively low levels (125 db) and with standard sound-level meters which in laboratory calibration at these levels show no such effect. The reason is the existence of low-frequency components of the sound fields which may excite vibration but which are not measured by the instrument. (Jet noise fields have considerable sound energy down to 1 cps.)

The instrumentation for the measurements on engines and stationary aircraft on the ground and the positions where these measurements are taken depend very much on whether the purpose of these measurements is general noise control, or research on the noise source or the noise-generating mechanism itself. Normally, in the first case, fewer measuring points are satisfactory with special emphasis on measurements in locations where personnel work. Standard sound-measuring techniques can be employed; sound-level meter readings and octave-band analysis give enough information in most cases. Positions around the source can be selected which give a rough measure of the noise output for noise sources of similar design. Such measuring positions have been standardized by the aircraft industry and are widely in use (Fig. 33.4).[10]

For more accurate investigations a more detailed study of the noise field is necessary to detect small changes in the noise field, and to evaluate modifications which may be introduced. An optimal description of such a three-dimensional sound field would require sound-pressure measurements on spheres surrounding the sources at

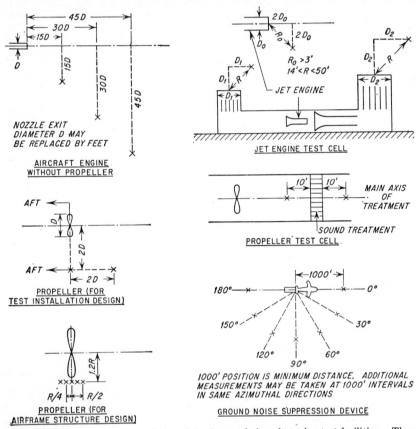

FIG. 33.4. EN-1 positions around aircraft engines and aircraft-engine test facilities. These positions, recommended by the Aircraft Industries Association to assure uniform practices for the measurement of aircraft noise, must be considered as a minimum number of positions for characterizing a noise source. For most purposes, noise measurements at more positions are required.

different radii. If the radius is large enough so that the measurements are made in the far-field, the total radiated acoustic power of the source is found by integrating the energy flux over the surface of the sphere. Usually it is possible to take advantage of the approximate symmetry of sound fields. As long as rotational symmetry around one axis exists, measurements must be made only on a half-circle around the sound source. This is usually assumed when such a rotationally symmetrical source (propeller, jet engine) is located with its axis parallel to the ground, close to the reflecting surface of the ground. Exact power measurements in this case would require sound measurements on arcs above the ground defined by constant radius r and constant angle θ (Fig. 33.5). Usually, the pressures as a function of angle are measured on the ground and assumed to be constant on the arcs in the upper hemisphere. The total power radiated is then given by

$$W_A = \frac{\pi r^2}{\rho c} \int_0^\pi p^2(\theta) \sin \theta \, d\theta \qquad (33.1)$$

where W_A = acoustic power

$p(\theta)$ = rms sound pressure on the ground at a circle of radius r, measured from the midpoint of the source

θ = angle between measuring point and symmetry axis of the sound field

c = velocity of sound in air

ρ = density of air

This integral can be evaluated by graphical or numerical methods. The actual power and the free-field power of the source without the presence of the ground might be somewhat larger than the value obtained by this method, depending on the distance of the source to ground, but under most circumstances probably not more than 3 db.

Sufficient accuracy usually is obtained by making measurements on the ground on half-circles around the engines. For single jet and propeller engines, a fairly constant acoustic power is obtained at radii of 50, 100, or 200 ft, even though 50 ft is not really in the far-field for low-frequency jet noise (the directivity pattern still changes with increasing radius). For large multiple-engine airplanes, the radii must be 500 to 1,000 ft. The larger distances are more correct theoretically, but atmospheric influences reduce the accuracy considerably for distances over a few hundred feet. The same large distances—and still greater distances—must be applied for the evaluation of the effectiveness of larger noise control structures (dimensions in the order of 100 ft) where the reduction in energy flux along the ground is the quantity defining the effectiveness with respect to the neighborhood. (Naturally, measurements closer to the structure also must be made, but

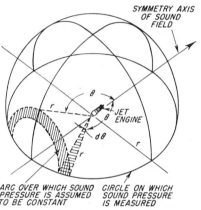

FIG. 33.5. Hemispherical surface used to calculate acoustic power radiated by noise source.

they give only the noise reduction at this point and cannot be used to determine the actual reduction of the power propagated along the ground.)

The angular intervals between the measurement positions on the circles should not be more than 10° to 15°. Whenever possible, the microphone should be kept in a fixed position and the sound source turned about its axis. In this way, atmospheric and terrain influences are constant for all angles of the directivity pattern and the relative accuracy is improved. This method has been applied successfully to measurements on airplanes. Turntable test stands for single engines would be desirable from the acoustical point of view.

For accurate analysis of the noise, it is advisable to make tape recordings at all points of the directivity pattern. Octave-band and narrow-band analysis, as well as special analysis of the wave shape, then, can be made in the laboratory. Measurements of the peak pressure level of the noise, which in the case of the turbojet engine exceeds the level of the rms pressure by 10 db and more, are important for physical and biological problems. Often, the long-time average spectrum is desired. For laboratory analysis, it is advisable to record samples of the noise of one or more seconds duration on an endless loop of magnetic tape. The spectral analysis of short, one-time noise events (spectrum at different moments of the overflight of an airplane, rocket noise) requires this or a similar technique.

Calibration of the microphone-amplifier-recording system in the field is advisable before, during, and after measurements by means of an acoustic calibrator or piston-phone. Atmospheric corrections for the microphone are thus automatically applied. Use of a dual-channel tape recorder, where the second channel takes explanations and remarks about the noise measurements, is often convenient.

The measurement of low-frequency noise, to which normal sound-measuring equipment does not respond, has become more and more necessary for investigations of jet noise. Components strong enough to have bio-acoustic and structural effects have been observed down to 1 cps and lower. Condenser microphones in high-frequency carrier systems, having a flat response down to zero frequency or variable-inductance-type pickups, are adequate for this frequency range. For measurements of the air-borne ultrasonic spectrum, condenser microphones (cylindrical in shape, diameter 0.4 in.) with a flat response up to about 100 kcps have been used in a common condenser-microphone circuit.

For research purposes the simultaneous or even synchronized recording of other quantities, such as aerodynamic thrust and its fluctuations, turbulence, temperature variations, high-speed motion picture of flame pattern of jet engine, may be desired, together with the noise.

The directivity pattern of the noise from an airplane in flight can be measured by two methods:

1. A microphone probe is towed by a second airplane at fixed distance with respect to the airplane under test. The microphone housing is streamlined to avoid turbulence and the sound inlet aperture is at such a position that the sound pressure is least affected by velocity. The disturbing pressure effects of inhomogeneities of the air, through which the microphone is towed, and of the noise from the towing airplane, must be considered. At speeds up to 435 miles per hour, sound pressure levels of about 75 db are still detectable by this method.[6b] To evaluate data obtained in this manner, the effect of the moving medium (Doppler effect) must be taken into account.

2. The airplane under test flies in straight-level flight with constant speed over a recording station on the ground.[113] The airplane's angle, as a function of time, is measured and recorded with proper correlation with the sound recording. For many measurements, an indication on the tape when the airplane is directly overhead and when it passes certain angles is sufficient. For other events, motion pictures or single-shot pictures, tied in with the noise recording, are required. From the two functions—noise and airplane's position as a function of time—the noise emitted from the airplane under a given angle can be calculated after taking into account the sound-propagation time, the varying distance, and the increase of atmospheric attenuation with distance The frequency spectrum emitted by the airplane is obtained by taking into account the motion of the source (Doppler effect). Thus, the directivity pattern for all spectral bands of the airplane in flight can be constructed. To obtain data on atmospheric attenuation and to increase the accuracy, the measurement should be immediately repeated with the airplane at a different altitude. For these measurements the weather must be calm and clear, and the terrain must be uniform. Recommendable altitude for these overflights depends on speed and size of the aircraft. However, it should be not less than 150 ft, and not more than 1,500 ft.

Noise measurements in aircraft cabins normally do not require special techniques except in the adaptation of the method to the type of airplane and the selection of characteristic points. It is often desirable in untreated cabins to make vibration measurements on the walls concurrently with sound measurements, to correlate noise components with vibrating surfaces.

Influence of the Atmosphere on the Propagation of Aircraft Noise. Changes in the composition of the atmosphere during the time of day and of year, and the inhomogeneity of the atmosphere at any given moment make the open atmosphere one of the most difficult and unpredictable transmission media for sound. Changes and inhomogeneities are related to wind, temperature, humidity, density, and turbulence (see Chap. 3).

The additional absorption due to nonlinear damping (shock-wave losses) is demonstrated in Fig. 33.6 for plane waves. An estimate of the shock-wave losses of a spherical wave gives the following approximate result: if at a distance of 50 ft from the source, sound pressure levels of 154 db are found at 1,000 cps, nonlinear damping in the first 1,000 ft attenuates the waves by 8 db in excess of viscous losses and spherical divergence. The sound pressure level assumed is not unrealistic for the most powerful present-day aircraft noise sources. For more powerful sources, still higher energy losses due to shock waves in the near field are to be expected, limiting the far-field noise levels.

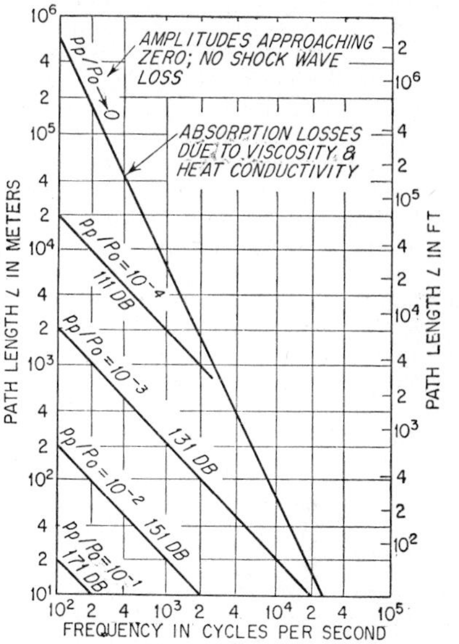

FIG. 33.6. Shock-wave losses in plane (originally sinusoidal) pressure wave of large amplitude as a function of frequency. The path length L, expressed in meters, indicates the distance over which the pressure wave is reduced by 3 db. The peak sound pressure level p_p is expressed in db re 0.0002 microbar rms pressure. P_0 represents the value of atmospheric pressure. (*From Ernsthausen and von Wittern.*[6])

AIRCRAFT PROPELLER AND RECIPROCATING-ENGINE NOISE

Noise Sources of Propeller-driven Aircraft. The noise from propeller-driven airplanes is a combination of two main sound sources—the propeller and the power plant. For most practical conditions, propeller noise is the more important noise source and generally exceeds the noise from the power plant with respect to its absolute level and especially with respect to its disturbing effect on man. Therefore, propeller noise has been studied the more extensively in theory and experiments.

The rotating propeller can produce sound by three different mechanisms. The first of these is given by bending vibrations of the propeller blade and is of no importance for the total noise of a practical propeller. The necessity of keeping propeller vibrations to a minimum reduces this noise source automatically so it will not be discussed here. However, this noise is sometimes detectable in the sound field at certain rotational speeds, and its observation can be of interest. The second and most important mechanism is the propeller-rotation noise generated by the pressure field which surrounds each blade as a consequence of its motion and which rotates with the rotating propeller blade. This noise is usually subdivided into noise due to torque and thrust (originated by blade angle and camber of the blades), and noise due to blade thickness. The third mechanism for noise generation by a rotating propeller is the vortex noise produced by vortices in the propeller wake which were shed by the blades during rotation. At very low propeller-tip speeds the vortex noise can be greater than the rotation noise; at higher tip speeds the vortex noise appears only in the higher frequency range of the propeller spectrum.

The noise from the power plant driving the propeller originally was restricted to the exhaust noise of reciprocating engines. Now gas turbines (turbo-propeller) are of practical importance. Additional noise from the power plant includes the noise produced by engine-excited vibration of single parts and of the fuselage. However, this noise has a low power output and only occasionally adds to the noise inside the airplane. It will, therefore, be discussed only in this connection.

Propeller-rotation Noise.[11] *Theoretical Analyses.* A propeller blade, rotating free in the air, is surrounded by a pressure field which results in a certain surface-pressure distribution on each blade element. Equal but opposite reaction forces are exerted by the propeller blade on the gas medium. For uniform rotation, these forces acting on the propeller are constant. The resulting force for each blade may be separated in a force component tangential to the circular path of the blade and associated with the torque Q opposing the rotation, and in a second component acting in the direction of the axis of rotation, the thrust force T. The propeller blade is a rotating airfoil with varying thickness and shape of the airfoil profile and with different angles of the profile (blade angle) relative to the direction of motion. These geometrical configurations determine, as shown by the aerodynamic airfoil theories, the drag and lift of the airfoil, which result in torque and thrust for the propeller.[12] The symmetrical profile with zero blade angle has no thrust component and only a minimum drag component as long as potential flow exists around the profile. At higher speeds, the drag or torque component is increased considerably by vortex separation. Increasing the blade angle from zero introduces the desired thrust and increases the torque to correspondingly much higher values. But, whereas the aerodynamic propeller theories usually consider only the forces existing in an incompressible fluid, this approximation becomes less justified with increasing rotational velocity because the radiation of sound energy results in a reaction of the sound field on the propeller, changing its drag and lift from its incompressible value.

No rigorous propeller theory exists at present, but an approximate analysis explains satisfactorily the propeller as a sound source for subsonic and moderate-supersonic tip-speed propellers, and is used for quantitative engineering calculations. The only rigorous theory applies to the noise from a propeller with symmetrical sections about the chord with zero blade angle and zero forward speed, the so-called *noise due to blade thickness*.[13,14] In this case, symmetry exists about the plane of the disk and the problem can be solved for potential flow around the blade. The rotating blade excites each stationary point of the propeller disk with a displacement given by the shape of the blade. Therefore, each point is excited by a periodic time function as illustrated in Fig. 33.7. All points on the propeller disk on a circle around the propeller axis are excited by the same function, but the phase of excitation is traveling around with the propeller velocity V. This boundary condition for the propeller disk is fulfilled, if we consider the propeller disk covered with simple sources oscillating with such strength and phase that the resulting displacement rotating over the propeller disk is equal and equivalent to the displacement of the rotating blade. The fundamental frequency $\omega = B\Omega$ is given by the rotational frequency Ω and the number of blades B, if the blades are equal in shape and at equal angular intervals. The sound fields (power radiated and directivity pattern) of this

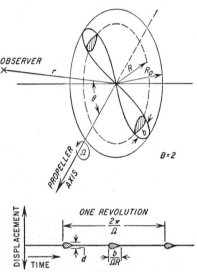

FIG. 33.7. Coordinate system for calculation of propeller noise. The propeller with zero blade angle is illustrated. The lower part of the graph gives the displacement caused by the rotating blade as a function of time for the elements of the propeller disk. Fourier analysis of this function gives the strength of the harmonics with which the simple sources considered to cover the propeller disk radiate.

source distribution with traveling phase have been investigated for a wide variation of the parameters and applied to the noise due to blade thickness of a propeller.[14–16] The rms sound-pressure amplitude of the mth harmonic at large distance from the propeller is given by

$$|p_m| = \rho m B \Omega \, \frac{V_m^0}{2\sqrt{2}\,r} \int_0^{R_0} R f(R) |I_{mB}(kR \sin \theta)| \, dR \qquad (33.2)$$

where ρ = density of air

m = order of harmonic

B = number of blades

Ω = angular velocity

V_m^0 = amplitude of the mth harmonic of the velocity function for a propeller-disk element

r, θ = polar coordinates with origin at center of propeller disk, θ is measured from propeller axis

R = radius to a blade element

R_0 = propeller radius

$f(R)$ = function characterizing the radial distribution of the velocity V_m^0 over the propeller disk

I_{mB} = Bessel function of first kind with index mB

$k = \dfrac{mB\Omega}{c}$

c = velocity of sound in air

d = thickness of blade

b = blade width

f_m = mth coefficient of Fourier series representing the velocity function

V_m^0 is given by the blade thickness $V_m^0 = (mB\Omega d/2)\, f_m$. Different simplifying assumptions have been made in arriving at values for f_m for special cases. Reference 15 gives calculations of the integral for four different velocity distributions, $f(R)$, and shows graphs for the directivity pattern and the radiated power as functions of m, B, and Ω. A more practical formula was obtained by assuming that d decreases linearly over R to zero at $R = R_0$, which results in an average blade thickness of $2/3d'$ (where d' is the blade thickness at $R_0/2$), and with $f(R) = 1$. The directivity pattern, for small values of $kR_0 = mBV_t/c$, has its maximum in the plane of rotation, and the sound pressure becomes zero on the propeller axis. For increasing values of kR_0 (increasing tip speed or higher harmonics) the directivity factor increases, and its pattern finally splits into two maxima—one in front and one behind the plane of rotation. The total radiated power is a function of the tip speed; at low velocities, the fundamental predominates, but with increasing speed the harmonics have relatively more power.

The reaction of the sound field on the propeller blade has been shown to result in a reaction force which is essentially an additional drag which is created by the sound radiation and has no relation to friction drag or vortex shedding. This "compressible drag" would be the same in a frictionless medium in which the torque delivered to a propeller without lift is completely converted into acoustic power. If we assume V_m^0 is constant over the propeller radius, this velocity is related to the mth component of the reaction force F_m^0 on the total area by a radiation impedance $Z_m^0 = S_m^0 + jM_m^0$. The radiation resistance S_m^0 is proportional to the acoustic power radiated by the mth harmonic; the radiation reactance M_m^0 is proportional to the air mass oscillating in the near-field of the moving blade, and describes the flow around the profile. Figure 33.8 demonstrates radiation resistance and reactance as a function of the tip Mach number $M_t = V_t/c$. This shows how the total radiated power increases with increasing tip speed and how at higher tip speeds more and more power is radiated by the higher harmonics and that, at extremely high tip speeds, the power radiated by all harmonics does cease to increase, but does approach a constant value. Equation (33.2) can be modified by replacing V_m^0 by the drag component $F_{D_m}^0$ of the force F_m^0 outside the integral, $V_m^0 = F_{D_m}^0/S_m^0$. Then experimental measurements of the drag distribution over the blade are sufficient to determine the resulting field if this drag due to sound radiation can be separated from the usually larger drag due to vortex separation in a medium with friction.

The sound radiated by *a propeller with angle of attack and camber* cannot be calculated with the same exactness as the preceding boundary-value problem of the symmetrical profile. Here, the velocity produced by the passing blade at each stationary point of the propeller disk is not known and is difficult to calculate. Hence, all approaches start with an approximated pressure distribution over the blade, and replace the action of this surface pressure distribution on the medium by fixed forces acting at the propeller disk. The first theoretical approaches to the problem of propeller-sound radiation[17,18,19] postulated certain source distributions without founding them in the aerodynamic properties of the propeller and were therefore not

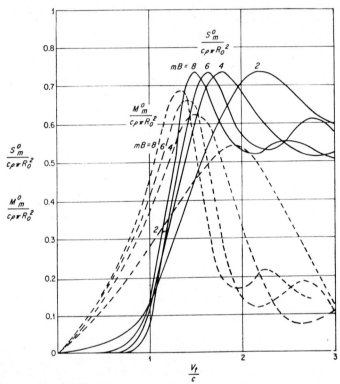

Fig. 33.8. Radiation resistance $S_m{}^0$ and radiation reactance $M_m{}^0$ for the mth harmonic of the sound radiation by the total propeller-disk area of a propeller with zero blade angle as a function of the tip Mach number V_t/c. (*After Ernsthausen.*[13])

too successful. Since then a theory has been developed which has been used commonly for practical noise calculations for the propeller at zero forward speed.[20,21] This theory starts with the force acting on each propeller element and resolves these forces into a thrust force in direction of the propeller axis and a torque force in the direction opposed to the direction of rotation. The forces on the medium are equal but opposite in direction. The stationary propeller disk is assumed to be of zero thickness and is considered covered with acoustic sources radiating with such phase and strength as to produce the pressure distribution of the blade traveling around over the disk. Each source element of the disk, therefore, must produce a force-time function $F_T(t)$ and $F_Q(t)$ for thrust and torque which follow from the spatial pressure distribution over the blade. The Fourier analysis of $F_T(t)$ and $F_Q(t)$ gives the harmonics of the thrust force and torque force experienced at each disk element.

As a simple, good approximation, a uniform, rectangular force distribution is generally assumed over the projected propeller width b, with the following Fourier coefficients for each blade element:

$$F_{T_m} = \frac{dT}{dR} \frac{1}{\pi} \frac{2\pi R}{mB\pi b} \sin \frac{mBb\pi}{2\pi R} \, dR \, d\theta = \frac{dT}{dR} \frac{1}{\pi} f_{T_m} \, dR \, d\theta$$

and

$$F_{Q_m} = \frac{dQ}{dR} \frac{1}{R\pi} \frac{2\pi R}{mB\pi b} \sin \frac{mBb\pi}{2\pi R} \, dR \, d\theta = \frac{dQ}{dR} \frac{1}{R\pi} f_{Q_m} \, dR \, d\theta$$

(33.3)

For this approximation $F_T(t)$ and $F_Q(t)$ are without phase shift relative to each other; T and Q are the total propeller torque and thrust, and are assumed to be functions of R. The quantities f_{T_m} and f_{Q_m} are the dimensionless Fourier coefficients given by the equation. The phases of the radiators covering the whole disk vary in proportion to the rotational angle; i.e., they travel with the blade. The single sources which are equivalent to concentrated periodic forces are represented by dipoles.[22] The resulting sound field of the rotating propeller is obtained by calculating the field of the torque and thrust dipoles uniformly distributed over the propeller area. For a field point at a large distance from the propeller, the following rms sound-pressure amplitude is obtained:

$$|p_m| = \frac{k}{2\sqrt{2}\,\pi r} \left| \int_0^{R_0} -\frac{dT}{dR} f_{T_m} \cos \theta \, I_{mB}(kR \sin \theta) \, dR \right.$$

$$\left. + \int_0^{R_0} \frac{c}{\Omega R^2} \frac{dQ}{dR} f_{Q_m} I_{mB}(kR \sin \theta) \, dR \right| \quad (33.4)$$

To simplify this equation for calculation purposes, the propeller disk can be replaced by an annular ring in which the entire thrust and torque are concentrated.[20,11] Assuming that this "effective radius" R_e is the same for torque and thrust, the following is obtained:

$$|p_m| = \frac{k}{2\sqrt{2}\,\pi r} \left| \left(-Tf_{T_m} \cos \theta + Qf_{Q_m} \frac{c}{\Omega R_e^2} \right) I_{mB}(kR_e \sin \theta) \right| \quad (33.5)$$

The frequency of the fundamental component is $B\Omega$, and of the mth harmonic is $mB\Omega$. The torque term in Eq. (33.5) results in a directivity pattern which is zero on the propeller axis and maximum in the plane of rotation. It is similar to the pattern given in Eq. (33.2) for the profile with zero blade angle since the thickness effect also results in a torque. The thrust term is zero on the propeller axis and in the plane of rotation. The torque and thrust term are out of phase in front of the propeller, but in phase in the space behind it. The resulting pattern, therefore, generally has a small maximum in front of the propeller and a large maximum somewhat behind its plane of rotation, usually approximately at 15°. Since with increasing tip speed and increasing number of m the ratio F_{Q_m}/F_{T_m} usually increases, it has the effect of shifting the maximum closer to the plane of rotation for the higher harmonics and for increased tip speed.*

The total torque can be calculated from the input power $W_M = Q\Omega$ or it can be measured; this value of the torque includes contributions due to skin friction and vortex separation which dissipate energy without producing rotational noise. Therefore, the sound effect calculated from this torque value results in somewhat too high values. The thickness effect should not be considered in addition to this torque effect, since it is already included.

The total thrust can be obtained either from measurements or from the simple aerodynamic momentum theory for the propeller in the form[20]

$$T = (2\pi\rho R_0{}^2 W_M^2 \eta^2)^{1/3} \quad (33.6)$$

* This effect can be seen in Fig. 33.12.

where η is an efficiency factor estimated to be about 0.75. The use of an empirical thrust value obtained from measurements may slightly underestimate the sound due to thrust.

The Fourier coefficients f_{T_m} and f_{Q_m} can be obtained from pressure measurements close at the blade or, as it is usually done, by approximate assumptions concerning the pressure distribution. In order to simplify Eq. (33.5) it is often assumed that f_{T_m} and f_{Q_m} are equal to unity. This is equivalent to assuming the blade to be of infinitely small width (i.e., the force pulses to be infinitely short). This assumption becomes less valid when $2mbB/R\pi$ exceeds unity. The quantities f_{T_m} and f_{Q_m} are given in Fig. 33.9 for different idealized pulse shapes of equal area or impulse (i.e., of equal average total thrust and torque). These clearly indicate that the low harmonics are almost independent of impulse width and shape, provided the total impulse is the same.[11] Therefore, Eq. (33.5) with $f_{T_m} = f_{Q_m} = 1$ is a good approximation at low frequencies. For constant thrust and torque the higher frequencies are reduced considerably by increasing the blade width. The impulse width

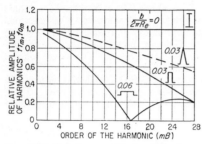

FIG. 33.9. Relative amplitude of the harmonics of propeller noise (f_{T_m} and f_{Q_m}) for various ratios of pulse duration to the time for a full revolution ($b/2\pi R_e$). The pulses shown exert equal resulting forces on the propeller. m = number of harmonic, B = number of blades. (*After Regier and Hubbard.*[11])

$$b/2\pi R_e = 0.03$$

represents a conventional propeller, whereas the 6 per cent width considered in Ref. 11 is rather extreme. As can be seen from Eq. (33.5) and Fig. 33.9, increasing the number of blades B always reduces the noise for a given power.

Several modifications and improvements have been made of the above theory. Equation (33.4) was used to calculate p and the power radiated by the propeller for realistic torque and thrust distributions dT/dR and dQ/dR.[21] However, these more exact results are not appreciably different from the above approximation.

The sound pressure at any field point without regard to distance has been calculated using the effective-ring approximation.[23,11] This solution proves very useful when the oscillating pressures near the propeller at wings or fuselages are of interest. This equation can be used also when the torque and thrust forces on the blade are functions of the position of the blade on the propeller disk. For example, this is the case for the dual rotating propeller, a propeller operating near a wing, or a propeller operating in the wake of a wing or strut.[24,25] The radiation pattern can change considerably in these cases from the field of a propeller with uniform loading.

A different approach to the noise of a propeller with thrust has been taken in which the thrust force is calculated from the incompressible-airfoil theory;[13,16] the sound field of the combination of this rotating force and the rigorous solution for the thickness effect is obtained. The results are similar to that of Eq. (33.4), yielding the same radiation characteristic, but since the thickness effect is equivalent only to a small part of the torque, the torque due to the impulse energy delivered to the slipstream is neglected; the radiation characteristics and the total sound power for the harmonics are evaluated rigorously for a wide variety of parameters. For the propeller disk with rotating thrust distribution, ($Q = 0$ in the theory previously reported), an approximate calculation of the reaction forces of the sound field on the propeller has been made: mass forces are determined which, with increasing tip speed, modify the thrust the propeller blade has in an incompressible medium; and drag forces are found which correspond to an additional drag or torque due to the radiated sound energy. Figure 33.10 shows the radiation reactance M'_m for the mth harmonic, which is given by the flow in the near field around the blade, and the radiation resistance S'_m for the mth harmonic which is proportional to the radiated sound power. These curves show that with increasing tip speed the propeller delivers more and more energy to the gas in the form of acoustic waves, whereas the thrust has a maximum and decreases thereafter. The increasing importance of the higher harmonics at higher tip speeds is obvious.

For the case of the *forward-moving propeller*, the sound-pressure relations valid for all field points are available both for the effective-ring approximation and for the

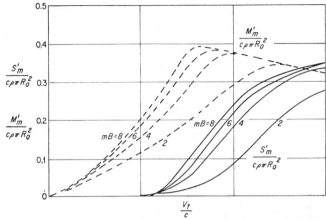

Fig. 33.10. Radiation resistance S_m' and mass reactance M_m' for the mth harmonic of the sound radiation by the total propeller-disk area of a propeller with thrust as a function of the tip Mach number V_t/c. (The torque force on the propeller blade is not considered in the derivation of this approximation.) S_m' is proportional to the radiated sound power and results in an increased drag force on the propeller. M_m' modifies the thrust value the propeller would have in an incompressible medium. (*After Ernsthausen.*[13])

general case involving integration over the total disk.[26] For the far-field and effective-ring approximation and $f_{T_m} = f_{Q_m} = 1$, the sound pressure for an observation point in the x-y plane moving with the propeller in the x direction is given by

$$|p_m| = \frac{mB\Omega}{2\pi c\bar{r}} \left| \left[T(M + \cos\bar{\theta})\frac{1}{\beta^2} - Q\frac{c}{\Omega R_e^2} \right] I_{mB}(kR_e \sin\bar{\theta}) \right| \qquad (33.7)$$

where $\beta = \sqrt{1 - M^2}$ where M is the forward speed Mach number

$\bar{r} = \sqrt{x^2 + \beta^2 y^2}$

$\cos\bar{\theta} = \dfrac{x}{\bar{r}}$

$\sin\bar{\theta} = \dfrac{y}{\bar{r}}$

x, y = Cartesian coordinates with their origin in the propeller center (x axis coincides with propeller axis and direction of motion)

The forward speed increases the sound-power output and affects the directivity pattern, the thrust term being considerably more affected than the torque term. For $M = 0$ Eq. (33.7) becomes equal to Eq. (33.5) for the statically operated propeller, which may give a reasonably good approximation up to $M = 0.3$($\beta = 0.95$).

For an actual propeller the thrust decreases with increasing forward speed when the torque is constant, so that the total noise output first decreases with increasing flight speed, but, at higher velocity, the effect of motion on sound generation prevails, resulting in a net increase of sound output with increasing M.[26] This effect is shown in Fig. 33.11 for a point near the propeller tip. An increase of the forward Mach number has an effect similar to an increase in rotational Mach number: the sound pressure shows a larger increase associated with the higher harmonics. For one

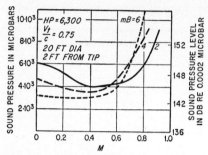

FIG. 33.11. Calculated effect of forward-speed Mach number M on sound pressure near the propeller tip. Rotational-tip Mach number, $V_t/c = 0.75$, is held constant. (*After Regier.*[5])

example, Ref. 26 gives the sound distribution from a propeller in the near- and far-field and also shows the relative contributions of the torque and thrust terms.

Measurements of Propeller-rotation Noise. Comparisons have been made of theoretical results with systematic measurements on the sound emitted by stationary propellers.[19,20,21,27,28] Fair agreement has been obtained for the fundamental frequency; increasing deviations occur at the higher harmonics. Measurements have been made of the rotation noise from symmetrical sections at zero blade angle and fair agreement has been found with theory up to the fifth harmonic and $M_t = 0.8$.[14] The sound due to blade thickness is small compared to the sound from a similar, thrust-producing propeller. Several detailed investigations of the sound from model airscrews have been made in a free-field (anechoic) room.[16] This, and the automatic method employed for plotting the directivity pattern of the propeller (rotation of the propeller-sound source around the axis perpendicular to the propeller axis; microphone stationary), makes these measurements and power calculations very exact. Data have been obtained from $M_t = 0.6$ to $M_t = 1.2$ for different profiles with and without blade angle. The

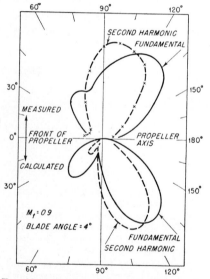

FIG. 33.12. Measured (upper half) and calculated (lower half) sound field of a model airscrew (blade angle 4°) at tip Mach number $V_t/c = 0.9$. The sound pressure is plotted in an arbitrary linear scale. (*After Ernsthausen.*[16])

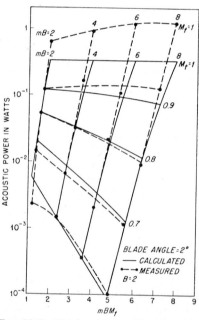

FIG. 33.13. Total acoustic power per harmonic radiated by model airscrews (blade angle 2°) as a function of the tip Mach number M_t and the number of blades B ($m =$ number of harmonic). Measured values for $B = 2$. The vertical lines indicate for constant mB the rapid increase of the acoustic power of all harmonics with tip speed. The horizontal lines give the power spectrum for constant-tip Mach numbers. (*After Ernsthausen.*[16])

general agreement with the theory of Ref. 16 is good, as is illustrated in Figs. 33.12 and 33.13. Figure 33.13 does not exhibit clearly at $M_t = 1$ what becomes more obvious in studies on the sound of a propeller at supersonic tip speed, namely, that although theory predicts increasing noise power for higher harmonics at supersonic tip speeds, measurements indicate a maximum of the spectrum followed by a decrease in level of the higher harmonics.[29] In Ref. 29, the maximum of the spectrum for $M_t = 1.2$ was found at the sixth harmonic. The reason for this finding, which limits the steep increase of noise power with tip speed, is not known exactly.

Measurements of the free-space pressure fields near the tips of propellers show good agreement with theory, even up to distances a few blade-chord lengths from the propeller.[23] The free-space oscillating pressures in the region where a wing might be located have been measured for $M_t = 0.5$ to 1.2 on a static pusher propeller.[30] Measurements on the same points have been made with a wing in place. It was shown that the side of the wing approached by the blade has considerably higher oscillating pressures than the side of the wing from which the blade recedes. The pressure on the side of the wing which the blade approaches, and the pressure differential across a thin wing, were found to be greater than the free-field value at corresponding points.

Tests on the dual counter-rotating propeller show that the sound field does not have rotational symmetry, but has a maximum in the direction of the blade overlap.[24] In this direction, the sound pressure and its spectrum are approximately the same as for a single propeller having the same number of blades as one stage of the dual. The sound minima in the direction midway between the intersection lines correspond closely to the sound of a single propeller with the blade number of the total unit. Another sound phenomenon is detected on the dual-rotating propeller. When the blades pass each other, unsteady air forces are generated in these positions, especially when the propellers are close to each other. The radiation from these nonrotating forces has its maximum on the axis of rotation, and is detectable only on this axis in the otherwise predominant torque and thrust noise field.

Similar unsteady air forces radiate sound and increase the noise level when the propeller passes closely to wings or struts. Qualitatively, their influence is well understood. Some model data have been given concerning the effect of propeller tip clearance on the total sound output.[6] A strut ahead of the propeller disk seems to have more effect on the noise output than a strut behind the propeller.[24,25]

Shrouded propellers have been studied for their reduced noise output, but as yet have no practical significance for propulsion.[31,32]

Near-field pressure measurements in flight of noise from a propeller in motion show results which agree qualitatively with the theory as indicated in Fig. 33.11.[33,34] Directivity patterns of noise from propellers in flight have been measured for only the fundamental and first harmonic.[35,6,7] These results show qualitatively changes similar to those calculated theoretically; i.e., more sound is radiated in the direction of flight.

Considerable information concerning the variation in propeller noise with different parameters has been obtained from extensive measurements of the noise in aircraft in flight.[36,37] These data do not allow checks on the complete sound field, but give the noise inside of the aircraft under a wide variety of conditions. In general, they are in agreement with the theory and free-field measurements, especially if modifications of the free-field sound from the propeller due to the presence of the fuselage are considered.

The effect of shielding of wing and fuselage on the sound has been somewhat investigated for the near field only, but is probably unimportant in the far field.

Vortex Noise. The nonperiodic part of the propeller-noise spectrum is produced by the generation of vortices in the wake of the moving profile. Ordinarily, this noise is small in comparison with the periodic part, but at frequencies above 1,000 cps it is always preponderant in the spectrum, except when M_t approaches and exceeds unity. At very low tip speeds, it exceeds the rotation noise at all frequencies and prevails especially near the propeller axis where the rotation noise is theoretically zero and the vortex noise has its maximum. The instability of flow behind a moving profile leads to the formation of vortices. For rectilinear motion of the profile and idealized flow the vortex formation follows the well-known periodic pattern of a "Karman vortex street," which has been studied intensively for the flow passing a cylinder. Here, the frequency f of the noise is $f = KV/d$, where V is the velocity, d the cylinder diameter, and K a constant (the so-called Strouhal number) with the experimental value of about 0.185. Frequency and sound-power output emitted by cylinders in such motion have been studied.[38] Profiles of shapes less regular than a cylinder shed vortices in a less periodic fashion, but still emphasize the frequency band around the Strouhal frequency, d being the projection of the profile width on the plane perpendicular to the direction of motion. The Strouhal number varies with the length of the profile between 0.2 for the infinite long cylinder and 0.09 for a body of relatively small length. A theoretical value 0.194 has been obtained for it, and it has been shown how the generation of the vortices is directly connected to the form drag of the profile.[39]

These results on sound emission from profiles in rectilinear motion have been applied to the vortex sound emission of the propeller.[40] Each blade element radiates at the Strouhal frequency as determined by its thickness and velocity. This results in a continuous noise spectrum corresponding to the velocities which vary from zero on the axis to the maximum velocity at the tip. For cylindrical rods, rotating about the mid-point of the rod, measurements have been made of vortex noise directivity pattern, the noise-power output, and the pressure along the rod in the near field. Periodic vortex generation behind a body is connected with periodic forces between the medium and the body, since the vortex circulation varies with time. On all types of vortex noise, these forces were found to act at a right angle to the flow so that the vortex generation is connected with an acoustic dipole with its axis rectangular to the flow. The assumption of such dipoles over the entire propeller blade results in a dipole characteristic for the vortex noise of the propeller with the maximum on the propeller axis and no sound in the plane of rotation. The vortex trail, once the vortices are generated, radiates with the very poor efficiency of quadrupoles similar to turbulent flow and, therefore, its sound can be neglected. The force of the vortex dipole has been calculated approximately from the pressure difference across the vortex street;[41] the acoustic power radiated by a rotating rod was found to be

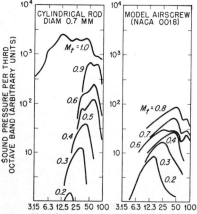

FIG. 33.14. Frequency spectra of the vortex noise of rotating cylindrical rods and of a model airscrew. The parameter shown is the tip Mach number M_t. (*After von Wittern*.[42])

$$W_A \propto \frac{\rho}{c^3} (c_\alpha{}^2 K)^2 V_t{}^6 R d \qquad (33.8)$$

c_α is the form drag coefficient, and K the Strouhal number; both in reference to a certain mean radius. The individual rod elements are assumed to be incoherent radiators. With c_α and K independent of velocity, the acoustical power is proportional to $V_t{}^6$. At lower Reynolds number with no fixed point of breakaway, c_α decreases with increasing velocity. This probably accounts for the 5.5 power law observed by Ref. 40, whereas Ref. 41 found the sixth power law for different profiles with a fixed point of breakaway. Although all the experiments mentioned thus far were restricted to tip Mach numbers below 0.3, in which range rotational sound is easy to separate from vortex noise, a similar mechanism must be assumed at higher tip speeds. The vortex formation becomes more and more irregular and even a small blade element will radiate a broad-band noise. This was shown by measurements of the vortex-noise spectra up to $M_t = 1$ for cylindrical rods and model airscrews as shown in Fig. 33.14.[42]   It can be seen how the maximum of the spectrum still shifts to higher frequencies with increasing M_t.   The relatively small size of the blades ($R_0 = 15$ cm) and small thickness resulted in high frequencies with appreciable spectral energy up to 100 kcps.   At $M_t = 1$ a sudden change to a wide spectrum was observed, which may be connected with the generation of shock waves or may mean that under this condition the rotational noise is no longer separable from the vortex noise.   Measurements were also made of the directivity pattern of the dipole vortex-noise generators in a coordinate system rotating with the rotating blade, and the effect of motion on these sound sources was demonstrated:[42] with increasing M_t the maxima of the dipole characteristic do not remain at a right angle to the direction of flow, but turn toward the direction of motion, in agreement with the calculations of Ref. 8.   For $M_t = 0.4$ the measured and calculated characteristic of the dipole in motion is shown in Fig. 33.15.   This directivity pattern rotates with the blade so that the vortex noise observed at a fixed point in space is modulated with the rotational frequency, since this point is struck during the course of one revolution from sound emitted under varying angles with respect to the moving dipole. (A similar modulation is known from the underwater noise of ship propellers.)   Maximum modulation occurs for $\theta = 35°$ to $50°$, since under this angle an observer receives noise from the maximum of the characteristic of the approaching blade and very little noise from the backside of the receding blade. No modulation occurs on the axis of rotation, where, or at least close by, the noise power integrated over one revolution still has its maximum. The time average directivity pattern changes somewhat with M_t.   In the plane of rotation, a minimum has always been observed.   Additional values for the acoustic-mechanical efficiency of the vortex-noise generator are given in Ref. 42 and show interesting correlations between form drag and acoustic radiation.   As a consequence of the effect of motion on

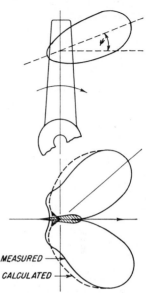

FIG. 33.15. Directivity pattern of the vortex-noise generators of a rotating profile (tip Mach number 0.4).   The sound pressure is plotted in an arbitrary linear scale.   The dotted curve is calculated for a dipole moving on a circle with $M = 0.4$.   The deflection of the dipole directivity pattern by the angle ψ is probably caused by the radial motion of the air due to friction and centrifugal forces, which were not considered in the calculation.   (*After von Wittern.*[42])

the dipole, the total acoustic vortex-noise power at high velocities increases at a value between the sixth power and tenth power, depending on the profile, instead of with the sixth power of M_t as it is for low velocities.

Unfortunately, the accumulated knowledge on vortex noise cannot be applied to the quantitative evaluation of vortex noise of actual propellers.   The high Reynolds numbers at which they operate are well in the turbulent flow range and exceed all Reynolds numbers used in the model experiments.   In practice, Eq. (33.8) is used with flow constants measured at low Reynolds numbers.   A dipole characteristic is assumed for the total resulting vortex noise with maxima on the propeller axis.   The few published data which exist on the spectrum indicate that it spreads over the entire audible range.   Only a few measurements in flight have been reported ($M_t = 0.8$, on propeller axis 100 dynes per sq cm at 10 kcps[6]); in most cases the vortex noise was not separated from the aerodynamic noise.

Noise from the Aircraft Reciprocating Engine.   *Exhaust Noise.*   The noise from reciprocating engines originates from the periodic expulsion of hot combustion gases through the exhaust.   Sound radiation from other parts of the engine is not appreciable and will not be noticeable unless extremely effective mufflers are used.   However, it occasionally may be detected as structure-borne noise inside the aircraft.

The exhaust noise has not been studied in as much detail as the propeller noise because the maximum, and usually more objectionable noise levels, are produced by the propeller. Furthermore, exhaust mufflers offer, in principal, the possibility of noise reduction, although they are seldom used in practice because of their weight.

The noise source of this exhaust noise is constituted by the periodic volume flow, which, to a first approximation, radiates equally in all directions like a monopole sound source. This assumption is made in all theoretical approaches, even when it is well known that velocity and temperature will modify this monopole radiation. Interference between several exhausts will lead to directional emission, becoming more pronounced at higher frequencies, where exhaust direction and reflection from the airplane structure become increasingly important. The lowest frequency of the exhaust noise spectrum is given by the number of exhaust discharges per cylinder per second, which usually corresponds to the firing frequency. Combining the exhausts of several cylinders into one exhaust port allows, at least in theory, the partial or even total cancellation of some components of the exhaust pressures. Two cylinders working in counterphase, for instance, cancel their fundamental frequency to an appreciable amount, and two cylinders firing at the same time count as one exhaust discharge, but of double strength. Thus possibilities of noise suppression are presented by proper arrangement of the manifold system and the use of collector rings. A combination of exhausts increases the frequency of the major noise-producing component, simplifying the muffling of this noise, and canceling some of the noise in the common pipe. This explains why the number of firings per second feeding into a common exhaust sometimes gives the fundamental frequency, and why the lower firing frequency of the single cylinder and its harmonics appear much weaker, depending on the symmetry of the firings and of the manifold system itself. But on most modern aircraft engines, the single cylinder firing frequency remains still very strong. When the exhaust valve of one cylinder remains opened after the valve of a neighboring cylinder opens in the same exhaust, the increased volume reduces the peak exhaust pressure.[43] These peak pressures in the exhaust tubing are in the order of 10^4 to 10^6 dynes per sq cm, so that the formation of shock waves and their attributed losses are always present. In addition to the monopole noise due to pulsating flow, some aerodynamic noise modulated with the pulse frequency is also present, originating at the edges, corners, and in the mixing region of the exhaust system.

A theory for the approximate calculation of the exhaust sound of a reciprocating engine has been given, in which the volume flow of the exhaust gases through the valve opening must be known from the engine characteristic.[44,6] The acoustically most effective part of the exhaust process is where the escape process of the gases is free of reaction and at supersonic velocity (high internal source impedance). The actual volume flow as a function of time can be idealized by a square wave of equal area, i.e., exhaust volume. As a simple approximation, it was assumed that the volume flow of one cylinder is formed out of rectangular impulses lasting over half the total cycle with a maximum of $i_{max} = S_v c_T$, where S_v is the cross-sectional area of the valve opening of one cylinder, and c_T is the sound velocity at the exhaust gas temperature. The volume flow is analyzed into its Fourier components i_m and the sound power output is calculated by means of the radiation resistance of the exhaust opening with the Area S. As long as the wavelength is small compared to the dimensions of the exhaust area, the sound power for the mth harmonic radiated by one cylinder is given by

$$W_{A_m} = \frac{1}{2} V_m^2 S^2 \frac{\rho}{c} m^2 \pi f_0^2 = \frac{2}{\pi} \frac{\rho}{c} f_0^2 i_{max}^2 \qquad (33.9)$$

where $i_m = i_{max} \dfrac{2}{m\pi} = V_m S$

V_m = peak value of the mth component of the velocity, with which the exhaust area S radiates

f_0 = fundamental frequency

$m = 1, 3, 5, \ldots$

The values for density ρ and sound velocity c are somewhat undefined in this approximation and are taken at the temperature of the surrounding air. At higher frequencies where the radiation resistance of the opening ceases to increase with frequency as it does in Eq. (33.9), but approaches a constant value, the acoustic output decreases by $1/m^2$. This limits the contribution of the higher harmonics to the total noise output of the exhaust. Assuming this limit for the usual exhaust ports to be in the order of $2\pi m f_0 = 6,000$, the total sound power output of one cylinder is

$$W_A \approx 1.13 \times 10^{-12} f_0 S_v^2 c_T^2 \qquad \text{watt} \qquad (33.10)$$

with S_v given in square centimeters and c_T in centimeters per second.

The velocity c_T may be in the order of 6×10^4 cm per sec and above. For an engine with z cylinders the upper limit for the total sound power output is given by $z \cdot W_A$ for the unfavorable case where no interference and cancellation between the cylinders is assumed. Usually the latter effect will result in a reduction of the lowest frequencies in the series up to the fundamental firing frequency of the total engine $[z f_0 = z\, n/(2 \cdot 60)$, where n is the engine rpm]. Calculations of the acoustic-mechanical efficiency of various German aircraft engines W_A/W_M (W_M = total mechanical power of engine) indicated them to be of the order of 1 per cent.[44,6,7] For the same engine the acoustic-mechanical efficiency decreases with increasing rpm; at the same rpm the less powerful engine has the lower efficiency. Knowledge of the exact function for the exhaust velocity would improve the above approximation, but it is doubtful if it would give more than the order of magnitude and the qualitative behavior. Many other factors of equal importance should be considered, such as the flow velocity, the temperature of the exhaust gas, and shock-wave losses. The latter will result in distortion and increased absorption of the higher frequencies in the pressure wave, both in the exhaust tubing and in the near field outside.

In addition to the effects already described, a tail pipe which cannot be considered small in comparison to the wavelength will affect the sound power radiated by the engine. At the pipe's resonance frequencies, the source is matched to the impedance of the air and more power is emitted. This tube's characteristic can be calculated with the required accuracy when the average exhaust gas temperature is known.[45,6]

Acoustically, it is advantageous to point the exhaust port or tail-pipe opening away from the observer, since the higher frequencies are stronger in the direction of the exhaust. These facts might influence the positioning of the exhaust tubing to reduce cabin noise and noise emitted toward the ground. An example of a noise reduction of 10 db and more for the exhaust noise of an aircraft in low-level flight directly overhead (100 ft) is reported.[46] In this case, initially the tail pipes of each cylinder bank discharged separately underneath the wings. The fitting of a cross-over exhaust with a common discharge from both banks above the wings reduced the noise at the firing frequency from a single bank of cylinders (120 cps) by some 10 to 15 db. In addition, the shielding of the exhaust orifices from the ground by the wings reduced the general level at high frequencies by some 10 db.

Exhaust Mufflers. Exhaust noise can be reduced considerably by the use of mufflers (see Chap. 21). The basic principles of muffler design for reciprocating engines are fairly well understood, although all theories start with the linearized equations of acoustic-filter theory and neglect the finite amplitude of the gas waves in the exhaust and the superimposed steady exhaust gas flow. Nevertheless, most studies and comparisons with models and actual mufflers show that the theoretical results are applicable within certain limits. Since the engine back-pressure must be kept to a minimum, only mufflers of the straight-through type, where the exhaust gas is not forced around sharp turns, are used for aircraft engines. In such mufflers, the steady-flow resistance always can be reduced to tolerable values by increasing the size of the exhaust pipe. Both types of mufflers—series filters (expansion chamber) and parallel or side-branch filters (resonators)—have been used successfully on aircraft engines. Single-element mufflers achieve attenuation over a relatively small frequency range but, for higher attenuation over a wide range, two or more chambers are required. Which type of muffler—series or parallel filter—is the more effective for otherwise equal size and back pressure, depends on the effect of finite amplitude and steady-flow velocity on the attenuation; as yet, a definitive answer cannot be given for large engines and pressures. In one study,[47] it was assumed that the expansion-chamber-type muffler performed more effectively at high pressure, but the effectiveness of resonator-type mufflers also has been demonstrated.[48] The effect of the steady exhaust-gas flow on the attenuation properties seems to be small for one-chamber models of both types but affects the multiple chamber types by changing the impedance of the connecting tube. However, only a little quantitative knowledge on these points is available.[45,49]

In practice, single-section, expansion-chamber-type filters provide above the cutoff attenuations up to 15 db (expansion ratio approximately 6), although theory and cold tests show that higher attenuations are possible. Two-section filters with a minimum attenuation of 18 to 20 db for all frequencies above cutoff have been designed and tested for large aircraft engines.[6] The passbands at higher frequencies can be dampened by filling the filter chambers with damping material, such as quartz wool. Dynamometer stand tests on actual engines with resonant chamber mufflers have been reported.[48,50] The mufflers designed to give maximum attenuation for the band between 70 and 350 cps were found to be in general agreement with the prediction from theory, although somewhat less attenuation was obtained. This fact is probably attributive to the finite amplitudes of sound waves. In practice, attenuations up to about 10 db have been achieved at some frequencies and a reduction of about 8 db for the over-all sound level has been obtained for the engine tested, where theory and cold tests predicted attenuation of 20 db and more.

The effect of the tail-pipe impedance which loads the filter output must be taken into account, so that its influence can be satisfactorily included.[45] All calculations for muffler and tail pipes must consider the exhaust-gas temperature, which results in sound velocities between 500 and 700 mps.[45,47]

Mufflers should be designed individually for a particular type of engine, considering all variables, such as the required attenuation, allowable weight and volume, engine-firing frequency, volume of gas flow, etc. The use of one muffler per engine, or two at the most, is desirable. Common exhaust for as many cylinders as feasible increases the frequency of the most intense noise, resulting in muffling with smaller volume and weight. Considered from this point of view, the engine firing frequency should be as high as possible.

Unfortunately, most mufflers are designed for completed aircraft without taking full advantage of all design possibilities if the muffler were an integrated part of the wing or the fuselage. An integrated muffler should be possible, since filters require specific volumes which are largely independent of shape. Disadvantages to consider in the use of mufflers are weight, increased drag, increased back pressure, increased thermal stress on the exhaust tubing, and exposure of certain areas of the airplane to heat.

A comparison of the exhaust noise from small aircraft engines in flight and on the ground, with and without mufflers, is given in Refs. 25 and 51.

Design Curves for Propeller and Reciprocating-engine Noise. *Propeller-noise Reduction.* The possibilities of reducing propeller noise for a given input power are evident from propeller theory. For the conventional propeller, an increase in the number of blades or a decrease in the tip Mach number reduces the noise output most effectively. For a given tip Mach number and number of blades, some noise reduction can be achieved by increasing the diameter of the propeller; a doubling of the propeller diameter will reduce the sound power level approximately 5 to 6 db. Limits for the noise reduction which is theoretically possible are set at a low tip Mach number by the vortex noise levels, and limits for an increased blade number or diameter are set by the increase in weight associated with each of these measures. An example has been given to show that for a given input horsepower and propeller diameter, a change from 3 to 8 blades would reduce the noise by 50 db but would approximately triple the propeller weight![11] In addition, changes in the cruise efficiency of the propeller must be considered.[11] For the practical requirements of noise control, charts have been prepared to show the approximate noise levels to be expected around practical propeller configurations.

Calculated Propeller-noise Charts.   Propeller loudness charts have been prepared for light (privately owned) airplanes of input powers between 100 and 300 hp operating under conditions corresponding to flight speeds up to 200 miles per hour.[52]   The effect of motion is considered only for the propeller performance, not for the noise radiation, which is based on Eq. (33.5).   The loudness charts for distances of 300 and 1,000 ft

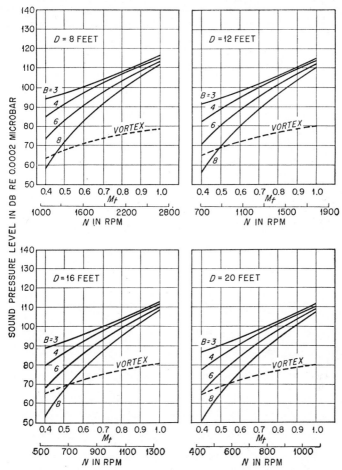

Fig. 33.16a. Sound pressure level of rotational propeller noise (sum of the first four harmonics) as a function of tip Mach number and number of blades for various propeller diameters.   The sound pressure levels are for a distance of 300 ft and for the angle of maximum radiation ($\theta = 105°$).   The curves are for an engine rating of 1,000 hp.   The broken-line curves are estimated levels for the vortex noise.   The approximate acoustic power level in dbp (re 10^{-12} watt) is obtained by adding 46 db to the sound pressure levels in the figure.   (*After Hubbard.*[53])

are given for propellers of 6- to 10-ft diameter and with the number of blades varied from 2 to 8.

For transport-type airplanes having engine ratings of 1,000 to 10,000 hp, propeller-noise charts and tables have been published for quick estimation of noise level and spectrum.[53]   For calculations, Eq. (33.5) was used, which, when adapted to engineering units, results for the root-mean-square sound pressure of a given harmonic in

$$p_m = 169.3 \frac{mBDM_t}{2rA} \left| \left[\frac{550W_M}{c(0.8M_t)^2} - T \cos \theta \right] I_{mB}(0.8mBM_t \sin \theta) \right| \text{ microbar} \qquad (33.11)$$

where r is the distance from propeller hub to observer in feet; D, the propeller diameter in feet; A, the propeller-disk area in square feet; W_M, the input horsepower; T, the thrust in pounds; c, the sound velocity in feet per second; m, the harmonic number; B, the number of blades; M_t, the tip Mach number; and θ, the angle between forward propeller axis and line to observer. The effective radius was taken as 0.8 of the total.

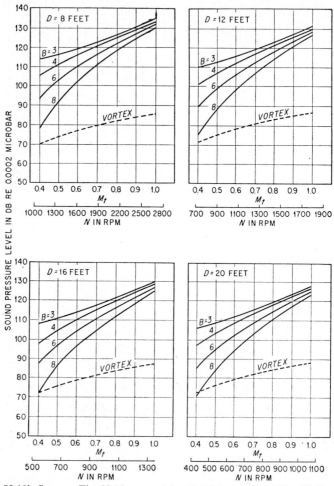

Fig. 33.16b. Same as Fig. 33.16a, except for 10,000-hp input. (*After Hubbard.*[53])

The charts are given for a distance of $r = 300$ ft and for $\theta = 105°$, the angle assumed to be close to the angle of maximum radiation for the investigated propellers. The sound pressure levels, summed over the first four rotational harmonics, are given in the graphs for $B = 3$, 4, 6, and 8, and for values of M_t from 0.4 to 1. In Fig. 33.16a and b, the charts for 1,000-hp and 10,000-hp engines are shown as two examples from a wide horsepower range. The thrust for these charts was calculated by Eq. (33.6) with a corrected value for η resulting in a lower thrust value (0.78, the value of Ref. 20). The assumptions for the static thrust appear to be valid for propellers near the point of stall. These propeller-noise charts are supplementary to propeller-performance charts for the same range of parameters.[54,55]

Another practical presentation of tables for the evaluation of Eq. (33.5) is given in Ref. 56, where the results are used and adapted to predict the propeller rotation noise inside multi-engine aircraft.

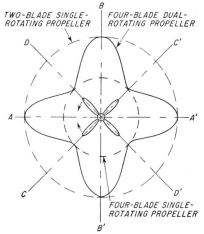

Dual-rotating Propeller. The sound field for a dual-rotating propeller can be obtained approximately from the set of charts for which examples were given in Fig. 33.16, if Fig. 33.17 is taken into consideration (from Ref. 53). The same principle applies to dual propellers with more blades.

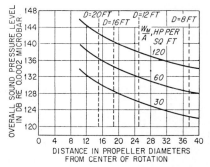

FIG. 33.17. Radiation pattern in the plane of rotation of a four-blade, dual-rotating propeller. The blades of the counter-rotating propeller overlap on axes AA' and BB' and are equally spaced along axes CC' and DD'. The dashed lines indicate how the radiation pattern can be composed from the noise fields of a two-blade, single-rotating propeller and a four-blade, single-rotating propeller. In addition, on axes AA' and BB' the spectrum has all the harmonics of a two-blade propeller, and on axes CC' and DD' only the harmonics of a four-blade propeller. (*After Hubbard.*[24])

FIG. 33.18. Over-all sound pressure level in the plane of rotation from a propeller with (low) supersonic tip speed as a function of the distance from the propeller center. Curves are given for various power loadings W_M/A of the propeller. (W_M = input horsepower; A = propeller-disk area in square feet.) The dashed lines indicate distances of 300 ft from the propeller center for different propeller diameters D. (*After Hubbard.*[53])

Vortex Noise. Equation (33.8) has been used to estimate the vortex noise level.[52] The following approximate formula was obtained for the over-all sound pressure level at 300 ft distance for the directions of maximum radiation ($\theta = 0°$ and $180°$):

$$L_p = 10 \log_{10} \frac{k A_B V_{0.7}{}^6}{10^{-16}} \quad \text{db} \tag{33.12}$$

where A_B is the total propeller blade area in square feet; $V_{0.7}$ the velocity at 0.7 of full propeller radius in ft per sec. The constant k was evaluated as $3.8 \cdot 10^{-27}$. For conditions below stall, this vortex noise level is estimated to be correct within ± 10 db. The levels obtained by Eq. (33.12) are plotted as dotted lines in the propeller-noise charts as shown in Fig. 33.16.

Supersonic Propeller. The theory of Ref. 20 does not give a good approximation for the supersonic propeller. At, or near tip Mach number one, the noise power output becomes nearly independent of tip speed and only a small reduction can be expected from an increased number of blades. For the low supersonic range, Fig. 33.18 has been published for estimating the noise output for a given power loading.[53] (The curves are extrapolated from a two-blade propeller at $M_t = 1.2$.) The noise maximum for the supersonic propeller is in the plane of rotation.*

* The noise spectra of supersonic propellers show an increase of the content of higher harmonics, a fact important for acoustical engineering purposes (see Fig. 33.23).

Pressures near the Propeller in the Region of the Wing and Fuselage. The pressures near the propeller are sometimes capable of exciting distinctive vibrations in nearby parts of aircraft structures. The fundamental blade-passage frequency and the lowest harmonics are structurally of primary importance. But the peak-to-peak pressure amplitudes, which exceed by far the values for the root-mean-square pressures of the single harmonics, are also of interest. Since calculations of the pressure in the near-field of propellers are very cumbersome, charts based on experimental results have been prepared to give the pressure in the region of the fuselage (Fig. 33.19) and wing (Fig. 33.20)—for M_t from 0.5 to 1.2.[30] The pressure per unit power is plotted as a function of M_t for different values of the parameter mB. The data, obtained from measurements on two-blade propellers, may also be applied to propellers with different numbers of blades. Figure 33.20 applies directly to pusher-type propellers, and it was also found to be approximately correct for tractor propellers. With a wing in place, the differential pressures across the wing and the pressures on the wing surface which the blade approaches, in general, will exceed the corresponding free-field pressures.[30]

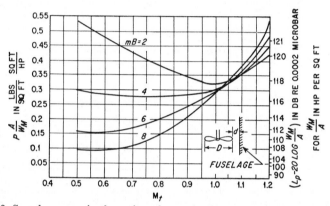

FIG. 33.19. Sound pressure in the region where a fuselage might be located: effect of tip Mach number at constant power loading on the maximum free-space sound pressure for a given value of $d/D = 0.10$ (m = number of harmonic, B = number of blades, p = root-mean-square sound pressure in pounds per square foot, W_M = input horsepower, A = propeller-disk area in square feet). (*After Hubbard and Lassiter.*[30])

Empirical Propeller Noise Power Chart. An empirical chart has been prepared for estimating the over-all power of propellers for the total tip Mach number range used in modern propellers.[4] This chart, Fig. 33.21, gives power level as a function of tip speed with input horsepower as the parameter. The supersonic portion of the curve, based on Ref. 29 and unpublished data from commercial firms, should be considered as tentative. The subsonic portion is based on the general dependence of propeller noise on input horsepower and tip speed as reported in Ref. 37. The curves show less dependence on tip speed than is expected from both the propeller theory and the measurements on static propellers. The chart is most nearly correct for 12-ft-diameter propellers, where it agrees within 3 db with the charts for the three-blade propeller, mentioned under *Propeller-noise Charts* (Fig. 33.16). A detailed study of the propeller as outlined there or the empirical charts given here should give the over-all noise of a static propeller within ±5 db.

Directivity of Propeller Noise. An average directivity pattern for the over-all sound pressure level (lower harmonics) of static propellers is given in Fig. 33.22.[29,4] The sound pressure level under the angle of maximum radiation is roughly 4 db above the space average; therefore, distribution in space of the total power obtained by Fig. 33.21 can be estimated from Fig. 33.22. For supersonic propellers, the maximum of the curve in Fig. 33.22 shifts to 90° (dashed line).

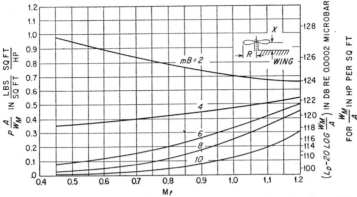

Fig. 33.20. Sound pressure in the region where a wing might be located: effect of tip Mach number at constant power loading on the maximum free-field sound pressure for a constant value $x/R = 0.25$. The maximum pressure values given in the graph occur inboard of the propeller tip for the fundamental frequency; for the higher harmonics they occur near the propeller tip and in some cases outboard of the tip. For the lower-order harmonics, the maximum sound pressure level will be about 5 db lower for $x/R = 0.5$, 14 db lower for $x/R = 1$, and 26 db lower for $x/R = 2$ (m = number of harmonic, B = number of blades, p = root-mean-square sound pressure in pounds per square foot, W_M = input horsepower A = propeller-disk area in square feet). (*After Hubbard and Lassiter.*[30])

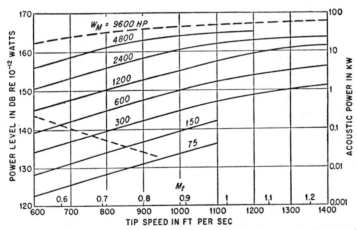

Fig. 33.21. Empirical power-level chart for estimating the noise from static propellers as a function of tip speed and input horsepower W_M. The chart applies directly to three-blade propellers approximately 12 ft in diameter. Use the following corrections for other numbers of blades: two blades + 2 db, four blades − 2 db. For operating conditions below the broken line at the lower left, reciprocating-engine exhaust noise may predominate over propeller noise. (*After Bolt, Beranek, and Newman, Inc.*[4])

Spectrum of Propeller Noise. The spectral distribution of the propeller-noise energy cannot be predicted accurately from theory. Good agreement between the measurements and the theories exists only for the lower harmonics which, due to their strength, are most decisive for calculating the over-all power. But for engineering purposes. the levels in the higher frequency bands are also very important. They increase in their relative strength for both the rotational noise and for the vortex noise as a function of the tip Mach number. Estimates for the relative sound-power levels of the different octave bands can be made from Fig. 33.23. The curve for the total propeller noise (i.e., rotational and vortex noise) is based on octave-band spectra measured beneath transport airplanes at full power shortly after take-off,[4,57] and is in general agreement with power-level measurements in propeller test cells. The propeller

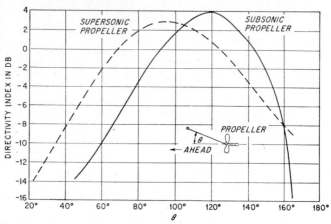

Fig. 33.22. Generalized directivity index of the noise field of a static propeller. (*From: Bolt, Beranek, and Newman, Inc.,*[4] *Ernsthausen,*[16] *and Hubbard and Lassiter.*[29])

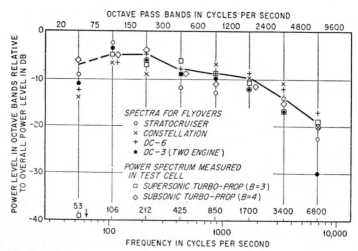

Fig. 33.23. Propeller-noise spectrum: power spectrum in octave bands relative to over-all power level. The curve, proposed as design curve in Ref. 4, is based on spectra beneath airplanes immediately after take-off measured by *Parkins and Purkis.*[57] Actual power-level measurements (unpublished) on a subsonic and a supersonic turbo-propeller in a test cell are also marked in the graph. Since the fundamental frequency of the noise from the supersonic turbo-propeller was 105 cps, practically no power was found in the 20- to 75-cps band.

engines with lower horsepower and tip speed have relatively less power in the higher frequency bands, but no precise data are available. The level in the first two bands depends very much on the exact frequency value for the fundamental frequency, i.e., where the fundamental and lower harmonics are located with respect to the octave bands. Therefore, it is more accurate to check the lower harmonics in the first two bands according to the method used in the section entitled *Propeller-noise Charts.* Figure 33.23 can also be used to give a rough estimate of the sound-pressure spectrum in the plane of rotation and under the angle of maximum radiation.

Sound-power Level of Exhaust Noise. An engineering formula for the prediction of exhaust noise, which is in general agreement with the theory resulting in Eq. (33.9), gives for the sound-power level (in decibels re 10^{-12} watt) of the lowest frequency component without exhaust muffler not less than[4]

$$L_w = 10 \log_{10} W_M + 112 \quad \text{dbp} \qquad (33.13)$$

In this equation, W_M is the total engine power in horsepower, which should include the mechanical losses of the engine. For the engine's total over-all exhaust sound-power level (in decibels re 10^{-12} watt), the following relations are given:[4]

$$L_w = 10 \log_{10} W_M + 115 \quad \text{dbp} \qquad \text{for engine power} < 150 \text{ hp or engines under}$$
$$\text{cruising conditions} \quad (33.14a)$$
$$L_w = 10 \log_{10} W_M + 120 \quad \text{dbp} \qquad \text{for engines} > 150 \text{ hp at full load} \qquad (33.14b)$$

The acoustical-mechanical efficiencies of the engines in Eqs. (33.13) and (33.14) vary from $\eta = 0.4$ per cent for the small engines to $\eta = 1.36$ per cent for large engines at full power in general agreement with the theoretical findings of Ref. 44.

Since the propeller noise increases faster with engine power than does the reciprocating engine noise output, the reciprocating engine noise predominates only at low engine power and low tip speed. The dotted line in Fig. 33.21 gives the approximate limit, where the sound-power level of the engine noise equals the propeller noise, indicating that in the area below this line the engine noise might predominate over the propeller noise. Naturally this line can be only an indication of the general trend, since the number of blades used and the engine characteristics and the exhaust system can influence the individual case considerably. In addition, for the sound pressure level at a given point, the different directivity patterns of the propeller and engine-noise source must be considered.

Spectrum of Exhaust Noise. For the engine under cruising condition and engines with less than 150 hp, Eq. (33.14a), the sound-power level in the octave band of the fundamental exhaust frequency is about 3 db below the over-all power level. The level of each consecutive band decreases at a rate of about 3 db per octave. For large engines under full load, nearly uniform power levels were observed in all octave bands at a level of approximately 8 db below the over-all.[4]

The Propeller-driven Aircraft in Flight. Design curves do not exist for the propeller-driven aircraft in flight. For ground operation, take-off and the following low-level flight, the static conditions discussed earlier can be assumed to be representative when changes in power setting (for example, from take-off to cruise condition) are taken into account. With increasing forward speed, the noise output from most airplanes becomes smaller. An increase in noise output above the static condition must be expected only for forward speed Mach numbers above 0.6.[34] For multi-engine aircraft, the noise powers of the single engines are assumed to be additive. This usually gives an upper limit for the sound levels at a given point calculated from the total sound-power level. The evaluation of a large number of take-off noise levels (engines ranging from 65 to 5,800 hp) has given good agreement with Fig. 33.21 for airplanes having more than 200 hp. For aircraft having less power, the noise from some airplanes agreed with Eq. (33.14a), and from others it agreed with Fig. 33.21. It seems that for take-off conditions, the over-all sound-power level L_w (in decibels re 10^{-12} watt) of an aircraft can be roughly approximated by[4]

$$L_w = 12 \log_{10} W_M + 111 \quad \text{dbp} \qquad (33.15)$$

where W_M is the total take-off horsepower of the aircraft.

The spectra of several commercial transport airplanes have been measured shortly after take-off at close distance,[57] and are plotted in Fig. 33.23 for the take-off condition. The over-all sound-power level estimated from these data appears to be 8 db below the prediction of Fig. 33.21.

For additional empirical data on noise from different types of propeller-driven aircraft in flight, see Chap. 34, under *Noise around Airports and Its Reduction.*

It must be emphasized that atmospheric attenuation and ground influence can result in a wider spread of the actual noise levels compared to the predicted ones than might be expected from the inaccuracy in the definition of the source.

Turboprop Noise. All noise measurements on propellers driven by gas turbines (turboprop) indicate that the propeller noise by far exceeds the exhaust noise of the jet, which contributes only in the order of 10 per cent of the total thrust of the combination. Sound-power levels of turboprop engines can be estimated or extrapolated, therefore, from Fig. 33.21. The noise from the jet exhaust, depending on the particular engine, might raise the noise level between the discrete frequencies of the propeller spectrum and the level in the highest bands for positions downstream from the exhaust. The level of this noise can be predicted from the design curves for turbojet-engine noise.

AIRCRAFT JET-ENGINE NOISE

Theories and Experimental Data on Jet-engine Noise. *Noise Sources of an Aircraft Jet Engine.* Jet engines effect propulsion through the acceleration of air masses. In the turbojet engine, air is compressed in an axial or centrifugal mechanical compressor, heated in a combustion chamber and then accelerated by expansion through a

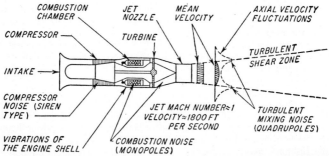

Fig. 33.24. Noise sources of a turbojet engine. The mean velocity of the gas jet and the distribution of the axial velocity fluctuations across the jet are shown schematically.

jet nozzle. A gas turbine in the path of the expanding gas serves solely to drive the compressor (Fig. 33.24). These processes, all connected with noise generation, produce three types of noise: (1) inlet noise radiated from the air intake, primarily as a result of compressor noise plus aerodynamic noise, (2) noise radiated from vibrations of the shell of the engine, and (3) exhaust noise leaving the engine through the tail-pipe opening. The exhaust noise includes contributions from noise sources inside the engine, such as combustion and turbine noise, but the principal exhaust noise is generated outside of the jet nozzle in the mixing region of the high-velocity jet and the surrounding air. This latter, so-called "aerodynamic jet noise," is the turbojet's principal noise source under normal, full-power operation, outweighing by far all the other noises on the basis of sound power and is completely responsible for the critical present-day jet-noise problem. Only at the engine's low-power setting does the compressor whine usually become the predominant noise. Under certain conditions at high-power setting or when engines are operated with afterburner, resonance phenomena can be observed, and can add appreciable power at discrete low frequencies to the wide-band aerodynamic noise. This low-frequency noise can usually be associated with resonances of the combustion chamber or tail pipe and is closely coupled with the combustion process itself with which it can interact. This operating condition is usually referred to as "rough burning" and, if it occurs at all, is observed in a given engine only for a certain fuel-air ratio. However, for engines used operationally in aircraft, smooth operation can generally be assumed.

Another mechanism for exhaust-noise generation can become effective when the Mach number in the jet increases above unity (choked jet), i.e., when the pressure ratio across the nozzle is raised above the critical pressure ratio resulting in sonic flow in the nozzle. Then the emerging gas expands and contracts periodically outside the nozzle and a periodic shock-wave pattern is set up along the jet. These shock waves can produce some additional noise when turbulent gas masses pass through the shock front. But more important is a high-frequency noise component of very high intensity overshadowing the other turbulence noise sources. It is produced when the total shock formation is set into oscillatory motion in the direction of the jet. This phenomenon is often referred to as the "screech" noise from supersonic jets. Jet engines are usually operated at low pressure ratios, at low altitude, and at low flight speeds. Hence, this shock noise has no great practical importance as yet for the more important noise problems. However, in cruising flight at high altitude, the engines are heavily overchoked and shock-wave noise will contribute to the noise in the aircraft and must be considered with respect to possible damage to the aircraft's structure.

Thus, the principal noise problem of a jet aircraft is the turbulent mixing-noise generated outside the nozzle by the high-velocity jet mixing with the surrounding air. But, under certain circumstances and operating conditions, internal noises such as compressor noise and combustion noise must be considered, and shock-noise generation should be kept in mind for jets operating under choked conditions.

Aerodynamic Generation of Noise. The comparison of the noise field of a turbojet engine at full power with the noise emitted by an air jet of equal diameter issuing from an air supply through a nozzle into the free atmosphere has shown that the noise emitted by both has the same directivity pattern, the same spectral distribution, and approximately the same sound power. This supports the assumption that both noises are generated by the same type of mechanism, namely, the turbulence in the mixing-region downstream from the jet exit. It proves that the influences of turbine, compressor, and combustion are small or even negligible at high-power setting of the jet engine, and that for this condition the noise can be considered of purely aerodynamic origin. Fortunately, therefore, this most important part of jet-engine noise can be studied successfully on cold model jets without the complicated and expensive operation of a jet engine and, after scaling laws have been established, basic investigations can be performed on small model jets. This tool of the scale model nozzle has led to a considerably improved understanding of the basic laws governing this type of noise generation and has enabled the testing and further development of a general theory of jet-noise generation. Although complete quantitative analysis of jet noise is still not possible, theory has proved to be very helpful in explaining and correlating the characteristics of the noise field and in guiding further experiments. This theory of sound generation by fluctuating gas flows has been given for the general case,[9,58] and an equation was obtained for the conversion of the kinetic energy of fluctuating shearing motion into acoustic energy of fluctuating longitudinal motion. Here, aerodynamic noise is defined in a stricter sense only as that part of the noise, produced by an airflow, which is generated in the absence of fluctuating forces between the fluid and solid boundaries. Such forces can produce dipole sound fields as discussed for the vortex noise of propellers, but are not considered of importance for the jet-noise generation. The turbulent flow itself was found to radiate in the same manner, acoustically, as a distribution of quadrupoles. These quadrupoles were found to have at any instant the following strength per unit volume:

$$T_{ij} = \rho v_i v_j + (p_{ij} - c_0{}^2 \rho \delta_{ij}) \qquad i, j, = 1, 2, 3 \qquad (33.16a)$$

Here ρ is the density, c_0 the sound velocity in the uniform medium, v_i is the velocity component in the x_i direction, p_{ij} is the compressive stress tensor which is, in a Stokesian gas, related to the velocity field by

$$p_{ij} = -p \delta_{ij} + \mu \left(\frac{\partial v_j}{\partial x_i} + \frac{\partial v_i}{\partial x_j} - \frac{2}{3} \sum_{k=1}^{3} \frac{\partial v_k}{\partial x_k} \delta_{ij} \right)$$

where $p = \frac{1}{3}(p_{11} + p_{22} + p_{33})$

δ_{ij} = the unit diagonal tensor

μ = the coefficient of viscosity

It has been shown that, in Eq. (33.16a), the principal source of noise generation is given by the first term of the right side—the fluctuation of the momentum flux across fixed surfaces. The second term on the righthand side representing the pressure fluctuations of the turbulent flow is partly balanced by the third term given by $c_0{}^2$ times the density fluctuations. But it was shown that even in the case where the whole pressure fluctuations are unbalanced—which occurs when the mean temperature in the turbulence and, hence, its sound velocity is notably different from that in the atmosphere— the effect of the pressure fluctuations on the quadrupole strength is a small one. Therefore, it follows that

$$T_{ij} \cong \rho v_i v_j \tag{33.16b}$$

The turbulent jet field is now represented by a distribution of quadrupoles of the strength given by Eq. (33.16b). The sound radiation from this turbulent field into the surrounding atmosphere, in which the only motions assumed are due to the acoustic disturbance from the jet, is given by summation over the radiation from all turbulent volume elements. Here, the statistical character of turbulence must be taken into account; roughly speaking, the sound power from different quadrupoles only adds up to the total power when the quadrupoles are statistically uncorrelated. Points with no eddy in common have completely uncorrelated values of momentum flux; points with many eddies in common show a higher degree of correlation. Only completely separated "average eddy volumes" give their quadrupole radiation independently to the total sound field. When this turbulence is superimposed on a mean flow of not-negligible Mach number, the separate eddy volumes move with a certain "local eddy-convection velocity" which is in the order of half the Mach number as observed on low-velocity jets.[59,60] This motion of the independently radiating eddy volumes modifies their sound radiation as discussed under *Acoustic Sources in Motion*. The main result of this motion is that far more sound is radiated in the direction of motion than backward. But the superimposed mean flow has still another more important effect: a given turbulence generates far more sound in the presence of a large mean shear. Then, the fluctuations in momentum flux consist either of a large mean momentum to be shaken about by the turbulent velocity fluctuations or of a large mean velocity transporting momentum fluctuations of the turbulence across fixed boundaries. This mechanism is significant only when there is a large gradient in the mean velocity causing a considerable change in velocity across a single eddy. Then the maximum rate of change of momentum, i.e., sound radiation, is generated by lateral quadrupoles given by the product of the pressure at a point and the rate of strain. In a flow of large mean shear, the maximum rate of change of momentum flux tends to occur at 45° to the direction of motion. In other words, the radiation of turbulent motion superimposed on a mean velocity gradient tends to be given by lateral quadrupoles orientated along the principal axes of rate of strain, which for a shearing motion are at 45° to the direction of motion. The mean velocity gradient amplifies the sound radiated from the turbulent flow and orients the quadrupoles so that their radiation maxima are at 45° to the direction of motion. In addition, the eddy convection effect increases these maxima toward the direction of eddy motion.

Quantitative estimates of the acoustic energy emitted from a turbulent jet can be made only when $\partial^2 T_{ij}/\partial t^2$ for the whole turbulent areas are known. This has been done for the case of isotropic turbulence,[61] where the noise field is omnidirectional. For the turbulent jet with a turbulent shear layer, no quantitative solution is yet given, although it should be possible to calculate the sound-power output once the average eddy volume, the pressure fluctuations in the shear layer, and the velocity gradient are measured.

Experimental research, together with additional support from dimensional analysis, suggests that the sound power radiated from a jet is given by

$$W_A = K \frac{\rho_1{}^2}{\rho_0} \frac{V^8}{c_0{}^5} d^2 = \eta W_M \quad \text{watts} \tag{33.17}$$

where ρ_1 = density in the flow
ρ_0 = density of the atmosphere
V = jet velocity
d = jet nozzle diameter
η = acoustic efficiency
W_M = mechanical power in jet

K is the "acoustical power coefficient" estimated to be approximately constant for different conditions of the jet.[9] Since $W_M = \frac{1}{2}\,\rho_1 V^3 \pi d^2/4$,

$$\eta = \frac{8}{\pi}\frac{\rho_1}{\rho_0}\,K\,\frac{V^5}{c_0^5} = \frac{8}{\pi}\frac{\rho_1}{\rho_0}\,KM^5 \tag{33.18}$$

where M is the mean Mach number at the jet orifice. Since quadrupoles are very inefficient sound producers, η is in the order of $10^{-4}M^5$.

The theoretical approach outlined is very valuable in explaining the aerodynamic noise from a subsonic jet, although it does not yet give quantitative data. Combined with the experimental data presented under *Experiments on Model Jets*, it suggests that the higher frequency sound in the broad noise spectrum is generated by the small-scale turbulence in the heavily sheared mixing region close to the orifice, whereas the low-frequency sound is emitted by the more nearly isotropic turbulence further downstream in the "core" of the jet. Several facts of the experimental data support these assumptions.[58,62]

At supersonic jet velocities the total sound power radiated by the jet can increase with a higher power of the jet velocity than at subsonic velocity and the directivity pattern changes slightly. Only qualitative explanations are given for the assumption of supersonic convection of quadrupoles.[58] Of greater importance seems to be the fact that turbulence energy, passing through the stationary shock-wave pattern in the jet, radiates part of its energy as sound, depending on the shock strength. A theory exists for the general case of this interaction of turbulence with a shock front.[63,64] But approximate calculations show that the efficiency of this radiation can easily exceed that of a jet without a shock pattern. The fact that this mechanism radiates noise upstream from the jet also can be explained qualitatively.[58] The discrete frequency sound radiation at supersonic velocities often referred to as "whistle" or "screech" has been explained successfully by a mechanism analogous to edge-tone production:[65,66] any especially strong eddy passing through a shock front in the jet radiates a sound wave which, in reaching the orifice of the jet, causes the formation of another strong eddy. This feedback mechanism results in a pure tone superimposed on the general turbulence, the frequency of which is given by the shock spacing and the eddy convection velocity. Conditions for the appearance of this whistle, its frequency and radiation pattern can be predicted by theoretical considerations. The whistle sound is a special case of the above-mentioned interaction of turbulence with a shock front, where, by a feedback mechanism, one frequency is selected and amplified.

Experiments on Model Jets. JET WITH SUBSONIC VELOCITY. Several studies on model air jets, reported in recent years, have contributed considerably to the understanding of jet noise. Most data are available on subsonic cold jets and were obtained by evacuating a reservoir of compressed air through a suitable nozzle.[67–73] The general findings of all observers agree fairly well within experimental limits. Insufficient data are available to allow a complete quantitative analysis with respect to sound power, power spectrum, and changes in directivity pattern. However, the following general conclusions can be drawn:

The sound power output of a jet varies as the sixth to eighth power of the exit velocity for $0.3 < M < 1$.[67,71,72] The value for the acoustic power coefficient K is between $0.3 \cdot 10^{-4}$ and $1.2 \cdot 10^{-4}$ with $0.6 \cdot 10^{-4}$ as a typical value. This results in acoustic efficiencies η of the order of magnitude of $10^{-4}M^5$. These findings have been substantiated on nozzle diameters from $\frac{1}{2}$ to 10 in. and are in agreement with the corresponding findings on turbojet engines at full power.[72,73] The increase of the sound power level of several jets as a function of velocity is shown in Fig. 33.25.

In other experiments the density of the jet was changed, both by heating the jet up to 1700°F,[72] and by using helium or SF_6 as gas for the jets.[69] Both experiments show a change in the power output roughly proportional to $(\rho_1/\rho_0)^2$ as would be expected from Eq. (33.17).

The geometry of the nozzle seems to have minor effect on the noise output since the nozzles tested had varying angles of divergence and also included straight pipes. Varying degrees of turbulence of the oncoming stream have some effect on the noise output. By changing the jet turbulence from a low value (axial-velocity fluctuations 1 per cent of the mean velocity) to a high one (velocity fluctuations 10 per cent) the acoustic efficiency increased up to 30 times.[68]

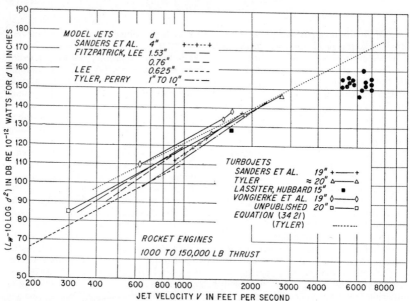

FIG. 33.25. Power levels of model jets, turbojet engines, and rocket engines as a function of the average jet velocity. The graph compares data measured by different investigators on an absolute scale. Curves averaging the results of the different investigators are shown. The graph includes data from model jets with between 0.625-in. and 10-in. diameter, and from turbojets with from 15-in. to more than 20-in. diameter. Nozzle shapes and techniques of measurements varied considerably for the different investigators. (*Data from Callaghan, North, and Sanders,*[73] *Fitzpatrick and Lee,*[67] *Lee,*[71] *Tyler and Perry,*[72] *Lassiter and Hubbard,*[69] *and von Gierke, Parrack, Gannon, and Hansen.*[76] *Rocket engine data from Lassiter and Heitkotter,*[99] *Cole et al.,*[116] *and Kyrazis et al.*[117])

The power spectrum of the noise from model jets is very flat. It has a peak in the neighborhood of $f_0 = 0.13\ V/d$ as shown by the generalized spectrum in Fig. 33.26. This agrees with the spectrum of turbojet engines at full power when plotted over the Strouhal number fd/V. It was measured by Refs. 71 and 72. In all measurements, the sound power level in the three octaves around the peak frequency is within 2 db.

The directional distribution of the acoustic power has maxima for all frequencies under an acute angle with the jet ($\theta > 90°$). The sound upstream from the jet is 15 to 20 db lower than the level at the maximum. The angle of maximum radiation θ_0 is probably a function of the Strouhal number: with increasing velocity the maximum shifts closer to the jet boundary, with increasing frequency it shifts away from the jet. With increasing jet diameter at constant velocity and frequency, the pattern also seems to broaden and the maximum shifts away from the jet. The general dependence is the same as for turbojet engines, for which directivity indices for different frequency bands are given in Fig. 33.28. On model air jets of Mach number close to unity, the following values were found (0° upstream of the jet, center at the nozzle):

$$\theta_0 \simeq 140° \qquad \text{for } \frac{df}{V} > 0.7$$

$$\theta_0 \simeq 150° \qquad \text{for } 0.8 > \frac{df}{V} > 0.3$$

$$\theta_0 \simeq 160° \qquad \text{for } \frac{df}{V} < 0.3$$

For the latter case the directivity increased monotonically with increasing θ at least until $\theta = 165°$, where the jet boundary was reached. The maximum of the over-all

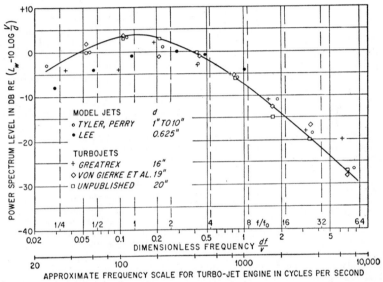

FIG. 33.26. Generalized power spectrum of model jets and turbojet engines: the spectrum level per cycle reference $[L_w - 10 \log (V/d)]$ is plotted as a function of the dimensionless frequency parameter df/V. The power spectra with reference to the total power are compared on an absolute scale for jets with from 0.625-in. to 20-in. diameter. (Same quantities for plotting the model jet data had to be estimated.) The full line is the proposed design curve for estimating the power spectrum of jet-engine noise. The approximate frequency scale for the jet-engine spectrum is correct for a nozzle diameter of 20 in. and an exit velocity of 1,665 ft per sec. (*Data from Tyler and Perry,[72] Lee,[71] Greatrex,[81] Mercer,[89] and von Gierke, Parrack, Gannon, and Hansen.[76]*)

sound level shifted for one nozzle from $\theta_0 = 135°$ at $M = 0.3$ to $\theta_0 = 165°$ at $M = 0.9$. Jets of equal exit Mach number but different sound velocity (cold jet, heated jet, helium) showed a decrease in θ_0 with an increase in sound velocity ($\theta_0 = 165°$, $\theta_0 = 150°$, $\theta_0 = 135°$, respectively).

Measurements in the near-field of the jet indicated that the low-frequency sound is radiated from a region 5 to 20 diameters downstream from the nozzle, whereas the high-frequency sound is radiated from regions closer to the orifice, roughly 1 to 9 diameters downstream. These determinations are very approximate, but far- and especially near-field studies point to such extensions of the noise sources. One consequence of this is that the directivity of jets (with the nozzle as origin of the coordinate system) changes considerably, when the radius around the nozzle, on which the measurements are made, is not large compared to the extensions of the noise source.

In the near field, the apparent θ_0 becomes smaller with increasing distance from the source; this can result in a comparatively smaller θ_0 for the higher frequencies, since, for them, far-field conditions are reached at smaller distances. For the low frequencies, far-field conditions are reached only at distances from the nozzle of several hundred jet diameters. The extension of the noise source is shown in Fig. 33.27, in which the pressure spectrum at several points close to the jet is given.[68] Turbulence measurements in the jet stream (axial-velocity fluctuations) were made and correlated with the pressure measurements just outside of the jet boundary at positions indicated in Fig. 33.27. The turbulence spectrum peaks in the same frequency range as a function of the position, where the pressure spectrum has its maximum. For the same location, the peak frequency in the turbulence increased in a similar manner with increased jet velocity, as was observed for the peak frequency of the pressure just outside the jet boundary. Other near-field studies give detailed constant sound pressure level contours for different noise bands for a wide variation of parameters.[70]

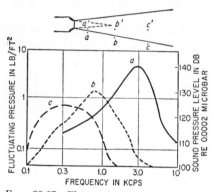

FIG. 33.27. Fluctuating pressure spectra near the boundary of a model jet. Frequency spectra outside the jet boundary (points a, b, c) correlate closely with turbulence spectra measured in the jet stream at corresponding positions (a', b', c'). The graph demonstrates that the high-frequency sources of jet noise are located close to the nozzle, whereas the low frequencies are radiated from sources farther downstream. (*From Hubbard and Lassiter.*[68])

Scaling laws have been established between model jets and full-scale turbojet engines which allow the use of model jets for basic investigations on jet noise. On the basis of the evidence summarized, it has been concluded that a division exists between high-frequency ($f > 0.7\ V/d$) and low-frequency ($f < 0.3\ V/d$) noise.[58] The high-frequency noise emanates from the heavily sheared mixing region near the nozzle, whereas the low-frequency sound is radiated by the region of more nearly isotropic turbulence farther downstream in the core of the jet. The effect of the eddy convection velocity modifies the directivity patterns and explains the shift of the maxima toward the direction of jet flow. The increase of sound power with a lower power of the jet velocity than the eighth can be explained on the basis of the theory of Ref. 58 only by assuming a decrease of turbulence with increasing jet Mach number. It is possible that when the velocity increases, the acoustic efficiency becomes so considerable that the turbulence loses appreciable energy by sound radiation.

The near-field noise studies on model jets can be used to predict the pressure distributions near fuselage and wing of jet-propelled aircraft. Measurements on aircraft models with model jets may become a valuable tool for such investigations. The effect of a panel placed in the pressure field 1.5 jet diameters from the jet boundary and parallel to it (the pressure on the panel was increased 3.5 to 5 db above the free-field pressure) and the effect of a simulated ground (3 diameters below jet axis) have been investigated by such model studies.[74] In the latter case the pressure on the ground was increased considerably only for distances of more than 12 nozzle diameters downstream. (At 20 nozzle diameters, the increase reached approximately 4 db.)

JET WITH SUPERSONIC VELOCITY. Some model tests on choked jets show that the noise energy emitted by the jet increases at a much greater rate once the jet Mach number is above unity. The intensity of the noise emitted at a certain angle was shown to increase with a power of the velocity as high as 17.[70] But in the only study where the total sound-power output of supersonic model jets was measured up to nozzle-pressure ratios of 2.75, the increase in sound power did not deviate significantly from a sixth- to an eighth-power law.[72] A large increase in sound output of a choked jet occurs only with the presence of screech noise, a discrete-frequency component. Such screech noise has not been observed in all test configurations or at all super-critical pressure ratios. The frequency of the screech noise is related to the shock spacing in the supersonic jet as shown by shadow-graphs[74] and Schlieren photo-graphs[75,65] and is roughly proportional to the inverse of the nozzle diameter and the inverse of the square root of the pressure ratio when it exceeds the critical pressure ratio. Oscillatory motion of the whole shock formation with the frequency of the screech also has been observed. The screech noise radiates sound upstream from the jet with a maximum at $\theta \simeq 60°$: this maximum can exceed by far the turbulence noise radiated downstream. (For the latter, the maximum is at 165° or more.) Another intense radiation of exactly twice the screech frequency was found within a narrow beam at about $\theta = 90°$. The experimental findings on screech noise support the theory of Ref. 66. Additional noise from shock waves generated by turbulence or eddies traveling supersonically, and from interaction of turbulence with the stationary shock pattern, was observed in several studies.

Turbine and Compressor Noise. The noise emanating from the engine air inlet has its main acoustic power concentrated at certain discrete frequencies, which are given by the rotational speed of the compressor, the number of compressor blades, and the stationary blades in the compressor inlet. These noises from turbojet engines are noticeable mainly at low engine speed when the exhaust noise is low. Although at higher power settings the acoustic power of the exhaust noise may exceed the power of the compressor by as much as 20 to 35 db, an observer in front of the engine at any power setting might notice the discrete air inlet frequencies above the exhaust-noise level. The absolute level of the compressor noise in front of the aircraft is high enough to endanger and annoy personnel working in this area. For their benefit, it is imperative to control the intake noise in addition to the exhaust-noise muffling. For aircraft in flight at low altitude, the compressor whine might have a more annoying effect on the ground observer than has been generally assumed on the basis of its relatively low power output, since the Doppler shift makes these discrete frequencies still more unpleasant.

The compressor noise of turbojet engines has never been studied in great detail. All studies on jet engines note it as the main noise source at idling speed,[76] and give its sound power and directivity, but no attempt has been made to compare the results on a quantitative basis for different engine designs and operating conditions.

The compressor noise is concentrated principally in a band smaller than one octave; on some jet engines it was found confined to a band less than 50 cps in width. Its main peak can be correlated with the siren-type noise (equivalent to the rotational noise of propellers) generated by the first compressor stage, although the noise from the following stages, having different numbers of blades and, therefore, different fundamental frequencies, still might be noticeable. Nonlinearities connected with the very high flow conditions in the compressor give rise to a rich harmonic content and to the generation of subharmonics, which may broaden the spectrum somewhat and shift its peak from the calculated fundamental. The noise output of the inlet opening might be considerably affected by the high mean intake velocity, which, when approaching sound velocity, should reduce the sound radiation from the inlet. Some measurements seem to support this assumption since a reduction in turbine noise was observed as the rpm increased.

Structure-borne sound, radiated from the compressor case in the immediate vicinity of the rotors, may also be important. The rotor blade tips apply oscillating forces to the compressor case similar to the vibrational forces applied to an airplane fuselage in the vicinity of a propeller.

Empirically, it has been found that often the second harmonic is the frequency of maximum sound output of a compressor:[4]

$$f_{max} = \tfrac{1}{30} \text{ (compressor rpm} \times \text{average number of rotor blades) cps}$$

The sound power output of centrifugal and axial-flow compressors seems to increase roughly 6 db for each doubling of horsepower, so that the acoustic efficiency increases. The validity of this finding at mean intake velocities close to Mach number 1 is doubt-

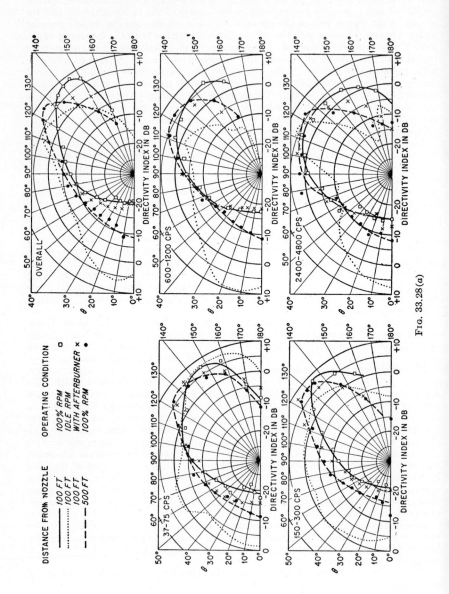

Fɪɢ. 33.28(a)

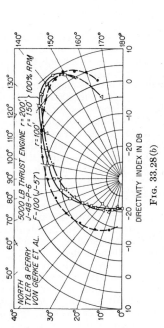

Fig. 33.28 (b)

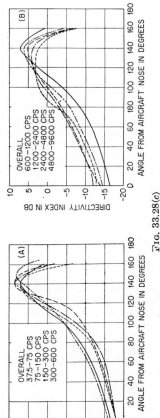

Fig. 33.28(c)

Fig. 33.28. (a) Directivity index of jet noise for the over-all sound pressure level and the levels in alternate octave bands. The directivity index is plotted for a jet engine at full power as measured at a radial distance of 100 ft. Data for afterburner operation of the same engine (increase in power level of 8 db) are also indicated. Measured at 500 ft radial distance, the directivity index at full power is changed as shown by the dashed curve. Although the data given were measured for one particular engine (J-57 in an F-100 fighter aircraft), they are representative for jet noise in general and are proposed as design curves for the directivity index. Fig. 33.28(b) For comparison, the directivity index for the over-all sound pressure level, as calculated from Refs. 72 (J-48 engine) and 83, is shown. The directivity of model air jets is roughly the same. Fig. 33.28 (c) Average directivity index of turbojet engines at full power. (A) — overall, --- 375–75 cps, ---- 75–150 cps, (--- 150–300 cps, ---- 300–600 cps. (B) —overall, ---- 600–1,200 cps, ----- 1,200–2,400 cps, --- 2,400–4,800 cps, ---- 4,800–9,600 cps. (After Cole et al.[116])

ful, and it may hold only for a comparison of compressors having the same intake velocities. In general, compressor noise will depend very much on the individual design.

Occasionally discrete frequencies, probably connected with compressor or turbine whine, have been noticed in the exhaust noise,[74] but their levels are not of practical significance.

The directivity pattern of the compressor noise has a sharp principal maximum toward the front of the engine ($\theta_0 = 0°$). The directivity index for the octave band 2,400 to 4,800 cps, the band in which the compressor noise is usually found, is approximately 7 to 8 db for θ_0. The directivity indices for idling speed, at which operating-condition compressor noise usually predominates in front of the engine, are plotted for one particular engine (J-57) in Fig. 33.28. The idling speed of this engine is relatively high so that the jet noise (maxima for $\theta > 90°$) is still very pronounced compared to other engines where it more nearly disappears (for example, J-47 engine[76]). The directivity indices for full power are given in Fig. 33.28c.

Combustion Noise. At normal operating speeds, the predominant noise from turbojet engines is that of the turbulent-mixing type, as shown by the fact that cold jets and jet engines radiate the same type of noise. But evidence of some influence of combustion irregularities and non-uniform fuel-burning rates can be found in most types of engines at certain operating conditions, although they are negligible for most jet aircraft used operationally. Only when the afterburner method for thrust augmentation of turbojet engines is used does combustion noise become more important. It consists of relatively random bursts in the frequency range up to 300 cps. Occasionally the irregular combustion, coupled to the resonance properties of the combustion chamber or the tail pipe, may be synchronized with, and may pulsate at, one of their resonance frequencies. In this case these discrete frequencies can have pressure levels exceeding the rest of the spectrum by 10 to 20 db; up to 50 per cent of the total acoustic energy may be at these frequencies.[73,77,78] Usually structural stability demands avoidance of such operating conditions. The primary combustion noise should be that of the exhaust noise type as discussed for reciprocating engine exhausts or pulse jets. But a secondary influence of the unsteady exhaust velocity associated with combustion irregularities may be found in a modulation of the aerodynamic noise and in changes in the shock-wave pattern at the nozzle exit. Both effects may be hard to detect and, so far, combustion noise has been separated from aerodynamic noise only when discrete frequencies appeared. But for basic studies, the coupling between the different noise-generating mechanisms cannot be neglected.

Experimental Data on the Noise of Static Turbojet Engines. Data on turbojet engines as noise generators have been obtained by two methods: (1) measurements on the engine mounted in a test cell, where reverberant room conditions are encountered, and (2) measurements on engines on an outdoor thrust stand or in an aircraft under practically free-field conditions. Although data obtained on the same type of engine under the two conditions show approximately the same results, good agreement cannot be expected, since in the test cell mounting part of the extended jet-noise source must be assumed to be so far downstream in the eductor tube that it cannot add its full share to the reverberant test-cell noise level. On the other hand, outdoor measurements are more subject to the influence of atmospheric and ground absorption and result in an unavoidable spread in the data. The stability of the turbojet engine itself as a random-type noise generator is surprisingly high:[79] in a test-cell run, the sound pressure levels, which were averaged over 5-sec periods for the third-octave bands from 50 to 10,000 cps, were for 75 to 100 per cent of a 5-min test time, within ± 1 db of the mean value. The largest deviation, which was in the 50- to 100-cps band, was $+3$ and -1.5 db. The maximum instantaneous peak levels of the random-type noise generated by a jet engine are approximately 12 db above the rms average.

The complete noise field of specific turbojet engines under free-field conditions has been reported by several workers[72,76,80–83] for different operating conditions. All these data give the total power and the power spectrum or allow its calculation, but the engine data are not always published in enough detail to allow their full use in supporting theoretical considerations. The directivity patterns are given for the octave bands.[76,81,82]   Early measurements indicate that measurements at a radius of 50 ft are within the near field of the engine.   More recently measurements at radii up to 300 ft have been made.

The published data from different sources have been analyzed and correlated to give the parameters of the noise field in generalized forms,[7,72,82,84] which are supplemented and explained by reported model tests.

The total acoustic power output of turbojet engines is a function of velocity, diameter, and temperature.   It increases with a somewhat higher power than the sixth (probably closest to the eighth power) of the jet exit velocity and roughly proportional to the jet area.[7,72,73,82,85]   Some of the newer, free-field data are shown in Fig. 33.25. To obtain this relationship, which agrees very well on an absolute level with the model jet data, only the aerodynamic noise of the turbojet engine must be considered, i.e., at low-power settings of the engine, the turbine noise must be subtracted from the over-all sound power.[76]   This process is necessarily an approximation, but since the compressor noise is usually concentrated in one or two octave bands and has a different directivity pattern, it can often be done.   The effective jet-engine-exhaust velocity is found by dividing the thrust by the mass flow of the engine.   The best correlation of data is found if the sound power is plotted as a function of the mechanical power of the jet stream or if the acoustic efficiency η is plotted as a function of the jet stream power.   The acoustic efficiency increases, on the average, with or slightly above the power of the jet stream,[7,58] although some investigators found it constant up to Mach numbers close to unity and then increasing with the third power of the jet stream power.[84]   The acoustic efficiency is in the order of 10^{-4} to 10^{-3} increasing with V^3 to V^4 and sometimes was even found to increase up to the order of 1 per cent.

A generalized power-spectrum level for jet engines is shown in Fig. 33.26, where only some of the individual points used to make up the curve are plotted.   The power-spectrum level is plotted as a function of the parameter df/V and compared with a spectrum observed on a model jet.   The second scale on the abscissa in cps is the frequency scale approximately valid for jet engines at higher power settings having a tail pipe diameter of roughly 20 in.   A few recent measurements in the frequency range 1 to 20 cps, which is usually not included in acoustic measurements, indicate that, as would be expected from extrapolation of the spectrum curve, considerable pressures can be found in this low, subaudible frequency range.   These levels are by no means negligible, neither with respect to man nor to structures.

The directivity index for alternate octave bands is plotted in Fig. 33.28a as it was derived from free-field measurements on one representative jet engine (J-57).   No significant deviation of these functions can be found if they are compared to other published data, especially considering the unavoidable spread of the data due to the distance of 100 ft or 500 ft respectively.   A slight change of the pattern is noticeable in going from a 100-ft to 500-ft radius.   The directivity index at the angle of the maximum for the over-all sound level was generally observed to be 8 db (± 2 db).   The sound power level radiated in the half space 0° to 90°, i.e., in front of the engine, is 13 db (± 2 db) lower than the power radiated backward (90° to 180°).   Increasing the jet velocity generally results in similar directivity patterns except that for the same octave bands, the maximum noise radiation peaks occur at rather smaller angles to the jet axis.   Since at the higher velocity the maximum noise radiation is at a higher frequency, the maximum of the directivity pattern for the over-all sound pressure level occurs at a larger angle to the jet axis.

If reheat or afterburning is used in the jet tail pipe to increase momentarily the thrust of an engine, the noise changes in correspondence to the increase in jet velocity. In afterburning, the airflow of the engine is maintained constant and by burning additional amounts of fuel the temperature and, therefore, the jet velocity is increased, resulting in a thrust boost.   In general, for afterburner operation, the noise output increases as the sixth to eighth power of the velocity, or with the third to fourth power of the thrust boost (or the jet temperature).   In addition, the sound-power output is increased to a small extent by the increased jet area (fins or clamshell opened).   For present-day jet engines, afterburning increases the sound power level by 6 to 8 db or even 10 db above the noise output at 100 per cent engine power, depending on the model. Theoretical considerations on engine performance[81] result in a theoretical limit—somewhere in the order of 20 db—for the noise increase by afterburning. However, in practice, the theoretically possible temperature increase has not been achieved yet, and obstructions required in the tail pipe for smooth burning reduce the theoretical thrust.

The directivity index is slightly changed by afterburner operation as shown in Fig. 33.28a as a result of the change in velocity and in jet diameter and, consequently, in spectrum. This change in the directivity pattern can increase the sound pressure level at some field points slightly (2 to 4 db) above the value expected from the increase in total sound power, assuming unchanged directivity. The increased jet stream turbulence in afterburning seems to have no noticeable effect on its noise output. As discussed earlier, rough burning in afterburners may give rise to additional combustion

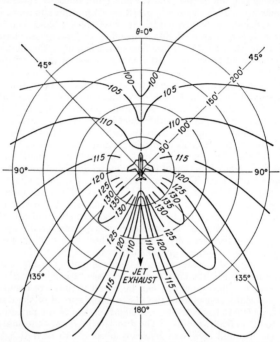

Fig. 33.29. Contours of constant, over-all sound pressure level around an F9F-6 jet aircraft operating at military power in a free field. (*From Pietrasanta.*[86])

noise in the low-frequency range. The total noise level may be modulated by rapid fluctuations within a range of 3 to 5 db. For some engines, the starting of the afterburner is followed by an initial afterburner blast exceeding the level for continuous afterburner operation by 1 to 3 db for a period up to 1 sec. Explosive-type afterburner starts may have initial peak levels up to 10 db above the steady value.

In several studies of jet noise, contours of constant sound pressure level were measured or constructed[80,81,82,86] as they are given in Fig. 33.29.

From theoretical considerations, it is clear that the sound pressure level at one of the so-called EN-1 positions—Fig. 33.4[10] (two jet diameters from the jet axis, two jet diameters downstream from the nozzle)—cannot be related accurately to the sound power radiated by the jet, and the pressure spectrum at this position is not representative of the power spectrum. As yet, the limits of accuracy have not been established within which the sound pressure level at this position can be related quantitatively to total sound power or power spectrum of the jet-noise source. Sound pressure levels at this EN-1 position of present-day high-thrust engines are in the range of 150 to 155 db.

The change of the sound pressure in the near-field of a full-scale turbojet engine (J-33) has been studied as a function of axial and radial distance from the nozzle.[74] In Fig. 33.30a, the pressure on a line parallel to the 15° jet boundary at two nozzle diameters distance from the boundary is given. In Fig. 33.30b the effect of radial distance on the pressure fluctuations in a plane normal to the jet axis and 15 diameters downstream is demonstrated.

For engine power settings lower than 100 per cent, the noise output, power spectrum, and directivity are changed mainly according to the decreased jet velocity and are only very slightly changed by the lowered jet temperature. The operating condition, where the turbine noise noticeably starts to influence the power level of the engine,

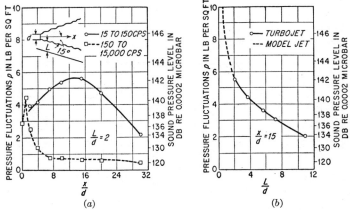

(a)   (b)

FIGS. 33.30. Pressure fluctuations in the near-field of a jet engine (J-33-A-17a, 3,825-lb thrust). d = tail-pipe diameter = $18\frac{3}{8}$ in., L = radial distance from 15° jet boundary. (a) Pressure fluctuations as a function of axial distance. The high frequencies have large random-pressure fluctuations close to the nozzle which decrease rapidly with distance downstream. (The maximum in the pressure distribution at one nozzle diameter downstream is largely due to compressor or turbine whine and not of basic significance for pressures near a gas jet.) The low frequencies have a maximum at 12 to 15 diameters downstream of the nozzle. (b) Pressure fluctuations as a function of the radial distance from the jet boundary in a plane normal to the jet 15 diameters downstream from the nozzle. At distances closer than two diameters the jet-engine data are supplemented by data from a 1-in. model jet. (*From Lassiter and Hubbard.*[74])

depends on the engine design and the operating characteristic. For the exhaust noise alone, no difference was observed between an axial or centrifugal engine when compared on the basis of equal velocity.[82]

For a large number of specific jet engines, useful aircraft noise characteristics have been compiled.[92,111]

Jet Aircraft in Flight. The sound pressure on the ground from jet aircraft in flight can be calculated from data taken under static conditions on the ground under the assumption that the forward speed does not affect the noise radiation. Whereas this assumption may be justified for take-off with relatively low speed, it becomes less valid for increasing flight speed. Theoretically, two effects may be expected: (1) the effect of motion on the sound source, which increases its power output and shifts its directivity pattern toward the direction of motion, and (2) a change in the output of the noise generator itself. Since the relative motion of the jet to the surrounding air decreases with increasing flight speed, the noise output of a jet should decrease. In practice, this second effect seems to prevail over the first one, so that the noise output of a jet aircraft decreases somewhat with flight speed.[112] In Fig. 33.31 the sound pressure level versus time curve recorded on the ground for a jet aircraft with six engines is shown for two different flight speeds and three altitudes.   The engines had the same power setting for both speeds.   The maximum sound pressure level decreased approximately 6 db due to the increase in flight speed from 185 to 490 miles per hour.   (It is interesting to note that because of the directivity pattern of the jet, an observer on the ground can be exposed to a noise above a specified level for a longer duration when he is at some distance from a passing airplane than when he is at a much closer range.) Each point on the curves of Fig. 33.31 is related to an angle under which it was emitted from the aircraft.   This is illustrated in Fig. 33.32 which shows that for the sound pressure level curve of a jet fly-over, the maximum over-all pressure level is not given by the radiation from the jet under 90° (i.e., by that noise radiated from the aircraft at the moment it has minimum distance from the observer).   From curves such as in Fig. 33.32, the directivity pattern in flight (reduced to constant distance from the source for sound emitted under all angles) can be constructed.[113]   Figure 33.33 shows how the over-all noise output of this particular aircraft decreased with increasing flight speed.

During a fly-over with pressure-time curves as in Fig. 33.31, the spectral composition of the noise changes continuously, as can be derived from Fig. 33.32.   This is to be

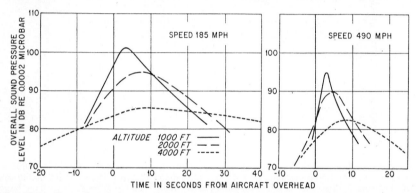

Fig. 33.31. Over-all sound pressure level as a function of time for a six-engine jet aircraft (B-47) passing overhead at different altitudes and flight speeds.   At zero time, the airplane is directly overhead.   The power setting of the engines was held constant for all fly-overs.

expected from the difference in the directivity patterns of the different octave bands: the low-frequency content increases as the aircraft passes overhead until the noise emitted from the receding aircraft under the angle of maximum radiation ($\theta \simeq 135°$) reaches the observation point.   Spectra, measured on a Comet aircraft with "Ghost" engines passing overhead at an altitude of 250 ft, are shown in Fig. 33.34.[46]   The data were taken one mile from the take-off and landing point, respectively.   During landing, at reduced engine-power setting, the compressor noise emitted forward is the predominant noise.   As a result, the frequency bands containing the compressor noise determine the over-all sound pressure level as the aircraft approaches and is just overhead.   The low-frequency noise reaches a maximum for the receding plane at a distance of about 500 ft beyond the overhead position.   To describe this type of passing plane accurately, the Doppler effect on the frequency spectrum must be considered, and it may play an important role in man's reaction to the noise.   In the example of Fig. 33.34, the received frequency of the impeller noise, at approximately 2,500 cps for the approaching plane at a great distance, shifted to 1,650 cps at the same distance for the receding plane.

For additional data on noise from jet aircraft in flight, see Chap. 34, under *Noise around Airports and Its Reduction.*

Possibilities for Jet-noise Reduction.   *Noise-suppression Devices and Configurations.* The first and most effective step in noise control is the attempt to prevent the generation of noise.   Theory and experiments point toward two basic possibilities in reducing aerodynamic noise from jets. The first is to reduce the jet's velocity prior to the radiation of sound, which should be very effective according to Eq. (33.18). The second is to reduce the turbulence of the jet, or to influence its frequency spectrum, or to change the rate of shear in the mixing region, which seems to act as an amplifier for the sound radiation from turbulence.[58] Based on these principles, different devices and methods have been tried with some success on model jets and full-scale engines. A reduction in total sound power level of 3 to 6 db is a major achievement when it is considered that such a decrease reduces the area exposed to a specified noise level by one-half to one-quarter.

One method of reducing the noise is by the conversion of the high-velocity, low-mass flow of a jet into low-velocity, high-mass flow. This can be achieved by converging-diverging aspirators and diffusers. At the same time, this arrangement should produce a less abrupt velocity gradient. No appreciable reduction has been obtained with such devices either on model jets[70,72] or on full scale engines.[73] Fan or bypass nozzles, where an annular low-velocity stream surrounds a high-velocity central jet, were also tested, but the results so far have been discouraging.[72] A detailed study was carried out on the influence of the exit-velocity profile on the noise of a subsonic jet,[87] which indicated that for jets of equal diameter and equal thrust any noise reduction obtained by a reduction of the velocity gradient near the boundary is more than offset by the increased velocities necessary near the center of the jet to obtain equal thrust. These experiments also lead to the conclusion that a thin sheet of slower-moving fluid around the high-velocity center jet cannot influence the subsonic noise levels noticeably. Various shapes of nozzles were tested: circular, square, rectangular, elliptical and truncated,[73,5] but none of these configurations brought about a definite change in noise power.

One possibility of reducing the intensity of shear already has been tried successfully in one of the earliest experiments on model jets.[70] "Tooth devices" around the lips of the nozzle increase the thickness of the mixing zone. Whether this is the mechanism which makes them effective or whether it makes them influence the scale of the

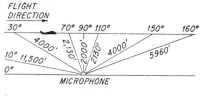

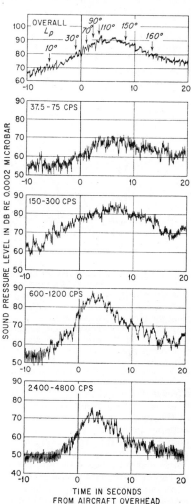

Fig. 33.32. Sound pressure levels in octave bands as a function of time for the six-engine jet aircraft of Fig. 33.31 passing at 2,000-ft altitude at a speed of 490 mph. The figure also illustrates under which angle the sound received on the ground was emitted from the aircraft.

noise-radiating turbulence, these tooth devices affect the sound power spectrum of the jet: the low-frequency noise intensity toward the rear of the jet is reduced, but the high-frequency noise in the direction perpendicular to the jet is increased. However, the total power radiated by the jet remains about constant. These results on model jets[70,72] have been verified by full-scale engine experiments,[73,81,83,88,89] where sound-power reductions of only 1.5 db were achieved. They resulted in a thrust loss of 2.5 per cent on nozzles with six teeth, which so far have proven most effective. Throttling the turbojet engine without teeth to the same reduced thrust results in an equivalent sound-power reduction, but not in the same spectral and spatial distribution of the power as obtained with teeth.[83] In spite of the practically unchanged total power output, these tooth devices should have a beneficial effect with respect to the community noise problem. Due to the increased absorption by air and ground for the higher frequencies, the effect of teeth, with the accompanying shift of the spectrum to higher frequencies, sufficiently influences the noise levels at a distance of 1 or 2 miles to lead one to expect a significant change in man's psychological response.[89] This

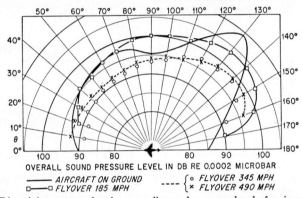

OVERALL SOUND PRESSURE LEVEL IN DB RE 0.0002 MICROBAR

——— *AIRCRAFT ON GROUND*   ---- $\left\{\begin{array}{l}\circ \;\; FLYOVER\; 345\; MPH\end{array}\right.$
□——□ *FLYOVER 185 MPH* $\left.\begin{array}{l}\times \;\; FLYOVER\; 490\; MPH\end{array}\right.$

Fɪɢ. 33.33. Directivity pattern for the over-all sound pressure level of a six-engine jet aircraft in flight, constructed from Figs. 33.31 and 33.32. The directivity patterns, derived from fly-overs at 2,000-ft altitude, are reduced to a constant radial distance from the aircraft of 1,000 ft. The pressure levels measured at a radius of 1,000 ft from the aircraft, stationary on the ground, are also indicated. (Measurements with sound source and receiver on the ground, over a distance of 1,000 ft, are more influenced by atmospheric conditions, especially since at such a distance they consume considerable time.) The curves show the trend of jet aircraft toward decreasing noise output with increasing flight speed.

effect is illustrated in Fig. 33.35. In addition, there may be occasions when a noise reduction in the downstream region of 5 to 6 db is well worthwhile, although obtained at the cost of increased high-frequency levels of 3 to 4 db at 90° to the jet. For example, personnel protection (earplugs and earmuffs) and noise control are achieved more easily at the higher frequencies than at the lower ones. The relatively small reduction in thrust of about 2½ per cent with a six-tooth nozzle compared to a standard nozzle makes the use of teeth in flight appear to be not impossible. As yet, however, no flight experiments with toothed nozzles have been reported.

An improvement of the toothed-nozzle idea was achieved by the use of "*corrugated nozzles.*"[82] By increasing the total perimeter of the nozzle so that equal nozzle area was obtained for the corrugated as for the standard circular nozzles, no effect on engine performance is observed. (In addition, the angle of convergence of the inner walls of the corrugations had to be limited to 12°.) The preliminary experimental results on such nozzles indicate that actual reductions in total acoustic-power output from 4 to 7 db can be achieved without thrust loss. Optimal effects have been obtained on nozzles with six corrugations and with depths of 2.65 in., 5.3 in., or 7.95 in. (standard nozzle diameter was 19.5 in.). A larger number of corrugations shifts the frequency range of their effectiveness to higher frequencies; deeper corrugations narrow the effective frequency range and somewhat increase the noise-reduction effect. The noise reduction achieved with the nozzle with six corrugations is demonstrated in Fig. 33.36. Final evaluation of the usefulness of corrugated nozzles for flight use must await the outcome of further experimentation.

Another jet exhaust silencing principle under investigation is based on the fact that the maximum of jet noise can be shifted to higher frequencies by decreasing the nozzle diameter,[90] Fig. 33.26. The arrangement of *multiple nozzles* of small diameter would replace the one large nozzle. The higher atmospheric attenuation of high-frequency sound, the more economical noise-control possibilities, and the hope of shifting

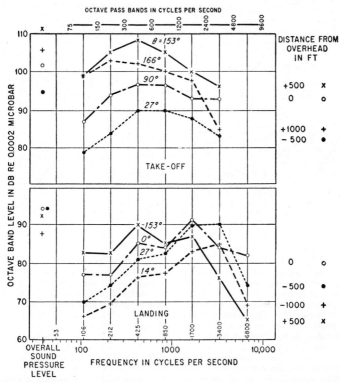

Fig. 33.34. Noise spectra from jet aircraft (Comet with four "Ghost" engines) passing at an altitude of 250 ft overhead. The spectra refer to the sound originating from different positions of the aircraft. Negative values for the distance from overhead indicate the approaching plane ($\theta < 90°$). (*After data from Fleming.*[46])

part of the noise energy into the inaudible range of the spectrum make this idea very appealing. Attempts with perforated sheet-metal tubes attached to the nozzle of the jet engine (0.085-in. holes, three diameters apart) show the desired noise-reduction effect, but due to the radial direction of the exhaust jets, most thrust is taken from the engine. Although similar arrangements with thrust-producing nozzles directed toward the rear have been proposed and their use during flight has been discussed, no experiments exist to demonstrate practical feasibility.

It is difficult to predict what noise reduction may finally be achieved with a practical device which is acceptable with respect to weight and effect on engine performance, but a power-level reduction of 5 to 8 db might be obtained (noise reduction at θ_0 approximately 10 to 14 db), with a performance penalty of 1 to 3 per cent.[114,115]

Very effective noise reduction on jets has been obtained by placing *screens normal to the jet* downstream from the nozzle. Screens with various wire diameters, wire spacing, and positions relative to the nozzle have been tried in model studies[74] and more recently on full-scale engines.[73,91] Screens seem to be most effective when placed at a point upstream from the region of greatest noise generation so that the flow is decelerated to lower velocities. Noise reduction is greatest for the low frequencies generated originally by a region downstream from the screen. The noise-reduction effect of screens results largely from the reduction of the effective jet velocity downstream from the screen, measured by the net thrust of the engine-screen combination.

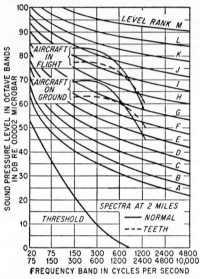

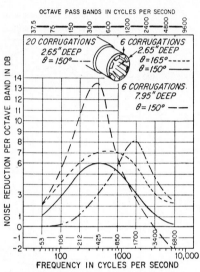

Fig. 33.35. Spectra of the noise from a turbojet engine with and without "teeth" at a distance of 2 miles. The spectrum is given for each case for the angle of maximum sound radiation. The curves for the aircraft in flight are based on the assumption of minimal atmospheric attenuation, whereas the curves for the aircraft on the ground are based on the increased atmospheric attenuation for sound propagation parallel to the ground. The level-rank curves superimposed on the spectra represent steps of significantly different reaction of people to noise[4] (see Chap. 36). Distance from aircraft at which a given annoyance is caused is reduced to nearly one-half by the fitting of teeth to a jet engine. (*From Mercer.*[89])

Fig. 33.36. Jet-engine noise reduction by corrugated nozzles. Noise reduction per octave band measured at a radius of 50 ft from the nozzle is shown for angles θ of 165° and 150° (0° upstream of the jet). For the nozzle with six corrugations and a corrugation depth of 2.65 in., a power-level reduction of 4 db is reported; increasing the depth of the corrugations to 7.95 in. reduced the power level by a total of 7 db. The standard nozzle of this engine has a diameter of 19.5 in. The data above were measured at a jet velocity of 1,800 ft per sec. (*Data from Greatrex.*[82])

The sound power generated by the engine-screen combination is a function of this effective velocity raised approximately to the 1.7th power. This small dependence of noise on the effective velocity is explained mainly by the screen-generated noise and also by the noise generation upstream from the screen. The screen position downstream from the nozzle is critical since small distances (<6 in.) result in back-pressure on the engine and large distances (>12 in.) for certain screens (fine mesh) result in resonant noises. Except for these resonant noises, little difference was observed between the effectiveness of small wires with small spacing and large wires with large spacing, as long as the screen was made equally rigid. On a jet engine of 19-in. nozzle diameter, best results so far were obtained with a screen (wire diameter $\frac{1}{4}$ in., distance between wires 1 in.) located 15 in. downstream from the nozzle which showed no reso-nances when placed as far as 27 in. downstream. The over-all sound level downstream from the engine at 150° was decreased by 14 db in this case, as demonstrated in Fig. 33.37, but the high frequencies to the side and front of the engine were increased some-what. The over-all sound power level was decreased by 5.5 db, the thrust loss was approximately 65 per cent. Therefore, screen configurations are very promising as a means of reducing the noise from engines or aircraft on the ground, but they are not proposed for use in flight.

The elimination of discrete screech frequencies of a jet operating at supercritical pressure ratios seems to be achieved easily, and nearly all devices discussed above have some effect on the screech. Model tests have shown that the increased turbulence obtained by radial blades upstream from the nozzle[72] or by four small auxiliary orifices bleeding air into the main stream just downstream from the exit[74] reduces the magni-tude of the screech component by a considerable amount. Toothed or notched nozzles, slotted cylinders, and a gauze cylinder extension to the nozzle to allow expansion of the supersonic flow without a regular shock pattern, are all successful in delaying the

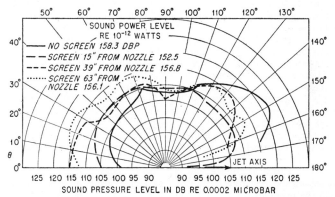

Fig. 33.37. Jet-engine noise reduction by screens. The graph shows the effect of distance screen nozzle on the sound output for the most effective screen used (1-in. mesh, $\frac{1}{4}$-in.-diameter wire). The engine, rated at 5,000-lb normal thrust, had a nozzle diameter of 19 in. (*Data from Callaghan and Coles.*[91])

onset of self-maintained, shock-produced noise.[62] Any mechanism breaking up the discrete pattern and diminishing the back reaction is beneficial. Noise reduction of maximum pressure levels of as much as 15 to 20 db have been reported, and changes in the exit-velocity profile alone reduced the noise up to 10 db.[87] Another possibility of reducing the noise from shock formation in the jet is the design of *convergent-divergent nozzles*. A convergent-divergent nozzle providing shock-free expansion of the jet at a pressure ratio of 3 reduced the noise-power level at this pressure ratio by 10 db com-pared to a convergent nozzle.[73] After elimination of the shock pattern, the noise power radiated by the choked jet agrees with the value following extrapolations from subsonic data (Fig. 33.25). So far, this shock-wave-produced noise is relatively unim-portant on full-scale turbojet engines on or near the ground, where nozzle-pressure ratios are never likely to exceed about 2.5. But an awareness has to be maintained of the possibility of screech components in the noise at high altitude where pressure ratios of at least 4 will occur compared to the choking-pressure ratio of 1.85. Control of this screech noise may be necessary for structural reasons or for minimizing noise in the rear section of the aircraft where passengers may be seated.

Water injection into the tail pipe or into the jet exhaust downstream from the nozzle has been tried; in general, it shows no marked noise reduction,[72,73] even for water flows up to a value equal to the airflow. However, successful noise reduction by waterspray rings on rockets indicates that, at supersonic flow velocity, waterspray apparently has the same effect as teeth or notches.[62]

Noise Reduction by Engine Design. The sound-power levels of present-day turbojet engines result from the fact that the engines are designed to give the highest specific propulsion using the simplest and most economical configuration. Consequently, all comparable engines show approximately the same noise power. If it should become necessary to design quieter jet engines, this can be achieved in a predictable way by reducing the jet velocity. But such a design results in less thrust obtainable for a given engine weight, and usually, especially for military use, the resulting performance penalties are considered excessive. Studies indicated that a reduction in noise of 8 db, achieved through reduction in jet velocity, resulted in payload losses from 15 to 50 per cent, depending upon the range over which the hypothetical aircraft was expected to operate. It appears possible, however, that propulsion efficiency may be retained with lower jet velocities if the bypass or ducted-fan principle is employed in engine design.[72,73] In a bypass engine, part of the air which flows through the early compressor stages is bypassed around the later compressor stages, combustor, and turbine by means of an external duct. The bypassed air then is discharged through a common nozzle with the exhaust gases. A greater airflow is required than for a simple jet engine to produce the same thrust; consequently, the relative noise level is lower. Although this type of engine is heavy, its fuel consumption is lower, so that it may be feasible for commercial and cargo operations. The Rolls-Royce Conway engine built according to this principle is, as expected, 6 to 9 db less noisy than a conventional turbojet engine of equivalent thrust.[82] This noise reduction corresponds to the amount expected, assuming the noise output to be a function of the mean velocity. The main benefit from the bypass principle also is obtained when mixing is incomplete in the exhaust nozzle. For example, for a bypass ratio of 1, an 8-db noise-power reduction is predicted, assuming that there is no mixing of bypass air to the primary jet, and an 11-db noise reduction, assuming that there is complete mixing of the jets.[73] Still higher reductions seem to be feasible by the use of this principle.

Besides these basic design considerations, the greatest possibilities for jet-noise research and for noise reduction by engine design are in the achievement of minimum noise production for a given jet velocity, i.e., the aerodynamic noise associated with this velocity. This also implies that combustion noise and screech—the additional noises at supersonic velocities from shock patterns—are reduced to a level below the noise from the jet mixing.

Design Curves for Turbojet Noise. *Power Output.* Two curves have been published for estimating the acoustic power output of turbojet engines. Both represent an empirical relationship between the sound-power output and the velocity and diameter of the jet stream. The relative accuracy of the two approaches, especially with respect to extrapolated ranges where no experimental data exist, cannot be evaluated yet. For higher performance engines operating at military thrust or with afterburner, the approach used for rocket engines, Fig. 33.42, would be more accurate.[116]

One relationship—an improved version of one published earlier—[4,84] relates the sound power to the engine parameters by means of a parameter X, where this term is given by

$$X = W_M \left[1 + \left(\frac{W_M}{2.7 \cdot 10^6} \right)^3 \left(\frac{19}{d} \right)^3 \left(\frac{1600}{T} \right)^{5.4} \right] \quad \text{watts} \quad (33.19)$$

where W_M = mechanical power in jet = $0.676 \, wV^2/g = 0.676 \, t^2 g/w = 21.77 \, t^2/w$ in watts

w = total weight flow of primary air and fuel through the engine in lb per sec

$V = \dfrac{tg}{w}$ = effective exit velocity in ft per sec, calculated from the engine thrust t in lb (g = gravitational constant = 32.2 ft per sec²)

d = tail-pipe diameter in in.

T = jet exhaust temperature in °Rankine ($T_{\text{Rankine}} = T_{\text{Fahrenheit}} + 459°$)

This relationship is based on dimensional analysis and on a large body of power measurements on different engines.[79,92] It is restricted to normal (i.e., not bypass) turbojet engines and considers only the noise from the jet stream.

For the parameter X calculated for a given engine, the anticipated sound-power level is given by the straight line in Fig. 33.38. (Of the 72 plotted points representing power measurements on different engines under test cell and free-field conditions, 70 per cent lie within ± 3 db of the design curve.) The sound-power level of an engine with afterburner cannot be found from the curve by inserting afterburner values in Eq. (33.19). Rather, it is obtained by adding 5 to 8 db to the level of the non-afterburning engine operating at 100 per cent power. This additional 5 to 8 db corresponds to the third or fourth power of the thrust boost.

The second relationship[85] gives the sound power as a simple sixth-power relationship of the jet velocity with empirically evaluated constants. This formula, which is in agreement with data on various turbojets and general findings on model jets, does not

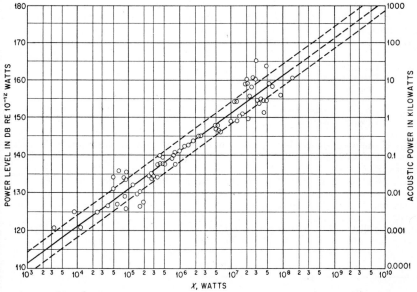

Fig. 33.38. Acoustic power output of turbojet engines as a function of the jet-stream parameter X according to Eq. (33.19). Of the 72 experimental points plotted (free-field and test-cell data covering a wide range of operating conditions), 70 per cent lie within ± 3 db of the straight-line relation. (*From Bolt, Beranek, and Newman, Inc.,*[4,92] *and Mercer.*[79])

require knowledge of the exhaust temperature. It is directly applicable to afterburner operation (assuming the sound power increases with the third power of the thrust boost). The sound power is

$$W_A = 1.8 \cdot 10^{-9} \tau^6 A \qquad \text{watts} \qquad (33.20)$$

where τ = "specific thrust" = t/w in lb per lb per sec (τ is proportional to the effective exit velocity $V = \tau g$)
A = nozzle area in sq in.
The sound-power level (in decibels re 10^{-12} watt) may be written as

$$L_w = (60 \log_{10} \tau + 10 \log_{10} A + 32.5) \qquad \text{dbp} \qquad (33.21)$$

Figure 33.25 shows this relationship and compares it with some turbojet-noise power data, other than the ones from which the formula was obtained. For low-power setting of the jet engine, the turbine noise becomes comparable to the jet noise, and values for the over-all sound-power level calculated from Eq. (33.20) are too small. Both relationships neglect the turbine noise.

It should be noted here that the performance of a turbojet engine and, therefore, its noise output are influenced by the ambient atmospheric conditions.[93] Nomograms have been prepared to predict the changes in acoustic power output for changes in ambient conditions when the engine characteristics are known.   Mass flow varies most with changing conditions.   For example, by changing ambient pressure from 30.5 in. to 25 in. of mercury, and by changing temperature from 70°F to 80°F—variations in conditions which are not yet representative for extremes within the United States—a decrease in acoustic power-level output by about 5 db has been predicted.

Power Spectrum.   For a given sound-power level, the spectrum level of the noise from a turbojet engine may be calculated from Fig. 33.26.   To obtain V/d, the velocity and jet diameter must either be taken in feet per second and feet or in m per second and m, respectively.   The frequency of the peak noise is at $f_0 = 0.13 \, V/d$ cps.   From the power spectrum level, the power level in various octave bands can be calculated.

Directivity.   The directivity indices for the different octave bands, given by Fig. 33.28 (especially Fig. 33.28c), may be used for engineering-design purposes.

Example.   A hypothetical turbojet engine is operated under the following conditions:

Thrust	5,100 lb
Thrust boost due to afterburner	18%
Fuel flow	1.8 lb per sec
Primary air	110 lb per sec
Tail-pipe temperature	$T = 1220°F = 1679°$ Rankine
Tail-pipe diameter	19.5 in.

What is the sound-power level of the total noise radiated by the engine?   What is the sound pressure level in octave bands at a distance of 100 ft at an angle of 35° under the jet axis?

According to Eq. (33.19), $X = 2.9 \cdot 10^7$ watts is obtained, for which value Fig. 33.38 gives a power level of $L_w = 156 \pm 3$ dbp.· For the same engine with $\tau = 45.7$ lb per lb per sec, Eq. (33.21) gives a power level $L_w = 156.9$ dbp.   The 18 per cent thrust boost for afterburning increases the power level from 157 db to 162 dbp.   From Fig. 33.26, the distribution of the power in the octave bands is obtained, which, for full power (non-afterburning) is given in Table 33.1.   The space-average sound pressure

Table 33.1

Bandwidth, cps	Sound power level, L_w (re 10^{-12} watt), dbp	Sound pressure level, in db L_p 100 ft from engine 35° to jet axis ($\theta = 145°$)
Over-all sound pressure level....	157	125
20–75......................	146	113
75–150.....................	151	118
150–300....................	153	120
300–600....................	152	118
600–1200...................	149	114.5
1200–2400..................	146	110
2400–4800..................	141	103.5
4800–9600..................	137	98

at a distance of 100 ft is $L_p = L_w - 40.5$ db re 0.0002 microbar.   Figure 33.28 gives the directivity index for $\theta = 145°$.   With a space-average over-all sound pressure level of 116.5 db and a directivity index of 8.5 db, the over-all sound pressure level at the location under consideration is 125 db.

Turbojet-engine Performance and Noise Output.   Since the acoustic output of an engine can be predicted from the engine data, design curves have been prepared which show the acoustic output as a function of the internal variables of an engine.[93] The charts, based on the relation of Eq. (33.19), give the total acoustic-power output as a function of the parameters compression ratio, specific thrust, and jet temperature. Efficiencies of the turbojet-engine components are shown to have only negligible influence on the noise.

Ramjet Noise. Ramjet engines, unlike turbojet engines, have no compressors for delivering the compressed air necessary for combustion. This air is obtained by ram pressure at high speed. To reach the required speed for this ram action, auxiliary propulsive devices are necessary, and blowers or wind tunnels must be used for ground tests to deliver the ram action. Except for the latter case and for their application as helicopter tip jets, ramjets have not created a noise problem, and it is not likely that they will be applied to civil aviation in the near future. Their main noise source is the random aerodynamic noise from the continuous jet. Although directivity and power spectra have not been investigated on a sufficient number of engines, there is no reason to doubt from qualitative reports and the few detailed measurements[4,7,77] that this noise obeys the same laws as does the aerodynamic noise from turbojet engines. Under the condition of rough burning—arising from periodic explosions of the fuel-air mixture or from fuel-flow pulsations—discrete, harmonically related, frequencies occur in the 100- to 400-cps range, which can override the continuous jet noise. These frequencies are of the pulse-jet-noise type and show similar angular distribution.[77] The so-called "buzz condition" in ramjets occurs in ramjets with external compression diffusers, with or without combustion in the engine, and consists of flow pulsations of approximately 1 to 80 cps. Stability investigations of these pulsations have been carried out both theoretically and experimentally, assuming the ramjet system to act as a Helmholtz resonator.[94] The directivity of ramjet noise, its sound power, and its spectrum, therefore, to a considerable extent, will depend on the steadiness of flow and burning state.

A generalized design curve for the sound power level of ramjet-engine noise as a function of fuel consumption[4,7] is given in Fig. 33.39. The range of uncertainty for this curve is ±3 db, but this range probably does not include rough burning. For smooth-burning ramjet engines having combustion-chamber diameters of less than 9 in., the octave-band spectrum was observed to peak in the 600- to 1,200-cps band; for large ramjets of combustion chambers with a diameter of more than 16 in., the spectrum peaked in the 300- to 600-cps band in approximate accordance with Fig. 33.26.

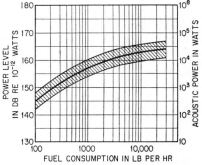

FIG. 33.39. Acoustic power level of ramjet engines as a function of fuel consumption in pounds per hour; based on test cell, semi-closed test cell, and open-field measurements. (*After Bolt, Beranek, and Newman, Inc.*[4])

Pulse-jet Engine Noise. The intermittent-jet or pulse-jet engine produces thrust by an intermittent flow rather than by a continuous stream leaving the exit nozzle. In the most common form, air is admitted into the tube-like engine through the shutter valve at the forward end of the engine and through the tail-pipe nozzle. The air is mixed with fuel in the combustion chamber. The combustion raises the pressure in the chamber sufficiently to close the intake vents so that the exhaust gases leave through the tail pipe and produce thrust. Then the valves open again and the cycle is repeated. The fundamental period of operation is determined by the resonant properties of the combustion-chamber–tail-pipe combination. This particular feature makes the operation relatively simple, so that pulse-jet engines require only a small amount of auxiliary equipment. This results in a high thrust-to-weight ratio, making the pulse jet attractive for many applications, such as propulsive units at the rotor tips of helicopters.

Acoustically, the pulse-jet engine behaves in a manner similar to the exhaust noise of reciprocating engines discussed earlier. The pulsating flow leaving the tail pipe radiates as a simple source whose strength is controlled by the volume flow leaving the nozzle. The fundamental firing frequency of the engine is usually about 100 cps and is the lowest and most powerful component of the discrete-spectrum-type noise. The higher harmonics are determined by the shape of the exhaust volume-flow vs. time function. Because of the exhaust velocity, the exhaust noise is slightly directional toward the direction of flow. If the flow parameters of the engine are known, the noise field of the fundamental frequency can be calculated with reasonable accuracy by the simple-source approximation. This has been verified for pulse jets of

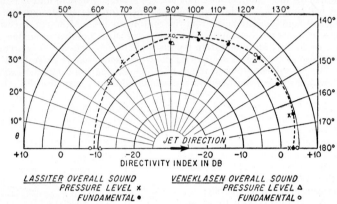

Fig. 33.40. Directivity index for the over-all sound pressure level and the fundamental frequency of pulse-jet noise. (*Graph based on data by Lassiter[77] and Veneklasen.[96]*)

2-in.[95] and 6-in.[77] diameter. The total acoustic power for the fundamental frequency is obtained from Eq. (33.9).

$$W_A = \frac{\pi}{2} \frac{\rho' c'}{c_0{}^2} V^2 f^2 S^2 \qquad (33.22)$$

where ρ', c' = assumed average values for density and sound velocity at the tube exit[77] or = ρ_0, c_0 of the surrounding atmosphere[94]

$V \approx \dfrac{V_{\max} - V_{\min}}{2}$, where $V_{\max}$ is the peak velocity during the exhaust half-cycle, $V_{\min}$ during the intake half-cycle

f = firing frequency

$S = \dfrac{d^2 \pi}{4}$ (d = nozzle diameter)

With $\rho' c' \approx \rho_0 c_0 = 41.5$ rayls, an approximation for the power level (in decibels re 10^{-12} watt) of a pulse-jet engine is given by

$$L_w = (21.5 + 20 \log V + 20 \log f + 40 \log d) \qquad \text{dbp} \qquad (33.23)$$

where V is expressed in feet per second and d is expressed in inches.

This approximation can be improved (as is shown for the exhaust noise), if the time function of the pulsating flow is known so that higher harmonics can be considered. Power levels re 10^{-12} watt measured in approximate agreement with this formula are 146 dbp for a 2-in. diameter, 18-lb thrust pulse jet,[95] and 158 and 156.5 dpb for pulse jets of 6-in. and 9.4-in. diameter of 90- and 97-lb thrust, respectively.[77,95] The firing frequency of these jets was 120, 100, and 93 cps. The acoustic efficiency is in the order of 1 per cent. The directivity index for the over-all sound level and the fundamental frequency was in agreement for all these jets, as shown in Fig. 33.40. The difference in level between the maximum downstream and the minimum upstream is 13 db. (Some measurements give a maximum at $\theta = 135°$ to $150°$, 1.5 db above the value at $180°$.)

In addition to the discrete frequency spectrum, in which the strength of the higher harmonics decreases, random noise of the aerodynamic-mixing type is observed in the higher frequency bands. As for continuous jets, this noise has its maximum between $130°$ and $150°$ where it is 10 to 15 db above the minimum of those bands. For a 2-in. pulse jet,[95] the frequency spectrum shows—in addition to the spectrum peak at the discrete frequency—a pronounced, rounded maximum of this random-noise spectrum in the frequency range of $f_{max} \approx 0.13\, V/d$, about 1,000 cps for the engine which was measured. The level of this aerodynamic noise was found to be about 20 to 30 db higher than the corresponding aerodynamic noise of a steady cold jet of equal thrust and diameter. This is reasonable, since the peak velocity of a pulse jet will be at least twice the velocity of the steady jet of equal thrust, and, assuming the noise power to increase with the sixth to eighth power of the velocity, the aerodynamic noise level of the pulse jet should be in the order of 20 db above the steady jet noise.

Since the pulse-jet exhaust noise increases as $V_{max}^2 d^4$, its acoustic efficiency decreases with increasing velocity; whereas the aerodynamic noise increases with $V^6 d^2$; therefore the aerodynamic noise should increase in relation to the exhaust noise with increasing exhaust velocity and decreasing diameter. This is probably why the aerodynamic noise was relatively pronounced for the 2-in.-diameter pulse jet and why it seems to become somewhat lower compared to the fundamental when the fuel flow (thrust) of an engine is reduced. Therefore, in estimating the relative importance of aerodynamic noise in pulse-jet noise, the sound power level obtained from Eq. (33.23) should be compared with the power level of aerodynamic noise resulting from Fig. 33.25 for the peak velocity of the pulse-jet exhaust.

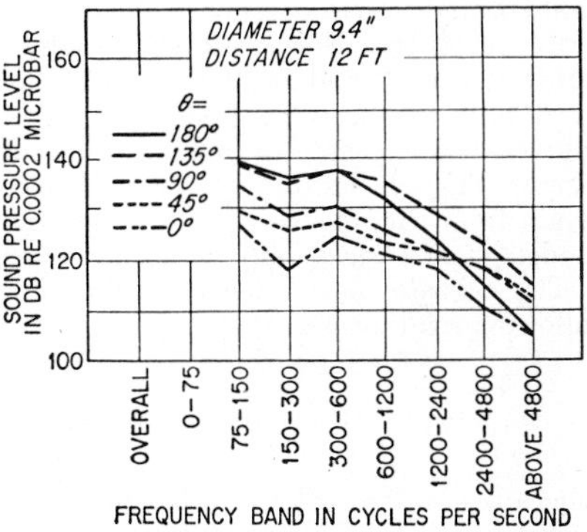

Typical pulse-jet spectra are shown in Fig. 33.41. Measurements at 1-ft distance from intake and exhaust clearly proved the assumption made in the analysis above, i.e., that the exhaust is the predominant noise source by approximately 15 db.

FIG. 33.41. Octave-band spectra of pulse-jet noise as a function of azimuth position on a radius of 12 ft. The levels in the first three octave bands are determined by the firing frequency (93 cps) and its harmonics. Above 600 cps the spectrum becomes continuous. Note how the aerodynamic noise increases the levels in the higher bands at the 135° position. (Engine diameter 9.4 in.; thrust approximately 100 lb.) (*From Veneklasen.*[96])

If, in Eq. (33.22), V_{min} is negligible compared to V_{max} and with the thrust

$$t \propto \rho_1 V^2 S = \frac{\rho_0 T_0}{T_1} V^2 S$$

it, follows that the sound power output as a function of pulse-jet design parameters is

$$W_A \propto T_1 t d^2 f^2 \tag{33.24}$$

where T_1 is the exit temperature. In general, T_1, t, and f will increase in the same direction.

Since the pulse-jet-noise source acoustically approximates a simple source, there is some possibility of noise reduction by mutual interference of two pulse jets. This can either be accomplished by having two pulse jets—side by side, close together—operating 180° out of phase, or by having them both operating in phase, but displaced by a half-wavelength. Experiments have been done on the effect of out-of-phase operation of two jets by appropriate acoustic coupling. The noise reduction obtained by mutual interference of two jets as a function of n—the distance between the exhausts in wavelength—and ϵ—the phase angle of the operation in cycles—is given by the directivity factor[95,62]

$$D = \cos \pi (\epsilon - n \cos \beta)$$

where β is the angle from the line joining the jet exits.

In experiments, where two 6.75-in. pulse-jet engines were operated synchronically side by side, an 8-db noise reduction of the over-all noise level and a 20-db reduction of the fundamental frequency were achieved compared to the out-of-synchronization operation of two engines.[97] The second engine can be replaced by a resonator tuned to the fundamental frequency.[98] Thus, an 11-db reduction of the fundamental frequency was obtained in practice on a single engine and still more effective noise control configurations seem possible.[97]

Rocket-engine Noise. Rocket engines are used to assist in take-off operations of military aircraft and for the propulsion of missiles. Few investigations on the noise of rockets have been reported; their use is infrequent compared to other aircraft noise sources, and exposure to rocket noise is of short duration during missile launching or aircraft take-off assistance. In principle, their major noise source is of aerodynamic origin from the jet—as can be shown by the similarity of this noise with that from model jets. Occasionally, it is increased by rough-burning and combustion noise.

The acoustic power level output of rocket engines can be estimated from the following relationship:[117]

$$L_w = (68 + 13.5 \log_{10} W_M) \qquad \text{dbp re } 10^{-12} \text{ watt} \qquad (33.25)$$

where $W_M = 0.676wV^2/g = 0.676t^2g/w = 21.77t^2/w$ in watts
with $\quad w$ = total weight flow of primary air and fuel through engine in lb per sec
$\quad\quad V = tg/w =$ effective exit velocity in ft per sec, calculated from engine thrust
$\quad\quad\quad t$ in lb
$\quad\quad g$ = gravitational constant = 32.2 ft per sec²

A plot of Eq. (33.25) is shown in Fig. 33.42 along with experimentally determined points from measurements on rocket engines of up to 150,000 lb thrust.[2,99,116,117] Power-level data on turbojet engines and on model jets given earlier in Fig. 33.25 are also replotted on this graph and demonstrate that the noise output of rockets is less than one would extrapolate from low-velocity model jets and turbojet engines.

Rocket engines have an acoustic power level output which is approximately 5 to 10 db higher than that of turbojet engines of equal thrust (see Fig. 33.2). This is caused by a high-exit Mach number—up to 3 or 4.

The exit diameters of the supersonic-nozzles studies were between 0.6 and 30 in. The power spectra indicate a random spectrum similar to that of jet-engine spectra which peak in the lower audible-frequency range in correspondence to the generalized power spectrum in Fig. 33.26. For exit diameters between 0.6 and 6 in., and at the velocities given above, the peaks of the spectra were observed between 600 and 2,400 cps (θ between 120° and 150°);[2,99] for the large rockets the spectrum peaked in the 75 to 150 cps band with exit velocities of about Mach 2.5.[117] There are indications that the high-frequency content of rocket spectra decreases somewhat with increasing distance from the nozzle. Since their acoustic power output is above the power output of turbojet engines of comparable thrust and since this acoustic power is radiated by jets which have a smaller diameter than turbojet engines, finite-amplitude effects and the consequent generation of higher frequencies and increased absorption will occur in the near field.

The angle of maximum radiation for rockets is between $\theta = 110°$ and $\theta = 130°$, with a pattern similar to but somewhat flatter than that observed for turbojets (Fig. 33.28). The directivity index of the over-all sound pressure is for θ_0, the angle of maximum radiation, 5 to 6 db. The low-frequency lobes have their maximum at a higher value of θ and the high-frequency lobes at a smaller value.

In general, both types, solid- and liquid-fuel rockets, result in approximately the same noise output for the same thrust and nozzle. Both types may burn roughly or smoothly depending on the burning process. The difference in noise levels between rough- and smooth-burning rockets may be as much as 15 db.[2]

Propellant geometry influences the burning process in the solid-fuel rockets, and, therefore, influences the noise output. In smooth-burning rockets of the 1,000- and 5,000-lb thrust class,[99] chamber pressures of 1,000 to 2,000 lb per sq in. absolute were observed upon which pressure fluctuations of ± 25 lb per sq in. were superimposed, presumably due to burning irregularities.

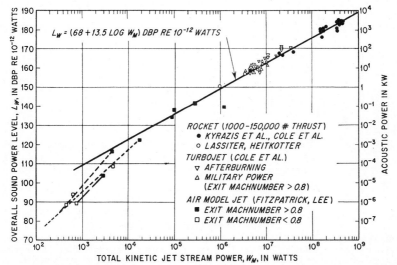

Fig. 33.42. Over-all sound-power level of rocket engines as a function of the total kinetic jet-stream power. Turbojet and model-jet data of Fig. 33.25 are also plotted in this graph. (*From Cole et al.*[116] *and Kyrazis et al.*[117])

Efforts to reduce rocket noise begin with smooth burning. Once smooth burning is achieved and aerodynamic noise becomes predominant, rocket-noise reduction should be possible by applying the same principles discussed earlier for turbojet engines. Configurations observed effective on supersonic jets should prove to be equally beneficial on rocket noise.[100] Convergent-divergent nozzles, designed for the pressure ratio at which the rocket operates, should be able to reduce the noise of many existing rockets by providing shock-free expansion of the jet and thereby eliminating additional noise due to shock formation.[73]

MISCELLANEOUS AIRCRAFT NOISE SOURCES

Helicopter Noise. Helicopters are not particularly powerful noise sources when considered either in an absolute sense or in relation to their thrust, Fig. 33.2. But the use of the passenger-carrying helicopter to provide traffic connection across or into residential districts creates a noise problem with respect to people living along the flight routes as well as to the passengers.

Helicopter noise is generated by several sources.[101] For the conventional helicopter, for which a typical spectrum is shown in Fig. 33.43, the reciprocating engine is the main noise source. Unless a muffler is used, the engine determines the over-all sound level; its operating frequency and its principal harmonics are in the frequency bands from 100 to 600 cps. This level can be estimated from the section on exhaust noise in this chapter.

Another major source of noise is produced by the meshing of gear teeth, which is predominant in frequency ranges from 600 to 4,800 cps. Since the transmissions to the main rotor and tail rotor usually are located directly over the cabin and behind the cockpit, this noise is especially deterrent to speech communication inside the helicopter. The gear-contact frequencies are the fundamental sources of noise; data on this noise source are available from studies on other types of transmissions (see Chap. 23).

The main and tail rotors of helicopters are propellers which generate rotational noise and vortex noise. Currently used blade dimensions and operating conditions are such that the rotational noise of the tail rotor (below 100 cps) and the vortex noise of the main rotor predominate in the over-all helicopter spectrum. Their relative strength

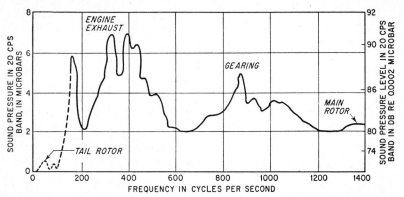

Fig. 33.43. Spectrum of a conventional (reciprocating engine, 600 hp) helicopter hovering 100 ft overhead. The frequency analysis was made with a 20-cps wide filter. Octave-band analysis of the noise from the same helicopter at 300 ft overhead is given in Fig. 33.44. The graph shows the main noise sources. The noise from about 1,200 to 15,000 cps was random in nature, originating mainly as vortex noise from the main rotor. (*From Hubbard and Lassiter.*[101])

can be calculated from the section on propeller noise in this chapter. Since the vortex noise has its maximum on the axis of rotation of the rotor, it is the major noise observed in the cabin or on the ground which is produced by the main rotor. It can be kept low by operating at a low tip speed. Other noise sources such as the engine-cooling fan, or the supercharger, can sometimes be detected depending on the design, but they are usually below the above-mentioned noise components.

If tip jets attached to the outboard end of the rotor blades are used to provide the driving power for the rotor, this type of engine will be 10 to 20 db noisier than the reciprocating-engine-type helicopter. All types of jet engines have been proposed to drive the main rotor; pulse jets, ramjets, pressure jets, and exhaust jets. In the pressure jets, the air compressed by an axial compressor passes along the blade into combustion chambers at the tips, which emit the product of combustion at supersonic velocity. In the exhaust jet system, the combustion product of a normal jet engine passes along the blades and leaves the tips at subsonic velocities. The noise from all these propulsion systems can be calculated from data given under jet engines.

In contrast to sources that have been considered previously, the sources here are rotating. As a result of this rotation, (1) the sound output of each engine can be reduced by as much as 10 db,[62] (2) an observer hears the variation in noise pattern (amplitude and frequency) as the azimuth angle of the engine changes in relation to the observer, (3) the pitch of the noise is modulated according to the Doppler effect, and (4) the use of two or four jets, one on each blade tip, causes a complex beating effect between the sources.

Measurements have been made on stationary and rotating helicopter tip jets, pulse jets,[95] and pressure jets.[62]   As expected, the pulse jet seems to be in the order of 5 to 10 db noisier than the pressure jet, although no comparison on an equal thrust or weight basis is available.   The use of two pulse jets operating in proper phase to reduce the noise of the fundamental frequency, which seems feasible for helicopter use, has not been tried in practice.   Teeth at the exit nozzle of helicopter pressure jets were employed and showed promising results.[62]

In general, it seems doubtful whether the tip-jet propulsion presently available is acceptable for civil aviation.[62,101]   Figure 33.44 shows an approximate comparison of the noise levels associated with different types of helicopter propulsion.

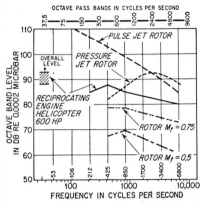

FIG. 33.44. Noise from helicopters: the estimated noise levels for comparably sized helicopters (7,000-lb gross weight) with different main rotor systems are given for an observer on the axis of rotation of the rotor at 300-ft distance. The noise from the main rotor alone for different tip Mach numbers M_t is estimated from data on propeller noise. An increase of the tip speed of current helicopters would make the rotor-noise level comparable to the over-all noise. For an observer in the plane of the rotor, the bare rotor noise would be less objectionable (decreased vortex noise) but the noise from both tip jet systems would increase. (*From data from Richards,[62] Veneklasen,[96] and Hubbard and Lassiter.[101]*)

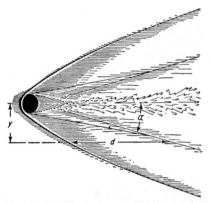

FIG. 33.45. Shock-wave pattern around a sphere in a wind tunnel at Mach number 3.0. (*Based on Schlieren photographs.*)

Noise from Supersonic Flight.   An aircraft flying at supersonic speed creates in addition to the noise radiated by its propulsion units, which is also present at subsonic speed, the so-called *sonic boom* or *bang* experienced by ground observers.   This acoustic phenomenon is not connected with the stationary emission of acoustic energy by the aircraft.   Therefore, it would exist even for "noiseless aircraft" and it can be observed on missiles.   It is an explosive type of noise and consists of two, three, or even more pressure pulses separated by a time delay of 0.1 to 0.2 sec, and it is generated by the shock-wave pattern formed around any body moving with supersonic speed.[102,103] Such a pattern is demonstrated by the Schlieren picture of a sphere in a wind tunnel at Mach number 3.0 in Fig. 33.45.   Measurements of the pressure across this pattern indicate a saw-tooth distribution.   In the front (bow) wave the pressure increases suddenly from the normal atmospheric pressure in front of this wave to a certain value; then it decreases continuously to a negative value of pressure and jumps back to normal pressure at the back wave.   The angle between the shock wave and the direction of motion is given by the Mach-angle $\sin \alpha = c/V$, where V is the flight velocity, and c is the velocity of sound.   The sonic boom may be classified in two types, according to its generation and propagation.   One type of boom is experienced by an observer on the ground when a supersonic airplane passes in steady supersonic flight overhead.   In this case, the aircraft "drags" a shock-wave formation over the ground, as is illustrated on the left side of Fig. 33.46. The second type of boom is generated in accelerated and decelerated flight, as in diving. Here the shock-wave pattern leaves the aircraft when it changes its velocity and the pressure discontinuity propagates from this instant on as a large amplitude (nonlinear) acoustic wave toward the ground. The right side of Fig. 33.46 illustrates how, in a diving maneuver at high altitude, the shock wave detaches from the nose of the aircraft and moves toward the ground. Aside from amplitude considerations, the noise heard on the ground is the same for both types of the sonic boom. At present, the second type is observed more frequently with current aircraft.

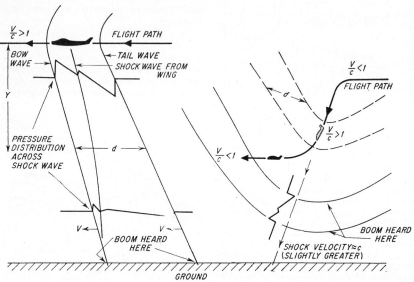

Fɪɢ. 33.46. Generation of the sonic boom for the steady case (straight and level flight at constant supersonic Mach number) and the unsteady case (varying supersonic Mach number during dive). (Velocity of aircraft V, sound velocity c.) Typical pressure distributions observed under a supersonic airplane at different distances by *Daum and Smith*[108] are given as an example. (*Based on Lilley, Westley, Yates, and Busing*[102] *and Daum and Smith.*[108])

For the steady flight boom in an idealized uniform atmosphere, the maximum pressure rise across the bow wave can be calculated for different shapes of the body, as, for example, an airfoil profile[104] or a parabolic body of revolution.[102,105,106] For the latter, used as an approximation for an aircraft, the following expression for the pressure jump Δp across the bow shock wave at a distance of many times the length of the body is obtained:

$$\frac{\Delta p}{P_0} \simeq 0.53(M^2 - 1)^{\frac{1}{8}}\frac{\delta}{(y/L)^{\frac{3}{4}}} \tag{33.26}$$

where P_0 = static pressure in undisturbed atmosphere

$M = \dfrac{V}{c}$ = Mach number of aircraft

δ = fineness ratio of body = maximum body diameter/body length

L = length of body

y = distance normal to the body and its flight path (zero body incidence)

The distance d, between the bow and tail shock wave, measured parallel to the motion, is

$$\frac{d}{L} \simeq \frac{1.82M^2\delta(y/L)^{\frac{1}{4}}}{(M^2 - 1)^{\frac{3}{8}}} \tag{33.27}$$

From Eq. (33.26), note that the magnitude of the shock decreases with the distance from the body proportional to $y^{-3/4}$, and from Eq. (33.27) that the time delay between bow and tail wave is proportional to the body dimension and increases with $y^{1/4}$ (as can be seen qualitatively from Fig. 33.45). Experiments on ballistic shock waves show fairly good agreement with the above relations.[107] Applied to the case of an aircraft flying at supersonic speed at high altitude, values of the order of those shown in Fig. 33.47 are obtained from Eq. (33.26) as estimates for the pressure rise across the bow wave. As this figure indicates, the strength of the steady flight sonic boom increases slowly with Mach number, once supersonic speed is reached, but increases rapidly with decreasing distance or altitude, respectively.

The nonsteady boom phenomenon has not been investigated quantitatively as thoroughly, but estimates can be made from a knowledge of the pressure jump when it detaches itself from the airplane, and from the laws of propagation for high-intensity

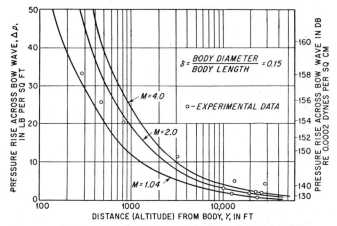

Fig. 33.47. Pressure rise Δp across the bow wave of a body flying with different supersonic speeds ($M = 1.04, 2.0, 4.0$) as a function of the distance from the flight path, y. The curves are calculated from the theory of Ref. 105 for a ratio of body diameter to body length of 0.15 and one-atmosphere uniform static pressure according to Eq. (33.26). The experimental points were observed on an airplane of 45-ft length in long, steady, supersonic dives (dive angle 15 and 20°) over a Mach number range of 1.02 to 1.4. (*From Daum and Smith.*[108])

acoustical waves. The pressure observed on the ground can be predicted when the shock-wave history is known, so that the boom can be described qualitatively for accelerated or decelerated motion, or for different flight maneuvers.[102] In these cases, as for example in the diving maneuver illustrated in Fig. 33.46, the sonic boom (or at least the shock wave's maximum intensity) strikes the ground over a smaller area and localized effects can be expected.

Only limited measurements on sonic booms under well-controlled conditions are available. They indicate that Fig. 33.47 gives the pressure to a good approximation. Supersonic dives (Mach number 1.04 to 1.4) between 25,000- and 10,000-ft altitude resulted in peak sound pressure levels on the ground of between 125 and 140 db. Some of the experimental data are plotted in Fig. 33.47.[108] Supersonic flight at lower altitude may produce pressures on the ground high enough to break ordinary window glass and to result in building vibration being felt by its inhabitants and in possible damage to buildings. The booms which were measured consisted of two to three pressure pulses separated by roughly 0.1 sec each. Their pressure spectra decreased 3 to 6 db per octave through the entire audible spectrum with a probable maximum in the subaudible range (10 to 15 cps). For supersonic dives at an angle of 30°, where the airplane decelerated to subsonic velocity at an altitude of 20,000 ft, the boom was heard on the ground over an area 15 to 35 miles wide and long.

Measurements of the shock wave close to the airplane (70 to 2,000 ft) have been made by flying a second aircraft instrumented for static-pressure measurements through the shock waves.[110] The peak pressures recorded were in agreement with Eq. (33.26).

Due to the nonuniformity of the atmosphere, where temperature and wind velocity vary with altitude, the sonic boom (shock wave) is refracted.[102,108] The deformation of the shock front by wind and temperature is shown qualitatively in Fig. 33.48. For level flight at uniform, low supersonic speed the shock wave pattern will not penetrate below altitudes at which the local speed of sound, due to the atmospheric temperature gradient, is greater than the speed of the aircraft. Therefore, the shock waves are refracted back to higher altitudes if the plane moves subsonically with respect to the

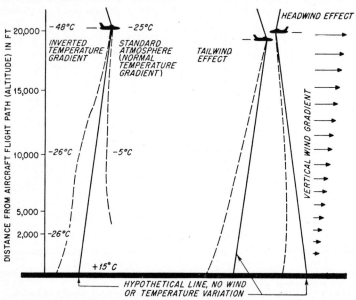

Fig. 33.48. Effects of atmospheric wind and temperature gradient on the shock waves around a supersonic aircraft.

speed of sound at ground level, although its Mach number is >1. For example, at 30,000-ft altitude, the aircraft's flight Mach number has to exceed 1.13 before the boom will be heard on the ground. This relation has been confirmed generally by audibility tests of the sonic boom on the ground.[108]

Although the shock-wave pattern accounts for the phenomenon of sonic boom and occurs for completely silent bodies, sound waves emitted by the moving body, such as jet noise, may contribute to the phenomenon or may modify it. These sound waves, believed to be insignificant, accumulate at the Mach cone, i.e., the shock front,[102,108] and never propagate into the space in front of the cone.

For practical considerations, Fig. 33.47 may be used to estimate the magnitude of the steady-flight sonic boom. If the aircraft flies supersonically at altitudes in excess of 20,000 ft, a sonic boom having a peak in excess of 120 db is not likely to occur. The sonic boom may be heard by the passengers of an aircraft decelerating from supersonic flight when its own tail wave passes the aircraft. But appreciable diffusion and, therefore, a decrease in noise level can be assumed for a shock wave passing through the subsonic viscous boundary layer adjacent to the aircraft. If the shock pattern of a supersonic aircraft passes over a low-speed aircraft, the latter will receive the sonic boom. Its strength and frequency spectrum with respect to an observer in the lower speed aircraft will depend on the relative velocity of the two aircraft. Problems of control and stability of aircraft must be kept in mind with respect to this phenomenon.

The transient-type noise of the sonic boom, so far as its effect on hearing and damage to buildings is concerned, can best be compared to explosive blasts. Considerable literature exists on this subject.

The control of the sonic boom is limited practically to operational control of supersonic flight. Only a small decrease in its intensity can be expected from the use of more slender wings and bodies, i.e., aircraft with less wave drag.

Aircraft Support-equipment Noise. Under certain conditions and at certain locations, in and very close to different types of aircraft, the noise from auxiliary aircraft equipment may exceed the noise connected with propulsion. Although a discussion of these noise sources is not included here, they must be considered in evaluating the effect of "aircraft noise" on ground crew, flight crew, and passengers. Types of equipment which, at certain spots, may exceed comfort and tolerance criteria, and thus require noise control, are starter compressors for jet engines, electrical equipment, pressurization equipment, and cooling fans or air-conditioning systems in the aircraft or movable units used on the ground.[118]

REFERENCES

1. Bolt, R. H.: *J. Acoust. Soc. Am.*, **25**: 363 (1953).
2. Hubbard, H. H.: *NACA Tech. Note* 2701 (1952).
3. Doolittle, J. H., C. F. Horne, and J. C. Hunsaker: The Airport and Its Neighbors, U.S. Gov't. Printing Office, Washington, D.C., 1952.
4. Staff of Bolt, Beranek, and Newman, Inc.: *WADC Tech. Rept.* 52-204, Office of Tech. Services, Dept. of Commerce, Washington 25, D.C., Vol. I, PB111200; Vol. II, PB111274 (1955).
5. Regier, A. A.: Why Do Airplanes Make Noise? *SAE National Aeronautic Meeting* (1954).
6a. Ernsthausen, W.: Sound and Vibration in Aircraft, "German Aviation Medicine, World War II," Vol. II, Chap. VII-A, Dept. of Air Force, U.S. Gov't. Printing Office.
6b. Ernsthausen, W., and W. von Wittern: Measurement of Sound and Vibration with Reference to Physical and Physiological Problems in Aviation, "German Aviation Medicine, World War II," Vol. II, Chap. VII-B, Dept. of Air Force, U.S. Gov't. Printing Office.
7. von Gierke, H. E.: *J. Acoust. Soc. Am.*, **25**: 367 (1953).
8. Oestreicher, H. L.: *Technical Data Digest*, **19**: 16 (1951).
9. Lighthill, M. J.: *Proc. Royal Soc. of London*, **A 211**: 564 (1952).
10. Uniform Practices for the Measurement of Aircraft Noise, *Aircraft Tech. Committee Report No.* ARTC-2, p. 21, 1952.
11. Regier, A. A., and H. H. Hubbard: *J. Acoust. Soc. Am.*, **25**: 363 (1953).
12. Theodorsen, T.: "Theory of Propellers," McGraw-Hill Book Company, Inc., 1948.
13. Ernsthausen, E. W.: *Zeitschrift fuer angewandte Mathematik und Mechanik*, **31**: Heft 1/2 (1951).
14. Deming, A. F.: *NACA Tech. Note* 679, 1938.
15. Ernsthausen, W.: *Jahrbuch der deutschen Luftfahrtforschung*, **III**: 46 (1938).
16. Ernsthausen, W.: *Akustische Zeitschrift*, **6**: 245 (1941).
17. Lynam, E. J., and H. A. Webb: *Aero. Res. Comm. Report, Memo. No.* 624, 1919.
18. Hart, M. D.: *Aero. Res. Comm. Report, Memo. No.* 1310, 1929.
19. Paris, E. T.: *Phil. Mag.*, **13**: 99 (1932).
20. Gutin, L.: *Phys. Zeitschrift der Sowjetunion*, **9**: 57 (1936); English trans., *NACA Tech. Memo.* 1195, 1948.
21. Deming, A. F.: *J. Acoust. Soc. Am.*, **12**: 173 (1940); also *NACA Tech. Note* 747.
22. Lamb, H.: "Hydrodynamics," Cambridge University Press, pp. 501ff., 1932.
23. Hubbard, H. H., and A. A. Regier: *NACA Tech. Report* 996, 1950.
24. Hubbard, H. H.: *NACA Tech. Note* 1654, 1948.
25. Roberts, J. P., and L. L. Beranek: *NACA Tech. Note* 2727, 1952.
26. Garrick, I. E., and C. E. Watkins: *NACA Tech. Note* 3018, 1953.
27. Kemp, C. F.: *Proc. Phys. Soc* (London), **44**: 151 (1932).
28. Obata, J. Y. Yosida, and S. Morita: *Rep. Aero. Res. Inst. Tokyo*, **6**: 361 (1932).
29. Hubbard, H. H., and L. W. Lassiter: *NACA Res. Memo.* L51C27, 1951 (Being converted into *NACA Tech. Report* 1079).
30. Hubbard, H. H., and L. W. Lassiter: *NACA Tech. Note* 3202, 1954.

31. Munk, Max M.: *Aero Digest*, **33**: 67 (1938).
32. Hubbard, H. H.: *NACA Tech. Note* 2024, 1950.
33. Hubbard, H. H.: Report on NACA Conference on Some Problems of Aircraft Operation, Cleveland, 1954.
34. Vogeley, A. W., and M. C. Kurbjun: *NACA Tech. Note* 3417, 1955.
35. Ernsthausen, W., and W. Willms: *Akustische Zeitschrift*, **4**: 20 (1939).
36. Beranek, L. L., R. H. Nichols, Jr., H. W. Rudmose, H. P. Sleeper, Jr., R. L. Wallace, Jr., and H. L. Erickson.: *OSRD Report No.* 1543, 1944.
37. Rudmose, H. W., and L. L. Beranek: *J. Aero. Sci.*, **14**: 79 (1947).
38. Holle, W.: *Akustische Zeitschrift*, **3**: 322 (1938).
39. von Karman, T., and Rubach, *Physikal. Zeitschr.*, **13**: 49 (1912).
40. Stowell, E. Z., and A. F. Deming: *NACA Tech. Note* 519, 1935.
41. Yudin, E. Y.: *Zhurnal Tekhnicheskoi Fiziki*, **14** (1944). (Translation: *NACA Tech. Memo.* 1136, 1947).
42. von Wittern, W. W.: *Tech. Data Digest*, **19**: 20 (1951).
43. Stokes, G. M., and D. D. Davis, Jr.: *NACA Tech. Note* 2943, 1953.
44. Willms, W.: "Der Flugzeugschall, seine Entstehung, Ausbreitung und Verminderung," Ringbuch V D 2 der Luftfahrttechnik, 1937.
45. Davis, Jr., D. D., G. L. Stevens, Jr., D. Moore, and G. M. Stokes: *NACA Tech. Note* 2893, 1953.
46. Fleming, N.: *J. Royal Aero. Soc.*, **58**: 245 (1954).
47. Martin, H., U. Schmidt, and W. Willms: *Motortechnische Zeitschrift*, **12**: 377 (1940); **1**: 11 (1941).
48. Davis, D. D., Jr., and K. R. Czarnecki: *NACA Tech. Note* 1838, 1949.
49. Davis, A. H. (with Appendix by N. Fleming): *Report No. N.* 108, *British N.P.L.* (*Report No.* 1421, *A.R.C.*), 1935.
50. Czarnecki, K. R., and D. D. Davis, Jr.: *NACA Tech. Note* 1688, 1948.
51. Beranek, L. L., F. S. Elwell, J. P. Roberts, and C. F. Taylor: *NACA Tech. Note* 2079, 1950.
52. Hubbard, H. H., and A. A. Regier: *NACA Tech. Note* 1358, 1947.
53. Hubbard, H. H.: *NACA Tech. Note* 2968, 1953.
54. Grigler, J. L., and R. E. Tagnis: *NACA Tech. Note* 1338, 1947.
55. Gilman, Jr., Jean: *NACA Tech. Note* 2966, 1953.
56. Rogers, O. R.: *Army Air Force Technical Report No.* 5446, 1946.
57. Parkin, P. H., and H. J. Purkis: *Acustica*, **4**: 439 (1954).
58. Lighthill, M. J.: *Proc. Royal Soc.*, **222A**: 1–32 (1954).
59. Brown, G. B.: *Proc. Phys. Soc.*, **49**: 493 (1937).
60. von Gierke, H. E.: *Zeitschrift fuer Angewandte Physik*, **2**: 97 (1950).
61. Proudman, I.: *Proc. Royal Soc.*, **214A**: 119 (1952).
62. Richards, E. J.: *J. Roy. Aero. Soc.*, **57**: 318 (1953).
63. Ribner, H. S.: *NACA Tech. Note* 3255, 1954.
64. Lighthill, M. J.: *Proc. Camb. Phil. Soc.*, **49**: 531 (1953).
65. Powell, A.: *Aircraft Engineering*, **XXVI** (299): 2 (1954).
66. Powell, A.: *Proc. Phys. Soc.* (1954).
67. Fitzpatrick, H. M., and R. Lee: *David W. Taylor Model Basin Report* 835, 1952.
68. Hubbard, H. H., and L. W. Lassiter: *J. Acoust. Soc. Am.*, **25**: 363 (1953).
69. Lassiter, L. W., and H. H. Hubbard: *NACA Tech. Note* 2757, 1952.
70. Westley, R., and G. M. Lilley: *The College of Aeronautics*, Cranfield, England, *Report No.* 53, 1952.
71. Lee, R.: *David W. Taylor Model Basin Report* 868, 1953.
72. Tyler, J. M., and E. C. Perry: Jet Noise, presented at the SAE meeting in New York, April 14, 1954. *Report No. PWA Inst. 451*, Pratt & Whitney Aircraft, 1954.
73. Callaghan, E. E., W. J. North, and N. D. Sanders: *Aero. Engrg. Rev.*, p. 66 (June, 1955). See also N. D. Sanders and E. E. Callaghan: Recent NACA Investigations of Noise Reduction Devices on Full-scale Jet Engines. Report on NACA Conference on Some Problems of Aircraft Operation, 1954, at Lewis Flight Propulsion Laboratory, Cleveland, Ohio.
74. Lassiter, L. W., and H. H. Hubbard,: *NACA Tech. Note* 3187, 1954.
75. Powell, A.: *J. Acoust. Soc. Am.*, **25**: 363 (1953).
76. von Gierke, H. E., H. O. Parrack, W. J. Gannon, R. G. Hansen: *J. Acoust. Soc. Am.*, **24**: 162 (1952).
77. Lassiter, L. W.: *NACA Tech. Note* 2756, 1952.
78. North, W. J., E. E. Callaghan, and C. D. Lanzo: *NACA Res. Memo.* E54G07, 1954.
79. Mercer, D. M. A.: "Correlation of Turbojet Noise with Engine Design," paper read at the 48th Meeting of the Acoust. Soc. Am., Austin, Texas, 1954.

80. Mercy, K. R., and M. Bernstein: Investigation of Jet Aircraft Noise for XF3H-1 and F7U-3 Aircraft on Board USS Coral Sea (CVA43), *Final Report*, 1953. *Naval Material Laboratory, New York Naval Shipyard*, 5280-9.
81. Greatrex, F. B.: *J. Royal Aero. Soc.*, **58**: 223 (1954).
82. Greatrex, F. B.: Jet Noise, *Fifth International Aeronautical Conference*, June, 1955, *Inst. Aero. Sci., Inc.*, preprint 559, *Aviation Age*, **25**: 59 (1956).
83. North, W. J.: *NACA Tech. Note* 3516, July, 1955.
84. Mawardi, O. K., and I. Dyer: *J. Acoust. Soc. Am.*, **25**: 363 (1953).
85. Tyler, J. M.: *Noise Control*, **1**: 46 (March, 1955). (Also: *General Turbine Information Letter, No. 14*. Installation Engineering, *Pratt & Whitney Aircraft*, November, 1954.)
86. Pietrasanta, A. C.: *J. Acoust. Soc. Am.*, **28**: 434 (1956).
87. Powell, A.: *Aeronautical Quarterly*, **IV**: 341 (1954).
88. Callaghan, E. E., W. Howes, and W. North: *NACA Res. Memo.* E54B01, 1954.
89. Mercer, M. A., and the Staff of Bolt, Beranek, and Newman, Inc.: *USAF, WADC Tech. Report* 54-224, July, 1954.
90. Tyler, J. M., and G. B. Towle: *Noise Control*, **1**: 37 (July, 1955).
91. Callaghan, E. E., and W. D. Coles: *NACA Tech. Note* 3452, 1955.
92. Bolt, Beranek, and Newman, Inc.: *USAF, WADC Tech. Report* 54-401, 1955.
93. Bolt, Beranek, and Newman, Inc.: *USAF, WADC Tech. Report* 55-471, 1955.
94. Sterbentz, W. H., and J. C. Evvard: *NACA Tech. Note* 3506, August, 1955.
95. Powell, A.: *J. Helicopter Assoc.*, Great Britain, **7** (1): (1953).
96. Veneklasen, P. S.: *J. Acoust. Soc. Am.*, **25**: 363 (1953).
97. Veneklasen, P. S., and L. Emmerich: *American Helicopter Company, Inc. Report No. 163-K-3*, 1952.
98. Veneklasen, P. S., and L. Emmerich: *American Helicopter Company, Inc. Report No. 163-K-2*, 1952.
99. Lassiter, L. W., and R. H. Heitkotter: *NACA Tech. Note* 3316, 1954.
100. Measurements of the Effect of Water Injection on the Noise of a Rocket Motor, National Physics Laboratory, *England Physics Dept. Report*, November, 1951. (Reported in Ref. 62.)
101. Hubbard, H. H., and L. W. Lassiter: *NACA Tech. Note* 3239, August, 1954.
102. Lilley, G. M., R. Westley, A. H. Yates, and J. R. Busing: *J. of Royal Aero. Soc.*, **57**: 396 (1953).
103. Warren, C. H. E.: *J. Royal Aero. Soc.*, **58**: 239 (1954).
104. Courant, R., and K. O. Friedrichs: "Supersonic Flow and Shock Waves," Interscience Publishers, 1948.
105. Whitham, G. B.: *Proc. Royal Soc. A*, **201**: 89 (1950).
106. Whithan, G. B.: *Communications in Pure and Applied Mathematics*, **5**: 301 (1952).
107. DuMond, J. W. M., *et al.*: *J. Acoust. Soc. Am.*, **18**: 97 (1946).
108. Daum, F. D., and N. Smith: *USAF, WADC Tech. Note* 55-203, 1955.
109. Walters, A. G.: *J. Royal Aero. Soc.*, **57**: 719 (1953).
110. Mullens, M. E.: *USAF, AFFTC Tech. Note* 56-20, 1956.
111. Eldred, K. M., and D. T. Kryazis: *USAF WADC Tech. Note* 56-280, 1956.
112. von Gierke, H. E., J. N. Cole, K. M. Eldred, M. Fass, L. O. Hoeft, and D. T. Kyrazis: *J. Acoust. Soc. Am.*, **28**: 804 (1956).
113. Cole, J. N., D. T. Kryazis, and H. L. Oestreicher: *USAF WADC Tech. Note* 56-448, 1956.
114. Sanders, N. D., and E. E. Callaghan: *Noise Control*, **2**: 43 (November, 1956).
115. Withington, H. W.: *Noise Control*, **2**: 46 (September, 1956).
116. Cole, J. N., K. M. Eldred, L. O. Hoeft, A. J. Humphrey, D. T. Kyrazis, and H. E. von Gierke: "Prediction of Rocket and Turbojet Noise," presented at 52d meeting of Acoustical Society of America, November 15, 1956. (To be published as *USAF WADC Tech. Report*, 1957.)
117. Kyrazis, D. T., and J. N. Cole: "Noise Generated by Solid Propellent Rockets," paper presented at 52d meeting of Acoustical Society of America, November 15, 1956. (To be published as *WADC Tech. Note*, 1957.)
118. Cole, J. N: *USAF WADC Tech. Note* 56-335. 1956.

Chapter 34

AIRCRAFT NOISE CONTROL

Henning E. von Gierke, Dr. Eng.

Aero Medical Laboratory, Wright Air Development Center

INTRODUCTION

Requirement for Noise Control. The acoustical power output of aircraft noise sources is discussed in Chap. 33. Methods of control of aircraft noise are presented in this chapter. Since noise fields in and around an aircraft on the ground or in flight can be predicted with sufficient accuracy to estimate their effects on man and structures when the aircraft is operated, it is no longer justifiable to neglect noise considerations in the design stage of aircraft and in planning certain aircraft operations. For once an aircraft is built or the site for an airport selected, noise-control possibilities are limited and may necessitate expenses which careful analysis of the noise problem at an early stage easily could have avoided. For this reason, it is necessary to consider the over-all system early in planning to arrive at the most practical and most economical solution of noise control. For example, mufflers for reciprocating engines should be designed as an integral part of the air frame and not as a later modification; this is equally true for acoustical treatment of the cabin. Ground run-up mufflers for jet aircraft should be developed and tested as part of the aircraft system, when need for them can be anticipated, instead of waiting until serious noise problems with the operational aircraft make their development unavoidable. Aircraft maintenance procedures determine noise levels and duration of the exposure of maintenance personnel and must, therefore, be analyzed together with the noise situation at an early stage, when modifications are still possible. The location and design of sensitive electronic and mechanical equipment in the aircraft must be selected to minimize the effects of noise on their operation. Airport planning should, through proper layout of the field and adequate zoning around the field, reduce possible future noise problems (see Chap. 35).

For assessing a noise situation, design criteria have been developed specifying human tolerance to noise exposure. In spite of the fact that most of these criteria must be considered as tentative, they can be used as general guide for arriving at certain noise-control specifications. They have to be modified and adapted to given situations. Operational or economic reasons might force a compromise between the desired and the practically attainable noise levels. They will also guide the decision as to whether noise reduction at the source or at the receiver is the better solution. Such design criteria for practical use are listed below for completeness, without an analysis of their scientific background and limitations.

Design Criteria. *Impairment of Human Hearing.* Negligible risk of damage to hearing is assumed if the noise to which people are exposed for an eight-hour work day

Note: References with * in this chapter refer to references in Chap. 33.

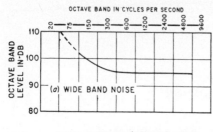

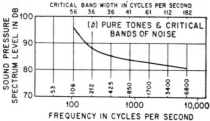

FIG. 34.1. Criteria for damage risk to hearing for lifetime exposure (8-hr work day) of the unprotected ear to noise. (a) Damage-risk criteria for octave-band levels of continuous wideband noise, (b) Damage-risk criteria for sound pressure level of pure tones and for levels in critical bands of noise (the critical bands in cps for the center frequencies of the octave bands are given above the graphs). (*From The Staff of Bolt, Beranek, and Newman, Inc.*[4*])

* See Reference 4, Chap. 33.

over months and years is kept below the criteria specified in Fig. 34.1.[4*] These criteria cannot be applied too precisely, but serve as a general guide to prevent noise-induced hearing loss (see Chap. 7). If personal protective equipment is worn (see Chap. 8), these criteria can be raised by the average amount of protection afforded. If the daily exposure time is less than a continuous eight-hour work day, the allowable noise levels can probably be increased by 3 db for each halving of the exposure time, assuming constant noise energy exposure. Criteria, based on this assumption, for short-time exposure to the spectrum of typical jet-exhaust noise are given in Fig. 34.2.[1]

Regardless of exposure time, the unprotected ear should not be routinely exposed to over-all sound pressure levels above 135 db (pain threshold for "tender" ears); the protected ear, regardless of the degree of protection, should not be exposed to over-all sound pressure levels above 150 db (limit for nonauditory effects). Occasional brief exposure of the unprotected ear to sound pressure levels above the pain threshold is usually without harmful effect as long as the level is below 150 to 160 db re 0.0002 microbar (the threshold range for mechanical damage to the

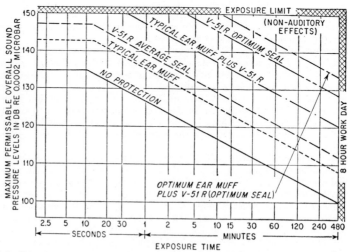

FIG. 34.2. Criteria for damage risk to hearing for short time exposure to jet-type noise. The maximum permissible over-all sound pressure level of jet-exhaust noise is given as a function of the average daily exposure time for the protected and unprotected ear. "V-51R" refers to data for the V-51R earplug. (*From Eldred, Gannon, and Von Gierke.*[1])

middle ear). The effects of such exposures are of an accumulative nature, and satisfactory protection is available; therefore, such unprotected exposures should be avoided.

Interference with Human Performance. Sound pressure levels of the order of 140 db and above are considered threshold levels for the initiation of disturbances to a large number of important body functions. Protecting the ear or head appears to prevent most of these disturbances.

No general criteria exist to assess man's complex, behavioral response to noise levels below 140 db when speech communication is not involved. Although significant decrements in the performance of mental or motor tasks have not been reported, increased fatigue and changes in motivation toward the job are, at least in some groups of individuals, indications that noise control is required, and in the long run will be more economical.

Noise principally affects human performance in tasks requiring communication. Therefore, speech-interference levels (Chap. 9) or more accurate methods of computing the interfering effects of noise on speech communication are sometimes used to specify noise environments for certain classes of people, as, for example, office workers, shop workers, or aircraft passengers. Recent investigations have shown that aircraft noise influences speech communication in offices in the same predictable way as industrial noise.[2] The allowable degree of interference with speech differs for the various groups of people and depends primarily on the quality of communication necessary and the required working time in noise. Jobs involving important operations (for example, pilots, control-tower operators, etc.) require very reliable communication. Message complexity and familiarity with subject matter also influence the allowable noise for a specified quality of communication.

Interference with Comfort and the Arousal of Annoyance. Since comfort and annoyance are very complex human responses,

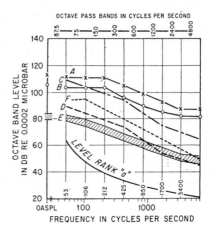

OCTAVE PASS BANDS IN CYCLES PER SECOND

(A) MILITARY AIRCRAFT (HIAD) ACCEPTABLE NOISE LEVELS FOR NORMAL RATED POWER CONDITION

(B) MILITARY AIRCRAFT (HIAD) ACCEPTABLE NOISE LEVELS FOR NORMAL CRUISE POWER CONDITION

(C) BORDERLINE QUASI-COMFORT AND UNCOMFORTABLE

(D) BORDERLINE COMFORTABLE AND IDEALLY QUIET

(E) DESIRABLE NOISE LEVELS FOR FUTURE AIR TRANSPORT

(F) BRITISH R.A.E. RECOMMENDED MAX LEVEL FOR CRUISE

FIG. 34.3. Design criteria for sound levels in aircraft (see text). Noise level rank "a" is given for comparison as the level not to be exceeded by continuous aircraft noises in suburban communities if any annoyance from the noise has to be avoided. [(A) and (B) from Ref. 12, (C) and (D) from Lippert and Miller,[3] (E) from McFarland,[4] (F) from Greatrex.[81*]]

criteria that establish their respective boundaries for noise exposure have not been accurately determined. Available criteria are very tentative and it is necessary to caution against their generalized use without reference to the specific condition for which they were established.

"Comfort" criteria for airline passengers, based on airline experience, are given in Fig. 34.3.[3] Higher noise levels than the borderline "quasi-comfort and uncomfortable" are definitely considered uncomfortable—optimum comfort exists only for levels well below this criterion. Comfort as defined by this criterion is probably closely related to good passenger-to-passenger speech communication.

Annoyance of people in residential areas on the ground due to aircraft noise has been a matter of increasing importance during the last years. Annoyance with the presence of noise can arise from interference with conversation; from interference with sleep; from its effect in rattling windows; from noise-stimulated fear reaction and many other causes. Criteria exist only to estimate the average expected over-all response of a normal population to all these disturbances and they are widely used in practical noise control (Chap. 36). Two things must be kept in mind: First, that these criteria are criteria for "expressed annoyance"—annoyance without expression will often exist at still lower noise ratings—and second, that these are over-all response curves for a population—annoyance to single individuals can be much more severe. For comparison, noise-level rank a (Fig. 36.4) is plotted in Fig. 34.3. Noise spectra of continuous noises being below this curve in all bands should result in no annoyance whatsoever in a suburban community with no previous adjustment to noise exposure. Criteria close to this level rank, or leveling off at a level of 32 db for the bands above 600 cps, are often referred to as "sleep-and-rest criteria," although the noise rating method by means of level ranks constitutes a refinement of these earlier criteria.

Effects of Noise on Structures and Equipment. No general criteria exist to assess damage of structures and malfunction of equipment due to noise. Fatigue failure of air-frame panels due to resonances has been observed in laboratory tests and in actual jet-noise fields of over-all sound levels above 150 db. In addition to material and plate thickness, the sound pressure distribution (frequency, amplitude, phase) over the exposed surface and the manner by which the panel is fastened at the edges to the supporting structure seem to be the principal variables.[46,47]

So far, structures on the ground have not been affected severely by aircraft noise and no problems are anticipated in this area. Rattling of windows and detectable vibrations of objects in residential buildings close to take-off flight paths of aircraft might be annoying and might result from relatively low sound levels, but actual mechanical damage is very unlikely and practically unreported. Exceptions include the effects of sonic boom (Chap. 33). Here, peak sound pressure levels of 130 db and above have caused the breakage of window panes. With increasing peak level, damages become more severe and can best be compared to the effects of explosive blast of the same amplitude. Other exceptions are given by the effects of aircraft engine noise on noise-control structures such as run-up noise suppressors or test cells, where the noise induced vibration levels must be well controlled.

Although some electronic equipment is affected by sound levels of the order of 120 to 130 db, it seems that for present-day standard aircraft components and installation practices a more severe limitation is reached in sound levels above 145 to 150 db. At these high levels special components, special mounting, and special noise control become necessary for the proper functioning of equipment.

Selection of Practical Design Criteria. For practical application, design criteria for noise control are usually a compromise between the different criteria and a technically and economically feasible solution. Desired speech communication may determine the noise-level requirements in the speech-interference bands, while comfort or damage risk to hearing may require restriction of the noise levels in other bands. Exposure time to noise, the feasibility of using personnel protective equipment, the possibility of improving mouth-to-ear communication by electronic systems in certain spaces, and the attitude of the exposed people toward the noise are only a few of the most important variables that the acoustical engineer must concern himself with before selection of a criterion.

NOISE INSIDE THE AIRPLANE AND ITS REDUCTION[4,36*,37*]

The Cabin. The noise inside an aircraft cabin has its origin in air-borne and structure-borne sound from the engine and in aerodynamic or boundary-layer noise associated with the flow of air over the fuselage skin. In addition, noise from auxiliary equipment, generators, and particularly ventilation-system outlets and air-conditioning systems ("de-ice" and "defrost" conditions in military jet aircraft) is often a serious problem. This noise from auxiliary equipment can exceed sound levels due to engine and aerodynamic noise unless special consideration is given this problem. There is no general, quantitative method for predicting the noise from structure-borne vibrations, and in most cases the noise radiated from the structure is less than the air-borne transmitted noise.[37]*

Vibration may be suspected as an important noise source only if the measured noise levels in the airplane exceed considerably the values calculated for the air-borne noise. (As a practical rule on propeller-driven aircraft, noise produced by engine vibration must be assumed to be significant if the octave level below 75 cps is considerably higher than the level in the 75- to 150-cps band.)   Engine vibration is reduced by selecting a low natural frequency for the engine suspension, i.e., less than 50 cps.   Then, for vibrations above the natural frequency, the attenuation increases 6 db per octave. Vibrational energy which is transmitted by the engine mounts is propagated to the cabin with little loss, vibrating the panels and thereby radiating sound.

The air-borne noise surrounding the cabin is reduced as it is transmitted through the fuselage from the outside to the inside of the compartment.   In estimating the sound reduction, one assumes a nearly uniform acoustical enclosure surrounded by a uniform outside sound field, which produces a nearly diffuse sound field inside.[37]* Under these assumptions the noise reduction equals

$$\text{Noise Reduction} = 10 \log \left(1 + \frac{\alpha}{\tau}\right) = 10 \log \left(1 + \frac{a}{T}\right) \quad \text{db} \quad (34.1)$$

Here α and τ are the average absorption and transmission coefficients of the bounding surfaces, which in the case of a non-uniform enclosure must be replaced by the total number of absorption units a and total number of transmission units T (Chap. 20). The transmission coefficient decreases with increasing frequency; above the panel's resonances it is only a function of the panel weight.   The absorption coefficient increases if porous trim cloth is used inside the cabin and decreases for non-porous trim cloth.   With these coefficients known, the levels inside the cabin can be calculated when the average outside sound field is known, and by proper selection of these coefficients the inside noise level can be controlled.

The cabin structure includes the "dural" skin, having a thickness of 0.02 in. to 0.05 in., and the windows.   Absorption within the cabin is furnished by the clothes of personnel, upholstery of seats, carpet, and acoustical material installed over the surface area of the cabin.   Multiple structures, composed of layers of acoustical material covered by an impervious septum, are installed for this purpose at some distance from the skin.

The Outside Noise Levels.   *Boundary-layer Noise.*   In modern high-speed aircraft traveling under cruising conditions (above 200 mph) aerodynamic noise of the boundary-layer noise type is the predominant noise source in the frequency range above 600 cps. Complete information on this type of noise and on its correlation with the turbulent boundary layer is still lacking but theoretical approaches have been published.[5,6]   It appears that the peak of the pressure spectrum acting on the outside cabin wall shifts to higher frequencies as the velocity increases.   High energy levels have been measured in the boundary layer from 500 cps up to 70,000 cps.[6]*   The measurements were made on the inner side of the cabin wall, and from these data the levels outside were calculated by considering the wall attenuation.   This noise level is called the "external noise field," but it is not a noise field in the usual sense.   The pressure fluctuations due to the turbulent boundary layer vibrate the fuselage skin in a manner equivalent to an excitation by an external noise field which is assumed to be uniformly distributed around the fuselage.   The most exact measurements exist for the important frequency bands 600 to 1,200 cps, 1,200 to 2,400 cps, and 2,400 to 9,600 cps,[7] for which boundary-layer noise was measured accurately both in a large glider and in a diving jet aircraft with idling engine.   The noise increased approximately as the 2.75th power of the indicated airspeed.   An evaluation of the noise levels in more than 20 multiengine propeller-driven aircraft, turbojets, and gliders showed that the noise levels at the outside cabin walls in these frequency bands were always within ± 4 db of the boundary-layer noise measured on the glider.   This indicated clearly that for all these airplanes, boundary-layer noise is the predominant noise source in the frequency bands 600 to

9,600 cps. The levels for these "external noise fields" are given in Fig. 34.4 as a function of the indicated airspeed. In this frequency range, within the limits of accuracy of the curves (± 4 db), the levels seem to be independent of aircraft size and shape. Altitude and temperature have little effect on the boundary-layer noise, and their

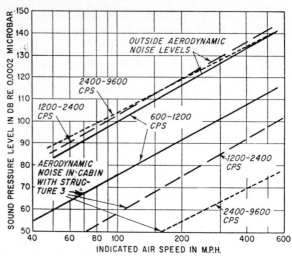

FIG. 34.4. Aerodynamic noise levels outside the aircraft fuselage as a function of the flight speed. The corresponding noise levels inside a cabin with soundproofing "structure 3" (see Fig. 34.9) are given by the lower three curves. (*From Rogers and Cook.*[7])

effects are not in the same direction in all frequency bands. In general, at higher altitude the noise at the same airspeed is somewhat less than at a lower altitude, but these influences can be neglected within the limits of accuracy of Fig. 34.4. Earlier measurements for higher frequencies[6]* indicate that the noise increases with velocity, up to the eighth power of the velocity. (A similar trend seems to be indicated by more recent unpublished data with microphones mounted flush on the outside of the fuselage skin, and these data also show considerable variation of the actual outside pressures for different microphone positions over the fuselage.)

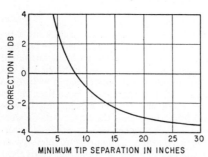

FIG. 34.5. Correction in db as function of minimum propeller-tip clearance for the calculation of propeller noise according to Eq. (34.2). (*From Rudmose and Beranek.*[37]*)

Boundary-layer noise is responsible for a noise level below which a change in engine, propeller, or jet noise cannot reduce the outside noise field. Noise control, therefore, must always reduce this noise under cruising conditions to acceptable levels inside the aircraft. Thus, Fig. 34.4 gives the basic data for such noise control considerations.

Propeller Engine Noise. In the octave bands up to 150 cps the propeller noise is usually the principal noise source on the outside wall of the fuselage, especially in the forward part of the airplane. It predominates up to 600 cps where, under cruising conditions, it disappears in the boundary-layer noise. However, for single-engine aircraft, vortex noise from the propeller may increase the levels indicated in Fig. 34.4 at frequencies above 600 cps. In general, it was found by measurements on some 50 aircraft of the 1941–1945 type[37]* that the low-frequency octave-band spectrum up to

600 cps is flat within ±3 db outside the fuselage, a characteristic now generally assumed in noise-control calculations. The average sound pressure level in the octave bands below 150 cps in a "typical cabin" can be found from the power-level chart of Fig. 33.21 by calculating the space-average pressure level at 20 ft distance from the propeller center, and subtracting 6.5-db average-noise reduction provided by the cabin. This value is assumed for a minimum propeller-tip clearance of 8 in. For

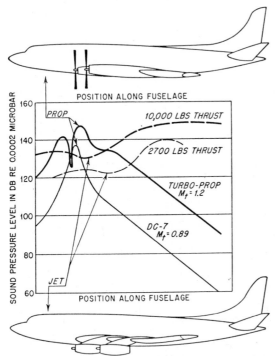

Fig. 34.6. Sound pressure distribution of propeller and jet noise along the fuselage of a transport aircraft with four engines. The heavy lines compare a hypothetical turboprop transport to a jet transport of the same airplane speed (480 mph) and the same operating altitude (35,000 ft). Both curves are calculated; aerodynamic noise is not considered. The fine lines give the calculated pressure distribution along the fuselage of a DC-7 and the jet noise distribution measured with a small jet engine (2,770-lb static thrust) placed in a realistic position under the wing of a transport airplane. (*From Miller and Pollock.*[8])

other values of propeller tip clearance, the corrections given by Fig. 34.5 must be applied. Thus, the over-all level in the cabin is

$$L_p = [L_w - 43 + \text{(correction tip clearance)}] \qquad \text{db} \qquad (34.2)$$

According to Fig. 33.23, the levels in the octave bands up to 150 cps are 2 to 5 db below the over-all level. This sound pressure level is found in a typical cabin, at about 2 ft from the wall in an area in the cabin within 6 ft of the plane of the inboard propellers.[37]* For propellers with supersonic tip speeds, the use of the same power-level chart is suggested, in the absence of more complete data.

Farther away from the plane of rotation the low-frequency noise levels outside and inside the cabin decrease considerably. As an example, Fig. 34.6 shows the calculated propeller sound pressure distribution along the fuselage of a turbo-propeller transport of the future.[8] The change of noise level with tip clearance as indicated in Fig. 34.5 (and which can be calculated for either the stationary propeller or the propeller in flight) is very pronounced only in a narrow area near the plane of rotation. Farther from the propeller in the axial direction, the noise level is only slightly influenced by increasing the tip clearance. Therefore, such a design change reduces excessive high noise levels only in restricted locations of the fuselage, but it does not influence larger areas. For design calculations of air-frame structures the noise measurement positions around propellers recommended by the aircraft industry (Fig. 33.4) are helpful in determining the air-borne forces acting on the fuselage.

Direction of rotation of the propellers changes the fuselage wall pressure and the cabin noise, since an advancing blade results in a higher pressure than a retreating blade.[11*,33*]

In multiengine aircraft, phasing between the propellers has considerable influence on the noise output. The noise is minimum in the out-of-phase position and maximum in the in-phase position; the absolute value of maximum and minimum depends on the spectrum. Differences of 6 db and more are often observed. Therefore, careful control of the engine phase in multiengine aircraft can be used to minimize the noise. Inaccurate synchronization results in a changing phase between the engines so that the blades vary between positions of maximum and minimum noise. When this occurs, undesirable beats are observed.

Jet-engine Noise. The noise field of a jet engine is not greatly affected by its installation in an aircraft. Noise levels around the forward section of the fuselage, where the pilot's compartment is located, are lower than those in comparable propeller-driven aircraft; in flight the jet noise is always negligible compared to the boundary-layer noise. In contrast to this (and to the pressure distribution on the fuselage of a propeller-driven plane), the maximum sound pressure levels in multijet aircraft are usually located toward the rear of the fuselage as shown in Fig. 34.6. Noise-level measurements in the same aircraft propelled either by propeller or jet engines of the same thrust demonstrate this difference between jet and propeller aircraft most clearly.[9] The fuselage may be exposed to the noise maxima found in the axial pressure distribution along the jet boundary (Fig. 33.27). Narrow areas of the fuselage wall may be exposed to sound maxima which differ in frequency, the higher frequencies being farther upstream. Model tests indicate that the presence of a fuselage panel parallel to the jet has little influence on the axial station of the maximum pressure, but increases the sound pressure level by as much as 5 db above the free-field value. Exposure of structures to the near-field pressure, which increases rapidly in the vicinity of the jet, should be avoided. Small differences in the radial distance from the jet boundary may change the sound pressure level considerably.

Specific problems can be evaluated in detail in the light of the existing model studies or free-field measurements on jets.[116*] Jet models combined with aircraft models provide a valuable tool for structural considerations.

For estimating the noise levels inside the fuselage, estimates of the levels around the fuselage can be obtained from Chap. 33 (see *Aircraft Jet-engine Noise*), although very little such information exists in published reports.[8,10] In the higher frequency range, where noise control becomes necessary and where it is effective, most of the jet noise is overshadowed by boundary-layer noise.[7,11]

In single-jet aircraft, engine noise from nonaerodynamic sources is easily transmitted to the cockpit and may require special attention.

Noise Control. *Desired and Measured Noise Levels inside the Aircraft.* When the noise levels outside the fuselage are known, the noise levels inside the fuselage can be calculated by means of Eq. (34.1). The transmission coefficient of single nonporous panels (dural skin, windows) decreases roughly as the square of the surface density and the square of the frequency (Chap. 20), and the noise reduction increases, theoretically, 6 db per octave and 6 db for double thickness. Without additional absorption inside the airplane's compartments, the levels will be too high to assure effective speech communication or moderate comfort; here, noise-control design must provide additional absorption. The design criteria for the level inside the airplane depend on the mission of the airplane, the exposure time of crew and passengers, and the desired comfort. Certain comfort criteria based on airline experience are shown in Fig. 34.3. A similar curve between the two comfort criteria is the British RAE recommended maximum noise level for cruising speed in civilian aircraft, which is also shown in Fig. 34.3. Typical average levels in current civilian and military aircraft are presented in Fig. 34.7 for comparison. Most civilian air transports are designed for noise levels well below the borderline "quasi-comfort and uncomfortable" criteria, with speech-interference levels around 70 db. For aircraft of shorter flying time, e.g., helicopters, higher noise levels might not be objectionable. The noise-level requirements for military airplanes, where mission capability and personnel protection, rather than comfort, are the basis for the tolerable noise levels, are also shown in Fig. 34.3, and they deviate somewhat from the comfort criteria.[12] The "acceptable noise levels" are based on a low risk of permanent hearing loss of regularly exposed personnel and on the need for direct mouth-to-ear communication.

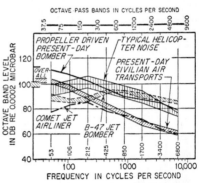

Fig. 34.7. Representative sound pressure levels in present-day civilian and military aircraft.

All comfort and design criteria published to date, including the speech-interference levels, are based only on experience with propeller-driven aircraft. There are indications that these criteria must be modified for jet aircraft, where the noise spectrum is flatter than for propeller-driven aircraft. Flat jet spectra which are below the RAE recommended levels F in Fig. 34.3 in the two lowest octave bands, but above these levels in the higher bands (10 db and more in the 4,800- to 9,600-cps band), are universally acknowledged as quiet and comfortable. Therefore, modifications of these criteria may be required for civilian jet aircraft.[81*]

Design criteria are usually specified for cruise conditions. For take-off in propeller and jet aircraft, the levels are usually 10 to 15 db higher than cruise levels; they may be as much as 5 db above cruise level for the climbing aircraft. For the pilot, even under take-off condition, reliable radio communication is necessary. In determining the speech interference of the noise and maximum permissible levels, the benefit the pilot obtains from wearing noise-shielding headsets (10 to 40 db in speech-frequency range) must be taken into account. For military aircraft, acceptable noise levels during take-off, afterburner operation, and other conditions not exceeding 5 min continuous operation are, for all octave bands, 7 db above the acceptable levels specified for the normal rated power condition (curve A, Fig. 34.3).[12] The noise levels inside the aircraft compartment vary somewhat with the position. This is caused by the nonuniformity of the outside sound field and standing waves in the compartment. The sound level rises toward the walls as much as 6 db in the higher frequency bands.

Noise-level measurements inside the airplane should be made at the pilot's or passenger's head positions. The noise levels for the entire passenger compartment should be reported as the plotted maximum and minimum noise level for each octave for all positions measured (cabin-noise envelope). Standard cabin noise-level test conditions[10*] are proposed as follows: aircraft in straight and level flight at 8,000-ft altitude for an unpressurized cabin (20,000 ft for pressurized cabin with inside pressure equivalent to 8,000 ft); all engines synchronized except right inboard engine, which will be out of synchronization so as to produce beats of 1 or 2 cps.

Noise-control Treatment. The requirements of adequate speech communication for pilot and crew as well as passenger comfort necessitate greatest noise reduction in the speech interference bands, i.e., the octave bands 600 to 1,200 cps, 1,200 to 2,400 cps, 2,400 to 4,800 cps. The required noise reduction is the difference between the design criteria (Fig. 34.3) and the estimated outside noise levels. Calculations or preliminary measurements in the untreated aircraft will supply the outside noise spectrum indicating whether the power-plant or aerodynamic noise is the predominant noise source.

[In practice, actual noise measurements in the aircraft, in aircraft of similar construction, or in special fuselage test sections exposed to aircraft noise fields on the ground are usually preferred to theoretical calculations of outside and inside noise levels. Noise treatment is then designed or modified from experience and the theoretical Equation (34.1) is used only as qualitative guidance.]

The outside noise level is first attenuated by the nonporous single panel of the structure. Its attenuation [the transmission loss of the panel is given by $TL = 10 \log (1/\tau)$] is primarily a function of the surface density for frequencies above 600 cps. It can be obtained from Fig. 34.8 for various thicknesses of the dural skin. Additional noise reduction is usually obtained by using a multiple wall structure which has a depth of 1 to 4 in. and is lined with sound-absorptive material. The acoustical material frequently is applied in the form of "insulating" blankets, consisting of a nonporous panel to which various layers of acoustical material have been added. This blanket (1 to 2 in. thick) is spaced at a distance of approximately 1 in. from the structure. For an especially effective structure this blanket may be followed by a second air-gap and a second blanket of lesser thickness. Sound transmission through such multiple structures consisting of two impervious layers, an air space, and two flexible acoustical blankets has been studied experimentally and theoretically for a wide variation of the parameters.[13,14,15] Depending on the acoustical material and the spacing, large differences in the transmission coefficient are obtained. For lightweight material [as, for example, the material described in specification MIL-B-5924 (USAF) Type 1] the transmission loss of the total structure depends only on the sum of the septa and acoustical material surface density and the surface density of the dural panel for frequencies above 600 cps, provided that the total weight of all septa does not exceed the weight of the acoustical material.[7] Fig. 34.9 shows three examples of structures of this type which are widely used. The transmission loss for these structures is shown in Fig. 34.8. The interrelation between attenuation, weight, and noise reduction is also illustrated by this graph. Taking the attenuation values at 600, 1,200, and 2,400 cps in Fig. 34.8 and subtracting them from the octave-band levels of aerodynamic noise in Fig. 34.4 gives the aerodynamic noise levels inside the different structures for the speech-interference bands (example in Fig. 34.4 for Structure 3).

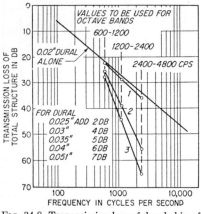

Fig. 34.8. Transmission loss of dural skin of different thickness and of the three aircraft-soundproofing structures given in Fig. 34.9. (*From Rogers and Cook.*[7])

On actual fuselages, deviations from the theoretical attenuation (calculated according to the method outlined in Ref. 15) are observed.[8] At low frequencies (below 200 cps) attenuation better than that predicted by simple mass law and detailed theory is obtained because of the beneficial effects of the fuselage's radial stiffness and panel curvature. At high frequencies the measured attenuation of a specific structure follows only the mass law and not the theoretical curve predicting greater attenuation, since flanking sound bypasses the soundproofing construction via windows, floors, hat racks, air-conditioning ducts, etc.

For calculating the total noise reduction according to Eq. (34.1), the absorption coefficient of the acoustical material covering the inside of the aircraft is required. Since inaccuracies of ±40 per cent in the total absorption produce errors in the calculated noise reduction given by this equation in the order of about ±2 db, only the approximate absorption coefficients for acoustical materials are required. Since all such commercial acoustical materials with a thickness greater than ½ in. have absorption coefficients greater than 0.44 at frequencies above 500 cps, the assumption of a nominal acoustic absorption coefficient of 0.72 is accurate enough for most calculations. For untreated areas of the cabin wall, e.g., windows, where the coefficient is frequently smaller than 0.1 and cannot easily be measured with an accuracy of ±40 per cent, the absorption coefficient need not be known within a factor of 150 per cent if these areas total less than the acoustically treated areas. Representative values of absorption

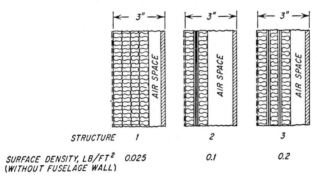

FIG. 34.9. Typical lightweight aircraft-soundproofing elements and constructions. Attenuation values obtained with these structures are given in Fig. 34.8. (*From Rogers and Cook.[7]*)

coefficients accurate enough to obtain a satisfactory estimation of the total absorption are given in Table 34.1.

With transmission and absorption coefficients of the total structure known, the total noise reduction afforded by the structure may be calculated from Eq. (34.1) by the proper estimation of different absorptive areas. The calculation may be repeated for different soundproofing structures until the design goal is achieved with an optimum compromise with respect to weight.

Table **34.1**. Representative Absorption Coefficients for Aircraft Cabin Materials[7]

Material	Frequency		
	600 cps	1,200 cps	2,400 cps
Acoustical material.....................	0.70	0.80	0.90
Wood, glass, metal.....................	0.05	0.05	0.05
Nonporous trim fabrics..................	0.60	0.40	0.20
One pilot or passenger..................	4.0 sabins	5.0 sabins	6.0 sabins

The acoustical materials used for sound insulation on aircraft must meet many requirements which are often not important for other noise-control applications: effective sound absorption, low weight, resistance to vibration, low thermal conductivity, high resistance to flame, low hygroscopicity, and chemical stability so that it will not corrode or lose its flame-resisting qualities. Materials such as cotton, glass, kapok, milkweed, plastics, mineral products, wool, rubber, and paper are most widely used. Trade names such as "Fiberglas," "Stonefelt," and "Kimsul" are the commercial designations of some of the most effective materials. Detailed evaluation reports of all these materials can be found in the literature, together with the derivation of the indices, such as "Merit Factor" and "Attenuation Efficiency Index," used for their evaluation.[36*,4,13,14] The requirement that materials used in aircraft do not readily absorb moisture and will dry quickly is very important for aircraft operating in areas of high humidity. For some materials (kapok), increases in the weight of the sound insulation of 30 per cent and more, due to the absorbed moisture,[4] were reported for operating periods of 18 months to several years. In general, mineral-base materials such as "Fiberglas" are superior to other materials with respect to hygroscopicity and weight.

For protection, cleaning purposes, and aesthetic reasons a trim cloth is usually applied to parts of the cabin wall surface of the insulation blanket. (On the average, approximately 50 per cent of the total absorptive area of the cabin interior is covered.) This material must be porous in order not to reduce significantly the effectiveness of the absorptive material (Table 34.1). Therefore, trim cloths such as wool and gabardine or perforation of otherwise nonporous fabrics are recommended.

As much as possible, acoustical insulation of aircraft should be combined with thermal insulation to save weight and to increase the effectiveness of the insulation. Air gaps required in the wall structure for acoustical purposes can serve as hot-air ducts for panel heating.[4]

Uniform distribution of the sound-absorptive material throughout the cabin or cockpit is very important. The calculation of an example using Eq. (34.1) will show readily the influence of untreated areas in the enclosure. It should be noted that this equation assumes uniform distribution of the sound energy—a condition fulfilled only if the enclosure wall is nearly uniform. A low transmission loss of a small wall area (for example, a window too thin compared to rest of skin) can raise the sound level in the vicinity of this area considerably without affecting the average level very much. (If the pilot's head is close to this window, the total sound treatment becomes ineffective for him.) Large areas of the enclosure without absorptive material may make the rest of the acoustic material almost useless. Therefore, it is better to install sound-proofing of lesser weight uniformly than to apply heavy treatment over a relatively small area.

Special emphasis must be placed on the detection and control of secondary noise sources, such as air-conditioning systems,[16] ventilators, electrical equipment, compressors, wind leaks, increased aerodynamic noise in certain areas of the fuselage, vibrating panels, ash trays, etc. These sources often nullify or reduce the benefit obtained from costly noise-control treatment, and proper attention with respect to noise control must be given these units individually, as early as possible in the design and installation stage.

The control of structure-borne noise and vibration goes hand in hand with air-borne noise control. Both must be reduced to the desired vibration levels and noise levels according to vibration-control practices (Chaps. 13 and 14).

THE NOISE AROUND AIRPORTS AND ITS REDUCTION

Prediction and Specification of Airport Noise Levels. The operation of an airfield presents a major aircraft-noise problem for ground personnel and nearby communities which calls for expert application of knowledge from all fields of noise control. This section considers only those noise-control procedures and methods which are peculiar to airfields.

On an airfield the noises resulting from the operation of different aircraft combine to become a complex *airfield noise source*—complex, not only because different aircraft having different power spectra and different times of operation are involved, but also because these individual noise sources are scattered over a wide area and many are in motion. It can be described in two ways: the airfield noise source is the sum of the single noise fields from the individual aircraft; this approach is useful in determining which individual source is most objectionable, and how much can be accomplished by noise control at this source. The second description is statistical. using the time pattern of the total noise at specific locations in the area around the field. This approach is preferable if one is interested in the correlation between the response of individuals or communities and the airfield noise source. Here the information concerning the origin of different noise components is usually omitted as not being pertinent to the particular problem.

Considering the first description, in terms of the individual noise sources, two classes of noise sources can be distinguished: (1) noise from flight operation, and (2) noise from ground operation. For both, the noise field around individual aircraft can be calculated from the information in Chap. 33 if complete data are available concerning

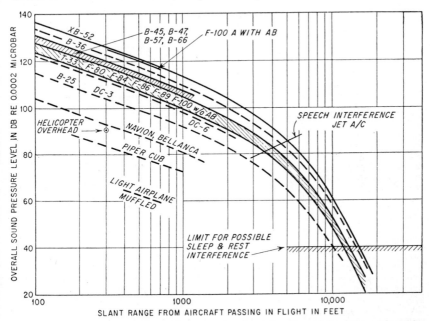

FIG. 34.10. Maximum over-all sound pressure level as a function of the distance from the aircraft's flight path. Data are given for commercial, military, and privately owned airplanes and jet and propeller aircraft. Minimum atmospheric absorption observed for the propagation of noise from aircraft in flight is assumed. For estimating noise from aircraft operating on the ground, increased absorption due to ground and terrain influences has to be considered.

the engines and the sound propagation through the atmosphere for the particular terrain existing at the airfield. At distances greater than 500 ft from a single source, fluctuations in the atmospheric attenuation usually set the limit on the accuracy of the noise-level predictions, rather than a restricted knowledge of the noise source. The sound from stationary aircraft on the ground or from very low-flying aircraft is much more rapidly attenuated than is sound from aircraft at higher altitudes; a knowledge and ability to predict both types of noise are required for distances up to 10 miles and more from the airport. In calculating the contribution of different airplanes to the total airfield noise source, certain (measured or estimated) standard meteorological conditions may be assumed. The noise field radiated from aircraft on the ground (pre-take-off run-up, or maintenance run-up) then can be calculated. Depending on the type of operation (for example, fixed position for run-up) the directivity pattern of a single source may be assumed to be oriented in a specified direction. If the aircraft may turn in any direction or if an arbitrary position for run-up is employed, it may be necessary to assume the maximum of the radiation pattern for every direction. For an aircraft taking off or landing, noise radiation from each point of its flight path must be considered.   The intersections of the ground plane with the surfaces of equal noise level surrounding the aircraft yield contours of equal noise level on the ground for each position of the aircraft.   The envelopes of such contours for a given flight path determine the locations on the ground which are exposed to the same peak noise level during the flight operation.   In this way the noise level versus time function for each point on the ground can be calculated and zones on the ground which are exposed to levels above certain criteria can be determined.   Alteration of these zones for different aircraft or flight patterns thus can be evaluated.   However, the change in the noise level versus time pattern and in the spectrum with distance from the airplane

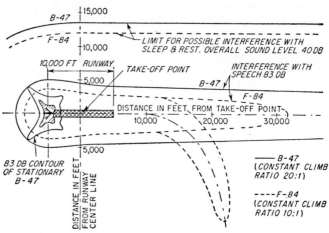

Fig. 34.11. Noise-level contours for climb-out of a jet bomber (B-47) and fighter (F-84) aircraft.   The contours are given for an over-all sound pressure level of 83 db, at which level the jet-type noise is assumed to interfere with speech communication (less than 90 per cent sentence intelligibility using a loud voice; speaker-to-listener distance, 3 ft).   The shaded area around the stationary aircraft indicates the "damage-risk zone" for continuous exposure.   The 40-db over-all sound pressure level contours are given to indicate the possible distance up to which the take-off noise might interfere with sleep and rest.   All contours are computed for minimal atmospheric absorption.

make a complete presentation of the results difficult.   Therefore, for practical application it is often more convenient to express the noise contours on the ground in terms of some psychological scale such as loudness level or speech-interference level which describes reactions to noise by a single quantity.   Unfortunately, there is no universal scale characterizing human reaction to aircraft noise.   Until a more suitable scale is available, noise zones must be expressed in terms of the different scales depending on the purpose for which they are to be applied.

As an example, Fig. 34.10 shows the approximate peak over-all sound pressure levels resulting from different aircraft passing in flight at varying distance.   The minimal atmospheric absorption, very frequently observed for aircraft at high elevation angle, is assumed for this graph.   Close to the ground the attenuation could become much higher for distances over 500 ft; this is always the case when the wind exceeds about 6 ft per sec.   For two of the aircraft in Fig. 34.10, the noise contours on the ground for different take-off angles are shown in Fig. 34.11.

Detailed equal-loudness contours on the ground for a number of small private and large commercial-type airplanes (take-off power: 65 to 2,400 hp) together with a large number of level versus distance plots are given in Ref. 17; the equal-loudness contours (100 phons to 60 phons) given there are based on actual measurements and realistic take-off flight paths.   Calculated constant noise-level contours are given elsewhere.[4*,85*,18]

The time-averaged speech interference level has been used as a noise criterion for offices.[48]   Similarly, to predict community reaction, time-averaged levels in certain frequency bands have been used.[49]   The averages can be calculated from the pressure-time curves of the individual fly-overs, either estimated or measured.[49]

An extremely large amount of information is necessary to calculate the over-all airfield noise sources from the individual noise sources, including operational data such as time and type of ground and flight operation, engine designation and its power setting, complete atmospheric attenuation data, runway utilization, etc.   Therefore, the statistical description of the airfield noise source is often simpler and probably more reliable when the noise levels in certain areas are of particular interest, for instance, when they will be correlated with a neighborhood response.   An extensive survey of aircraft noise in the vicinity of eight major civilian airports has been reported.[19]   In this survey measurements were made in over 20 areas, each about four square blocks, within a radius of 12 miles of the airport.   The results show a decrease of the average noise level of 20 db or more for the low frequencies and of more than 30 db for the high frequencies as the distance is increased from one to ten miles from the end of the runway.   No systematic differences between the levels from take-offs and landings were observed.   Although the observation points were "under the flight paths," the levels observed showed a statistical spread of at least 20 db.   Figure 34.12 shows that there is a low probability that the idealized maximum sound level possible will be reached (take-off power of large four-engine aircraft estimated at 20 kilowatts of acoustic power).   This spread is brought about by variations in type of aircraft, power setting, meteorological conditions, and flight path.

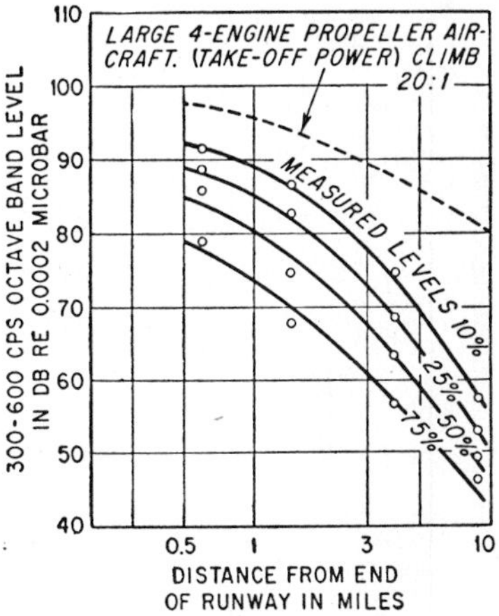

For noise control and planning purposes (see Chap. 35) the individual aircraft approach and the statistical approach are both helpful and they should be combined for optimum benefit. Before noise-control measures are planned, the relative importance of the individual sources with relation to the over-all statistical noise situation must be evaluated.   This relative importance will shift considerably from one

Fig. 34.12. Distribution of measured sound levels in the 300- to 600-cps band in areas under take-off path of major commercial airports.   The areas are located at different distances from the end of the runway.   The dotted curve gives the computed maximum sound pressure level expected for the largest aircraft operated.   The reasons for the deviations from this calculated curve are operation of other types (smaller) aircraft; variations in power settings; meteorological conditions; and aircraft flight path.   (*From Stevens.*[19])

case to the other.   If several individual noise-control devices or procedures are used, their effectiveness must be evaluated separately in each case by measuring the total noise-power reduction or the spatial shift of noise zones.   In addition, it must be shown that the anticipated result, a reduction in the over-all statistical noise, has been achieved.

Noise Control of Ground Operations.   Noise from ground operations includes noise from aircraft power plants operated for maintenance and overhaul work on both the flight line and test stands.   Although control of this noise usually is undertaken to reduce neighborhood complaints, the principal reason for controlling this noise should be the protection of service crews and other nearby personnel.   The effectiveness of run-up noise suppressors with respect to a neighborhood can be estimated from a consideration of ground versus flight operation.   Such data might change considerably from one airport to another.   However, the following figures collected on military bases are of interest.   In the long time average, each take-off requires at least 3 to 4 min running time per engine on the ground, at 80 per cent power and above.   The total time including all power settings is four to five times as much, about 12 to 15 min per start per engine. Since each take-off or fly-over will disturb people on the ground for a maximum of one minute, these figures indicate that people living in areas exposed to the same noise level from both flight and ground operations are disturbed by run-up noise four times longer or four times more frequently than by flight noise of equal loudness. In general, it is sufficient to reduce the ground noise to a level well below the flight-noise level; ground noise reduction in excess of approximately 20 db is not often required.

Frequently, a noise reduction of 10 db or more in certain areas near an airport can be obtained by making proper use of the noise sources' directivity pattern. Reloca-

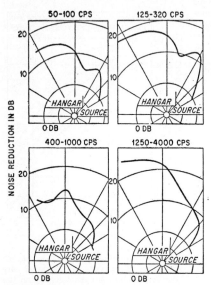

FIG. 34.13. Shielding effect of airplane hangar: average measured attenuation at 600-ft distance in four frequency ranges is shown, when the source is located close to the edge of the hangar (height 33 ft). The attenuation caused by the presence of the hangar is given for various angles with respect to the edge of the geometrical shadow created by the hangar (marked by line at 45°). (*From Stevens and Bolt*[20] *and Bolt, Beranek, and Newman, Inc.*[4*])

tion of run-up areas to places farther removed from the community, taking advantage of any special meteorological and terrain conditions, are other alternatives which may (after detailed study of the propagation conditions) be practical in many places in spite of sacrifices in the form of increased operation time. Certain times of the day, depending on the part of the country and the season, are especially good for sound propagation; maintenance operations at this time should be avoided (night time). The variations in sound level due to atmospheric attenuation at the distances from the airport, which are of interest here, can be more than 20 db.

Another possible method of ground-noise reduction is by the use of the sound shadows of buildings. If airplanes are run-up close to hangars or buildings, the shielding effect of the hangar can reduce the noise radiated in the direction of the hangar by as much as 10 to 25 db. Design charts for calculating the noise reduction provided by a wall of infinite length in terms of wall height, the source, and receiver location are given in Chap. 3. These have been applied and modified[20] for aircraft running very close to a hangar or wall. Although ground reflection, attenuation of sound, scattering of sound by turbulence and inhomogeneities, and flanking around the side edges of the hangar influence the calculated values somewhat, the simplified theory gives good results. Figure 34.13 shows the measured attenuation provided by a 33-ft-high hangar. More effective use of hangars as noise shields could be made if such buildings were constructed with this function in mind. Protection of flight-line offices and shops from noise (by having either no windows or double-glazed windows on the noise exposed side of the building) would allow engine run-ups close to the building.

Similar noise reduction can be achieved with specially built acoustic shielding walls.[21] These may be of fairly light construction, such as ¼-in. thick asbestos cement. Such walls can be located away from the flight line wherever they are needed; but they have the disadvantage that they must be at least 40 ft high to be effective. For buildings and experimental walls, noise reductions of 20 db in the 300- to 600-cps band at a distance of 400 ft have been measured.

The most effective method of reducing the noise from maintenance (not pre-take-off) run-ups of jet aircraft is the use of run-up noise suppressors. Portable or stationary suppressors provide 10 to 25 db noise reduction, depending on the seal of the muffler to the airplane and the acoustic treatment itself. Above 1,000 cps they give attenuation of 30 db or more. The limit of their effectiveness is probably set by the sound radiated by the skin of the aircraft, which, in the 300- to 600-cps band, may be about 30 to 35 db below the level of the exhaust noise. The intake noise of the jet engine must be muffled by special, movable, intake silencers. The exhaust muffler may be up to 75 ft long, the intake silencer up to 30 ft. Proper use of such silencers increases maintenance time because of the time consumed in the alignment of the muffler to the airplane and the necessary movement of the intake silencers. Run-up hangars built of concrete and large enough to house the whole airplane may prove to be the better technical solution for the operation of future jet aircraft. The technical details on these structures are given in the section *Aircraft-engine Test Cells and Run-up Noise Suppressors*.

Smaller and less expensive noise-reduction devices than those mentioned may be possible in the future (as, for example, the multiple nozzle silencer[90*] and other thrust-reducing devices or tail-pipe configurations tolerable for ground run-up); but at present they are not in practical use.

Noise Control of Flight Operation. Very limited possibilities exist for controlling the noise from flight operations in addition to the obvious but limited noise-reduction possibilities at the source. Once the aircraft is designed and in operation, the power setting of the aircraft engines is the only change one can make in the noise source itself. The remaining noise-control measures consist of modifications of flight operational procedures such as changes or reorientation of flight patterns (especially at low altitudes during landing and take-off) and the time of day when the aircraft are operated.

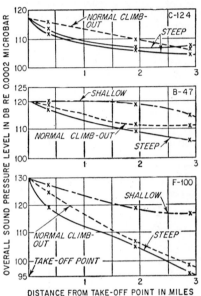

FIG. 34.14. Over-all sound pressure levels under the take-off path of a jet fighter (F-100), a jet bomber (B-47), and a propeller-driven cargo aircraft (C-124). Sound pressure levels are given for "normal" climb-out procedure and for the steepest and the shallowest climb-out considered feasible by pilots. Each cross indicates average of data measured on two repeat take-offs. (*From Eldred, et al., to be published as WADC Tech. Report.*)

From the noise standpoint the flight pattern should be oriented so as to maximize the distance between aircraft and communities. Whenever possible, the aircraft should fly over unpopulated or sparsely populated areas. Noise contours (Fig. 34.11), plotted on a map indicating population density around the airport, will show what orientation (direction of take-off) or deformation (turn after take-off) of the contours will keep the exposed population to a minimum. To accomplish a particular, selected take-off orientation, the preferential runway-utilization scheme must be used; it has already proved beneficial at many commercial airports[22] and some military bases. Since the complaints in a noise zone are a function of the frequency of fly-overs, the use of a preferential runway markedly reduces complaints from the noise zones under other take-off directions. The use of crosswind landing gears (considerable research indicates that landings in crosswinds up to 40 mph are no problem) would increase the effectiveness of the preferential runway scheme. As yet, at civilian airports, the preferential program is restricted to winds of 15 mph or less and to winds within 80° of the runway heading.[22] (With winds of 5 mph, an angle of 90° is permissible.)

A faster climb angle reduces the size of the noise zones (Fig. 34.11), assuming the noise generated by the aircraft is the same for both climbs. However, the faster climb usually requires a higher power setting, increasing the radiated noise power, partly offsetting the advantage of the faster climb. In general a flat climb makes the noise zones narrow but extending over a long distance under the flight path; a steep climb with high power setting makes the noise zones wider and shorter, i.e., relatively more noise is spread to the side of the flight path and less in its direction. The type of aircraft and the location of the communities determine which climb-out procedure is more advantageous with respect to noise. The range of variation in noise levels obtainable with such changes in the take-off profile are illustrated by Fig. 34.14. In this study pilots were instructed to follow first the "normal" take-off profile and then to modify the climb-out as "shallow" and as "steep" as considered feasible. Take-off procedures for jet aircraft are markedly different from procedures for propeller airplanes. These differences are not only reflected in the over-all sound pressure levels

Table 34.2. Estimated Noise Data under Flight Path of an F-89C Jet Taking Off with Afterburner[49]

Distance from beginning of runway (miles)	Altitude range (ft)	Range of peak L_p 300–600 cps band (db)	Duration of peak L_p within 10 db of peak level (sec)	Duration of SIL of 70 db (sec)
1	0–100			
1½	50–280	119–134	1	7
2	150–400	116–124	2	8
3	320–780	109–118	3	10
4	500–1700	102–114	4	12
5	700–3100	95–110	7	17
6	1300–4400	90–104	13	20
7	2600–5800	86–97	20	18
8	4000–7200	82–91	25	10

but also in such quantities as "duration of peak" or "duration of speech interference level of 70 db," which are used for correlation with community annoyance. Table 34.2 shows such data for a jet fighter taking off with afterburner.

The time pattern of the "airport noise source" should be adjusted as far as possible so as to minimize community annoyance. This requires the avoidance of noisy flight operations during the night and early morning. Such operations will be least annoying during rush hours, say 7 to 9 A.M. or 4 to 6:30 P.M.

The effect of all of the above noise-control procedures is limited, since in individual situations many other operational and special factors must be considered. Greatest benefit can be expected by utilizing all information at hand for the planning of future airports. Acquisition or zoning of land under the runway extending for two miles outside the airport has been recommended for commercial airports[3]* and may be the ultimate answer to this problem. Although this recommendation was mainly based on hazard considerations, experience shows that the effect of noise and hazard cannot easily be separated (see Chap. 36).

With the advent of supersonic flight, control of the sonic boom at low altitude and in the vicinity of populated areas will become a major problem with respect to control of noise from flight operations. As a result of the increased frequency of operation of civilian helicopters, operating at extremely low altitudes and near the centers of population, the control of their noise and the routing of their noise zones (preferably over areas of high background noise) pose another problem.

AIRCRAFT–ENGINE TEST CELLS AND RUN–UP NOISE SUPPRESSORS

General Design.[23,24] *Special Acoustic Requirements.* The aircraft-engine manufacturer has faced the problem of noise control for development and production testing of engines for many years. During World War II, propeller-engine test facilities were quieted by 15 to 25 db. However, present-day jet engines have raised the noise-reduction requirements by an additional 20 to 30 db. In addition, noise control of ground operation of aircraft has become a problem for both the airframe manufacturers and the military. Ground run-up of jet aircraft requires an attenuation in the order of 20 db and more not only for development and production, but also for the operational use of jet aircraft, whether from a military base or a civilian airport. On the basis of limited operational experience, one may estimate that one ground run-up noise suppressor will be required for every 10 operational aircraft.

The design of all engine test facilities follows a similar approach, since the following factors characterize them as a special class of noise-control structures:

1. High acoustic power output (power level up to 170 dbp or more).
2. High air-mass flow (exhaust-mass airflow up to 300 lb per sec and above).
3. High heat release due to the large fuel consumption.
4. Special aerodynamic requirements that jet-engine or propeller operation is not influenced by noise-control structure.

Although the following discussion of these points applies mainly to turbojet-engine test facilities, similar problems are found in propeller engine test stands.

1. The high acoustic power output requires noise control for the engine operator and for personnel in adjacent work areas, as well as for those who live in the vicinity of the airport. Since the operators of engine test cells can be protected relatively easily by special enclosures, and maintenance crews of aircraft during ground run-up are not exposed for excessively long time periods and can be partially protected by personal protective equipment, the required amount of noise reduction for the design of a special facility is usually determined by the requirements of the surrounding neighborhood.

   Because of the high acoustic power of airplane engines, effects of nonlinear acoustics enter many problems and considerations. In addition, the low-frequency components of the sound source result in vibration problems.

2. The high air-mass flow required by the combustion and cooling air of the jet engine or the load on the propeller requires open cross-sectional areas of air intake and exhaust of the cell of several hundred square feet when the exit velocity is maintained in the range of 50 to 200 ft per sec. Higher exit velocities are not desirable since the "self-noise" produced by the exhaust flow of the cell might be higher in level than the engine noise which is propagated through its muffler, and since acoustical materials are hard to protect against destruction from higher velocities.

3. The temperature of the exhaust gases of a jet engine without afterburner is about 1300°F and about 3000°F with an afterburner. There are no sound-absorptive materials that will withstand these high temperatures, so that cooling of the hot gases down to 450°F (more recently to 700°F) is required either by additional air or by water spray. The large quantity of water required makes it too expensive for use during continuous jet-engine tests so that most present-day cells are built to operate with cooling air for normal jet operation. But, for short-time afterburner operation, water cooling is used as a compromise, if possible, since otherwise the large cooling-air quantities would result in an uneconomically large test-cell structure. The amount of water needed in actual installations varies between 50 and 800 gallons per min.

   For a jet engine in the high-thrust class of today's production, which consumes 250 lb of combustion air, the exhaust volume flow is given as a function of the exhaust temperature for air and water cooling in Fig. 34.15. In Fig. 34.16 the relation between open intake or exhaust cross-sectional area and flow velocity is shown for the same engine.

4. Aerodynamic requirements of jet-engine test installations are not fixed but vary with the test purpose. Cells used in research might have stricter requirements than production cells or noise suppressors used for maintenance work. The maximum exhaust-suppressor pressure drop is in the order of 5 to 10 in. of water.

Propeller-engine Test Cells. The earliest aircraft engine test cells[25,26] constructed were for engines of the propeller type. Such cells designed during World War II provided reductions of 25 db in the overall sound level and between 40 and 50 db for the bands above 600 cps.

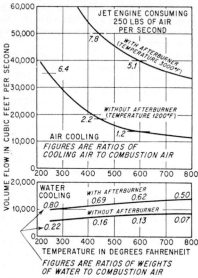

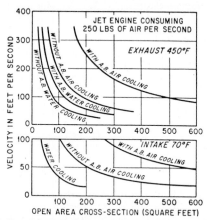

FIG. 34.15. The total volume airflow (combustion plus cooling volume) for a jet engine consuming 250 lb per sec of air in combustion as a function of the average exhaust-duct temperature. The upper curves are for air cooling; the lower curves for cooling with water only. When water cooling is used only when the afterburner is on, the lower curve of the upper section should be used. Most modern test cells and suppressors are being built for at least the capacities shown. (*From Hardy.*[23])

FIG. 34.16. Relation of the gas velocity in exhaust (upper graph) and intake (lower graph) of a noise-control structure for a jet engine consuming 250 lb per sec of combustion air to the open cross-section area of the structure. (Intake-air temperature 70°F; exhaust-duct temperature 450°F. Depending on structure and noise-control treatment, the "open" cross section may be one-half or less of the total cross section.) (*From Hardy.*[23])

Propeller-engine test cells are of the straight-through type or U-shaped with turning vanes, having acoustical treatment for air inlet and exit. A transition cone is usually ahead of the propeller which reduces the flow area from the basic cross-sectional area of the cell to the propeller disk area. In the basic design of the cell the required aerodynamic characteristics control the application of noise control. The pressure losses of the air flowing through the obstructions, contractions, and turns of the cell must be kept small to avoid operating the propeller against a large back pressure. If the back pressure becomes too large, it results in disturbed airflow in the test house and the propeller blades, forced to operate in a turbulent state, may be exposed to vibratory stresses. A criterion for the severity of this problem, which gives an estimate of the permissible test-cell pressure loss as a function of the velocity head in the plane of the propeller, has been established analytically.[27] Therefore, pressure loss of all acoustical treatments must be considered carefully and properly designed turning vanes must reduce the losses at each turn. With increasing acoustic radiation efficiency of new propellers, even acoustic reaction of the sound field might have to be considered with respect to its aerodynamic effect on the blade; since many test cells allow standing waves inside, a considerable deviation exists from the free-field condition of normal operation.

Jet-engine Test Cells. Jet-engine test cells[23,28,29] for development and production testing are usually designed and built according to the specific needs of each plant. The increase of engine power has required, in many cases, costly modification of the cell after a few years' operation and made some of the older facilities obsolete. As a consequence, noise-control planning of such facilities is now made for many years

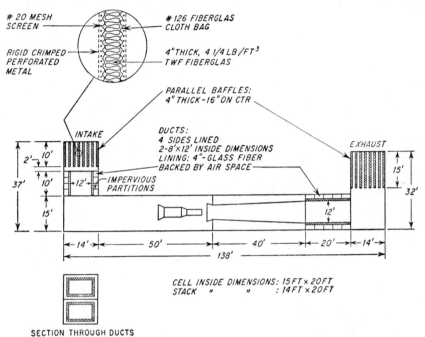

FIG. 34.17. Turbojet-engine test cell utilizing parallel baffles and tuned ducts as noise-control elements. Data for this cell are given under *Example of the Acoustic Design of a Turbojet-engine Test Cell.* Engine characteristics are given under this subject; noise-control design data in Tables 34.5, 34.6, and 34.7.

ahead. Modern jet-engine test cells are shown in Figs. 34.17 and 34.18 as two examples of a wide variety of equivalent designs.

The test cell consists of the test section, where the engine is located, and an acoustically treated intake duct and exhaust duct. The cooling air is either supplied by the intake duct (Fig. 34.17) or an extra, acoustically treated secondary air intake duct (Fig. 34.18). The hot gases of the jet stream issue from the tailpipe into an eductor tube, aspirating a sufficient amount of cooling air. The design of the secondary air augmenting system, so that it does not result in back pressure or excessive turbulence affecting engine operation, is an important factor in test cell and run-up noise-suppressor design.[30] If used, water-spray rings provide additional cooling in this region. The eductor tube is followed by the acoustically treated exhaust. Many cells are U-shaped, taking advantage of directivity and height above ground of vertical intake and exhaust stacks. A control room for the engine operators is located at one side of the test section, allowing visual observation and control of the engine. The test section must have a door large enough to allow the fast replacement of engines. Occasionally a need exists for semiportable test cells, which can be moved to various loca-

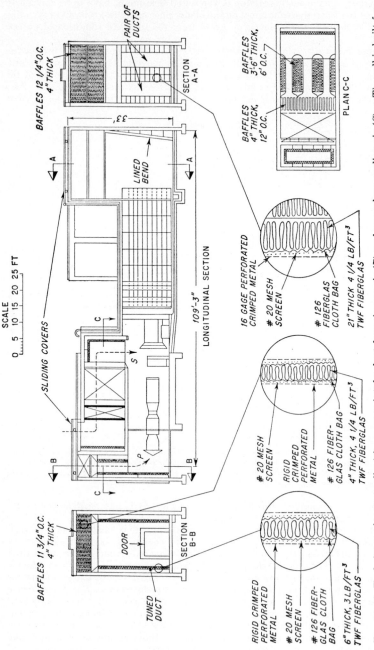

FIG. 34.18. Turbojet-engine test cell with separate intake duct for primary air (P) and secondary cooling air (S). The cell is built for turbojet engines of 10,000-lb thrust and more. (The directivity patterns measured on this cell are given in Fig. 34.29. The contributions to the measured total sound pressure level at a radius of 250 ft around the cell made by the sound radiated from intake and exhaust openings and the wall are given in Fig. 34.31.)

tions around a plant.   The U.S. Air Force has a requirement for such semiportable cells for engine run-up following overhaul at maintenance air bases.

Jet Aircraft Run-up Noise Suppressors.   Jet aircraft run-up noise suppressors[31–34] require a jet exhaust noise suppressor and one or two air-intake noise suppressors per engine.   These components must be contoured to fit the engine intake and exhaust area with an acoustically tight seal.   This requires the custom-fitting of the suppressor to each model or type of aircraft.   The contoured seal is followed by an adjustable alignment section connecting the seal with the suppressor proper.   Similar engines used on different aircraft can, in this way, use the same suppressor with interchangeable coupling sections.   The coupling section must accommodate motions of the aircraft's tailpipe, resulting from changes in thrust.   Attenuation of these suppressors is limited to 30 to 40 db by noise radiation through the engine structure.   Main emphasis in the design of these mufflers is placed on the possibility for rapid connection to the

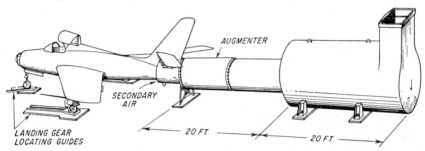

Fig. 34.19.   Run-up noise suppressor for jet aircraft (F-84 powered by J-65, 7,200-lb thrust) utilizing mainly nondissipative elements for noise suppression (sound-absorbing resonant chambers).   This muffler is reported to reduce the over-all jet noise under the angle of maximum radiation for the unmuffled aircraft by 23 db.   No water cooling is used with this particular design.   (*Courtesy Industrial Acoustics Co.*)

aircraft, for the best muffler is worthless if the time required for muffler-aircraft line-up is too long to allow its operational use, or if the silencers are not used to their full effectiveness.   An example of a run-up noise suppressor is given in Fig. 34.19.

The disadvantages of run-up noise suppressors can be overcome by building run-up hangars large enough to house the whole airplane.   They have an acoustically treated intake and exhaust stack like a test cell and a heavy access door with a good seal.   They are relatively fast in operation, versatile, and frequently without difficult individual fitting problems.   Such a permanent run-up hangar is shown in Fig. 34.20.

A compromise between a run-up noise suppressor and a hangar is often used on multiengine jet aircraft: the noise-control structure encloses the total jet engine, but seals at the strut, which holds the engine pods, or at the wing, wherever the seal offers less difficulties.   An example is shown in Fig. 34.21.

Noise-control Elements.   *Walls.*   The walls of propeller- and jet-engine test cells and permanent-type run-up hangars are normally constructed of reinforced concrete. The strength required mechanically to assure the necessary protection and resistance to vibrations usually insures an acoustic attenuation of the order of 50 db.   Total acoustic power transmitted through the walls must be small in the over-all design. Flanking transmission by walls must be avoided by using structural discontinuities. Tilt-up concrete slabs are used for the wall construction of semiportable cells.

Steel is used for the ductwork and sometimes for the total structure of a run-up noise suppressor.   Sound transmission through the steel pipe walls (augmenter tube) is reduced by either internal liners or external absorbent walls.   Earth covering and sand jacketing also have been used.   Walls consisting of two concentric Quonsett huts with the space between the walls filled with sand also proved satisfactory for some test-cell applications (Fig. 34.21).   Run-up mufflers were built out of cinder building blocks[31] as combined structural material and sound-absorptive material.   The blocks were supported in a framework of steel I-beams.

The effects of the high temperature gradients, especially in concrete walls, and of vibrations must be considered in the selection of all structural materials.

Doors, Other Openings, Control Room. The seal for all access doors to the test cell must be properly designed so that there are no acoustical leaks. Rubber gaskets, inflated after the door has been closed, have been used to achieve this. The control room should be mechanically isolated from the test-cell structure and have interior acoustical treatment. Observation of the engine in the test cell is usually required.

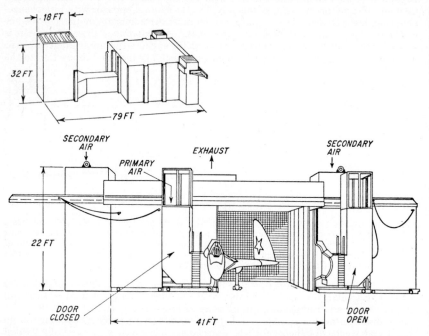

FIG. 34.20. Run-up hangar for the F4D aircraft (J-57 jet engine with afterburner). The 8-in.-thick concrete door is contoured to fit snugly around the fuselage just aft of the cockpit, permitting the operator to remain outside the structure during run-up tests. The door, built in four 8-ft sections, allows partial enclosure during low-power runs. Rubber seals on all sides of the door are pneumatically actuated. Cooling water is used only during afterburner operation. Acoustic effectiveness of this hangar is shown in Fig. 34.30. (*Built by Kittell Lacy, Inc.*)

Several panels of bulletproof glass in an observation window allow direct view of the engine. Other designs use periscope observation. Fuel lines and ducts for instrumentation wiring must be introduced into the cell with properly designed sound and vibration breaks. Carelessness in this respect easily raises the sound level in otherwise perfect control rooms.

Sound Treatment of Intake and Exhaust Duct.[4*,23,25,36,37] Practically all noise-control techniques have been applied to attenuate the noise in the intake and exhaust duct, including:

1. Conventional straight-through steel mufflers including expansion chamber and resonator-type mufflers.
2. Masonry duct with continuous resonant lining.
3. Splitting of duct in many small ducts.
4. High-frequency and low-frequency baffles.
5. Lined bends.

6. Lined chambers (continuous labyrinth chamber).
7. High vertical stacks to take advantage of increased distance and directivity of openings.

Most treatments applied in practice, including those known by specific trade names, employ a number of these acoustical techniques. The effectiveness of dissipative muffler elements, which all in one way or the other have the lined duct as their basic element, is improved by nondissipative (reflective or reactive) filter elements like curvature, bends, and tuned chambers (see Chap. 21). In Fig. 34.22 some frequently used dissipative muffler elements are shown with their typical attenuation characteristic. Although in principle acoustic theories on lined ducts have been tremendously refined and the general case, where the energy is distributed among the various modes of travel, can be solved, practical design relies quite heavily on scale-model data and on experimental design charts.[36] But theoretical tables are very useful in giving a qualitative picture and the correct scaling factor to transfer model data to the full-scale case. For optionally designed ducts theory and measurements indicate that the maximum attenuation is approximately 6 db per duct width for a two-sided duct and 12 db for a four-sided duct. These maximum values are reached at a ratio of width to wavelength between $\frac{1}{2}$ and 2. Lined ducts are used for low-frequency attenuation; for the middle-frequency range, parallel baffle arrangements are frequently used, i.e., ducts of very small width. Depending on the spacing, attenuations between 1 and 9 db per ft can be obtained in practical installations with 4-in. thick baffles as shown in Fig. 34.23. If duct bends treated with acoustical material are incorporated in the design (Fig. 34.22), the attenuation increases rapidly for values of $d/\lambda > 0.5$ (λ = wavelength). Design curves for lined bends are given in Fig.

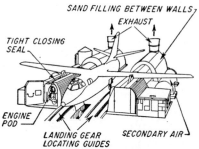

FIG. 34.21. Noise-control installation for the RB-66 (two J-71 engines rated at 10,000-lb thrust without afterburner). The construction is all steel. Double walls are filled with sand, with the exception of the engine section, which has perforated lining backed with glass wool. Bulk head sealed around the tail pipe separates the engine and exhaust sections. Air enters exhaust section through a 30-in. diameter Maxim silencer, and the jet exhaust goes out through a 66-in. diameter Maxim silencer surrounded by sand. Automatically controlled water spray maintains exhaust temperature below 400°F. [*From* Cover, *Noise Control*, **1** (March, 1955).]

34.24. The thickness of the lining is not critical if its absorption coefficient is 0.8 or above for all frequencies for which $d/\lambda > 1.5$. For practical lining materials the thickness, therefore, should be of the order of $d/10$ or greater.

Specific duct treatments such as the ones indicated by Fig. 34.22d and e reach, in the range of maximum attenuation above 400 cps, attenuation values between 40 and 60 db for a duct length of 20 ft.[35] The maximum attenuation of a 30-ft long helix muffler (Fig. 34.22f) is approximately 40 db. The above values give only the approximate range of attenuation obtainable with different treatments. There is considerable variation with individual configurations and materials. (For more detailed data see Chap. 27 and Refs. 4* and 36.)

The performance of sound-attenuation structures such as baffles, ducts, bends, and resonators is considerably affected by increased temperature. The speed of sound and the density and viscosity of gases are all a function of temperature[4*] so that the attenuation properties, resonant frequencies and the sharpness of resonances must be calculated for the elevated temperature of the gas during normal operation of a test cell. With increased temperature the characteristic frequency of the treatment (frequency of maximum attenuation in Fig. 34.23 or frequency where the attenuation starts to rise in Fig. 34.24) is shifted to higher frequencies proportional to the square root of the absolute temperature. In general, the attenuation decreases with increasing temperature. For example, because of the elevated temperature, a baffle treatment in an exhaust stack will have slightly less attenuation than the same treatment in the intake stack.

High gas velocities and high sound pressures demand caution in the application of small-amplitude acoustical theory and acoustical filter theory. In the application of

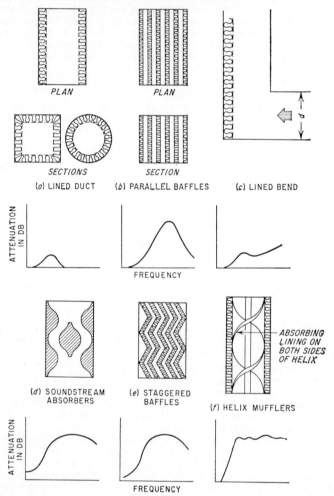

Fig. 34.22. Examples of dissipative noise-control elements with their corresponding approximate noise-attenuation characteristics. (*From Dyer.*[36])

sound-absorptive treatments it is important to remember that the location of the noise source is not at the nozzle of the jet engine but in the turbulent-gas flow downstream from the nozzle. All principles discussed in Chap. 33 which influence the generation of jet noise, i.e., screens, teeth, multiple-nozzle silencers, etc., must be investigated carefully for possible beneficial application in jet-engine noise suppressors. Since low-frequency attenuation is the more expensive and difficult part in jet-noise suppression, any shift of the power spectrum to higher frequencies by such means will result in a saving of space and money.

Many jet-engine test facilities use water-spray for cooling the hot engine-exhaust gases. One or more rings spray water concentrically into the exhaust stream directly behind the nozzle. Under certain conditions the water may cause energy losses through scattering and viscous losses[4*,35] which increase with the diameter of the

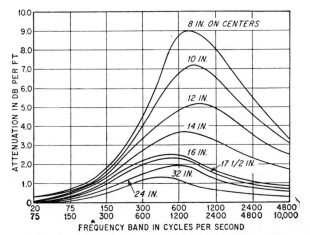

Fig. 34.23. Attenuation in octave bands for a family of parallel baffles with varying spacing. In all cases each baffle is 4 in. thick and filled with either PF Fiberglas of density 4 lb per cu ft or rock wool of density 6 lb per cu ft. The results as shown apply to continuous spectrum noise. (*From Staff of Bolt, Beranek, and Newman, Inc.[4*]*)

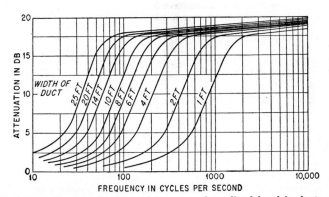

Fig. 34.24. Attenuation as a function of frequency for a lined bend in ducts of various widths. The design curves are based on scale-model tests and tests on large installations and are given for a sound velocity of 1,120 ft per sec. (*From Staff of Bolt, Beranek, and Newman, Inc.[4*]*)

drops. For most existing exhaust treatments this additional attenuation is not significant and cooling is the only practical consideration for using water in the design. Water injection may also influence, in the same manner as teeth, the noise generation itself.[62*]

In some installations attenuation by water spray has been deliberately sought in the design of the treatment. Some idea of the magnitude of the noise reduction possible by water spray under favorable conditions can be obtained from Fig. 34.25. The high water flow rates used for this test on a jet-engine installation may be prohibitive for continuous operation but are worth further study for use during short afterburner operations or rocket tests. Generalized information for predicting the effectiveness of water-spray systems is still lacking at present.

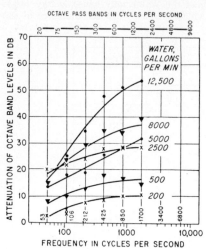

FIG. 34.25. Sound attenuation in octave bands as measured through a water-spray system of unconventional length and capacity for a jet-engine test facility. Attenuation values are relative to the values obtained for operating the facility without water for constant engine-operating conditions. The graph is not a design chart for water-spray systems but is based on one particular facility only. (*From Watters, Labate, and Beranek.*[35])

Noise-control Materials.[38,39] The destructive effects of high gas temperatures, velocities, vibrations, and corrosion have led to the development of special acoustical treatments for test cells. In early propeller-engine test cells, porous concrete blocks were used for intake and exhaust treatment of many cells. The required large absorptive areas were obtained by subdividing the duct in many small ducts, which resulted in the inevitable disadvantage of this type of treatment: low-percentage open area and high pressure drop. In addition, the high susceptibility of this material to erosion by vibrations and to temperature gradients during the cell's operating cycle limited its use in modern test cell structures.

Fibrous acoustic material mounted in metal panels is most commonly used today in jet- and propeller-engine test cells. Maximum allowable temperatures for different porous materials are indicated in Table 34.3. The gas surface velocity determines the sensitivity of the material to vibrations and erosion and, therefore, determines the type of metal facing used for protection. Materials used for the different velocity ranges up to 400 ft per sec are shown in Fig. 34.26. Stainless-steel or copper wool, packed to a minimum density of 25 lb per cu ft, is used as sound-

Table 34.3. Porous Materials for Use in Hot Gas Streams[39]

Material	*Maximum Allowable Temperature, °F*
Fibrous materials:	
1. Some mineral wools (e.g., J-M Airacoustic)	125–150
2. Wool felts	150–200
3. Hair felts	200–250
4. Bonded glass fibers* (Microlite, PF Fiberglas, Aerocor, Ultralite, Ultrafine)	350–400
5. Asbestos fibers (J-M Spintex and Spincoustic)	800
6. Unbonded glass fibers (TWF and TWL Fiberglas)	1000–1100
7. Mineral-wool felted block (Baldwin Hill Rockwool)	1200
8. Basaltwool (Hoeganaes Sponge Iron Corp.)	1450
9. Vitreous fiber-silica (H. I. Thompson Refrasil)	1800–2000
10. Refractory fiber (J-M Thermoflex)	2000
Other Materials:	
1. Haydite block (cracks under high transient temperatures)	900
2. Porous firebricks (including ceramic)	1600–3000
3. Gravel	3000

* In these materials the temperature limits generally apply to the binder; the glass fibers themselves are good to about 1000°F–1100°F. After the binder melts, the glass fibers may have a tendency to sift under vibration.

absorptive material for extremely high temperatures (700°F) and velocities. Absorptive materials such as metal wool, glass, and mineral wool must be protected against

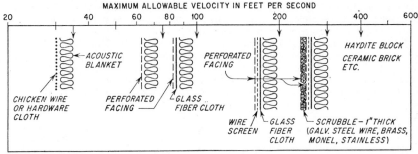

FIG. 34.26. Protective facings for acoustical panels subjected to high-velocity gas streams. The arrows indicate the maximum allowable velocities for the illustrated structures. Values are for smooth, diffuse gas flow at grazing incidence and are believed to be conservative. The placing of acoustical structures in places of high gas turbulence is not recommended, because erosion is there highly probable. (*Based on Labate[39] and Lemmerman.[38]*)

settling under vibration. This is accomplished by the use of separators in the metal panel, reducing the height of unsupported packing material to 18 to 30 in. This distance varies with the hardness of the packed material and its density. A layer of metal wool in front of other acoustical material in order to protect it does not influence adversely the acoustical effectiveness of the material behind it.

For the metal facing used to protect the absorptive material, the high temperatures of the gas must be considered (reduction of tensile strength, allowance for thermal expansion), together with its corrosive atmosphere. To prevent corrosion, a ceramic coating has been applied to the metal surface.

Fibrous, porous, or shredded sound-absorptive material used in most aircraft-engine test cells require some maintenance, cleaning, and replacement. Therefore, noise-control materials should be easily replaceable. The trend in materials and designs of jet-engine noise-control facilities is necessarily toward materials that will stand higher temperatures and velocities, and toward over-all design principles requiring a minimum amount of sound-absorptive material.

Directivity.[4*,35,40] Proper use of the height of intake and exhaust opening above the ground and use of the directivity of these openings are additional factors to be considered in the design of aircraft test facilities. Directivity measured on test cells and scale models (1:16) and

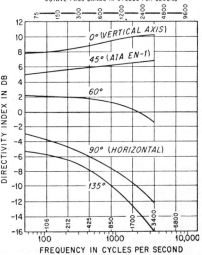

FIG. 34.27. Directivity index as a function of frequency band for six angles relative to the vertical axis of a square exhaust stack. The curves represent average values, since, for example, values at the different EN-1 positions are 3 to 6 db different. Note that the EN-1 positions are 5 to 7 db above space average. The data were measured on a 16-by 16-ft stack. (*From Watters, Labate, and Beranek.[35]*)

the results of theoretical calculations agree fairly well.[35,40] The directivity index as measured on a square exhaust stack (at a distance of one-stack diameter from the stack axis) is shown in Fig. 34.27. The level at the EN-1 position (Fig. 33.4) can be as much as 5 to 7 db above the value obtained by assuming non-directional radiation; the sound radiated toward the ground is below this value. Design charts for estimating the effect of directivity at some distance from the stack openings have been published.[4*] An example is given in Fig. 34.28. The directivity pattern in the ground plane around a U-shaped test cell is shown in Fig. 34.29.

Evaluation of Acoustical Performance.[41] *Measurements on Test Cells.* Acoustic measurements on aircraft-engine test cells are made for two principal purposes: (1) to determine the over-all effectiveness of the noise-control installation, and (2) to obtain specific information with regard to the effectiveness of various noise-control measures. In (1), measurements are made on the ground on a circle with a radius of 250 to 500 ft around the noise-control facility (Fig.

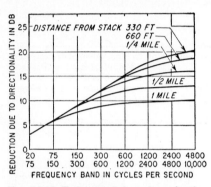

FIG. 34.28. Estimate of the noise reduction at ground level resulting from directional radiation of sound from a vertical-exhaust stack containing hot gases. The curves are for approximately square or circular openings of 50-ft perimeter. To obtain values for vertical stacks containing normal gases, as much as 5 db should be added. (*From Staff of Bolt, Beranek, and Newman, Inc.*[4*])

34.29). The average sound pressure level on this circle compared to the average levels on the same circle around the same noise source without any noise-control measures provides a measure of the effectiveness of the noise-control installation. The reduction of the noise-energy flux along the ground can so be expressed in db for the spatial average (attenuation of power propagated along the ground) or for specified directions. These attenuation figures include all factors affecting noise reduction in the neighborhood of the test cells as well as directional effects, but not special far-field atmospheric diffraction effects. The over-all effectiveness of a noise-control installation is specified most realistically in these terms for the various frequency bands. Control rooms and other positions, wherever human operators must work, are specified separately and checked by measurements at these specific locations. For example, for a jet aircraft run-up noise suppressor the over-all evaluation would be made on a circle of 250 to 500 ft radius around the aircraft, both with and without the suppressor. In addition, measurements close to the aircraft and the silencer (for example, on a rectangle enclosing aircraft and structure as close as possible) should be made to determine the noise levels to which maintenance personnel will be exposed. (Noise-control structures effective for far-field noise reduction may be practically ineffective on a few but vital positions of the near-field.) Figure 34.30 gives the evaluation of the effectiveness of a run-up hangar of the type illustrated in Fig. 34.20 at a distance of 250 ft.

Measurements (2) may be made to evaluate the effectiveness of various details of the noise-control facility, for example, the following: (1) the acoustical treatments in the stacks, (2) the sound insulation of doors, windows, and walls, (3) the stack-directivity patterns (Fig. 34.27), (4) the cell-radiation patterns (Fig. 34.29), (5) bend effects, etc. This type of measurement should allow the separation of the total noise radiated by the cell into three components: (1) the power radiated by the intake, (2) the power radiated by the exhaust, and (3) the power radiated by walls and leaks of the structure. Such an analysis into these three components of the average sound pressure level at a circle of 250 ft around the test cell of Fig. 34.18 is illustrated in Fig. 34.31. A comparison of these three components does not always reveal such a well balanced over-all design as the one given here as an example. The power radiated by intake and exhaust duct openings should be calculated from sound pressure level measurements across the openings. Similarly, the effectiveness of different treatments can be evaluated by measuring the sound pressure level across cross-sectional areas at both ends of each treatment and from these data calculating the energy reduction. Grids consisting of up to five microphones have been used to measure the average sound pressure level of a test-cell cross section.[41] Unfortunately,

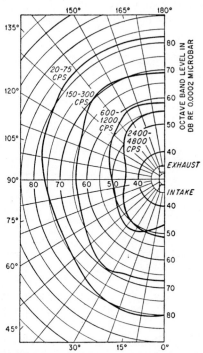

FIG. 34.29. Sound pressure levels in octave bands measured on a circle of 250-ft radius from the mid-point of the test cell shown in Fig. 34.18. The measurements were made with a J-57 turbojet engine operating in the cell at 96 per cent rpm, which has in a free-field an acoustic-power output of 170 dbp (re 10^{-12} watt). The over-all effectiveness of the cell is given by the net reduction in the average acoustic intensity at 250-ft distance compared to the average intensity produced by the engine in free field. This over-all effectiveness (power reduction) of the test cell is:

Over-all sound pressure level.........	43 db
20–75 cps......................	29
75–150........................	34
150–300.......................	50
300–600.......................	59
600–1200......................	65
1200–2400.....................	61
2400–4800.....................	63
4800–9600.....................	60

(From data taken by Bolt, Beranek, and Newman, Inc., to be published as a WADC Tech. Report, 1957.)

such an exact evaluation during full power operation of a jet engine can be made only on the intake duct since the hot gases in the exhaust make the measurements difficult to perform. Only special probe-tube microphones which withstand the high temperatures and gas velocities of exhaust ducts allow measurement in the exhaust stream itself.[42]

Frequently, for practical evaluation of exhaust duct treatments, only the sound pressure levels at the inside and outside EN-1 positions (Fig. 33.4) are measured, and their difference is assumed to represent a measure for the attenuation along the exhaust. The sound pressure level at the outside EN-1 position is, based on spherical divergence only, generally assumed to be 14 db below the pressure across the exhaust stack opening. As exact measurements of the stack directivity (Fig. 34.27) and calculations show, this value may be in error by 5 db or more.[35,40] In addition, the levels at the different EN-1 positions for the same stack, under otherwise identical conditions, have a spread of 3 to 5 db.[35]

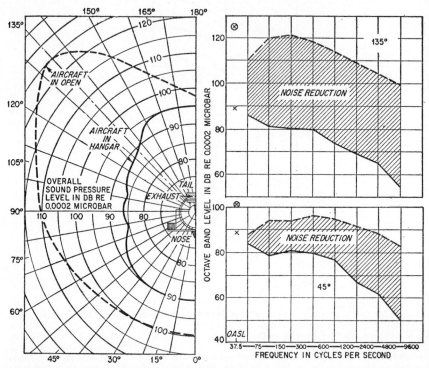

Fig. 34.30. Acoustic evaluation of the run-up hangar for the F4D aircraft illustrated in Fig. 34.20.   Measurements are made at a radius of 250 ft from the center of the test facility or from the tail-pipe exit of the aircraft in the open, respectively.   The J-57 turbojet engine was running at full power for the test.   The spectra for two angles (45° and 135°) are given in the right graph.   (*From Eldred et al., to be published as WADC Tech. Note.*)

Whenever possible, it is preferable to use the actual engine, for which the test facility was designed, as the noise source for the evaluation measurement.   If such a source is not available, or if a detailed analysis of the elements of the exhaust treatment requires measurements inside the exhaust duct, a "cold" noise source may be used as substitute.   An explosive noise source radiating a power spectrum approximately similar to a jet-engine spectrum has been used for this purpose and seems to be preferable to a loudspeaker source.[43]   Neither type of "cold" noise source can be expected to give results for the exhaust-duct attenuation, which is in complete agreement with results obtained with an actual engine, even when the exhaust treatment was heated to the correct temperature by a jet engine run immediately prior to the "cold" noise-source evaluation.   The reason for this discrepancy is because the jet-engine noise source extends over part of the exhaust duct.   Therefore, the estimation of the attenuation from the EN-1 positions using a jet-engine noise source usually results in a lower value than that measured from the test-cell exit (eductor tube) to the stack opening with a cold noise source placed in the test cell. The same fact and the possibility of "self-noise" generated by the gas flow explain, also, the experimental finding why noise reductions measured by the EN-1 positions vary in the order of 5 db and more with the power setting of the jet engine. Location of the jet-noise source along the exhaust duct, downstream from the tailpipe, is also a reason why sound pressure level measurements in the actual test cell containing the engine cannot be used, applying room acoustics approaches (source contained within reverberant enclosure), to the

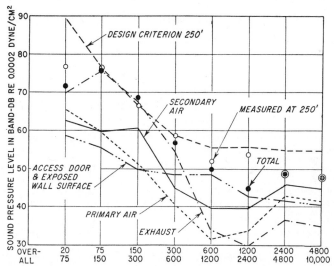

Fig. 34.31. Contributions of the various test-cell noise sources to the average sound pressure level at 250-ft distance around the test cell illustrated in Fig. 34.18. The sound pressure levels produced by the various components at 250 ft were calculated from the levels measured across primary air, secondary air, and exhaust opening, taking into account inverse-square law and stack directivity. The sound radiated by the exposed walls was estimated from the sound pressure levels inside the test cell, taking into account the noise reduction of the 12-in. concrete wall and inverse-square law. The sound pressure levels across the access door were obtained from level measurements outside, rather than from calculations based on levels measured inside. The single heavy points indicate the total level at 250 ft obtained by summing the estimated contributions from the four sources considered. These points should be compared with the measured average sound pressure levels at 250 ft, marked by the open circles. The original design criterion for this cell is also indicated. (*From data taken by Bolt, Beranek, and Newman, Inc., to be published as a WADC Tech. Report, 1957.*)

calculation of the total power radiated by the engine. Such attempts result in sound power level values which are 10 to 20 db too low. On the basis of this experience the power radiated into the exhaust duct is, for design purposes, usually assumed to be at least 10 db above the acoustic power radiated toward the intake duct.

For the above reasons, at the present time the difference between the sound pressure levels on the inside and outside EN-1 positions of an exhaust (Fig. 33.4) cannot be assumed to represent an ideally accurate evaluation of the noise-control treatment. Additional measurements with a cold noise source are desirable to obtain the attenuation values provided by the different elements of the exhaust treatment.

To indicate attenuation values measured with a cold (loudspeaker) noise source over the length of a modern noise-control facility, Table 34.4 gives the data for the treatment of the NACA supersonic wind tunnel designed for the operation of jet engines under conditions of supersonic speeds (Fig. 34.32).[44] The acoustical performance of the resonators for attenuating the low frequencies from 5 to 20 cps was also tested with loudspeakers; attenuation values in excess of 20 db were observed over the frequency range for which they were designed.

Model Studies. Scale models with a scale factor $1/n = \frac{1}{2}$ to $\frac{1}{16}$ have been used successfully for testing the acoustical performance of a proposed structure at frequencies n times those of interest in the full structure. They are recommended in the study of new designs. Absorption coefficients of treatments in the model must be simulated at frequencies n times those of interest in the full-scale structure.[45] Either a model of the total installation may be built or different scale factors may be applied

Table 34.4. Over-all Acoustical Behavior of NACA Supersonic Wind-tunnel Treatment[44]

	Frequency band in cps							
	20–75	75–150	150–300	300–600	600–1200	1200–2400	2400–4800	4800–9600
Measured levels in test section, 16-in. ram jet operating at Mach 2 (3000 lb/hr fuel consumption), in db	146	151	153	153	151	148	143	138
Loss due to wave expansion in diffuser, in db	10	10	10	10	10	10	10	10
Loss in first plenum and bend, in db	13	16	15	15	16	17	19	20
Loss at junction between concrete and glass section, in db	4	4	4	4	4	4	4	4
Loss in 90 ft of Fiberglas, in db	50	49	44	45	2	0	0	0
Loss in second plenum, in db	0	0	0	3	11	16	17	18
Loss in parallel baffles, in db	1	4	14	26	30	21	14	10
Total loss (exclusive of flanking noise leaks), in db	78	83	87	103	73	68	64	62
Resultant noise at exit of baffles (exclusive of flanking noise), in db	68	68	66	50	78	80	79	76

to the single components of an installation. For example, in the course of the design of the noise-control structure illustrated in Fig. 34.32, the section with the 5- to 10-cps resonators was tested in a model with a scale factor $\frac{1}{12}$. The resonators for the frequency range 11 to 20 cps were built with a scale factor $\frac{1}{6}$; the lined, tuned duct was constructed as a model with $n = 1/2.5$.[44] The radiation pattern of exhaust stacks has also been tested by model studies.[35,40] In addition, aerodynamic factors such as pressure drop and turbulence, important in propeller test-cell design, can be studied on scale models.[27]

Example of the Acoustics Design of a Turbojet-engine Test Cell. The over-all acoustic design of a test cell is best illustrated with a practical example. Suppose a turbojet engine of the 10,000-lb-thrust class is to be tested in a location approximately 600 ft from the nearest residential urban neighborhood. Six runs per day of approximately one-half hour duration are anticipated; 80 per cent of each run is at full rpm of the engine. Year around testing of the engine is expected during daytime only. The residents of the neighborhood have been exposed to aircraft noise before. The acoustic treatment of the test cell is to be so designed that the noise from the test cell does not result in observable complaints or community reaction.

Using the method proposed for engineering design to predict community reaction (Chap. 36) the desired "no complaint" reaction (Scale Numbers I to II in Table 36.5) requires a Composite Noise Rating of B (Fig. 36.3) at a distance of 600 ft from the cell. Applying the correction numbers (Table 36.6) for a residential urban neighborhood (-1), only daytime operation (-1), repetitiveness of the noise (-1), year around operation (0), continuous spectrum (0), peak factor (0), previous exposure (-1), to Eq. (36.1) results in a desired noise-level rank:

$$(\text{Noise-level rank}) + [(-4)] = B$$

Hence the noise-level rank is ($B + 4$) or f at 600 ft. Allowing only for the minimal atmospheric and terrain attenuation to be expected and for spherical spreading, this desired noise-level rank (Fig. 36.4) is equivalent to the design criterion at 250 ft distance given in Fig. 34.33.

The design selected as an example to meet the required criterion is the U-shaped test cell given in Fig. 34.17. As noise-reduction elements, only the most basic elements are selected (duct, bend, parallel baffles, and directivity) to make the design simple and to exclude proprietary designs. Details of the design are given in Table 34.5 for the exhaust and in Table 34.6 for the intake treatment. The power level (in decibels re 10^{-12} watt) of the jet engine is assumed to be 170 dbp. The power spectrum in octave bands is assumed to be known from measurements and is given in the first column of Tables 34.5 and 34.6. The primary air of the engine is given as 160 lb per sec. To keep the exhaust temperature, through air cooling alone, at 450°F, cooling air in the ratio 2:1 has to be aspirated. This results in a total intake airflow of 480 lb per sec, which corresponds to a total intake-volume flow of approximately 6,350 cu ft

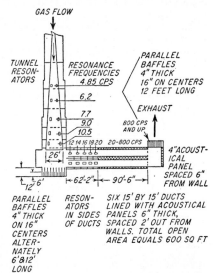

FIG. 34.32. Acoustical treatment for the 8 ft by 16 ft NACA supersonic wind tunnel. Noise-reduction treatment is designed for the frequency range 5 cps to 10,000 cps. Acoustical behavior of the treatment is given in Table 34.4. (*From Beranek, Labate, and Ingard.*[44])

Table **34.5**. Design of Exhaust Treatment Power
Output of Jet Engine $L_w = 170$ dbp (Re 10^{-12} Watt)

Octave band (cps)	Power level in octave band (dbp)	L_p at entrance to exhaust treatment (db re 0.0002 microbar)	Estimated noise reduction at 450°F due to			Total estimated NR of exhaust (db)	L_p at stack exit (db re 0.0002 microbar)	Stack directivity (db)	L_p at 250 ft (db re 0.0002 microbar)
			Duct, 20 ft (db)	Bend diffraction (db)	Baffles, 15 ft (db)				
20–75	154	139	8	7	2	17	122	6	85
75–150	159	144	14	11	6	31	113	8	74
150–300	164	149	10	11	17	38	111	11	69
300–600	165	150	2	15	30	47	103	14	58
600–1200	163	148	0	20	37	57	91	17	43
1200–2400	158	143	0	21	30	51	92	19	42
2400–4800	154	139	0	21	19	40	99	20	48
4800–10000	150	135	0	19	14	33	102	21	50

per sec (ambient temperature 60°F). The volume flow in the exhaust stack at a temperature of 450°F is then 11,100 cu ft per sec. For stack dimensions and treatments indicated in Fig. 34.17, these volume flows result in average linear velocities of approximately 28 ft per sec between the intake baffles and in approximately 50 ft per sec between the exhaust baffles. In the ducts the velocities are only negligibly higher so that no materials problems with the acoustical treatment are to be expected (Fig. 34.26).

Table 34.6. Design of Intake Treatment

Octave band (cps)	Power level in octave band (dbp)	L_p at entrance to intake (db re 0.0002 microbar)	Estimated noise reduction due to			Total estimated noise reduction of intake (db)	L_p at stack exit (db re 0.0002 microbar)	Estimated stack directivity (db)	L_p at 250 ft (db re 0.0002 microbar)
			Bend diffraction (db)	Duct, 10 ft (db)	Baffles, 10 ft (db)				
20–75........	154	129	10	5	2	17	112	9	72
75–150.......	159	134	11	7	8	26	108	12	65
150–300.......	164	139	13	3	17	33	106	15	60
300–600.......	165	140	18	0	25	43	97	18	48
600–1200......	163	138	20	0	22	42	96	19	46
1200–2400......	158	133	21	0	16	37	96	20	45
2400–4800......	154	129	21	0	10	31	98	21	46
4800–10000.....	150	125	19	0	7	26	99	21	47

Table 34.7. Cell-wall Considerations

Octave band (cps)	Estimated average sound pressure level over inside face of wall (db re 0.0002 microbar)	Noise reduction of 12-in. concrete, db (T.L. + 6 db)	Sound pressure level at 250 ft distance (db re 0.0002 microbar)
20–75........	134	44	67
75–150.......	139	49	67
150–300.......	144	54	67
300–600.......	145	59	63
600–1200......	143	64	56
1200–2400.....	138	64	51
2400–4800.....	134	64	47
4800–10000....	130	64	43

From the octave-band power level of the engine, the sound pressure level at the entrance to the exhaust treatment (15 ft by 20 ft) is calculated by subtracting [10 log (15 × 20) − 10] db, or 15 db, from the power-level values. The sound pressure levels at the entrance to the intake treatment are, as discussed under *Measurements on Test Cells*, assumed to be 10 db lower, i.e., 25 db below the power-level values. The estimated noise-reduction values given in the tables for bend diffraction, duct, and baffles were taken from actual measurements on similar designs and are, therefore, only in approximate agreement with Figs. 34.23 and 34.24. The values for the exhaust treatment are for a temperature of 450°F. The estimated stack directivity is interpolated for the stack-opening perimeter of 68 ft from Fig. 34.28 and a similar graph published for opening perimeters of 100 ft.[4*] Reduction due to directivity differs for intake and exhaust because of air-velocity and temperature considerations. The reduction due to inverse-square law from stack opening to the circle at 250 ft distance is calculated as $10 \log [2\pi (250)^2/(20 \times 14)] = 31$ db. The transmission of sound through the test-cell wall is estimated in Table 34.7. The sound pressure level over the inside face of the test-cell wall is estimated as the mean value of the levels at the entrances to intake and exhaust treatment. The noise reduction provided by the 12-in.-thick dense concrete walls is estimated from the transmission loss $T.L.$ by assuming reverberant condition inside the cell and absorbent conditions outside, as $T.L. + 6$ db.[4*] The sound pressure level at 250 ft distance from the wall is calculated by assuming both side walls as being exposed and vibrating. The radiating area is, therefore, on both sides from the eductor tube entrance to the intake

$$64 \text{ ft} \times 15 \text{ ft} = 960 \text{ sq ft}$$

The sound pressure level at 250 ft is obtained by subtracting

$$10 \log \left(\frac{2\pi (250)^2}{1870} \right) = 23 \text{ db}$$

The average sound pressure levels at a distance of 250 ft from the test-cell center (mid-way between intake and exhaust) as calculated in Tables 34.5, 34.6, and 34.7 are plotted in Fig. 34.33 together with the design criterion. The total sound pressure resulting from intake, exhaust, and wall radiation is calculated as the space average, i.e., by neglecting the directivity of the cell structure (Fig. 34.29). The estimated total sound pressure at 250 ft meets the design criterion. Once the test cell is built, its effectiveness should be checked by measurements at this distance.

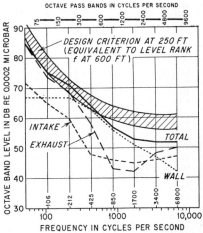

FIG. 34.33. Estimated sound pressure level at 250 ft from test cell shown in Fig. 34.17, used as design example. The noise levels from the three sources "exhaust," "intake," and "wall" are calculated in Tables 34.5, 34.6, and 34.7. The shaded region designates the design criterion, as explained in text.

Although the test-cell design given above is realistic and the noise-reduction values used have been confirmed by measurements on similar installations, the acoustic treatments used are not necessarily the most desirable nor the most economic ones. Solutions involving specific commercial products were avoided for the sake of simplicity.

REFERENCES

Note: See footnote on p. 34–1 regarding references with asterisks.

1. Eldred, K. M., W. J. Gannon, and H. E. von Gierke: *WADC Technical Note 55-355*, September, 1955.
2. Beranek, L. L.: *J. Acoust. Soc. Am.*, **28**: 833 (1956); also *USAF, WADC Technical Note 56–58*, 1956.
3. Lippert, S., and M. M. Miller: *Journal of Aviation Medicine*, **23**: 54 (1952).
4. McFarland, R. A.: "Human Factors in Air Transport Design," McGraw-Hill Book Company, Inc., New York, 1946.
5. Phillips, O. M.: Surface Noise from a Plane Turbulent Boundary Layer, Trinity College, Cambridge, 1954, *NACA Report* N-36622.
6. Kraichnan, R. H.: *WADC Technical Report 56-263.* See also papers *J. Acoust. Soc. Am.*, **28**: 378 (1956); and **29**: 65 (1957).
7. Rogers, O. R., and R. F. Cook: *WADC Technical Report 52-341*, ASTIA No. AD 13026.
8. Miller, M. M., and R. Pollock: *Noise Control* **1**: 50 (1955).

9. Ghose, S. C.: *Jour. of the Royal Aeronautical Soc.*, **54**: 697 (1950).
10. Miller, M. M., and J. E. Calkins: *J. Acoust. Soc. Am.*, **27**: 203 (1955).
11. Rogers, O. R.: *AMC Memo Report No.* MCREXA5-4551-4, Jan. 28, 1949.
12. Handbook of Instructions for Aircraft Designers, *Air Research and Development Command Manual* 80-1, revised April, 1957, also "Acoustical Noise Levels in Aircraft," General Specifications for MIL-A-8806, Oct. 25, 1956.
13. Nichols, Jr., R. H., H. P. Sleeper, Jr., R. L. Wallace, Jr., and H. L. Ericson: *J. Acoust. Soc. Am.*, **19**: 428 (1947).
14. Geiger, P. H., and R. N. Hamme: Sound Transmission through Aircraft Soundproofing Structures, *University of Michigan, Project* M820, Oct. 27, 1949.
15. Beranek, L. L., and G. A. Work: *J. Acoust. Soc. Am.*, **21**: 419 (1949).
16. Bonvallet, G. L., and H. B. Karplus: *USAF, WADC Technical Report* 53-522, December, 1953.
17. Field, R. L., T. M. Edwards, P. Kangas, and G. L. Pigman: *U.S. Department of Commerce, Civil Aeronautics Administration*, Washington, D.C., *Technical Development Report No.* 68, July, 1947.
18. Kamrass, M., and K. D. Swartzel: *Noise Control*, **1**: 30 (November, 1955).
19. Stevens, K. N.: *NACA Technical Note* 3379, December, 1954.
20. Stevens, K. N., and R. H. Bolt: *J. Acoust. Soc. Am.*, **26**: 938 (1954).
21. Hayhurst, J. D.: *J. Royal Aeronautical Soc.* (January, 1953).
22. *The National Air Transport Coordinating Committee, NATCC Noise Abatement Procedures*, Jan. 1, 1954.
23. Hardy, H. C.: *J. Acoust. Soc. Am.*, **25**: 423 (1953).
24. Hazard, D. M.: *J. Acoust. Soc. Am.*, **25**: 412 (1953).
25. *Pratt and Whitney Aircraft, Report No.* PWA-130, 1936.
26. *Hamilton Standard Propellers, Report* HSP-25, 1936.
27. Mercer, J. R.: *United Aircraft, VAC Research Dept.*, M-22502-1, 1951.
28. Fehr, R. O., R. J. Wells, and T. L. Bray: *J. Acoust. Soc. Am.*, **24**: 480 (1952).
29. Fehr, R. O., and B. E. Crocker: paper presented at *SAE National Aeronautic Meeting*, 1954.
30. Lemmerman, Richard D., and H. J. Lockwood: *Aeronautical Engineering Review*, **14** (3) (1955).
31. Veneklasen, P. S.: *J. Acoust. Soc. Am.*, **25**: 417 (1953).
32. Fogel, R. E. L., and H. W. Withington: paper presented at *SAE National Aeronautic Meeting*, 1954.
33. Acceptance Report: Jet Engine Noise Suppression Device, *The Glenn L. Martin Co., Dept.* 866, 1954.
34. Hemond, C. J., Jr., and R. D. Lemmerman: *J. Acoust. Soc. Am.*, **27**: 203 (1955).
35. Watters, B., S. Labate, and L. L. Beranek: *J. Acoust. Soc. Am.*, **27**: 449 (1955).
36. Dyer, I.: *Noise Control*, **2** (May, 1956).
37. Hirschorn, M., R. Zecca, and S. M. Potter: 49th *Meeting Acoust. Soc. Am.* (1955).
38. Lemmerman, R. D.: *J. Acoust. Soc. Am.*, **25** (3): 438–442 (1953).
39. Labate, S.: *Noise Control*, **2** (1): 15 (1956).
40. Wells, R. J., and B. E. Crocker: *J. Acoust. Soc. Am.*, **25**: 433 (1953).
41. Doelling, N., W. J. Galloway, and A. C. Pietrasanta: paper presented at 50th Meeting, *Acoust. Soc. Am.* (1955), to be published as *WADC Technical Report*.
42. Goff, K. W., and D. M. A. Mercer: *J. Acoust. Soc. Am.*, **27**: 1133 (1955).
43. Galloway, W. J., William G. Waters, and J. J. Baruch: *J. Acoust. Soc. Am.*, **27**: 220 (1955).
44. Beranek, L. L., S. Labate, and U. Ingard: *J. Acoust. Soc. Am.*, **27**: 85 (1955). (Also *NACA* TN 3378 by the same authors.)
45. Galloway, D. B., and R. D. Lemmerman: *J. Acoust. Soc. Am.*, **25**: 429 (1953).
46. See papers presented at 52d meeting of *Acoust. Soc. Am.*, November, 1956, in session "Noise Induced Vibrations in Aircraft Structures," *J. Acoust. Soc. Am.*, **29**: 176 (1957).
47. Rogers, O. R., and R. F. Cook: *USAF WADC Technical Note* 57–68, 1957.
48. Pietrasanta, A. C.: *Noise Control*, **3**: 2 (November, 1957).
49. Stevens, K., A. Pietrasanta, and the staff of Bolt, Beranek, and Newman, Inc.: *USAF WADC Technical Note* 57-10, 1957.

Chapter 35

COMMUNITY NOISE AND CITY PLANNING

K. N. Stevens, Sc.D., and J. J. Baruch, Sc.D.

Bolt, Beranek, and Newman, Inc., and Massachusetts Institute of Technology

PHYSICAL DESCRIPTION OF COMMUNITY NOISE

Statistical Aspects of Community-noise Sources and Propagation Paths. People who live in residential communities are exposed to noise from many different sources. Most of the noise usually originates from transportation vehicles: automobiles, trucks and other motor traffic, trains, airplanes, and perhaps motorboats. In some neighborhoods machinery in factories or in homes is also an important source of noise. Children playing, dogs or other animals, radios, etc., frequently make further contributions to community noise.

With such a multiplicity of noise sources, some stationary and some moving, it is difficult to describe in a simple fashion the noise measured at a given point in the community. Each of the noise sources generates a different amount of sound power and has different frequency and directional characteristics, and each of these properties of the sources may vary with time. The sound energy that reaches a given point must propagate over distances that may vary from a few feet to a mile or more. The manner in which sound propagates over this path depends markedly on the type of terrain and on the atmospheric conditions, especially on gradients of wind velocity and temperature. The wind and temperature conditions change with time, with resultant large fluctuations in the propagation of sound through the medium.

Within a community comprising several blocks, there are usually substantial differences in the noise characteristics from point to point, depending upon the location of roads, factories, airplane flight paths, etc. In view of this complexity of noise sources and propagation paths, it is clearly difficult to obtain a meaningful description of the noise in a community in terms of a single number. One must resort to the language of statistics to specify the characteristics of community noise.

What physical dimensions should be used to describe the noise in a community? Since the interaction of the noise with people in the community is of ultimate concern, dimensions must be selected that provide enough information to permit estimation of this interaction.

Laboratory data in psychoacoustics and field experience have shown that the frequency characteristics of the noise are of primary importance, as well as the over-all noise level. Thus, the description of community noise should include a specification of the sound pressure levels in bands of frequencies such as octave bands. When the noise exhibits appreciable fluctuations, a single number such as the average sound pressure level in decibels does not provide an adequate description of the noise. A statistical distribution must be given, indicating the percentage of time that various sound pressure levels are exceeded in a given period of minutes or hours.   The distribution usually changes throughout a typical day, and hence more than one distribution must be given to specify the background noise completely.

In principle, if the appropriate statistical properties of the sources and propagation paths are given, it is possible to compute the relevant characteristics of the noise at a given point in a community.   Such a computation is often difficult, however, and adequate data on the sources and propagation paths are frequently not available. Community noise is usually determined, therefore, from direct measurements of sound pressure levels at various points in the community.   In the following sections of this chapter the results of a number of direct measurements of noise in communities are

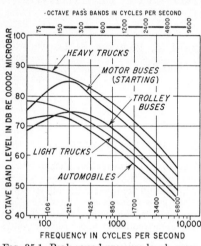

FIG. 35.1. Peak sound pressure levels measured at a distance of 20 ft from various motor vehicles. Vehicle speeds on roadways were those commonly used, except for motor buses, which were in a starting condition. (*After Bonvallet.*[1])

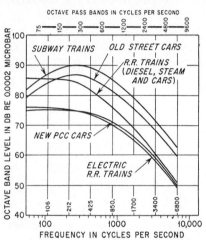

FIG. 35.2. Peak sound pressure levels for vehicles operating on rails at commonly used speeds. Distances to the vehicles were 20 ft except in the case of steam and diesel trains, for which the distances were 100 ft. (*After Bonvallet.*[1])

presented and procedures for computing the statistical properties of community noise are outlined.

Principal Sources of Community Noise.   The principal sources of community noise may be divided into three classes: (1) sources of transportation noise, (2) fixed sources of industrial noise, and (3) noise produced by people, especially children.   The sources of transportation noise are usually the most important since the noise measured at a point in the community is usually controlled by ground and air traffic.   A considerable number of measurements of sources of transportation noise have been made in the past, and the distribution of levels and spectra are now fairly well established, especially for automobiles and trucks.   The characteristics of sources of industrial noise and of noise made by people are less simple to specify in general terms, and only approximate data are given for these cases.

Automobiles, Buses, and Trucks.[1]   Average sound pressure levels in octave bands of frequency, measured at a standard distance of 20 ft, are shown in Fig. 35.1.   Spectra are given for automobiles, light trucks, heavy trucks, trolley buses, and motor buses under starting conditions.   There is, of course, a variation in the peak level for one particular type of vehicle, and variations from the average are given in Table 35.1. The numbers in this table indicate the decibel range within which one-half the measurements on a particular type of vehicle are obtained.

Trains, Streetcars, and Subways.[1]   Average spectra for various types of trains, streetcars, and subways are given in Fig. 35.2.   Variations about the mean are shown as before in Table 35.1. There is a fairly wide spread in the data for railroad trains, since there is usually a difference between steam and diesel locomotives, and between the level measured as the locomotive passes and the level measured as the train of cars passes.

Table 35.1. Decibel Variations from the Average for Measurements of Transportation Noise in the 300- to 600-cps Frequency Band*[1]

Vehicle	Variation, db
Automobiles	±3
Trolley (electric) buses	±3
Motor buses	±3
Light trucks	±3
Heavy trucks	±3
Steam, diesel trains	±6
Electric trains	±2
Subway trains	±4
Old streetcars (trams)	±3
New PCC streetcars	±2

* One-half of the measurements for each type of vehicle are within the range defined by this variation. Measurements for all vehicles were made at 20 ft except steam and diesel trains, which were at 100 ft. Speeds were those usually employed except for motor buses, which were in the accelerating condition.

Airplanes.[2,3] The sound pressure levels measured a fixed distance underneath aircraft in flight depend markedly on the type of aircraft and on the operating conditions or power settings of the aircraft engines. The variation of noise-source characteristics with engine power and other engine characteristics is discussed in Chap. 33. Some typical measurements of peak sound pressure levels underneath various types of aircraft under several operating conditions are given in Fig. 35.3. The data are all adjusted for a standard distance directly beneath the aircraft, as indicated in the figure.

Industrial Noise.[4] The sound pressure levels produced by industrial sources other than transportation vehicles are difficult to specify in simple terms because industrial buildings have many sizes and shapes, and the composite sources of sound may have a complicated configuration. One method of characterizing industrial-noise sources is to show a statistical distribution of sound pressure levels measured at some average distance, for many different industrial areas. Such a characterization depends, of course, upon the particular sample of industrial areas selected for study. If the sample is sufficiently large, however, the measurements provide an approximation to the distribution of sound pressure levels near industrial areas in general.

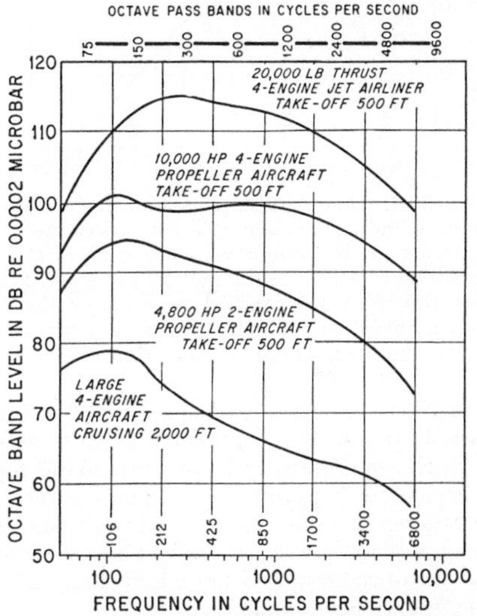

One survey has reported the results of measurements made at over a hundred

FIG. 35.3. Peak sound pressure levels on the ground for typical aircraft passing directly overhead, for the distances and power settings shown. (*Data from Parkin and Purkis*[2] *and Stevens.*[3])

places in various industrial areas during usual business hours.[4] These measurements were made at an average distance of about 25 ft from the industrial property line, without regard to the proximity of residences. The distribution of measurements from this survey is shown in Fig. 35.4. Some of the measurements were made at locations where the particular industrial noise under study was above the background of industrial, traffic, or unidentifiable noise. In other cases, the background noise, generally from traffic, was above the industrial noise. After the usual business hours there is, of course, a decrease in the noise of industrial operations and of traffic, since the traffic is usually reduced. The data in Fig. 35.4 are typical of summertime, when factory windows are usually open. The average levels decrease by about 5 db in areas where windows must be closed in the winter.

Determination of Community Noise from Statistical Properties of Noise Sources and Propagation Paths. As already noted, community noise is determined largely by sources of transportation noise—automobiles, trucks, trains, aircraft, etc. These noise sources usually move in relatively straight lines along roads, tracks, or flight paths. If certain assumptions are made concerning the number of noise sources, their location,

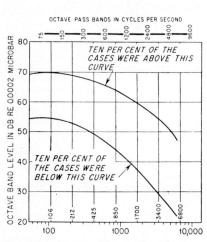

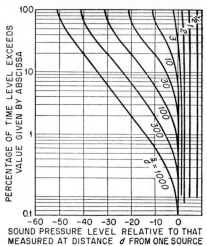

Fig. 35.4. Distribution of sound pressure levels in industrial areas. The approximate distance to the property line was 25 ft in each case. Data from about 90 per cent of the 100-odd areas studied were below the upper curve, and about 10 per cent were below the lower curve. (*After Bonvallet.*[4])

Fig. 35.5. Computed curves showing cumulative distributions of sound pressure levels measured at distance *d* from a line along which sound sources move with spacing *s*. The parameter is the ratio *s/d* (see text).

and their properties as generators of sound, it is possible to compute the statistical distribution of sound pressure levels at an observer's position.

Such computations have been made for particular sets of conditions by several authors. For example, relations between the average over-all sound pressure level at a given distance from a roadway and the number of vehicles per minute passing on the roadway have been derived and verified by actual measurements.[5,6] Also, calculations of room noise from a knowledge of statistical properties of noise sources in the room have been made.[7,8]

Suppose that a number of equally spaced, nondirectional sound sources move with a fixed velocity along a straight path, each radiating the same amount of sound power, and let *s* be the spacing between the sources. Compute the distribution of sound pressure levels at a point *A* which is at distance *d* from the path. If it is assumed that the propagation of sound from a source follows the "inverse-square law," the computation of the distribution is straightforward. The results of such calculations are shown in graphical form in Fig. 35.5. In this figure the horizontal axis is the difference between the measured sound pressure level and the sound pressure level that would be obtained at distance *d* from one source. The vertical axis gives the percentage of time the level exceeds the level given by the abscissa. The parameter is the ratio of the spacing between the noise sources to the perpendicular distance from the observer to the path, i.e., the ratio *s/d*. If the spacing between the noise sources is not uniform, the shape of the curves in Fig. 35.5 will be slightly modified. The minimum level, or the level that is exceeded 100 per cent of the time, will be somewhat lower, but the maximum level will probably not be changed. In cases where noise sources at a distance of a few hundred feet or more make a substantial contribution to the result, the computations should include corrections for sound attenuation over terrain and through the atmosphere (see Chap. 3). The inverse-square law is usually not a good approximation for propagation over distances of more than 1,000 ft.

To illustrate the use of the curves in Fig. 35.5, consider a hypothetical situation in which four automobiles per minute pass along a road at about 30 mph. Determine the distribution of sound pressure levels in the 300- to 600-cps band at a distance of, say, 200 ft from the road. From Fig. 35.1, the sound pressure level at a distance of 20 ft from one automobile is 68 db. At 200 ft the level is about 48 db, from the inverse-square law. The ratio s/d is 3.3, and hence, from Fig. 35.5, the distribution shown as curve A in Fig. 35.6 may be plotted. The fluctuations in level are relatively small, from 45 db to about 49 db.

Next, assume that, in addition to the automobile traffic, one heavy truck passes along the road every 2 min. In the 300- to 600-cps band, the sound pressure level 200 ft from a heavy truck is 64 db, from Fig. 35.1. The ratio s/d is about 26 for the trucks. The distribution in levels as a result of the trucks is shown as curve B in Fig. 35.6. When the trucks and automobiles are combined, the distribution curve labeled C is obtained. In a similar fashion, contributions from other sources, such as trains, streetcars, and airplanes, can be added to those already plotted in Fig. 35.6, to obtain a distribution for the combination of all sources. In addition, contributions from fixed sources such as manufacturing operations can also be added. If all important noise sources are included in the calculation, the computed distribution should be the same as the distribution in levels that would be measured in a noise survey.

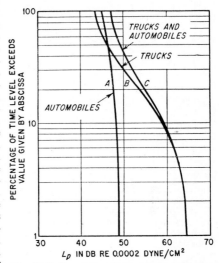

Fig. 35.6. Examples of computed cumulative distribution curves of sound pressure levels for automobile and truck traffic (see text).

Table **35.2.** Median Sound Pressure Levels and Range of Sound Pressure Levels Measured in Residential Areas[9]

	Median L_p, db re 0.0002 microbar	Range of L_p within which 90% of Measurements Were Made, db
New York City..................	66	59–72
Other than N.Y.C.—summer...........	55	43–67
Other than N.Y.C.—winter.............	53	40–66

Results of Community Noise Surveys.   During the past few years several extensive surveys of community noise have been reported. Since the objectives of these surveys were somewhat different, a direct comparison of their results cannot easily be made. Consequently, data from the surveys are described separately.

In the first survey, over-all levels of room noise and outdoor noise were measured under various conditions.[9] Measurements of outdoor noise were made in residential communities and in business areas at the edge of the street for (1) summer conditions in New York City, (2) summer conditions in locations other than New York City, and (3) winter conditions in locations other than New York City. The data for the residential areas are summarized in Table 35.2.

In another survey, measurements were made in a large number of residential and industrial areas in or near the city of Chicago.[4]   In each neighborhood, measurements of an average level of background noise were made when there was no noise due to nearby sources, such as children at play, vendors, dogs, etc.   Ranges of sound pressure levels in octave bands of frequency in the various residential areas are given in Fig. 35.7.   The upper two curves define the range of average levels measured in areas where there is considerable industrial activity and reasonably heavy traffic.   Below this is a range of levels measured in residential areas where noise is caused by distant traffic or industry, and where the sources of noise are unidentifiable.   In general, the noise in residential areas selected at random would not be distributed uniformly throughout the two ranges shown in Fig. 35.7.   Only a rather small number of neighborhoods would have noise conditions as severe as those in the upper range.   In most residential areas the daytime noise levels would be in the lower range.   In the Chicago survey a number of measurements were made at nighttime, and the lowest curve in Fig. 35.7 represents the lowest nighttime levels that were measured.   At the right side of this figure is

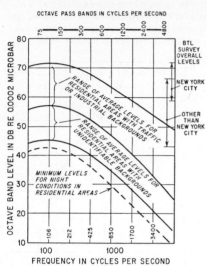

Fig. 35.7. Average sound pressure levels measured in residential areas. (*After Bonvallet.*[4])

plotted, for comparison, the ranges of over-all sound pressure levels measured in residential areas in the survey of Ref. 9.   The ranges in over-all levels for the two sets of data are very nearly the same.

In the third survey considered here, the communities in which measurements were

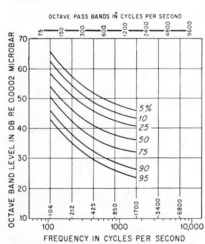

Fig. 35.8. Average sound pressure levels measured in residential areas in the daytime. The numbers labeling each curve indicate the percentage of residential areas in which the spectrum represented by that curve was exceeded. (*After Stevens.*[3])

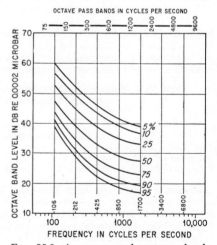

Fig. 35.9. Average sound pressure levels measured in residential areas at nighttime. The numbers labeling each curve indicate the percentage of residential areas in which the spectrum represented by that curve was exceeded. (*After Stevens.*[3])

made were selected in a somewhat different fashion.[3] All measurements were made in populated communities within 12 miles of the commercial airports in eight major cities in the United States.   In each city data were taken in about 24 different neighborhoods.   Most of the communities were selected to be under or near regularly used aircraft flight paths, although the measurements of background noise were always made in the absence of aircraft noise.   The communities represent all types, from quiet suburban, or even rural, areas to commercial-residential areas along heavily traveled highways.   Measurements representative of both daytime and nighttime conditions were made.   Daytime readings were between 9:30 A.M. and 4:30 P.M.; nighttime readings were from 1:00 A.M. to 5:00 A.M.   Measuring locations were always close to typical residences in each area.

The results of the survey are summarized in Figs. 35.8 and 35.9.   Each curve in these figures indicates a spectrum that is exceeded in x per cent of the areas, where x is the number that labels the curve.   A curve labeled "25%," for example, depicts an average background-noise spectrum that is exceeded in 25 per cent of the areas in which measurements were made. Since most of the measurements were made in only three octave bands of frequency, each noise spectrum is defined by only three points.   The background-noise spectrum is usually rather smooth, however, and joining the points in Figs. 35.8 and 35.9 by smooth curves and extrapolating the curves below 75 cps and above 2,400 cps are usually justified.   Comparison of the data in Fig. 35.7 with those in Fig. 35.8 indicates that the daytime average levels (curve labeled "50%" in Fig. 35.8) are about in the middle of the "range of average levels for residential areas with unidentifiable backgrounds" reported in Ref. 4.   In the survey of Ref. 3, a considerable number (about 30 per cent) of nighttime measurements were below the minimum levels in Fig. 35.7.

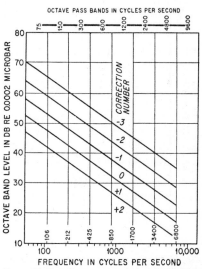

FIG. 35.10. Summary curves indicating ranges of average sound pressure levels measured in typical rural, suburban, and urban residential areas. (*From Fig. 36.5.*)

From the data in Figs. 35.7 to 35.9, summary curves have been drawn in Fig. 35.10 to indicate the average background-noise levels to be expected in communities with various amounts of traffic and industrial activity.

These curves correspond roughly to those in Fig. 36.5, which are used to assess the effect of background noise in predicting community reaction to noise.   The curves divide the octave-band levels into six regions, labeled from +2 to −3.*   Each curve slopes downward at a rate of 5 db per octave and represents an "average" shape for the background-noise spectrum in residential areas.   In the region labeled +2 are found background levels that are measured in rural areas remote from busy highways and industrial areas.   The nighttime background levels in some quiet suburban communities lie within this region, but in only a few such communities would the daytime levels be this low.   The region labeled +1 depicts nighttime background levels that are frequently measured in suburban areas near cities, provided there are no industrial activities, trucking, or busy streets within a few hundred yards.   In the daytime, levels in this region are measured in some reasonably quiet suburban communities with no nearby industrial activity, but they are rarely found within the boundaries of large industrial cities.   The daytime background level in many suburban commu-

* The regions are labeled in this manner to be consistent with the labeling of Fig. 36.5. The positive and negative numbers are used as correction numbers in one of the predictive schemes discussed in Chap. 36.

nities lies in the region labeled 0, provided the communities are not located near any industrial activity or trucking.   Nighttime levels in this region usually designate populated residential areas in cities, provided there are no nearby trucking routes or heavily traveled roads.   The background levels in the region labeled −1 are found in the daytime in many urban residential areas.   At nighttime, levels in this region in Fig. 35.10 would occur in a relatively noisy community, probably located near main thoroughfares or near industrial areas with nighttime operations.   The region labeled −2 characterizes a residential area located near relatively busy roads, or near industrial areas.   Considerable numbers of communities are exposed to such levels nowadays, and hence this cannot be considered as an extreme condition.   Nighttime back-ground-noise levels in this range are generally found only in residential communities in industrial cities, with a considerable amount of nighttime traffic and trucking nearby.   Background levels in the region labeled −3 are usually found in urban residential areas close to busy thoroughfares with trucks, buses, etc., and in areas where there is considerable industrial activity.   Such areas are generally in large cities that have a network of busy streets and highways.

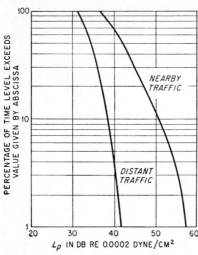

FIG. 35.11. Cumulative distribution curves showing sound pressure levels in 300- to 600-cps frequency band for typical traffic conditions in a residential community.   (*After Stevens.*[3])

The data in Figs. 35.7 to 35.10 present *average* sound pressure levels of background noise in octave bands of frequency.   Measurements at a given point are obtained by averaging the fluctuations of sound pressure level indications on a sound-level meter or octave-band analyzer.   In two communities with the same average background-noise spectrum but with different amounts of fluctuation about this average, the subjective reaction of residents to the noise might be quite different.   It is important, therefore, to obtain a measure of the fluctuations in order to describe adequately the background noise in a community.   Unfortunately, quantitative data on the distribution of levels have not usually been obtained in most community-noise surveys.

Some examples of cumulative distributions of measured levels are shown in Fig. 35.11.   One of the distributions is typical of a situation where the level is controlled primarily by steady distant traffic; the other distribution is typical of a case where there is steady distant traffic but also a considerable volume of local traffic passing within 300 ft of the measuring location.   Since the curves in Fig. 35.11 are based on a limited number of measurements, they cannot be extended below 1 per cent.   Very occasional occurrences of high noise levels, from large trucks or aircraft, for example, would cause the curves to extend into regions of higher sound pressure level for percentage values less than 1 per cent.

NOISE AND COMMUNITY PLANNING

General Problem of Community Planning against Noise.   Intelligent community planning and its subsequent implementation by zoning regulations are essentially protective measures insofar as noise is concerned.   The protection they afford is three-fold.   The resident must be protected from the intrusion on his privacy caused by outside noise.   The community must be protected from having the property value, and hence the tax revenue of land surrounding a noise-generating operation, reduced.   Last, but by no means least, the manufacturer or operator of a noisy process must be protected from lawsuits and post-facto expenditures for noise control.

Many original approaches have been made to the problem of noise zoning in the past. For example, "heavy factories" have long been prohibited in residential areas on the basis that they produced too much noise. As time went on, however, it became apparent that such zoning laws were inadequate. In spite of these laws, people were building factories which produced vigorous complaints on the grounds of excessive noise; similarly, factories operating in a quiet fashion were being relegated to undesirable districts. The reason for this apparent anomaly soon became evident. First of all, noise is a subjective term by its very definition: "any unwanted sound." Thus, it implies not only a source generating a sound but a listener "unwanting" that sound. Obviously, then, any zoning procedure which concerns itself only with the source must deal in terms of sound and not of noise.

The second factor leading to the difficulties experienced with older zoning systems arises from the assumption that similar industries perforce produce similar amounts of sound. While there was some basis for this concept in the past, modern technological advances in understanding the generation and control of sound have virtually eliminated the utility of such a view. Thus, for example, if a modern jet engine were tested on an old-fashioned test stand, the facility would radiate about 10,000 watts of acoustic power. If the same tests were performed on a modern acoustically designed stand, the radiation would amount to less than 0.01 per cent of this quantity! Evidently, then, one jet-engine manufacturer might be a perfectly acceptable neighbor while another would be an anathema.

Newer methods of planning, in order to avoid the inconsistencies of older methods, try to base their requirements on a close understanding of the tolerance of the people involved as well as on the actual performance of the potential offender. Thus, a jet-engine manufacturer would not be prohibited from building in a given spot because of noise, but would be told that, if he does build there, his radiated power may not exceed so many watts with such and such a spectrum. In addition, this requirement would vary from spot to spot within the city depending on the characteristics of the neighboring communities.

Planning of Communities in Relation to Industrial Noise. The new manufacturer entering an established community has many problems in choosing a location for his plant. Not only must he comply with local ordinances, but the enlightened manufacturer wishes to become an accepted part of the community, with the ancillary benefits in worker morale and efficiency which accrue to such acceptance. Thus, when the noise question is broached, the community and the manufacturer have a common interest in its solution. The zoning procedure to be presented here is based on the criteria discussed in Chap. 36 and is designed not only to protect the community, but also to enable the manufacturer to determine the degree of noise control (and hence its cost) for any given location in a well-mapped city. The discussion of community reaction to noise in that chapter points out that community response is dependent upon a number of different factors.[10] Some of these factors are determined by characteristics of the community, independent of the particular noise source under consideration; others are determined by characteristics of the noise source.

The characteristics of the community fall into two classes: the first class specifies sociological and psychological factors, and the second specifies physical quantities related to noise in the community. The sociological and psychological variables are difficult to quantify, and relatively little is known concerning their relation to the community response. At present, there is no satisfactory way of accounting for such factors in the planning of particular communities in relation to noise. Therefore, consideration is restricted to communities for which the influence of these nonacoustic factors is expected to be "normal." It is assumed that the deviation from this norm is not too great in most cases. The second class of community factors includes the background-noise levels in the community in the absence of the particular industrial-noise source under consideration, and the amount of previous exposure of the community to noise like that generated by the industrial-noise source. Numerical descriptions or ratings can be attached to different communities or portions of communities depending upon the background-noise levels and upon the previous exposure. A community with relatively high background noise and with considerable previous exposure to noise would have a relatively high rating; a community with low background noise and little previous exposure would have a low rating. For a given industrial noise, one would expect a more severe response from the latter community than from the former.

Characteristics of the noise source that are likely to influence community response are the sound power radiated by the source at different frequencies; the presence or absence of predominant single-frequency components in the noise spectrum; the peak factor of the noise, i.e., the presence or absence of sharp impulses; and the time schedule of the operation of the source, i.e., the time of day or night and how often and for how long the source operates. Chapter 36 suggests procedures for estimating the relative contribution of these various characteristics of the noise source in evaluating the community response.

The zoning procedure described here attempts to account for the two types of variables—one associated with the community and the other associated with the noise source—in a reasonably quantitative fashion. To establish procedures for zoning residential communities, a number of steps are required.

1. The community or communities surrounding an existing or potential industrial-noise source must be studied and surveyed to determine the background-noise levels and previous noise exposure. The measurements of background-noise levels are plotted in Fig. 35.10, and correction numbers* from $+2$ to -3 are assigned, depending upon the region in Fig. 35.10 within which the spectrum lies. If there has been some previous exposure of the community to the particular industrial noise under consideration, an additional correction number of -1 is applied; no additional correction is applied if there has been no previous exposure. These correction numbers are used to divide the community into zones. Seven different kinds of zones are possible, ranging from zones labeled $+2$ to zones labeled -3.

2. Since a change of one rank represents a change of about 5 db, it is evident that a given noise source can be placed closer to a zero zone than to a $+1$ zone. How much closer can be determined from the equation

$$5 \text{ db} = 20 \log \frac{\text{distance to } +1 \text{ zone}}{\text{distance to zero zone}}$$

Solving this equation, we have

$$\frac{\text{Distance to } +1 \text{ zone}}{\text{Distance to zero zone}} = 1.8$$

Thus, a given source must be 1.75 times farther from a $+1$ zone than a zero zone and $(1.8)^2$, or 3.2, times farther from a -1 zone, etc. As a result, the divider numbers of the table below may be assigned to each zone and marked on the map. After this has been done, the basic zoning map is complete.

Zone Number	Divider Number
$+2$	1
$+1$	1.8
0	3.2
-1	5.6
-2	10
-3	18
-4	32

3. As a policy matter, a decision must be made to determine the degree of community reaction that is to be considered acceptable. Thus, using the scale given in Fig. 36.3 officials may decide that a response of "no observed reaction" will be acceptable. From Fig. 36.3 and from this policy decision, a tolerable Composite Noise Rating is then established.

* The use of correction numbers in the evaluation of community reaction to noise is discussed in Chap. 36 and in Ref. 10.

4. The industrial noise source is then rated according to the character of the noise it generates by using the numbers given in Table 36.6, and a correction number is assigned to account for the character of the noise source. Pertinent portions of Table 36.6 are reproduced in Table 35.3. If, for example, the correction number is −2, a

Table 35.3. Correction Numbers to Account for Character of Industrial Noise Source*

Influencing Factor	*Correction Number*
Temporal and seasonal factors:	
a. Daytime only..............................	−1
Nighttime.................................	0
b. Repetitiveness (see Fig. 36.6)................	0 to −6
c. Winter (for northern climates)...............	−1
Summer...................................	0
Character of the noise:	
a. Continuous spectrum.......................	0
Pure-tone components......................	+1
b. Smooth time character.....................	0
Impulsive.................................	+1

* Also see Table 36.6.

noise-level rank of **d** will be permissible in the example which follows, as calculated from the relation [see Eq. (36.1)]:

(Noise-level rank) + (correction number) = (Composite Noise Rating)

5. Having thus decided that the noise source will be permitted to create a sound pressure level spectrum equal to that bounding the upper edge of space **d** in Fig. 36.4 at a zero-zone residence, a calculation must be made to determine the acoustic power which the factory may radiate and not exceed this spectrum. This calculation involves not only the distance to a given zone, but, as explained under (2), the kind of zone (and hence its divider number). Only the closest zone of each type is of concern. From the zoning map, the zone is selected whose distance from the proposed factory divided by its divider number yields the smallest quantity. (This is a simple task if a transparent movable overlay marked with concentric circles is used over the zoning map.) (This smallest value of distance)/(divider number) is used in conjunction with the following table to find the number of decibels to be added to the level-rank curve in order to determine the maximum permissible radiated power level. The resulting

$\dfrac{Distance\ in\ feet}{Divider\ number}$	*Decibels to Be Added to Noise-level Rank Curve*
40–70	40
70–125	45
125–225	50
225–400	55
400–700	60
700–1,250	65
1,250–2,250	70
2,250–4,000	75
4,000–7,000	80

curve gives the maximum permissible power level, in octave frequency bands, which may be generated by a factory producing one specific type of noise under a specific set of conditions of operations (as given in Table 35.3) at that site.

While this system may seem complex, it must be realized that no single number can be a solution to a problem involving as many parameters as the determination of community reaction to noise. Actually, the intelligent use of a prepared rating form incorporating the questions of Table 35.3 reduces (4) in the above procedure to a routine. In addition, the use of an overlay having concentric circles marked on it reduces (5) to a fairly simple routine.

Example. In order to illustrate the application of the above procedure, consider a hypothetical example. In Fig. 35.12 is shown a portion of a community close to the intersection of two highways. A factory is to be built at the location marked A in the figure, and the factory building is to be about 250 ft from the nearest residences as shown. The residents of the community have had no previous exposure to noise of the type that is to be radiated by the factory, and consequently no correction number is applied for previous exposure. From a survey of background noise in the community, the dashed contours shown in the figure are plotted. The numbers labeling the zones between the contours are obtained by comparing the measured background levels with the levels given in Fig. 35.10.

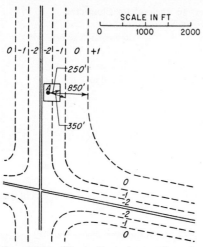

In this example it is assumed that a Composite Noise Rating of B is considered to be acceptable. The factory is to operate continuously during the daytime only, and hence a correction of -1 can be applied in the manner shown in (4) of the procedure outlined above. Thus the noise source is permitted to create sound pressure levels equal to those bounding the upper edge of space c in Fig. 36.4 at a zero-zone residence. The closest distances to the various zones are 250 ft for a -1 zone, 350 ft for a zero zone, and 850 ft for a $+1$ zone. (The smallest value of distance)/(divider number) is $350/3.2 = 110$. From the table in (5) of the description of the procedure above, observe that 45 db must be added to the noise-level rank to give the maximum permissible power level. In this example, the maximum permissible power level, in octave frequency bands, is tabulated as follows:

FIG. 35.12. Illustration of procedure for preparing performance standards for industrial noise. The numbers -2, -1, etc., characterize the background noise in a community that lies near the intersection of two roads. The proposed industrial site is designated by A (see text).

Frequency Band, cps	Maximum Permissible Power Level, db re 10^{-12} watt
37.5–75	115
75–150	101
150–300	94
300–600	88
600–1,200	84
1,200–2,400	81
2,400–4,800	78
4,800–10,000	75

A Typical Zoning Ordinance. At the present time, standardized techniques for the measurement of the total sound power radiated from a source such as a factory have not been agreed upon. Consequently, present zoning ordinances that are concerned with noise usually specify the maximum values of sound pressure level that may exist at residences that are nearest to the noise-producing facility. These values of sound pressure level should be given with due regard for the characteristics of the community and of the noise source, as discussed above. A zoning ordinance written in this manner was recently proposed for the town of Stony Point, New York. The proposed ordinance appeared in The Rockland County Times of Haverstraw, New York, on December 16, 1954. The ordinance contained nine articles, and portions pertaining to noise control are reproduced below. (For a general discussion of anti-noise ordinances, see Chap. 39.)

Article 2

ESTABLISHMENT OF
DISTRICTS, MAP, DISTRICT
BOUNDARIES, AND SCOPE
OF CONTROLS

2.1   Establishment of Districts
The Town of Stony Point is hereby divided into the following districts, the respective symbol for each type of district being set forth opposite its title:

Symbol	Title
RA-1	One-Family Residence-Agriculture District (40,000 sq ft)
R-1	One-Family Residence District (15,000 sq ft)
R-2	General Residence District
RO	Residence-Office District
C-1	Retail Commerce District
C-2	General Commerce District
M-1	Light Manufacturing District
M-2	General Manufacturing District

Each such district is designated on the map referred to in Section 2.2, in the Use and Bulk Tables in Section 3.1 and elsewhere in the text of this ordinance by its symbol only.

Article 4

OTHER USE REGULATIONS

4.15   Locations where Determinations Are to be Made for Enforcement of Performance Standards.   The determination of the existence of any Dangerous and Objectionable Elements shall be made at the location of the use creating the same or beyond (herein referred to as "at any point") except as follows: the measurements necessary for enforcement of performance Standards set forth in Section 4.163, . . . shall be taken at different districts in relation to the establishment creating the element being measured, as follows:
   (a) In any R district and C-1 and C-2, 25 ft from the establishment or at the lot line if closer.
   (b) In M-1 and M-2, the boundary of the nearest R district.
4.16   Restrictions on Creation of Dangerous and Objectionable Elements.   Every use subject to Performance Standards shall conform to the restrictions set forth in this Sec.
4.163   Noise.   At the specified points of measurement the sound pressure level of noise radiated continuously from a facility at nighttime shall not exceed the values given in Table I in any octave band of frequency.   The sound pressure level shall be measured with a Sound Level Meter,[1] and an Octave Band Analyzer[2] that conform to specifications published by the American Standards Association.

Table I. Maximum Permissible Sound Pressure Levels at Specified Points of Measurement for Noise Radiated Continuously from a Facility at Nighttime

Frequency Band, cps	Sound Pressure Level, db re 0.0002 microbar
20–75	69
75–150	54
150–300	47
300–600	41
600–1,200	38
1,200–2,400	38
2,400–4,800	38
4,800–10,000	38

[1] American Standard Sound Level Meters for Measurement of Noise and Other Sounds, Z24, American Standards Association, Inc., New York, New York.
[2] American Standard Specification for an Octave-band Filter Set for the Analysis of Noise and Other Sounds, Z24, 10-1953, American Standards Association, Inc., New York, New York.

Table II

If the noise is not smooth and continuous and is not radiated at nighttime, one or more of the following corrections shall be added to or subtracted from each of the decibel levels given above in Table I.

Type of Operation or Character of Noise	Correction, db
Daytime operation only	+5
Noise source operates less than 20 % of the time	+5[a]
Noise source operates less than 5 % of the time	+10[a]
Noise source operates less than 1 % of the time	+15[a]
Noise of impulsive character (hammering, etc.)	−5
Noise of periodic character (hum, screech, etc.)	−5

[a] Apply one of these corrections only.

Planning of Communities in Relation to Sources of Transportation Noise. In the first section of this chapter the results of measurements of sound pressure levels around various sources of transportation noise were given. Also presented were the results of some surveys of community noise, together with a method for computing the composite effects of many noise sources to yield an estimate of the statistical variation of community noise. The computational procedures show that one can compute the distribution of sound pressure levels at any given location in a community if the distribution of automobile and truck traffic on nearby highways is known, and if data on air traffic and flight paths (if air traffic makes an appreciable contribution to noise in the community) and on other moving sources of transportation noise, such as trains, can be obtained.

Other chapters in the Handbook discuss the ways in which noise can interact with people and show how the effects on people can be predicted if certain physical characteristics of the noise are known. In particular, Chap. 36 shows that the reaction of communities to noise can, under some circumstances, be estimated if the spectral and temporal characteristics are known and if the background noise and previous noise exposure of the community are known. The effects of noise on speech communication are discussed in some detail in Chap. 9. Both of these effects—community reactions to noise and interference with speech—may be involved in cases where the effects of transportation noise are to be evaluated.

If one is able to predict reasonably accurately the physical characteristics of noise produced by sources of transportation noise, and if one can estimate the effects of such noise on people living or working in the communities, then he can devise rational procedures for the planning of communities in relation to highways, railroads, airports, and other sources of transportation noise. The procedures suggested here are similar to those outlined in the previous discussion of community planning relative to fixed sources of industrial noise. However, the present state of the art leaves many uncertainties and inaccuracies in our estimates both of the physical characteristics of the noise and of the effects of the noise on people. The planning procedures suggested here are subject to modification and refinement as more reliable data become available.

First consider the general approach to community planning relative to sources of *ground*-transportation noise. Suppose one is concerned with the planning of a community through which a rather heavily traveled highway is to pass. The first step is to obtain estimates of the volume of automobile and truck traffic on the highway at various times during the day and night. Then compute the noise spectra and the distribution of sound pressure levels at various distances on either side of the highway, using the data given in the first section of this chapter. Suppose, for example, the estimated traffic count during the day is eight cars per minute, and the average speed of these vehicles is 30 mph. It is then a simple matter to compute the spacing s between vehicles (330 ft), and to estimate the average sound pressure levels at various distances d from the highway, following the procedures outlined previously. The peak and median sound pressure levels in the 300- to 600-cps band for this example are plotted as a function of d in Fig. 35.13. Estimates of attenuation in excess of inverse-square sound reduction are made in Fig. 35.13 for large values of d. The next step is to decide upon the noise exposure that will be acceptable. This will depend to some extent upon the use to which the land is to be put. If the land is to be a residential area, then the acceptable levels should be consistent with levels that people living in such a residential area would normally expect. Such levels should presumably give rise to negligible or, at most, relatively mild community reaction. Figure 35.10 has given a summary of the levels that have been measured in many suburban and urban residential areas during the day and night. These data can be used as a guide for the selection of acceptable levels. If, for example, the community is an urban community, then daytime levels in the region designated −1 in Fig. 35.10 would be expected under normal conditions. In suburban communities, lower levels would be expected. According to the scheme presented in Chap. 36, such levels would elicit "no observed reaction" from the community. For the example illustrated in Fig. 35.13 one concludes that the nearest residence should be at a distance of 400 ft from the highway.

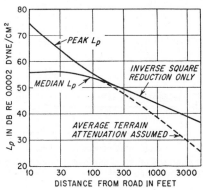

Fig. 35.13. Estimated sound pressure levels in 300- to 600-cps frequency band as a function of distance from a highway. Traffic count is eight automobiles per minute at a speed of 30 mph. Geometrical spreading of the sound is assumed for the solid curves.

To determine whether this distance is acceptable under nighttime traffic conditions we must compute the levels resulting from the estimated volume of nighttime traffic and compare these levels with acceptable nighttime levels. Many highways have a relatively large volume of heavy truck traffic at night, and for such cases the zoning of the community may be controlled by nighttime conditions.

Areas that are closer to the highway than the critical distance discussed above would not be suitable for residences if "no observed community reaction" is to be maintained. Such areas can often be used for commercial or office activities, however. The acceptable sound pressure levels for office spaces are determined primarily by speech-communication criteria, as discussed in Chap. 9. If, for example, private offices are to be located near the highway, speech-interference levels of 45 db outside open office windows would, in most cases, be acceptable. For the example illustrated in Fig. 35.13, the speech-interference levels would be about 10 db less than the levels in the 300- to 600-cps band (see Fig. 35.1) and it would be concluded that such private offices could be located as close as 100 ft from the highway. Private offices with closed windows, less critical office spaces, or other commercial areas could usually be located even closer to the highway.

In the planning of communities, noise from road traffic is likely to be an important factor only in cases where relatively heavy traffic is expected. In such cases the traffic noise is relatively uniform, and the distribution of levels is rather narrow, as indicated in Fig. 35.5 for small values of s/d or in Fig. 35.13 for d greater than about 100 ft. Since the noise is relatively uniform, it can be specified simply in terms of the average level and spectrum.

A consideration of the possible effects of noise from airports and air traffic on community planning shows a considerable difference in the character of the noise exposure. In general, the noise is characterized by relatively high peaks of sound pressure level but by a rather low frequency of occurrence of these peaks. The noise exposure must now be specified by both the peak sound pressure levels and the repetitive character. The effect of repetitive character on the prediction of community reaction to noise is discussed in Chap. 36. It is clear from that discussion, however, that the prediction of community reaction to noise is usually less reliable for cases where the noise exposure is intermittent than for cases of uniform noise exposure.

Noise from air traffic will obviously have the greatest effects on communities that are within a few miles of airports, since the sound pressure levels measured on the ground are highest when aircraft are at low altitudes, i.e., during take-off and landing operations. If the peak sound pressure levels at various points on the ground are computed or measured as an aircraft makes a straight take-off from an airport runway, it is found that contours of equal sound pressure level take the cigar-shaped form shown in Fig. 35.14.[11] Contours of high sound pressure level are narrow and short, whereas contours of lower sound pressure level are broad and long. The shape of a contour and the level associated with it depend upon the number and type of aircraft engines, the engine power settings, and the climb angle.

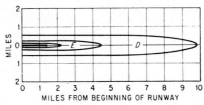

Fig. 35.14. Examples of contours of equal composite noise rating at the end of an airport runway. The letters D and E designate the composite noise rating (see text).

Communities within 1 or 2 miles of airports are usually exposed to the noise of ground run-up operations in addition to the noise of take-offs and landings. Such ground noise originating from stationary sources falls into the general category of industrial noise, which has been discussed in the last section.

The general approach to community planning relative to the noise of air traffic follows the same pattern as the approach that was used in connection with highway-traffic noise. First, either by measurement or by computation, contours of equal peak sound pressure levels for take-offs and landings of typical aircraft used at the airport under consideration are established. Next, information is obtained on the number of take-offs and landings for each airport runway, and other data are obtained that are pertinent to computation of the "Composite Noise Rating" by the method outlined in Chap. 36. In addition, data are required on the background noise in the community and on the previous exposure of the community to aircraft noise, since these factors associated with the community contribute to the final computation of the composite noise rating.

The contours in Fig. 35.14 are computed for a particular set of conditions in order to illustrate the general procedure. It is assumed that there are four take-offs per hour during the daytime, on the average, and that the aircraft maintain a straight flight path with a climb of 20:1. Typical commercial propeller aircraft with two engines are assumed (see Fig. 35.3). The letters D and E labeling regions between the contours represent values of Composite Noise Rating. Correction numbers to account for repetitiveness and other factors have already been applied to the noise-level rank corresponding to the peak levels, following the procedures outlined in Chap. 36.

If the area on either end of the runway is to be zoned, a decision must be made to establish the degree of community reaction that is to be considered acceptable. In this case, since the area involved is reasonably small, a response of sporadic complaints may be considered acceptable. From Fig. 36.3, the maximum Composite Noise Rating would be D. In the example illustrated in Fig. 35.13 then, the contour between the zones labeled D and E would mark the edge of the area considered as acceptable for a residential community. Within this contour, the land could have other uses. Some commercial and agricultural operations could be carried on under the noise conditions existing in this area.

This example shows that it is possible to develop procedures for the planning and zoning of land near airports. As the number and size of aircraft operating from military and commercial airports increase, with accompanying increase in noise exposure in nearby areas, planning for compatible land use in the vicinity of airports will become a virtual necessity.

REFERENCES

1. Bonvallet, G. L.: *J. Acoust. Soc. Amer.*, **22**: 201 (1950). Also see F. J. Meister: *J. Acoust. Soc. Amer.*, **29**: 81 (1957).
2. Parkin, P. H., and H. J. Purkis: *Acustica*, **4**: 439 (1954).
3. Stevens, K. N.: *NACA Technical Note* 3379, December, 1954.
4. Bonvallet, G. L.: *J. Acoust. Soc. Amer.*, **23**: 435 (1951).
5. Galt, R. H.: *J. Acoust. Soc. Amer.*, **2**: 30 (1930).
6. Takeuchi, R.: *Mem. Inst. Sci. and Ind. Research*, Japan, **9**: 53 (1952).
7. Dietze, E., and W. D. Goodale: *Bell System Tech. J.*, **18**: 605 (1939).
8. Takeuchi, R.: *Mem. Inst. Sci. and Ind. Research*, Japan, **11**: 69 (1954).
9. Seacord, D. F.: *Elec. Eng.*, **58**: 255 (1939); *J. Acoust. Soc. Amer.*, **12**: 183 (1940).
10. Stevens, K. N., W. A. Rosenblith, and R. H. Bolt: *Noise Control*, **1**: 63 (January, 1955).
11. Beranek, L. L.: *J. Acoust. Soc. Amer.*, **24**: 769 (1952).

Chapter 36

COMMUNITY REACTION TO NOISE

Horace O. Parrack, Ph.D.

Wright Air Development Center, USAF

INTRODUCTION

In modern, industrial countries many persons must live and work in environments that contain undesired, obnoxious, or potentially harmful physical agents. Acoustic energy (air-borne sound) frequently is one of these agents. Sounds are by-products of the mechanized operations that characterize modern industries. Factories, railroads, streetcars, trucks, buses, automobiles, airplanes, and their supporting facilities are accepted as essential to modern industry and modern living. All these machines and many others continuously radiate acoustic energy in their immediate vicinity. This acoustic energy is then widely distributed, by propagation in air, so that residential and business areas may be filled with sounds which originated from a variety of more-or-less distant sources. Details concerning the generation, propagation, and pressure levels of these varied sounds are to be found in earlier chapters. Here we are primarily concerned with the problems that arise when these sounds propagate into areas occupied by persons whose activities are not connected with the operation of the sound-producing sources.

Noise is defined as unwanted sound. The sounds, just described, are forced upon the occupant of an area. He must live and carry on his daily activities in their presence. He cannot control them directly. Frequently the source operation contributes nothing to his welfare. Indeed, the sounds usually disturb or disrupt many of his daily activities. Under these circumstances the sounds are definitely unwanted. To the occupant of the area these ambient sounds are simply noises. When the ambient sounds to which a majority of the occupants of an area are exposed can be described as noise we may call the sounds community noise.

Practical experience has shown that community noise may create individual and group resentments toward a noisy operation and its operator. Sometimes when the community noise levels were high, these annoyances and resentments have been accompanied by positive, concerted action to remove the offending source. Industrial plants and other noise-producing operations have been forced to shut down. The area of human knowledge concerned with individual and group attitudes and actions and the way these are related to pressure levels and other parameters of the noise field in a community are extremely complex. There have been few serious attempts to acquire data that could provide a better understanding of these problems. However, interest in these interrelations increases daily. This chapter describes these complex problems, indicates why we need information about them, and describes some practical applications for reliable data. Finally, some schemes are considered that have been proposed as predictors of reaction to community noise. The limitations of these schemes are described, and some suggestions for improving them are offered. Thus, an individual faced with a community-noise problem will be better informed concerning the tools now available to him and their limitations. Finally, some approaches are suggested that may improve our future capability for describing or predicting reaction to community noise.

COMMUNITY REACTION

The responses or reactions of individual men to sounds, including those described as noises, have been studied extensively. However, few studies have been made on the responses of groups of men (communities) to such sounds. In studies that have been made, the meaning assigned to the term "community" has not been consistent. To avoid further confusion, in future studies it will be necessary to use a commonly accepted definition of community or to specify exactly, for each case, the kind of group called a community. In addition, it will be necessary to specify, exactly, the type of group activity described by the term "reaction." A description of the characteristics of a community and some consideration of the restrictions these characteristics place upon group activity that may be called "community reaction" will simplify the interpretation of proposed methods for evaluating community reaction to noise.

The Community.[1] Before discussing community reaction to noise a definition of the term community is required. The sociologist applies the term community to a group of people, of all ages, having a common culture and living in a limited region which provides the group with a geographical center for most of their common interests and activities. In contrast, the sociologist defines a "neighborhood" as a subdivision of the community. A neighborhood is simply a group of families living conveniently near together. The community consists of several neighborhoods and is the smallest social unit that will hold together. The term community also is applied to larger groups such as a national or a world community. However, these groups are too large to be of interest here in considering group reactions to noise.

The term community usually has a different meaning for the ordinary citizen. In general, when individuals are asked to describe a community their descriptions define a neighborhood rather than a community. Examination of the studies that have been made on group responses to noise also reveals that, in nearly all cases, the group exposed to noise was a neighborhood rather than a community. These facts indicate that the *neighborhood*, a subdivision of the *community*, should be the organizational unit employed in studies on group response to noise.

The Neighborhood and Noise. Individual men respond to noise in a varied and complex way. Loudness is a perceptual parameter of noise as experienced by the individual. It would be convenient if loudness were related to noise level in a rather simple way. However, a multitude of studies have not produced a simple statement of this relation that is generally accepted today. Group responses to noise have received far less attention than have individual responses, such as perceived loudness. Therefore, virtually no information is available on the factors that may be important in determining the group response. However, a complex group response is to be expected. It may be highly unstable also. In considering neighborhood response to noise the best that can be done is to enumerate some of the factors that must be considered. Much will have been achieved if a proper appreciation of the complexity of the problem is created. One basic step is to distinguish "neighborhood attitudes" from "neighborhood action" in dealing with responses to noise.

ATTITUDES. Attitude is used to describe the state of mind of the neighborhood resident with respect to the noise situation; for example, he feels annoyed, resentful, or not disturbed by the noise. Attitude certainly is related to noise level, but little information concerning this relation is available. The attitudes or feelings of persons living in a neighborhood toward the noise stimulus have been investigated in one preliminary study. This study indicated that many factors other than noise level are important in determining attitude. Some of these factors are attachment to the local area, dislike of the local area, interest in the noise-producing operation, degree of individual social adjustment, economic level of the individual, individual educational achievements, etc. Thus, the attitudes of individuals toward neighborhood noise are influenced by many factors that have no definite relation to the noise stimulus. These facts always should be remembered by those who seek solutions to neighborhood-noise problems. It is reasonable to expect that neighborhood attitudes are the foundations upon which neighborhood actions are based. Therefore, an understanding of the action a neighborhood may take against a noise source requires information about the attitudes of the group. Attitudes of extreme annoyance usually lead to action.

ACTION. Neighborhood action against the operator of a disturbing noise source results from extreme group annoyance with the noise. In addition to the widespread feelings of annoyance, means for communicating these feelings throughout the group also must be at hand. Group action will result, provided leaders are available who are aware of appropriate methods for taking group action. Once again, the factors that determine the type and extent of group action are not related to the noise stimulus but are inherent in the neighborhood organization, its leadership, and the extent of its knowledge about effective procedures.

Community Action. Examination of the responses of the larger unit of social organization, the community, reveals that all the factors which operated to determine the neighborhood reaction are present. The pooled attitudes of the neighborhoods determine the community attitude. The community reaction simply reflects an integration of the reactions of the neighborhoods composing the community. If action is initiated, it is usually more effective because a larger number of more experienced leaders are available. On the other hand, communication is more complex, individual neighborhoods may be influenced by special interests, and concerted action may develop more slowly. The same factors that influenced the neighborhood may influence the community reaction. The following factors are considered most important: social status, economic level of community residents, political interest and affiliations, understanding of legal rights, knowledge of agencies empowered to control the agency creating the annoyance, general educational level of residents, the effectiveness of the public-relations program of the noise-source operator. Thus community reaction to noise is so complex in nature that one well may ask, "Can community response to noise be predicted?" If a predictive tool can be developed, it will have a variety of uses.

NEED FOR DATA ON COMMUNITY RESPONSE TO NOISE

The analysis of the factors relevant to the generation of a community's response to noise shows the problem to be so complex that many specialists are required in obtaining a solution for any single practical problem in this area. There are major needs, in connection with many specific subsidiary problems, for data that relate the community response to the community noise levels. Not only do we need a method that will predict the over-all or aggregate community response, but this method should also provide the means for evaluating specific effects of the noise on community residents. Some of the special problems that could be solved by adequate data on community reaction to noise are now considered.

Public-health Problems. "This noise injures health" is one of the first claims made when a community is subjected to intense noise. Community health is a responsibility of public-health agencies. Community officials and industrial-hygiene engineers need data that specify the relation between community noise level and health. The tool for predicting community response to noise should provide these data directly or it should ensure that community health is protected when no adverse community reactions are indicated. Knowledge of the noise levels that are consistent with community health also will allow engineers to calculate the extent of noise control that must be applied to any specific source.

Economic Problems. In discussing the factors that influence community reaction to noise, several economic factors were pointed out. In addition, noise in the community may influence property values, may render certain areas unsuited for certain business activities, or in other ways may influence the economic welfare of the residents. A method for predicting the extent of these economic effects when the community noise levels are known or can be computed would be of great value to community leaders, industrialists, engineers, and others who are held responsible for adequate control of community noise.

Engineering Problems.   Data that relate noise level to specific types of community response are essential to the acoustical engineer who must design the noise-control features of a factory or other industrial installations.   These data, when compared with data on source noise level, provide the means for computing the required noise reduction.   Only when such data are available is it possible to provide noise control in the initial facility design that will ensure adequate community protection from noise.

USES FOR DATA PREDICTING COMMUNITY RESPONSE TO NOISE

Complaints or other antagonistic action by the community have been the first indicators of excessively high community noise levels in the past.   Today the situation is essentially the same.   That is, industrial officials, community planners, and other responsible personnel have no means for evaluating in advance the community response to noise.   If a means for relating probable community response to specific noise levels can be developed, advance estimates of the community reaction can be made.   These data then can be used in several ways which will tend to eliminate adverse community reaction to noise by appropriate advance planning.

General Community Planning.   Any tool for predicting community response to noise would be extremely valuable in formulating general community plans.   It would be useful to city planners and to persons responsible for preparing broader general community plans for large districts or other areas that are mutually interdependent. Community planners would find a reliable means for estimating community response to noise useful in many specific areas.

Zoning.   In zoning a city or other area a method for predicting community response to specific noise levels would be of value in establishing appropriate zone borders.   The method could also be employed to determine what zones can advantageously be contiguous.

Industrial-area Selection.   The selection of industrial areas and the appropriate orientation of heavy and light industrial areas with respect to each other and with respect to areas assigned for other uses could be greatly improved if the planners had available an effective predictor of community response to noise.   Undesirable interactions among industrial areas and among these and residential or business areas could be avoided by adequate initial planning based upon the predicted community reaction to noise.

Industrial-area Layout.   Data that would specify the community reaction to particular noise levels would constitute important guides for the internal layout of areas designated for industrial use.   If the data prescribed the response of different types of communities, their value would be enhanced.   With such data, the orientation of intense noise sources and the spacing between them could be selected to minimize noise interferences while assuring maximal effective utilization of these areas.

Site Selection for Special Facilities.   A reliable predictor of community reaction to noise would make possible better site selection and facility orientation within particular zones.   In addition better choices could be made in selecting areas for special facilities such as airports, railway terminals, maintenance shops, and like facilities.

Industrial-facility Planning.   A technique that predicts community reactions to noise from specific data on noise levels could be used extensively by engineering and management personnel in planning industrial facilities.   The capability for predicting probable community reaction to noise would increase the effectiveness of several phases of general planning.

Location.   The industrial-facility planner faces a major problem when he selects the site for his plant.   Site selections require consideration of many factors, including the estimation of the effects of plant noise on surrounding communities.   At present these estimates, if made at all, are essentially guesses.   If community reaction to noise could be reliably predicted in advance, a site could be selected to ensure adequate isolation of the noise sources so that future costly arguments and possible closure of the plant would be avoided.

Design and Construction. The initial design and construction of any factory, airport, or other possible source of intense noise should provide the necessary noise-control and noise-reduction installations. The amount of reduction in noise level required can be determined only when data are available to specify acceptable noise levels in areas near the facility. An adequate method of relating community response to specific noise levels is the only means for estimating the noise control required to prevent undesired responses of persons located outside the plant. When a tool of this kind is available, industrial designers can provide for noise control in the original design and construction, where the costs are usually reduced to a minimum.

Operational Guidance. Noise control that will alleviate antagonistic community action frequently can be achieved by controlled operational procedures. This means of control is particularly applicable to existing facilities where noise-control measures were not applied in the original design. The method also may be required to supplement other noise-control measures applied to extremely noisy facilities. Selection of operational controls and their evaluation after application would be more effective if the operator had a reliable technique for predicting community response from the measured noise levels. When this tool is available the effectiveness of a given operational change can be estimated in advance. This would permit selecting an operational procedure that would be effective and that would minimize possible internal difficulties generated by its application.

In the case of factories or other manufacturing facilities an adequate method of predicting community response to noise could be used in establishing schedules of operation, particularly in selecting the time of day for operation of any source of unusually intense noise. Airport operators could use a predictor of community response to noise in selecting runways for maximum use, in selecting sites for maintenance operations, and in instituting other operational measures to reduce noise disturbances in surrounding communities. Similar applications for data on community response to noise could be made by operators of trucking lines, buses, street railways, and like transportation facilities. Undoubtedly many other applications for predictions of community response to noise could be made in devising operational procedures for noise control as soon as the predictive procedure is available.

RESPONSES OF COMMUNITY RESIDENTS TO NOISE

The important characteristics of the community have been described together with those factors other than noise that influence the generation of the community attitude. It has been suggested that attitudes may determine the action taken by a community against an operator of a source of disturbing noise. Requirements for a method of predicting community response to noise have been described, together with suggested uses for the predictive method. All these discussions have been general. The data that are available for use in constructing a predictor of community response to noise are now to be examined. Some predictive methods, based on empirical observations, have been suggested. These methods will be evaluated and discussed. This will provide a realistic summary of the current state of the art for stating the relations among community noise levels and the attitudes and actions of the residents of the community.

The principal sources of community noise were named in the introduction to this chapter. Specific data concerning the noise levels generated by many of these sources are to be found in Chap. 35. Other data on the noise radiated by various sources are to be found in earlier chapters.

Responses of Community Residents. "Response" is here used to mean recognition followed by development of an attitude or state of mind, as well as any observable positive action taken by members of the community as a result of their exposure to noise. A feeling of annoyance is just as much a response or reaction to noise on the part of a community resident or a group of residents as is a telephone call to the noise-source operator, a letter of complaint to officials, or the initiation of legal action to suppress the noise-producing activity. Community feelings or attitudes about noise, usually, are not directly observable. They have been investigated in a very limited way only.   However, feelings and attitudes certainly must develop before any kind of overt action is initiated.   As community responses, they are, therefore, just as important as, perhaps even more important than, the directly observable, positive actions induced by the exposure to noise.   Community attitudes are discussed here to the extent permitted by available data.   Thereafter, community action will be considered.   No one has yet attempted to formulate a method for predicting community attitudes toward a specific noise situation from the physical specifications of the noise stimulus.   In contrast, several groups have proposed methods for estimating the probable level of community action when the physical parameters of the community noise stimulus are known.

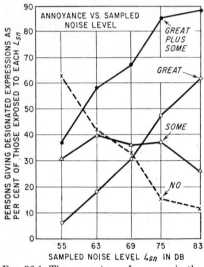

Fig. 36.1. The percentage of persons, in the areas sampled, whose expressions indicated varying degrees of annoyance are compared with the noise levels in the community. (*H. O. Parrack, from data contained in Ref.* 2.)

Community Attitudes.[2]   Community attitudes toward noise are the product of complex interactions among many factors. Some of these factors describe the noise stimulus.   Other factors describe the individuals of the community, and still others describe the community as a specific reacting organism.   Thus general feelings and attitudes concerning the community will influence an individual's perception of the noise stimulus, and his feelings about the noise situation will influence his perception of other environmental factors.   In the study of community feelings or attitudes toward noise level or other parameters of the noise stimulus, one deals with the response to a *total complex stimulus situation* rather than with an *independent response* to noise alone.   The single study, mentioned earlier, dealing with these aspects of industrial noise was confined primarily to the responses of community residents to environmental noise generated by the operation of aircraft.   The results of this

preliminary study may serve as useful guides for more general studies on community attitudes toward environmental noise of industrial origin.

In the study to be discussed, noise levels were measured in various communities in accord with a sampling plan that would provide a range of noise levels.   The sites for measurement were also located at different distances from the sources of noise.   An interview method was employed to obtain information concerning the responses (i.e., the attitudes) of the residents of the selected areas to the noise generated by the sources under study.   The noise stimulus was described in terms of "sampled noise levels." A special averaging technique was employed to obtain the sampled noise level in decibels,* so that the noise level data are not directly comparable to the over-all noise levels as measured by standard sound-level meters.   Responses of the community residents are given as degree of expressed annoyance.

The subdivisions of expressed annoyance used are no annoyance, some annoyance, and great annoyance.   The data, given in Fig. 36.1, show trends for the annoyance expressed by community residents as the sampled noise level varies.   The number of persons expressing a given degree of annoyance is shown as a percentage of the total number exposed to a given sampled noise level.   The number of persons expressing

* The sampled noise level (L_{SN}) is a single number used to define the sound field in communities.   To obtain it, the noise levels were measured and the levels that were exceeded by 25 per cent of the aircraft that passed the measuring position were selected for averaging. The single number used is the arithmetic mean of the measured levels for the following octave bands: 75 to 150, 300 to 600, and 1,200 to 2,400 cps.

great annoyance increased steadily as the sampled noise level increased. In contrast, those expressing no annoyance decreased in number as the noise levels increased. Those expressing some annoyance remained fairly constant in number, except at the lowest and highest noise levels to which persons were exposed, where the number expressing some annoyance decreased. The group that expressed annoyance of any degree, i.e., those expressing some plus those expressing great annoyance, increased in size as the noise level increased. These trend curves suggest that the attitudes of community residents are related directly to noise level and that one may estimate the probable response from the measured noise level even when the total situation is very complex. Since the responses of more than 3,500 persons, located in eight widely separated localities, are included in these data the relations found may turn out to be generally applicable to estimating the responses of community residents to environmental noise of industrial origin. However, general applicability is yet to be proven, and the data should be used, at present, only as tentative guides to probable community response. Examination of the suggested relations may lead to new approaches to be used in future studies.

In Fig. 36.1, annoyance (a complex response to a complex stimulus situation—operation of aircraft near a community) is related to only one aspect of the stimulus situation, namely, sampled noise level. Although the data indicate that it is possible to estimate the annoyance level from the noise level data alone, one should remember that many factors other than noise level may influence response. Some of the other factors were studied; however, the data collected were not sufficient for a complete evaluation of their significance. Among the factors investigated the following may be important: *Emergent-noise level* describes the degree to which a specific noise, under study, stands out above the more usual level of ambient noise. The emergence of a particular noise at night is frequently more pronounced than during daylight hours. Night operations may, therefore, create greater community annoyance. The frequency of exposure to the noise may influence reaction. In this study, frequency of exposure was clearly important when the sampled noise level was low, 50 to 60 db. When the frequency of exposure to these noise levels was high the number of persons expressing great annoyance was three times the number expressing this reaction when the exposure frequency was low. Certain factors not related to the noise or noise source also influence response to the noise situation. Some of the important factors in this category are over-all attitude toward local area; particular aspects of the local area, such as convenience of location, convenience of facilities, general physical aspects of the area, traffic and traffic noise; and social problems (class, race, etc.).

The persons that express different degrees of annoyance with the aircraft-noise-stimulus situation may vary in their perception of other noises and in their response to them. Some comparisons of perception and reaction to various noises are given in Table 36.1. The number of mentions of the presence of the noise and also the presence or absence of annoyance are given in relation to the response to the aircraft situation—no annoyance, some annoyance, or great annoyance. Mention of aircraft noise increases as annoyance increases. For other noises their mention is independent of the degree of annoyance or may decrease slightly as annoyance with aircraft noise increases. Annoyance with other types of noises in general is greater the greater the annoyance with the aircraft-noise-stimulus situation. Perception of various factors relating to the operation of the noise source may be influenced by the degree of annoyance. In Table 36.2, data are presented that show how persons in various annoyance categories perceive the same aircraft operations. The factors shown are frequency of passage of aircraft and the altitudes at which the aircraft passes. The data in this table certainly make it clear that one should not accept the observer's opinion as a satisfactory specification of the way in which a noise source is operated.

Annoyance has been used to describe a complex response of individuals to a noise-stimulus situation. Some of the factors that enter into the over-all annoyance attitude are indicated in Table 36.3. Most of these factors are related to effects of noise on human activities. Effects of aircraft noise are compared with effects of traffic noise. Interference with rest, relaxation, and sleep is one important generator of annoyance. However, traffic noise created interferences to a larger number of persons than did aircraft noise. Interference to the detection of a spoken signal (voice) is of major importance with respect to aircraft noise but is of less importance upon exposure to traffic noise. The effects of noise on normal, daily human activities are related by the exposed individual as a major factor in creating his state of annoyance with the noise-stimulus situation.

Fear, in the case of aircraft operations, appears to be a factor of considerable importance in creating annoyance with the over-all situation. In Table 36.4 data are given

Table 36.1. Perception of Aircraft Noise, Preception and Annoyance with Other Noises as Related to Annoyance with Aircraft-noise-stimulus Situation

Response	Degree of annoyance (aircraft situation)		
	None	Some	Great
Mention aircraft noise.....................	31%	56%	83%
Annoyed by aircraft noise................	.....	22%	71%
Mention traffic noise......................	72%	70%	67%
Annoyed by traffic noise................	25%	30%	40%
Mention human noise......................	39%	47%	41%
Annoyed by human noise................	9%	13%	16%
Mention other noise*.....................	28%	32%	29%
Annoyed by other noises................	11%	13%	17%
Number of persons.......................	1,148	1,237	1,250

* Includes such noises as garbage cans, fire trucks, drunks, dogs, etc.

Table 36.2. Perception of Aircraft Operational Conditions as Influenced by Degree of Annoyance (Per Cent of Persons in Each Annoyance Category That Perceive the Operation as Described)

Description of perceived condition	Degree of annoyance		
	None	Some	Great
Airplanes fly over very often.............	21%	32%	59%
Airplanes fly over fairly often............	34%	41%	31%
Airplanes fly over occasionally...........	45%	27%	10%
Airplanes fly very low..................	31%	60%	91%
Low-flying airplanes pass often..........	20%	29%	57%

which show the percentage of annoyed persons who stated that fear of aircraft was a cause of the annoyance. Fear may be less important in other noise-stimulus situations, but there are indications that it is of importance in creating attitudes toward noise from motor-trucking operations.

Other factors that must be considered in evaluating the response of community residents to noise from a given operation are familiarity with and the rated importance of the source operation, age of persons exposed, educational level of residents, sex, time spent in noisy area, income, occupation, and family size. No attempt is made to assess the relative importance of the factors listed above. They are given simply to remind those concerned with community reactions to noise that the problem is extremely complex. Therefore, data such as appear in Fig. 36.1 must be used with extreme caution. Such data do suggest, however, that more effort expended in well-planned studies of community reaction to noise may provide a future means for predicting community attitudes from physical specifications of the noise stimulus.

Community Action. Persons faced with finding a practical solution to a community-noise problem or those seeking to evaluate the potentiality of adverse response to the

Table 36.3. Reasons Why Aircraft Noise and Traffic Noise Annoy, Expressed as Per Cent of Persons in Each Category of Annoyance (with Aircraft Noise) Who State That the Listed Interference Is Cause of Annoyance

Reason for annoyance	Degree of annoyance (aircraft)				
	Airplane noise		Traffic noise		
	Some	Great	None	Some	Great
Annoyed because the noise interferes with:					
Sleep, rest, relaxation...............	20 %	39 %	48 %	41 %	40 %
Hearing, radio or television..........	39 %	37 %	18 %	21 %	13 %
Hearing, conversation...............	25 %	26 %	12 %	17 %	11 %
Television picture..................	17 %	11 %			
Work, housework, study............	3 %	6 %	6 %	6 %	8 %

Table 36.4. Fear of Airplane Crashes as It Relates to Annoyance

Reaction	Degree of annoyance		
	None	Some	Great
Direct expressions of fear...............	...	25 %	60 %
Indirect expressions of fear.............	...	38 %	20 %
No expressions of fear.................	...	37 %	20 %

noise from specific operations are usually more interested in overt action (i.e., antagonistic activity) than in attitudes. However, an understanding of the factors that underlie community action is essential to the development of the most economical and most effective noise-control plan. The data reviewed here suggest some factors that may be important. These data also suggest that, when sufficient information has been accumulated, it may be possible to predict the probable level of community action from data on attitudes, particularly data showing prevalence of certain attitudes in the community.

In the study considered above, the original plan provided for study of an equal number of areas designated "complaint" areas and "noncomplaint" areas. The selection of complaint and noncomplaint areas was based upon public records of complaints, the opinions of the operators, and the records and opinions of governmental agencies responsible for control of the operations. Therefore, data were available indicating which areas had already initiated overt action and which areas had taken no such action.   In Fig. 36.2 data are presented on the number of persons expressing great annoyance in each class of area and also on the number expressing no annoyance in the same area.   It is clearly shown that great annoyance increases with increasing noise level and that for all noise levels great annoyance is more prevalent in the areas predesignated as complaint areas.   There is definitely a relationship between the prevalence of great annoyance and complaints.   Also, it clearly is apparent that the number of persons expressing no annoyance is smaller in complaint areas and that the number of persons registering no annoyance decreases as the noise levels (sampled noise levels L_{SN}) increase.   Again a relationship between annoyance expressed and complaint (action) is indicated.   The data available are not sufficient to establish a quantitative statement of this relationship.   However, the recorded statements of the persons interviewed in this study as to action they have taken may serve as a useful guide in making a crude preliminary estimate of possible reaction to specific noise levels.   In the great-annoyance group living within 2 miles of the airport, 6 per cent stated they had taken action to express their feelings to authorities.   If the great-annoyance group is examined in relation to complaint vs. noncomplaint areas we find that in complaint areas 7 per cent of them had expressed their feelings, while only 2 per cent of them had done so in the noncomplaint areas.   If the entire group interviewed is considered, only 0.5 per cent of those expressing "some annoyance" ever took positive action to express their feelings, while 5 per cent of the entire great-annoyance group took positive action in expressing their feelings.   It is not possible, using currently available data, to specify the degree of annoyance that will result in significant action against the operator of a noise source.   However, the presence of feelings of great annoyance among some 70 per cent of the area

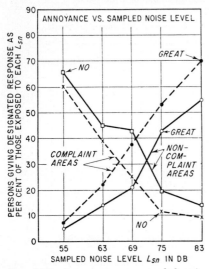

FIG. 36.2. Annoyance vs. sampled noise level as expressed by residents of complaint areas and noncomplaint areas. (*H. O. Parrack, from data contained in Ref. 2.*)

residents appears to connote probable action of importance.   At this level of annoyance these data suggest that approximately 5 per cent of the population will take action, at least to the extent of making formal complaints.   These data also suggest that methods for predicting overt action with respect to a noise situation must deal with, at most, some 7 per cent of the area's total population.   In many instances the portion of the population whose activities are predicted must be much less than this figure of 7 per cent.

PREDICTING COMMUNITY REACTION TO NOISE

In developing noise-control procedures and equipment for solving practical problems, data have been accumulated that relate to the noise levels and to the community reaction before control measures were instituted.   A few attempts have been made to organize, analyze, and arrange these sets of empirical data into a method for estimating the probable community reaction from the physical specifications of the noise-stimulus situation.   These empirical methods will now be examined and described.   Their use may provide improved practical solutions in many cases.   In addition, it is hoped that they will stimulate the acquisition of additional data that will make possible their improvement or permit the development of replacement methods that are more reliable.

Methods for Direct Operational Use. Operators of some specialized facilities have developed a method for directly relating noise level to community action. The noise level, monitored at the plant, is directly compared to complaints received. After some experience is gained, operation of the facility may be altered, based on the monitored noise level, to avoid community complaints. This direct method is useful, but the details of the method must be tailored to each individual case. The following steps are necessary:

1. A noise-control office for the plant is established.
2. A monitoring station is established at the plant which furnishes the control office a continuous record of the noise level.
3. Incoming complaints from the community also go directly to the control office.
4. When a complaint is received a field measurement crew goes to the appropriate community area and measures the noise level.
5. These data are compared to establish a noise level, measured by the monitoring station, that will ensure satisfactory levels in the community, i.e., no complaints.
6. The control office regulates the plant operation, as required, to maintain the specified noise level at the monitoring station.

Some time is required to accumulate the data necessary to control satisfactorily the operation of the plant so that the community noise levels are maintained at values which assure the absence of community complaint or other adverse action. In initiating a program of this kind it is necessary, before experience is gained, to select arbitrarily some community noise level to be used as an index of probable community complaint. One could select for this purpose a noise level that falls within the range of noise levels that have been measured in communities and described as unidentifiable background noise. Another possibility is to measure the noise levels, in one or two community areas, while complaints are being received and to use these to establish a tentative index noise level, at the plant monitoring station, which is used until additional data and more experience provide a more reliable index.

Records of the plant noise level, the community noise levels, and the community complaints must be maintained over a sufficiently long time to establish a reliable monitored plant noise level to ensure the absence of community complaints during various seasons of the year and under the varying weather conditions that occur during these seasons. After perhaps 1 year of observation the plant noise-control office need only consider the monitored plant noise level and the meteorological data to control the plant operation so that the desired, preselected noise level is maintained in surrounding communities.

This method is direct and basically simple. However, as has been pointed out, the observations on plant noise, on weather conditions, on community noise level, and on community reaction must be carried out over a considerable length of time before one can rely on the use of the noise level, monitored at the plant, to ensure satisfactory conditions in the surrounding communities. The data accumulated can of course be used for other purposes, as, for example, to determine the amount of sound attenuation on propagation through air over varying distances. Estimates can also be obtained of the importance of meteorological variables in varying sound attenuation by air. Study and application of this additional information can improve the reliability of the method.

This direct method is applicable to the local situation only. It is of value only when the operation can be altered to change the noise output. The method has been found very useful in several situations and is described here in general terms for possible use by operators of facilities to which it may be applicable. Usually the allowable noise level must be determined for each facility, and so no data are given here concerning specific noise levels.

Empirical Predictive Methods. Neighborhoods or communities may be exposed to industrial noises generated by a variety of sources. Frequently it is necessary for the operators of the noise-generating facility to introduce control measures. Such measures may consist of the installation of sound absorptive on insulative treatments, the use of special equipment for noise reduction, or the development and use of facility operating procedures that reduce the noise output or control its spreading to areas adjacent to the facility.   Studies on the noise levels in affected communities and observations on the community activity that results from exposure to noise frequently are made to determine the amount of noise control required and also to evaluate the effectiveness of noise-control measures instituted.   These studies provide data that may possibly be integrated and arranged to describe the "stimulus-response relations" existing at the time of the study.   These specific descriptions of stimulus-response relations may be combined to formulate more general statements of the stimulus-response relations that exist when communities are exposed to noise.   Such statements of stimulus-response relations may be considered as general summaries of the responses of communities to noise exposures.   When a sufficient number of cases are utilized in its preparation, a summary of this kind may be used as a tool for predicting the probable responses of other communities when adequate descriptions of the noise-stimulus situation are available.   A reliable method for predicting public or community response from data on the noise stimulus would be of great value to all persons interested in noise, its generation, its effects, and its control.

The use of any predictive method implies that definable and continuing relationships exist between definable noise stimuli and the activities generated in a group of persons living in the noisy area, neighborhood, or community.   That is, a definitive stimulus-response relation must exist.   It is clearly recognized that an individual's response to sounds may vary considerably, so that it is to be expected that the responses of a group of individuals to these stimuli will be both complex and variable. However, it may be that the average over-all responses of different groups to specific effective noise stimuli are sufficiently constant to permit deriving a relationship between the stimuli and the average group responses.   In using such a scheme as a predictive tool it is also assumed that people will, on the average, behave in the future in the same way they have behaved in the past.   That is, on the whole, social groups will be stable in their responses to noise stimuli.

One early scheme, which was put forth as a tentative method for evaluating the probable responses of neighborhoods or communities to noise in their environment, described the effective noise stimulus in terms of a complex variable, the *Composite Noise Rating*, which is derived fron data that describe the physical characteristics of the noise field and includes the influence of several other variables.   It was formulated on the basis of data acquired in the study of several actual communities.   All the important characteristics of the noise were measured.   The behavior of the persons exposed to these noises was studied and recorded.   Community response was indicated on a six-point scale.   Then the relations between the noise, considering all its aspects, and the observed community behavior were summarized in charts and tables and were then applied to new communities in an effort to predict their behavior in some new stimulus situations.   On the average the method worked well enough to create the hope that it may be valuable as a predictive method for establishing design goals for noise control in the community.   The method presented in the next section is a modification of the one just described.   The same data, general approach, and stimulus factors are considered.

A METHOD OF PREDICTING PUBLIC RESPONSE

The following method of predicting public response to a noise stimulus is based on the scheme cited above.[3]   In order to develop such a method, these steps were taken:

1. To establish a scale of rating public response called "observable public reaction." (This rating is expressed on a scale from I through VII—the magnitude of reaction increasing with number.)
2. To establish a scale for the noise stimulus called the "Composite Noise Rating." (This rating is expressed by capital Roman letters A through J—the letter A indicating the quietest condition.)
3. To establish a relationship between the observable public reaction and the Composite Noise Rating.   (This relationship is shown in Fig. 36.3.)

This section describes the scale for observable public response and shows how the Composite Noise Rating can be computed for a specific problem. Then by the use of the relationship between these two quantities, Fig. 36.3, the public response can be predicted.

A Scale for Public Response. The proposed response scale is shown in Fig. 36.3, and the description of the responses anticipated, at various points on the scale, is given in Table 36.5. At the low end of the scale (I) no spontaneous complaints can be observed. This implies that carefully planned observations will reveal no spontaneous complaints about the effects of the noise. The next point on the scale (II) is reached when careful observation reveals a few spontaneous complaints. Scale Number III is reached when sporadic complaints are detected by casual observation or where the complaints are made directly to the operators of the noise source. If the complaints increase in number and regularity we have the situation designated by the next Scale Number (IV), widespread complaints. The next higher level of community response (Scale Number V) is reached when the group begins to organize and lodge complaints as a unit or when some individuals threaten the noise-source operators with the use of legal or police agencies to force reduction of the community disturbance. When organized group action is casually observable, the community response has reached the level of Scale Number VI. The highest Scale Number (VII) is reached when community action is fully integrated and employs all available legal or public police

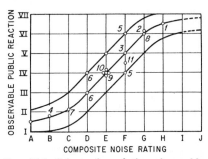

FIG. 36.3. Scheme for relating observable public response to a complex factor describing the noise, the Composite Noise Rating. (*Modified scheme by H. O. Parrack, from data and figures in Ref. 4.*)

Table 36.5. Description of the Actions or Activities That Characterize the Subdivisions of the Observable Public Response Scale of Fig. 36.3

Scale Number	Description of the Activity or Action That Constitutes Each Level of Observable Public Response
I	No observable spontaneous complaints to operators or to other community members, and no community discussion.
II	A few spontaneous complaints can be observed. Usually these complaints are made to other residents and are detected only by carefully planned observation.
III	Sporadic spontaneous individual complaints to noise-source operators or to officials. Limited or irregular in number, time, and area of origin.
IV	Widespread individual complaints, regularly received from all noise-exposed areas.
V	Just observable initiation of group organization to lodge complaints with officials or operators. Some individual threats of the use of public-health, police, or legal enforcement agencies.
VI	Organized group action readily observable. Tendency toward integration of actions by community groups. Police power sometimes used to halt noisy operation.
VII	Group and community action completely integrated and supported community wide. Employs all police authority, legal action, or other public power to oppose noise-source operation.

power to oppose noise-producing operations. This response scale describes only overt, observable community activity. The response range extends from "no" observable overt complaints or opposition to "all-out," organized community opposition using all legal means to enforce the group opinion. It should be borne in mind that the response scale, as used here, does not deal with community attitudes or feelings about the noise stimulus. It deals only with action taken by individuals within the community or by the fully organized community acting as a single unit. In evaluating case histories one must rely on casual observations or unsolicited complaints in estimating the level of community response. To apply this method effectively and to evaluate it completely, future studies should include definitive and improved observations on the level of community activity generated by each noise-stimulus situation.

The Composite Noise Rating. The noise stimulus in a community cannot be described simply as the noise level at any given time. Several characteristics of the noise stimulus, in addition to level, must be incorporated in measurements or computations. The various physical aspects that describe the noise must be combined to provide a satisfactory composite description of the effective stimulus in terms of a

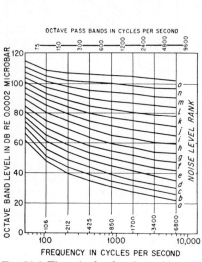

FIG. 36.4. The noise-level ranks used in computing the Composite Noise Rating. (*Modified by H. O. Parrack, from figure in Ref.* 4.)

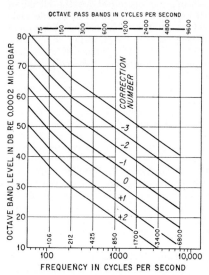

FIG. 36.5. Correction numbers to be applied to the noise-level rank to obtain the Composite Noise Rating when background-noise level varies. (*Modified by H. O. Parrack, from figure in Ref.* 4.)

single rating. This description is defined as the "Composite Noise Rating," which may be computed from the following equation:

$$\text{(Composite Noise Rating)} = \text{(Noise-level rank)} + \text{(correction number)} \quad (36.1)$$

The noise-level rank, obtained from Fig. 36.4 by the procedure described below, is expressed by lower-case boldface letters *a* through *o*. If the correction number is equal to zero, then the Composite Noise Rating is the same letter in the alphabet as the noise-level rank. For example, if the correction number is zero and the noise-level rank is *f*, then from Eq. (36.1) the Composite Noise Rating for this situation is *F*. If the correction number is other than zero, the Composite Noise Rating is expressed by a letter which is shifted in the alphabet from the noise-level rank by a number of letters numerically equal to the total correction number. For example, if the noise level rank is **f** and the correction number is +1, the Composite Noise Rating is *G*. On the other hand, if the correction number in this case is −1, then the Composite Noise Rating is *E*. To determine the value of the correction number in any given situation, see *Correction Numbers* below.

Noise-level Rank. The over-all noise level and the spectrum of the noise are of primary importance. The spectra are measured as sound pressure levels in octave bands of frequency. These are measured out of doors near the residences. Final values are obtained by averaging over a reasonable time interval and over a reasonable number of locations within the community. A family of curves that define the noise-level rank is shown in Fig. 36.4. The ranks are designated, on an ascending scale, by letters *a* to *o*. Rank *f* is higher than rank *b* but not necessarily three times *b*. Each rank denotes the area between two adjacent curves. Rank *a* is at the low end, and its lower boundary is the average threshold of hearing for octave bands of noise. The highest rank, *o*, denotes a noise level in which direct person-to-person communication by shouted voice signals is impossible. This choice of scale implies that unheard noise does not generate a community response and that a noise level in which voice communication is impossible may be considered socially unacceptable. To determine the level rank of a community noise, the measured or calculated octave-band pressure levels are superimposed on Fig. 36.4. The noise-level rank is given by the highest area into which the spectrum protrudes in any octave band.

Table 36.6. Correction Numbers to Be Applied to Noise Level Rank*

INFLUENCING FACTOR	CORRECTION NUMBER
1. Background noise (see Fig. 36.5 or Table 36.7)..........	+2 to −3
2. Temporal and seasonal factors:	
a. Daytime only.....................................	−1
Nighttime...	0
b. Repetitiveness (see Fig. 36.6 and text)..............	0 to −6
c. Winter...	−1
Summer...	0
3. Character of the noise:	
a. Spectrum character:	
Continuous spectrum...........................	0
Pure tone.....................................	+1
b. Peak factor:	
Smooth time character.........................	0
Impulsive.....................................	+1
4. Previous exposure:	
None..	0
Some..	−1

* See Eq. (36.1).

Correction Numbers. For any given situation where the public response to noise is to be predicted, a correction number must be applied which depends on the following factors: background noise, temporal and seasonal factors, character of the noise, and previous exposure of the neighborhood. The numerical values for the various factors are summarized in Table 36.6 and described in detail below. These various corrections are then totaled and applied in Eq. (36.1).

1. *Background Noise.* In considering community (public) response to noise stimuli, attention is usually fixed on the noise generated by particular sources. As shown in the preceding chapter, noise in a given community environment may originate from many different sources. The sound field created by these sources is called the "ambient noise." This noise generally is accepted by residents as part of the environment. It usually does not disturb them particularly—i.e., they do not react to it, or they have adapted to it. This level of the general community noise (ambient noise) is a factor that modifies the specific effective stimulus. The noise from a given source may be masked by ambient noise in one area while it is strikingly above the ambient noise in another. Persons residing in the two areas will respond quite differently. The ambient noise level, in a sense, serves as a reference level against which the specific noise stimulus is compared. To take account of ambient noise the average ambient noise is measured in octave bands of frequency and the spectrum is plotted on the chart shown in Fig. 36.5. This figure is divided into zones which designate the correction number to be used. These numbers range from −3 to +2. Table 36.7 lists the types of localities in which the various ambient noise levels may be found.

2. *Temporal and Seasonal Factors.* If a source of noise operates uniformly and continuously over an appreciable period of time, its noise field may be adequately described by the levels in octave frequency bands. Typical sources, however, gen-

erally operate on a specific time schedule. That is, they may operate only between certain hours, say 8 A.M. to 4 P.M., or the noise they generate may be heard in a residential area for only three or four 15 to 20 sec periods per hour (for example, when

Table 36.7. Correction Numbers to Account for Daytime Ambient Noise Levels in Typical Neighborhood[*4]

(On the average, the correction numbers should be increased by 1 for nighttime conditions.)

NEIGHBORHOOD	CORRECTION NUMBER
Very quiet suburban.....................	+1
Suburban...............................	0
Residential urban.......................	−1
Urban near some industry................	−2
Area of heavy industry..................	−3

* See Fig. 36.3 and text.

an aircraft operates over a residential area). The methods that may be used in correcting the composite noise rating for these irregular operations are as follows:

   a. DAY OR NIGHT. If a noise source operates only during daytime hours many persons are away from their residences; they do not hear the noise. Those at home are engaged in many activities that may mask the noise or divert the hearer's attention so that a given noise is less disturbing. On the other hand, more persons are at home during night hours and noise tends to interfere with rest, relaxation, or sleep. Therefore, a noise source usually creates less community disturbance if it operates only during the day. Empirical evidence suggests a correction number of −1 when the sources operate only during the daytime. No correction is applied if the source operates at night (7 P.M. to 7 A.M.).

   b. REPETITIVE CHARACTER. Here we are concerned primarily with sources that operate on a more-or-less regular schedule throughout the week. In general, if the source operates only for a fraction of each day, the disturbances will be less than for continuous operation, i.e., continuous stimulation. A negative correction number is used to account for a restricted time schedule of operation. Only preliminary data are available now, and these suggest the correction number is a function of the percentage of time the noise source operates within, say, an 8-hr period. The correction number appears to be related to the total time of operation and relatively independent of the length of time in any one period. Three periods of 10 min are the same as one 30-min period is within the day. A proposed evaluation of repetitive operation is shown in Fig. 36.6. If the daily schedule of operations varies, other corrections may be required. If

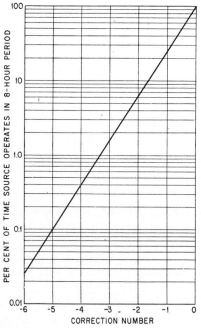

FIG. 36.6. Chart for computing correction factor that allows for the variation in the time a noise source is operated. (*H. O. Parrack, from data and tables in Ref.* 4.)

operation is restricted to 1 or 2 days per week an additional correction number of −1 is suggested.

    c. WINTER OR SUMMER. In northern climates living habits differ greatly in winter and summer. Houses are usually closed tightly in winter, and activities are much more frequently carried on inside. A given outside noise is usually not so disturbing. In summer in northern climates and at all times in southern climates windows and doors are open and outside activities are much more numerous. A given outside noise is more disturbing. These differences are taken into account by using a correction number of −1 if the source is operated only in winter in northern areas. No correction is applied for either summer or winter in warm climates.

3. *Character of the Noise.*

    a. SPECTRUM CHARACTER. A noise that contains audible pure-tone components is usually judged to be more disturbing than a continuous spectrum. If the level rank of a given octave band is attained because of the pressure of a single-frequency component, a correction number of +1 should be applied. For example, if the observed level rank is *d*, this will give an equivalent level rank of *e*. This implies that a pure-tone component must be held about 5 db below the level of a continuous-spectrum noise in the same octave band to produce the same effects.

    b. PEAK FACTOR. Noises that are reasonably continuous in time, at least for several seconds or longer, appear to be less disturbing than impulsive noise, such as the sounds of a drop forge or gunshots. In general a correction number of +1 should be applied to the level rank if the noise is impulsive. Considerable judgment must be exercised in classifying noise as continuous or impulsive.

4. *Previous Exposure.* Persons differ in their ability to adapt to intruding noise on repeated exposure. People near a railroad may become accustomed to noise even though they reacted upon first exposure. Most people now accept the noise from an occasional passing aircraft, and they may be considered to be adapted or adjusted to it. However, the adaptation is unstable, and accidents or other unusual events may change the reaction sufficiently to make a reevaluation necessary. No correction is applied if there has been some previous exposure to the same or similar noise. A correction number of −1 is suggested if there has been no previous exposure.

Examples of Application of the Predictive Method.
A scale for measuring responses of communities to noise has been described. The methods for obtaining data and arranging them so that the scale may be used have also been described. The question is, "How well does the scheme work?" A summary of the cases examined is given in Table 36.8. These cases are shown by the Arabic numerals on Fig. 36.3. They tend to cluster around the middle S-shaped curve of the figure. This curve may be said to define the average expected response from a normal community. Note that there is spread and that a range of response is anticipated. This procedure attempts to evaluate a very complex response to a complex stimulus situation. In the future it may require complete replacement, but for the present it provides some engineering guidance where none has existed before. Attempts to apply it to new situations should bring forth additional data that must improve our understanding of a community reaction to noise. Additional discussions of the method and its implications are contained in Refs. 4 and 5.

A Modified Predictive Method. The scheme for relating public or community response to environmental noise to a specifiable characteristic of the noise field or of the noise source was applied originally to situations where noise levels were measured out of doors. One modification has been suggested[5] which extends the coverage to sources inside buildings and also to noise levels inside buildings that are generated by the operation of out-of-door sources. This modified method uses a form of the noise-level rank which describes the noise source in terms of the power level in octave bands.

Table 36.8. Summary of Typical Case Histories of Response to Noise in Residential Areas[3]

Case No.	Description of facility and noise	Noise-level rank	Background noise	Day or night	Repetitive character	Winter or summer	Spectrum character	Peak factor	Previous exposure	Composite Noise Rating	Observed Community Response
1	Large wind tunnel in Middle West, jet engine operating	h	+1	0	0	−1	0	0	0	H	Municipal authorities forced facility to shut down
2	Large wind tunnel in Middle West, no burning	f	+1	0	0	0	0	0	0	G	Vigorous telephone complaints and injunction threats
3	Exhaust for air pumps, factory in industrial area	j	−3	−1	−0	0	+1	0	−1	F	Lodginghouse owner entered complaints with operator of factory and with local department of health
4	Engine run-ups at aircraft manufacturing plant	e	0	−1	−1	0	0	0	−1	B	No complaints reported
5	Aircraft in flight 1 mile from airport	l	−1	0	−4	0	0	0	−1	F	Vigorous complaints by letter and telephone; one community attempted to prevent passage of aircraft
6	Aircraft in flight 4 miles from airport	j	−1	0	−4	0	0	0	−1	D	Sporadic complaints in some communities, widespread complaints in others
7	Aircraft engine manufacturing plant; test cells	f	−1	−1	0	0	0	0	−1	C	No complaints reported for daytime operation
8	Transformer noise from power company	f	+1	0	0	0	+1	0	−1	G	Injunction threats
9	Large fan at power company	e	0	0	0	0	+1	0	−1	E	Residents complained consistently, company took steps to reduce noise
10	Weapons range, intermittent firing	l	−1	−1	−5	−1	0	+1	0	E	Vigorous complaints from nearby residents
11	Loading platforms with trucks, men shouting, etc.	g	−1	0	0	0	0	0	0	F	Vigorous complaints to management, some threats of legal action

(The noise output of the source might equally well have been described in terms of watts. The power-level terminology was introduced merely for convenience and in itself is not essential to the modified predictive scheme.) A nomogram (Ref. 5) is used to relate sound level, as determined from the power-level contours, to the various classes of areas occupied by people. When the line drawn between the power level and the specific occupied area intersects the chart showing human responses (essentially Fig. 36.3), predicted response may be read off, and the response is interpreted as annoyance. The monogram consists of two parts. One applies to various indoor spaces occupied by men and considers the noise source to be in the occupied area. The other part applies when the sources are outside the structures occupied by men and relates the outside noise to the inside noise and also the responses of those persons occupying the inside space. If experience confirms the validity of the assumptions underlying this predictive tool, it will provide a means for estimating public response to noise under a much greater range of situations than is covered by the basic scheme.

LIMITATIONS OF CURRENT PREDICTIVE METHODS

Community response to any situation is a complex function. The response elicited depends on the definition of community. If one is concerned with the responses of individuals that inhabit a common area, several techniques may be employed to determine their response to a stimulus, even a noise stimulus. If a sufficiently large sample is obtained one may be able to state, for example, that 70 per cent behave thus and 20 per cent behave so or that the mean response of the group is thus and so. These are *public responses*, because they define the behavior of a specific number of persons in the population of an area. The community response is predicted in these cases only in the sense that it can be stated (if a sufficiently large number of samples have been obtained from a sufficiently large number of communities) that some definite percentage of the various community populations responds in a particular way. Public responses are not, in reality, community responses; i.e., they do not represent the behavior of a social organization. A community is a social unit, it can and does behave as a unit, but its behavior as *an organism* is not the same as the behavior of the individual persons, *the public*, composing the community. The community has a structure, a communication system, a motor system, so to speak, and so has a specific behavior pattern. These patterns and the way they are influenced by a noise stimulus or, more exactly, a noise-stimulus situation have not been studied sufficiently to obtain the information necessary for predicting real community response. Therefore one must conclude that none of the responses that have been observed or predicted by various methods are real *community responses;* they are, almost universally, *public responses*. From sufficient knowledge concerning *public response* one may be able to make some inferences about probable *community reaction*, but not more than this. All the responses discussed as community reaction have been public reactions in the sense described above. Therefore, the basic limitation of any and all current methods for predicting community reaction is that they measure public response only.

The fact that community reaction has not been measured need not dismay us. In fact, we are probably much more interested, at least initially, in public response. It is of interest to know how the individuals in an area react to community noise—to know what action they will take to eliminate the noise! Accepting the fact that one is dealing with, at best, the average response of a group or groups of persons, let us examine more extensively the limitations of the methods described above.

Public Response. Public response should include both the overt (observable) activity or reactions and the feelings, attitudes, or state of mind of the public with respect to the stimulus. Both feelings and action are important. Feelings are basic to action. To understand public action completely it is necessary to know how the public feels or thinks about the noise situation.

Public Attitudes. As indicated earlier, only *one* type of noise-stimulus situation has been studied. That study, concerned with aircraft noise, was preliminary in nature. The data may serve as a general basis for predicting attitudes of the public toward noise, but it is not known whether the public attitude would be the same if the same noise levels were produced by a different noise source. Furthermore, we do not know the relative importance of the *noise* in the *aircraft-noise-stimulus complex*. Other factors may be more important than the noise itself. All we can do now is observe carefully, obtain more data, and then explore the possibilities of formulating improved generalizations about *public attitudes* as responses to community noise.

Public Reactions (Activity).   A second aspect of public response is public action, or overt activity. The predictive schemes we have described have dealt with public action only. Even this limited area of community response is very complex. It is suggested that the predictive schemes be tried, with caution. They should be used, particularly, for the purpose of obtaining new data that will either validate proposed schemes or provide a basis for new ones.

In using these schemes for predicting public reactions the following limitations should be kept in mind: The number of cases upon which they are based are limited in number. The types of noise sources are limited. Identification of specific sources may influence reaction to such an extent that no general scheme can be devised. Caution is necessary when applying the present schemes to noise from sources that were not included in the original studies. The noise-stimulus situation is always very complex, and current methods of prediction may not include all significant physical factors. Present schemes may not take sufficient account of variation and instability of public reaction.

IMPROVING COMMUNITY NOISE SOURCE RELATIONS

The relations between the community and the noise-source operator will depend on many factors other than community noise level. If these relations are already strained because of noise in the community, improvement can come only through a thoughtful approach by both sides. Both parties must understand the problem, including the difficulties that may lie in the way of adequate noise reduction. The operator of the noise source must take action, i.e., institute all reasonable measures to control the disturbing noise. Where action has been taken, the community attitude and activity can usually be made more favorable by making the public aware of what has been done.

Agreeable relations between the community and operators of noisy facilities can best be maintained by adequate advance planning. This means that noise output should be estimated in advance. Probable public response should be estimated and facility location, design, and construction planned to maintain satisfactory noise levels in residential areas of the community. Advance planning should include appropriate zoning and site designation within zoned areas. The predictive methods described in this chapter are useful as a starting point for the necessary planning and engineering design.

REFERENCES

1. Young, K.: "Sociology," p. 19, American Book Company, New York, 1942.
2. Unpublished Preliminary Study on "Community Aspects of Aircraft Annoyance," conducted by the National Opinion Research Center, University of Chicago, under the technical supervision of P. N. Borsky, for the National Advisory Committee for Aeronautics, 1954.
3. Rosenblith, W. A., and K. N. Stevens: *WADC Technical Report* 52-204, p. 18, Wright Air Development Center (June, 1953).
4. Stevens, K. N., W. A. Rosenblith, and R. H. Bolt: *Noise Control*, **1**: 63 (January, 1955).
5. Fehr, R. O., and R. J. Wells: *Noise Control*, **1**: 30 (January, 1955).

Chapter 37

LEGAL ASPECTS OF THE
AIRPLANE NOISE PROBLEM

KENNETH J. LUCEY, L.L.M.

Legal Department, New York Telephone Company

INTRODUCTION

Airplane noises have created many interesting legal questions to which the courts and the legislatures have adopted a very cautious approach. The noise of an aircraft engine as it is being tested upon an engine test block or as it is being warmed up upon an airfield preparatory to flight presents the same legal problems as that of noise emanating from any industrial establishment. The legal effects of personal injury to an airplane ground or flight crew from exposure to intense noise may be treated in the same light as the workmen's compensation problem of the foundry worker. It is the airplane in flight over the property of others that has created the complex conflicts of legal rights.

The legal questions that have arisen over the airplane noise problem are related only indirectly to sound. The surface proprietor has, from time to time, challenged the right of the airplane to fly over his property. The more intense the sound of aircraft over his domain the more likelihood there is that legal action may be taken, directed not against the noise factor alone but to the right of the airplane to occupy the airspace over the property.

The noise output of an aircraft engine of any type is generally greatest during the period of maximum power output. Generally speaking the nearer the airplane to those below, the greater will be the objectionable noise. During take-off and to a lesser degree during landing operations, the nuisance factor of noise creates a situation that is most likely to result in conflict between the legal rights of the airplane and the property owner.[1] The basic questions are, "Who has the title to the airspace?" and "What rights if any has the airplane in airspace?" If the landowner can exercise absolute dominion over the air above his property, then he can, by preventing flights overhead, eliminate the noise factor. If the airplane has any legal rights in the air over private property, then the nature and extent of its rights will determine the airplane noise to which those below may be legally subjected. In an attempt to understand the rights of aircraft to fly over private property it is necessary to trace briefly the history of "title to airspace."

RIGHTS OF SURFACE OWNERS

Before the advent of aviation there existed a maxim in the law of real property, *cujus est solum ejus est usque ad coelum* (he who owns the soil likewise owns to the sky).[2] If this maxim were to remain unchanged and inviolate there could not have been the expansion and development of the air industry that have taken place since the first flight.[3]   Contrary to the beliefs of many, it is the "traditional policy of the courts to adapt the law to the economic and social needs of the times."[4]

As early as 1815, in discussing the *ad coelum* doctrine, doubt was expressed that a balloonist would be legally liable because his balloon happened to pass over a person's property.[5]   Today the *ad coelum* theory has been rejected as far as its application to aviation is concerned.[6]

The airspace that has been physically used by the surface proprietor by the erection of a tall building or other structure therein belongs to and is owned by the surface owner.   This is true even though such building or structure may be considered by the Civil Aeronautics Authority to be a menace to aviation under its rules and regulations.[7]   The landowner's title to airspace, however, is not limited to that portion of the airspace that he may have physically reduced to possession by the erection of a structure into it.   The majority of legal authorities now seem to agree that the surface owner has the right to exclusive possession of so much of the airspace over his property as may be necessary for the full use and enjoyment of the land beneath.[8]   In considering what may be necessary for full use and enjoyment we must consider not only the present utilization but any future utilization and enjoyment to which the land might reasonably be put by a present or future owner.[9]

The future use and enjoyment to which the land might reasonably be put is of course indefinite and varies with the circumstances.   Reasonable speculation must be allowed the surface owner.   This does not mean that we should foresee an Eiffel tower in a Nebraska cornfield or, as the court indicated in the *Causby* case, an Empire State Building on a North Carolina chicken farm.[10]

The fact that all buildings and structures are limited to a fixed maximum height by a valid local zoning ordinance does not mean that the landowners in such zone have lost the right to challenge noisy aircraft in the airspace over the height restriction. Although a structure may not be erected into the space, the landowner has the right to light and air from above, and it would seem that in order fully to use and enjoy his land below he has the right to be free from the objectionable noise of aircraft in the area above the height restriction.[11]

The unauthorized use of airspace may constitute what is known in law as a trespass or a nuisance.   Trespass may be defined as the unlawful disturbance of the right to enjoy the possession of one's property.[12]   A nuisance consists of the unreasonable or unwarranted use by a person of his property resulting in actual or threatened material discomfort or damage to others.[13]

The early attempts of landowners to assert ownership of airspace were based upon a claim of trespass.[14]   This claim was based on the theory of ownership "to the sky." With the repudiation of the *ad coelum* doctrine in relation to airspace the courts were reluctant to hold the mere flight of aircraft over property as a technical case of trespass.[15]   In a trespass action the plaintiff need not establish damage.[16]   Little if any damage would seem to result from the mere flight of aircraft high over property.   In the absence of provable damage, trespass was the form of legal action selected by the surface owner, and if the act of trespass consisted of flights at high altitudes, the aircraft operator had little fear that he would be subjected to substantial monetary damage in the event of a verdict against him.

The majority of surface owners that have been successful in their airspace litigation have based their claims upon the nuisance theory.[17]   The bulk of the litigation based upon the nuisance theory has involved property in close proximity to airports.[18]   The nuisance factors were dust, night lighting, fear of crash, and noise.   At a modern airport the dust problem is negligible, and the night lighting of the airport or aircraft does not appear to have been particularly stressed in any of the decided cases.

The apprehension of danger and the noise factor seem to be the dominant features causing the nuisance.   The noise factor and the fear problem are growing in importance and are of sufficient interest to have been made the subject of study by a special presidential commission.[19]

The public fear of airplanes crashing onto property is a variable thing and reached one of its peaks as a result of the series of fatal crashes in the period between December,

1951, and February, 1952, all of which took place in the populated area surrounding Newark Airport.[20] It would seem that as the memory of air crashes fades the fear lessens, but to be revived again in the event of a spectacular and fatal crash into a populated area.

The noise factor is an aspect of the nuisance theory that continues to cause increasing concern to landowners and to aircraft and airport operators. Indeed, it is related to the problem of fear. The roar of the airplane engine close overhead gives rise to the thoughts of a crash. When the noise causes discomfort, loss of business revenue, or even personal injury to the surface owner, a cause of action in nuisance may arise and the aircraft operator may be made to pay substantial money damages or be prohibited by court order from any threatened or future nuisance.

When we consider the growing number of aircraft, the increasing number of flights, and the more powerful and thus noisier airplane engines in use today the legal aspects of the airplane noise problem assume increasing importance.

The remedies of the surface owner against the intrusion of airplanes into the space over his property are varied. As we have already indicated, an action for trespass has in a few cases been sustained. It is believed that the courts will continue to look with disfavor upon such actions and where no substantial damage is found will refuse to grant relief for any purely technical trespass of the aircraft.

It is interesting to note that one may be guilty of a trespass without physically going onto the property of another. Trespass has been found in cases where missiles were thrown upon the land of the plaintiff,[21] where water was turned into it,[22] and in the withdrawal of subterranean water by pumps outside the property limits.[23]

Noise enters upon a person's domain in the nature of a sound-wave motion in air set up by a vibrating body. It would seem that the person that placed such sound waves in motion and thus projected them into the property of another might be liable for a trespass, not because of any physical personal intrusion but by virtue of the physical intrusion of the force of the wave set in motion by him.[24] This theory as yet does not seem to have been advanced in any of the decided cases. Even under such a theory it is believed that if no injury is proven the courts would refuse to grant relief under the *de minimus* doctrine (the law does not concern itself with trifles). However, if the noise factor does cause substantial injury or damage, relief under this aspect of the trespass theory might well be granted.

The nuisance theory appears to be the best approach on the part of the landowner to the airspace problem and particularly toward the airplane noise factor.[25] Unlike the trespass theory, wherein the plaintiff must establish an intrusion into an area to which he has the right to possession, under nuisance no claim of possession to the airspace need be established but only the basic fact that the airport or airplane operator unreasonably used his property to the actual damage of another. The flight of an airplane over property or the operation of an airport is, in and of itself, not a nuisance but may become a legal nuisance depending upon the method of flight or the manner of operation of the airport.[26]

In addition to a claim for money damages, an aggrieved surface owner may seek, in a trespass or nuisance action, a court order or injunction against the offending aircraft or certain specific airport operations, preventing the actual or threatened trespass or nuisance in the future.[27] Such a court order if violated, especially in a willful manner, would give rise to a citation for contempt of court which would be punishable by a fine or even a jail sentence.

Rather than meeting the problem of overhead flight by court action, the surface proprietors have attempted to sponsor, upon occasion, legislation directed against aircraft. These legislative efforts have been directed primarily against the plane itself rather than against the noise or other nuisance factor as such. On occasion property owners have been successful in securing an award by legislation for private relief.[28] The legislation may be either state or municipal in origin and tends to regulate aircraft traffic.

Many of the states have adopted laws, rules, or regulations for the purpose of controlling air traffic.[29] These laws generally follow and in many instances have been taken bodily from, or incorporate by reference, the Federal rules. In a field as vast and growing as aviation and with the ever increasing ability of speedy aircraft to conquer the problems of time and space, uniform regulations of air-traffic control are desirable and best accomplished through Federal regulation rather than diverse state regulation.[30] The reported cases that deal with the enforcement of state air-traffic regulations are few and add nothing of consequence to the legal aspects of the airplane-noise problem.

Local municipal authorities have entered into the field of aircraft-flight legislation.[31] Rules and regulations, the purpose of which is to control flight in an orderly manner and promote safety as between aircraft and aircraft, can best be left to Federal enactment and certainly should not be in the area of municipal regulation.

The public health and safety of the citizens of a state are the concern of the state, and it may legislate reasonably to protect its citizens in such matters. It may delegate such authority to local city or village authorities.[32]

When the local municipality under such a grant from the state attempts by legislation to protect its citizens from repeated trespasses or nuisances by aircraft over its land, a conflict may arise between the Federal and local rights. The right of the state and local authorities to protect the health and safety of its citizens must be weighed against the Federal government's right to regulate air commerce. This is a serious question that has been presented for determination in the Federal Court.[33]

RIGHTS OF AIRCRAFT

The legal aspects of the airplane noise problem may also be examined from the viewpoint of the aircraft or airport operator. In the law of real property there is a principle by which a person may acquire a right or even title to land of another by open, notorious, and continuous use thereof even though such use was unauthorized. This principle has been termed an easement by prescription, a prescriptive right, or title by adverse possession.[34]

Aircraft and airport operators have argued that numerous flights over property for a considerable period of time have given them right of use of the airspace by prescription. In those cases where this contention has been raised, the courts have held that such prescriptive right cannot be acquired, on the theory either that such flights though considerable in number are not each in the same place as to linear space or altitude[35] or that such flights do not merely use space (speaking of space as a nonentity) but more properly use the air in such space.[36] This latter approach enabled the court to follow the established line of judicial decisions that no prescriptive right can be obtained for light or air.[37]

At times it has been argued that the admiralty jurisdiction as set forth in the United States Constitution[38] might be the basis for Federal legislation. The courts, however, have refused to consider an aircraft a "vessel"[39] or aviation to be a "maritime" activity.[40]

The first comprehensive Federal legislation that sought to resolve the right of aircraft to fly in airspace over property was the Air Commerce Act of 1926.[41] Certain portions of this act might well be analyzed as having a bearing on the aircraft noise problem.

Section 176(a) of the Air Commerce Act provides that the United States of America has "complete and exclusive national sovereignty in the airspace above the United States." The act further provides in Sec. 403 that there exists "in behalf of any citizen of the United States a public right of freedom of transit in air commerce through the navigable air space of the United States." Reading these two sections we can see that in a sincere attempt to regulate and promote the growing aviation industry Congress saw fit to place sovereignty in airspace in the Federal government and gave at the same time free public transit in navigable airspace to its citizens.[42] No reasonable property owner can take serious issue with the rights established in Secs. 176(a) and 403. The next step in the analysis of the rights, if any, given by the act to aircraft operators is to determine what constitutes navigable air space.

Navigable airspace is defined in Sec. 180 as "air space above the minimum safe altitudes of flight prescribed by the Civil Aeronautics Authority." Section 401(24) also defines navigable airspace as "air space above the minimum altitudes of flight prescribed by regulations issued under this chapter."

Provisions of the Code of Federal Regulations, Title 14, Civil Aviation, Part 60.17, have been promulgated pursuant to the authority granted in the Air Commerce Act and define minimum safe altitudes. In general and for the purposes of discussing the airplane noise problem, the regulations provide that the minimum safe altitude over congested areas is 1,000 ft above the highest obstacle within a horizontal radius of 2,000 ft from the aircraft and over noncongested areas is 500 ft above the surface. It is interesting to note that in fixing minimum safe altitudes no consideration appears to have been given to the nuisance factor of airplane noise when the act was originally passed or since 1926, with the advent of the jet age of aircraft and its greater noise production.

As we have already indicated, the airplane noise factor is of greatest concern to the surface operator during the landing and take-off phase of aircraft operation. What if any are the minimum safe altitudes during landing and take-off? Section 60.17 of the Air Traffic Rules seems to except from its definition of minimum safe altitudes the altitudes necessary for landing and take-off, for it provides "except when necessary for take-off or landing, no person shall operate an aircraft below the following altitudes . . . "[43]

This exception has a twofold effect. Quite logically it removes the minimum-safe-altitude requirement of level flight from landing and take-off, where it is inapplicable, but, more important, it does not provide the aircraft operator with the right of freedom of transit in the airspace used in such landing and take-off operation below the 1,000- or 500-ft level. Although some writers[44] on the subject have expressed the opinion that various other regulations controlling landing and take-off[45] are in the nature of "minimum safe altitude" and thus establish freedom of air transit in such strata of flight, the Supreme Court of the United States has preferred to rule that the path of glide taken by aircraft in the process of landing or take-off is not the minimum safe altitude and no right of transit exists therein.[46]

Aircraft noise and other nuisance factors, particularly when in close proximity to the surface during landing and take-off, become more than an inconvenience that must be borne in silence because they are a part of our modern life.[47] Noise and other airplane nuisances may be of such intensity and frequency as to interfere substantially with the enjoyment and use of the land beneath. When such noise is present a substantial part of the land has in reality been taken away.[48]

The Civil Aeronautics Board on July 22, 1954, adopted and published in 19 Federal Regulations 4602 an interpretation of Part 60 of its Air Traffic Rules. The Board confined its interpretation to the approach-zone problem and said, "The particular part of the regulations to which this interpretation relates is that contained in the initial clause of the section: 'Except when necessary for take-off or landing, no person shall operate an aircraft below the following altitudes.'" The Board intended only to construe the words "Except when necessary for take-off or landing, . . . " as related to the problem of air safety and said, "*b*. The duty of the Board under the act is primarily to prescribe safe altitudes of flight, not to proclaim what is navigable airspace. Although navigable airspace has been defined by the Congress in terms of minimum altitudes, these must be fixed by the Board solely on the basis of safety." The interpretation of the exception was as follows: "In consideration of the foregoing, the Board construes the words 'Except when necessary for take-off or landing, no person shall operate an aircraft below the following altitudes' where such words appear in § 60.17 of the Civil Air Regulations as establishing a minimum altitude rule of specific applicability to aircraft taking off and landing." Even if the Board had not thus limited its interpretation such a construction of the Air Traffic Rules could not be used so as to define property rights in airspace as between surface owner and aircraft. The Federal government cannot, under the guise of air-traffic regulation or an interpretation thereof, give a right of transit in airspace that would result in the taking of a part of a person's property without compensation for such taking.[49] To do so would be a violation of the Fifth Amendment of the Constitution of the United States. Any law of regulation that results even indirectly in such a taking is of necessity unconstitutional.

There are valid and constitutional methods of establishing the right of transit in airspace in the lower strata of such space which we will later examine.

In England, where there are few if any constitutional provisions affecting rights in property, the problem of title to airspace was rendered much simpler of solution. The English Air Navigation Act of 1920 outlawed legal actions of trespass or nuisance against aircraft in flight if such flights were reasonably made and otherwise legally conducted pursuant to statute.[50]

On occasion various state air-traffic laws and regulations may come in conflict with the Federal air-traffic rules and regulations. Any state regulations that were enacted primarily for the purpose of traffic control rather than for the protection of the public health and safety of the citizens of the state must yield to the Federal provisions.[51] Any state air-traffic rule or regulation that seems to give the aircraft a right in airspace at such a low level that the noise factor becomes a "taking" of the landowner's property would likewise be unconstitutional, not only under the provisions of the state constitution but also under the Fifth Amendment of the Federal Constitution. Thus the problem of aircraft noise is essentially the same whether we consider it under state or Federal enactment.

In studying the problem of airplane noise in particular relation to the rules and regulations of the Civil Aeronautics Authority it is interesting to note that the air-traffic rules are binding upon military planes where there are no military service regulations to the contrary and where the appropriate service has not given prior notice of its intended departure from the regulations to the Authority.[52] Any attempt to promulgate military regulations that would permit military aircraft to operate at such low altitudes as to constitute a "taking" of the property below would not only be unenforceable as against the surface owner but unconstitutional. Most of the litigation involving aircraft nuisances has involved commercial operations. This may be based upon the natural reluctance of most persons to take issue with measures adopted for reason of national security and is particularly true in times of national emergency. Fundamentally the airplane noise problem in its legal aspects is the same whether civil or military in origin.

APPROACH-ZONE NOISE

There are many solutions presently available to the airplane or airport operator that minimize or cure the legal aspects of the airplane noise problem particularly in its most troublesome phase, that of landing and take-off. The first solution is that of purchase. In planning future airports, in enlarging present airports, and in an attempt to correct some of the noise nuisance problems presently existing in the vicinity of airports, the airport or airplane interests may purchase sufficient land surrounding the airport so that the landing and take-off operations, particularly at the lower levels, occur over airport-owned property. This of course is the most expensive solution and in many areas may be prohibitive from a cost viewpoint. The size of the area to be purchased can be determined by a study of the noise patterns that might be expected.

A less costly but equally effective method of approach to the noise problem is that of purchase of an avigation right over the land surrounding the airport. In such a case the title to the land itself remains in the surface owner but he sells a well-defined right of flight in the airspace over his land. The sale may be in perpetuity or in the nature of a lease for a term of years. The space in which the right of flight is given should be defined as to its width and its height either above the land surface or sea level.

The most effective method of establishing the size and extent of the airspace in which an avigation easement is given is to determine an "approach zone" at the ends of the runways.[53] The specifications of course will vary according to the type of aircraft, length of the available runways, and weather conditions prevalent in the area. The approach zone most commonly in use at civil and military airfields has the shape of a huge trapezoid extending fanlike from the end of each runway for a distance of about

2 miles. At the end nearest the runway it is about 1,500 ft wide and a mile or more in width at its outer edge. Superimposed upon this huge trapezoid is the so-called glide-angle plane into which no obstructions may extend. The glide-angle plane is likewise trapezoidal in shape and at its narrowest end rises at an angle from the ground beginning at the end of the runway or some distance out from the runway end. The angle of the glide plane in relation to the ground will vary with the type of aircraft in use and other conditions. The rise is in many instances at the rate of 1 ft vertically for each 50 ft horizontally for the 2-mile length of the zone.

The length and width of the zone, together with the angle of the glide, may well vary with the development of future aircraft. In planning the approach zone, careful consideration should be given to the airplane noise factor. It is in this approach-zone area that legal conflict with the rights of the surface owner is most apt to occur.

In those situations where the property owner refuses to sell either his land or an avigation right over it, the airport or aircraft operator may, in the proper case, proceed through condemnation action to acquire either title to the land[54] or an avigation interest.[55]

For our purposes condemnation may be described as the process by which a sovereignty exercises its right as a state to acquire private property within its domain for public use upon making just payment therefor to the owner.[56]

The right of condemnation exists in the Federal and state governments, in many local municipal authorities, and in a few private and quasi-governmental corporations.[57] The procedure varies with the different states and with the Federal government.[58] Under every procedure it is necessary that the landowner receive notice of the nature of the interest sought to be taken. The notice given is usually in the form of a complaint or petition issued out of a court of competent jurisdiction. The property owner has the right to appear, defend, and be represented by counsel. Assuming the case is a proper one for condemnation, the most important question and usually the only question is that of the amount of compensation to be awarded.

If the parties cannot agree upon the question of compensation, testimony may be presented by the litigants and a determination made by a judge, a jury, or by commissioners duly appointed by the court. The general procedure is essentially the same in condemnation of the land itself or of the right of flight. When the land itself is taken in condemnation the owner is entitled to receive in return the fair market value of the property as of the time of the taking of the property.[59]

When the right of flight is condemned the noise factor becomes important. In evaluating this right, consideration must be given not only to the amount of space taken, but also and more important to the effect such taking will have upon the land below, title to which still remains in the original owner.[60] The surface property suffers consequential damage not so much because a portion of the airspace above is taken away, but more so by reason of the use to which such airspace may be put under the terms of the avigation easement that has been taken.[61]

When the avigation easement taken is a "perpetual easement and right-of-way for the free and unobstructed flight of aircraft in, through and across the airspace above the 'glide angle plane,'"[62] the party owning such easement will be entitled to make full use of the airspace by small and giant aircraft of the single- and multiengine variety, including those driven by piston engine, jet engine, jet engine with after burner, rocket engine, and supersonic propeller. Keeping in mind the continued rapid development being made in aviation, the noise factor in the space taken might reasonably be expected to be of a considerable intensity level in the lower reaches of the approach zone.

Some writers on the subject take the position that an avigation easement merely places a height limitation on the property below and that this limitation constitutes the main element of damage to the property.[63] Such a position is unrealistic and shows a lack of appreciation of noise and the part it plays in our daily personal and business life.

It has long been recognized in the law of condemnation that a valid claim for compensation exists on behalf of a person for the depreciation in value of property retained by him as a result of the taking of a portion of the property.[64] When an avigation easement is taken, a part of the property is taken and any damage that is suffered by the remaining portion (surface property) is a proper item for compensation.   It should be stressed that the important consequential damage to the property remaining below the glide-angle plane occurs not by reason of the space taken but by reason of the use to which the space may be put, i.e., flights of aircraft with their attendant noise at very low altitudes.   The closer such property is to the beginning of the glide-angle plane, the lower will be the flight and, generally, the greater will be the noise nuisance.

In the process of condemning an avigation easement the party seeking the easement usually prepares and in many instances files maps or charts showing the height and width of the glide-angle plane over the various tracts of land.   Any competent real-estate appraiser can evaluate the damage to the land below solely by reason of the space taken.

In order to evaluate the damage to the land below by reason of the noise factor it is necessary to make a study of the various features that will influence the noise problem.   Consideration must be given to the size and type of airfield involved, type of aircraft that might reasonably be expected to use the airspace, the probable frequency of such use, and the background-noise level existing at the time of flight.

Knowing the type of aircraft, the probable frequency, and the height of the aircraft above the ground at a given point, an analysis of the noise problem can then be made by the physicist or acoustical engineer for the benefit of the real-estate appraiser. With the calculation of the noise zones that might be expected from the possible use of the airspace the noise intensity may to some extent be determined sufficient to appraise what might be termed the noise damage to the underlying property.[65]

In investigating the problem of consequential damage to the surface-property owner by reason of airplane noise in the superjacent airspace, the first consideration must be given to the type of property involved.   The problem may vary somewhat depending on whether the property is suited for residential or commercial use (commercial use to include industrial and farm purposes).

Aircraft noise in the immediate superjacent space over a residence presents many factors that may be considered in estimating consequential damage.   Intense noise overhead is distracting and at night it may interfere with sleep.[66]   Interference with speech communication may be annoying.   Vibration and sonic bang might cause minor property damage.   There may be the possibility of some loss of hearing over a period of time.   This problem as yet does not seem to have been sufficiently investigated and, whether or not a factor in any given case, is a problem for the otologist after consultation with the physicist or acoustical engineer.

The homeowner naturally prefers to live elsewhere than under a glide-angle plane. Such preference will be reflected in the readiness with which the premises may be sold.   The marketability is some barometer of its value.   Although some real-estate appraisers have gathered statistics tending to show that residential property value is not affected by the proximity of an airport,[67] the better-considered opinion based on an appreciation of the noise problem is to the contrary.[68]

Commercial or business property may likewise be afflicted by airplane noise in an approach zone close overhead.   Interference with speech communication may cause costly errors and misunderstandings.   Recruitment of personnel may be rendered difficult.   People who would hesitate to live under intense aircraft noise may not desire to work under such noise nuisance.   A noisy aircraft may be distracting.   Distraction from work in or about dangerous machinery creates an additional work hazard.   Noise from low-flying aircraft affects farm animals.   In the case of a chicken farm the court recognized that as a result of such noise chickens flew into walls from fright, killing themselves, and egg production declined, and it took these items into consideration when fixing the damage award.[69]   The question of personal injury to employees as a result of intense aircraft noise is comparable to personal injury in residences.

In arriving at both consequential damage and the value of the space taken, consideration must be given not only to the present use of the property, but to that which real-estate appraisers term "the highest and best use" of the property.[70]   Although at the time of the taking the surface property may be vacant land, if a study of the real-estate trend in the area indicates a future use of the property for residential, business, or industrial use, such prospective use can be evaluated by competent real-estate appraisers by the use of various methods.

Where part of the land is taken (as is the case where an avigation easement is condemned) the measure of damage is the difference between the market value of the land prior to the taking in condemnation and the market value after such taking. If an aircraft does not have the legal right to fly over a particular tract of realty at a given altitude then such flights do not and cannot affect the market value of the land for they are acts of trespass or nuisance or both for which the property has legal redress. If an aircraft does have the valid right to fly over such realty then such flights are legal, and the value of the property already has been depressed by reason of the legal use of the airspace.

We can see, therefore, how necessary it is to study the question of the right of flight in airspace before we can approach a problem of proper compensation for an avigation easement based on the difference between the before and after value. In arriving at the value of property before the taking of an avigation easement in those cases where the aircraft or airport operator is condemning the approach zone to an airport already in existence, care must be taken to determine whether or not the real-estate appraiser in fixing the "before" value understood that the aircraft did not have any rights in the approach zone. If the appraiser assumed that the prior low flights were lawful, then his "before" value will already be mistakenly depreciated by reason of the airplane nuisance, and the differential of value will not be as great as it should be.

In further considering the consequential damage to the property not appropriated in condemnation and caused by the noise nuisance the terms of the avigation easement must be carefully examined. If the easement is in perpetuity and is as comprehensive as the usual easement which we have mentioned[71] care must be exercised to ascertain that the real-estate appraiser understands the legal aspects of the easement and the potential noise problem. If the appraiser mistakenly believes that the use of the approach zone will legally or actually be limited to the same type and frequency of aircraft as in the past, the "after" value will be inaccurate and too high, and such error will be reflected in an unjust differential.

The avigation easement that is usually sought is broad in its terms. The owner of the easement is and will be entitled to the highest and best use of the airspace. The fact that the aircraft do not presently fly at low level over the land, or the fact that the airport is presently used only by a comparatively low-powered plane such as the single-engine piston-driven variety must not be taken as an indication that such use will necessarily continue. The appraiser must be advised of the potential noise factor of jet type aircraft at low levels of flight and must take it into consideration in fixing an after value.

One of the best methods of arriving at just compensation in condemnation cases is based upon a comparison in sales prices of similar property sold in the vicinity just before and just after the imposition of the easement.[72] This method contains some element of danger when applied to aviation situations.

A fair sales price is one arrived at by negotiation between a willing and informed buyer and a willing and informed seller.[73] In this writer's experience very few buyers and sellers of real estate understand or are at all informed as to the rights of aircraft in airspace over their property, the extent of the rights that may be acquired by an avigation easement, or the nuisance and damage potential of intense aircraft noises. Ignorance of any of these factors must invariably lead to a false sales price in either the price before or the price after the imposition of the easement.

In some cases the proximity of real property to an existing or proposed airport causes an appreciation in the value of the property. Many civil airports have highly developed industrial areas in their vicinity which create an additional demand for housing units so long as they are not in the approach zone. Civil airports attract a certain amount of business such as instrument and engine supply facilities, repair and service establishments, restaurants, shops, etc., and these appreciation factors must also be taken into consideration in fixing values.

The solution of the airplane noise problem, particularly during landing and take-off operations, is at the present time based mainly upon purchase of air rights after negotiation and, failing in that, condemnation of an avigation easement.[74]   Other solutions have been suggested and may in the near future be made available.

ZONING PROBLEMS

It has been suggested that a Federal zoning act might be enacted and utilized to regulate the approaches to airports.[75]   It would seem that Congress, for various reasons, has the power to regulate air navigation to the exclusion of any local regulation by the several states in direct conflict with the congressional Air Commerce Act.[76]   It must be borne in mind, however, that the exercise of the power to zone is limited. It must not be unreasonable or open to charges of discrimination.[77]   As was pointed out in the Doolittle Report the most important limitation is the fact that the zoning "cannot go beyond the line of the regulation and become an actual 'taking' of property, without just compensation."[78]   Zoning is the exercise of a form of police power, and of necessity even its valid exercise results in the deprivation of some property rights in the public interest.[79]   When the rights deprived result in a substantial diminution of property value it becomes an illegal taking.[80]   The deprivation, whether legal or illegal, is a question of degree to be determined by the evidence in each particular case.   A detailed study of the potential noise intensity over a given tract of land and the manner in which the noise factor will affect the use and enjoyment of the best use to which the land may reasonably be put is necessary to determine if any future zoning regulation would constitute a valid or invalid regulation.

The power to zone is inherent in the sovereignty of the several states.[81]   This zoning authority may be delegated to a municipality or public body by the legislative of the state, and most of the state legislatives[82] have provided the authority to municipalities for the adoption of zoning ordinances.   The zoning ordinances of state, municipal, and public bodies are subject to the same limitation in that such ordinances must not result in the deprivation of any substantial interest in property.

It has been suggested that zoning for airport purposes be in the first instance the responsibility of the individual states.   Unless some uniformity in zoning practices can be achieved in all the states and territories it would seem that the necessary zoning should be accomplished under Federal authority.

Under present judicial interpretation the Air Commerce Act offers little protection to aircraft operators in any dispute with surface owners.   Any future amendment that might seek to determine the relative rights to airspace as between surface owner and aircraft would be ineffective in those cases where it can be established that the amendatory legislation constituted a "taking" of property without compensation.   The noise factor in the approach zone may in the future continue to increase in such intensity that the complaints of the underlying landowners may be legally solved not by air-traffic rules or zoning, but by purchase or condemnation of avigation easements and in the extreme lower levels of airspace by purchase or condemnation of the land itself.

Since the dawn of the aviation era there has been what might be termed a diminution in land ownership.   The owner of the surface no longer owns to the heavens.   The courts have become inclined toward refusal to enjoin a mere technical trespass in the sky.   As aviation advances we may expect some further diminution of land ownership. If aviation is to continue to grow and progress as it must and will, the surface occupants must be prepared to surrender some of their ancient rights and concepts of ownership.

There is a corresponding duty on the part of aviation industry to recognize certain growing responsibilities to the surface owner.[83]   The increase in frequency, size, and power of modern aircraft will cause an understandable annoyance as a result of the increased noise level.   In order to keep these annoyances at a minimum, flight traffic patterns that will produce the least noise over populated land areas must be used whenever possible.[84]   In the approach-zone areas the airport operator must be prepared to pay a fair price for an avigation easement or the land itself.[85]

In times of national emergency or international crisis involving the safety of the nation, the surface occupier may not be inclined to protest against the noise nuisance of military craft. Such forbearance, however, cannot be expected to extend to private or commercial aircraft in peace time.

The legal aspects of the airplane-noise problem are of recent origin, and the future trend of the law will be affected by the methods adopted by aviation science to meet the challenge of airplane noise.

The first challenge should be met by the aircraft engineer. What, if anything, can be done to lessen noise ouput without any substantial interference with the power output? If some degree of scientific control of noise output can be exercised at the source of the noise the possibility of noise litigation will be lessened without any necessity of further weighing the respective rights of surface owner and the aircraft in airspace.[86]

A second challenge is directed to the aircraft designer. The more vertical a take-off or landing of aircraft, the less will be the noise factor in its most troublesome area, that of the approach zone.

Careful attention should be given to the calculation and plotting of noise zones in and about airports so that maximum benefit can be obtained by operational procedures that decrease noise intensity in approach zones.

Some writers feel that the landowners will gradually become acclimated to intense airplane noise similar to the manner in which the public became accustomed to the horseless carriage. Indeed, the general public already has exhibited such acclimation, but to assume at this stage that it can or will ever completely ignore the growing noise intensity possible from aircraft powered by jet engines appears to be wishful thinking.

REFERENCES

1. The Airport and Its Neighbors, Report of the President's Airport Commission, p. 47 (May, 1952).
2. *1* Coke, "Institutes," 19th ed., chap. 1, sec. 1 (4a), 1832. *3* Kent, "Commentaries," Gould ed., p. 631, 1896. *2* Blackstone, "Commentaries," (Lewis ed., p. 18, 1902), s. 52 Code Napoleon.
3. 6 Am. Jur. (rev. ed.).
4. Swetland vs. Curtiss Airports Corp., 55 F 2d 201, 203 (6th Cir. 1932).
5. Pickering vs. Rudd, 1 Stark N.P. 56, 171 Eng. Rep. 400 (1815).
6. United States vs. Causby, 328 U.S. 256, 261 (1945). Lacroix vs. The Queen, 4D.L.R. 470 (Can-Exchequer Ct. 1954). For comprehensive review see Fixel, "The Law of Aviation," The Mitchie Co., Charlottesville, Va., 1948.
7. Roosevelt Field vs. Town of North Hempstead, 88 F. Supp. 177 (E.D. N.Y. 1950).
8. Northwest Airlines vs. Minnesota, 322 U.S. 292 (1943). Swetland vs. Curtiss Airports Corp. *supra*. Delta Air Corp. vs. Kersey, 193 Ga. 862, 20 S.E. 2d 245 (1942). Thrasher vs. Atlanta, 178 Ga. 514, 173 S.E. 817 (1934). United States vs. Causby, 328 U.S. 256 (1945). Crew vs. Gallagher, 358 Pa. 541, 58 A. 2d 179 (1948).
9. Smith vs. New England Aircraft Co., 270 Mass. 511, 170 N.E. 385 (1930).
10. United States vs. Causby, 75 F. supp. 262, 264 (Ct. Claims 1948).
11. Swetland vs. Curtiss Airports Corp., *supra*. Spite structures will be prohibited: United Airport vs. Hinman, 1940 U.S. Av. Rep 1 (U.S.D.C.S.D. Cal. 1939); Liles vs. Jarigan, 1950 U.S. Av. Rep 90 (Chan. Ct. Roane Co. Tenn. 1949); Commonwealth vs. Bestecki, 1937 U.S. Av. Rep. 1 (Ct. Com. Pl. Dauphin Co. Pa., 1937); City of Iowa vs. Tucker, 1936 U.S. Av. Rep. 10 (D.C. Johnson Co. Iowa 1935).
12. 63 C.J. 893. Fallen aircraft as trespass: see Hahn vs. U.S. Airlines, Inc., 127 F. Supp. 950 (E.D.N.Y. 1955). Margosian vs. U.S. Airlines, Inc., 127 F. Supp. 464 (E.D.N.Y. 1955).
13. 66 C.J.S. 727.
14. Smith vs. New England Aircraft Co., 270 Mass. 511, 170 N.E. 385 (1930). Burnham vs. Beverly Airways, 311 Mass. 628, 42 N.E. 2d 575 (1942). Vanderslice vs. Shawn, 26 Del. Ch. 225, 27 A. 2d 87 (1942). La Com, *et al.* vs. Pacific Gas & Electric Co., 132 Cal. App. 2d 114, 281 P. 2d 894 (1955).
15. Swetland vs. Curtiss Airports Corp., *supra*. Delta Air Corp. vs. Kersey, *supra*. Thrasher vs. Atlanta, *supra*. Brandes vs. Mitterling, 67 Ariz. 349, 196 P 2d, 464 (1949).
16. Dixon vs. Clow, 24 Wend. 188 (1840).
17. Swetland vs. Curtiss Airports Corp., *supra*. Hinman vs. Pacific Air Transport Corp., 84 F 2d, 755 (9th cir. 1936) cert. denied 300 U.S. 654 (1936).

18. Note 8, *supra*. Gardner 382 Pa. 88, 114 A. 2d 491 (1955). Money damages awarded: Grey vs. United States, D.C.N.D. Texas (November 26, 1952); Anderson vs. Lockheed Aircraft Corp., no. 638,719 Sup. Ct. Calif. L.A. Co. (April 26, 1955). Recovery denied: Fitch vs. United States D.C. Kan. (March 22, 1957).
19. Presidential Directive, February 20, 1952, establishing President's Airport Commission.
20. Three airplane crashes in the Newark–Elizabeth, N.J., area on December 16, 1951, January 22, 1952, and February 11, 1952, all in the landing or take-off phase and within 5 miles of the airport, caused fatal injuries to persons on the ground and aroused much public indignation and temporary closure of Newark Airport. The surrounding communities subsequently commenced proceedings in the Federal court for an injunction and damages. Cities of Newark et al. vs. Eastern Airlines, Inc., et al. (D.C. N.J. 1954).
21. Hay vs. Cohoes Co., 2 N.Y. 159 (1849).
22. Byrnes vs. City of Cohoes, 67 N.Y. 204 (1876). Mairs vs. Real Estate Association, 89 N.Y. 498 (1882).
23. Forbell vs. City of New York, 164 N.Y. 522, 58 N.E. 64 (1900).
24. 63 C.J. 897.
25. Noise under certain circumstances may constitute a nuisance, 66 C.J.S. 722.
26. 6 Rev. Am. Jur., Aviation, sec. 4, 140 A.L.R. 1362. Smithdeal vs. American Airlines, 80 F. Supp. 233 (N.D. Texas 1948). City of Phoenix vs. Harlan, 1953 U.S. & C. Av. R. 222 (Ariz. Sup. Ct. 1953).
27. Anderson vs. Souza, 1952 U.S. Av. Rep. 216 (Sup. Cal. 1952).
28. An example of such legislation wherein a property owner secured monetary relief for low-flying military planes may be found in Relief of Sara Davies, 152 U.S. & C. Av. R. 572.
29. N.Y. General Business Law, secs. 240–250.
30. Neiswonger vs. Goodyear Tire & Rubber Co., 35 F. 2d 761 (D.C. Ohio 1929).
31. Administrative Code, New York City, sec. 435.16.0. General Ordinance No. 34, Village of Cedarhurst, N.Y., adopted March 31, 1952, effective June 15, 1952, presently challenged by the airport and aircraft interests by legal proceedings in the Federal District Court for the Eastern District of New York.
32. Yara Engineering Corp. vs. City of Newark, 132 N.J.L. 370 (Sup. Ct. N.J. 1945). Rice vs. City of Newark, 132 N.J.L. 387 (Sup. Ct. N.J. 1945).
33. All American Airways, Inc., et al. vs. Village of Cedarhurst et al., preliminary injunction prohibiting enforcement of local ordinance granted, 106 F. Supp. 521 (E.D. N.Y. 1952) on appeal preliminary injunction sustained pending trial 201 F. 2d 273 (2nd Cir. 1953). County government cannot regulate where State and Federal authorities have taken jurisdiction. County Control of Airports 1954 U.S.C. Av. R. 25 (Cal.-Op-Co.-Counsel 1954).
34. 28 C.J.S. 641.
35. Smith vs. New England Aircraft Co., 270 Mass. 511, 170 N.E. 385 (1930).
36. Hinman et al. vs. Pacific Air Transport, 84 F 2d 755 (9th Cir. 1936).
37. Hinman et al. vs. Pacific Air Transport, *supra*, p. 759.
38. U.S. Constitution, art. III, sec. 2.
39. Foss vs. The Crawford Brothers No. 2, 215 Fed. 269, 271 (1941). See also Reinhardt vs. Newport Flying Service Corp., 232 N.Y. 115; 133 N.E. 371, 1921.
40. United States vs. Cordava, 89 F. Supp. 298 (E.D. N.Y. 1950). Noakes vs. Imperial Airways, 29 F. Supp. 412 (S.D. N.Y. 1939).
41. 44 Stat. 568 (1926), 49 U.S.C., sec. 171 et seq. (1946 ed.).
42. The right of foreign airlines to operate presents an interesting question.
43. Similar language defining "minimum safe attitudes" may be found in some of the state air regulations, e.g., N.Y. General Business Law, art. 14, Aircraft, sec. 245(a) to (d).
44. See *Aviation Law—Fifty years after Kitty Hawk—Evolution of Federal Jurisdiction Over Airspace*, 29 N.Y.U.L. Rev. 180 (1954).
45. 14 C.F.R. sec. 60, 16(d) (1952 ed.) (Acrobatics). 14 C.F.R. sec. 60, 17(c) (1952 ed.) (Heliocopters). 14 C.F.R. sec. 609, 5(e), (l), (i) (1952 ed.) (Low Clouds).
46. United States vs. Causby, 328 U.S. 256, 263 (1945).
47. The Airport and Its Neighbors, *supra*, part III, sec. 3, p. 45.
48. United States vs. Causby, *supra*, pp. 261–262. Boyd vs. United States, 222 F. 2d 493 (8th Cir. 1955).
49. Roosevelt Field vs. Town of North Hempstead, 88 F. Supp. 177 (E.D. N.Y. 1950).
50. 10 & 11, Geo. 5, c. 80 5.9 (1920).
51. Salem Air Service vs. Delany, 197 U.S. Av. Rep. 629 (Ore. Cir. Ct. 1947). In re Veteran Air Express Co., 76 F. Supp. 684 (N.J. 1948) *contra*, Aviation Credit Corp. vs. Gardner, 174 Misc. 798, 22 N.Y.S. 2d 37 (1940). Rosenham vs. United States, 131 F 2d 932

(10th Cir. 1942) cert. denied, 318 U.S. 790 (1943); United States vs. Drumm, 55 F Supp. 151 (Nev. 1944).

52. Cameron vs. Civil Aeronautics Board, 140 F 2d 482 (7th Cir. 1944) 14 C.F.R., sec. 60.1(a).

53. Fabian, *The Appraisal Journal*, **XII**: 9, (January, 1944).

54. Rhyne, Airports and the Courts, Inst. Mun. Law Officers, Washington, D.C., 1944.

55. Oklahoma Airport Zoning Act of 1943, sec. 13, 1946 U.S. Av. Rep. 221. Friendship Cemetery vs. Baltimore, 3 Avi 17, 289 (Cir. Ct. Anne Arundel Co. Md. 1950). 49 U.S.C.A. Sec. 452(c) (1946 ed.) empowers the Civil Aeronautics Administrator to acquire easements in airspace on behalf of the United States.

56. Jahr, "Eminent Domain," sec. 1, p. 1, Clark Boardman Company, Ltd., New York, 1953.

57. One of the most outstanding examples of such a corporation is the Port of New York Authority, which operates four airports in the vicinity of New York City and has condemnation powers. New York Laws of 1947, c. 819, sec. 1(a), in defining "real property" for condemnation by the Authority, includes "air space and air rights."

58. Dolan, *The Appraisal Journal*, **XXII**: 26 (January, 1954).

59. Jahr, "Eminent Domain," *supra*, secs. 66 and 70.

60. United States vs. Dickinson, 331 U.S. 745 (1947). Lyons vs. United States, 99 F. Supp. 429 (W.D. Pa. 1951). United States vs. Hyman, 115 F. 2d 599 (7th Cir. 1940). Watervliet Hydraulic Co. vs. State of New York, 119 Misc. 743, 753 197 N.Y. Supp. 348 (1922).

61. United States vs. Grizzard, 219 U.S. 180, 182 (1910). South Buffalo Railway Co. vs. Kirkover, 176 N.Y. 301, 68 N.E. 366 (1903).

62. Language used in condemnation of an avigation easement for approach zone to Mitchel Air Force Base, Hempstead, New York, United States of America vs. 26.07 acres of land, 126 F. Supp. 374 (E.D. N.Y. 1954). United States of America vs. 1040.30 Acres of Land, 144 F. Supp. 199 (W.D. La. 1956).

63. Howard, *The Appraisal Journal*, **XXII**: 336 (July, 1954). Schmutz, *The Appraisal Journal*, **XX**: 465 (October, 1952).

64. Note 56, *supra*.

65. Randall, *The Appraisal Journal*, **XXII**: 39 (January, 1954). The burden of proof of such "proximity damage" is upon the property owner; the proof of the experts must not be too speculative or conjectural, and the diminution in market value must be established by factual data. United States vs. 26.07 acres of land, 126 F. Supp. 374 (E.D. N.Y. 1954).

66. United States vs. Causby, *supra*, p. 259.

67. Walther, *The Appraisal Journal*, **XXII**: 15 (January, 1954).

68. Note 65, *supra*. See also Beeth, *NAHB Correlator*, p. 178 (August, 1954).

69. Causby et ux. vs. United States, 75 F. Supp. 262, 263–264 (Ct. Claims 1948).

70. City of Syracuse vs. Stacey, 45 App. Div. 249, 61 N.Y. Supp. 165 (1899). Matter of City of New York (East River Waterfront), 213 App. Div. 187, 210 N.Y. Supp. 387 (1925).

71. Note 62, *supra*.

72. Jahr, "Eminent Domain," *supra*, and cases cited therein.

73. Causby et ux. vs. United States, 75 F. Supp. 262, 263–264 (Ct. Claims, 1948).

74. United States vs. 357.25 acres of land, etc., 55 F. Supp. 461 (W.D. La. 1944). United States vs. Hayman, 115 F 2d 599 (7th Cir. 1940). United States vs. 0.15 of an acre of land, 78 F. Supp. 956 (S.D. Me. 1948). See note 62, *supra*. Another method adopted is for the government to condemn only the right to keep the glide path clear of obstructions, leaving unresolved the question of the right of flight. United States of America vs. 4.43 Acres of Land, 137 F. Supp. 567 (N.D. Tex. 1956). See also United States of America vs. 48.10 Acres of Land, 144 F. Supp. 258 (S.D. N.Y. 1956).

75. The Airport and Its Neighbors, *supra*, p. 72 et seq.

76. Rice vs. Santa Fe Elevator Corp., 331 U.S. 218, 230 (1946). Northwest Airlines vs. Minnesota, 322 U.S. 292, 303 (1943). Chicago & Southern Air Lines vs. Waterman Steamship Corp., 333 U.S. 103 (1948).

77. 58 Am. Jur., Zoning, secs. 20, 21 (1948).

78. The Airport and Its Neighbors, *supra*, p. 72.

79. Airports and the Courts, *supra*, pp. 177–179.

80. Pennsylvania Coal Co. vs. Mahon, 260 U.S. 393 (1922).

81. Village of Euclid vs. Ambler Realty Co., 272 U.S. 365 (1926); 58 Am. Jur., Zoning.

82. Note 32, *supra*.

83. Airport Safety, an Air Coordinating Committee Review of Policies and Action in the

Fields Covered by the Doolittle Airport Commission released by the President May 26, 1954.

The National Air Transport Coordinating Committee, New York, N.Y., has undertaken the task of promoting better relations between communities in the aviation-terminal areas and the civil aviation industry by a continuing study of community complaints, field studies, and recommendations for airport operational procedures designed to lessen noise annoyance.

Various aviation associations have formed aircraft-noise committees to study the problem.

84. Airport Safety, *supra*, Recommendation No. 17.
85. Airport Safety, *supra*, Recommendation No. 4.
86. Airport Safety, *supra*, Recommendation Nos. 17, 18.

Chapter 38

LEGAL LIABILITY FOR LOSS OF HEARING

HARRY A. NELSON

Director, Workmen's Compensation Division
Industrial Commission of Wisconsin

INTRODUCTION

Problem and Background. Why does loss of hearing present such an extreme problem in workmen's compensation? To the informed the answer is simple. Noise is almost ubiquitous. There are so many possible claimants. Many industrial operations engender noise sufficient in time to cause loss of hearing. Many employees lose some hearing because of industrial exposure to noise. Few employees actually lose wages because of their partial deafness, few (if any) become absolutely deaf because of prolonged exposure to noise, but the price to be paid for loss to the employee may be substantial and produces much controversy.

Since about 1945 the problem of occupational loss of hearing has grown increasingly important. This is especially true as to the medico-legal phases of the subject. The determination of the numerous issues which present themselves is fraught with much difficulty. The question of interpretation of present laws and decision as to the sort of legislation to be enacted for the future occupies the attention of many persons concerned.

It is said that occupational loss of hearing could result in billions of dollars of claims in this country and that some employers and insurance companies might even become insolvent if all these claims were allowed. Hundreds of claims have been filed in New York and Wisconsin. In New Jersey over 200 claims were filed against a single employer. It is stated that possible claims in Wisconsin under the law as it existed to July 1, 1953, might call for payment of as much as 200 million dollars and that possible claims under New York law might amount to as much as 1 billion dollars. Just how reliable these figures are is unknown. That the problem is serious is obvious. Its gravity will depend upon interpretation of laws by compensation administrators and courts, and by legislative action. Laws undoubtedly will be changed, as has already been accomplished in Wisconsin. New methods of determining and measuring loss are in the process of development. The problem needs the best available thought and attention with as rapid action as possible to make up for lost time.

The fixing of the *cause* of loss has been given considerable study by medical men. When a case is presented a factual determination must first be made as to whether loss of hearing actually exists. If it does, the question must be asked as to whether it is the type of loss which *could* result from prolonged exposure to noise. Then follows inquiry as to whether the quantity and quality of noise exposure were such as has resulted in loss.

What shall be the standard upon which compensation or damages are to be predicated? Shall it be based solely on wage loss or on physical loss regardless of loss of wage?

38-1

When compensation laws were first enacted certain basic principles were recognized. A primary tenet was that benefits were to be based on wage loss. Why, then, is wage loss not measured as and when it occurs and compensation awarded accordingly? Those who are acquainted with workmen's compensation administration recognize the almost insuperable task that a system of that kind would involve. Benefits would vary from week to week, and continuing claims would require repeated adjudication on the subjects of cause and extent of wage loss. The factors of speed, security, and certainty—implicit in good compensation administration—would be lost.

As a workable scheme of practical administration of approximate justice, most states have adopted schedules of benefits based on physical loss. Originally, at least, this measurement was contemplated to produce compensation for "average" wage loss in an "average" case and to be consistently related as between schedule items. As they have developed, schedules frequently bear little relation to actual wage loss. They leave much to be desired as to meticulous relativity and uniformity.

Warnings have been advanced that unless the wage-earning concept is followed, compensation laws may suffer. Judge Harold R. Medina has said: "The wage earning concept is the only principle that holds compensation law together as a consistent whole."[1]

Undersecretary of Labor Arthur Larson has commented: "I have always felt, and I still feel, that if we cut loose from the earning capacity concept, and start recognizing the principle that compensation is payable for physical impairment as such, we will have no way of knowing where the process will stop."[2]

It may well be contended that compensation which is paid for disabilities which cause little, if any, wage loss could much better be used to pay more adequate compensation for disabilities where actual and serious wage loss results. If schedules are to be used, they may well be examined as to their relativity to schedules for other disabilities which cause actual wage loss.

The problem of accrued liability created great difficulty when silicosis was first held to be compensable. Symons has stated that it threw 35,000 to 50,000 men out of work in New York and required corrective legislation.[3] In Wisconsin the impact was cushioned by court construction and legislation over a period of years. Other states made use of "escalator" clauses and other devices to meet the problem of accrued liability and to defer payments and thus avoid full initial liability for injury due to past exposure, often over many years.

The widespread prevalence of deafness and industrial noise raises the question as to the wisdom of suddenly imposing full liability on employers for the results of long-past exposures. The problem of what premiums are to be charged where no statistics are available and future experience cannot be accurately predicted presents considerable difficulty. The payment for accrued liability may be embarrassing to those employers and carriers who may be faced with numerous and substantial claims founded on past exposures. Henry D. Sayer, General Manager, Compensation Insurance Rating Board, New York, has stated: "In assuming now to make provision, out of the moneys of industry, for the effect of years of work in an environment of noise, we are assuming an ability to do the impossible."[4]

If the test is to be that of physical or "social" loss, measurement of the loss must be made by use of some formula or scheme which will translate the inability to hear certain sounds into a percentage of loss of hearing. If there is loss of hearing in both ears, there must be a further plan for determining binaural loss. Obviously, a person with total deafness of one ear does not have a 50 per cent binaural loss. Loss of hearing of the second ear is cumulatively of much greater concern than monaural loss.

The problem is complicated by the question of which employer shall make payment, and in what amount, where successive employments have existed. Should there be allocation as between employers? How can that be done where noise has varied in quality and intensity? How far back should a claimant be permitted to reach in order to charge an employer with loss? Should statutes of limitations bar such loss as has occurred anterior to a given period? When no physical examinations have been made before and during employment, how is it possible to allocate loss among respective employers and over different periods of time?

The impact of a great economic burden suddenly charged to an unprepared employer or insurance carrier may be so great in totality that it cannot be assumed without financial distress or even extinction.   Should, therefore, liability be assumed on a limited basis, paying only for a portion of the loss in claims made as of a given date and a greater or total liability in later claims made over a period of time?   This is the method accomplished by so-called "escalator" clauses.   Liability may be deferred or eliminated by providing for payment of compensation only after some period of removal from noise, retirement, severance of the employer-employee status, or layoff, as has been done in Wisconsin.   Liability may be reduced by formulas for determination of loss and by schedules on lesser bases, recognizing possible undue cost to employers and the fact of little wage loss to employees.

Conflicting interests make varying demands.   Industry has contended that physical losses which do not cause economic loss to the employee should be lightly, if at all, compensated.   Workers who suffer loss of hearing consider that, by analogy with other laws, some payment should be made, even though no wage loss may occur.   The ultimate consumer, who finally assumes the bill when he purchases goods, may (if, indeed, he gives any thought to the subject) have ambivalent conceptions of what should be paid.   The growing trend in workmen's compensation, and the practice firmly established under common-law provisions, is for benefits or damages to be paid on the basis of physical and social, as well as purely economic, loss.   Whether the result is wise will be determined by process of legislative examination and factual experience.

At common law, generally speaking, an employer cannot be held liable for the result of personal injury unless, prospectively, the result of work exposure can reasonably be anticipated and the cause prevented.   Under workmen's compensation neither foreseeable consequences nor possibility of prevention of disability are factors.   The sole question is: "Did the injury arise out of employment, i.e., was it caused by a hazard of the work?"   If it was, the question of negligence is immaterial and benefits are to be paid as part of the cost of production and ultimately charged to the consumer of products.

If a compensation act does not cover loss of hearing, it is foreseeable that as more is learned about the whole subject and as the employer is able to foresee and prevent some of the loss for which a claim may be made, at least in some jurisdictions, a common-law action grounded on negligence may be maintained.

If there is to be a legal remedy, should it be under workmen's compensation or by suit at common law?   What forum should act to determine liability?

The real, and perhaps a rather rough, test of good law is often stated in the simple terms of "the greatest total good for the greatest possible number."   On one side of the scale must be placed the factors which cause burden to the employer and consumer.   On the other side must be placed those which weigh validly in favor of persons who, because of their work, have lost a portion or all of the faculty of hearing.   As laws are considered by legislative bodies, the weight to be accorded to these elements will determine the sort of law which will be enacted.   Sympathy, group pressure, public opinion, and interpretation of probable economic consequences in varying proportions will actuate legislators in reaching a conclusion as to desirable legislation.   Each jurisdiction must assign the importance to be given to the components to be considered in arriving at benefits to be accorded.

The final product will usually be attained by compromise between divergent views, as is customary in the exercise of the democratic process.

The immediate burden imposed will be met by employers and insurance carriers.   The cost will finally be charged to the consumers of products of employers whose processes produce damaging noise.

COMPENSATION IN GENERAL

Early History.   In his recent book on workmen's compensation, Somers states: "Workmen's compensation was not invented; it evolved.   It developed out of a series of social adjustments to meet a social need."[5]

Before the advent of workmen's compensation acts, the legal remedy of an employee for industrial injury was governed largely by common law. This system had been developed to a point of refinement, technicality, and expense which made recovery of damages well-nigh impossible in the great majority of cases. Legal negligence of the employer was required to be shown. The employer had available the three common-law defenses of assumption of risk, fellow-servant rule, and contributory negligence. If these difficult hurdles were surmounted by a worker there was no assurance that damages could be collected from employers financially unable to make payment.

As a result of this situation great hardship resulted to injured employees and their dependents. Public and private charity were frequently invoked. Legal expenses imposed on both employer and employee were substantial. Friction between them was engendered, which impaired otherwise good relationships and consequently production.

As stated by the Wisconsin Supreme Court in *Falk vs. Industrial Commission*, 147 Wis. 327:

It was admitted by lawyers as well as laymen that the personal injury action brought by the employee against his employer to recover damages for injuries sustained by reason of the negligence of the employer had wholly failed to meet or remedy a great economic and social problem which modern industrialism has forced upon us, namely, the problem of who shall make pecuniary recompense for the toll of suffering and death which that industrialism levies and must continue to levy upon the civilized world . . . . To speak of the common-law personal injury action as a remedy for this problem is to jest with serious subjects, to give a stone to one who asks for bread. The terrible economic waste, the overwhelming temptation to the commission of perjury, and the relatively small proportion of the sums recovered which comes to the injured parties in such actions, condemn them as wholly inadequate to meet the difficulty.

In an attempt to relieve some of the strictures of the common-law system, almost all states before 1910 had acted to modify the common-law defenses. Some had enacted so-styled employer's liability laws in order to give injured workers a more effective remedy. These efforts were not sufficient to answer a growing demand for a truly revolutionary remedy based upon newer and more salutary principles.

The major defects imputed to the older system were those of the necessity for establishing fault on the part of the employer and freedom of fault of the employee and his fellows; the uncertainty and inadequacy of remedies; the delay and high costs attendant upon suit in court; lack of uniformity in awards; lack of incentive for adoption of safety measures for prevention of injury; and the burden imposed upon the public of caring for many victims of industrial injury.

Elihu Root described the system as "foolish, wasteful, ineffective and barbarous." The so-called industrial revolution, which commenced in the nineties with the rise of the factory system, brought a great increase in industrial accidents and demand for a radical departure from the older system.

Development. As early as 1854 Prussia required employers to contribute to sickness association funds. In 1884 Germany adopted the first compensation system, based primarily on the thesis that industrial injury was part of the cost of manufacture to be added to the price of the product. The test was not that of negligence on the part of the employer, but was that of logical allocation of an economic expense entailed in production. The British law followed in 1897.

The first compensation law in the United States was passed in 1908 under President Theodore Roosevelt and covered civil employees of the Federal government. By 1910 the first state law had been formulated, and by 1915, 30 states had compensation laws. Since that time all states have passed laws, the last being Mississippi in 1949.

General Philosophy. These laws are of varying types and with considerable diversity in benefits and procedure. Nearly all of them have been held constitutional as a valid exercise of the police power of a state in acting for the welfare of its people. Thus we find elective and compulsory coverage of specified industries, numerical exceptions, and varying coverage of accidents and diseases. Procedure varies from that of courts to that of administrative bodies, usually known as boards or commissions, and with wide differences in practice and procedure. Even among administrative bodies these differences are notable.

Security for payment of benefits is provided by funds built up by assessments on employers in the case of state funds and by premiums paid by them to insurance companies with various provision for reserves in private-insurance states. Some states utilize both systems.

The ideal compensation system would almost automatically produce benefits on a definite and adequate basis without litigation or expense, and with certainty and security of payment. Benefits would consist of all necessary medical and hospital care, adequate monetary benefits, rehabilitation for those whose permanent disabilities handicap them in employment, and death benefits for dependents of those whose injuries result in death.

The student of workmen's compensation will speedily learn that this ideal has not been attained. Most acts belie the broad definition of compensation in the sense of something which tends to make a worker whole, at least financially, following his loss. Some of the better acts approach more nearly the optimum but are criticized because of deficiencies in varying respects, one of which is inadequacy of at least some benefits. Criticism is also advanced that benefits are not properly allocated for specified losses as between claimants even in the same state.

Estimates as to coverage of employees in the United States vary from two-thirds to four-fifths of all employees.[6] Principal broad exclusions are agricultural and domestic employees and those employed by "small" employers.

As originally enacted, compensation laws covered only accidental injuries and not occupational disease. Gradually it was recognized that disease due to occupation was largely preventable by employers but not by employees, and that there was sound reason for including conditions which arose, not at one time and by single impact, but over a considerable period by a myriad of exposures.

By January, 1954, only two states had failed to provide some sort of compensation for occupational diseases.[7] Some states compensate a limited number of diseases, even as few as one, some according to a list of selected diseases, and some by blanket coverage of all diseases attributable to industrial exposure. Complaint has been voiced that sometimes the very diseases which cause the greatest disability are excluded from coverage. Response has been made that the cost of "unknown hazards" could become immense; that compensation laws would in effect become health insurance, and that administrative difficulties in determination of cases would prove insuperable.

Actually the result of blanket coverage of occupational disease has not been serious on a long-range basis. The immediate impact of a new law on employers and carriers has at times proved embarrassing.

The first occupational disease which created real concern was silicosis, which, largely because of the incidence of superimposed tuberculosis, called for considerable payments of benefits. If the liability could have been gradually assumed over a protracted period, the problem would not have been great. Many employees had been exposed for years and were affected with silicosis in different stages. Many of them, during a period of economic depression, filed claims.

Passage of laws calling for payment for so-called "accrued" liability produced fear of oppressive awards with consequent competitive disadvantage between employers in different states. Employers were held liable for the end result of exposures extending in cases over many years, and in service for other employers.

Some states eliminated liability for a preexisting condition; others provided a sliding scale of increased benefits over a period of time; others faced the problem head on and charged an employer with liability when his employment produced, not the whole condition, but the final disability. Insurance problems arose because of succession of carriers on a given risk for varying periods, thus necessitating decision as to which of the carriers should respond in compensation.

COMPENSATION IN HEARING-LOSS CASES

Federal Laws. The oldest workmen's compensation law in the United States, enacted in 1908, is the Federal Employees' Compensation Act, which covers civil employees of the Federal government. It also provides the largest allowances for occupational loss of hearing. For total loss in one ear an employee may receive as much as $6,300, and for total loss in both ears as much as $24,200.

The Longshoremen's and Harbor Workers' Compensation Act, enacted in 1927, which covers workers in maritime employment, allows up to $1,820 for total loss in one ear, and $7,000 for loss in both ears.

An act with almost identical provisions covers private employees in the District of Columbia.

Railway workers and seamen do not come under compensation acts but are accorded special treatment under the Federal Employees' Liability Act and the Jones Act (Merchant Marine Act), respectively. With limited exceptions the remedies of these workers are founded on negligence, with reductions where comparative contributory negligence can be shown.

State Laws. It is not possible to delineate with exactness and in detail all the remedies provided by the various state compensation acts. To the student who is willing to spend sufficient time, reference to statutes, court interpretations, and administrative rulings reveals as much variation as in general is found among the many other acts of the several states.

Rather generally, schedules of fixed benefits control payment for permanent loss of hearing. Some state laws still cover only accidental injuries. Other laws have not received construction by the courts, so it is not known whether schedules may apply to loss of hearing due to prolonged noise, although they may apply in case of accidental injury. Loss of hearing which results from a single impact of noise or single trauma from other cause is, of course, accidental and is covered by all state acts. Gradual loss due to countless impacts over considerable periods of time is usually placed in the category of occupational disease and treated under provisions governing liability for occupational disease. Some states which have covered only for accidental injuries have later passed separate laws for occupational disease, while others have included these diseases under modifications or extensions of previous laws.

In some states schedules list certain diseases which are covered, excluding others which are not named. In such states, unless loss of hearing is listed, it is not covered under occupational-disease provisions. Other states use special language defining that a disease must be due to a specific industrial hazard, which leaves the court to construe what that hazard may be.

Proponents of full coverage believe that "listings" fail to keep pace with newer processes and hazards, while opponents express the fear that the cost of unrecognized and unknown hazards could become disastrous and that compensation laws would assume a role not intended.

The variations in allowances for loss of hearing among states range from a high of $12,333, in Wisconsin, to a low of $1,560, in Maine, for total loss in both ears. For loss in a single ear the high is $2,700, in Oregon, and the low is $625, in Kansas. The range between allowances for one and two ears varies in a ratio of from 1 to 5⅔, in Wisconsin, to 1 to 2, in Delaware. Some states allow compensation for temporary disability in addition to allowance for permanent disability. This is ordinarily rather unimportant in the case of loss due to prolonged exposure to noise where, as a rule, no temporary disability (inability to work) occurs.

It will be seen that a detailed study of provisions in state laws, as well as study of court decisions, is necessary to learn whether liability exists in a given state under compensation acts for loss of hearing due to noise over a period of time. If there is no liability under a compensation act, there may still be liability at common law on a showing of negligence or of failure under statutory provisions to supply a safe place and methods of work. This affords material for prolific discussion as to the remedy of election for legislative action.

Loss of Hearing. In May, 1948, the New York State Court of Appeals decided the case of *Slawinski vs. Williams and Company*, 298 N.Y. 546, and held that the compensation schedule applied to permanent hearing impairment found to be caused by work in a noisy environment. Soon after, the Court of Appeals affirmed in *Rosati vs. Despatch Shops*, 298 N.Y. 813, a schedule award for permanent loss of hearing likewise due to damaging noise. Slawinski worked on heavy forging hammers. Rosati was a riveter in a railroad-car-repair shop.

Two other cases have been decided by the New York Courts: *Russo vs. Despatch Shops, Inc.*, 280 App. Div. 1008, which raised issue as between liability of two insurance carriers; and *Gabor vs. American Magnesium Corporation*, 275 App. Div. 1014, in which the claim was not for loss of hearing but for tinnitus (buzzing and ringing in the ears). Liability was held for a period of temporary partial disability.

Although occupational loss of hearing has thus been found compensable in New York, the Industrial Commission, on testimony produced in a number of cases, held that there could be no determination until the injured worker had been removed from his noisy environment for at least 6 months. The stated reason for this deferment of decision is that testimony has established that there is some recovery of hearing after removal from noise for some time, and that until 6 months' removal, ultimate loss of hearing cannot properly be determined. (In this regard the Wisconsin commission held that although some recovery results, the testimony in its test case established that not more than 25 per cent recovery could occur; therefore, compensation could be awarded for 75 per cent of the loss found, with further finding when and if 6 months' removal from noise has taken place.) The New York holdings have deferred the necessity for decision in many cases and have prevented the filing of many others—this because employees continue working at regular wages and will not cease work for 6 months in order to collect compensation. It has also been stated that numbers of employees have failed or refused to file claims because of the possible financial impact on employers who might be embarrassed by payment of large sums and ultimately might have to close down or leave the state of New York, and thus leave employees without jobs.

In New Jersey 232 claims were filed against the Bethlehem Steel Company by workers who claimed over 5 million dollars in damages. Claims were filed at common law, under the Longshoremen's and Harbor Workers' Compensation Act and the New Jersey Workmen's Compensation Act. One case was heard in the Hudson County Court on the question of jurisdiction. The court held that jurisdiction was under the New Jersey Workmen's Compensation Act or under the Federal act. An appeal was taken to the Appellate Division of the Superior Court, but before the appeal was heard all the claims were settled under the New Jersey Workmen's Compensation Act. In addition, payments were made under executed releases in the suit started in the Hudson County Court. The claims filed under the Federal jurisdiction were discontinued.[8] The New Jersey act was amended effective January 1, 1950, to provide compensation for all occupational diseases, although previously there had been provision only for those diseases included in a schedule listing.[9]

Under the Longshoremen's and Harbor Workers' Compensation Act the United States District Court for the Eastern District of New York has approved payment of compensation for permanent partial loss of hearing due to injurious industrial noise over varying periods. The court stated that previous administrative interpretation placed upon the statute by the agency charged with administration was entitled to considerable weight.

In Wisconsin before the end of 1951 about 40 claims had been filed with the Industrial Commission based on gradual loss due to noise exposure. Additional claims were filed until over 500 had accumulated by August 1, 1953.

A test case was heard by the commission, which found liability, holding that the schedule of fixed benefits applied even though no wage loss could be shown. On appeal to the Circuit Court of Dane County the decision was reversed, based on absence of wage loss which the court held was essential in occupational disease, as had previously been held by the Supreme Court in silicosis cases, where, however, no schedule of benefits was involved.

On appeal to the Supreme Court the decision of the Circuit Court was reversed, and the holding of the commission affirmed. The court stated that wage loss was not an essential prerequisite to liability in occupational loss of hearing, that the schedule applied, and that the last day of work (defined in the law as the date of injury in occupational disease) was properly taken as the day before the filing of application. (The testimony established loss up to a short time before filing of application.) (*Green Bay Drop Forge Company vs. Albert Wojcik*, 265 Wis. 38.)

The testimony clearly established that noise can and does result in loss of hearing and that the employee had worked in noise of a kind and over a sufficient period to result in permanent loss. It was held that there should be a reduction in the recorded percentage of loss because of hearing loss common at the age (sixty) of the claimant. The testimony established the average natural loss at age sixty to be 7.07 per cent. Although some restoration of hearing might be anticipated if the employee were removed from noisy environment, at the most it could not amount to more than 25 per cent, leaving 75 per cent of residual loss as attributable to work exposure.

In determination of loss, the American Medical Association method[10],[*] with the use of the pure-tone audiometer was considered to be the most reliable evolved to the date of the decision. Under the Wisconsin statute [Sec. 102.52 (17) and (18)], the value of binaural hearing loss (i.e. a single number representing the combined hearing loss for both ears) was computed from the monaural hearing losses as follows: The average monaural loss for the better ear was multiplied by 5⅔; this figure was then added to the monaural loss for the worse ear; then, the sum was divided by 6⅔. The figure so obtained was considered as the binaural hearing loss. After further deduction, as required by the statute (the claimant's age was over fifty), the final result called for payment of 13.511 per cent of binaural loss, or 45.04 weeks of compensation, in the sum of $1,575.46.

The commission's advisory committee on workmen's compensation legislation was impressed with the possible serious impact on industry of a multitude of claims. It was, therefore, proposed to the legislature that, at least temporarily, a change in law was desirable. As a result, effective July 1, 1953, the schedule was abrogated as to loss of hearing from prolonged exposure to noise but retained as to accidental loss. It was provided that an employee must establish loss of hearing as a result of prolonged exposure to noise for a total period of at least 90 days; and that because of his loss he had been discharged or transferred from employment, or that he had ceased such employment since it was inadvisable for him to continue in it because of impairment of hearing. If he could then establish wage loss he might receive benefits not to exceed $3,500.

To discourage unnecessary discharge or transfer, the employer was charged with uninsurable primary liability where discharge or transfer was not necessary.

The advisory committee continued to study the question of a more desirable formula and possible new legislation. A medical subcommittee was appointed, which advised that pure-tone air-conduction audiometric tests be taken at readings of 500, 1,000, and 2,000 cps.[11] These were stated as the frequencies most highly correlated with the ability to understand speech.[†] (The American Medical Association table also includes the frequency of 4,000 cps.)

Losses averaging 16 db or less are to be held not to constitute hearing disability, and losses of 80 db and over are to constitute total deafness. Between these points, for each average decibel loss between 17 and 80 is prescribed a percentage of compensable hearing loss.

Loss for presbycusis[‡] (age deafness) is to be subtracted at the rate of one-half per cent at age fifty, plus an additional one-half per cent for each year thereafter. Some recovery of hearing may be expected after removal from a noisy environment. Just how much will depend on factors of years of exposure, degrees of loss, and individual susceptibility. After 48 hours' removal from noise, a first examination is made, followed by closely spaced periodic tests, with deduction of 5 db from the average ratings of the 500-, 1,000-, and 2,000-cps frequencies, to allow for auditory fatigue. The result will be the final permanent loss, except for those individuals who have been removed from noise for 6 months or longer, whose loss will be established without the 5-db deduction.

The Wisconsin commission's advisory committee on workmen's compensation legislation proposed a bill to the 1955 legislature, enacted into law effective on July 1, 1955[12] (this act is reproduced as Appendix 38.1), which will continue to provide compensation for *actual* wage loss up to $3,500. This provision applies only where an employee,

---

[*] This method is discussed in Chap. 6.
[†] See *Speech Average Loss*, Chap. 7.
[‡] See Figs. 7.1 and 7.2.

because of occupational deafness, is transferred by his employer to other *noisy* employment. Time of injury in such case is to be the date of wage loss.

This provision will probably seldom, if ever, be invoked. It is difficult to conceive of transfer from one noisy employment to another *because* of deafness. The possibility was, however, recognized.

The most important feature of the act is the adoption of a schedule which provides payment of 160 weeks for total deafness and 32 weeks for total deafness of one ear, with proportionate allowances for partial deafness. These allowances are to be made regardless of wage loss. The allowances are about one-half of those which were formerly assigned.

In order to invoke the schedule, the employee must be transferred by his employer to another job, have retired, have terminated his status as an employee, or completed a layoff of 1 year. His claim will be enforceable only after six consecutive months from one of these events, except that as to total layoff the 6-month period may commence in the last half of the layoff-year period. Compensation will be payable only by an employer for whom the employee may have worked on each of 90 days in noisy employment.

If the last employer fails to have a preemployment examination, or otherwise fails to establish loss not due to his employment, he will be liable for all deafness to which his employment has contributed. Aggregate liability, however, will not be greater against all employers than could result for total deafness of both ears.

The effect of this provision will be to postpone and spread liability over a longer period of time than under a law which would call for liability of accrued loss as of a given time. Compensation will be payable in the vast majority of cases to persons who are either temporarily or permanently removed from the labor market. They will receive compensation at a time when their wage has been reduced, or when no wage is being received. Payments will be entirely avoided in many cases in which liability would have been held prior to July 1, 1953. In case of death of an employee who is still in service, no payment will be made except as liability has been admitted or an order made. Payments will be considerably reduced from the former schedule which preexisted July 1, 1953, both because of change in formula for determining loss and the more limited schedule to be adopted.

(The Wisconsin experience has been rather extensively detailed because of the greater activity which has developed in this state, both by way of claims filed and legislation adopted and proposed to meet the problem.)

Trends. Great concern has been expressed generally by industry in this country as to the cost of compensation for the many hearing-loss cases which may be attributed to employment. Labor has also been concerned by this factor and by its desire to see compensation paid for industrial loss of hearing.

Insurance carriers are concerned because of fear that they may not be able to absorb the large losses which would result from a flood of awards, because reserves have not been set up to meet the many claims which had not been anticipated. Symons has stated that "direct insurers can no more absorb the catastrophic losses which would result from a flood of occupational deafness awards than they could absorb the losses for injuries or deaths resulting from an atomic bomb attack."[13]

New York has reached a partial solution of great immediate fiscal impact on employers by withholding decisions upon the postulate that until 6 months' removal from noise, and the cessation of auditory fatigue, extent of loss cannot be determined. Wisconsin's proposal will accomplish the same purpose as to postponement of liability, with additional relief because of reduction in schedule allowances, and avoidance of many claims which would have been allowed under former provisions.

Other states are pursuing a policy of watchful waiting and exploring the possibilities of legislation in the light of what has occurred in New York, Wisconsin, and New Jersey. Some claims have been filed in Missouri and Indiana but have not reached the point of decision.

There can be no doubt but that the greatest good which can result from a medicolegal program is the prevention of loss of hearing to the extent that that may be accomplished. Most employers are strongly actuated by humanitarian motives.

They must also, however, consider economic problems and competitive factors. The fact that occupational disease has become expensive in terms of money has hastened programs of safety and prevention, which, in the case of silicosis and lead poisoning, have produced gratifying results. Employers should use all diligence in surveying conditions in their plants, ascertaining whether detrimental noise is present, and doing whatever is feasible to eliminate as much noise as possible. Physical examinations for loss of hearing should be made promptly and at intervals. Regardless of the basis of recovery, either under compensation acts or at common law, workers are rightfully going to insist that working environments are provided which will, within reasonably attainable bounds, eliminate the hazard which produces loss. Workers are entitled to work in environments which, within practicable bounds, will not impair their faculties. When the time comes when codes and standards can be written into law with sanctions for violations, steps in that direction should be cautiously taken. This should not be done until it is certain that rules can be established which are physically and economically feasible and which are based upon sound medical, engineering, and safety principles. Employers who act promptly and effectively will be able to congratulate themselves on the fact that they are carrying out the golden principle of man's humanity to man, that they are acting to preserve the precious heritage of hearing, and that their industries will not be embarrassed by claims founded on avoidable hazards.

Methods of Testing and Rating Disability. In view of liability involved under schedules which call for payments based on percentage of loss, the methods to be adopted are of great importance. The ability to hear sounds in the high-frequency ranges may be important to persons in certain professions, such as piano tuners and musicians. At the other end of the scale, inability to hear sounds of extremely low frequency interferes little with ability to work and earn in most industrial activities. One who cannot hear the gentle rustling of leaves in the summer breeze lacks a portion of normal hearing. One who cannot hear the noise of a drop hammer finds scant comfort in being able to discern faintly the roaring of a jet plane. To the ordinary worker, however, the ability to hear speech and sounds embraced within the speech range are of the greatest utility.

It must be a matter of considered judgment as to which frequencies and intensities are to be considered in measuring the hearing loss for which the employer is to pay and the employee is to collect. Schedules are, at least theoretically, based on "average" wage loss in "average" occupations, with some possible concessions to elements of physical and social loss. The measure of loss, for lack of a better and more accurate method, is grounded on *physical* inability to hear, based on formulas which weight more heavily ability to hear most "useful" sounds.

As ability to hear speech is of great importance, testing for this factor is emphasized. There are drawbacks and difficulties which attend such testing, as will be pointed out in other chapters. So far, use of the pure-tone audiometer has been stated as the most practicable method, with interpretation of findings into percentages of loss according to various tables proposed. Progress has been made which has dictated changes in earlier methods employed.

Methods adopted for use under compensation acts will undoubtedly vary, but will tend to attain some uniformity as experience is gained. This has been the case in methods and formulas for testing vision.

THE ROLE OF THE PHYSICIAN

Otologists have been largely instrumental in bringing the subjects of industrial noise and occupational deafness to light. They have played a commendable role in calling attention to the hazards of noise, the necessity of conservation of hearing, and the methods of appraisal of loss and treatment of those conditions susceptible of treatment. The otologist's interest should be factual and truly scientific. As a doctor he is not concerned with amounts to be paid for loss, but is interested only in arriving at proper medical conclusions, leaving to legislators and administrators the question of benefits.

Increasingly the doctor will be called upon to render medical and otological services to employers and employees by way of physical examinations of workers, measurement of loss, treatment of conditions amenable to treatment, and appraisal of hazards in noisy operations. He will be asked to supervise those who make audiometric tests and to make reports upon which loss can be measured. He will cooperate with engineers and safety experts in advising as to protective equipment and their fitting and use, and as to reduction and prevention of deleterious noise and of deafness. As a witness, he will be prepared to give his opinion and findings as to causation and extent of loss, with sound reasons to support his testimony. As an adviser to industry he will be able to counsel as to facts upon which denial or acceptance of claims can be predicated.

LABOR AND MANAGEMENT COOPERATION

Because of the stake which both labor and management have in the progress and outcome of legal aspects of the hearing problem, the closest of cooperation is needed. Neither workers nor industries can afford to neglect conservation of hearing, the loss of which entails for the worker physical impairment, and for industry an economic burden which, while potentially great, is reducible by medical and engineering control methods. Labor has, at times, resisted medical examinations of employees. Such examinations have on occasions been used to bar from employment employees capable, with proper placement, of productive service. Enlightened employers have used examinations for placement rather than for exclusion of capable employees. They will continue to do so. Labor will increasingly realize that physical examinations, properly used, conduce to health and welfare of employees.

Both labor and industry need to get together on measures for safety and prevention of loss of hearing. Industry must supply devices, equipment, and procedures which will tend toward these objectives. Labor must make use of measures provided and make certain that its members carry out to the full extent their share of the program.

When legislation is proposed, labor and industry must join hands in study and research, and then, by the system of give and take, reach conclusions which will not endanger the healthful economic existence of industry or the reasonable welfare of the employee. To accomplish their purpose, the best help of engineers, doctors, safety personnel, legislators, and lawyers will be needed.

By the process of education, legislative approach, and medical and engineering control and research, the end result, it is expected, will be the same sort of accomplishment which has been attained in similar fields where hazards are largely prevalent but can be reduced or eliminated by good preventive and safety measures.

REFERENCES

1. Iscone vs. Cardillo, 208 Fed. 2d 696.
2. Industrial Noise and Claims for Occupational Loss of Hearing, *Insurance Counsel Journal*, International Association of Insurance Counsel (April, 1954), as quoted by Noel Symons.
3. Symons, N. S.: 17th Annual Meeting, Industrial Hygiene Foundation, *Transactions Bull. No.* 24, 1952.
4. Legal Aspects of Noise in Industry, 17th Annual Meeting, Industrial Hygiene Foundation, 1952.
5. Somers: "Workmen's Compensation," p. 17. John Wiley & Sons, Inc., New York, 1954.
6. McCamman and Skolnik: Social Security Bulletin, p. 4 (March, 1954).
7. The following jurisdictions have coverage of a varying number of occupational diseases as listed: Alabama, Arizona, Colorado, Georgia, Idaho, Iowa, Kansas, Kentucky, Louisiana, Maine, Montana, New Hampshire, New Mexico, North Carolina, Oklahoma, Pennsylvania, Puerto Rico, South Dakota, Tennessee, Texas, and Vermont.
    The following jurisdictions have full coverage of all occupational diseases: Alaska, Arkansas, California, Connecticut, Delaware, District of Columbia, Florida, Hawaii, Illinois, Indiana, Maryland, Massachusetts, Michigan, Minnesota, Missouri, Nebraska, Nevada, New Jersey, New York, North Dakota, Ohio, Oregon, Rhode Island, South

Carolina, Utah, Virginia, Washington, West Virginia, Wisconsin, Federal Employees' Act, and Longshoremen's Act.
Mississippi and Wyoming have no coverage of occupational disease.

8. Spair, W. C.: Problems 1954; *Bull.* 180, U.S. Department of Labor.
9. Paper by Commissioner Carl Holderman, New Jersey Department of Labor and Industry, at convention of International Association of Industrial Accident Boards and Commissions, Quebec, 1954.
10. *J. Am. Med. Assoc.* (February 9, 1947).
11. Report of Medical Subcommittee to Advisory Committee of Wisconsin Industrial Commission, 1954.
12. Chapter 281, Laws of 1955, Wisconsin Statutes.
13. Symons, N. S.: The Legal Aspects of Occupational Deafness, Problems of Noise in Industry, Conference Atlantic City, April 23, 1951.

APPENDIX 38.1

[No. 341, S.]

CHAPTER 281, LAWS OF 1955

An Act

AN ACT to repeal 102.565 (6); to amend 102.01 (2), 102.11 (1) (intro. par.), 102.49 (5), 102.565 (1), (2) and (4), and 102.59 (2); and to create 102.555 of the statutes, relating to compensation for injuries under workmen's compensation.

The people of the state of Wisconsin, represented in senate and assembly, do enact as follows:

SECTION 1.   102.01 (2) of the statutes is amended to read:

102.01 (2) "Act" as used in this chapter means "chapter"; "compensation" means workmen's compensation; "primary compensation and death benefit" mean compensation or indemnity for disability, or death benefit, other than increased, double or treble compensation or death benefit; "injury" is mental or physical harm to an employe caused by accident or disease, and also damage to or destruction of artificial members, dental appliances, teeth, and eyeglasses, but, in the case of eyeglasses, only if such damage or destruction resulted from accident which also caused personal injury entitling the employe to compensation therefor (either for disability or treatment); * * * "municipality" includes county, city, town, village, school district, sewer district, drainage district, and other public or quasi-public corporations; and "commission" means the industrial commission of Wisconsin.   "Time of injury", "occurrence of injury", "date of injury" is the date of the accident which caused the injury, or in the case of disease, the last day of work for the last employer whose employment caused disability, *except that in case of occupational deafness the definition in s. 102.555 shall control.*

SECTION 2.   102.11 (1) (intro. par.) of the statutes is amended to read:

102.11 (1) (intro. par.)   The average weekly earnings for temporary disability shall be taken at not less than $12.50 nor more than * * * *$65;* for permanent total disability or death at not less than $20 nor more than * * * *$65;* and for permanent partial disability at not less than $20 nor more than $52.86.   Between said limits the average weekly earnings shall be determined as follows:

SECTION 3.   102.49 (5) of the statutes is amended to read:

102.49 (5)   In each case of injury resulting in death, leaving no person wholly dependent for support, the employer or insurer shall pay into the state treasury such an amount, when added to the sums paid or to be paid on account of partial dependency, as shall equal the death benefit payable to a person wholly dependent, such payment to the state treasury in no event to exceed * * * *$5,500.*   The payment into the state treasury shall be made in all such cases regardless of whether the dependents or personal representatives of the deceased employe commence action against a third party as provided in s. 102.29.   If such payment is not made within 20 days after the commission makes request therefor, any sum payable shall bear interest at the rate of 6 per cent per annum.

SECTION 4.   102.555 of the statutes is created to read:

102.555   OCCUPATIONAL DEAFNESS: DEFINITIONS.   (1) "Occupational deafness" means permanent partial or permanent total loss of hearing of one or both ears due to prolonged exposure to noise in employment.   "Noise" means sound capable of producing occupational deafness. "Noisy employment" means employment in the performance of which an employe is subjected to noise.

(2) No benefits shall be payable for temporary total or temporary partial disability under this act for loss of hearing due to prolonged exposure to noise.

(3) An employee who because of occupational deafness is transferred by his employer to other noisy employment and thereby sustains actual wage loss, shall be compensated at the rate provided in s. 102.43 (2), not exceeding $3,500 in the aggregate from all employers. "Time of injury," "occurrence of injury," "date of injury" in such case shall be the date of wage loss.

(4) Subject to the limitations herein contained and the provisions of s. 102.53 (2) there shall be payable for total occupational deafness of one ear, 32 weeks of compensation; for total occupational deafness of both ears, 160 weeks of compensation; and for partial occupational deafness compensation shall bear such relation to that named herein as disabilities bear to the maximum disabilities herein provided. In cases covered by this subsection "time of injury," "occurrence of injury," "date of injury" shall be exclusively the date of occurrence of any of the following events to an employe:

(a) Transfer because of occupational deafness to nonnoisy employment by an employer whose employment has caused occupational deafness;

(b) Retirement;

(c) Termination of the employer-employe relationship;

(d) Layoff, provided the layoff is complete and continuous for one year;

(e) No claim under this subsection shall be filed, however, until 6 consecutive months of removal from noisy employment after the time of injury except that under par. (d) such 6 consecutive months period may commence within the last 6 months of layoff.

(5) The limitation provisions in this act shall control claims arising under this section. Such provisions shall run from the first date upon which claim may be filed, or from the date of subsequent death, provided that no claim shall accrue to any dependent unless an award has been issued or liability admitted.

(6) No payment shall be made to an employe under this section unless he shall have worked in noisy employment for a total period of at least 90 days for the employer from whom he claims compensation.

(7) An employer shall become liable for the entire occupational deafness to which his employment has contributed; but if previous deafness is established by a hearing test or other competent evidence, whether or not the employe was exposed to noise within the 6 months preceding such test, he shall not be liable for previous loss so established nor shall he be liable for any loss for which compensation has previously been paid or awarded.

(8) Any amount paid to an employe under this section by any employer shall be credited against compensation payable by any employer to such employe for occupational deafness under subs. (3) and (4). No employe shall in the aggregate receive greater compensation from any or all employers for occupational deafness than that provided in this section for total occupational deafness.

SECTION 5. 102.565 (1), (2) and (4) of the statutes are amended to read:

102.565 SILICOSIS, NONDISABLING; MEDICAL EXAMINATION; CONDITIONS OF LIABILITY. (1) When an employe working subject to this chapter is, because he has a nondisabling silicosis * * *, discharged * * * from the employment in which he is engaged, or when an employe ceases such employment and it is in fact inadvisable for him on account of a nondisabling silicosis * * * to continue in it, and suffers wage loss by reason of such discharge, * * * or such cessation, the commision may allow such compensation on account thereof as it may deem just, not exceeding $3,500. In case of such discharge prior to a finding by the industrial commission that it is inadvisable for him to continue in such employment, the liability of the employer who shall so discharge his employe * * * shall be primary, and the liability of the insurer shall be secondary, under the same procedure and to the same effect as provided by s. 102.62.

(2) Upon application of any employer or employe the commission may direct any employe of such employer or such employe who, in the course of his employment, has been exposed to the inhalation of silica, * * * to submit to examination by a physician or physicians to be appointed by the industrial commission to determine whether such employe has silicosis * * *, and the degree thereof. The cost of such medical examination shall be borne by the person making application. The results of such examination shall be submitted by the physician to the industrial commission, which shall submit copies of such reports to the employer and employe, who shall have opportunity to rebut the same provided request therefor is made to the commission within 10 days from the mailing of such

report to the parties. The commission shall make its findings as to whether or not it is inadvisable for the employe to continue in his employment.

(4) No payment shall be made to an employe under this section unless he shall have worked for the employer from whom he claims compensation in work exposing him to inhalation of silica * * * for a total period of at least 90 days.

SECTION 6.   102.565 (6) of the statutes is repealed.

SECTION 7.   102.59 (2) of the statutes is amended to read:

102.59 (2)   In the case of the loss or of the total impairment of a hand, arm, foot, leg * * * or eye, the employer shall be required to pay * * * *$850* into the state treasury. The payment shall be made in all such cases regardless of whether the employe, his dependents as personal representatives, commence action against a third party as provided in s. 102.29.

SECTION 8.   This act shall take effect on July 1, 1955.

Chapter 39

ANTI-NOISE ORDINANCES

LYLE F. YERGES

United States Gypsum Company

ROSE L. WEISLER, L.L.B.

Legal Bureau, New York City Police Department

NOISE AS A NUISANCE

According to the American Standard Acoustical Terminology, Z 24.1, *"Noise is any undesired sound";* law dictionaries do not include a definition of this term. The judiciary's closest simulation to definition is "noise imports a confused and discordant sound."[1] However, the concept that noise, under a given set of facts, may be a nuisance and accordingly dealt with by law has long prevailed.

"Generally, noise is not *ex necessitate* a nuisance, even when disagreeable. It has been stated that no one is entitled to absolute quiet in the enjoyment of his property, but is limited to a degree of quietness consistent with the standard of comfort prevailing in the locality in which he dwells. Thus, it has been held that, as many useful acts are necessarily attended with more or less noise, reasonable noises in an appropriate locality are not necessarily nuisances, even though they are disagreeable and annoying. On the other hand, noise may be a nuisance, even though such noise may result from the carrying on of a lawful business, industry, or trade in a town or city, but to have this effect, the noise must be excessive and unreasonable, producing actual physical discomfort and annoyance to a person of ordinary sensibilities . . . . A nuisance by noise is a question of degree, and should be considered in connection with the locality and in connection with the nature of the trade, the magnitude of the industry complained of, the use of the property producing it, and its intensity and effect. In determining whether noise is a nuisance, the time when the noise is made should be considered. Noise may constitute a nuisance abatable during certain hours. Noises alone may be of such character and volume as to constitute a nuisance when they occur during the hours usually devoted to sleep, even though the same might not be so at other times; but in such cases the question is one of degree as well as locality."[2]

Or, as another authority on nuisance puts it,

"If unusual and disturbing noises are made, and particularly if they are regularly and persistently made, and if they are of a character to affect the comfort of a man's household, or the peace and health of his family, and to destroy the comfortable enjoyment of his home, a court of equity will stretch out its strong arm to prevent the continuance of such acts."[3]

It appears, then, that

". . . noise alone may constitute a nuisance, although in determining whether it is in fact such a nuisance as to entitle the complaining party to relief at law or in equity, the character, volume, time, place and duration of its occurrence as well as the locality, must be taken into consideration, . . ."[4]

Having determined that noise must be a nuisance before legal remedy may be resorted to, some thought should be directed to the legal conception of nuisance. Again, definition is elusive and subject to lengthy treatment.[5] However, it may be said that it is "something offensive or annoying to individuals or to the community, to the prejudice of their legal rights."[6] And, "it may be at the same time of both a public and private character, which status may give an individual a civil right for damages, and may abate it as a private nuisance, although it might also be abated as a public nuisance."[7] To distinguish private nuisance from public nuisance would be merely of academic interest. The problem concerns itself with the public nuisance, which may be defined as "the doing of or the failure to do something that injuriously affects the safety, health, or morals of the public, or works some substantial annoyance, inconvenience, or injury to the public, and as a nuisance which causes hurt, inconvenience, or damage to the public generally, or such part of the public as necessarily comes into contact with it."[8]

FORM OF LAW

The history, customs, traditions, provincial traits, industry, and working habits, even the geography and climate, of a locality must be considered in determining whether a particular noise is a nuisance. Therefore, an ordinance, or local law, appears to be the proper and effective instrument for a public authority to adopt in its approach to a local community problem.

"An ordinance, as a term of municipal law, is the equivalent of legislative action, and it may be included within the meaning of the term, 'law,' since it is a law passed by the governing body of a municipal corporation for the regulation of its affairs . . . it is a local rule, a police or domestic regulation . . . ."[9] "The main feature of such enactment is its local applicability, as distinguished from the general applicability of the state laws."[10] "In the United States, cities, towns, and villages are usually municipal corporations."[11] "A municipal corporation is a body politic created by organizing the inhabitants of a prescribed area, under the authority of the legislature (state) into a corporation with all the usual attributes of a corporate entity, but endowed with a public character by virtue of having been invested by the legislature with subordinate legislative powers to administer local and internal affairs of the community."[12] "One of the most usual powers enjoyed by municipal corporations is that of abating or suppressing nuisances."[13]

Thus, ordinances usually may be directed

". . . against offenses affecting the public order and peace, as those forbidding riotous assemblies, disturbing the peace, forbidding abusive or indecent language, cursing, swearing, or any loud or boisterous talking, or other disorderly conduct within the corporate limits, . . . blowing whistles of factories, shops, and the like, parading in public thoroughfares with bands of music, and various kinds of noises, without legal permits . . . ringing bells for auction sales, and so forth, playing on hand organs and other musical instruments . . . ."[14]

The more modern sources of noise include mechanized traffic and transportation; radio, television, and juke-box; airplane and airport; recreation and hobby; and home power equipment, industrial plant, advertising by sound devices, and loading.

Past experience with anti-noise ordinances indicates that great care must be taken in their planning, lest they be subject to attack in the courts.

"It is definitely settled, without dissent, that a state legislature may lawfully delegate to municipal corporations, to be exercised within their corporate boundaries, the power to declare what shall constitute nuisances, and to prevent or abate them; such power, as a matter of fact, is generally given to the municipalities either in their specific charters or general state statutes. The regulation and abatement of nuisances is one of the ordinary functions of the police power,[15] and municipalities are generally considered as having been given the right, in connection with their exercise of such power, to suppress them."[16]

"In order to be valid and to have force and effect, ordinances enacted by municipal corporations must be constitutional, within the powers of the municipality, reasonable (insofar as the question of reasonableness is justiciable), equal, general and impartial in operation, certain and definite in their provisions, not in conflict with general laws of the state, in some states, although not in others, must not forbid or regulate the same matters as are forbidden or regulated by the laws of the state, and where the state Constitution, general statutes, or a specific municipal charter so require, the subject matter of the ordinances must conform to the title, although unless specifically so designated, there is no such requirement."[17]

Review of some of the leading cases in which anti-noise ordinances have been attacked on one or more of the aforementioned qualifications should be helpful in ascertaining whether a contemplated ordinance would stand up in the courts.

In one case, the city of Chicago had been empowered to regulate traffic and sales on the streets, and to license, regulate, and suppress peddlers. Pursuant thereto, it had enacted an ordinance prohibiting peddlers on the streets from advertising their wares by public outcry, but permitting peddlers on licensed amusement grounds and in certain other places to so do. The fruit and vegetable peddlers, who engaged in their business on the streets, sought to restrain the enforcement of the ordinance on the grounds that it discriminated against them and that it deprived them of their right to engage in the business of peddling on the streets. The court sustained the constitutionality of the ordinance, holding that it was not discriminatory inasmuch as these peddlers could frequent the places that were excepted for the purpose of making sales. It felt that the conditions in the permitted places differed greatly from the conditions which are found in and upon the public streets and alleys of Chicago. The court pointed out that the peddlers had no vested property right resting in them to make a noise upon the streets by advertising their wares by public outcry, any more than they had a right to advertise such articles by any other means, the result of which would be to disturb the peace and quiet of the neighborhood in which they pursued their calling.[18]

In another case a similar ordinance was the issue, and the court, in sustaining it, said:

"In the exercise of the police power, the city council has some discretion. The ordinance was not wanton nor arbitrary. A person engaged in peddling and hawking fruits has no right to bawl away in a manner that is annoying to others. The mere fact of selling was not the cause of the prosecution, but the manner of the peddler or hawker in offering to sell, which was, as we are led to infer by the charge and by the surrounding circumstances, loud and boisterous and within the terms of the ordinance, which sought to regulate the occupation and keep it in such bounds as that it would not be felt to be a nuisance. We are not concerned with the right or authority of the city council to prohibit the peddling or hawking of wares; but we do think that that body has the right and authority to put a stop to loud and boisterous outcries of overzealous and anxious sellers of goods and wares on the public street."[19]

In another case, the court said:

"The control it (municipality) may exercise over business and trade, is such as belongs to the necessities and demands of local government, such as have relation to the general prosperity of the citizen, the public health, order, and morals of the community. It cannot, outside of these considerations, enter into the area of business competition, to advance a favored class and retard others. All citizens in pursuit of legitimate, honest occupations, stand equal before the law, and a police power entrusted to a corporation is unreasonably exercised in making invidious distinctions between citizens endowed with equal rights."

But this same court said: " . . . rules directing the manner of using the public streets by such persons, prohibiting the use of horns or bells in the public streets, or the public outcry of vendors, and restrictions of like character, are proper regulations."[20]

An ordinance which imposed a penalty for making or aiding in making an improper noise, riot, disturbance, breach of peace, or diversion tending to a breach of the peace within the limits of a city was sustained as being sufficiently certain and definite to permit an average person after reading it to determine whether he would incur a penalty under its provision.[21]

Ordinances prohibiting the blowing of locomotive whistles within corporate limits present difficulty because of the aspect of interstate commerce but have been sustained.[22]

An ordinance prohibiting the use of machines causing annoying noises during certain periods of weekdays and at any time on Sunday was declared not per se void and unconstitutional.[23]

Because of two decisions by the United States Supreme Court,[24] in which the majority opinions were supplemented by the individual opinions of concurrence or dissent of several other justices, prohibition and regulation pertaining to sound devices such as sound trucks should be the subject of special enactment and not be incorporated into general anti-noise ordinances. Such prohibition and regulation are fraught with danger of violating the provisions of the United States Constitution relative to freedom of speech, of assemblage, and the right to communicate information and opinions to others, as well as the "due process" clause, under which the ordinance may not be so vague, obscure, and indefinite as to be impossible of reasonably accurate interpretation. However, the danger may be overcome by adherence to the principles laid down by these two leading cases, particularly by avoiding a previous restraint provision and by establishing specific standards. To date, standards of noise and noise levels are still rather moot, but it is significant that the United States Supreme Court held that the phrase "loud and raucous noises" provided adequate limits on the discretion of city officials and sustained the validity of an ordinance which forbids the use, for non-commercial purposes, of any sound truck which emits "loud and raucous noises." As to commercial advertising by the use of sound trucks, it is now settled that such use may be completely banned from the city streets.[25]

PROBLEMS IN ENFORCEMENT

Local Problems. Invariably a city has industries and activities of such vital economic importance to some of its citizens that it will not or cannot enact ordinances which hamper those activities. Just as dispersal of existing industries as a defense against air attack appears to be usually prohibitive and impracticable, blanket ordinances against all annoying noises may be unreasonable. A municipality cannot reasonably assume that its problem is identical with that of any other, or that arbitrary and inflexible application of existing provisions is in the best interest of the community.[26]

Police and Law Enforcement. Most police forces, today, are understaffed, overworked, and hard put to cope with the many duties imposed upon them. It appears that noise ordinances do not get much attention unless a police, municipal, or civic official is particularly interested in the problem or has been goaded into action by civic protest. In Memphis, Tennessee, and in New York City, the public officials are much concerned with the problem, and noise ordinances are effective. Other communities either lack proper ordinances or fail to enforce them because the seriousness of the problem is not fully recognized. Generally, some regulation is attempted by means of zoning and building codes, but such measures are only a partial solution.

"Zoning, while helpful, is not decisive. It has been held recently in Massachusetts, that a zoning ordinance which impresses an industrial character upon a neighborhood does not sanction practices not naturally incidental to ordinary and reasonable use. It has been said that where industrial works are collected in an appropriate locality and are prudently carried on during working hours, noise inseparable from such enterprises must be endured by those who by choice or necessity live in the vicinity . . . . On the other hand, the noise or noisome factory cannot with immunity invade territory stamped by use for residence."[27]

Public Cooperation. Public cooperation is a prime requisite to successful enforcement of any law. When responsible officials conduct educational campaigns against unnecessary noises, the public becomes increasingly aware of the nuisance, and response is usually good.[28]

Inspectors. It would seem to be good practice for a municipality to use inspectors to check on noise levels in industrial areas, transportation centers, and the like, and to take action similar to that taken by building and smoke inspectors. Perhaps the building and smoke inspectors should be empowered to serve summonses for the noise nuisance to supplement and assist the police with respect to this problem.

Violations. Until recently, the feeling persisted that the noise laws are of minor moment and that infractions thereof should not be dealt with in other than token fashion. However, the growing gravity of the problem is bringing recognition that offenders must be treated more severely. Experience demonstrates that token fines do not serve as deterrents. Thus, New York City, in 1954, amended its anti-noise law to increase sharply the punishment for violation.[29] This appears to be fair and equitable in view of the fact that the policeman is instructed to "make every effort to suppress unnecessary noise on his post. He shall exercise reason and discretion in the suppression of unnecessary noise, and common sense and judgment in determining what is purely unnecessary noise. Admonition and warning will be used to correct such conditions, but if there are repeated offenses, after the offender has been admonished and warned, then a summons will be served."[30] It is recognized that too severe a penalty may defeat the purpose since a court is sometimes reluctant to convict if it believes that the punishment imposed is too harsh. However, if it is scaled according to the repetition of offense, objection is not valid.[31]

NOISE PROBLEMS COVERED BY ORDINANCES

The number of noise sources in modern life is truly amazing. New York City's records of violations are indicative of the variety. It is significant that the actions total approximately 300,000 per year. For example Fig. 39.1 shows the number of actions taken each month during a typical year.

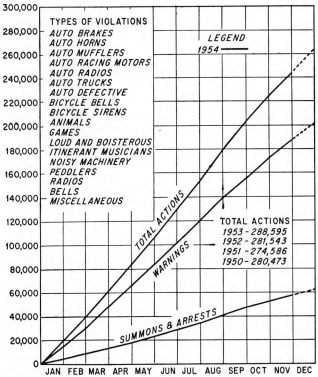

Fig. 39.1. New York Police anti-noise campaign, as reported by Safety Bureau. (*Chart prepared by League for Less Noise, Inc., N.Y.*)

In 1950, a noise survey was conducted which included measurements and analyses of vehicle-traffic, residential-area, and industrial-area noise.[32] One answer to the question, "How is quiet to be obtained?" was felt to be enactment of ordinances which make use of the available noise yardsticks. It was further found that traffic noises require most attention because of their prevalence. The following sections include data from this survey, as well as from other studies.

Traffic Noises. *Automobile Horns.* Most ordinances prohibit horn blowing, except as a warning to persons and animals or to prevent property damage. Some prohibit horn blowing entirely in specific areas or at specific times, such as in hospital zones or residential areas during night hours. Others limit the noise level of the horn or the distance at which it can be heard.

Mufflers. Nearly all ordinances require a muffler in good working order on the exhaust of all engines, moving or stationary. Most of them specifically prohibit cutouts or mufflers altered to reduce their effectiveness.

The muffler problem has been taken seriously by almost everyone concerned with it. Truck manufacturers and trucking associations are doing an unusually effective job in quieting truck exhaust, even on large diesel engines. Only the "hot rod" presents much of a problem today.[33]

During 1954, the police of Milwaukee, Wisconsin, began a campaign against noisy trucks. Truck drivers and owners protested vigorously the new noise ordinance setting 95 db as the loudest maximum exhaust noise permissible. The Wisconsin Motor Carriers Association protested that the decibel meter test was unrealistic because it did not measure the annoyance factor of the noise but only the volume. The police gave truckers a "breather" to work out the problem with muffler manufacturers and turned to prosecuting "hot-rod" drivers.

Vehicle Noise. Many ordinances require that vehicles be kept in good repair so that "unusual, loud, and disturbing" noises do not emanate from them. However, the noise level from the newest and best trucks can be as high as 90 db at the street curb line. This is a difficult problem for legislation, and the "rule of reason" must prevail.

Whistles, Signals, and Sirens. Generally, ordinances forbid the use of whistles, sirens, and other startling noise-signaling devices. Exception is made for police and fire vehicles, ambulances, and emergency vehicles of federal, state, or municipal departments or public-service corporations. Recently, some cities have discarded the use of the traffic policeman's whistle and have outlawed the hotel doorman's whistle. Many suburban communities forbid railroad-crossing signal whistling, especially at night.

Other Transportation Noises. *Airports.* This problem is so new that virtually no major city has adopted an ordinance regulating specifically this noise source. Glendale, California, has an ordinance which refers to warming up of aircraft engines and to take-offs. Airports are the subject of considerable study and controversy. Indications are that solution may eventually be found in zoning and building codes (see Chaps. 35 and 40).

Airplanes. This problem is similar to that of airports because of the newness of it. Some ordinances restrict the minimum height at which a plane may fly over a city, except on specific take-off paths. It, likewise, is a subject of considerable study which is complicated by an apparent conflict as to jurisdiction between the Federal government and the municipality (see Chap. 37).

Railroads. Railroads, railroad stations, yards, roundhouses, back shops, and repair and service installations have been an essential part of transportation for so long that the public tends to accept their noise. However, the blight of these installations has spread in ever-widening circles throughout cities. Except for whistle and signal noises, little seems to have been done about these noises (see Chap. 32).

Trucks. In addition to truck noises discussed under *Mufflers* and *Vehicle Noise*, there is the objectionable scream when starting a large load from a dead stop at traffic lights. While better mufflers and better body and chassis construction have been developed over the years, the larger and more powerful engines in modern trucks are more objectionable than ever. Partial solution may be obtained by routing heavy trucks away from specific areas such as hospital, school, residential, and office districts.

Ships. Because of the locations of docks, piers, and waterways, the noise problem from ships is rarely very serious. The whistles or signals used are rarely of long duration or annoying. Little has been done in the way of ordinances.

Streetcars and Elevated Trains. These vehicles have been serious offenders.[34] Legislation covering them requires that they be kept in good repair. They are rapidly becoming obsolete, being replaced by the bus and the subway.

Buses. The modern city bus is usually in good repair. However, it presents the same problem as the truck (see *Trucks* above).

Subways. Apparently, no ordinances cover this source. Since their noise rarely bothers others than those who use them, it is not in the area of a general nuisance. However, the users are part of the general public and are entitled to relief by means of acoustical treatment of stations and tubes.

Personal Noises. *Radios, Television, Juke Boxes, and Musical Instruments.* Almost every city includes these sources in its anti-noise ordinances. Usually it is provided that excessive volume during certain hours is particularly annoying and disturbing to the quiet, comfort, or repose of persons, and the court will particularly note such fact.

Disorderly Conduct. Noisy, rowdy, and drunken conduct, excessive hilarity and celebration, and similar sources are usually well covered by the law.

Recreation and Hobby Noises. Noises from games, model airplanes, bicycles, and such are difficult to control. Usually games that attract large audiences are confined to stadiums which are located so that the public will not be annoyed. However, the sand-lot game, the street game, the model-airplane enthusiast, and similar sources are difficult to regulate. "Among the noises which, if they do not cause substantial discomfort, residents in large industrial cities may have to put up with, is a certain amount of the noise which accompanies and is incident to the reasonable recreation of a crowded population."[35]

Home Power Equipment. The tremendous increase in the use of power equipment for and about the home detracts from the peace and tranquility of residential neighborhoods. Such equipment, however, is generally used during the day hours, and the neighbors tolerate the noise because they, too, use such equipment. However, much complaint is made about the individual who mows his lawn at 6:00 A.M. on a Sunday morning. If cooperation is not forthcoming, he may be taken to task in most communities under the Sabbath Law, which prohibits all labor on Sunday excepting the works of necessity and charity. In works of necessity or charity is included whatever is needful during the day for the good order, health, or comfort of the community. Occasionally, the "do-it-yourself" fan disturbs his neighbors with his new saw by working into the early hours of the morning. Usually neighborhood pressure is sufficient to make him desist. The latest woe is the operation of a home window air-conditioner unit, especially when the neighbors are lacking such improvement. In a recent case, the court found that the air-conditioner was not per se an unnecessary noise nor did it constitute a public nuisance. The court said:

"The air-conditioning machine is a product of man's constant search for the improvement of his own comfort and enjoyment of life. That its use may cause some annoyance to others does not justify denouncing its use as criminal. It is an unfortunate truth that virtually every scientific invention has carried with it not only advantages but burdens . . . . No doubt the manufacturers of air-conditioning units are aware of the desirability and necessity of producing their machines in such a manner as to render them as noiseless as is consistently possible with their efficient operation. No doubt the course of time will result in progress in that direction. The present case involves the operation of a properly functioning air-conditioning unit. Another question would be presented if, due to defective construction or disrepair, the unit were to be excessively noisy."[36]

Industrial Noises. *Plant Noises.* Noise is especially obvious near industrial zones. Modern technology has created loud noise sources faster than it has learned to cope with them. Zoning by law and zoning by free choice of people who move because of the nuisance have handled some phases of the problem. Plant construction, acoustical treatment of buildings, and better design of machines have eliminated other parts of the problem. There remains, however, a distinct need for standards, codes, and other specific requirements on industrial installations. One method of approach to the zoning problem has been described in Chap. 35.

The survey showed that industrial noise heard in residential areas was usually substantially below the level of traffic noises in the same area.[37] Nevertheless, residents complained only of the industrial noise. It is true that the scream of saws and cutting tools and the impact sounds of forges and hammers are very disturbing, particularly at night. This further complicates the problem of noise standards in ordinances, since it is not likely that a court will deprive a person of a livelihood if the noise level created by his plant is below the level of surrounding traffic. To date, only zoning laws and individual actions in nuisances have been utilized in treatment of this problem. Success, at best, is moderate.

The growing pressure for sound control in plants to protect the working personnel may ultimately solve the entire problem for municipalities. It seems reasonable that a plant operating at a noise level safely below the danger point for employees may not be a nuisance to surrounding areas.

Engine Test Cells. The tremendous expansion of the aircraft industry during World War II brought with it the serious noise problem arising out of tests of large, powerful engines. It was obvious from the outset that soundproof cells were an absolute necessity to make the operation feasible. It has become standard practice in most of the industry today to try to overcome the nuisance by designing proper structures to house engine test stands. For the uncooperative, ordinances must be invoked to prod such cooperation.

Impact and Explosive Sounds. Another serious industrial-noise problem is the one arising from impact sounds and explosions. The low-frequency vibrations from heavy forges and similar equipment often disturb the neighborhood. However, the development of huge, large-capacity presses is tending to make hammer forging obsolete in many cases. Explosive sounds are especially annoying. Handling them is difficult and expensive. In Milwaukee, Wisconsin, for example, a manufacturer of high-voltage circuit breakers found that the explosive report resulting from destructive test procedures was so objectionable that the company was faced with moving miles out into the country or spending over $100,000 for a soundproof test cell. It chose the latter course because it was evident that a rural location would ultimately be surrounded with residents, and complaints would recur. Related to impact and explosive sounds are those of construction. Ordinances usually limit the hours during which pile drivers, pavement breakers, steam hammers, and other noisy construction equipment may be used. While present construction practices continue, this is about the only way to control such noises.

Special Noises. *Sound Trucks and Other Sound Devices.* As mentioned heretofore, these noise sources present special legal problems in abatement ordinances. Many cities ban loudspeakers or amplifying devices entirely for advertising purposes and regulate, by licensing provisions, the use of such devices for non-commercial purposes. These regulations apply to such devices irrespective of their location (e.g., on a sound truck or inside a store), provided noise is heard on the street.

Animals. Almost every city has legislated about the noises from animals, including roosters, cattle, dogs, and so forth. Since little livestock is kept in cities today, these provisions are useful principally to quiet the neighborhood pets.

Loading Noises. Restrictions of sounds emanating from loading, crating, and similar operations have long been enacted in many communities. Municipal garbage collectors seem to be the worst offenders, but such activity is usually limited to certain hours.

Loose Manhole Covers. Some ordinances require that manhole covers over access tubes to under-the-street facilities of public utilities be kept from rattling. Unfortunately, the municipality itself is usually the worst offender.

MODEL ORDINANCES

The following regulation of sound devices or apparatus, in its present form, has been in effect in New York City since October 1, 1948,[38] which is subsequent to the *Saia* case discussed in *Form of Law* (see Refs. 9 to 25), and appears to have met no challenge.

Regulation of Sound Devices or Apparatus.

a. Legislative declaration. It is hereby declared that the use or operation of any radio device or apparatus or any device or apparatus for the amplification of sounds from any radio, phonograph or other sound-making or sound-producing device, or any device or apparatus for the reproduction or amplification of the human voice or other sounds, in front of or outside of any building, place or premises, or in or through any window, doorway or opening of such building, place or premises, abutting or adjacent to a public street, park or place, or in or upon any vehicle operated, standing or being in or upon any public street, park or place, where the sounds therefrom may be heard upon any public street, park or place, or from any stand, platform or other structure, or from any airplane or other device used for flying, flying over the city, or on a boat or on the waters within the jurisdiction of the city, or anywhere on or in the public streets, parks or places, is detrimental to the health, welfare and safety of the inhabitants of the city, in that such use or operation diverts the attention of pedestrians and vehicle operators in the public streets, parks and places, thus increasing traffic hazards and causing injury to life and limb. It is hereby further declared that such use or operation disturbs the public peace and comfort and the peaceful enjoyment by the people of their rights to use the public streets, parks and places for street, park and other public purposes and disturbs the peace, quiet and comfort of the neighboring inhabitants. Therefore, it is hereby declared as a matter of legislative determination that the prohibition of such use or operation for commercial or business advertising purposes and the proper regulation of such use and operation for all other purposes is essential to protect the health, welfare and safety of the inhabitants of the city, to secure the health, safety, comfort, convenience, and peaceful enjoyment by the people of their rights to use the public streets, parks and places for street, park and other public purposes and to secure the peace, quiet and comfort of the city's inhabitants. It is hereby further declared as a matter of legislative determination that the expense of supervising and regulating the use and operation of such sound devices and apparatus for purposes other than commercial and business advertising purposes should be borne by the persons using or operating such devices and apparatus and that the requirement of a nominal fee for the issuance of a permit for such use and operation as hereinafter prescribed is intended to defray the expenses of regulating such use or operation for the health, welfare and safety of all the people.

b. Definitions. As used in this section:

1. The term "sound device or apparatus" shall mean any radio device or apparatus, or any device or apparatus for the amplification of any sounds from any radio, phonograph, or other sound-making or sound-producing device, or any device or apparatus for the reproduction or amplification of the human voice or other sounds;

2. The phrase "to use or operate any sound device or apparatus in, on, near or adjacent to any public street, park or place," shall mean to use or operate or cause to be used or operated any sound device or apparatus in front or outside of any building, place or premises, or in or through any window, doorway or opening of such building, place or premises, abutting on or adjacent to a public street, park or place, or in or upon any vehicle operated, standing or being in or on any public street, park or place, where the sounds therefrom may be heard upon any public street, park or place, or from any stand, platform or other structure, or from any airplane or other device used for flying, flying over the city, or on a boat or on the waters within the jurisdiction of the city, or anywhere on the public streets, parks or places.

c. Use and operation of the sound devices and apparatus for commercial and business advertising purposes. It shall be unlawful for any person to use or operate any sound device or apparatus in, on, near or adjacent to any public street, park or place, for commercial and business advertising purposes.

d. Use and operation of sound devices and apparatus for other than commercial and business advertising purposes; permit required. It shall be unlawful for any person to use or operate any sound device or apparatus, in, on, near or adjacent to any public street, park or place, unless he shall have first obtained a permit to be issued by the commissioner in the manner hereinafter prescribed and unless he shall comply with the provisions of this section and the terms and conditions prescribed in such permit.

e. Applications. Each applicant for a permit to use or operate a sound device or apparatus in, on, near or adjacent to any public street, park or place shall file a written application with the commissioner, at the police precinct covering the area in which such sound device or apparatus is to be used or operated, at least five days prior to the date upon which such sound device or apparatus is to be used or operated. Such application shall describe the specific location in which such sound device or apparatus is proposed to be used or operated, the day and the hour or hours during which it is proposed to be used or operated, the volume of sound which is proposed to be used measured by decibels or by any other efficient method of measuring sound, and such other pertinent information as the commissioner may deem necessary to enable him to carry out the provisions of this section.

f. Issuance of permit; terms. The commissioner shall not deny a permit for any specific time, location or use, to any applicant who complies with the provisions of this section, except for one or more of the reasons specified in subdivision *g* hereof or for non-payment of the fee prescribed in subdivision *h* hereof, or to prevent over-lapping in the granting of permits. Each permit issued pursuant to this section shall describe the specific location in which such sound device or apparatus may be used or operated thereunder, the exact period of time for which such apparatus or device may be operated in such location, the maximum volume of sound which may be employed in such use or operation and such other terms and conditions as may be necessary, for the purpose of securing the health, safety, comfort, convenience and peaceful enjoyment by the people of their right to use the public streets, parks or places for street, park or other public purposes, protecting the health, welfare and safety of the inhabitants of the city, and securing the peace, quiet and comfort of the neighboring inhabitants.

g. Special restrictions. The commissioner shall not issue any permit for the use of a sound device or apparatus:

1. In any location within five hundred feet of a school, courthouse or church, during the hours of school, court or worship, respectively, or within five hundred feet of any hospital or similar institution;

2. In any location where the commissioner, upon investigation, shall determine that the conditions of vehicular or pedestrian traffic or both are such that the use of such a device or apparatus will constitute a threat to the safety of pedestrians or vehicular operators;

3. In any location where the commissioner, upon investigation, shall determine that conditions of overcrowding or of street repair or other physical conditions are such that the use of a sound device or apparatus will deprive the public of the right to the safe, comfortable, convenient and peaceful enjoyment of any public street, park or place for street, park or other public purposes, or will constitute a threat to the safety of pedestrians or vehicle operators;

4. In or on any vehicle or other device while it is in transit; or

5. Between the hours of 10 P.M. and 9 A.M.

h. Fees. Each applicant for a permit issued under the provisions of this section shall pay a fee of five dollars for the use of each sound device or apparatus for each day, provided, however, that permits for the use of such sound devices or apparatus shall be issued to any bureau, commission, board or department of the United States Government, the state of New York, and the city of New York without fee.

i. The provisions of this section shall not apply to the use or operation of any sound device or apparatus by any church or synagogue on or within its own premises, in connection with the religious rites or ceremonies of such church or synagogue.

j. Violations. Any person who shall violate any provision of this section, upon conviction thereof, shall be punished by a fine of not more than twenty-five dollars or imprisonment for thirty days, or both.

k. Rules and regulations. The commissioner shall have the power to make such rules and regulations as may be necessary to carry out the provisions of this section.

The foregoing ordinance should meet the problem of unnecessary and unreasonable noises arising from the indiscriminate use of sound-amplification devices by persons who make a captive audience of the general public. It is comprehensive, not only as to the type of sound device, but as to its location. It includes any sound device that is located inside, as in buildings, boats and aircraft, from which the sound is cast into public places, as well as any that are operated in a public place. All other unnecessary and unreasonable noises may be prohibited in a blanket provision similar to the one set forth hereafter. With the exception of an omission of one section, which, it is felt, is provided for in the preceding ordinance and the amendment of the section on penalties, which provides that a violator shall be deemed guilty of a misdemeanor, the model is based on one proposed by the National Institute of Municipal Law Officers.[39]

Unnecessary Noises: Prohibited.

Section 1. It is found and declared that

(*a*) The making and creation of loud, unnecessary or unusual noises within the limits of the City of _____ is a condition which has existed for some time and the extent and volume of such noises is increasing;

(*b*) The making, creation or maintenance of such loud, unnecessary, unnatural or unusual noises which are prolonged, unusual and unnatural in their time, place and use affect and are a detriment to public health, comfort, convenience, safety, welfare and prosperity of the residents of the City of _____; and

(c) The necessity in the public interest for the provisions and prohibitions hereinafter contained and enacted, is declared as a matter of legislative determination and public policy, and it is further declared that the provisions and prohibitions hereinafter contained and enacted are in pursuance of and for the purpose of securing and promoting the public health, comfort, convenience, safety, welfare and prosperity and the peace and quiet of the City of _____ and its inhabitants.

Section 2. It shall be unlawful for any person to make, continue, or cause to be made or continued any loud, unnecessary or unusual noise or any noise which either annoys, disturbs, injures or endangers the comfort, repose, health, peace or safety of others, within the limits of the city.

Section 3. The following acts, among others, are declared to be loud, disturbing and unnecessary noises in violation of this ordinance, but said enumeration shall not be deemed to be exclusive, namely:

(1) HORNS, SIGNALING DEVICES, AND SO FORTH. The sounding of any horn or signaling device on any automobile, motorcycle, street car or other vehicle on any street or public place of the city, except as a danger warning; the creation by means of any such signaling device of any unreasonably loud or harsh sound; and the sounding of any such device for an unnecessary and unreasonable period of time. The use of any signaling device except one operated by hand or electricity; the use of any horn, whistle or other device operated by engine exhaust; and the use of any such signaling device when traffic is for any reason held up.

(2) RADIOS, PHONOGRAPHS, AND SO FORTH. The using, operating, or permitting to be played, used or operated any radio receiving set, musical instrument, phonograph, or other machine or device for the producing or reproducing of sound in such manner as to disturb the peace, quiet and comfort of the neighboring inhabitants or at any time with louder volume than is necessary for convenient hearing for the person or persons who are in the room, vehicle or chamber in which such machine or device is operated and who are voluntary listeners thereto. The operation of any such set, instrument, phonograph, machine or device between the hours of 11 P.M. and 7 A.M. in such a manner as to be plainly audible at a distance of fifty (50) feet from the building, structure or vehicle in which it is located shall be prima facie evidence of a violation of this section.

(3) YELLING, SHOUTING, AND SO FORTH. Yelling, shouting, hooting, whistling, or singing on the public streets, particularly between the hours of 11 P.M. and 7 A.M. or at any time or place so as to annoy or disturb the quiet, comfort, or repose of persons in any office, or in any dwelling, hotel or other type of residence, or of any persons in the vicinity.

(4) ANIMALS, BIRDS, AND SO FORTH. The keeping of any animal or bird which by causing frequent or long continued noise shall disturb the comfort or repose of any persons in the vicinity.

(5) STEAM WHISTLES. The blowing of any locomotive steam whistle or steam whistle attached to any stationary boiler except to give notice of the time to begin or stop work or as a warning of fire or danger, or upon request of proper city authorities.

(6) EXHAUSTS. The discharge into the open air of the exhaust of any steam engine, stationary internal combustion engine, motor boat, or motor vehicle except through a muffler or other device which will effectively prevent loud or explosive noises therefrom.

(7) DEFECT IN VEHICLE OR LOAD. The use of any automobile, motorcycle, or vehicle so out of repair, so loaded or in such manner as to create loud and unnecessary grating, grinding, rattling or other noise.

(8) LOADING, UNLOADING, OPENING BOXES. The creation of a loud and excessive noise in connection with loading or unloading any vehicle or the opening and destruction of bales, boxes, crates, and containers.

(9) CONSTRUCTION OR REPAIRING OF BUILDINGS. The erection (including excavating), demolition, alteration or repair of any building other than between the hours of 7 A.M. and 6 P.M. on weekdays, except in case of urgent necessity in the interest of public health and safety, and then only with a permit from the Building Inspector, which permit may be granted for a period not to exceed three (3) days or less while the emergency continues and which permit may be renewed for periods of three days or less while the emergency continues. If the Building Inspector shall determine that the public health and safety will not be impaired by the erection, demolition, alteration or repair of any building or the excavation of streets and highways within the hours of 6 P.M. and 7 A.M., and if he shall further determine that loss or inconvenience would result to any party in interest, he may grant permission for such work to be done within the hours of 6 P.M. and 7 A.M., upon application being made at the time the permit for the work is awarded or during the progress of the work.

(10) SCHOOLS, COURTS, CHURCHES, HOSPITALS. The creation of any excessive noise on any street adjacent to any school, institution of learning, church or court while the same are in use, or adjacent to any hospital, which unreasonably interferes with the workings of such institution, or which disturbs or unduly annoys patients in the hospital, provided conspicuous signs are displayed in such streets indicating that the same is a school, hospital or court street.

(11) HAWKERS, PEDDLERS. The shouting and crying of peddlers, hawkers and vendors which disturbs the peace and quiet of the neighborhood.

(12) DRUMS. The use of any drum or other instrument or device for the purpose of attracting attention by creation of noise to any performance, show or sale.

(13) METAL RAILS, PILLARS, AND COLUMNS, TRANSPORTATION THEREOF. The transportation of rails, pillars or columns of iron, steel or other material, over and along streets and other public places upon carts, drays, cars, trucks, or in any other manner so loaded as to cause loud noises or as to disturb the peace and quiet of such streets or other public places.

(14) STREET RAILWAY CARS, OPERATION THEREOF. The causing, permitting or continuing any excessive, unnecessary and avoidable noise in the operation of a street railway car.

(15) PILE DRIVERS, HAMMERS, AND SO FORTH. The operation between the hours of 10 P.M. and 7 A.M. of any pile driver, steam shovel, pneumatic hammer, derrick, steam or electric hoist or other appliance, the use of which is attended by loud or unusual noise.

(16) BLOWERS. The operation of any noise-creating blower or power fan or any internal combustion engine, the operation which causes noise due to the explosion of operating gases or fluids, unless the noise from such blower or fan is muffled and such engine is equipped with a muffler device sufficient to deaden such noise.

Section 4. Violations. Any person who shall violate any of the provisions of this section shall be punished as follows: Upon conviction for the first offense, by a fine of not less than two dollars and not more than ten dollars, or by imprisonment for one day; upon conviction of every other offense thereafter, by a fine of not less than ten dollars and not more than twenty-five dollars or by imprisonment for ten days, or by both said fine and imprisonment.

Section 5. Separability. It is the intention of the City Council that each separate provision of this ordinance shall be deemed independent of all other provisions herein, and it is further the intention of the City Council that if any provision of this ordinance be declared to be invalid, all other provisions thereof shall remain valid and enforceable.

A separability section, as set forth above, should be likewise included in an ordinance regulating sound devices or apparatus.

WHY ANTI-NOISE ORDINANCES ARE REQUIRED

Educational campaigns are helpful in making the public understand the extent of the noise nuisance. For the duration of such campaigns, the public is demonstrably cooperative. However, as publicity lapses, so does public interest, and the same inconsiderate practices reappear. Therefore, law must be invoked to cope with the nuisance. "In working to secure quieter environments, sacrifices must be required of some persons for the sake of others, and also a mutual forbearance must be shown . . . Where a reasonable number of people request the removal of noises that can be easily removed, the burden of proof should lie with the opponents; and the fact that the latter do not mind the noises objected to should not count too strongly for them."[40]

Since conditions vary in local communities, an ordinance or local law is the proper form of legislation, as distinguished from state-wide laws. The community usually has the power to enact a noise-abatement ordinance under the police power delegated to it by the state.

In drafting such ordinances, great care must be exercised not to violate constitutional provisions, particularly as to the freedom of speech, of assemblage, and the right to communicate information and opinions to others, as well as the "due process" clause.

When responsible officials make a determination that noise is a nuisance in the community and legislation is enacted, the seriousness of the problem warrants that such legislation be enforced. Many police forces are overburdened, and it may be judicious to empower other public officers, such as building and smoke inspectors, to deal with the noise nuisance. It appears harsh to denominate a person a criminal because of violation of a noise ordinance. Making him guilty of an offense and scaling his fine or imprisonment, or both, according to repetition should act as a deterrent.

The model ordinances set forth are intended to act as a guide to what sources of noise may be properly regulated or prohibited. Some communities may find it expedient to adopt them *in toto*. Others may need only to cull from them those provisions which they lack. Until designers are able to conquer the concomitant noises of their products and human behavior is ready to discipline itself for the sake of others, the people will seek solution to the noise nuisance by calling upon the law.

REFERENCES

1. Vaszil vs. Molnar, 133 N.J. Eq. 577, 33 A 2d 743 (1943).
2. 66 C.J.S. 772.
3. Joyce on Nuisances, sec. 174 (Noise as a Nuisance, Generally).
4. Lloyd, W. H.: *University of Pennsylvania Law Review*, **82** (6): 567 (1934).
5. Law Dictionaries: Black's, Ballentine, Rapalje and Laurence, Bouvier, Wharton's Law Lexicon (England), Stroud's Judicial Dictionary (England).
6. The American College Dictionary.
7. Birmingham News Company vs. Little, 226 Ala 642, 148 So 398 (1933).
8. 39 Am. Jur. 285.
9. 62 C.J.S. 785.
10. 37 Am. Jur. 755.
11. 37 Am. Jur. 622.
12. 37 Am. Jur. 618.
13. 62 C.J.S. 629.
14. McQuillan on Municipal Corporations, secs. 1069 and 1070.
15. "Police power is the exercise of the sovereign right of a government to promote order, safety, health, morals, and the general welfare of society, within constitutional limits." 16 C.J.S. 537.
16. 37 Am. Jur. 933.
17. 37 Am. Jur. 767.
18. Goodrich vs. Busse et al., 247 Ill. 500, 93 N.E. 292, 139 Am St. Rep 335 (1910).
19. City of New Orleans vs. Fargot, 116 La 370, 40 So 735 (1906).
20. Mulenbrinck vs. Commissioners, 42 N.J.L. 364 (1880).
21. City of Chicago vs. Hunt, 374 Ill 234, 29 N.E. 2d 86 (1940).
22. Larson vs. Lowdern, 204 Minn 80, 282 N.W. 669 (1938). See also Soucie vs. Payne, 299 Ill 552, 132 N.E. 779 (1921). Frazier vs. Northern Pacific Railway Co., 28 F. supp 20 (1939). Gilluno vs. Pacific Coast Railroad Co., 152 Wash. 657, 279 Pac 114 (1929). Anno, 4 A.L.R. 1342.
23. Singer vs. Ben How Realty, 160 Fla 53, 33 So 2d 409 (1948).
24. Saia vs. New York, 334 U.S. 558 (1948). Kovacs vs. Cooper, 336 U.S. 77 (1949).
25. Note 24, *supra*.
26. O'Harrow, D.: *Proc. Fourth Annual National Noise Abatement Symposium*, **4** (1953).
27. Note 4, *supra*.
28. Yaffe, C. D.: *Proc. National Noise Abatement Symposium*, **1**.
29. Administrative Code of the City of New York, sec. 435-5.0.
30. Manual of Procedure, New York City Police Department.
31. Note 29, *supra*.
32. Bonvallet, G. L.: *Proc. Fourth Annual National Noise Abatement Symposium*, **4** (1953).
33. Kibbee, L. C.: *Proc. Fourth Annual National Noise Abatement Symposium*, **4** (1953).
34. Note 32, *supra*.
35. Note 4, *supra*.
36. People vs. Arkow, 204 Misc. 635, 124 N.Y. S. 2d 704 (1953).
37. Fugill, A. P.: *Proc. Fourth Annual National Noise Abatement Symposium* (1953).
38. Administrative Code of the City of New York, sec. 435-6.0.
39. National Institute of Municipal Law Officers, Report No. 123.
40. Putnam, J. J.: *Trans. Fifteenth International Congress on Hygiene and Demography*, III (1912).

Chapter 40

NOISE-CONTROL REQUIREMENTS IN BUILDING CODES

Richard V. Waterhouse

National Bureau of Standards

INTRODUCTION

The Need for Noise-control Requirements in Building Codes. Since 1938 the more progressive national building codes throughout the world have had noise-control requirements added to them, particularly requirements for the sound insulation of dwellings. There is good reason for the inclusion of these noise-control requirements. Noise levels have increased markedly owing to greater mechanization in and out of doors. Furthermore, modern building techniques with their emphasis on economy and lightweight construction have tended to produce dwellings with poorer sound insulation.

It is perhaps surprising that although the building codes of Canada and several European countries contain noise-control requirements, in the United States, where mechanization and noise levels are so great, the building codes possess none.*

It is broadly true that countries with high population density have the greatest need for effective sound insulation, but it is really the concentration of dwellings and the local noise levels that count. When these factors are considered, it becomes evident that an apartment block in Manhattan needs as much sound insulation as an apartment block in London. At present the chances are that it does not get it.

The subject of sound-insulation requirements for buildings has received some discussion in the United States. However, none of the four principal national codes of the United States, nor any of the city codes, contain noise-control requirements at the time of publication. Consequently, this chapter is chiefly a summary of the progress of other countries in this field. Some sound-insulation standards that have been drawn up for the United States are presented.

Basis for Selection of Sound-insulation Requirements. The noise-control requirements that have been written into building codes abroad are as follows:

1. Acceptable sound-insulation values for walls and floors in houses, apartments, and other buildings. Insulation values for both air-borne and impact sound are generally given.
2. Acceptable location of buildings with respect to noise sources, such as highways.

Before examining in detail these noise-control requirements, it is worth while to consider their basis. Before numerical requirements could be formulated, quantitative answers had to be given to the questions, "How disturbing are various degrees of noise?" and "How far is it practicable to go in reducing noise?"

The earliest noise-control requirements in building codes were introduced without

*An exception is the advisory code, Ref. 18.

having much information on which to base answers to these questions. However, during the last 12 years extensive surveys have been made in Britain to obtain accurate answers to these questions. In these surveys[1,2] the sound insulation of about 1,000 walls and floors was measured in houses and apartments occupied by lower- and middle-income families, who were questioned on how adequate they found the sound insulation. Some interesting data were obtained. For example, tenants in semi-detached houses were asked "Would you rather hear some noise or no noise at all

Table 40.1. Noise-control Requirements in Building Codes of the World

Country	Date of code	Sound-insulation requirements, db					Other noise-control requirements
		Dwellings			Class-rooms	Hos-pitals	
		Party walls	Party floors				
			Air-borne sound	Impact sound			
Germany.......	1938 Revised 1953	48*	50*	*	—	—	—
Canada........	1941 Revised 1953 1954	50 45	50 45	—	40	40	—
Britain.........	1944 Revised 1948 Revised 1954	I 46* II 41*	55 46* 41*	15 wood 20 conc. * *	45	—	Site-noise figures
Sweden........	1946 Revised 1950	48	48	*	44	48	Yes *
Norway........	1948	50	50	12	44	50	—
Netherlands....	1952	a 52 ab 50 b 50	52 52 50	—	—	—	—

The above figures are given for comparison purposes and may be read as average transmission-loss figures, except for the impact figures, which give the required sound-level improvement over a bare concrete floor. In the codes some of the above figures are expressed differently, as explained in the text.
* See text.

from the adjoining house?" Sixty-four per cent replied "some noise," and twenty-five per cent replied "no noise." The remaining 11 per cent had no opinion. The same tenants, whose party walls were of 9-in. solid brick with 50-db transmission loss,† were asked further whether a slight increase in rent would be considered worth while to ensure greater quiet: 20 per cent said yes.

Apartment dwellers were asked how disturbing they found the noise through party floors. In the group having party floors with about 50-db transmission loss (air-borne), 26 per cent described the noise as disturbing, while in the group having floors with about 45-db transmission loss, 42 per cent described the noise as disturbing or very disturbing. A 30- to 35-db transmission loss for floors was termed the "deputation level," since a group of tenants living in apartments having such floors petitioned

† See Chap. 20 for further information on *transmission loss*.

the local authority which built them, which was then forced to modify the construction at considerable expense.

The most important findings of these surveys were as follows:

1. In apartments of modern frame construction, 1 person in 2 is bothered by neighbor noise. In apartments of older-type construction the proportion is 1 person in 3.
2. In semidetached and row houses, 1 person in 4 is bothered by neighbor noise.

These results were obtained in Britain, but it seems reasonable to assume that they apply equally well in the United States.[3] A more detailed discussion of community noise is given in Chaps. 35 and 36.

NOISE-CONTROL REQUIREMENTS IN EXISTING BUILDING CODES

Table 40.1 gives the salient features of the noise-control requirements of six national building codes, listed in chronological order. These will now be discussed separately in more detail.

German Code.[4] The noise-control requirements of the German code are about the most detailed and comprehensive in existence, and reflect the long experience and considerable accomplishment of Germany in this field.

The first noise-control requirements were introduced in 1938* and specified a mini-

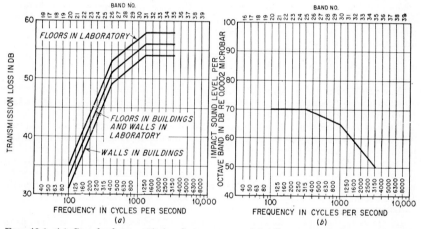

Fig. 40.1. (*a*) Standard transmission loss curve used in German code for assessing the (air-borne) noise reduction of walls and floors. (*b*) Corresponding curve for assessing the impact-sound insulation.

mum air-borne transmission loss for party walls by three average figures, 42 db for the frequency range 100 to 550 cps, 54 db from 550 to 3,000 cps, and 48 db over-all. For party floors the figures were 2 db lower, and in addition the impact-sound level produced by a standard tapping machine had to be less than 85 db re 0.0002 microbar. However, since 1953 new requirements have been in force, as laid down in a tentative standard DIN 52211.[4] Here a new method of specifying sound insulation is adopted; transmission loss values are specified for all frequencies throughout the range 100 to 3,200 cps, as follows: At 100 cps the transmission loss figure is 35 db and rises uniformly to 53 db at 400 cps. From 400 cps it again rises uniformly, though at a slower rate, to 58 db at 1,250 cps; the transmission loss then remains constant at 58 db for the frequencies 1,250 to 3,200 cps (see Fig. 40.1*a*).

* DIN 4110.

This curve is the standard for the air-borne transmission loss of floors as measured in the laboratory.   For walls measured in the laboratory and floors measured in buildings the curve is similar but 2 db lower at all points.   The 2-db difference between laboratory and field measurements accounts for the flanking transmission* generally present in the latter case.   For walls measured in buildings the curve is again similar, but 4 db lower at all points.

To determine whether a partition meets the air-borne sound standard, its transmission loss vs. frequency curve is compared with the standard curve.   Where the curve for the partition exceeds the standard curve, it is ignored.   Where it falls below it, the deficiency is averaged over the whole curve, except that only half the deficiencies at 100 and 3,200 cps are counted.   Then if the average deficiency is not more than 2 db, the partition meets the standard.   The average transmission loss figures† from these curves, for comparison with other codes, are approximately 52, 50, and 48 db for the air-borne sound, and, deducting the 2-db deficiency allowed, these figures become 50, 48, and 46 db.   For impact-sound insulation, the standard curve for the impact-sound level in the room below the standard tapping machine is 70 db from 100 to 320 cps, diminishing uniformly from 70 db at 320 cps to 65 db at 1,000 cps, then diminishing again, though more rapidly, to 50 db at 3,200 cps (see Fig. 40.1b).   To determine whether a partition meets the impact-sound standard, the method is similar to that given above except that in this case it is the parts above the standard curve that count.   The transmission-loss figures for partitions have to be measured under the conditions of a very thorough standard[5] on transmission-loss measurement.

In 1952, a list[6] was published of various partitions, including several modern ones, which met the requirements listed above.   At the same time a large-scale educational drive was launched by the West German government, using films, lectures, and articles to make builders, architects, and the public more conscious of the matter of sound insulation in dwellings.

The sound-insulation requirements given have been adopted in most of the states of Germany, including the East Zone, supervision and administration being on a local basis.

Canadian Code.[7]   The National Building Code of Canada, Part 3, entitled "Use and Occupancy" contains a section on sound insulation and lists transmission loss requirements for a large variety of buildings and rooms.

These requirements are given an original form, by postulating the maximum air-borne noise levels likely to be produced by the occupancy and then assigning maximum tolerable levels for air-borne extraneous noise; the required transmission loss for a partition is then the difference between these two levels.   For example, for all rooms in dwellings the occupancy noise is given as 80 db and the tolerable extraneous-noise level as 30 db.   The required transmission loss for all partitions is thus 50 db.   In classrooms and hospitals the corresponding figures are 80 and 40 db, while in concert halls the corresponding levels are given as 85 and 30 db.

In practice, the noise-control requirements for dwellings in the above code have been superseded by the standards published in 1954 by the Central Mortgage and Housing Corporation of Canada.[8]   These standards require at least 45-db transmission loss for the party walls and floors of all multi-unit dwellings built under its jurisdiction.   Multi-unit dwellings include two-family houses, row houses, and apartments.

The corporation estimates that these standards are currently in operation for about 50 per cent of all multi-unit dwellings being built in Canada.   For example, in the first 9 months of 1954, about 20,000 such dwelling units were constructed, and about half of these were estimated to have been built under the jurisdiction of the corporation and in accordance with the transmission loss standard.   A useful list is given of wall and floor constructions which meet the 45-db standard.

British Code.[9]   The British Code of Functional Requirements of Buildings devotes Chapter 3 to sound insulation.   A draft edition was published in 1944, and a finished version followed in 1948.   It specifies average transmission loss figures as follows for houses and apartments: 55 db between a living room in one dwelling and a living room

---

* See Chaps. 19 and 20 for a discussion of flanking transmission.
† Based on the frequencies: 125, 175, 250, 350, 500, 700, 1,000, 2,000, and 4,000 cps.

or bedroom of the adjacent dwelling, 45 db elsewhere between dwellings, and 35 db between rooms of the same dwelling.

Impact-noise insulation of 20 db better than for bare concrete is specified for wood floors, while for concrete floors the figure is 15 db.   For floors above classrooms the figures are 15 and 10 db, respectively.

Recommendations are given for the siting of buildings with respect to noise sources. Dwellings and schools should be at least 100 ft and preferably 200 ft from a main highway or railroad.   (At distances 150 to 200 ft from these, average weighted sound pressure levels are given as 70 db.)   Where such siting of a building is impracticable, special sound-insulating treatment for windows is discussed.   A table is given of the sound insulation of various kinds of windows.   It is suggested that playgrounds, being noisy, should be screened with trees 15 to 20 ft high.

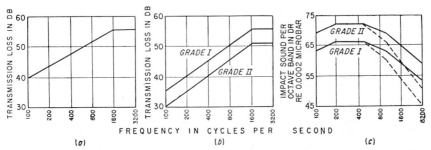

FREQUENCY IN CYCLES PER SECOND

(*a*) (*b*) (*c*)

Fig. 40.2. (*a*) Standard transmission loss curve for assessing the (air-borne) noise reduction of walls and floors for houses, as proposed for British code.   (*b*) Corresponding curves for the walls and floors of apartments.   (*c*) Corresponding curve for assessing impact-sound insulation; dotted line for floors with linoleum, solid line for floors without.

An 18-page appendix to the British Code gives details of sound-insulating techniques in building.   Transmission loss figures are given for various common constructions, some of which meet the sound-insulation requirements.   The effect of flanking transmission is discussed in assessing the sound reduction between rooms, and examples are worked out showing how to take it into account.

The sound-insulation requirements contained in this 1948 standard are, however, slated for revision.   In place of the average transmission loss figures, it is proposed[2] to specify entire curves for the transmission loss and impact-sound level vs. frequency, which will be similar but not identical to those in the new German standard (see Fig. 40.2).

Three grades of air-borne sound insulation are proposed.   (The curves specified are converted in the following to average transmission loss figures for comparison purposes.)   There is one grade for house walls, requiring 48-db transmission loss, and two grades for the party walls and floors of apartments, 46 db and 41 db.   These are significantly lower than the old grade of 55 db, which was rather high.

For impact-sound insulation, two grades are specified.   The maximum permitted impact-sound levels in a room below the panel under test are specified throughout the band 100 to 3,200 cps.

For apartments, grade I insulation is such that the neighbors' noise is only as disturbing as several other factors, while grade II is such that the neighbors' noise is to some of the tenants the worst thing about living in the apartments, but is still not sufficient to disturb seriously the majority of the tenants.

Swedish Code.[10]   A code of noise-control requirements was first introduced in Sweden in 1946.   In 1950 a revision was issued, containing the following requirements:

In dwellings and hospitals an air-borne transmission loss of 48 db is specified, the figure for classrooms being 44 db and for offices 40 db.   The corresponding figures for the insulation of impacts for concrete and wooden floors are 55 and 46 db (dwellings), 55 and 48 db (hospitals), 50 and 44 db (classrooms), and 50 and 42 db (offices).

These impact-sound-level figures (L_i) are defined by the equation

$$L_i = 130 - L - 10 \log a \qquad \text{db}$$

where L is the level measured with a 30- to 60-db weighting-network in the room underneath the partition, with a standard tapping machine in operation, and a is the absorption of the room in square meters, averaged over the frequency range 600 to 1,200 cps.

In addition to these sound-insulation requirements, maximum levels are specified for noise that may be produced in dwellings and other buildings.

Norwegian Code.[11] Sound-insulation requirements were added to the building code of Norway in 1948. In apartments, hotel rooms, and hospital rooms an average airborne transmission loss of at least 50 db is required; in classrooms the value is 44 db, and in offices 40 db.

For impact-sound insulation a value of 12 db better than bare concrete is required in all these cases, as measured with a 40-db weighting network.

The transmission loss and impact-sound insulation figures for various wall and floor constructions are given.

Netherlands Code.[12] In 1952 a tentative national code of sound-insulation requirements was published in the Netherlands.

The code specifies three grades of sound insulation, a good, ab medium, and b fair. The corresponding sound insulation is then expressed by an arbitrary quality number P whose value is given for various common constructions. Thus for party walls between living rooms a minimum P of 10 is required for grade b, and a brick wall 1 ft thick and weighing 73 lb per sq ft is given as an example of a wall having a P number of 10. The P numbers of 22 wall and floor constructions are given, together with the variation of P with some of the construction details.

To obtain P for other partitions, rules are given for determining the effective mass per unit area of a partition, which is then related to P as follows: For partitions with an effective mass of about 13 lb per sq ft, $P = 5$, and for each doubling of this mass P is increased by 2. Thus the classification is based on the mass law.

The phrase "effective mass" means the mass that is effective in reducing sound transmission. Thus for a wooden floor nailed across wooden studs, only the mass of the flooring is effective, assuming that it is airtight, while the mass of the studs is not effective. But if a substantial ceiling is now added underneath, the whole mass of the construction becomes effective.

The advantage claimed for these P numbers is that they give a more accurate measure of noise reduction than the average transmission loss figure, while avoiding the complication of specifying the complete transmission loss vs. frequency curve, as is done in the German code.[4]

The theoretical assessment of P allowed by the code doubtless represents a convenience, as it is quicker to make than a test measurement. However, it is difficult to predict accurately the effective mass of partitions where porosity, spring elements, or complicated coupled masses are present, and so the usefulness of this scheme may be somewhat limited.

Turning now to the sound-insulation requirements in the code, and converting the P numbers into average transmission-loss figures for comparison with other codes, grade b requires at least 50 db for party walls and floors between living rooms. For grade ab the floor requirement is raised to 52 db, and for grade a both walls and floors must meet this figure. For party walls between rooms other than living rooms the figures are the same or slightly lower. A difference of only 2 db in transmission loss between grade a and grade b is rather small, in view of the limited discrimination of the ear and the limited accuracy of present measurements and calculations of the transmission loss of partitions.

General Comments on Existing Sound-insulation Requirements. All the above building codes contain values for the sound insulation of partitions, and there is no doubt that this is the most important noise-control feature to have specified. The average air-borne transmission loss specified in these codes for party walls separating the living rooms of two dwellings varies from 41 to 55 db. The average of these transmission loss figures cited is about 49 db.

Impact-sound insulation is mentioned in only four of the six codes, although it is probably as important as air-borne sound reduction in the case of apartments. One reason for this may be that the impact-sound insulation will be affected by the floor coverings to be used, and at the building stage this is an unknown variable. This is a slight argument, however, and there seems good reason for specifying impact-sound insulation figures in addition to air-borne transmission loss figures.

It is interesting to note that the latest codes[2,11] tend to specify more than one grade of sound insulation. This gives scope for setting a minimum requirement to apply to all new construction, and higher standards for better-quality construction.

Making recommendations for the maximum background-noise levels for building sites, as is done in the British code,[9] is a complex problem. There is no doubt that quiet sites are very desirable, particularly for dwellings, hospitals, and schools, but the expense of obtaining them may be exorbitant in urban districts. In such cases, improved transmission loss of partitions may prove a cheaper solution. For this reason, site-noise recommendations can only be fairly general in character.

A Method of Specifying Sound Insulation. In the past an average figure has generally been used to express the transmission loss of a partition, this being the arithmetic mean of the transmission loss figures in decibels at various frequencies spaced over the range 100 to 4,000 cps. This range is commonly used in architectural acoustics and is considered to contain most of the energy of noises heard around buildings.

The disadvantage of using this average transmission loss figure is that it leaves indefinite the noise reduction of the partition, even when the noise is specified.

For example, if a partition has a transmission loss of 24 db at 250 cps, and 42-db transmission loss at all the other frequencies used in the average, its average transmission loss is 40 db. However, it will reduce the level of noise containing equal energy per octave by only 30 db. Thus although the average transmission loss is a sufficiently accurate guide in most cases, it can be quite misleading for some partitions. This point was well demonstrated in one survey[2] in which an 11-in. cavity wall with average transmission loss of 55 db was found in practice to give no better sound insulation than a 9-in. brick wall with average transmission loss of 50 db. The reason was that the cavity wall picked up its 5-db advantage over the brick wall at the higher frequencies, where it did not matter since the noise at these frequencies was already sufficiently reduced. At the lower frequencies, where a few extra decibels would have helped, the transmission loss of the two walls was not appreciably different.

This disadvantage, inherent in the use of the average transmission loss figure, can be minimized by using in its place an index more directly related to the noise reduction of the partition. Such an index can be obtained by specifying a certain curve of transmission loss vs. frequency as a standard, and basing the index of a partition on the average number of decibels its transmission loss falls below the standard curve, ignoring the parts where it exceeds it. This principle is used in the new German code[4] and has been proposed for the British code.[2]

The idea behind this index is given in the following translation of the German code.

A mean divergence from the Standard Curve in the unfavorable direction must be permitted, as the evaluation depends upon the determination of the mean of a number of measurements. Thereby, since only those values diverging in the unfavorable direction are taken into account when determining the mean, bad zones in the frequency range are prevented from being compensated by needlessly good ones.

The impact-sound insulation can be specified in a similar way, by giving the maximum permitted sound levels in the various octave bands in a room when a standard tapping machine is operating above it. A partition is then rated by the average amount its curve exceeds the standard curve.

Experience with these methods of rating is limited, but there is little doubt that they will provide a more accurate measure of the ability of a partition to keep out noise than the old transmission loss and impact-loss averages.

LEGAL AUTHORITY OF CODES

In all cases discussed above, the sound-insulation requirements of building codes have no legal force at the national level. It is left to the local authorities of cities and communities to make the building codes or parts of them compulsory if they so wish, and to enforce them as they see fit.

Enforcement is usually carried out, as with other building code requirements, by withholding building permits if the inspection of building plans shows that the requirements will not be met. This is generally followed up by inspection of buildings during construction. In several European countries mobile laboratories (generally small trucks containing test equipment) are available for measuring the transmission loss of partitions in the field. This provides a valuable additional check on construction.

The transmission loss values of most partitions are known, so it is generally easy to check whether plans meet transmission loss requirements. If the transmission loss of a proposed partition is not known, the local authority requires a measurement of transmission loss by an accredited laboratory.

The above system has proved satisfactory, as far as is known, and the acoustic requirements generally seem to have been accepted as reasonable and legitimate standards.

In some cases the requirements of a national code have been modified to meet local conditions. For example, in Scotland, where tenement dwellings are common, a bylaw has been passed requiring a minimum transmission loss of 43 db for all party walls and floors, which is lower than the figure recommended in the British code.

FUTURE PROSPECTS

The Growth of Noise-control Requirements in Building Codes. There is little doubt that noise-control requirements in building codes are here to stay. Figure 40.3 shows the growth of the idea internationally. It is notable that no country that

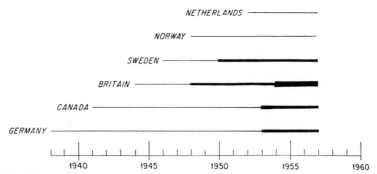

Fig. 40.3. The growth of noise-control requirements in building codes. Heavy line denotes revision of requirements.

has once included such requirements in its building code has subsequently omitted them. On the contrary, in the four countries where they have been longest in force they have been revised and made more comprehensive. This point seems significant.

The spread of noise-control requirements in building codes has resulted from the general recognition that better sound insulation is needed in many buildings being constructed today and that it can often be obtained with little extra expense if present knowledge is applied. The use of the codes has reflected the wish to use building materials in the most economical way and to make sure that good sound-insulating properties of buildings are not lost merely through ignorance of what is obtainable.

In the future it is certain that considerations of economy and efficiency will become more rather than less important. Since also noise levels are almost certain to increase, it appears that the reasons for including noise-control requirements in building codes will become more compelling as time goes by and that eventually most domestic building will be covered by such codes.

Status of Sound-insulation Requirements in Building Codes in the United States. There are four principal building codes[13] in the United States, but none of them contains sound-insulation requirements. Apparently no sound-insulation requirements are in operation in any building code in the country at the time of publication,* and the proportion of building in which sound insulation is considered at all is negligible.

There has been some discussion of the need for better sound insulation in dwellings.[14] However, there appear to have been relatively few concrete proposals of sound-insulation figures for buildings. Between 1942 and 1946 the Federal Housing Administration (FHA) required 45-db transmission loss for party walls in the dwellings for which it was responsible, but this requirement has now been discontinued. It was discontinued partly owing to the time and expense involved in having partitions tested, and partly because it was felt this level was perhaps too high, since the standards set were considered minimum standards. After 1946 it was left to the discretion of the field offices of the FHA whether the 45-db standard was to be used in any particular case.

In 1950 recommendations were made for acceptable noise levels in different kinds of rooms, from which it is possible to deduce corresponding transmission loss figures for partitions by assuming some arbitrary level for the external noise.[15]

In 1951 two sets of definite proposals for the sound insulation of dwellings were published, one of which included comprehensive recommendations for sound insulation.[16] Different transmission loss values are given for low-, medium-, and high-cost buildings, and for two different levels of external noise.

For example, for bedrooms where the external-noise level is 65 db (this level is cited as average), transmission loss values of 46 to 50, 51 to 55, and 56 to 60 db are recommended for low-, medium-, and high-cost dwellings. For an external-noise level of 75 db, the transmission loss levels given are 10 db higher. No impact-sound-insulation figures are included. These recommended transmission loss figures tend to be on the high side. For instance, with an external-noise level of 75 db, transmission loss values of 56 to 60 db are recommended for "low-cost building," which is optimistic.

A more conservative set of acoustic standards for dwellings has been proposed in a publication[17] of the American Public Health Association. These standards include recommended noise levels for housing sites, sound-insulation figures for partitions, and sound-absorption figures for rooms. (These latter figures are generally controlled by the furnishings introduced by the occupant after the building is finished, and thus such recommendations would normally fall outside the scope of a building code.) The sound-insulation requirements proposed in this publication cover three grades of attainment, minimum, standard, and optimum. Thus for party walls between a living room of one dwelling and a living room or bedroom of another, the recommended sound-insulation figures are 40, 50, and 55 db. For all other party walls, and for all floors, the corresponding figures are 40, 45, and 50 db. Between rooms of one dwelling where privacy is required the figures are 30, 35, and 45 db, and the impact-sound insulations recommended for floors are 10, 15, and 20 db better than a concrete slab. These proposals seem a reasonable compromise between what is desirable and what is economically feasible.

Some sound-insulation standards are proposed for dwellings in the next section of this chapter.

It is difficult to assess how much influence these sound-insulation recommendations have had on construction in the United States. The general opinion seems to be that they have influenced only a few of the most progressive builders and architects; the general result has been small. Of course, the situation could hardly be expected to be otherwise, since the recommendations have not been vigorously promoted or written into any building codes.

It has been argued that the recommendations have not been adopted because they were couched in nonlegal terms. This seems unlikely, however, since their transla-

*See footnote on p. **40**-1.

tion into a legal ordinance would be a simple and routine job for the legal staff of any interested municipality.   None of the codes mentioned in this chapter was issued in legal form.   They were translated later, as required, into the form of legal ordinances, or specifications for building under loans or mortgages from official bodies.

The key problem, for those who feel that sound-insulation requirements should be more widely used, thus appears to be how best to publicize and promote the proposals that exist.

American building codes have in the past included only requirements that were considered necessary to make buildings safe and sanitary.   Considerations of aesthetics and convenience have not been included, because it has been felt that these were personal and controversial matters in which it was better to let people suit themselves. This appears a very reasonable way of defining the scope of a building code, but it has the disadvantage that it excludes sound insulation and other noise-control factors, since it can hardly be argued that noise in dwellings represents a hazard to health or life, in the general case.   The reason for requiring adequate sound insulation in dwellings and elsewhere is that life is so much more uncomfortable and inconvenient without it.   This is a powerful argument and does not need laboring to most people.

SUGGESTED SOUND-INSULATION STANDARDS FOR THE UNITED STATES

The sound-insulation standards given in Tables 40.2 and 40.3 are proposed by the author for American communities.   They are intended to contain the essential points of the various codes discussed above, modified where necessary to suit American conditions.

Table 40.2. Proposed Standards for the Sound Insulation of Party Walls and Floors in Apartments, Semidetached Houses, and Row Houses

Type of Sound	Class A (standard), db	Class B (minimum), db
Air-borne sound insulation		
Party walls and floors separating the living rooms and bedrooms of one dwelling from the living rooms, bathrooms, and kitchens of adjacent dwellings, shall have a transmission loss of at least..	50	40
All other party walls and floors shall have a transmission loss of at least..	45	40
Impact-sound insulation		
All party floors shall have an impact-sound insulation of at least..	15	10

NOTES: *a.* The airborne-sound insulation figures cited in this table are to be taken as the average transmission loss values of partitions, over the frequency range 125 to 4,000 cps.
b. The impact-sound insulation is the decibel difference between the sound levels measured under test conditions for the floor in question and a 4-in. floor of bare concrete.

The standards have been reduced to a form as compact and readily understandable as possible.   All requirements that could be considered nonessential have been omitted, so that the main issues would not be clouded with less important details. Site-noise figures have not been included in these standards, because of the difficulty of deciding what are practical levels to specify.   Impact-sound-insulation figures have been included; few data measured in the United States are available, but there are enough data from foreign sources on standard floor constructions to be used for comparison purposes.

The sound-insulation standards are intended to be applicable to all new apartment buildings, semidetached and row houses, hospitals, and schools. The minimum standards of class *B* are low enough to be fairly considered an irreducible minimum level that ought to be met in all new construction. Thus it is hoped that any community can adopt this code and require that its buildings meet the requirements of class *B*, without feeling that it has overreached itself. Class *A* is intended to be a reasonable level for average construction.

It is suggested that communities adopting these standards should enforce them by checking building plans to see that wall and floor constructions meet the requirements and withholding building permits if they do not. Chapter 20 gives the average transmission-loss figures for a number of constructions.

If the transmission loss of a proposed partition is unknown, a measurement should be required.*

Table 40.3. Proposed Standards for the Sound Insulation of Walls and Floors in Hospitals and Schools

Type of sound	Class A (standard), db	Class B (minimum), db
Air-borne sound insulation Walls and floors shall have a transmission loss of at least....	50	40
Impact-sound insulation Walls and floors shall have an impact-sound insulation of at least...	15	10

NOTES: *a.* The airborne-sound insulation figures cited in this table are to be taken as the average transmission loss values of partitions, over the frequency range 125 to 4,000 cps.

b. The impact-sound insulation is the decibel difference between the sound levels measured under test conditions for the floor in question and a 4-in. floor of bare concrete.

If a construction has a much higher transmission loss than the standards require, this could probably be predicted without the need of a test. However, in general it is to be expected that proposed constructions would not exceed the standards by a wide enough margin to make this possible.

REFERENCES

1. "A survey of noise in British homes." National Building Studies Technical Report No. 2. Obtainable from H. M. Stationery Office, London, England, price 9d (10¢).
2. "Recent research on sound insulation in houses and flats." Parkin, P. H., and E. F. Stacey, *J. Roy. Inst. Brit. Arch.* (July, 1954). Also "Noise in Three Groups of Flats with Different Floor Insulations" (to be published). Also article in *Noise Control*, **1**: 41 (1955).
3. Beranek, L. L.: *J. Acoust. Soc. Amer.*, **21**: 302 (1949).
4. DIN 52211 (Sept., 1953), sold by Beuth-Vertrieb GmbH, Cologne, Germany. Obtainable from American Standards Association, Inc., 70 East 45th St., New York 17, N.Y.
5. DIN 52210. Obtainable from source of note 4.
6. DIN 4109, Beiblatt, March, 1952. Obtainable from source of note 4.
7. Part 3, National Building Code of Canada, 1953. Sold by the Secretary, Associate Committee on the National Building Code, National Research Council, Canada, price 10¢.
8. Building Standards of the Canadian Central Mortgage and Housing Corporation, Ottawa, Canada, 1954.
9. Sound Insulation (Housing, flats, and schools) 30 pp. Chapter 3 from the Code of functional requirements of buildings. Sold by the British Standards Institution, 28 Victoria St., London S.W.1, England, price 2s (25¢).

* The National Bureau of Standards, Washington, D.C., and the Riverbank Laboratories of the Armour Research Foundation in Geneva, Illinois, are available for such measurements. The test fee at the former is $260 per panel.

10. Swedish building code, part on heat and sound insulation.   Obtainable from the American Standards Association, 70 East 45th St., New York 17, N.Y.
11. Norwegian building code, part entitled Anvisningar till byggnadsstadgan.   Obtainable from American Standards Association, 70 East 45th St., New York 17, N.Y.
12. Naturkundige grondslagen voor bouwvoorschriften, Deel III, NGB III 1951, v. 1070. 30 pp.   Obtainable from American Standards Association, 70 East 45th St., New York 17, N.Y.
13. Building Code of the National Board of Fire Underwriters.   Code of the Building Officials   Conference   of   America.   Southern   Standard   Building   Code.   Uniform building codes of the Pacific Coast Building Officials Conference.
14. Knudsen, V. O.: *J. Acoust. Soc. Amer.*, **21**: 296 (1949).
15. Knudsen, V. O., and C. M. Harris, "Acoustical Designing in Architecture," p. 221, John Wiley & Sons, Inc., New York, 1950.
16. Ramsey, C. G., and H. R. Sleeper, "Architectural Graphic Standards," 4th ed., p. 301, 1951.
17. Construction and Equipment in the Home, 1951, 77 pp.   By the American Public Health Association.   Obtainable from the Public Administration Service, 1313 East Sixtieth St., Chicago 37, Illinois.   Price $1.
18. "State Building Construction Code Applicable to Multiple Dwellings," State of New York, Dec. 15, 1953.   See Section B 206–3, "Miscellaneous Requirements."

INDEX

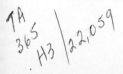